Essentials of Texas Water Resources

Seventh Edition

Essentials of Texas Water Resources

Seventh Edition

Mary K. Sahs and Holly Heinrich
Editors

A project of the

Austin 2022

The State Bar of Texas, through its Texas Bar Books Department, publishes practice books prepared and edited by knowledgeable authors to give practicing lawyers as much assistance as possible. The competence of the authors ensures outstanding professional products, but, of course, neither the State Bar of Texas, the editors, nor the authors make either express or implied warranties in regard to their use. Each lawyer must depend on his or her own knowledge of the law and expertise in the use or modification of these materials.

IRS CIRCULAR 230 NOTICE: To ensure compliance with requirements imposed by the IRS, we inform you that (1) this written material was not intended or written by the author(s) to be used for the purpose of avoiding federal penalties that may be imposed on a taxpayer; (2) this written material cannot be used by a taxpayer for the purpose of avoiding penalties that may be imposed on the taxpayer; (3) this written material cannot be used in promoting, marketing, or recommending to another party any tax-related transaction or matter; and (4) a taxpayer should seek advice based on the taxpayer's particular circumstances from an independent tax advisor.

ISBN (print): 978-1-938873-98-0
ISBN (digital download): 978-1-938873-99-7
Library of Congress Control Number: 2022930846

Austin, TX 78711

Printed in the United States of America

Seventh Edition, 2022

STATE BAR OF TEXAS
Created in 1939

STATE BAR OF TEXAS

Contents

Plates

(Plates follow chapter 19.)

Foreword

The Texan ethos is marked by ambition, opportunity, independence, and resilience. This cultural spirit has a wide appeal and is an important reason why the state is projected to reach 50 million citizens by 2070. But Texans also believe strongly in responsibility and stewardship. The well-known "Don't Mess with Texas" slogan, for example, captures the fierce pride we have in protecting our natural resources. However, these values inevitably come into conflict with one another, and reconciling competing priorities can be complex and problematic. Private property rights and economic growth often collide with depleting water sources, aging or undersized infrastructure, scientific uncertainty, budget constraints, and regulatory requirements. Building a deep, cross-disciplinary base of knowledge is key to untangling these issues.

This book describes well the rich, historical background of Texas water, providing helpful context to today's water disputes and thorniest policy issues. Understanding where we have come from is absolutely critical in illuminating a viable and productive path forward. At the Texas Water Development Board, our integrated approach to securing the state's water future combines science, planning, and finance to best serve Texan taxpayers and ratepayers. Similarly, the *Essentials of Texas Water Resources* effectively weaves together the collective wisdom of experts in a variety of fields. It provides incredible value to new water professionals and seasoned veterans alike, in addition to serving as a blueprint for how we might handle emerging water issues. The lessons contained within this book will better enable practitioners to assist clients and stakeholders in resolving conflicts quickly, amicably, and cost effectively.

Texans have been coping with drought for decades, but the last few years have focused more of our attention on other water-related challenges. Following Hurricane Harvey in 2017, it became clear that Texas would need to start fighting flood in an innovative and deliberate manner. Although there is still much work to be done, I am proud to report that my agency and our partners are well on our way to implementing the landmark mapping, planning, and mitigation strategies enacted by the Texas legislature in 2019. Additionally, Winter Storm Uri in February 2021 and the subsequent water service disruptions introduced many Texans—in a very painful way—to the existence of a water-energy nexus. The final chapters in this book do an excellent job of describing these newer challenges in detail and identifying opportunities going forward.

Today, the future of Texas water is at a significant juncture. The state's population growth is climbing rapidly while its water supplies become more limited. Identifying strategies that are financially, technologically, environmentally, and legally sustainable will be at the forefront of the policy agenda over the coming decades. The state's water leaders have achieved meaningful progress in this regard, and continuing that positive trajectory is crucial.

I cannot thank enough the many people who contributed their time and talent to this latest edition of the *Essentials of Texas Water Resources*. Ensuring a sustainable water future for Texas is a daunting task that can only be achieved with Texas's sharpest minds working together, leading all Texans toward a shared solution.

—Brooke Paup
Chair, Texas Water Development Board

Foreword

Water is essential for life. *Essentials of Texas Water Resources* is an indispensable reference book for understanding the complex laws, policies, and issues affecting this natural resource so vital to all of us in Texas, especially in this challenging twenty-first century.

Texas is blessed with a rich diversity of topography, climate, flora, fauna, natural resources, cultures, and people. That diversity is no more evident than in the state's water resources: aquifers as different as the Ogallala, the Edwards, and the Gulf Coast; springs such as Comal and San Marcos that have served humans and other species for thousands of years; the ephemeral playa lakes of the Panhandle; rivers flowing across Texas, some serving as international and interstate boundaries; the languid bayous of southeast Texas; human-engineered impoundments for flood control, recreation, and water supply; the fertile bays and estuaries along the Texas coast; and the vast Gulf of Mexico that borders us.

Capturing the essence of those varied water resources, and explaining how Texans use and manage (and sometimes misuse and mismanage) those resources, requires a large book, many voices, and periodic updating. *Essentials of Texas Water Resources* checks all those boxes. This book draws strength from its thorough discussion of a wealth of Texas water topics, the knowledge and experience of its numerous authors, and its frequent new editions. *Essentials* benefits from the perspectives of lawyers well versed in Texas water law but also from the viewpoints of other water professionals who are noted for their work in areas as diverse as water conservation, endangered species, flood management, water project financing, and water planning, among others.

As a former educator and an environmental advocate in Texas for over four decades, I believe firmly that "knowledge is power" and that the more informed policymakers and people are, the better the potential for sound policies and practices. The Environmental and Natural Resources Law Section of the State Bar of Texas and Mary Sahs, the longtime editor of *Essentials of Texas Water Resources*, are to be commended for providing an opportunity for Texans to enhance our knowledge of water and thus our potential for responsible water stewardship. This is a legacy on which Texans will continue to draw to secure our water future. With the passing of the baton to Holly Heinrich, coeditor of the seventh edition, this compilation of information and insight will itself remain a critical water resource.

—Ken Kramer
Water Resources Chair
Sierra Club—Lone Star Chapter

Preface

The vagaries of weather—swinging between severe drought and damaging floods—shift the focus of *Essentials of Texas Water Resources* from edition to edition. Then the freeze of February 2021 resulted in the temporary loss of drinking water for millions of Texans. Experts agree that the frequency and intensity of such severe weather conditions are likely to increase due to anthropogenic climate change. The sixth edition added a chapter on the effects of weather and climate change on water resources. Several chapters now address this issue.

My colleagues and I are saddened at the untimely passing in 2020 of Brad Castleberry. Brad was a licensed professional engineer and an attorney. His legal career was spent at Lloyd Gosselink Rochelle & Townsend, where he practiced in water resources planning, water rights, and environmental law, relying on his engineering background to provide stellar legal services to the firm's clients. He taught water law as an adjunct professor at Texas Tech University and was a frequent speaker and writer on water law, including being an author of *Meeting Water Supply Needs: Planning, Permitting, and Implementation* for almost every edition of this book. His scholarship remains a crucial part of this edition. He was active in many professional water organizations and was recognized for his achievements. He served as an EnviroMentor for the Texas Commission on Environmental Quality, providing pro bono legal services. But his community involvement did not end with professional actions; he coached Little League baseball at the YMCA and South Austin Little League for many years. He is sorely missed by the water resource community.

Those of you who watch this space know that I have expressed the hope of finding someone to take over the reins as managing editor of this book. I am pleased to introduce you to the coeditor of the seventh edition and future managing editor of this publication, Holly Heinrich. She has taken to the coeditor tasks, if you will excuse me, "like a duck to water." Holly has long been involved in reporting about and studying water issues. She interned at *Texas Monthly*, *Texas Tribune*, and *StateImpact Texas*—reporting and editing. She also studied and interned internationally—earning a Master of Public Policy at the University of Cambridge focusing on water security and policy—and at the UN Mechanism for International Criminal Tribunals and the International Energy Agency. Additionally, she interned at the White House Council on Environmental Quality. Holly currently is an attorney at the City of Austin. She brings this wealth of experience and interest in water issues to this treatise.

Additional thanks go to Texas Bar Books. I never could have anticipated their support over sixteen years ago when I first pitched this project. Despite the relatively small sales of this work, they have continued to publish this treatise because they understand the importance of water management in our state and believe that publication of books such as this have broader value than generation of profit. For this, I will always be grateful. My personal thanks go to the new project publications attorney, Sarah Henson, and the project's other legal editors, Derek Smith and James Norman; Michael Ambrose, senior editor; Travis Riddle, production supervisor: and Sharon Sandle, Texas Bar Books director.

My special thanks go to Steve Kosub and Robert Martinez. Steve has been my "go to" person on all aspects of this undertaking—from suggesting new authors and selecting topics to peer review to being a project cheerleader. Robert is always responsive when this editor believes an agency lawyer is the right fit for a particular chapter. He thoughtfully selects and suggests new authors from the TCEQ staff.

Others who deserve mention are Dr. David W. Yoskowitz and Dr. Quinn McColly, whose many hours of work did not make their way into this edition. Thank you also to Ed McCarthy, Doug Caroom, and Susan Maxwell for their peer reviews.

Also, I would like to acknowledge the contributions of the following authors (in alphabetical order) who participated in previous editions but who do not appear as authors in this edition. Many of these authors have contributed to the treatise from its inception and have stepped aside to allow talented newer professionals to participate: Barney Austin (ASR); Darcy Alan Frownfelter (Edwards Aquifer Authority); Ian Groetsch (water rights enforcement); Ross Henderson (drought planning and surface water availability); Shana Horton (state water planning); Jace Houston (flood management); Charles Irvine (ESA); Sharlene Leurig (economics of water); Robert Martinez (water rights enforcement); Janet McQuaid (dredge and fill permits); Howard Slobodin (TPDES for water supply projects); Cynthia Smiley (state water planning); Mary E. Smith (multijurisdictional water rights); Robin Smith (environmental flows and water rights enforcement); Dinniah Tadema (water rights enforcement); and Constance Courtney Westfall (governmental entities).

You will see many new authors and existing authors changing their topics (in alphabetical order): Kellie E. Billings-Ray (multijurisdictional water rights); Jim Bradbury (land use and water); Forrest Cobb (land use and water); Marc Friberg (EAA); Todd Galiga (environmental flows); Jason Godeaux (environmental flows); Daryn Hardwick (GAMs); Kathy Humphreys (governmental entities); Tiffany Lashmet (land use and water); Kim Nygren (drought planning); Chris Smith (flood management); Clayton Smith (water rights enforcement); Tony L. Smith (state water planning); Justin Sutherland (desalination); Ruth Takeda (surface water availability); Lauren C. Thomson (meeting water supply needs); Brandon Tuck (dredge and fill permits); and Reem Zoun (flood management).

Royalties from this publication continue to fund Environmental and Natural Resources Law Section projects designed to maintain the high standards of the environmental and natural resources bar in the State of Texas.

I will always be entranced by the technical and legal complexities of water resources in general, and those in Texas in particular. Although I am resigning as editor, I continue to practice law in this field and woe to the unsuspecting dinner guest or new acquaintance who asks me a question about what I do. I could talk and write for hours on these topics and will miss being the guiding force behind this book. Hopefully I won't turn into an FIP (formerly important person), hovering in the background giving unsolicited advice as Holly takes over. Now for a word from Holly.

—Mary K. Sahs
Editor

***Mary K. Sahs** has an active legal practice, focusing on environmental and administrative law, with an emphasis on water law. With many years of experience as an attorney at the state's environmental agency as well as in private practice, she is familiar with the roles and views of government, the public, and the regulated community in the management, conservation, and protection of water resources. A 1985 honors graduate of the University of Texas School of Law, Ms. Sahs is a frequent speaker and author on environmental and water law issues, and from its first edition served for many years as coeditor of West's Texas Practice Series on Environmental Law. Since 2009, she has annually been selected by her peers for inclusion in Woodward/White, Inc.'s* The Best Lawyers in America—Texas, *in the field of Water Law.*

I am honored that Mary Sahs has invited me to serve as her coeditor for this edition and to serve as future managing editor of *Essentials of Texas Water Resources*. I have admired this publication since 2011, when I began writing my undergraduate honors thesis on water rights in the midst of what became the most recent drought of record for significant portions of Texas. *Essentials* served as my introduction to the fundamentals of Texas water law and policy. This aptly titled book truly has been an essential resource that helped me transform a passion for Texas water resources into a meaningful career in Texas water law.

As the founding editor of *Essentials of Texas Water Resources*, Mary Sahs has created a commendable resource that has been invaluable to a generation of Texas water professionals. This book is extraordinary because she has ensured that its scope is both broad and deep—the chapters cover a wide range of important Texas water issues, and yet each chapter imparts deep knowledge about its subject. These pages reflect the time and thought that our dedicated authors have put into sharing their legal, scientific, governmental, and other professional knowledge with our readers.

I hope to continue the legacy that Mary has begun by ensuring that this publication remains the essential guide to Texas water resources, providing present and future generations with the tools needed to navigate droughts, floods, storms, legislative sessions, water rights disputes, and the other water-related challenges of our time.

—Holly Heinrich
Editor

***Holly Heinrich** is an Assistant City Attorney for the City of Austin, Texas, in the Utilities and Regulatory Division. She holds a JD from the University of Texas School of Law, an MPhil in Public Policy from the University of Cambridge, and a BA in Government, with highest honors, from the University of Texas at Austin. She has written extensively, both academically and professionally, about water issues. Prior to working at the City of Austin, Ms. Heinrich interned at the Mechanism for International Criminal Tribunals in The Hague and in the White House Council on Environmental Quality.*

Acknowledgments

Water resources and water law remain critical and evolving topics for Texas, with its growing population and economy, and with geography and water issues varying around the state. Our section fosters education resources within our field and has proudly sponsored the development of this book, which serves as a valuable reference for all those exploring these subjects in more detail. Since the publication of the first edition of *Essentials of Texas Water Resources* in 2009, the editors and the many chapter authors—who are themselves practitioners, agency experts, and scholars from a variety of disciplines—have worked hard to capture and describe long-standing principles along with recent developments affecting Texas water resources and water laws. This single volume is designed to serve not only attorneys but also industry representatives, academics and students, public officials, and other water stakeholders. This seventh edition of the book incorporates an even broader scope of relevant and timely information, with updated chapters addressing the latest emerging water topics.

Our section appreciates the generous contributions of time and talent provided by the contributing authors for this seventh edition, as well as by the authors in each of the earlier editions. We have enjoyed a great working relationship with the team at the State Bar and Texas Bar Books who have so professionally developed and promoted this project. And we are especially grateful for the dedicated work of the original editor, Mary Sahs, new coeditor Holly Heinrich, and their assistants for their substantial ongoing efforts required to produce and continually update this unique and impressive book.

Thank you to all of those involved in this publication.

—Nathan M. Block
Chair, Environmental and Natural Resources
Law Section, State Bar of Texas

Essentials of Texas Water Resources

Seventh Edition

CHAPTER 1

Scientific, Legal, and Ethical Foundations for Texas Water Law

Gabriel Eckstein[1] and Amy Hardberger [2]

I. Introduction to Water Law

§ 1.1 Introduction

Water law is the field of law concerned with the ownership, allocation, and use of water resources, both surface and subsurface. Although most closely related to property law, recent developments in other legal fields, especially in environmental law, have heavily influenced the interpretation, application, and development of water law. As a result, water law today encompasses a broad perspective and often takes into account individual and community rights, environmental issues, commerce and economics, and other societal and legal concerns.

Significantly, modern water law is an interdisciplinary practice. In light of the continuously expanding body of knowledge of the hydrologic cycle, groundwater flow, wetlands, and freshwater resources in general, the field has expanded to include scientific considerations related to the management, use, and allocation of water resources. It is now no longer enough merely to be versed in water law. Rather, a water lawyer today must understand technical concepts such as hydrostatic pressure and Darcy's law, flow regimes, drainage basins, ecosystems needs, consumptive uses, and crop yields.

Ultimately, though, water law advances societal values and goals related to water management and conservation. It is a means for bridging the gap between the demand for water and the availability of the resource. And therein lies the challenge—learning to practice water law to better society as well as to ensure the client's interests.

Part I of this chapter provides an overview of the scientific, legal, and ethical foundations that are pertinent to Texas water law. Part II discusses the availability of water in Texas and beyond, and part III addresses the hydrologic cycle and its relevance to water law. Part IV covers some of the basic concepts of the science of water that are particularly significant for understanding and applying water law. Finally, parts V and VI discuss the value and ethic of water.

---

1. Gabriel Eckstein is a Professor of Law and Director of the Program on Natural Resources Systems at Texas A&M University School of Law. He also serves as President of the International Water Resources Association, Executive Council Member of the International Association for Water Law, and Director of the International Water Law Project.

2. Amy Hardberger is the McCleskey Professor of Law and Director of the Center for Water Law and Policy at Texas Tech School of Law.

II. Water, Water Everywhere

§ 1.2 Available Water Resources in Texas

§ 1.2:1 Surface Water

With 191,000 miles of streams and rivers, 15 major river basins, 8 coastal basins, and 196 major reservoirs of which 175 are designated for water supply, surface water in Texas is an integral part of the Texan culture, history, and economy. Texas Water Development Board, *River Basins and Reservoirs*, www.twdb.texas.gov/surfacewater/rivers/index.asp [hereinafter *River Basins and Reservoirs*]; Ronald Kaiser, *Drought: An Opportunity for Legal and Institutional Change in Texas*, *in Water Policy and Planning in a Variable and Changing Climate* 402 (Kathleen A. Miller et al. eds., 2016). Surface water is also a significant water source for Texas citizens, constituting approximately 42 percent of the total water used in 2015. Texas Water Development Board, *Texas Water Use Estimates—2016 Summary*, www.twdb.texas.gov/waterplanning/waterusesurvey/estimates/index.asp [hereinafter *Texas Water Use Estimates—2016 Summary*].

Many rivers start their journey at springs, where water bubbles out of the ground to start its passage above ground. Springs are responsible for the location of numerous Texas cities and are an integral part of Texas culture. *See* Gunnar A. Brune & Helen C. Besse, 1 *Springs of Texas* (new ed. 2002) [hereinafter Brune & Besse]; Larry McKinney, *The State of Springs*, *Texas Parks & Wildlife* 26, 29 (July 2005), www.tpwmagazine.com/archive/2005/jul/ed_1/ [hereinafter McKinney, *The State of Springs*]. A 2003 U.S. Geological Survey database listed 1,891 springs in Texas, although some experts think the total is more than twice that. Franklin T. Heitmuller & Brian D. Reece, *Database of Historically Documented Springs and Spring Flow Measurements in Texas*, U.S. Geological Survey Open-file Report 03-315 (2003), https://pubs.usgs.gov/of/2003/ofr03-315/; McKinney, *The State of Springs*, at 29. The majority of the springs cataloged are in the Hill Country region of Central Texas; historically, however, springs have flowed throughout Texas even if they do not do so today. *See* Brune & Besse. The disappearance of Texas springs over the past half-century marks the loss of both a water resource and a piece of the state's history. Wendee Holtcamp, *Aquatic Islands in a Sea of Land*, *Texas Parks & Wildlife* 36, 41 (July 2005), www.tpwmagazine.com/archive/2005/jul/ed_3/.

In addition to its river basins, Texas has a large system of reservoirs that provide water to its citizens. Much of Texas's potable surface water supply comes from state reservoirs with storage capacities of at least 5,000 acre-feet. Texas Water Development Board, *Water for Texas 2022* 105 (2022), www.twdb.texas.gov/waterplanning/swp/2022 [hereinafter 2022 State Water Plan]. These reservoirs were constructed primarily in the 1960s and 1970s to provide a source of freshwater for municipal, industrial, agricultural, flood control, and electricity generation purposes. Today, reservoirs constitute more than half of the state's available surface water. Although the 2012 State Water Plan recommended construction of twenty-six new major reservoirs by 2060, all of which were designated "sites of unique value for the construction of a reservoir," the 2017 State Water Plan did not repeat the recommendation. Texas Water Development Board, *Water for Texas 2012* 236 (2012), www.twdb.texas.gov/waterplanning/swp/2012 [hereinafter 2012 State Water Plan]; Tex. Water Code § 16.051(g–1).

§ 1.2:2 Groundwater

In addition to surface water, Texas is heavily dependent on its groundwater resources. Nearly 140,000 water wells have been inventoried by the Texas Water Development Board (TWDB). *See* Texas Water Development Board, *Groundwater Data*, www.twdb.texas.gov/groundwater/data/. In 2015, the state officially recognized nine major and twenty-one minor aquifers that, together, provided

56 percent of the water used in Texas. *See* Texas Water Development Board, *Water for Texas 2017*, 65–66 (2017), www.twdb.texas.gov/waterplanning/swp/2017 [hereinafter 2017 State Water Plan]; *Texas Water Use Estimates—2016 Summary*. Since then, another minor aquifer has been recognized, bringing that number to twenty-two. 2022 State Water Plan, at 69. These thirty-one aquifers, however, do not represent all the state's groundwater. Although excluded from the official count because of their size, significance, or salinity levels, numerous other aquifers scattered throughout the state are important locally to homeowners, farmers, ranchers, and various businesses. 2012 State Water Plan, at 204.

As a result of Texas's heavy reliance on groundwater, many of the state's aquifers have been pumped in excess of natural recharge. For example, while the Panhandle gets 88 percent of its water from the Ogallala Aquifer, that aquifer's supplies are expected to decline 25 percent by 2070. 2022 State Water Plan, at 173. Other regions heavily dependent on groundwater include the San Antonio region, which relies on the Edwards Aquifer for more than 80 percent of its drinking water, and far west Texas, where two major and six minor aquifers meet 75 percent of the region's water needs. San Antonio Water System, *Edwards Aquifer*, www.saws.org/your-water/aquifer-level-statistics/about-the-edwards-aquifer/; 2012 State Water Plan, at 58. If Texas follows global trends, dependency on aquifers will continue to increase. *Cf.* Jean Margat & Jac van der Gun, *Groundwater Around the World: A Geographic Synopsis* (CRC Press 2013) (asserting that groundwater today is the most extracted natural resource on the planet, amounting to more than 1,000 km^3 of water annually).

Due to the decline of several aquifers, groundwater availability statewide is projected to decrease 25 percent from 2020 to 2070. 2022 State Water Plan, at 73. Some of these reductions in available water have already been observed, including declining water tables averaging three to eleven feet annually in the Trinity Aquifer and approximately thirteen feet per year in the Ogallala Aquifer. Environmental Defense Fund, *Groundwater in Texas: Case Studies of Effective Management—Hays Trinity Groundwater Conservation District* 7 (Mar. 2021), https://texasgroundwater.org/wp-content/uploads/2021/02/Hays-Trinity-Case-Study-March-2021.pdf; V.L. McGuire, *Water-Level and Storage Changes in the High Plains Aquifer, Predevelopment to 2011 and 2009–11*, U.S. Geological Survey Scientific Investigation Report 2012-5291 9 (2013). https://doi.org/10.3133/sir20125291.

Because aquifers are not visible, the state is continually updating their boundaries and trying to understand their characteristics. The TWDB, in cooperation with other state and federal agencies, conducts groundwater availability and water use studies across the state. 2022 State Water Plan, at 165. Local groundwater conservation districts also track changes in water levels and attempt to quantify available water in their areas. In addition, the Texas Commission on Environmental Quality regularly tests both surface and groundwater quality with the goal of ensuring clean drinking water. 2022 State Water Plan, at 166. For effective water planning, water source characteristics must be evaluated in relation to how the water is currently used as well as how it will be needed in the future.

§ 1.2:3 Brackish and Saline Water

In addition to fresh groundwater resources, studies estimate that there are 880 trillion gallons (2.7 billion acre-feet) of brackish water below the surface in Texas. Texas Water Development Report, *The Future of Desalination in Texas 2020 Biennial Report on Seawater and Brackish Groundwater Desalination in Texas* 17 (2020), http://www.twdb.texas.gov/innovativewater/desal/doc/2020_The FutureofDesalinationinTexas.pdf?d=1623.0700000000002. Brackish refers to nonpotable water with a high total dissolved solids (TDS) content. Brackish TDS content typically ranges from 1,000 milligrams per liter (mg/L) to 10,000 mg/L. Seawater has over 35,000 mg/L TDS, and potable water is below 1,000 mg/L.

Until recently, brackish and saline water resources received very little attention in Texas. As the state's population and water demand have increased, and as better treatment technology has become available, these nonpotable sources are now recognized for their potential. Texas currently has forty-six desalination plants with a collective capacity of 123 million gallons per day (MGD) (approximately 375 acre-feet per day), and many more are proposed. Texas Water Development Board, *Answers to Frequently Asked Questions*, www.twdb.texas.gov/innovativewater/desal/faq.asp#title-16. The world's largest inland brackish desalination treatment plant is in El Paso, which can produce up to 27.5 MGD (approximately 84.5 acre-feet per day). Currently, there are no large-scale seawater desalination plants in Texas. Although the technology exists, it is still seen as cost-prohibitive. In addition to treating the water, there are large energy costs associated with transportation, since most of the major municipal centers are located away from the coast.

In 2015, the Texas legislature passed House Bill 30 and appropriated $2 million to study brackish groundwater resources. *See* Act of May 26, 2015, 84th Leg., R.S., ch. 990 (H.B. 30). Part of the authorization required the TWDB to research four specific aquifers by the end of 2016: the Carrizo-Wilcox, Gulf Coast, Blaine, and Rustler. The resulting studies identified production zones, suggested sustainable pumping volumes that would not significantly impact water quality and availability, and provided recommendations for monitoring the effects of pumping brackish groundwater from these aquifers. *See* Texas Water Development Board, *Brackish Groundwater Production Zones*, www.twdb.texas.gov/innovativewater/bracs/HB30.asp. While H.B. 30 also directed the board to identify and designate brackish groundwater production zones for the rest of the state by December 1, 2022, Senate Bill 1041, adopted in 2019, extended that deadline to 2032 due to insufficient funding and a lack of qualified contractors. Act of May 31, 2019, 86th Leg., R.S., ch. 990, § 4(b) (S.B. 1041) (codified at Tex. Water Code § 16.060). Building on the growing interest in brackish groundwater, House Bill 722, also enacted in 2019, authorized groundwater conservation districts to implement an independent permitting scheme for the production of brackish groundwater in designated production zones. Act of June 14, 2019, 86th Leg., R.S., ch. 36, § 36.1015 (H.B. 722) (codified at Tex. Water Code § 36.1015). For further discussion of H.B. 30 and related issues, see Chapter 25 of this book.

§ 1.3 Water Use Patterns in Texas

Water availability and use patterns in Texas have experienced dramatic changes over the past century. A growing population and a dynamic economy, coupled with all too frequent droughts (at least one severe drought every decade for the past century), engendered an evolution in water resource management that has forever left its mark on the state. *See* 2022 State Water Plan, at 36, 155; Joe G. Moore, Jr., *A Half Century of Water Resources Planning and Policy, 1950–2000, in Water for Texas* 7 (Jim Norwine et al. eds., Texas A&M University Press 2005); Rima Petrossian, *Water Use Patterns and Trends: The Future in Texas, in Water for Texas* 52.

In recent years, for example, the state's burgeoning population has spurred a shift from agricultural to municipal water use. In 1974 irrigation accounted for more than 70 percent of the total water used in the state, but by 2014 that percentage had dropped to less than 58. *See* Texas Water Development Board, *Historical Water Use Estimates*, www.twdb.texas.gov/waterplanning/waterusesurvey/estimates/index.asp [hereinafter *Historical Water Use*]. Water use attributable to irrigation is projected to further decline by 20 percent of total water use from 2020 to 2070. 2022 State Water Plan, at 53. In contrast, between 1974 and 2014, municipal use grew from 11 percent to nearly 30 percent of the total water used in Texas. The bulk of that increase came from municipal use of surface water resources, which increased from 18.8 percent to nearly 50 percent of all surface water used in Texas, while municipal use of groundwater accounted for 8 percent of all groundwater used in the state in 1974, peaked at 20.5 percent in the late 1980s, and then has fluctuated between 13.75 and 19.5 percent ever since. *See Historical Water Use*. In addition to population growth, other reasons for the decrease in water use for irrigation include a decrease of irrigated land from 8.6 million acres in 1974 to 6.17 million acres in 2008 and the use of improved water conservation techniques. *See* Texas A&M Agrilife Research Extension, *Status and Trends of Irrigated Agriculture in Texas* 2 (2012), http:

//twri.tamu.edu/docs/education/2012/em115.pdf; Amy Hardberger, *From Policy to Reality: Maximizing Urban Water Conservation in Texas* 3, Environmental Defense Fund (2008), https://ssrn.com/abstract=1873540 [hereinafter *From Policy to Reality*]. Future demand for irrigation is expected to decline from 9.4 million acre-feet in 2020 to about 7.6 million acre-feet in 2070, due in part to improvements in irrigation efficiency, reduced groundwater supplies, and the transfer of water rights from agricultural to municipal users. 2022 State Water Plan, at 6.

Other noteworthy trends in Texas water-use patterns can be identified. Between the 1950s and late 1970s, the average per capita municipal use statewide rose from around 100 gallons per day to 182 gallons per day. *See From Policy to Reality*, at 3. That rate declined in the 1980s and leveled off at around 158 gallons per capita per day in the mid-1990s. Over the last decade, it has fluctuated between 150 and 182, with the highest rates coinciding with drought periods. *See* Texas Water Development Board, *Annual Statewide Water Use—Updated June 12, 2015*, www.twdb.texas.gov/waterplanning/waterusesurvey/estimates/data/TexasStatewideReport_6_12_15_Revision.pdf. During dry conditions, water consumption can increase considerably due to outdoor watering, accounting for 50 to 80 percent of a home's water use. Texas Water Development Board, *Conserving Water Outdoors*, www.twdb.texas.gov/publications/brochures/conservation/doc/ConservingWaterOutdoor.pdf.

Another significant trend is evident in the state's industrial and manufacturing sector, whose water use has been relatively consistent over the past thirty years. In 1974, the sector used almost 1.6 million acre-feet of water. That number fluctuated downward on occasion, reaching 1.37 million acre-feet in 2000. In 2010, it was at 1.7 million acre-feet and projected to increase to 3 million acre-feet by 2070. *See Historical Water Use*; 2022 State Water Plan, at 53. As a percentage of the total water used in the state, the industrial and manufacturing sector uses between 8.4 and 10.8 percent. *See Historical Water Use*.

In addition, the growth in shale gas and oil drilling in Texas, especially efforts using hydraulic fracturing techniques ("fracking"), greatly increased the amount of water use for hydrocarbon extraction through the end of 2015. *See* Ceres, *An Investor Guide to Hydraulic Fracturing and Water Stress*, https://eplanning.blm.gov/epl-front-office/projects/nepa/68426/102904/125791/CERES_2016_An_Investor_Guide_to_Hydraulic_Fracturing_and_Water_Stress.pdf. This was especially prevalent in the Eagle Ford Shale and Permian Basin, where production relies almost entirely on groundwater for the fracking process. With the recent downturn in oil and gas prices, drilling activities have slowed substantially across the state, with active rigs in Texas declining from 840 in January 2015 to 321 in January 2016. Reid Frazier, *When A Fracking Boom Goes Bust*, *Inside Energy* (Mar. 28, 2016), http://insideenergy.org/2016/03/28/when-a-fracking-boom-goes-bust/. That downturn, however, is unlikely to continue. *See* Institute for Regional Forecasting, *Houston's Outlook for 2017: Is the Worst Behind Us?* (Jan. 2, 2017), www.bauer.uh.edu/centers/irf/houston-updates-jan17.php. The 2022 State Water Plan notes that projections for water use in all mining activities in the state is likely to increase through 2030 before declining again. Nonetheless, it also suggests that water demand for all mining activities will "account for roughly 2 percent of total water use statewide." 2022 State Water Plan, at 59.

See Chapter 20 of this book for a discussion of regional and state water planning.

§ 1.4 Future Uses and Needs in Texas

Although everyone agrees that the demand for water in Texas will increase, the amount of that increase and the best way to prepare for that need are the subjects of ongoing debate. The state is projected to grow from approximately 29.7 million people in 2020 to 51.5 million by 2070. 2022 State Water Plan, at 47. Moreover, water use by the industrial and manufacturing sector is expected to intensify and grow from 1.3 million acre-feet in 2020 to more than 1.5 million acre-feet by 2070. 2022 State Water Plan, at 53. These additional people and the increased business and industry in Texas will require more water. To complicate issues, growth is not predicted to be equal across the state. Some areas will grow more than others, and additional water resources will be needed.

Based on current water use rates, between 2020 and 2070 municipal water demands for the state are expected to increase approximately 63 percent, from 5.2 million acre-feet to 8.5 million acre-feet. 2022 State Water Plan, at 53. Assuming Texas maintains the use patterns of the 2000s and no additional supplies are created, in the event that a drought of record returns to Texas in 2020, water users across the state will face water shortages of 4.8 million acre-feet annually; a drought of record in 2070 will result in shortages of 8.9 million acre-feet per year, leaving one-third of Texans with less than half of the municipal water supplies they require. The good news is that water demand is not predicted to escalate at the same ratio as population. Texas's water demand is expected to increase only 9 percent, from 17.7 million acre-feet in 2020 to 19.26 million acre-feet in 2070. 2022 State Water Plan, at 53. One significant reason for the moderate total increase is that more water is expected to shift from agricultural to municipal uses. 2022 State Water Plan, at 56.

Using water differently through a better understanding of conservation and efficiency can also alter these predictions. The city of El Paso exemplifies the impact that conservation and efficiency measures can have on reducing demand. In 2000, some experts projected that El Paso's water supplies would be completely depleted by 2025. E. Dan Klepper, *¡Agua Caliente!*, *Texas Parks & Wildlife* 16–17 (July 2002). Using a combination of diversification of supply, technology, and efficiency programs, the city was able to stabilize its water usage even though its population increased. Conservation efforts have reduced per capita consumption from 205 gallons per day in 1985 to less than 130 in 2017. Zoë Schlanger, *El Paso Is on the Cutting Edge of Water Conservation. It Really Has No Choice*, *Texas Observer* (Aug. 23, 2018), www.texasobserver.org/el-paso-is-on-the-cutting-edge-of-water-conservation-it-really-has-no-choice/. Over a similar time period, San Antonio reduced its per capita water use by nearly 50 percent despite a 150 percent population increase. San Antonio Water System, *SAWS Customers Make San Antonio a Conservation Star*, *San Antonio Report* (Oct. 8, 2017), https://sanantonioreport.org/saws-customers-make-san-antonio-a-conservation-star/.

Although conservation measures should be included in any water planning effort, the future of Texas water cannot rely entirely on conservation. Other solutions must be found. The 2022 State Water Plan reviews the state's current water resources and summarizes sixteen regional plans created by local planning groups. 2022 State Water Plan, at 17. See also Chapter 20 of this book for further discussion of state water planning. Based on this information, the 2022 State Water Plan proposes a series of water management strategies in an effort to plan for Texas's water future.

These include (1) designating the five river or stream segments of unique ecological value recommended by the 2021 regional water plans (Alamito Creek, Black Cypress Bayou, Black Cypress Creek, Pecan Bayou, and Terlingua Creek) for protection under Texas Water Code section 16.051(f); and (2) designating for protection under Water Code section 16.051(g) three sites of unique value for the construction of reservoirs (Coryell County Off-Channel Reservoir, Millers Creek Off-Channel Reservoir, and Parkhouse II (North)) as recommended in the 2021 regional water plans. 2022 State Water Plan, at 30–33.

In contrast to the 2017 State Water Plan, the 2022 plan recommendations were rather modest. The recommendations from the 2017 plan included a requirement that the next set of groundwater desired future conditions be adopted collectively by the district representatives of each groundwater management area by January 5, 2022, and every five years thereafter, and required that the regional water plans under development as of that same date be consistent with those adopted desired future conditions in effect on that date. 2017 State Water Plan, at 24–27. In spite of the debates over which approaches should be pursued, one thing is clear: the future of Texas is inextricably tied to the threat of water scarcity, and solutions must be found. For these solutions to be effective, the science must be understood.

III. Water and the Hydrologic Cycle

§ 1.5 Understanding the Hydrologic Cycle

Unlike other natural resources, "the total volume of water in nature is fixed and invariable." David Keith Todd, *Groundwater Hydrology* 13, 14–16 (John Wiley 2d ed. 1980) [hereinafter Todd]. Although the total quantity is unchanging, the form and the location of the water are constantly shifting. The hydrologic cycle, also known as the water cycle, is the continuous circulation of water—solid, liquid, or gas—on earth (see Plate 1). *See* C.W. Fetter, *Applied Hydrogeology* (Prentice Hall 3d ed. 1994) [hereinafter Fetter]; Michael Price, *Introducing Groundwater* (Routledge 1996) [hereinafter Price]. This persistent and perpetual cycle has no beginning or ending. Water falls to the earth's surface as precipitation, such as rain, snow, or sleet, and flows over the earth's surface into fluid bodies, including rivers, lakes, and wetlands, or solid bodies, such as snow and ice, or seeps into the ground to become groundwater. Fetter, at 5–6; Price, at 15–16. Throughout its surface travels and especially when it reaches large bodies of water, much of the water evaporates through the effects of solar energy and returns to the atmosphere, where it continues in the cycle. Fetter, at 5–6; Price, at 15–16.

As for the water that seeps into the ground, in most cases the earth acts as a conduit allowing it to travel back to the surface where it can discharge, only to evaporate into the atmosphere to start the cycle again. Todd, at 13–15. Water typically percolates into the earth vertically downward until it reaches the groundwater table, where it flows in more lateral directions through the porous spaces in the geologic formation. The rate of percolation into the subsurface and the flow of groundwater within aquifers are considerably slower than surface water flow, but both eventually allow water to return to the atmosphere and continue in the cycle. Price, at 17.

Normally, groundwater emerges in natural discharge sites, such as springs, rivers, lakes, lagoons, swamps, and the sea. Herman Bouwer, *Groundwater Hydrology* 293 (McGraw-Hill 1978) [hereinafter Bouwer] (noting that springs are the most conspicuous avenues for the natural return of groundwater to the surface). Plants also consume or absorb some groundwater, which they then transpire through their leaves back into the atmosphere. Price, at 15–16 (discussing the processes of interception and transpiration of water by foliage). Other groundwater can remain in the ground as aquifer storage, which serves as an underground reservoir from which humans can withdraw needed freshwater. However, due to the growing need for water, pumping of groundwater from wells is one of the greatest sources of aquifer discharge, the consequence of which is to divert water, at least temporarily, from the hydrologic cycle. Although the cycle may appear complex, its foundation hinges on the relationship between water in its various settings, including the surface and subsurface.

§ 1.6 Surface Water and Groundwater Interrelationship

Groundwater is a significant component of the hydrologic cycle. This is especially evident given the vast quantity of water found under the ground. Price, at 2. From a hydrologic point of view, however, groundwater is neither similar nor dissimilar to surface water resources. Ground and surface waters are, in fact, part and parcel of the same thing, namely, water moving through the various stages of the hydrologic cycle. Thomas C. Winter et al., *Ground Water and Surface Water, A Single Resource*, U.S. Geological Survey Circular 1139, 76 (1998), https://pubs.usgs.gov/circ/circ1139 [hereinafter Winter et al.] (emphasizing the importance of considering groundwater and surface water collectively). Groundwater can assist surface water by sustaining stream flows when surface runoff is low; likewise, surface recharge features, including stream beds, can assist in aquifer replenishment. Todd, at 16. The relationship between these water sources is natural; however, it is not inalterable and can be influenced by external factors. See Chapter 6 of this book regarding conjunctive management and use.

§ 1.7 Climate Change and the Hydrologic Cycle

Unfortunately, the hydrologic cycle is not immune to human impact. In addition to the dewatering of surface water and groundwater resources created by pumping, climate change affects many aspects of the hydrologic cycle. Intergovernmental Panel on Climate Change, *Climate Change 2014: Synthesis Report, Contribution of Working Groups I, II and III to the Fifth Assessment Report of the Intergovernmental Panel on Climate Change* 6 (R.K. Pachauri & L.A. Meyer eds., 2014), www.ipcc.ch/report/ar5/syr/ [hereinafter IPCC Assessment]. Human activities, such as burning fossil fuels and clearing forests, have released large quantities of carbon dioxide and other global warming gases into the atmosphere. *Massachusetts v. Environmental Protection Agency*, 549 U.S. 497, 504–07 (2007). These gases trap the sun's heat and slow its escape back into space, thereby threatening to disrupt the delicate balance needed to sustain earth's ecosystems.

During the past one hundred years, average temperatures worldwide have risen more than one degree Fahrenheit. The year 2014 was the warmest year on record since recordkeeping began in 1880, and 2011 was the driest in Texas. *See* National Aeronautics and Space Administration, *NASA, NOAA Find 2014 Warmest Year in Modern Record* (Jan. 16, 2015), www.nasa.gov/press/2015/january/nasa-determines-2014-warmest-year-in-modern-record; State Impact Texas, *Everything You Need to Know About the Texas Drought*, https://stateimpact.npr.org/texas/tag/drought/. One of the most important potential impacts of climate change is its effect on water resources. A 2014 report of the United Nation's Intergovernmental Panel on Climate Change projected that climate change will reduce both surface and groundwater availability in dry, subtropical regions (such as Texas), thereby increasing the frequency of droughts. IPCC Assessment, at 69.

The 2010–2014 drought ranked as the second-worst and second-longest statewide drought on record, with 2011 ranking as the worst one-year drought on record. 2022 State Water Plan, at 36. If model predictions about climate change are correct and such droughts become more common, global warming could significantly impact Texas's water resources. Models project that Texas will experience increasing temperatures that will reduce soil moisture. This, in turn, will affect agricultural water needs as well as the amount of water percolating through the subsurface. *The Impact of Global Warming in Texas* 42 (Gerald R. North et al. eds., University of Texas Press 1995). More heat will also result in increased evaporation, possibly affecting the economics and reliability of reservoirs and other surface water resources. Furthermore, climate change will alter precipitation patterns in Texas, shifting or decreasing rainfall across parts of the state. Decreased rainfall will diminish river flows and aquifer recharge and affect water supply planning.

The hydrologic cycle and climate change are natural processes. Because water is an integral part of human life and development, law and policy are injected into the natural process as a means for managing water resources for the benefit of people and communities. This interaction creates new and varying definitions and interpretations of nature's mechanisms that must be understood in their proper context.

Unfortunately, climate change and its potential impacts have not been integrated into the Texas State Water Plan or Texas policy. For further discussion of the effects of climate change on water resources, see Chapter 2 of this book.

§ 1.8 Relationship of the Hydrologic Cycle to Water Law

"Water law is a function of the incomplete fit between water availability and the demand for various uses." A. Dan Tarlock, *Law of Water Rights and Resources, Environmental Law Series* 2-2 (West 1998 & Supp. 2006). A common shortfall in water law is the failure to consider the entire hydrologic cycle. In Texas, for example, surface water and groundwater are regulated under different legal regimes. Whereas surface water is primarily managed under a state-run prior appropriation permit system, groundwater is owned by surface owners under the right of capture. Ownership rights can be regulated by local groundwater conservation districts where they are present. See Chapter 4 of this book regarding surface water law, Chapter 5 regarding groundwater law, and Chapter 6 regarding conjunctive management and use.

The consequence of these disparate regulatory structures is that interrelated surface water and groundwater are often managed independently and with little thought to their impact on each other. An example of this situation is the elimination of Comanche Springs in Fort Stockton, Pecos County, Texas, in the late 1950s. These surface springs became dry because of overpumping of the Edwards-Trinity Plateau Aquifer, which was drained in accordance with the rule of capture. Brune & Besse, at 357. Pumping for fruit irrigation dried up this "oasis in the desert" and severely affected the local community, which had used the springs as a tourist attraction. Art Chapman, *Running Dry*, *Fort Worth Star-Telegram* (Feb. 14, 2007), at B4; *see also Pecos County Water Control & Improvement District No. 1 v. Williams*, 271 S.W.2d 503 (Tex. App.—El Paso 1954, writ ref'd n.r.e.).

Some water law principles can be considered in the context of the hydrologic cycle. Perhaps the simplest way is through the application of conjunctive use principles. Though not incorporated into Texas law, conjunctive use principles recognize the relationship between surface water and groundwater and seek to regulate water as a system and not as individual resources. While not mandated under Texas law, conjunctive use is applied in the management of the Edwards Aquifer and the various springs fed by that aquifer. *See* Todd H. Votteler, *The Little Fish That Roared: The Endangered Species Act, State Groundwater Law, and Private Property Rights Collide over the Texas Edwards Aquifer*, 28 Envtl. L. 845 (1998) [hereinafter Votteler].

IV. The Legal and Scientific Language of Water Resources

§ 1.9 Introduction

One of the more troublesome aspects of water law can be the divergence often encountered between legal and scientific definitions, as well as among subfields of the law. Although the vocabulary used by the various communities can overlap, the meanings ascribed by each to various terms and concepts may differ significantly. For example, the scientific understanding of "surface water" is markedly different from the legal meaning provided under the Texas Water Code (see section 1.10 below). Moreover, that term has different legal definitions depending on whether it is used in the context of water quality standards or water rights (see section 1.10:3 below). At the very least, such differences can result in confusion or misunderstanding. At worse, they can result in distinctions that fail to reflect scientific reality or misapply the law. Accordingly, it is imperative that anyone who enters the field of water law be well versed in the scientific and various legal understandings of the terms and concepts relevant to the subject matter.

§ 1.10 Understanding Surface Water

Surface water is the water resource most familiar and understandable to people because, unlike groundwater, it is visible and tangible. Generally, surface water is water that exists on the surface of the earth. It can take many forms but most commonly occurs as rivers, streams, lakes, wetlands, and reservoirs. Surface water also includes the solid forms of water—snow and ice. Winter et al., at 1.

As a legal matter, when "surface water" is discussed with reference to water rights the phrase is often used interchangeably with the term "state water." Under section 11.021(a) of the Texas Water Code, "state water" is defined as "[t]he water of the ordinary flow, underflow, and tides of every flowing river, natural stream, and lake, and of every bay or arm of the Gulf of Mexico, and the storm water, floodwater, and rainwater of every river, natural stream, canyon, ravine, depression, and watershed in the state." Tex. Water Code § 11.021(a). By definition and by case law interpretation, it does not include "diffused surface water." *See Dietrich v. Goodman*, 123 S.W.3d 413, 417–18 (Tex. App.—Houston [14th Dist.] 2003, no pet.).

Diffused surface water refers to "water or natural precipitation diffused over the surface of the ground until it either evaporates, is absorbed by the land, or reaches a bed or channel in which water is accustomed to flowing." *Raburn v. KJI Bluechip Investments*, 50 S.W.3d 699, 704 (Tex. App.—Fort Worth 2001, no pet.) (citations omitted); *Dietrich*, 123 S.W.3d at 418–19. As a result, and in contrast to the scientific understanding of the term, diffused water is never found in a natural watercourse. *Dietrich*, 123 S.W.3d at 418. Accordingly, diffused water belongs to the landowner until it enters a natural watercourse. State water in Texas does not include diffused surface water or groundwater and is the property of the state. *See* Tex. Water Code § 11.021(a).

Based on the above definition, only water in a watercourse constitutes state water. As defined by Texas case law, a "watercourse" is any "body of water flowing in a reasonably definite channel with bed and banks." *Watts v. State*, 140 S.W.3d 860, 866 (Tex. App.—Houston [14th Dist.] 2004, pet. ref'd) (quoting *Black's Law Dictionary* 1585 (7th ed. 1999)). To constitute a watercourse, the body of water must have (1) a bank and bed, (2) a current of water, and (3) a permanent supply source of water. *Hoefs v. Short*, 273 S.W. 785, 786–87 (Tex. 1925); *see also* 30 Tex. Admin. Code § 297.1(60) (defining a "watercourse" as "[a] definite channel of a stream in which water flows within a defined bed and banks, originating from a definite source or sources" and noting that the "water may flow continuously or intermittently, and if the latter with some degree of regularity, depending on the characteristics of the sources").

Permanent does not mean continuous, but rather an established source of water that occurs with some regularity such that it "establish[es] and maintain[s] a running stream for considerable periods of time." *Hoefs*, 273 S.W. at 788. In some cases, it can include streams that may be dry for extended periods of time. *Hoefs*, 273 S.W. at 787. Moreover, according to *Watts*, a watercourse "may be either artificial, *i.e.*, man-made, or natural." *Watts*, 140 S.W.3d at 866 (citing *Black's Law Dictionary* at 1586). As a result, under Texas law, the vast majority of Texas lakes, rivers, streams, channels, and other conduits of water are watercourses.

Outside of the Water Code, the legal definition of "surface water" in Texas varies. One Texas court of appeals indicated that "[i]n common usage, the term simply means 'natural water that has not penetrated much below the surface of the ground.'" *Dietrich*, 123 S.W.3d at 417 (citing *Webster's Third New International Dictionary* 2300 (1993)). This "common" understanding appears to comport with the general definition provided for surface water under chapter 30 of the Texas Administrative Code, which encompasses—

> [l]akes, bays, ponds, impounding reservoirs, springs, rivers, streams, creeks, estuaries, wetlands, marshes, inlets, canals, the Gulf of Mexico inside the territorial limits of the state [from the mean high water mark (MHWM) out 10.36 miles into the Gulf], and all other bodies of surface water, natural or artificial, inland or coastal, fresh or salt, navigable or nonnavigable, and including the beds and banks of all water-courses and bodies of surface water, that are wholly or partially inside or bordering the state or subject to the jurisdiction of the state; except that waters in treatment systems that are authorized by state or federal law, regulation, or permit, and which are created for the purpose of waste treatment are not considered to be water in the state.

30 Tex. Admin. Code § 307.3(a)(70). That definition, however, is applicable only in the context of surface water quality standards. See also Chapter 39 of this book discussing the definition of surface water in relation to flood management.

§ 1.10:1 Headwaters and Mouth of a River

Rivers are large natural streams of water flowing in channels and emptying into larger bodies of water. Brian J. Skinner & Stephen C. Porter, *Physical Geology* 270 (John Wiley 1987). The beginning of a river is its source, also called the headwaters. Located at higher elevations, the source may be fed by an underground spring or by runoff from rain, snowmelt, or glacial melt. E.C. Pielou, *Fresh Water* 81–82 (University of Chicago Press 1998) [hereinafter Pielou]. In contrast, the river mouth is the end point of a river; it is where a river flows into a larger body of water, such as another river, a lake, or an ocean. V.N. Mikhailov, *Principles of Typification and Zoning of River Mouth Areas*, 31 Water Res. 1 (Jan. 2004).

§ 1.10:2 Tributary

River systems consist of a network of links and nodes that make up the middle portion of a river. These links and nodes are called tributaries. Michael A. Summerfield, *Global Geomorphology* 208–09 (Longman 1991) [hereinafter Summerfield]. A tributary is a stream that flows into and contributes to a larger stream or another body of water. *Cf.* Tex. Water Code § 41.009, art. I(e) (defining "tributary" in the Rio Grande Compact to mean "any stream which naturally contributes to the flow of the Rio Grande"), *and* Tex. Water Code § 46.013, art. III(e) (defining "tributary" in the Red River Compact to mean "any stream which contributes to the flow of the Red River"). As more and more tributaries join together, the flow accumulates and expands the size of the river. Summerfield, at 208–09. Some rivers have many branches, or bifurcations, of tributaries, while others do not. Because water supply in a river is achieved through accumulation, the flow of each tributary is important, and its absence can have impacts downstream. Summerfield, at 208–09.

§ 1.10:3 Watershed, Drainage Basin, and Catchment Area

A watershed, also referred to as a drainage basin or catchment area, is the area of land surface in which water, generated by precipitation, flows or drains from the land into a particular river, stream, or the ocean. Summerfield, at 207; U.S. Geological Survey, Water Science School, *Dictionary of Water Terms*, www.usgs.gov/special-topic/water-science-school/science/dictionary-water-terms. Watersheds are generally well defined and can be identified by tracing a line along the highest elevations between two areas on a map. Areas of higher elevation that form the boundaries of a watershed are called drainage divides. Summerfield, at 207. These irregular boundaries generally follow local topography. William S. Carlsen et al., *Watershed Dynamics* 4 (National Science Teachers Association 2004) [hereinafter Carlsen et al.].

Watersheds vary greatly in size and shapes depending on regional geology. Carlsen et al., at 4–5; Pielou, at 84–86. Large watersheds, like the area that drains into the Mississippi River, contain many smaller watersheds, or subwatersheds, that flow into the river. Carlsen et al., at 5; Coastal America, *Toward a Watershed Approach: A Framework for Aquatic Ecosystem Restoration, Protection, and Management* (1994). Under Texas case law, "[a] 'watershed' is a topographical designation to describe an area in which surface water flows during a rain event because of gravity toward a 'watercourse' such as a river, bayou, ditch or creek." *Texas Woman's University v. The Methodist Hospital*, 221 S.W.3d 267, 275–76 (Tex. App.—Houston [1st Dist.] 2006, no pet.). Under title 30 of the Texas Administrative Code, a "watershed" "designate[s] the area drained by a stream and its tributaries, or the drainage area upstream from a specified point on a stream." 30 Tex. Admin. Code § 297.1(62). This latter definition applies to procedural and substantive water rights (30 Tex. Admin. Code chs. 295 and 297, respectively) as well as water conservation and drought contingency plans (30 Tex. Admin. Code ch. 288).

§ 1.10:4 Base Flow

The water in a river consists of water from various sources. River discharge is the volume of water that passes through a given cross section of the river in a set amount of time. The quantity of discharge sustained without the addition of water from precipitation, runoff, or melting snow is called "base flow." Summerfield, at 193. Under title 30 of the Texas Administrative Code, base flow is "[t]he portion of streamflow uninfluenced by recent rainfall or flood runoff and is comprised of springflow, seepage, discharge from artesian wells or other groundwater sources, and the delayed drainage of large lakes and swamps." 30 Tex. Admin. Code § 297.1(6). Under certain circumstances, "[a]ccountable effluent discharges from municipal, industrial, agricultural, or other uses of ground or surface waters may be included" in determining base flow. 30 Tex. Admin. Code § 297.1(6). Base flow is important because it is a quantity of water that maintains a perennial or continuous stream.

§ 1.10:5 Underflow

Under Texas law, "underflow" refers to water found within the bed and banks of a river. Although this water is found within the ground, it is regarded as "state water" and is subject to prior appropriation. According to title 30 of the Texas Administrative Code, the underflow of a river refers to—

> [w]ater in sand, soil, and gravel below the bed of the watercourse, together with the water in the lateral extensions of the water-bearing material on each side of the surface channel, such that the surface flows are in contact with the subsurface flows, the latter flows being confined within a space reasonably defined and having a direction corresponding to that of the surface flow.

30 Tex. Admin. Code § 297.1(56).

§ 1.10:6 Environmental Flows

"Environmental flows" refers to both instream flows and freshwater inflows into bays and estuaries. At its most basic level, "instream flows" means the water in streams, rivers, and lakes. *See* Tom Annear et al., *Instream Flows for Riverine Resource Stewardship* 1 (Instream Flow Council 2002) [hereinafter Annear et al.]. Instream flows support a variety of fishery and aquatic wildlife resources and the ecological processes of riverine systems. Annear et al., at xix. Freshwater inflows into bays and estuaries contain the water necessary to sustain a broad range of biological needs in those coastal systems. Rivers serve many functions, including moderating floods and droughts, renewing soil fertility, often recharging certain aquifers, and providing habitat and breeding sites for fish and wildlife. Sandra Postel & Brian Richter, *Rivers for Life: Managing Water for People and Nature* 2 (Island Press 2003). Freshwater from rivers meets and mixes with seawater in estuaries, dynamic systems that in Texas create diverse wetlands that support the production of 100 million pounds of seafood annually and sustain a birding paradise. Larry McKinney, *Texas: The State of Rivers*, *Texas Parks & Wildlife* 23 (July 2004), www.tpwmagazine.com/archive/2004/jul/ed_2/. In 2007, as part of the omnibus bill Senate Bill 3, the legislature enacted a new statutory scheme for protecting the environmental flows that support the state's riverine and bay systems. See Chapter 11 of this book regarding environmental flows.

§ 1.11 Understanding Groundwater

Groundwater makes up only three-quarters of 1 percent of the total volume of fresh and saltwater found in nature. Nonetheless, it makes up nearly 97 percent of the freshwater readily available on earth for human use. *See* Bouwer, at 1–3.

Water is found throughout the subsurface in various quantities. The term "groundwater," however, does not encompass all subsurface waters. Rather, it specifically pertains to subsurface water found within the saturated zone of a porous geologic formation that may be naturally or mechanically extracted. The saturated zone is the "[p]ortion of the geologic profile below the groundwater table, in which the pores or voids between the soil particles are filled with water." *Kansas v. Colorado*, No. 105, 1994 WL 16189353, at *1 (U.S. Oct. 3, 1994); *see also Shurbet v. United States*, 242 F. Supp. 736, 740 (N.D. Tex. 1961) (describing the saturated zone as "the underground area containing water-bearing material from which water can be artificially extracted"); *cf.* 30 Tex. Admin. Code §§ 330.3(134), 334.481(51), 335.1(142) (defining the saturated zone as "[t]hat part of the earth's crust in which all voids are filled with water" in the context of rules for industrial solid and municipal hazard wastes). Groundwater does not include water found in the unsaturated zone of such formations. *See Price*, at 7 (describing the difference between surface water and groundwater); Ralph C. Heath, *Basic Ground-Water Hydrology*, Water Supply Paper 2220, at 1, 4 (U.S. Geological Survey, 10th prtg. 2004, rev.) [hereinafter Heath]. In the context of underground and aboveground storage tanks, the unsaturated zone is defined in title 30 of the Texas Administrative Code as—

> [t]he subsurface zone containing water under pressure less than that of the atmosphere (including water held by capillary forces within the soil) and containing air or gases generally under atmospheric pressure. This zone is bounded at the top by the ground surface and at the bottom by the upper surface of the zone of saturation (i.e., the water table).

30 Tex. Admin. Code § 334.2(123); *cf.* 30 Tex. Admin. Code § 334.481(62) (applicable in the context of the storage, treatment, and reuse procedures for petroleum-substance contaminated soil related to underground and aboveground storage tanks), *and* 30 Tex. Admin. Code § 335.1(177) (applicable in the context of industrial solid and municipal hazardous wastes) (describing the unsaturated zone as "[t]he zone between the land surface and the water table"). It is economically infeasible and often physically impossible to pump water from the unsaturated zone.

In Texas, "groundwater" is defined as "water percolating below the surface of the earth." Tex. Water Code §§ 35.002(5), 36.001(5); *cf.* 30 Tex. Admin. Code § 297.1(21) (defining groundwater as "[w]ater under the surface of the ground other than underflow of a stream and underground streams, whatever may be the geologic structure in which it is standing or moving"); Tex. Spec. Dist. Code § 8801.001(4) (defining groundwater as "water located beneath the earth's surface" but excluding "water produced with oil in the production of oil and gas"); 30 Tex. Admin. Code §§ 330.3(61), 334.481(28), 335.1(68); 31 Tex. Admin. Code § 601.3(6) (defining groundwater as "[w]ater below the land surface in a zone of saturation"). A groundwater reservoir is a "specific subsurface water-bearing reservoir having ascertainable boundaries containing groundwater." Tex. Water Code §§ 35.002(6), 36.001(6). Groundwater in Texas is specifically excluded from the definition of state water and is subject to the rule of capture as modified by the various groundwater conservation districts across the state. See Chapter 5 of this book for a discussion of the rule of capture. This is true even where percolating water supplies a surface stream. *See Denis v. Kickapoo Land Co.*, 771 S.W.2d 235, 236 (Tex. App.—Austin 1989, writ denied).

The scientific definition of groundwater does not include a water quality metric. This means that nonpotable water with high TDS is included; however, Texas law does not clarify whether current groundwater laws and regulations apply to brackish groundwater. The issue was raised in the 2013 legislative session and will likely arise again.

§ 1.11:1 Aquifer

An "aquifer" is a relatively permeable geologic formation (composed of unconsolidated material such as sand or gravel) that has sufficient water storage and transmitting capacity to provide a useful water supply via wells and springs. *See* Heath, at 6; Price, at 9; *cf.* 30 Tex. Admin. Code §§ 330.3(8) (describing an "aquifer" as "[a] geological formation, group of formations, or portion of a formation capable of yielding significant quantities of groundwater to wells or springs"), 335.1(8) (describing an "aquifer" as "[a] geologic formation, group of formations, or part of a formation capable of yielding a significant amount of groundwater to wells or springs"), 230.2(2) (defining an "aquifer" as "[a] geologic formation, group of formations, or part of a formation that contains water in its voids or pores and may be used as a source of water supply"), *and Mitchell Energy Corp. v. Bartlett*, 958 S.W.2d 430, 434 (Tex. App.—Fort Worth 1997, writ denied) (asserting that "[a]n aquifer is an underground rock stratum with sufficient permeability to permit movement of water through it"). Accordingly, an aquifer encompasses the saturated portion or saturated zone within a porous geologic formation.

It is noteworthy that aquifers are very often in a state of flux, meaning that the volume of water contained or flowing through the geologic formation is constantly changing. These changes are the result of variations in the amount of water flowing into (recharge) and out of (discharge) the saturated zone. When the water table (see definition at section 1.11:2 below) drops during a drought or when human withdrawals exceed recharge, the portion of the geologic formation that is described as an "aquifer" decreases in volume. Conversely, when the water table rises as a result of rainfall or another increase in recharge, or even a reduction in human withdrawals, the portion of the geologic formation that conforms to the definition of an "aquifer" increases in volume.

All aquifers have an impermeable base layer that prevents water from seeping to lower-lying strata, thus creating a natural water reservoir within the porous geologic formation. *See* Bouwer, at 4 (listing some materials that constitute the impermeable layer, including clays or "other fine-textured granular material, or of shale, solid limestone, igneous rock, or other bedrock"). At any given location, the land surface may be underlain by one or more distinct aquifers separated by impermeable layers (like different apartments separated by floors in a multilevel apartment building), depending on the composition of the underlying strata. *See* Fetter, at 511.

Unconfined or Water-Table Aquifer: An *unconfined aquifer* (see Figure 1) is an aquifer bounded by an impermeable base layer of rock or sediments and overlain by layers of permeable materials extending from the land surface to the impermeable base of the aquifer. *See Shurbet v. United States*, 242 F. Supp. 736, 741 (N.D. Tex. 1961) (defining an "unconfined aquifer" as an aquifer "in which the water is not confined between two impervious layers and in which the water level in a well drilled in the aquifer reflects the general level of the water table throughout the aquifer"); *see also* Heath, at 6; Price, at 10–11. Such an aquifer also may be referred to as a *water-table aquifer* because its upper limit is defined by the water table. *Cf.* Heath, at 6.

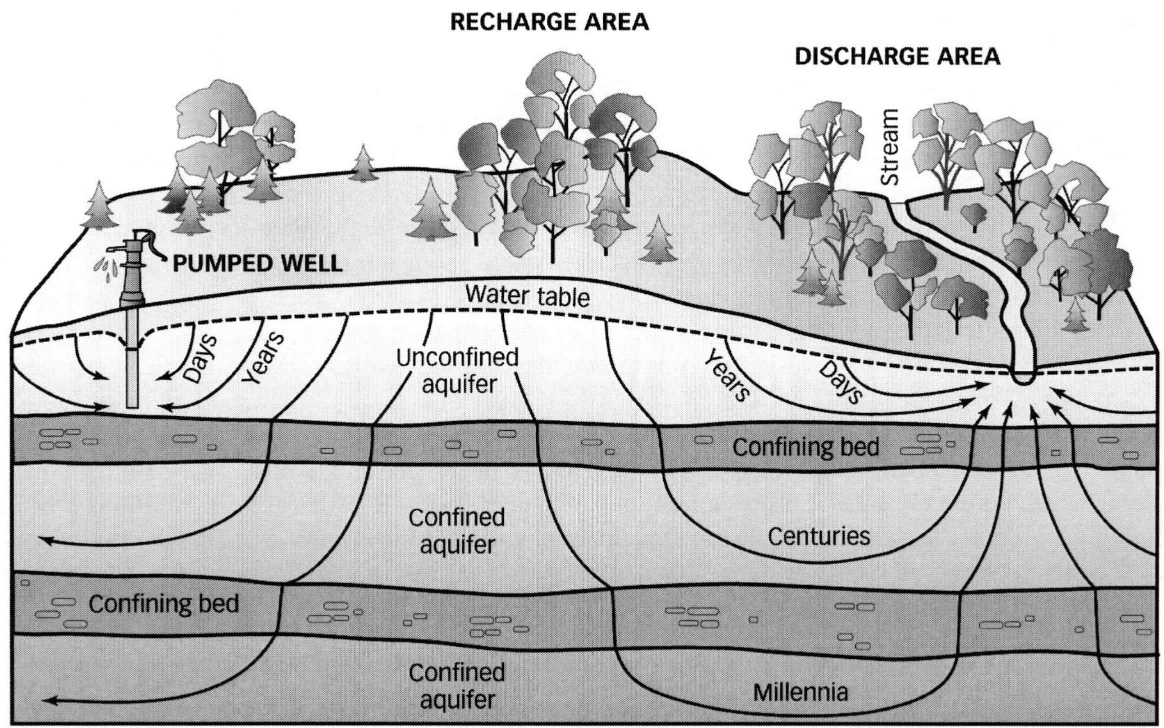

Figure 1. Diagram of an unconfined aquifer overlaying confined aquifers and groundwater flow paths with general length, depth, and travel time from points of recharge to points of discharge. Thomas C. Winter et al., *Ground Water and Surface Water, A Single Resource*, U.S. Geological Survey Circular 1139, 5 (1998), https://pubs.usgs.gov/circ/circ1139.

Although not always the case, unconfined aquifers are often directly related to a surface water body, such as a river or lake. *See* Bouwer, at 4, 6 (explaining that seepage and drainage from rivers and lakes connect unconfined aquifers to surface bodies of water). Rivers, for example, tend to have interrelated unconfined aquifers located directly underneath and following the course of the riverbed. *See* Bouwer, at 3–4 (noting that, depending on the strata underneath and beside the river, an unconfined aquifer hydraulically related to a river is generally spread out laterally on both sides of and below the river). This scenario can create significant complications when considering the legal distinctions between a river's underflow and an interrelated aquifer (see definition of underflow at section 1.10:5 above). Unconfined aquifers, however, can also exist independent of a surface body of water. The Ogallala Aquifer is an example of an unconfined aquifer with little hydraulic connection to any surface water bodies. Rex C. Buchanan et al., *The High Plains Aquifer*, Publ. Info. Circular 18, at 1 (KA Geol. Survey, 2001), www.kgs.ku.edu/Publications/pic18/index.html [hereinafter Buchanan et al.].

Confined or Artesian Aquifer: In contrast, a *confined aquifer* (also known as an *artesian aquifer*) (see Figure 1) is an aquifer contained between two impermeable layers—the base, or "floor," and the "ceiling" strata—that subject the stored water to hydrostatic pressure exceeding atmospheric pressure. *See Shurbet*, 242 F. Supp. at 741 (defining a confined aquifer as an aquifer that "is confined under hydrostatic pressure between two relatively impermeable beds, and in which the water level in a well drilled in the aquifer will rise above the top of the aquifer"); *see also* Heath, at 6; Price, at 10–11. If a well is drilled through the impermeable upper layer of the aquifer, the confining or hydrostatic pressure within the confined aquifer propels water through the well toward the surface. *See Shurbet*, 242 F. Supp.

at 741; *see also* Fetter, at 110. The water may rise a considerable distance above the top of the aquifer and may spout above the ground surface. *See* Fetter, at 110.

As an example, consider a U-shaped tube filled with water. If one were to attach a vertical pipe (or "well") in the center of the tube between the two raised arms, water would be propelled upward into the vertical pipe at the point where it is attached. The water in the pipe would rise as a result of the pressure until it reached a point where the hydrostatic pressure equals atmospheric pressure.

Where a well is drilled into a confined aquifer, the well acts as a partial relief valve for the confining pressure in the aquifer. Water in the well will rise until the hydrostatic pressure equals atmospheric pressure. If the water level in the well rises and spouts above the ground surface, the well is called a *flowing artesian well*. *See* Heath, at 6.

Despite their name, confined aquifers are not devoid of any connection to surface water or other water resources. *See* Bouwer, at 4–5 (relating that confined aquifers may transmit water vertically to surface waters, and vice versa, through an aquitard—a layer of strata less permeable than the aquifer, but not totally impermeable). Such aquifers must have a water source and often are recharged through lateral flow of water from recharge zones located at distant higher elevations, such as mountains or high plateaus, where the aquifer crops out on the land surface. *See* Bouwer, at 5. In addition, confined aquifers can themselves discharge into rivers and lakes at lower elevations. *See* Bouwer, at 6 (noting that "[h]illside seeps and springs occur where the aquifer and its lower impermeable boundary are exposed to the atmosphere at hillsides, canyons, etc.").

Nonrecharging Aquifer: Aquifers that receive little or no recharge are described as nonrecharging aquifers. *Cf.* Fetter, at 288. The water in such aquifers is typically stagnant, with little if any flow. In most cases, these aquifers contain very old groundwater that has been trapped in a geologic formation for centuries or eons because the aquifer is physically isolated from sources of recharge, the surrounding formations are impermeable, or there is a paucity of recharge in an arid region. *See* Bouwer, at 7; Fetter, at 364.

Often found in arid and semiarid climates, nonrecharging aquifers are important sources of water for many parts of the United States. The Ogallala Aquifer in the central United States is an example of an unconfined aquifer with relatively limited recharge. Located at depths ranging from a few meters to hundreds of meters below the surface, the water in this aquifer is estimated to be thousands to millions of years old. *See* Manjula V. Guru & James E. Horne, The Kerr Center for Sustainable Agriculture, *The Ogallala Aquifer* (2000), http://kerrcenter.com/wp-content/uploads/2014/11/ogallala_aquifer.pdf. While the overlying strata are still relatively permeable, present-day recharge rates range from minuscule to nil. Buchanan et al., at 2, 5.

§ 1.11:2 Water Table

The term "water table" generally refers to the upper limit of a saturated geologic formation (see Figure 1). *See Shurbet v. United States*, 242 F. Supp. 736, 740 (N.D. Tex. 1961); *see also* Winter et al., at 6. This definition, however, is more applicable to unconfined aquifers. (See discussion of "unconfined aquifer" at section 1.11:1 above.) A water table is more correctly described as the level in the saturated zone of a saturated geologic formation in which the hydraulic pressure is equal to atmospheric pressure. *See* Heath, at 4; *see also* 30 Tex. Admin. Code § 330.3(176) (describing the water table in the context of municipal solid waste as "[t]he upper surface of the zone of saturation at which water pressure is equal to atmospheric pressure, except where that surface is formed by a confining unit"). Thus, in an unconfined aquifer, the water table is represented by the top of the saturated zone of the geologic formation. In a confined aquifer (see discussion of "confined aquifer" at section 1.11:1 above), the water table is evidenced by the level to which the water naturally rises in an unused well.

§ 1.11:3 Functioning of an Aquifer

The "functioning" of an aquifer refers to how a particular aquifer works or operates as an aquifer. Aquifers typically store and transport water and dilute wastes and other contaminants; provide a habitat for aquatic biota; and serve as a source of freshwater and nutrients to aquifer-dependent ecosystems. Some aquifers even provide geothermal heat. Each of these is a function of an aquifer. All functions are dependent on the particular aquifer's hydrostatic pressure, hydraulic conductiveness, and mineralogical, biological, and chemical attributes. Moreover, those functions may be interdependent to the extent that the aquifer's continued operation depends on the continuation of the particular function or series of functions. *See generally* Heath, at 14–15 (describing the basic "functions" of groundwater systems).

§ 1.11:4 Groundwater Flow

Aquifers and groundwater are sometimes mistakenly perceived as underground lakes or rivers. In reality, they are neither. In most aquifers, water is rarely stagnant (except in aquifers with no recharge) and tends to flow toward natural discharge sites, such as springs, rivers, lakes, lagoons, swamps, or the sea. *See* Bouwer, at 36 (asserting that "[u]ndergroundwater is almost always in motion"); Heath, at 20. Water in an aquifer resides in the pore spaces of a geologic formation similar to water in a sponge, where the water fills all the small holes. The material found in a geologic formation, though, is far less elastic or pliable than that of a sponge. Accordingly, water flowing through an aquifer does so by seeping through the available pore spaces.

One notable consequence of this water flow process is that the rate or velocity of flow is typically far slower than any water flow perceived on the land surface, such as in rivers and streams. Groundwater velocities commonly range from one meter per day to one meter per year. *See* W. Kenneth Hamblin & Eric H. Christiansen, *Earth's Dynamic Systems* 325 (Prentice Hall 10th ed. 2001); *see also* Heath, at 25 (noting that "[t]he rate of movement of groundwater is greatly overestimated by many people, including those who think in terms of groundwater moving through 'veins' and underground rivers at the rates commonly observed in surface streams. . . . It would be more appropriate to compare the rate of movement of groundwater to the movement of water in the middle of a very large lake being drained by a very small stream."). Although water generally flows at low velocity underground, an exception can occur in karst aquifers, such as the Edwards Aquifer. Karst aquifers generally consist of limestone. Because of the chemical composition of limestone (calcium carbonate), such aquifers are more prone to having their matrix dissolved by the water, which results in the formation of larger pores and cavities through which the water can flow at much faster rates. See Chapter 17 of this book regarding the Edwards Aquifer Authority.

The rate at which water flows in an aquifer is a function of hydraulic potential. *See* Heath, at 25. Hydraulic potential is the ability of an aquifer to transmit water. Hydraulic potential of surface water is primarily dependent on gravity and the slope of the land surface. Although gravity plays a central role in determining the hydraulic potential of groundwater, aquifer porosity and permeability (the ability of the aquifer to transmit water), the gradient or slope of the groundwater table (or the hydraulic gradient in the case of a confined aquifer), and temperature also play a significant role in determining the rate at which water will flow through the geologic formation. *See* Heath, at 20–25.

§ 1.11:5 Aquifer Recharge

Aquifers may recharge from precipitation-soaked ground, from lakes and streams, and, to some extent, from other aquifers. *See* Bouwer, at 4–6 (explaining that seepage and draining from rivers and lakes connect unconfined aquifers to surface bodies of water and that water in confined aquifers is derived mostly from rainfall in higher elevations where the aquifer is exposed to the surface); Fetter, at 512 (noting that confined aquifers may recharge from other aquifers). A recharge zone is the area from which a body of water is recharged. R. Allen Freeze & John A. Cherry, *Ground Water* 194 (Prentice Hall 1979); *see* 30 Tex. Admin. Code § 285.2(22) (defining "recharge zone" in the context of the Edwards Aquifer as "[t]hat area where the stratigraphic units constituting the Edwards Aquifer crop out, including the outcrops of other geologic formations in proximity to the Edwards Aquifer, where caves, sinkholes, faults, fractures, or other permeable features would create a potential for recharge of surface waters into the Edwards Aquifer. The recharge zone is identified as a geographic area delineated on official maps located in the agency's central office and in the appropriate regional office, or as amended by Chapter 213 of this title."); 30 Tex. Admin. Code § 213.3(27). Significantly, certain human activities, such as irrigation operations, dike and canal building, and damming projects, may also recharge aquifers. *See* Winter et al., at 57, 68. Aquifer recharge is a function of both gravity and the permeability of the strata lying between the aquifer and the source of the recharge. As a result, aquifers can transmit to and serve as a source of water for lakes, streams, and other aquifers. Many argue that enhanced aquifer recharge and storage should be used as a water management strategy.

§ 1.11:6 Aquifer Discharge

Most aquifers have natural discharge points that allow their water to exit the aquifer. Such natural discharge zones include springs, rivers, lakes, lagoons, swamps, and the sea. *See* Bouwer, at 293. Aquifers, however, may also be discharged artificially. A well, for example, is an artificial means of aquifer discharge.

Cone of Depression: Water from water wells is usually produced by the use of a pump intake lowered into a water well. *See* Heath, at 30 (stating that the pump-intake action causes the water level of the well to fall). As a result of the pumping action, a pumping water well typically generates a flow of groundwater in the immediate vicinity of the well. The water converges radially from all directions on the well's intake pipe, resulting in a *cone of depression*—a curved, funnel-shaped depression in the water levels—centered at the pumping well. The largest drop in the groundwater level occurs in the center of the "funnel," that is, at the pumping well, and diminishes with distance from the pumping well. The shape and dimensions of the cone of depression—the amount of drop in the groundwater table at any given point around the pumping well—depend on the permeability of the aquifer material and the rate of pumping. *See* Heath, at 30–32.

Radius of Influence: The radial distance from a pumping well at which the drop in the groundwater table declines to nil is the *radius of influence* or the *radius of the cone of depression* for that particular water well at the specified rate of production. *See* Heath, at 30 (explaining that "because water must converge on the well from all directions and because the area through which the flow occurs decreases toward the well, the hydraulic gradient must get steeper toward the well"). Water outside the radius of influence (beyond the influence of the pumping well) does not flow toward the pump intake but rather in its normal flow pattern.

§ 1.12 Surface Water and Groundwater Interaction

Surface water and groundwater are interrelated parts of a larger system and can interact in a range of ways. Water does not flow in only one direction; therefore, surface water can contribute to groundwater, and vice versa. As discussed at section 1.6 above, groundwater and surface water are fundamentally interconnected in the hydrologic cycle. Understanding a water resource is incomplete without realizing the relationship between the surface and subsurface waters. Surface water percolates down into the ground to become groundwater. This water then flows laterally and eventually returns to the surface at a spring, the ocean, or other low-lying areas.

One of the more common routes of interaction is through streams. Streams can gain or lose water to the subsurface or both. This direction of flow is affected by many factors, including season, altitude, storm events, or local pumping. William M. Alley et al., *Sustainability of Ground-Water Resources*, U.S. Geological Survey Circular 1186, 30 (1999), https://pubs.usgs.gov/circ/circ1186/pdf/circ1186.pdf [hereinafter Alley et al.]. Lakes, wetlands, and reservoirs can have similar relationships with groundwater. Groundwater also discharges into the ocean in regions where there are low scarps and terraces and where surface water and groundwater mix in the tidal zones. Winter et al., at 42. Estuaries, which are common in Texas, create an interface between the ocean and discharges of freshwater. The addition of freshwater from rivers and groundwater is important to the maintenance and health of an estuary. Larry McKinney, *Why Bays Matter*, *Texas Parks & Wildlife* 24–25 (July 2003), www.tpwmagazine.com/archive/2003/jul/ed_2/ [hereinafter McKinney, *Why Bays Matter*].

Relationships between surface water and groundwater resources can vary in time and space. Price, at 10–11, 16. A river, for example, may discharge water into a related aquifer at one point of its course and receive water from groundwater at another, or a given stretch of a river may discharge into an aquifer during the autumn season and receive water in the spring. Understanding this association is important in water planning and anticipating water quantity and protecting water quality.

The interaction of water above and below ground extends beyond the movement between bodies of water. Groundwater flows laterally to areas of lower elevation before eventually discharging at the surface. Although this discharge can be into surface water bodies, it can also be in the form of springs or seeps. Springs occur where the water table intersects with the surface or where water from a confined aquifer is forced to the surface through fissures or fractures. Alley et al., at 43; William F. Guyton & Assoc., Texas Department of Water Resources Report 234: *Geohydrology of Comal, San Marcos, and Hueco Springs* 20 (June 1979), www.twdb.texas.gov/publications/reports/numbered_reports/doc/R234/r234.pdf. This means that a change in the water table or hydrostatic pressure can influence spring flow. If the water table drops below the surface, or if the hydrostatic pressure drops sufficiently, water in the spring ceases to flow. Springs often form the headwaters for rivers and can be an important water source as well as a cultural feature, especially in Texas. McKinney, *The State of Springs*. Therefore, their protection is intrinsic to the understanding and security of groundwater resources.

See Chapter 6 of this book regarding conjunctive management and use.

§ 1.12:1 Chemical and Physical Interaction

As water flows in both directions between the surface and the subsurface, chemical elements move with it. This transfer affects the supply of carbon, oxygen, nutrients, and other chemicals that enhance biogeochemical processes on both sides of the interface. When water enters the land surface, the chemistry of the soil is affected. The organic matter in the soil starts to degrade, lowering the pH of the water. Depending on the amount of time the groundwater remains in the ground, a range of chemical changes can take place. Winter et al., at 22–23. Groundwater chemistry cannot be separated between a surface water body and its interrelated groundwater.

Because of this interaction, contaminants can also be transported from one water resource to another, damaging the quality of both. This problem is exacerbated in a gaining stream (see definition at section 1.12:2 below) when groundwater reductions decrease the surface water flow, thus further concentrating contamination in the stream. Alley et al., at 62. Almost all human activity can be a source of contamination. For example, agricultural fertilizers and pesticides can be as harmful to water quality as industrial discharges and by-products. Alley et al., at 60–61. Therefore, protection of water quality must take all related bodies into consideration.

§ 1.12:2 Influent and Effluent Relationship

One of the primary ways that groundwater and surface water interact is through streams. Although this interaction can happen in various landscapes, it occurs in three basic ways: (1) the stream can gain water from the groundwater, (2) the stream can lose water to the groundwater, or (3) both can happen. Surface water resources hydraulically linked to an aquifer are often described as *influent* or *effluent* bodies of water, depending on the direction the water is flowing. *See* Fetter, at 58–59.

Water generally flows from higher elevation to lower elevation. An *influent*, or *losing*, stream or lake (see Figure 2) occurs when the groundwater table is below the bottom of a surface body of water and the soil is relatively permeable. In this situation, water percolates from the surface water body downward and recharges the underlying aquifer. Winter et al., at 9. In contrast, an *effluent*, or *gaining*, stream or lake (see Figure 2) results where the groundwater table is at an elevation higher than the intersected stream channel or lake and recharges the surface water resource. *See* Fetter, at 58–59. It is also possible that a stream can gain in some parts and lose in others. *See* Fetter, at 58–59.

This differentiation is important, especially in the context of water quality and contamination. For example, a polluted river that is effluent will not contaminate the related groundwater on either side of the river because it does not contribute water to the aquifer. Likewise, polluted groundwater on one side of an effluent river will contaminate the river but may not affect the quality of the groundwater on the other side of the river.

Although seemingly straightforward, the relationship between rivers and groundwater can become complex. As explained, rivers that hydraulically link to an aquifer can be influent at one point of the river and effluent at another point with the same or a different aquifer. Winter et al., at 9. Moreover, a river that is influent during normal climatic conditions may temporarily become effluent during heavy rains and flooding, when the ground becomes saturated and the water table rises above the intersected river. Alley et al., at 30. Such changes can also be very localized—for example, where one side of a river is effluent and the other side is influent. Such conditions might occur as a result of heavy groundwater pumping on the second side of the river resulting in a localized lowering of the water table. Whether a river is influent or effluent at any particular point is dependent on various factors such as topography, amount and rate of precipitation, soil permeability, and hydraulic conductivity of the soil underlying the river, as well as human intervention. Alley et al., at 30.

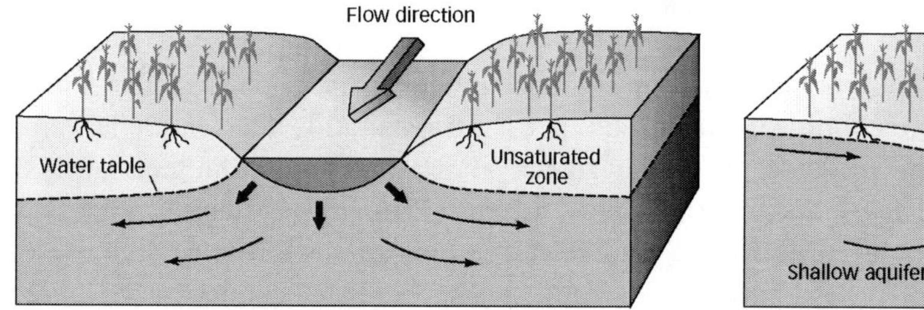

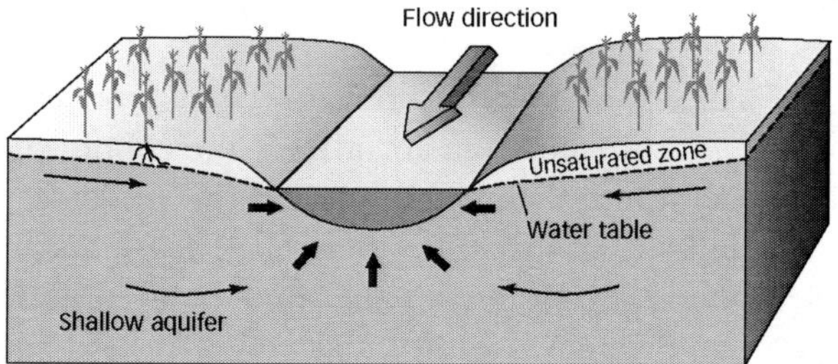

Figure 2. Aquifer-stream relationships showing an influent, or losing, stream at left and an effluent, or gaining, stream at right. Thomas C. Winter et al., *Ground Water and Surface Water, A Single Resource*, U.S. Geological Survey Circular 1139, 9 (1998), https://pubs.usgs.gov/circ/circ1139.

Groundwater can also interact with the surface water in lakes or reservoirs. A lake can receive groundwater inflow through its entire lake bed or through portions of the lake bed, or it can lose water to the subsurface through infiltration. Winter et al., at 18. Although this is similar to the stream dynamic, it is also different in several ways. Because the quantity of water in a lake is larger than in a stream, more water can be lost through evaporation than from infiltration, especially in arid climates. Also, deposits on lake bottoms and wetlands are different from those found on stream beds. This can affect water's ability to permeate the surface. Generally, lake sediments are not fine grained, particularly around their perimeters where wave motions remove fine particles, thus allowing water to flow freely between the surface and subsurface. Wetlands often have finer grained deposits and rooted vegetation, which inhibit water flow. Winter et al., at 21. Reservoirs are usually sited in stream beds so the water characteristics mirror those of rivers rather than lakes; however, over time, reservoirs can behave more like lakes. Winter et al., at 21.

§ 1.13 Water Measurements

Water is measured using different units depending on the purpose of the measurement. For example, water can be measured for its rate of flow or storage capacity. The unit of measure typically used to measure the rate of water flow is *cubic feet per second* (cfs). A cubic foot of water contains 7.48 gallons. The cfs is computed by measuring the number of cubic feet of water that pass a given location in one second. Thus, a flow of 1 cfs over a 24-hour period produces approximately 1.98 acre-feet, or 646,317 gallons of water. The cfs measurement is typically used for assessing water flow rates in rivers, pipelines, canals, and other water conduits. Reed D. Benson et al., *Water Resources Management: A Casebook in Law and Public Policy* 8–9, 1085 (Foundation Press 8th ed. 2021) [hereinafter Benson et al.]; Joseph L. Sax et al., *Legal Control of Water Resources* 18–19 (West 3d ed. 2000) [hereinafter Sax et al.].

Storage capacity for large water resources (such as reservoirs, aqueducts, canals, and rivers) is typically measured in acre-feet. An acre-foot is the amount of water that covers 1 acre of surface area to a depth of 1 foot. One acre is roughly the size of a football field, and 1 acre-foot of water is equivalent to approximately 325,851 gallons, or 43,560 cubic feet of water. It is also roughly the quantity of water used by an average family of five in a year at a rate of 180 gallons of water per person per day. Benson et al., at 8; Sax et al., at 18–19.

One notable exception to the use of acre-feet as a measurement is with large quantities of freshwater, such as the amounts provided by municipal water suppliers. Such supplies are often measured in million or billion gallons per day (mgd or bgd). Benson et al., at 8; Sax et al., at 18–19.

Table of Common Water Measurements and Equivalents

1 gallon	=	8.34 pounds or 0.134 cubic feet
1 million gallons	=	3.07 acre-feet
1 million gallons per day	=	1.55 cfs or 3.07 acre-feet per day
1 cubic foot	=	7.48 gallons
1 cubic foot per second (cfs)	=	646,317 gallons or 1.98 acre-feet per day
1 acre-foot	=	325,851 gallons or 43,560 cubic feet

§ 1.14 Effects of Human Activity

Human activity can severely affect the distribution, quantity, and quality of water resources both above and below ground. These impacts can be short term or long term and on a range of scales. Increased pumping, pesticide usage, and urban runoff can damage the water relationship above and below the earth's surface. Winter et al., at 54. This is most easily seen where excessive withdrawal depletes the water resource. For example, well pumping near an effluent stream can lower the water table in the immediate area around a well and thereby shift the stream-aquifer relationship to an influent relationship. *See* Heath, at 32–33 (describing the response of groundwater systems to withdrawals from wells). The converse is also possible. Extensive dewatering of an aquifer can reduce or potentially stop spring flow, stream flow, or flow into a wetland. Alley et al., at 31; Votteler, at 845.

The impact of pumping on spring flow is especially important in Texas. Many springs in North and West Texas have disappeared because of aquifer dewatering. Springs in Central Texas such as Comal Springs and San Marcos Springs are a major source of municipal water, provide habitat to several threatened and endangered species, and offer a cultural tradition. The flow in these springs is directly related to the water level in the Edwards Aquifer, which creates a complex situation in which human pumping must be carefully monitored. *See* Votteler, at 845. See Chapter 17 of this book regarding the Edwards Aquifer Authority.

Texas has more than 350 miles of coastline. Texas State Historical Association, *Texas Almanac*, http://texasalmanac.com/topics/environment/environment. Coastal areas are an interface between the continents and the ocean. Alley et al., at 44. The health of the bays and estuaries can depend on water that emanates from underground. Maintaining spring and surface water flow protects the wildlife found at the coast, which is sometimes miles away from the headwaters. McKinney, *Why Bays Matter*, at 24–25.

Another significant impact of human activity is increased evaporation. This occurs in a number of ways but primarily through the construction of reservoirs. Micheal Overman, *Water: Solutions to a Problem of Supply and Demand* 45 (Doubleday 1969) [hereinafter Overman]. In lakes or reservoirs, up to 25 percent of the water can be lost to the atmosphere, particularly in hot climates like Texas. Overman, at 45. Widespread pumping of groundwater for irrigation purposes also increases evaporation from the increased soil moisture. Any water gained by the atmosphere is water lost in another part of the hydrologic cycle, such as stream flow or aquifer storage.

Urban construction also affects water and its relationships. Increased impervious cover can greatly reduce groundwater recharge. Overman, at 51. Precipitation falling in municipal areas is generally channeled as runoff and treated as wastewater, preventing it from adding to ground or surface water resources as it would under natural conditions. In addition, pumping and piping of water from one basin to another or inland from the sea to meet water needs alter the natural system in an area. The extent to which society allows water resources to be affected by its actions depends on the importance placed on those resources.

V. The Value of Water

§ 1.15 Introduction

The following sections offer a perspective on the value and ethics of water as a means of encouraging cooperation over the sound management of freshwater resources. Although these notions presented are not legal or scientific principles, familiarity with these concepts is critical to the water professional who must daily make decisions about writing water legislation, drafting rules, issuing permits, entering water contracts, and dealing with a myriad of other water issues.

§ 1.16 Valuing Water

The value of water is often expressed in terms of its numerical or economic worth. As of October 1, 2018, for example, in addition to a base charge tied to the size of the water meter, the average Dallas, Texas, homeowner pays $1.86 per 1,000 gallons of treated water up to 4,000 gallons; $4.00 per 1,000 for the next 4,001 to 10,000 gallons used; $6.50 per 1,000 for quantities between 10,001 and 20,000 gallons; $9.30 per 1,000 for quantities between 20,001 and 30,000 gallons; and $10.70 per 1,000 for usage above 30,000 gallons. City of Dallas, Dallas Water Utilities, *Water & Wastewater Retail Rates, Effective October 1, 2018*, https://dallascityhall.com/departments/waterutilities/DCH%20Documents/monthly_rate_sheet.pdf. Thus, Dallas homeowners value water at between $1.86 and $10.70 per 1,000 gallons of water (plus the base charge). Similarly, in 2004 in Medina and Uvalde counties, which overlie the Edwards Aquifer, irrigated cropland sold for between $3,000 and $4,000 per acre when water rights were included, while dry cropland without water rights sold for between $700 and $1,200 per acre. Charles E. Gilliland et al., *Water Power, 11, No. 4 Tierra Grande, Journal of the Real Estate Center at Texas A&M University* (Oct. 2004). Here, landowners placed an $1,800- to $3,300-per-acre premium on the value of water. In both cases, water was treated as a marketable commodity and assigned an economic value.

But water often defies such commodification efforts. The value of water can permeate the social fabric of peoples and communities and includes factors and characteristics that cannot easily be appraised. For example, the valuation of water may be related to the desire to maintain soil moisture levels, spring flows, and base flows in rivers and streams; a personal assessment of water's importance to human and nonhuman life; an exercise of belief related to faith or history; or the need to preserve a cultural heritage or way of life. Although not a comprehensive list of valuation methodologies, the process of valuing water is highly dependent on how the one conducting the valuation perceives water. Factors that can influence how water is perceived, and therefore valued, may include perspectives on life and the value of life itself; social and economic ideals; cultural, religious, and societal backgrounds and proclivities; and even politics. Ultimately, it must be recognized that the scales used to assess the price homeowners and landowners may be willing to pay for freshwater and those used for noneconomic valuation are often incongruous. Accordingly, to ensure that all perspectives are given their due regard, these disparate assessments must be reconciled to find some basis on which to fairly and justly allocate this singular resource.

§ 1.16:1 Economic Valuation of Water

In an entrepreneurial society, people often consider water in terms of its economic potential, viewing it as a commodity—a "thing" or good that is subject to market forces, that can be bought, sold, and owned, and whose value depends on supply and demand. Under this approach, where freshwater resources are plentiful and easily accessible, water should be inexpensive. Conversely, where water is scarce, the value of water should be directly related to what the market will bear. In its purest form, the commodification of water would be available only to those who could pay for it and only in quantities they could afford. Accordingly, this valuation methodology is most in harmony with capitalist-based societies. *See generally* Andrew Morriss, *Real People, Real Resources, and Real Choices: The Case for Market Valuation of Water*, 38 Tex. Tech L. Rev. 973 (2006).

But establishing an economic valuation for water can be challenging. The value of water rights, for example, can vary greatly depending on the physical quality, reliability, availability, and amount of water tied to those rights, conditions that are subject to hydrologic and climatic changes over time. Additionally, there may be legal limits on surface water rights related to a right's priority date, as well as restrictions on groundwater pumping based on well spacing and other criteria imposed by water conservation districts. In addition, the possible uses for water in a given location can be consequential for determining the value of water and water rights. Water used to extract oil typically costs more than municipal water, which in turn costs more than water for agricultural use. *See* Gabriel Collins, *Economic Valuation of Groundwater in Texas*, 9 Tex. Water J. 56–57 (2018) [hereinafter Collins].

Nevertheless, many parties enter into the water market despite these obstacles. For example, courts sometimes must value water to resolve cases. In 2015, the city of Amarillo bought the groundwater estate lying under ranching land to its northwest, basing the price on feet of saturated water available under each surface acre. The city paid $250 per surface acre with a saturated layer of less than 200 feet, $300 per acre with an average saturated thickness between 200 and 257 feet, and $1.16 per average saturated foot for each acre with a saturated layer of 258 feet or greater. Collins, at 60. As another example, in 2016, a Medina County district court jury determined the value of groundwater pumping rights denied to pecan orchard owners, finding that one orchard was worth $1.67 million with full access to groundwater but only $300,000 with limited access. Jess Krochtengel, *Texas Jury Awards Pecan Farmers $2.5M In Water Takings Suit, Law 360* (Feb. 23, 2016) www.law360.com/articles/762833/texas-jury-awards-pecan-farmers-2-5m-in-water-takings-suit.

§ 1.16:2 Noneconomic Valuation of Water

Anthropocentric Valuation of Water: Under the anthropocentric perspective, the value of water is directly related to its irreplaceability as a fundamental component of life. Proponents of this perspective believe water has an intrinsic value that is incalculable and therefore it is beyond valuation. This position is grounded in the belief that life itself, at least human life, is sacrosanct and that the valuation of life is inappropriate, if not completely impossible. Just as the buying and selling of people is regarded by most as an inconceivable evil, under this perspective, so is the valuation of the substance that is so necessary for creating and sustaining life. The anthropocentric perspective is often at the base of arguments for the human right to water. *See generally* Salman M.A. Salman & Siobhan McInerney-Lankford, *The Human Right to Water* (World Bank Publications 2004) [hereinafter Salman & McInerney-Lankford]; Amy Hardberger, *Life, Liberty, and the Pursuit of Water: Evaluating Water as a Human Right and the Duties and Obligations It Creates*, 4 Nw. J. Hum. Rts. 331 (2005), http://scholarlycommons.law.northwestern.edu/njihr/vol4/iss2/3/ [hereinafter Hardberger].

Ecocentric Valuation of Water: In a similar vein, water is regarded by some as an intrinsic component of the natural environment with a value that is incalculable. In contrast with the anthropocentric notion of the inviolability of human life, the value of water to the environment is grounded in an ecocentric perspective of life in which humanity is merely a component of the natural environment. In this view, the life of all creatures, including but not limited to humans, is inviolable. Moreover, because water is a principal source of sustenance for all life, it is likewise regarded as sacrosanct and incapable of valuation. *See generally* Kerry Turner et al., *Chapter 5 Conclusions, in Economic Valuation of Water Resources in Agriculture: From the Sectoral to a Functional Perspective of Natural Resource Management* (U.N. Food & Agricultural Organization 2004), www.fao.org/3/y5582e/y5582e09.htm; Captain Paul Watson, *Clarification on Where Director Paul Watson Stands on Various Issues*, www.ecospherics.net/pages/wonw.htm.

Cultural or Traditional Perspective on the Valuation of Water: The cultural or traditional perspective of water valuation is dependent on individual or collective beliefs that water has a value more significant than that based on personal enrichment or sustenance. This distinct notion of valuation is typically related to a system of beliefs based on cultural, social, religious, or historical custom. The value of water becomes incalculable, at least in the economic sense, by its very nature of being abstract and ethereal and built on a foundation of tradition, social norms, or faith. Moreover, water is incapable of valuation because it is regarded as a blessing rather than a commodity. In some communities, water is considered the lifeblood of the earth, which should not be exploited or extracted to excess lest the earth be injured or killed. In other communities, water is sacrosanct to the extent that it is a gift of the creator, a gift that cannot be withheld from anyone in need. In still others, water defines the culture to the extent that it characterizes a people's identity, religious beliefs, ceremonial practices, and daily life. In most of these cases, water is regarded as an absolute necessity, not merely to maintain individual life but as a means of maintaining the life of the people. *See generally* Katosha Nakai, *Water: It Always Has Been; It Is; It Will Be—A Cultural Perspective on the Valuation of Water*, 38 Tex. Tech L. Rev. 1027 (2006); William Greenway, *Dominion and Domination: Living Life and Living Earth, in Symposium Proceedings: Precious, Worthless, or Immeasurable: The Value and Ethic of Water*, Center for Water Law & Policy and International Center for Arid & Semi-Arid Land Studies, Texas Tech University (A.C. Corrêa & Gabriel Eckstein eds. 2006).

§ 1.17 Overcoming Valuation Differences

To a great extent, the perspectives outlined above are described in absolute terms. Reality, however, is rarely based on absolutes, and perspectives often are combined to form unique viewpoints. For example, many environmentalists have adopted a combination of the ecocentric and economic approaches to valuation and created the hybrids of environmental and ecological economics. *See, e.g.*, James Boyd, *Procurement of Water's Ecosystem Services: An Economic and Ecological Perspective, in Symposium Proceedings: Precious, Worthless, or Immeasurable: The Value and Ethic of Water*, Center for Water Law & Policy and International Center for Arid & Semi-Arid Land Studies, Texas Tech University (A.C. Corrêa & Gabriel Eckstein eds. 2006). Although none of these perspectives can claim to be definitive, it is evident that they employ disparate and often contradictory methodologies that have the potential for fomenting conflict among the proponents of the respective approaches. This is particularly likely when the water resources assessed are inadequate to meet everyone's wants or needs.

A recent controversy in Central Texas over the sale of 50,000 acre-feet of Carrizo-Wilcox Aquifer water to San Antonio for $3.4 billion provides a clear illustration of disparate perspectives and value systems that can lead to friction among stakeholders. The Vista Ridge water deal involved two private water marketers who purchased water rights from individual landowners and obtained pumping and export permits from the local groundwater district. In this unique project, the sellers are required to transport the water 142 miles from its source to the city limits before they can be paid for the water. Neena Satija, *San Antonio Approves Historic Water Project*, *Texas Tribune* (Oct. 30, 2014), www.texastribune.org/2014/10/30/san-antonio-votes-historic-water-project/. Because of concerns over groundwater depletion and dependent ecosystems, economic values clashed against Central Texas community and environmental sensibilities, and the arrangement remains highly controversial.

Overcoming these fundamental and often ingrained viewpoints and methodologies is clearly not an easy proposition. Such perspectives are often at the core of disputes and greatly depend on personal perspectives; national interests; social and economic ideals; cultural, religious, and societal backgrounds; and politics. Moreover, they often serve as the basis for legislative and regulatory action and business decision making, as well as the justifications for aggravating controversies over limited freshwater resources. Common ground may be inconceivable, but it may be found in the ethics of water.

VI. The Ethics of Water

§ 1.18 Introduction

Ethics are fundamental to human existence. They are at the core of societal decision making and define what people and communities consider important and how people interact with each other. Ethics are the tacit rules of behavior and consequences that regulate people's lives, activities, and decision making. They function as a moral compass, guiding us to what we can or cannot do, and about the amount of harm, pain, loss, and deprivation we can inflict on each other. Poul Harremoës, *Water Ethics—A Substitute for Over-Regulation of a Scarce Resource*, Stockholm Water Symposium, Aug. 16, 2001, at 5.

In a sense, ethics are a structured system of principles, codes of conduct, or prime directives that aid humanity in determining appropriate conduct. To some extent, ethics can be both elective and prescriptive in that they direct people's actions toward what they should or ought to do and which values they should or ought to hold. To the extent that civil society can identify fundamental ethical bases related to freshwater, it can then begin constructing laws and policies that best reflect society's collective ideals of right and wrong.

§ 1.19 Water Ethics in History

Water has been the focus of ethics in every corner of the world for millennia. Irrigation and other water management practices, for example, were the developmental cornerstone of numerous communities in the Americas, Asia, Africa, the Middle East, and elsewhere thousands of years before the Industrial Revolution. *See* Fekri A. Hassan, *A Historical Perspective, in Water and Ethics* 11–15 (UNESCO 2004), https://unesdoc.unesco.org/ark:/48223/pf0000136341.locale=en [hereinafter Hassan]. These communities formulated strict rules of behavior governing the use and management of freshwater. *See* Hassan, at 47–49 (discussing principles of distribution, use, upkeep, and overall management dating back to the Code of Hammurabi 3,700 years ago). Cultures in arid parts of the world, such as Muslim communities, are especially noteworthy for developing allocation priorities for limited water resources. *See, e.g.*, Melanne Andromecca Civic, *A Comparative Analysis of the Israeli and Arab Water Law Traditions and Insights for Modern Water Sharing Agreements*, 26 Denv. J. Int'l L. & Pol'y 437 (1998). Considered collectively, water ethics have formed the foundation on which every aspect of a society's management of freshwater resources has developed.

Water ethics reflect the relative importance water plays in people's lives and provide guidance in decision making related to the use, management, allocation, and protection of freshwater resources. Even the concept and the act of valuation, regardless of methodology, are fundamentally based on notions of good and bad, right and wrong. For example, communities that apportion freshwater based on historical use hold a water ethic that values prexisting uses. In contrast, those that apportion water based on ownership rules value the property aspects of water. But both communities value water in relation to what they define as morally appropriate and correct. Thus, the valuation of water is a function of water ethics in that valuation reflects the evaluator's belief of how water should be managed.

§ 1.20 Identifying Universal Water Ethics

Ethics generally focus on individual conduct, yet they are profoundly influenced by societal norms and beliefs. Writing about the related notion of a "land ethic," noted philosopher Aldo Leopold explained that "[a]ll ethics rest upon a single premise: that the individual is a member of a community of interdependent parts." Aldo Leopold, *The Land Ethic, in A Sand County Almanac* (Oxford Univ.

Press 1949). The extent to which that interdependence is taken lies at the core of whether an ethic can be said to cut across diverse cultural, political, economic, religious, and national beliefs and proclivities. Yet any effort to identify one or more universal water ethics is not an easy task. In fact, recent cases suggest that different societies have distinct viewpoints related to water management. For example, in 1992 the International Conference on Water and the Environment formulated recommendations, including one providing that "[w]ater has an economic value in all its competing uses and should be recognized as an economic good." *The Dublin Statement on Water and Sustainable Development*, International Conference on Water and the Environment (Jan. 1992), www.ircwash.org/sites/default/files/71-ICWE92-9739.pdf. This portrayal of water as an economic good generated considerable concerns in Islamic countries, which regard water as the source of all life and a gift from God that cannot be bought or sold. *See* Jerome Delli Priscoli et al., *Overview*, *in Water and Ethics* 8–9 (UNESCO 2004), http://unesdoc.unesco.org/ark:48223/pf0000136343 [hereinafter Priscoli et al.].

One starting point in seeking universal water ethics may be the fact that all individuals, communities, nations, and societies value water. The specific reasons that different societies treasure water may be particularly significant, because if common justification can be identified, it may serve as a basis for articulating shared ethical bases for water valuation. This in turn could evolve into a foundation for cooperation on managing water resources.

§ 1.20:1 Life as a Water Ethic

Possibly the simplest and most obvious universal factor in valuing water is the value of water for life. Water is absolutely fundamental to human life. It nourishes people and facilitates health and well-being in ways that no other resource can. The adult human body is composed of up to 60 percent water, while a human brain is more than 70 percent water and human lungs are about 83 percent water. *See* U.S. Geological Survey, Water Science School, *The Water in You: Water and the Human Body*, www.usgs.gov/special-topic/water-science-school/science/water-you-water-and-human-body?qt-science_center_objects=0#qt-science_center_objects. Accordingly, it is easy to concede that water is universally valued for its life-giving and life-sustaining qualities. Combined with the broadly accepted notion that human life is invaluable and should be protected, a water ethic emerges: All human beings should have water in a quantity and quality that ensures and sustains life. The practical consequence of such an ethic mandates that, regardless of any other objective, water for human life should be ensured and guaranteed in the quantity and quality necessary to maintain that life. *See* Gabriel Eckstein, *Precious, Worthless, or Incalculable: The Value and Ethic of Water*, 38 Tex. Tech L. Rev. 963, 969 (2006).

This particular water ethic, however, is rudimentary and does not address the mechanisms for its realization. Rather, it is a simple statement designed to capture the fundamental and universal notion that everyone—regardless of cultural, religious, political, economic, or other background—values freshwater for sustaining human life. Whether there exists another identifiable water ethic related to the *provision* of water, however, is a separate matter. Such is the position argued by those who espouse the human right to water. *See* Salman & McInerney-Lankford; Hardberger.

§ 1.20:2 Participation as a Water Ethic

Participation in institutions and the decision-making process is one of the fundamental rights upheld in most democracies. Thus, in a democracy and in the context of water management, such a right comprises an ethic to the extent that all stakeholders are afforded the opportunity to become involved in assessing how freshwater resources should be managed and allocated. *See* Priscoli et al., at 16. Accordingly, it is important that the ethic of participation in water-related decisions be substantial and applied at all levels of involvement. Moreover, it especially should be ensured and protected for those who are least able to assert their rights and interests and for whom water is vital to their fulfillment as humans. *See* Priscoli et al., at 16.

§ 1.20:3 Equality as a Water Ethic

Equality is at the heart of the American experience and is enshrined in many of its constituent documents, including the Declaration of Independence. It is a notion that appeals to the near primordial sense of fairness and justice and that is intrinsic to our nation's ideals. The antithesis of discrimination, it is a principle intended and designed to apply to all people with regard to rights, opportunities, and the application of law. In this respect, the ethic of equality applies to all aspects of water and suggests that everyone is equally entitled to the water due them. In practical terms, the ethic of equality refers to the actual allocation of water as well as opportunities related to water, such as access to water, decision making affecting freshwater resources, and commercial and other prospects related to water. *See* Priscoli et al., at 16.

§ 1.20:4 Stewardship as a Water Ethic

The ethical principle of stewardship reflects a moral responsibility for creation. It both teaches respect for creation and establishes an obligation to use wisely all components of creation. Moreover, it offers a reminder that, absent sound stewardship, the ability to achieve the full human potential, now and in the future, will likely be compromised. Without good water management, human potential and human dignity are diminished for all and denied for some. The practical consequence of such an ethic challenges people to consider and respect all interests and perspectives in the efforts to manage freshwater resources. It also binds people to formulate management schemes that ensure and promote the human potential of current generations without compromising those of future generations. *See* Priscoli et al., at 16.

§ 1.21 Ethical Base for Water Law and Policy

The purpose of the above discussion is to encourage the sound management of freshwater resources by balancing and ensuring adequate water supplies for all stakeholders. Although different peoples, communities, and stakeholders often have disparate objectives for limited water resources, they often possess common ethical beliefs and values related to water on which they can agree. And although the use of ethics is but one method for analyzing how freshwater resources are managed, it is a lens that, unlike other approaches, allows a more direct view of the social, environmental, cultural, and other values that are so important to stakeholder groups and people in general. By pursuing such commonalities, disputes can be replaced by cooperation.

Under this ethical lens, when considering how to pursue a water permit, a wholesale water sales agreement, new water legislation, or a lawsuit challenging or defending a client's water rights, lawyers should endeavor to incorporate considerations of ethics and values into the decision-making process. Examples of questions and issues to consider might include the following:

- Who will the decision or planned action affect and how? Have those who may be affected been offered a voice in the decision-making process? Do they even know about the pending decision or action?
- What are all the economic and noneconomic values involved in the decision or planned action? Have they been integrated into the cost-benefit analysis of the deal? Have they been given equal treatment?

- What are the consequences of the decision or planned action for the water resource? Will it leave adequate freshwater resources for other stakeholders and future generations?

The integration of such ethics and values into the decision-making process offers a unique opportunity to seek common ground and to pursue compromise. Moreover, it permits the creation of a foundation on which to construct rules and regulations and to make business and court decisions that are inclusive and just, as well as principled.

VII. Conclusion

§ 1.22 Conclusion

The field of water law is today an established and growing specialization whose importance is well recognized around the country. The reasons are quite clear: water is critical, not only to human survival but also for other human interests and endeavors, including development, the environment, and recreation. Moreover, there is now a greater appreciation that while our water needs continue to expand, our water resources are finite. Accordingly, the sound management and regulation of all water resources are critical to ensuring both our present and our future. Without water, nothing is possible.

Water law, however, is a complex subject matter and requires a broad understanding of not only the law but also the science of water as well as people's relationship to this critical resource. Accordingly, water law today is an interdisciplinary practice encompassing a broad perspective that incorporates individual and community rights, environmental issues, commerce and economics, and other societal and legal concerns. Moreover, it is interdisciplinary in the sense that it requires a firm understanding of the science of water, including knowledge of the hydrologic cycle, groundwater flow regimes, agricultural practices, ground and surface water interaction, wetlands and dependent ecosystems, and much more.

Ultimately, the application of water law is a means to advance societal values and goals related to terrestrial water resources. It is a tool for bridging the gap between our societal water needs and the actual availability and distribution of the resource. The challenge we face as water lawyers is to practice water law in a manner that will ensure our clients' interests as well as those of society's in this precious and irreplaceable resource.

CHAPTER 2

Understanding Texas Weather and Climate and How Climate Change Might Impact Water Resources

Carlos Rubinstein[1] and Robert E. Mace[2]

I. Introduction

§ 2.1 Introduction

Nothing impacts Texas water resources, use, and policy more than weather and climate. Weather—as measured day to day and week to week—controls how wet or dry our soils are; how full our rivers, lakes, and aquifers are; how well our crops grow; and how much water is available for use by our cities, industries, power plants, and farms. The polar vortex storm of February 2021 also reminds us, unfortunately, of how weather can negatively affect our ability to treat and convey potable water and wastewater. Climate—the average of weather over a long period of time, generally thirty years—also affects water resources as reflected in seasons and expected variations from year to year. *See* National Aeronautics and Space Administration, *NASA—What's the Difference Between Weather and Climate?* (Feb. 1, 2005), www.nasa.gov/mission_pages/noaa-n/climate/climate_weather.html.

Both weather and climate have sparked water policy changes in Texas from its beginning. Examples include the creation of state geological surveys to investigate water supplies; the establishment of the rules of capture for groundwater and prior appropriation in surface water; state water planning after the drought of the 1950s and regional water planning after the drought of 1996; and groundwater regulation and infrastructure funding. *See* Carlos Rubinstein, *Texas Water Policy Appendix: The Weather*, 6 Tex. Water J. 121 (2015), https://journals.tdl.org/twj/index.php/twj/article/view/7033/pdf_8. Weather and climate happen; policy and law respond.

Climate is changing over time, impacting both long-term trends and day-to-day weather. Global warming trends over the last century suggest that Texas can expect a much warmer climate in the future, which will have consequences for water resources and policy. Furthermore, as we develop more land and increase impervious cover, we must deal with increased storm flows, water-quality

---

1. Carlos Rubinstein is Principal of RSAH2O, LLC and a former chair of the Texas Water Development Board and commissioner of the Texas Commission on Environmental Quality.

2. Robert Mace is the executive director and chief water policy officer at The Meadows Center for Water and the Environment and a professor of practice in the Department of Geography at Texas State University. He has a BS in geophysics and an MS in hydrology from the New Mexico Institute of Mining and Technology and a PhD in hydrogeology from the University of Texas at Austin. Robert worked at the Texas Water Development Board for eighteen years before joining Texas State University.

impacts, and associated flooding. This, too, impacts our water resources and associated planning. See Chapter 41 of this book for a discussion of how land use impacts water resources.

Consider as well that in just the past decade Texas has experienced the harshest one-year drought of record (2011), the rewriting of the continental U.S. record for total rainfall from a tropical cyclone as part of Hurricane Harvey (2017), and a record-setting subfreezing period associated with the polar vortex storm of 2021. To be sure, these weather extremes foster renewed policy and response considerations.

Human activity already impacts our environment; however, impacts attributable to human activity are less accepted by some when it applies to climate. In our experience, people generally accept human impacts and intervention on the environment when we can measure localized effects and the efficacy of mitigation programs. This is true for air, water, and waste. To that end, both federal and state regulations have been implemented to mitigate and reverse the degradation of our water resources and air quality, protect and preserve water and air quality, and protect land through the management of solid waste. These actions have benefited our planning for and preservation of water resources. Even without the consensus of policymakers and lawmakers on whether a changing climate is attributable to human activity, much can be done to plan for and mitigate the effects of change on water resources.

Climate change (long-term changes in regional and global climate caused by human activity) is a global concern with worldwide greenhouse gas concentrations as the focus. Unlike ozone and its precursors that impact, for example, the city of Houston, where we can measure how effective local emission control programs have been in reducing ozone levels through time in the same area, greenhouse gas emission reductions by one city, state, or country are easily dismissed as minimal or of no consequence when compared to global concentrations. Perhaps this lack of direct correlation of action and benefit at a local level contributes to the dismissive way some treat the subject of human impacts on climate. But, in our opinion, it is inescapable that weather and climate have, are, and will continue to impact our water resources.

This chapter describes the weather and climate of Texas as well as what climate change predicts for the state, with a focus on water resources and policy implications. Broadly, information on climate and water resources in Texas comes from three sources of information: (1) global, continental, and regional assessments such as those provided by the International Panel on Climate Change and the National Climate Assessments; (2) peer-reviewed literature from academic journals that may be global, continental, regional, or local in scope; and (3) unpublished local assessments intended to assist with local water planning.

Global, continental, and regional assessments are aggregators of peer-reviewed studies with the added benefit of (1) providing a peer review of the body of literature on a particular topic and (2) assigning certainty to conclusions and projections. Although warming of the climate is *unequivocal* and it is *extremely likely* that humans have influenced the climate (*see* Intergovernmental Panel on Climate Change, *Climate Change 2014: Synthesis Report* (2015), www.ipcc.ch/site/assets/uploads/2018/05/SYR_AR5_FINAL_full_wcover.pdf [hereinafter IPCC Report]), the science behind potential effects of climate change on a variety of fronts in Texas is still developing, including, but not limited to—

- weather (*see* Christian M. Appendini et al., *Effect of Climate Change on Wind Waves Generated by Anticyclonic Cold Front Intrusions in the Gulf of Mexico*, 51 Clim. Dyn. 3747 (2018));
- rainfall (*see* Xiaoyan Jiang & Zong-Liang Yang, *Projected Changes of Temperature and Precipitation in Texas from Downscaled Global Climate Models*, 53 Clim. Res. 229 (2012); John F. Joseph & Hatim O. Sharif, *A Methodology for Assessing Extreme Precipitation Trends Applied to Three South Texas Basins, 1898–2011*, 41 Arab. J. Sci. & Eng. 4945 (2016); Naga Raghuveer Modala et al., *Climate Change Projections for the Texas High Plains and Rolling Plains*, 129 Theor. & App. Clim. 263 (2017));

- drought (*see* Kartik Venkataraman et al., *21st Century Drought Outlook for Major Climate Divisions of Texas Based on CMIP5 Multimodel Ensemble: Implications for Water Resource Management*, 534 J. Hydr. 300 (2016));
- crop yields (*see* Pradip Adhikari et al., *Simulating Future Climate Change Impacts on Seed Cotton Yield in the Texas High Plains Using the CSM-CROPGRO-Cotton Model*, 164 Agric. Water Mgmt. 317 (2016); Yong Chen et al., *Modeling the Effects of Land Use Change from Cotton (Gossypium hirsutum L.) to Perennial Bioenergy Grasses on Watershed Hydrology and Water Quality under Changing Climate*, 192 Agric. Water Mgmt. 198 (2017); Ripendra Awal et al., *Assessing Potential Climate Change Impacts on Irrigation Requirements of Major Crops in the Brazos Headwaters Basin, Texas*, 10 Water 1610 (2018));
- environmental impacts (*see* Anna R. Armitage et al., *The Contribution of Mangrove Expansion to Salt Marsh Loss on the Texas Gulf Coast*, 10 PLoS ONE 17 pp. (2015); Jaehak Jeong et al., *Effects of Urbanization and Climate Change on Stream Health in North-Central Texas*, 43 J. Environ. Qual. 100 (2014); Hae-Cheol Kim et al., *Linkage between Freshwater Inflow and Primary Productivity in Texas Estuaries: Downscaling Effects of Climate Variability*, 68 J. Coast. Res. 65 (2014); Reynaldo Patino et al., *Retrospective Analysis of Associations between Water Quality and Toxic Blooms of Golden Alga (Prymnesium parvum) in Texas Reservoirs: Implications for Understanding Dispersal Mechanisms and Impacts of Climate Change*, 33 Harmful Algae 1 (2014); Michael J. Osland et al., *Assessing Coastal Wetland Vulnerability to Sea-Level Rise along the Northern Gulf of Mexico Coast: Gaps and Opportunities for Developing a Coordinated Regional Sampling Network*, 12 PLoS ONE 23 pp. (2017); Amanda M. Schwantes et al., *Measuring Canopy Loss and Climatic Thresholds from an Extreme Drought along a Fivefold Precipitation Gradient across Texas*, 23 Glob. Change Bio. 5120 (2017));
- human health (*see* Janet L. Gamble & Jeremy J. Hess, *Temperature and Violent Crime in Dallas, Texas: Relationships and Implications of Climate Change*, 13 West. J. Emerg. Med. 239 (2012); Roelof J.M. Boumans et al., *Developing a Model for Effects of Climate Change on Human Health and Health-Environment Interactions: Heat Stress in Austin, Texas*, 8 Urb. Clim. 78 (2014); Kathryn Conlon et al., *Potential Impacts of Future Warming and Land Use Changes on Intra-Urban Heat Exposure in Houston, Texas*, 11 PLoS ONE 19 pp. (2015); Natasha Prudent et al., *Assessing Climate Change and Health Vulnerability at the Local Level: Travis County, Texas*, 40 Disasters 740 (2016); Peter J. Hotez, *The Rise of Neglected Tropical Diseases in the "New Texas"*, 12 PLoS Neglected Tropical Diseases 15 pp. (2018); Amy Marsha et al., *Influences of Climatic and Population Changes on Heat-Related Mortality in Houston, Texas, USA*, 146 Clim. Change 471 (2018));
- water use (*see* Megan Mullin & Meghan E. Rubado, *Local Response to Water Crisis: Explaining Variation in Usage Restrictions during a Texas Drought*, 53 Urb. Aff. Rev. 752 (2017):
- water availability (*see* Joonghyeok Heo et al., *Impacts of Climate and Land-Cover Changes on Water Resources in a Humid Subtropical Watershed: A Case Study from East Texas, USA*, 29 Water & Env't J. 51 (2014); Tom Brikowski, *Applying Multi-Parameter Runoff Elasticity to Assess Water Availability in a Changing Climate: An Example from Texas, USA*, 29 Hydro. Proc. 1746 (2015); Dagbegnon Clement Sohoulande Djebou, *Spectrum of Climate Change and Streamflow Alteration at a Watershed Scale*, 76 Envtl. Earth Sci. 76 (2017); Goutam Konapala et al., *Teleconnection between Low Flows and Large-Scale Climate Indices in Texas River Basins*, 32 Stochastic Envtl. Res. & Risk Assess. 2337 (2018); Yiwen Zhang & Ralph Wurbs, *Long-Term Changes in River System Hydrology in Texas*, 379 Proc. Int'l Ass'n Hydro. Sci. 255 (2018)); USBR. Rio Grande Basin—SECURE Water Act Section 9503(c) Report to Congress (2021));

- flooding (*see* Gang Zhao et al., *Effects of Urbanization and Climate Change on Peak Flows over the San Antonio River Basin, Texas*, 17 J. Hydrometeor. 2371 (2016));
- perceptions (*see* Amber Campbell et al., *Climate Change Beliefs, Concerns, and Attitudes of Beef Cattle Producers in the Southern Great Plains*, 152 Clim. Change 35 (2019));
- policy (*see* Carolyn Ginno, *DO Mess With Texas . . . ? Why Rolling Easements May Provide a Solution to the Loss of Public Beaches Due to Climate Change-Induced Landward Coastal Migration*, 8 San Diego J. of Clim. & Energy L. 225 (2017));
- economic impacts (*see* David Yoskowitz et al., *Integrated Ecosystem Services Assessment: Valuation of Changes Due to Sea Level Rise in Galveston Bay, Texas, USA*, 13 Integrated Envtl. Assess. & Mgmt. 431 (2016);
- energy efficiency (*see* Ann W. Foss, *Climate Change and Political Discourse: Analysis of Energy Efficiency and Conservation Block Grants in Dallas-Fort Worth*, 61 J. Envtl. Plan. & Mgmt. 230 (2018); and
- rats (*see* Guy N. Cameron & David Scheel, *Getting Warmer: Effect of Global Climate Change on Distribution of Rodents in Texas*, 82 J. Mammalogy 652 (2001)).

The global, continental, and regional assessments present the science that has greater certainty. Because an analysis of all of the different categories of effects is beyond the scope of this chapter, we relied in large part on the U.S. Global Change Research Program's recently released National Climate Assessment, which conducted a thorough multidisciplinary review of effects (*see* U.S. Global Change Research Program, *Fourth National Climate Assessment*, https://nca2018.globalchange.gov/ [hereinafter 2018 Climate Assessment]) and is more recent than the most recent IPCC Report.

Inasmuch as Texas's current water-resource regulations focus on a single weather phenomenon—drought—a question arises: Going forward, how do we distinguish the difference between the weather we experience and the climate trends impacting Texas? Put another way, we are pretty good at focusing on the here and now (weather), but how well have we taken into account long-term trends (climate)?

II. Weather and Climate in Texas

§ 2.2 Texas Weather

Texas weather is the temperature, relative humidity, precipitation, sunny, cloudy, and overcast conditions, visibility, wind direction and speed, and atmospheric pressure Texans experience over a short period of time—be it minutes, hours, days, or months, with seasonable variability. Components of our weather include what we are experiencing at any moment in time: drought or flooding, a hailstorm or thunderstorm, freezing conditions or extreme heat, rain or snow, or other conditions. Although considered over a longer period, drought is considered weather. Weather is not the same as climate, but our climate impacts our weather. We know Texas summers are hot: that is our climate. When we experience a 104°F day or a thunderstorm: that is our weather.

Every Texan knows that the weather can get a bit wacky around here. As the saying goes: *If you don't like the weather in Texas, just wait fifteen minutes.* Weather variability in our state is quite high, and that's not surprising given our unique location. Texas's weather is affected by the Rocky Mountains (which impede the flow of air from the west), the Great Plains (where Arctic air can rush south unimpeded), the Atlantic Ocean (a source of moist, tropical air and tropical systems), and the Pacific Ocean (another source of moist, tropical air and tropical systems). *See* Texas Water Development Board, 2 *Water for Texas* 130–31 fig. 5-1 (2007), www.twdb.texas.gov/waterplanning/swp/2007/ [hereinafter 2007 State Water Plan]; John W. Nielsen-Gammon, *The Changing Climate in*

Texas, *in The Impact of Global Warming on Texas*, at 39–68 (Jurgen Schmandt et al. eds. 2011). See Figure 1. Weather variability is highest in winter and lowest in summer. For example, we're almost guaranteed to have a sweltering hot day on August 15 in any given year, while we don't know if we'll be huddled against a bitterly cold wind or in shorts barbecuing on New Year's Day.

§ 2.3 Texas Climate

Time matters—and how the atmosphere has behaved and is predicted to behave over long periods of time is climate. Climate is what you expect; weather is what you get. Just as our weather is affected by the Rocky Mountains, the Great Plains, and the Atlantic and Pacific Oceans, so is our climate, which conveys the long-term signals of these influences. Texas's climate is semi-arid between the more humid Southeastern United States and the arid Southwest. Average annual maximum daily temperature ranges from less than 70°F in the Texas Panhandle to more than 82°F in the lower Rio Grande Valley. *See* 2007 State Water Plan, v. II, at 130–32 fig. 5-2. See Figure 2. Average annual precipitation ranges from less than 10 inches in the El Paso area to more than 55 inches in the southeast. *See* 2007 State Water Plan, v. II, at 130–32 fig. 5-3. See Figure 3. Average gross lake-surface evaporation (the total amount of evaporation from a lake surface) ranges from more than 90 inches in the Big Bend area to less than 45 inches in the east. *See* 2007 State Water Plan, v. II, at 130–33 fig. 5-4. See Figure 4.

Based on vegetation, temperature, humidity, rainfall, and seasonality, the National Climatic Data Center divides Texas into ten climate divisions. *See* 2007 State Water Plan, v. II, at 132, 134 fig. 5-5. See Figure 5. As expected, the pattern of monthly temperatures is the same among the different divisions with higher temperatures in the summer and lower temperatures in the winter. The pattern for precipitation changes across the state with two peaks—one in the spring and one in the fall—for the eastern two-thirds of the state, with more of a single summer peak in the west.

§ 2.4 Sea-Surface Temperature Effects on Weather and Climate

Interestingly, sea-surface temperatures in distant oceans affect our weather and climate as well. Most well-known is the El Niño Southern Oscillation, which concerns sea-surface temperatures in the eastern equatorial Pacific as well as a corresponding influence on the atmosphere. El Niños occur with a warming of the sea surface, and La Niñas occur with a cooling (what are being colloquially called "La Nadas" occur when sea-surface temperatures are near normal). Each of these phases generally occurs every two to seven years and lasts nine months to two years. *See* Michelle L'Heureux, National Oceanic and Atmospheric Administration, *What Is the El Niño-Southern Oscillation (ENSO) in a Nutshell?*, ENSO Blog (May 5, 2014), www.climate.gov/news-features/blogs/enso/what-el-niño southern-oscillation-enso-nutshell.

For much—not all—of Texas, El Niño conditions may result in wetter and cooler winters and springs, fewer tropical systems, and weaker tropical systems. El Niño conditions do not always affect Texas weather; about 75 percent of strong or moderate El Niños result in wetter winters in Texas (based on data from Rebecca Lindsey, National Oceanic and Atmospheric Administration, *U.S. Winter Precipitation during Every El Niño Since 1950* (Oct. 24, 2018), www.climate.gov/news-features/featured-images/us-winter-precipitation-during-every-el-niño-1950). For much—not all—of Texas, La Niña conditions may result in dryer and warmer winters and springs, more Atlantic tropical systems, and stronger tropical systems. La Niña conditions do not always affect our weather; 76 percent of La Niñas result in dryer winters for Texas (based on data from Tom Di Liberto, National Oceanic and Atmospheric Administration, *Precipitation Patterns during Every La Niña Winter Since 1950* (Oct. 12, 2017), www.climate.gov/news-features/featured-images/precipitation-patterns-during-every-la-niña-winter-1950).

There are also longer term sea-surface temperature oscillations that appear to affect the weather and climate in Texas. The Pacific Decadal Oscillation relates to sea-surface temperatures in the northern Pacific and has cooling and warming phases that generally last twenty to thirty years. Depending on the phase, the Pacific Decadal Oscillation can intensify or diminish the effects of the El Niño Southern Oscillation. For the warming phase, the Pacific Decadal Oscillation may result in below-average temperatures and above-average precipitation; for the cooling phase, the oscillation may result in above-average temperatures and below-average rainfall. *See* Nathan J. Mantua & Steven R. Hare, *The Pacific Decadel Oscillation*, 58 J. Oceanography 35 (2002).

The Atlantic Multidecadal Oscillation relates to sea-surface temperatures in the northern Atlantic Ocean with cooling and warming phases that generally last twenty to forty years. In the warming phase, the Atlantic Multidecadal Oscillation may result in above-average temperature, below-average rainfall, and more tropical systems turning into hurricanes (twice as many during the warm phase than cool phase) but with fewer entering the Gulf of Mexico (tropical systems tend to swing up the Atlantic Coast during the warm phase). For the cooling phase, this oscillation may result in below-average temperatures and above-average rainfalls. The Dust Bowl and the 1950s drought occurred during the warm phase of the Atlantic Multidecadal Oscillation. *See* David B. Enfield et al., *The Atlantic Multidecadal Oscillation and Its Relation to Rainfall and River Flows in the Continental U.S.*, 28 Geophys. Res. Lett. 2077 (2001). From the mid-1960s to the mid-1990s, when the oscillation was in a cooling phase, Texas experienced cooler than normal temperatures and higher than normal precipitation. The Atlantic Multidecadal Oscillation switched from its cooling phase to its warming phase in the mid-1990s, about the same time as the 1996 drought that led to Texas regional water planning and the long-term drought in the southwest, including far West and West Texas. A number of droughts since the mid-1990s have occurred during the recent warm phase, including the recent state-wide drought from 2010 to 2015. The warming phase for the Atlantic Multidecadal Oscillation is still in place. See Figures 6 and 7. Recent research suggests that the Atlantic Multidecadal Oscillation may be driven more by external forces such as volcanic eruptions rather than an internal oscillation of the climate system. *See* Michael E. Mann et al., *Multidecadal Climate Oscillations During the Past Millennium Driven by Volcanic Forcing*, 371 Science p. 1014 (2021).

III. Climate Change in Texas

§ 2.5 Climate Change in Texas

The climate of our planet has indisputably changed over time as a result of a number of geologic, biologic, and meteorologic factors. Just a short 11,000 to 12,000 years ago, what is now Texas was experiencing the end of the last ice age. *See* Sam Houston State University, *Prehistoric Discovery Connects Texas Town to Ice Age* (Sept. 20, 2010), www.shsu.edu/~pin_www/T%40S/sliders/2010/katyconnection.html. Over the past 1 million years, the globe has experienced 100,000-year warming-and-cooling cycles. Before that were about 1.5 million years of 41,000-year warming-and-cooling cycles. Over the past 3 million years, global temperatures have declined, on average, about 5ºC. Over the past 50 million years, global temperatures have declined by 13ºC (the Antarctic ice sheet began to form when it was 11ºC warmer than today, and the northern ice sheets formed when it was 8ºC warmer). *See* Thomas E. Ewing, *Texas Through Time: Lone Star Geology, Landscapes, and Resources* (Bureau of Economic Geology, University of Texas at Austin, 2016).

As mentioned above, the term "climate change" generally refers to long-term changes in regional and global climate caused by human activity. Geologic, biologic, and meteorologic factors are still in play in the global climate, but changes in those factors over the past 140 years are small compared to the net sum of human influence (see Figure 8) resulting in a global average temperature increase of about 1.8°F from 1901 to 2016. *See* 2018 Climate Assessment, at 103. Warmer temperatures result in more water in the active hydrologic cycle (from melting glaciers and ice caps), a greater ability for the atmosphere to hold water (7 percent more per 1.8°F of warming), more energy in the atmosphere (resulting in more active storms), and greater evaporation and transpiration.

Measured temperature increases are greater at the poles than toward the equator. At its latitude, Texas can be expected to have shown a 1°F increase in temperature; however, the measured data is unclear at this point, largely because of the size of natural variation and the apparent effects of the Pacific Decadal and Atlantic Multidecadal oscillations on Texas climate. Analyses that show temperature trends over the past fifty years in Texas are misleading because much of the increase in temperatures over that time period is due to natural variation, not human-induced climate change. The amount of temperature change in Texas depends on the length of the climatic record and where you start and stop amidst the decadal variations. In fact, through more nuanced analysis, Texas is part of a "warming hole" where the data is not showing a systematic long-term increase in temperature. This doesn't mean temperatures aren't increasing or won't increase in Texas (as they clearly are elsewhere); it just means that our climatic record isn't long enough when compared to hypothesized increases to show the increased temperatures.

Rainfall in Texas has also remained relatively stable—again influenced by the decadal oscillations—but John Nielson-Gammon, the state climatologist, has seen an increase in rainfall in south and southeast Texas of 20 percent per century based on data collected between 1895 and 2006. Nielson-Gammon has also seen a 20 to 40 percent increase in extreme rainfall in Texas. Personal Communication from John Nielson-Gammon, Texas State Climatologist, Texas A&M University, to Robert Mace, Interim Executive Director and Chief Water Policy Officer of the Meadows Center for Water and the Environment (Sept. 2018).

§ 2.6 Projected Climate Change and Water Resources in Texas

§ 2.6:1 A Warming Climate and Precipitation

A warming climate will likely affect water resources from both the supply and demand sides. On the supply side, changes in the timing and intensity of precipitation would have an effect on water supplies—after all, that is where the water comes from. However, anticipated changes in precipitation by the end of this century are expected to be small compared with natural variation for much of the state, with a few exceptions. *See* 2018 Climate Assessment, at 88–89. Anticipated changes include 10 to 15 percent drier conditions over the entirety of the Rio Grande Basin in the winter, 10 to 15 percent drier conditions in far West Texas, and 15 to 20 percent drier conditions in the lower Rio Grande Valley in the spring. See Plate 9.

Climate change projections for the city of Austin's hundred-year water plan (*see* Katherine Hayhoe, ATMOS Research & Consulting, *Climate Change Projections for the City of Austin* (Apr. 2014), https://austintexas.gov/sites/default/files/files/Katherine_Hayhoe_Report_-_April_2014.pdf) show that there's little change in total precipitation for Austin under high and low greenhouse gas emission scenarios but increases in the number of—

- dry days per year (from ~275 in 1970–2000 to ~285 in 2071–2100);
- maximum consecutive dry-day length (from ~57 days in 1970–2000 to ~60 in 2071–2100);
- days with more than 2 inches of precipitation (from ~2.2 in 1970–2000 to ~2.8 in 2071–2100); and
- maximum five-day precipitation (from ~5.9 inches in 1970–2000 to ~7.9 in 2071–2100) (the models overshoot the historical record by an inch, so perhaps ~6.9 inches for 2071–2100 is more appropriate).

It's unclear what the future holds for tropical systems, an important and frequently destructive source of precipitation. Overall, with increasing temperatures, tropical systems are expected to be stronger and rainier; however, it's unclear how climate change may impact other factors (such as the El Niño Southern Oscillation and the Atlantic Multidecadal Oscillation) that will influence tropical system development and storm paths.

Increased and more intense rainfall may induce greater sedimentation of the state's reservoirs, thus affecting firm and safe yields. At present, Texas loses about 90,000 acre-feet (AF) per year of storage from its reservoirs because of sedimentation. See Chapter 27 of this book discussing reservoirs.

Although located outside of Texas, the headwaters of the Rio Grande in southern Colorado are the primary source of water for Elephant Butte Reservoir, an important source of water for irrigators and municipal users in the El Paso area. Similar to Texas, changes in precipitation amounts along the Rio Grande upstream of Elephant Butte Reservoir are expected to be small compared to natural variations, although there's the suggestion that winter precipitation could be slightly higher by 2100. See Plate 9.

§ 2.6:2 Increasing Temperatures Affect Water Resources

Temperature is easier to model and project than precipitation, with emissions controlling how warm the climate might get. Under the higher emissions scenario (Representative Concentration Pathway 8.5 (RCP8.5)), temperatures in Texas are expected to increase by about 4°F by midcentury and about 8°F by the end of the century. *See* 2018 Climate Assessment, at 87. See Figure 9. Increased temperatures can have profound effects on water resources.

Evaporation increases with increasing temperature, so we can expect increased evaporative losses from reservoirs. Monthly pan evaporation increases by about 0.1 inches per degree Fahrenheit in northeastern Texas to 0.3 inches in the Big Bend area. *See The Impact of Global Warming on Texas* (Gerald R. North et al. eds., 1st ed. 1995). A reservoir in the Central Texas area might expect to have 19 inches more evaporation in 2100 (under RCP8.5) than today. Increasing water temperatures can also reduce dissolved oxygen in water and increase eutrophication—degrading water quality and increasing treatment costs. See Chapter 33 of this book discussing water quality standards.

This increased evaporation would also affect soil moisture, which in turn affects runoff to rivers and reservoirs and infiltration to aquifers. Comparing runoff during the 1950 to 1956 drought of record period to normal conditions during the period 1971 to 2000 shows that runoff decreased 60 percent although there was only a 25 percent decrease in rainfall. An increase in temperature of 3.6°F and a decrease in rainfall of 5 percent results in a decrease in runoff of 17 percent and decreased flows to the coast of 26 percent.

Water availability modeling for Austin's hundred-year water plan shows that, without climate change and with increasing demand, the Highland Lakes can provide reliable water through 2115; however, with climate change added (and no new water supply strategies), the Highland Lakes go dry for years at a time. One could easily argue that the cost of implementing Austin's water plan is the cost of climate change on providing the city with reliable water.

Many, but not all, aquifers in Texas are buffered from climatic changes, at least on a human time scale. *See* Robert E. Mace & Shirley C. Wade, *In Hot Water? How Climate Change May (or May Not) Affect the Groundwater Resources of Texas*, 58 Gulf Coast Association of Geological Societies Transactions 655–68 (2008). Groundwater resources with high recharge rates, such as karstic aquifers like the Edwards (Balcones Fault Zone) Aquifer, and highly permeable clastic aquifers, like the Lipan Aquifer, are susceptible to changes in climate while others with much slower recharge rates would not show effects for decades, if not centuries. Furthermore, in many dipping clastic aquifers (such as the Trinity Aquifer north of the Colorado River, the Carrizo-Wilcox Aquifer, and the Gulf Coast Aquifer), it's unlikely that climate change will have much impact on down-dip groundwater resources because the flow of water down-dip is small compared to the flow of water discharging to local streams and rivers.

§ 2.6:3 Rising Sea Levels

With a warming climate, meltwater from land-based ice caps and glaciers and the thermal expansion of water are causing sea levels to rise. Rising sea levels submerge land along our coast and increase the impacts of storms on infrastructure. Rising sea levels and increasingly intense storm surges will affect bays and estuaries and may also affect upstream freshwater resources. Some have expressed concerns that rising sea levels might increase saltwater intrusion into the Gulf Coast Aquifer, which serves as the water source for communities all along the Gulf Coast of Texas. While this is a legitimate concern for shallow, unconfined aquifers along the coast, the primary water-bearing strata for the Gulf Coast Aquifer are separated by confining layers between the aquifer and the Gulf of Mexico. Land subsidence caused by groundwater pumping increases relative sea level rise by lowering land elevations.

IV. Weather and Climate: Shaping Texas Water Policy

§ 2.7 Texas Water Policy Reacts to Weather Events

Our recent history of the last 150 years is full of examples of how weather events prompted and resulted in policy changes. *See* Rubinstein, *Texas Water Policy Appendix*, 2015. These policy changes have assisted Texans in preparing for and responding to such weather manifestations and in part mitigating future disastrous impacts. But as very recent experience with Hurricane Harvey and the 2021 polar vortex storm have shown, we are far from done.

§ 2.7:1 State Water Policy Driven by Drought

Droughts (which are considered to be weather rather than climate) in Texas have resulted in significant modifications of Texas water policy and creation of many of our water management entities and programs. The success, unintended consequences, and less than desirable outcomes of some of these strategies is readily apparent in the history books. The drought of 1856 resulted in the creation of the state geological survey for scientific recommendations on soil utilization and water resources, which was never completed because the survey was interrupted by the Civil War.

The drought of 1886–87 led to the creation of a second state geological survey (completed for artesian wells) and proposed new reservoirs built by convict labor to make such projects affordable. The second geologic survey also introduced the prior appropriation allocation system for surface water rights. See Chapter 4 of this book for a discussion of this system. The drought of 1901 contributed to the establishment of the rule of capture regarding groundwater by the Texas Supreme Court in *Houston & T.C. Ry. Co. v. East*, 81 S.W. 279 (Tex. 1904). See Chapter 5. Drought conditions from 1909 to 1912 led to the establishment of the Texas Board of Water Engineers and centralization of water rights claims. See Chapter 4.

The drought of 1916–18 contributed to significant water policy changes in Texas. It led to the Conservation Amendment, article XVI, section 59, of the Texas Constitution, which allowed the legislature to (1) create conservation and reclamation districts to develop water resources and build dams and delivery systems, and (2) declare water resources public rights and duties while vesting water rights acquired prior to the act. See Chapter 4 for a discussion of the Conservation Amendment.

Lastly, the Conservation Amendment led to the establishment of special purpose districts called river authorities, including the Brazos River Authority in 1929, the Guadalupe-Blanco River Authority in 1933, and the Lower Colorado River Authority in 1934. See Chapter 9 for a discussion of river authorities and other regional water districts.

The Dust Bowl drought of 1933–34 led to the eventual creation of groundwater conservation districts but not without a few failed starts. Legislation to regulate groundwater failed in 1937. The Board of Water Engineers in 1938 called for state ownership of groundwater. Legislation to regulate groundwater again failed in 1941 and 1947. Legislation allowing for the creation of groundwater conservation districts passed in 1949 with the first district created in 1951 (High Plains Underground Water Conservation District No. 1). See Chapter 5 for a discussion of groundwater history and regulation. Of additional significance, this same drought period resulted in the establishment of the Wagstaff Act (partially repealed in 1997), which provided protection to upstream municipal water suppliers and stipulated that new appropriations would be granted subject to the right of municipalities to make further appropriations without the necessity of condemnation. See Chapter 4 for a discussion of the Wagstaff Act.

The statewide drought of record from 1950 to 1957 led to the creation of the Texas Water Development Board (TWDB) in 1957. This drought also resulted in a fivefold increase in groundwater pumping, primarily for agriculture. Concurrently, *State v. Hidalgo County Water Control & Improvement District No. 18*, 443 S.W.2d 728 (Tex. App.—Corpus Christi–Edinburg 1969, writ ref'd n.r.e.), referred to as the *Valley Water* case, settled claims for water on the Rio Grande below Falcon Reservoir, created a new priority system for the lower Rio Grande based on type of use, and established the first watermaster program, followed in 1967 by the enactment of the Water Rights Adjudication Act. The Texas response to the drought of record also resulted in the construction of twenty-three major reservoirs in the 1950s (with 5.9 million AF of firm yield) and thirty-four more in the 1960s (with 14.3 million AF of firm yield). Additionally, our response to the drought of record contributed to the 1968 state water plan that proposed bringing Mississippi River water to Texas. See Chapter 4 for a discussion of these events.

The next significant drought impacting Texas water policy was the drought of 1996. This led to the passage of Senate Bill 1 in 1997, establishing the regional water planning process we rely on today. See Chapter 20 for a discussion of state water planning. S.B. 1 also created the junior provision for interbasin transfers of surface water and repealed parts of the Wagstaff Act, replacing it with an emergency authorization provision for municipal water rights codified at Texas Water Code section 11.139. See Chapter 10 for a discussion of surface water permitting.

In 2001, the legislature passed Senate Bill 2, which created the Texas Water Advisory Council to heighten the level of discussion, in an advisory role only, on various significant water policy issues, including desalination, public-private partnerships and other financing methods to advance water projects, regionalization, brush control, water conservation and drought management, and regional, interstate, and international water planning efforts focused on environmental quality.

S.B. 2 also required the TWDB to develop groundwater availability models (GAMs) and for water plans to include water conservation and drought management practices. See Chapters 19 (GAMs), 22 (drought planning), and 23 (water conservation). Additionally, S.B. 2 codified that groundwater conservation districts are the state's preferred method of managing groundwater resources and charged the TWDB with designating groundwater management areas (GMAs). See Chapter 5 for a discussion of GMAs. In 2007, Senate Bill 3 established the process for environmental flow standards for new water right permits. See Chapter 11 of this book.

After the drought of 2009, the legislature granted new authority to the Texas Commission on Environmental Quality to manage shortages of surface water and senior priority calls. As the drought intensified into the worst one-year statewide drought in 2011, the legislature acted to provide incentives to implementation of water management strategies in the state water plan by passing House Bill 4 in 2013, which established the State Water Implementation Fund for Texas and restructured the

TWDB. See Chapters 37 and 7, respectively, for discussion of funding mechanisms and the TWDB restructure.

§ 2.7:2 Water Policy and Flooding

As discussed above, drought has impacted our water policy. Similarly, our changing rainfall patterns, perhaps indicative of a changing climate, have resulted in record-setting floods. The recently released 2018 Climate Assessment indicates that—

> The U.S. record for greatest single-day rainfall is 43 inches, set in Alvin, Texas, in July of 1979, as Tropical Storm Claudette moved through the area. Houston, Texas, in particular, experienced several record-breaking floods in 2015, 2016, and 2017, with Hurricane Harvey rewriting the continental U.S. record for total rainfall from a tropical cyclone. Cedar Bayou, Texas (30 miles from Houston), recorded 51.88 inches of rain during the multi-day onslaught of Hurricane Harvey.

2018 Climate Assessment, at 992.

The Memorial Day floods of 2015 and the record-breaking flooding caused by Hurricane Harvey in 2017 have caused the state to enact flood planning, mitigation, and funding legislation. The 86th legislative session passed and the governor signed into law H.B. 5, H.B. 7, S.B. 6, and S.B. 7. Collectively, these bills call for catastrophic debris management planning, navigating disaster contracting and waiver requirements, and the provision of significant funding for Harvey relief and flood mitigation project implementation. *See* Press Release, Office of Governor Greg Abbott, *Governor Abbott Signs Disaster Relief And Preparedness Legislation Into Law* (June 13, 2019), https://gov.texas.gov/news/post/governor-abbott-signs-disaster-relief-and-preparedness-legislation-into-law.

We believe that identification of flood mitigation projects and funding their implementation to reduce repetitive loss and catastrophic impacts is clearly in line with the recognition that a changing climate with increasing extreme weather events is impacting and will continue to impact Texas. Chapter 39 of this book, dealing with flood management, covers this subject in greater detail.

§ 2.7:3 Water Policy and Freezing

The 2021 polar vortex storm event, which occurred as the Texas Legislature was starting the second month of the 87th legislative session, quickly led to a declaration of emergency legislative action relating to the need for winterization of power and water utilities and associated funding. *See* https://gov.texas.gov/news/post/governor-abbott-declares-power-system-winterization-related-funding-as-emergency-items-provides-update-on-winter-weather-response. In issuing his emergency declaration, Governor Abbott stated, "The past several days have been beyond challenging, but with every passing hour we are restoring power and water for families across Texas." Press Release, Office of Governor Greg Abbott, Disaster Proclamation (Feb. 12, 2021) ("certifying under Section 418.014 of the Texas Government Code that the severe winter weather poses an imminent threat of widespread and severe property damage, injury, and loss of life due to prolonged freezing temperatures, heavy snow, and freezing rain statewide"), renewed Mar. 15, 2021.

The storm event led to the loss of electricity for a substantial part of the state due to cold-weather issues for power generators, but there were also local issues affecting power. In some cases, power went out to drinking water treatment plants, thus affecting supply. Some water suppliers switched to backup power before losing power, thus gaining control of their systems as well as dropping load from the power grid. Cold water moving through municipal water distribution systems caused some pipes to contract to the point of failure, resulting in water system pressure losses and the activation of boil-water notices. As power returned and pipes in structures thawed, pipes broken by the freeze began to produce water, creating another pressure loss in the system. *See* Will Groggin, *Texas Water System, Like the Grid, Failed in Winter Storm*, The Daily News (Apr. 5, 2021), www.galvnews.com/opinion/guest_columns/article_c45f95c3-3669-5fab-bb09-7a214b275f2b.html; Phil Helsel & Yuliya Talmazan, *Texas Water Shortage Adds to Power Crisis as New Winter Storm Moves In*, NBC News (Feb. 27, 2021), www.nbcnews.com/news/us-news/texas-contending-water-nightmare-top-power-crisis-n1258208.

§ 2.8 How Climate Change Is, Is Not, and Should Be Considered in Texas

We have witnessed firsthand that it is well accepted, both here and across the country, that Texas serves as a national model when it comes to statewide planning relative to water supply. There are many reasons for this recognition:

- We enjoy a planning process that requires local participation and identification of future strategies to meet projected increasing demands for water.
- Our planning horizon is fifty years.
- We enjoy enviable and highly competitive funding structures to assist in the cost-effective implementation of recommended water supply strategies.
- We have a water rights permitting process that calls for consistency with the state water plan.
- We plan to have sufficient water to be able to respond to a repeat of the drought of record.
- We revisit and modify our plan every five years, allowing us to adjust as changed conditions dictate, to project both population growth and demand forecasts, as well as how weather and climatic conditions have impacted our assumptions. When a new drought of record is established, water availability projects are adjusted.
- We allow the plan to be amended as needed during a five-year cycle to account for dramatic change conditions or to advance new strategies.

In our opinion, as good as our planning process is, it could be and needs to be better. Our current statewide planning is centered on our ability to endure a repeat of the drought of record with sufficient water availability. We have been planning for this outcome for the past twenty-four years. However, the goal of enduring a repeat of the drought of record with sufficient water availability may not be protective enough, considering what is known about historical climate conditions in Texas and climate change.

To complicate matters, Texas is not ready for a repeat of the drought of record, let alone a drought worse than the drought of record. The current state water plan reports that only about 39 percent of the recommended strategies over time either have been implemented or have some reported progress toward implementation. *See* Texas Water Development Board, *Water for Texas* 144 (2022), www.twdb.texas.gov/waterplanning/swp/2022/. Although Texas is unquestionably better prepared for drought—note how much better the state fared during the 2010–15 drought as compared to the 1996 drought that led to Senate Bill 1—we have unfortunately fallen more and more behind in being ready for a repeat of the drought of record. The difference between statewide water supplies and water demand in the immediate planning decade has decreased from a statewide surplus of 0.9 million AF in 2002 to a deficit of 3.2 million AF in 2017. Needs (additional water needed to meet demands during a repeat of the drought of record) have increased from 2.4 million AF in 2002 to 4.7 million AF in 2017. We are losing ground on preparing for future water supply needs, even without considering our climate or climate change.

Putting aside the fact that our water supply planning is not resulting in the full implementation of management strategies, climate and climate change have not been incorporated into the planning.

Deeper histories indicate that Texas droughts have been much worse than the drought of record in the 1950s. Tree-ring studies indicate that West Texas experienced a much more severe drought in the thirteenth century. Central Texas's worst droughts, based on tree-ring studies, occurred in both the sixteenth and eighteenth centuries, with the sixteenth-century drought representing a "megadrought" that impacted most of the continent. From such findings, a case can be made that planning for a repeat of the drought of record alone may not be enough.

A 2010 *Texas Water Journal* article relative to climate change and impacts on Texas water included a recommendation that large droughts of the past should be incorporated into our water planning process. *See* Jay L. Banner et al., *Climate Change Impacts on Texas Water: A White Paper Assessment of the Past, Present and Future and Recommendations for Action*, 1 Tex. Water J. 1, 14 (2010), https://journals.tdl.org/twj/index.php/twj/article/view/1043. More recent climate projections suggest drier conditions in the latter half of this century than have been seen in the past 1,000 years, including megadroughts. *See* John Nielsen-Gammon et al., *Unprecedented Drought Challenges for Texas Water Resources in a Changing Climate: What Do Researchers and Stakeholders Need to Know? Earth's Future* (2020), https://agupubs.onlinelibrary.wiley.com/doi/10.1029/2020EF001552. To the extent that megadroughts have been documented in Texas via tree-ring studies and with an anticipation that climate change is likely to result in a warmer Texas climate, the need to consider long-term climate trends in Texas in addition to the current practice of considering short-term weather manifestations is not only highlighted but is also prudent water planning. Put another way: if we experience a new drought of record, many water sectors in Texas today are not prepared to mitigate its impacts. Absent such consideration, however, a planning exercise focused on a drought worse than the drought of record might be sobering and critically useful in ensuring that Texas has enough water for the future.

The legislature established our planning process via Senate Bill 1 in 1997. Legislative action to incorporate a more detailed assessment of how Texas's climate has impacted and may impact our water resources has been attempted. We are unaware of any legislatively mandated statewide assessment of water impacts on Texas because of climate change. A review of past legislative action as documented in the Texas Legislature Online website, https://capitol.texas.gov/, reveals that most climate bills seldom go beyond the point of being filed, with just a few having enjoyed at least one committee hearing. Recent catastrophic flooding events led to several additional bills relative to climate impacts on water resources being filed during the 86th legislative session. In the sixth edition of this book we enumerated seven bills that had been filed to address weather and climate change concerns.

What a difference a severe cold snap makes.

As previously noted, in February 2021 Texans experienced record-setting and prolonged periods of subfreezing temperatures. These conditions contributed to significant power reductions—if not out-and-out failures—frozen natural gas production facilities, and significant failures of water and wastewater systems. We recognize that power generation and water treatment are inextricably interconnected. Texans appreciate that reality now.

If we were to list all bills filed after the storm passed in early February 2021 that speak to the need for ensuring that power and water systems are resilient in the face of extreme weather events, including subfreezing temperatures, as well as the need to study, consider, adapt, and mitigate the impacts of a changing climate, we would have to list more than 140. And if we added bills that call for significant changes at the Public Utility Commission of Texas and the Electric Reliability Council of Texas—all associated with the recent experience from the Arctic storm—the list would be much longer.

As the 87th session came to an end, and as experienced in previous sessions, many bills on climate change failed to get a single committee hearing. However, a more than fair number of bills that call for winterization and increased reliability and resiliency in our power and water systems have been considered and acted on. Climate change by any other name is still a recognition of a changing climate.

As with the previous edition's version of this chapter, we leave it to the readers to draw their own conclusions regarding the historical lack of legislative action on specific climate bills. Likewise, we leave it to the readers to consider the substantial commitment the legislature made to address flood-related disaster relief and preparedness during the 86th legislative session, as well as the admirable work of the Texas Water Development Board in implementing the legislatively mandated program. We also highlight the following legislative actions taken during the 87th session that address extreme weather and climate-associated impacts:

- H.B. 2089—we note this bill because it includes, among the characteristics to consider relative to agricultural pest control, the area's climate.
- H.R. 186, expressing the Texas House of Representatives' support for Taiwan's meaningful participation in the United Nations Framework Convention on Climate Change.
- H.R. 378, recognizing Teresa Feria of the University of Texas Rio Grande Valley for her areas of expertise, which include climate change.
- H.R. 142, recognizing the efforts of Houston mayor Sylvester Turner for his efforts to strengthen communities and address climate change.
- S.B. 3, the comprehensive winter storm reform bill relating to preparing for, preventing, and responding to weather emergencies and power outages, including conditions that present danger of climactic activity, such as precipitation severe enough to constitute a disaster.
- S.B. 1118, adding to the priority conservation measures of the State Soil and Water Conservation Board those measures that "improve resilience to weather extremes, climate variability, and nature disasters."

Because there is still uncertainty on exactly how climate change will manifest itself in Texas and how that manifestation will affect water resources, adaptive planning is key to responding to changes as they occur—something Texas already does with its water planning process. Impacts of climate change on water resources become clearer thirty years out from present, which is included in the current planning horizon. Thus, the adaptive planning structure already exists, but consideration of climate change data is needed. If climate change is too politically charged, as it is today, perhaps a good start would be to incorporate into the existing planning template historical climate data beyond the drought of record as an acknowledgement of climate variability in Texas and its impact on our water resources. Such historical data could include an assessment of climate change or tree-ring analyses. Some water planning groups address climate variability beyond what has been observed through using safe yields for reservoirs instead of firm yields. We know that real data is needed on which to base multibillion-dollar investments in infrastructure, but without considering climate and climate change in our water supply planning, the real data is lacking. In other words, without state investment in quantifying the risks of climate and climate change to our water supplies, water planners do not have the information they need to make decisions on how best to ensure the resiliency of Texas's water resources.

V. Conclusion

§ 2.9 Conclusion

Texans recognize the need to plan and respond to changing weather patterns. We have mandated water conservation and drought contingency plans. We have also developed a planning process to meet future water demands projecting a response to a repeat of the drought of record. Further, we are seriously looking at ways to protect Texans from devastating and repetitive losses due to flood events, and more recently from prolonged subfreezing events. Likewise, Texans recognize and accept natural phenomena that impact our weather and climate, from increased solar activity to our topography and geographical location to changing ocean temperatures and impacts via events such as El Niño.

Our water resources are impacted by our own use of water, population growth, development of water management strategies, weather patterns, and a changing climate. Nothing has impacted or will impact our water availability more than weather and, over time, our climate. Flood events replenish our reservoirs and contribute to groundwater recharge. Hot and dry patterns increase our consumptive use of water and evaporation rates. Extended periods of dryness or drought have devastating impacts on our economy. Drought is not new to Texas; megadroughts have visited the state before. Projected changing climate, irrespective of cause, will only make these impacts on our water resources worse. Thus, consideration of our climate and climate change are essential tools in Texas's water supply planning.

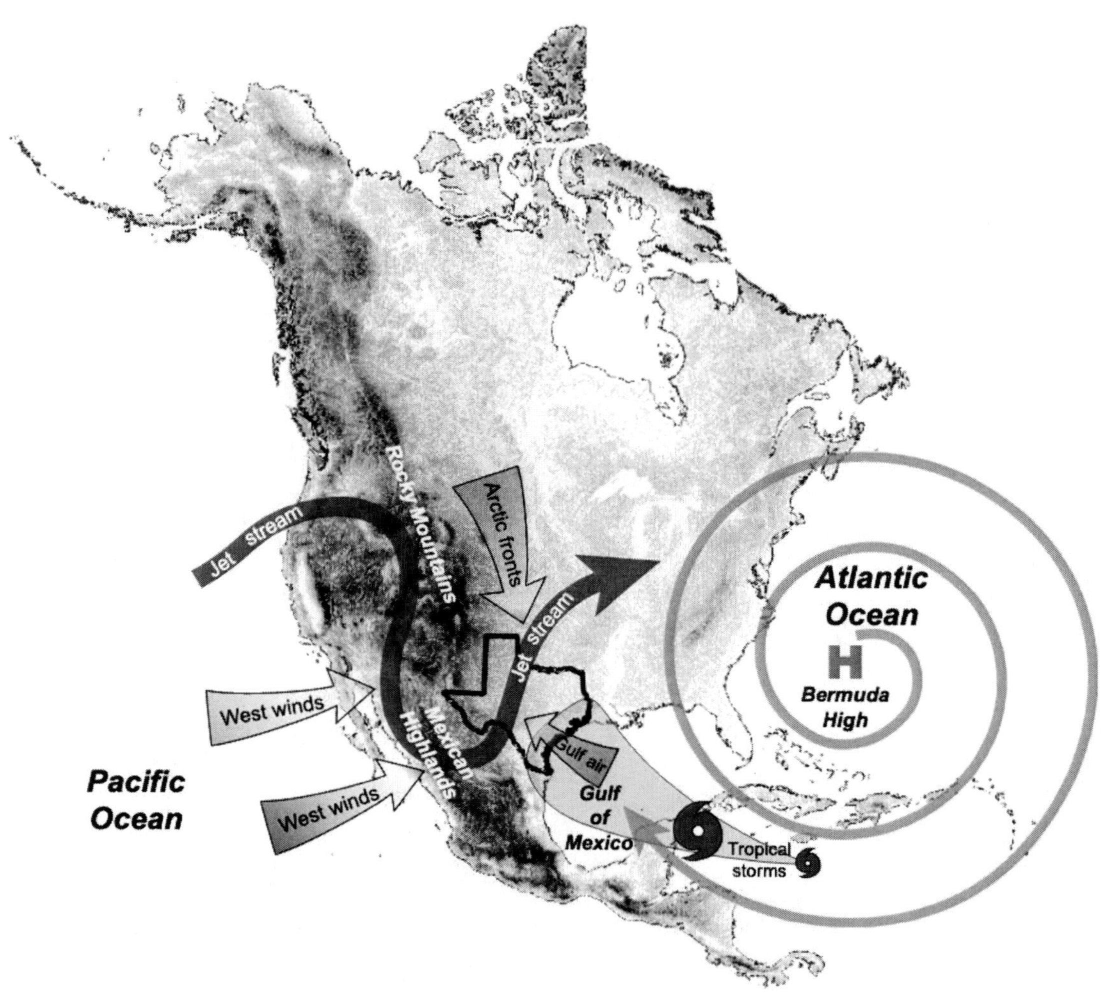

Figure 1. Factors affecting weather and climate in Texas. Texas Water Development Board, 2 *Water for Texas* 131 fig. 5-1 (2007), www.twdb.texas.gov/waterplanning/swp/2007/.

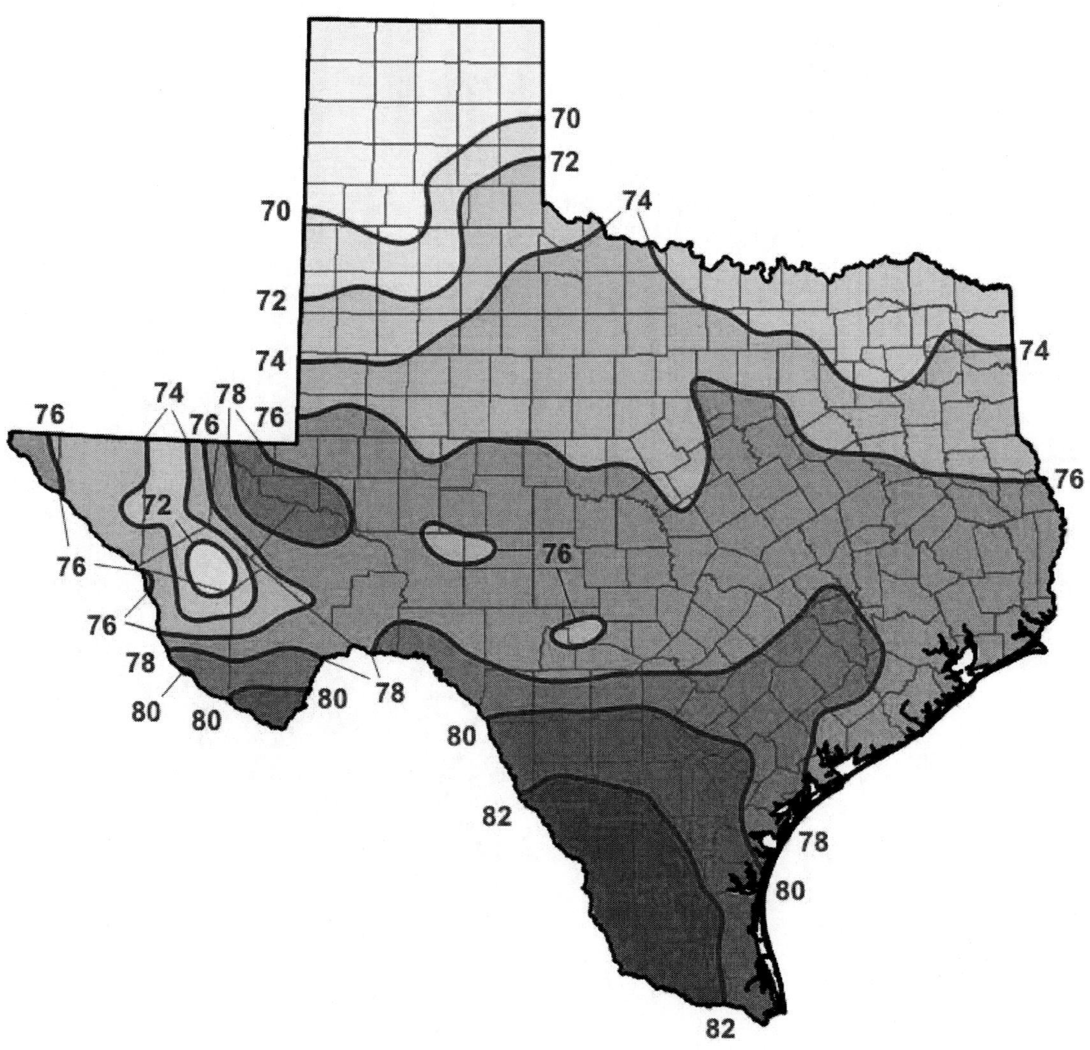

Figure 2. Average annual maximum daily temperature (in degrees Fahrenheit), 1971–2000. Texas Water Development Board, 2 *Water for Texas* 132 fig. 5-2 (2007), www.twdb.texas.gov/waterplanning/swp/2007/.

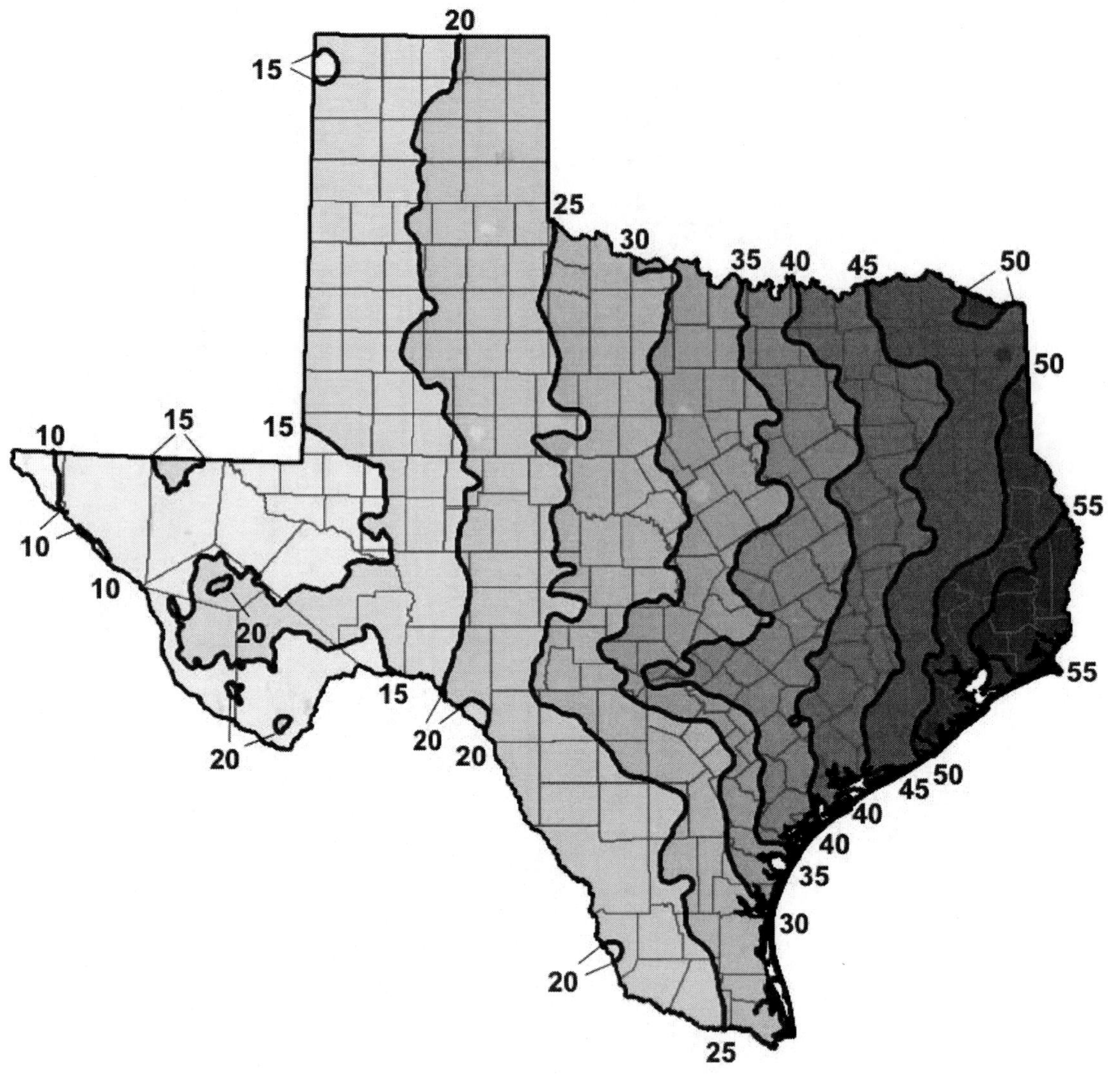

Figure 3. Average annual precipitation in inches, 1971–2000. Texas Water Development Board, 2 *Water for Texas* 132 fig. 5-3 (2007), www.twdb.texas.gov/waterplanning/swp/2007/.

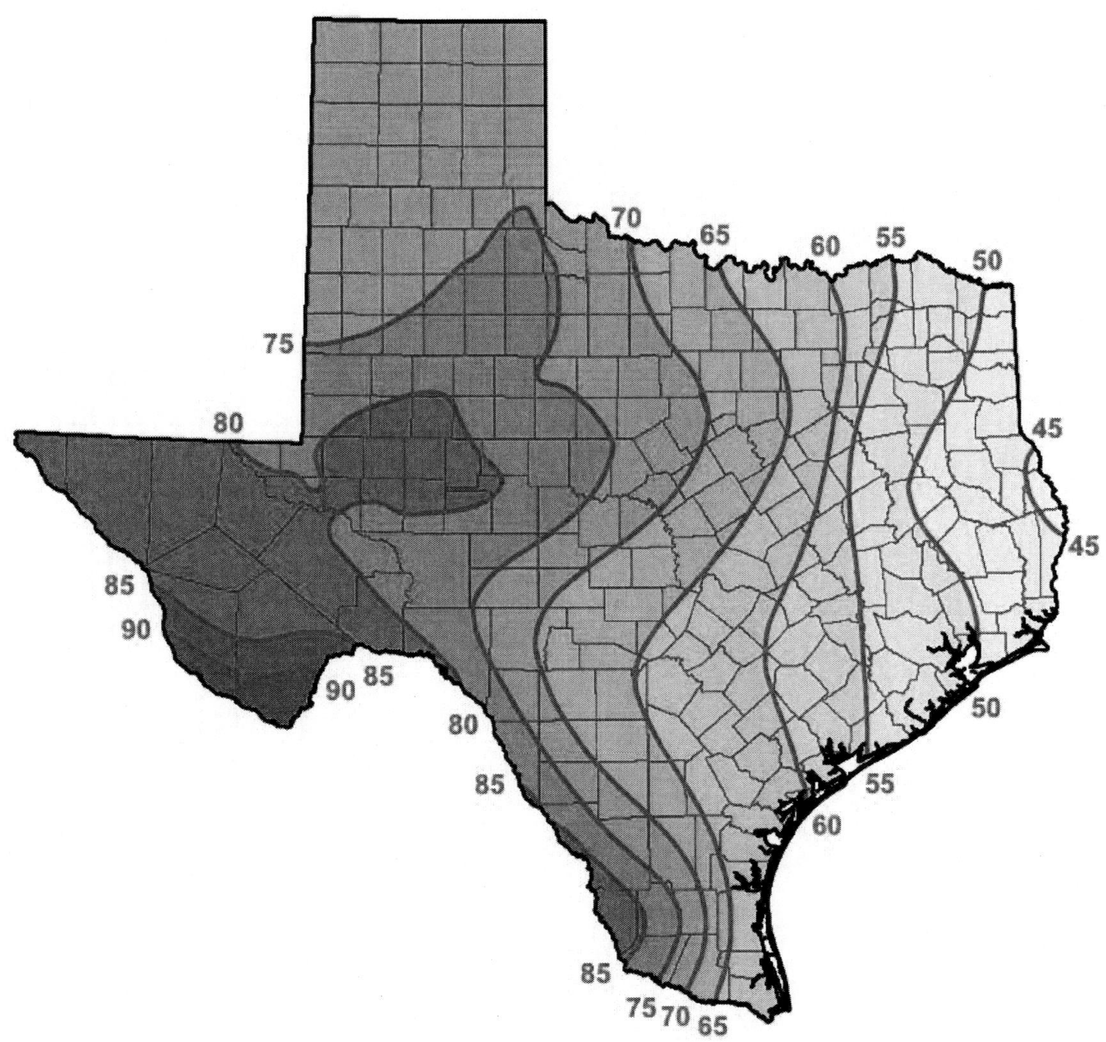

Figure 4. Average annual gross lake-surface evaporation in inches, 1950–1979. Texas Water Development Board, 2 *Water for Texas* 133 fig. 5-4 (2007), www.twdb.texas.gov/waterplanning/swp/2007/.

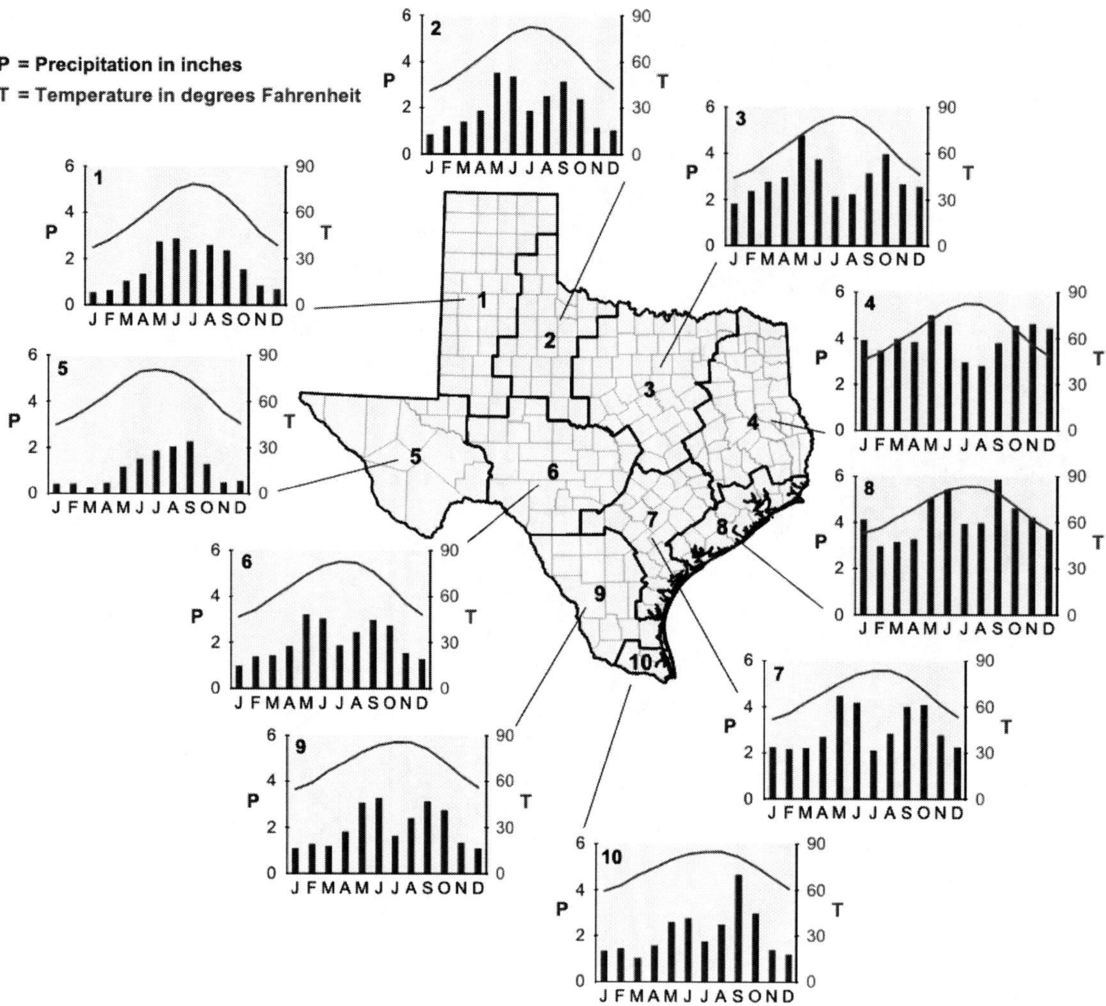

Figure 5. Climate divisions of Texas showing average monthly temperature (T, line) and precipitation (P, bars). Texas Water Development Board, 2 *Water for Texas* 134 fig. 5-5 (2007), www.twdb.texas.gov/waterplanning/swp/2007/.

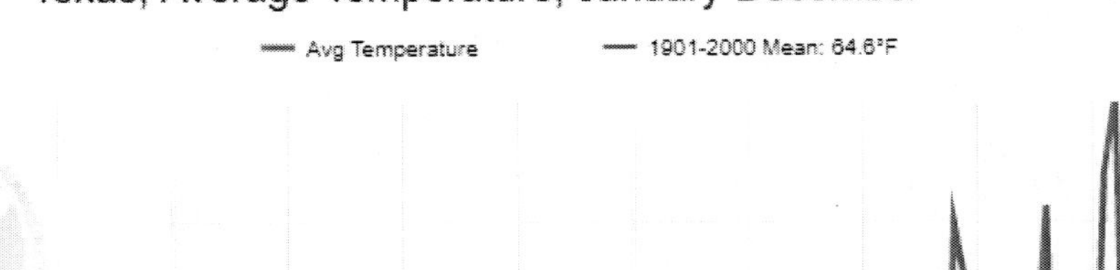

Figure 6. Average annual statewide temperature for Texas, 1895–2018. The long-term average for 1895–2018, as indicated by the horizontal gray line, is 64.8°F. National Oceanic and Atmospheric Administration, National Centers for Environmental Information, *Climate at a Glance: Statewide Time Series*, www.ncdc.noaa.gov/cag/statewide/time-series/41/tavg/12/12/1895-2018?base_prd=true&firstbaseyear=1901&lastbaseyear=2000.

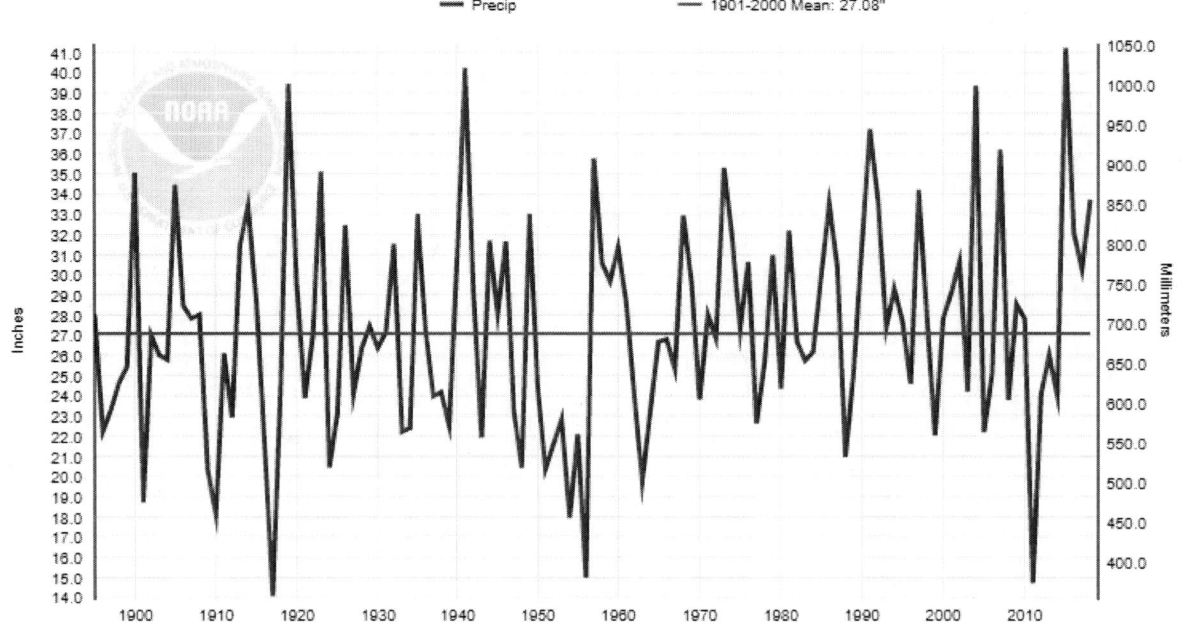

Figure 7. Average annual statewide rainfall for Texas, 1895–2018. The long-term average for 1895–2018, as indicated by the horizontal gray line, is 27.3 inches. National Oceanic and Atmospheric Administration, National Centers for Environmental Information, *Climate at a Glance: Statewide Time Series*, www.ncdc.noaa.gov/cag/statewide/time-series/41/pcp/12/12/1895-2018?base_prd=true&firstbaseyear=1901&lastbaseyear=2000.

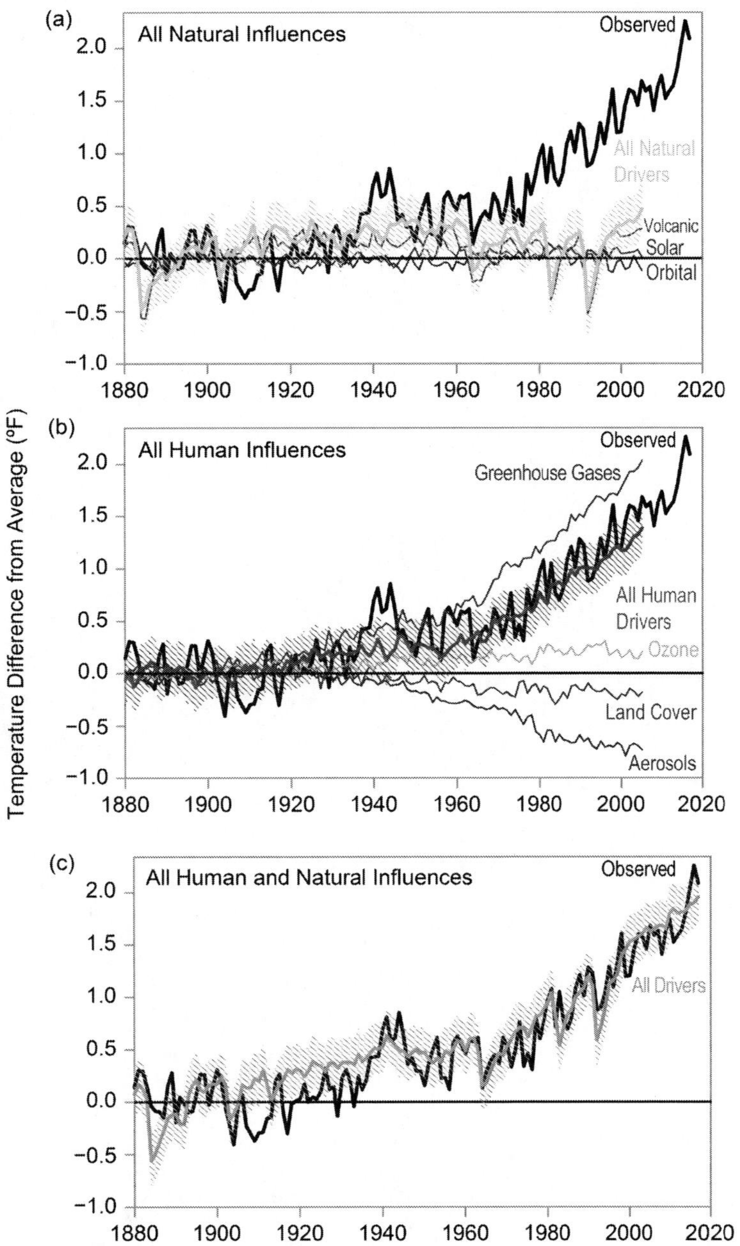

Figure 8. Changes in global temperature caused by natural and human-induced influences. U.S. Global Change Research Program, *Fourth National Climate Assessment: Impacts, Risks, and Adaption in the United States*, vol. 2, ch. 2, *Our Changing Climate* 79 fig. 2.1 (2018), https://nca2018.globalchange.gov/downloads/NCA4_Ch02_Changing-Climate_Full.pdf.

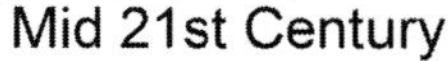

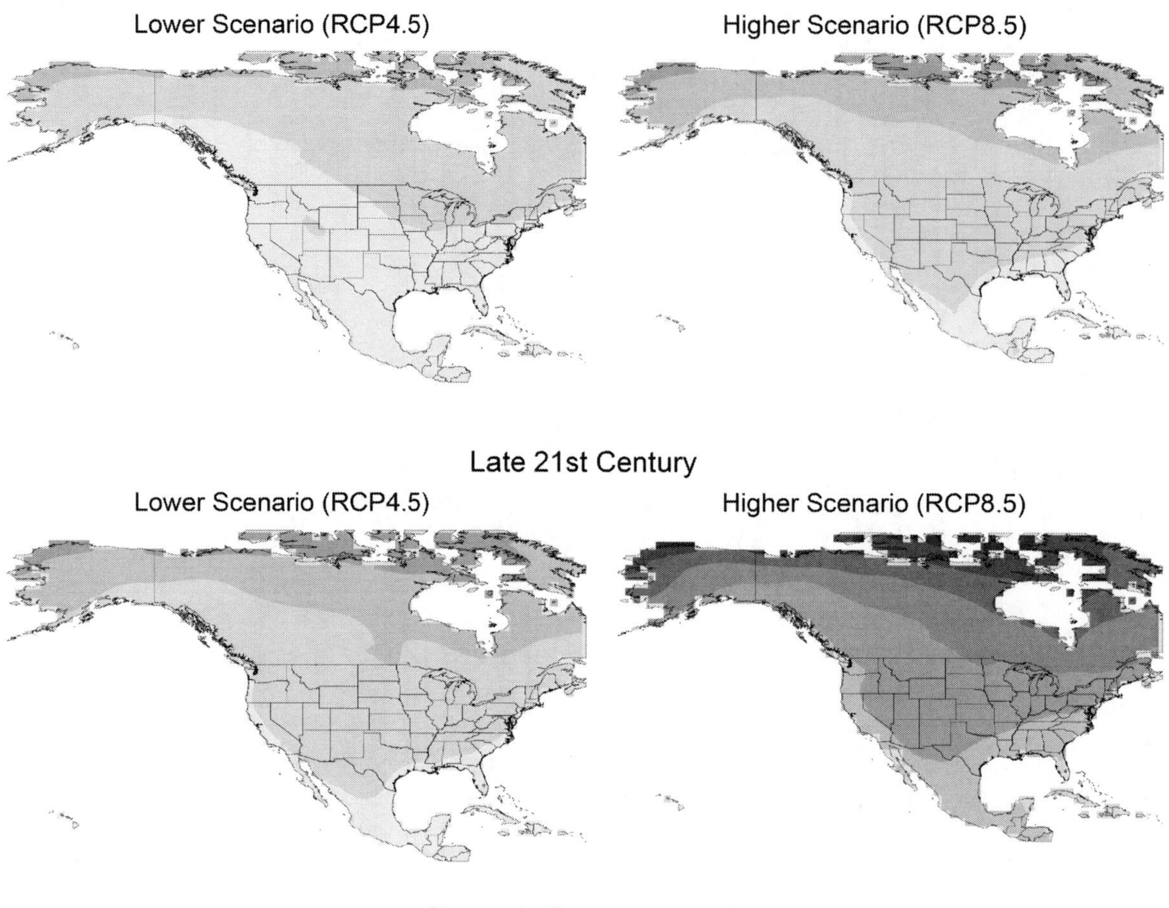

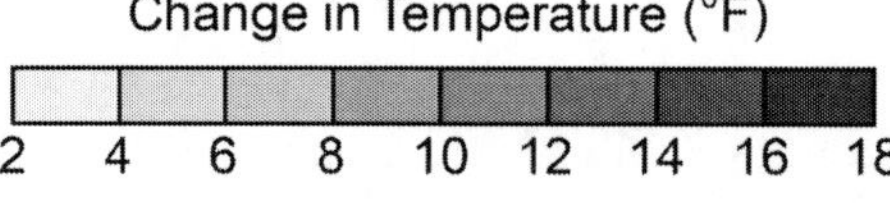

Figure 9. Projected changes in average annual temperature for ~2050 and ~2100 for lower and higher emission scenarios. U.S. Global Change Research Program, *Fourth National Climate Assessment: Climate Science Special Report*, vol. 1, ch. 6, *Temperature Changes in the United States* 196 fig. 6.7 (2017), https://science2017.globalchange.gov/downloads/CSSR_Ch6_Temperature.pdf.

References

Adhikari, P., Ale, S., Bordovsky, J.P., Thorp, K.R., Modala, N.R., Rajan, N., and E.M. Barnes. 2016. *Simulating future climate change impacts on seed cotton yield in the Texas High Plains using the CSM-CROPGRO-Cotton model.* Agricultural Water Management, v. 164, pp. 317–30.

Appendini, C.M., Hernandez-Lasheras, J., Meza-Padilla, R., and J.A. Kurczyn. 2018. *Effect of climate change on wind waves generated by anticyclonic cold front intrusions in the Gulf of Mexico.* Climate Dynamics, v. 51, pp. 3747–63.

Armitage, A.R., Highfield, W.E., Brody, S.D., and P. Louchouarn. 2015. *The contribution of mangrove expansion to salt marsh loss on the Texas Gulf Coast.* PLoS ONE, v. 10, no. 5, 17 pp.

Awal, R., Fares, A., and H. Bayabil. 2018. *Assessing potential climate change impacts on irrigation requirements of major crops in the Brazos headwaters basin, Texas.* Water, v. 10, 1610, 15 pp.

Banner, Jay L., Jackson, C.S., Yang, Z.L., Hayhoe, K., Woodhouse, C., Gulden, L., Jacobs, K., North, G., Leung, R., Washington, W., Jiang, X., and R. Castell. 2010. *Climate change impacts on Texas water: A white paper assessment of the past, present and future and recommendations for action.* Texas Water Journal, v. 1, pp. 1–19.

Boumans, R.J.M., Phillips, D.L., Victery, W., and T.D. Fontaine. 2014. *Developing a model for effects of climate change on human health and health-environment interactions: Heat stress in Austin, Texas.* Urban Climate, v. 8, pp. 78–99.

Brikowski, T.H. 2015. *Applying multi-parameter runoff elasticity to assess water availability in a changing climate: An example from Texas, USA.* Hydrological Processes, v. 29, pp. 1746–56.

Cameron, G.N., and D. Scheel. 2001. *Getting warmer: Effect of global climate change on distribution of rodents in Texas.* Journal of Mammalogy, v. 82, no. 3, pp. 652–80.

Campbell, A., Becerra, T.A., Middendorf, G., and P. Tomlinson. 2019. *Climate change beliefs, concerns, and attitudes of beef cattle producers in the Southern Great Plains.* Climatic Change, v. 152, pp. 35–46.

Chen, Y., Alea, S., Rajan, N., and R. Srinivasan. 2017. *Modeling the effects of land use change from cotton (Gossypium hirsutum L.) to perennial bioenergy grasses on watershed hydrology and water quality under changing climate.* Agricultural Water Management, v. 192, pp. 198–208.

Conlon, K., Monaghan, A., Hayden, M., and O. Wilhelmi. 2015. *Potential impacts of future warming and land use changes on intra-urban heat exposure in Houston, Texas.* PLoS ONE, v. 11, no. 2, 19 pp.

Di Liberto, T. 2017. *Precipitation patterns during every La Niña winter since 1950.* National Oceanic and Atmospheric Administration (Oct. 12, 2017), www.climate.gov/news-features/featured-images/precipitation-patterns-during-every-la-niña-winter-1950.

Djebou, D.C.S. 2017. *Spectrum of climate change and streamflow alteration at a watershed scale.* Environmental Earth Science, v. 76, 13 pp.

Enfield, D.B., Mestas-Nuñez, A.M., and P.J. Trimble. 2001. *The Atlantic multidecadal oscillation and its relation to rainfall and river flows in the continental U.S.* Geophysical Research Letters, v. 28, no. 10, pp. 2077–80.

Ewing, T. 2016. *Texas through time: Lone Star geology, landscapes, and resources.* Bureau of Economic Geology, The University of Texas at Austin, 431 pp.

Foss, A.W. 2018. *Climate change and political discourse: Analysis of energy efficiency and conservation block grants in Dallas-Fort Worth.* Journal of Environmental Planning and Management, v. 61, no. 2, pp. 230–48.

Gamble, J.L., and J.J. Hess. 2012. *Temperature and violent crime in Dallas, Texas: Relationships and implications of climate change.* Western Journal of Emergency Medicine, v. 13, no. 3, pp. 239–46.

Ginno, C. 2017. *DO Mess With Texas . . . ? Why rolling easements may provide a solution to the loss of public beaches due to climate change-induced landward coastal migration*. San Diego Journal of Climate and Energy Law, v. 8, pp. 225–48.

Intergovernmental Panel on Climate Change. 2014. *Climate change 2014: Synthesis report.* Contribution of Working Groups I, II and III to the Fifth Assessment Report of the Intergovernmental Panel on Climate Change. Core Writing Team, R.K. Pachauri and L.A. Meyer (eds.). Geneva, Switzerland, 151 pp.

Joseph, J.F., and H.O. Sharif. 2016. *A methodology for assessing extreme precipitation trends applied to three South Texas basins, 1898–2011*. Arabian Journal for Science and Engineering, v. 41, pp. 4945–51.

Kim, H.-C., Son, S., Montagna, P., Spiering, B., and J. Nam. 2014. *Linkage between freshwater inflow and primary productivity in Texas estuaries: Downscaling effects of climate variability*. Journal of Coastal Research, v. 68, pp. 65–73.

Konapala, G., Veettil, A.V., and A.K. Mishra. 2018. *Teleconnection between low flows and large-scale climate indices in Texas river basins*. Stochastic Environmental Research and Risk Assessment, v. 32, pp. 2337–50.

Hayhoe, K. 2014. *Climate change projections for the City of Austin*. ATMOS Research & Consulting, 9 pp., https://austintexas.gov/sites/default/files/files/Katherine_Hayhoe_Report_-_April_2014.pdf.

Heo, J., Yu, J., Giardino, J.R., and H. Cho. 2014. *Impacts of climate and land-cover changes on water resources in a humid subtropical watershed: A case study from East Texas, USA*. Water and Environment Journal, v. 29, pp. 51–60.

Hotez, P.J. 2018. *The rise of neglected tropical diseases in the "new Texas"*. PLoS Neglected Tropical Diseases v. 12, no. 1, 15 pp.

Jeong, J., Kannan, N., and J.G. Arnold. 2014. *Effects of urbanization and climate change on stream health in north-central Texas*. Journal of Environmental Quality, v. 43, pp. 100–09.

Jiang, X., and Z.-L. Yang. 2012. *Projected changes of temperature and precipitation in Texas from downscaled global climate models*. Climate Research, v. 53, no. 3, pp. 229–44.

L'Heureux, M. 2014. *What is the El Niño-Southern Oscillation (ENSO) in a nutshell?* ENSO Blog, National Oceanic and Atmospheric Administration (May 5, 2014), www.climate.gov/news-features/blogs/enso/what-el-niño-southern-oscillation-enso-nutshell.

Lindsey, R. 2018. *U.S. winter precipitation during every El Niño since 1950*. National Oceanic and Atmospheric Administration (Oct. 24, 2018), www.climate.gov/news-features/featured-images/us-winter-precipitation-during-every-el-niño-1950.

Mantua, N.J., and S.R. Hare,. 2002. *The Pacific decadal oscillation*. Journal of Oceanography, v. 58, pp. 35–44.

Marsha, A., Sain, S.R., Heaton, M.J., Monaghan, A.J., and O.V. Wilhelmi. 2018. *Influences of climatic and population changes on heat-related mortality in Houston, Texas, USA*. Climatic Change, v. 146, pp. 471–85.

Modala, N.R., Ale, S., Goldberg, D.W., Olivares, M., Munster, C.L., Rajan, N., and R.A. Feagin. 2017. Climate change projections for the Texas High Plains and Rolling Plains. Theoretical and Applied Climatology, v. 129, pp. 263–80.

Mullin, M., and M.E. Rubado. 2017. *Local response to water crisis: Explaining variation in usage restrictions during a Texas drought*. Urban Affairs Review, v. 53, no. 4, pp. 752–74.

National Aeronautics and Space Administration. 2005. *NASA—What's the difference between weather and climate?* (Feb. 1, 2005), www.nasa.gov/mission_pages/noaa-n/climate/climate_weather.html.

Nielsen-Gammon, J.W. 2011. *The changing climate in Texas*, *in* Schmandt, J., North, G.R., and J. Clarkson, eds., *The impact of global warming on Texas*. Austin, TX: University of Texas Press, 2d ed., pp. 39-68.

North, G.R., Schmandt, J., and J. Clarkson, eds. 1995. *The impact of global warming on Texas.* Austin, TX: University of Texas Press, 1st ed., pp. 254.

Osland, M.J., Griffith, K.T., Larriviere, J.C., Feher, L.C., Cahoon, D.R., Enwright, N.M., Oster, D.A., Tirpak, J.M., Woodrey, M.S., Collini, R.C., Baustian, J.J., Breithaupt, J.L., Cherry, J.A., Conrad, J.R., Cormier, N., Coronado-Molina, C.A., Donoghue, J.F., Graham, S.A., Harper, J.W., Hester, M.W., Howard, R.J., Krauss, K.W., Kroes, D.E., Lane, R.R., McKee, K.L., Mendelssohn, I.A., Middleton, B.A., Moon, J.A., Piazza, S.C., Rankin, N.M., Sklar, F.H., Steyer, G.D., Swanson, K.M., Swarzenski, C.M., Vervaeke, W.C., Willis, J.M., and K.V. Wilson. 2017. *Assessing coastal wetland vulnerability to sea-level rise along the northern Gulf of Mexico coast: Gaps and opportunities for developing a coordinated regional sampling network.* PLoS ONE, v. 12, no. 9, 23 pp.

Patino, R., Dawson, D., and M.M. VanLandeghem. 2014. *Retrospective analysis of associations between water quality and toxic blooms of golden alga (Prymnesium parvum) in Texas reservoirs: Implications for understanding dispersal mechanisms and impacts of climate change.* Harmful Algae, v. 33, pp. 1–11.

Prudent, N., Houghton, A., and G. Luber. 2016. *Assessing climate change and health vulnerability at the local level: Travis County, Texas.* Disasters, v. 40, no. 4, pp. 740–52.

Rubinstein, C. 2015. *Texas water policy appendix: The weather.* Texas Water Journal, v. 6, pp. 121–35.

Sam Houston State University. *Prehistoric discovery connects Texas town to Ice Age* (Sept. 20, 2010), www.shsu.edu/~pin_www/T%40S/sliders/2010/katyconnection.html.

Schwantes, A.M., Swenson, J.J., Gonzalez-Roglich, M., Johnson, D.M., Domec, J.-C., and R.B. Jackson. 2017. *Measuring canopy loss and climatic thresholds from an extreme drought along a fivefold precipitation gradient across Texas.* Global Change Biology, v. 23, pp. 5120–35.

Texas Water Development Board. 2007. *Water for Texas 2007*, www.twdb.texas.gov/waterplanning/swp/2007/.

Texas Water Development Board. 2017. *Water for Texas 2017*, www.twdb.texas.gov/waterplanning/swp/2017/.

U.S. Global Change Research Program. 2018. *Fourth national climate assessment*, https://nca2018.globalchange.gov/.

Venkataraman, K., Tummuri, S., Medina, A., and J. Perry. 2016. *21st century drought outlook for major climate divisions of Texas based on CMIP5 multimodel ensemble: Implications for water resource management.* Journal of Hydrology, v. 534, pp. 300–16.

Yoskowitz, D., Carollo, C., Pollack, J.B., Santos, C., and K. Welder. 2016. *Integrated ecosystem services assessment: Valuation of changes due to sea level rise in Galveston Bay, Texas, USA.* Integrated Environmental Assessment and Management, v. 13, no. 2, pp. 431–43.

Zhang, Y., and R. Wurbs. 2018. *Long-term changes in river system hydrology in Texas.* Proceedings of the International Association of Hydrological Sciences, v. 379, pp. 255–61.

Zhao, G., Gao, H., and L. Cuo. 2016. *Effects of urbanization and climate change on peak flows over the San Antonio River basin, Texas.* Journal of Hydrometeorology, v. 17, pp. 2371–89.

CHAPTER 3

Meeting Water Supply Needs: Planning, Permitting, and Implementation

Nathan Vassar[1] and Lauren C. Thomson[2]

I. Overview of Issues

§ 3.1 Introduction

The climate and hydrology of Texas vary greatly from one area of the state to the next. Because of its sheer size, Texas encompasses multiple ecological and hydrologic zones, each with different resources, climates, and demands for water. The varied nature of water resources in Texas is particularly evident when examining the state from east to west. The eastern part of Texas is blessed with abundant rainfall in most years, with up to 55 inches per year over large areas of the region, which provides plentiful water resources in many parts of east Texas. West and south Texas are not as blessed, with much of these areas receiving less than 10 to 20 inches of rainfall annually. *See* Texas Water Development Board, *Lake Evaporation and Precipitation*, https://waterdatafortexas.org/lake-evaporation-rainfall. Not surprisingly, water supply has played a large role in development and population growth throughout the state's history. The Trinity River provides the vast majority of the existing water supplies for the two largest metropolitan areas in the state: the Dallas–Fort Worth metroplex and the Houston metropolitan area. Other rivers and river basins in the state—notably the Sabine and Neches in the east and the Brazos, Colorado, and Guadalupe basins to the west—are also prolific, resulting from sizable drainage areas, plentiful rainfall in most years, and spring flow contributions. These basins each generate water supplies for cities, industries, and agricultural interests. *See* Texas Water Development Board, *Water for Texas 2022* 66–69 (2022), www.twdb.texas.gov/waterplanning/swp/2022 [hereinafter 2022 State Water Plan].

---

1. Nathan Vassar is a principal at Lloyd Gosselink Rochelle & Townsend, P.C. in Austin, Texas. Nathan assists communities and utilities with environmental permitting and enforcement matters. His involvement includes the state and federal development of water supplies for Texas communities and permitting processes. Mr. Vassar also counsels clients with respect to water and wastewater compliance strategies. He received his BA in history and government from the University of Virginia and his JD from the University of Texas School of Law.

2. Lauren Thomson is an associate at Lloyd Gosselink Rochelle & Townsend, P.C. Ms. Thomson assists clients with water quality matters, water resources development, regulatory compliance, permitting, enforcement, and litigation. Ms. Thomson earned her BS in environmental studies from the College of Geosciences at Texas A&M University and her JD from Texas A&M University School of Law.

The authors gratefully acknowledge the contributions and research assistance of Richard Arnett during his time as a law clerk with LLoyd Gosselink Rochelle & Townsend, P.C.

The history of water development in Texas begins at the end of the nineteenth century, when the state passed legislation allowing for the formal recognition of water rights and the issuance of debt for water supply projects. *See* Irrigation Act of Mar. 19, 1889, 21st Leg., R.S., ch. 88, §§ 1–17, 1889 Tex. Gen. Laws 100, 100–03, *reprinted in* 9 H.P.N. Gammel, *The Laws of Texas 1822–1987*, at 1128–31 (Austin, Gammel Book Co. 1898); Irrigation Act of Mar. 21, 1895, 24th Leg., R.S., ch. 21, § 1, 1895 Tex. Gen. Laws 21–26, *reprinted in* 10 H.P.N. Gammel, *The Laws of Texas 1822–1897*, at 751–56; *see generally* Ronald A. Kaiser, *Texas Water Marketing in the Next Millennium: A Conceptual and Legal Analysis*, 27 Tex. Tech L. Rev. 183, 229–44 (1996) (discussing the history of water rights and surface water law in Texas); Dylan O. Drummond et al., *The Rule of Capture in Texas—Still So Misunderstood after All These Years*, 37 Tex. Tech L. Rev. 1 (2004) (noting the extensive history of the rule of capture and water rights in Texas). See Chapter 4 of this book for a discussion of the history of surface water development. With the passage of the Conservation Amendment to the Texas Constitution in 1917, the legislature enabled the creation of political subdivisions entitled to issue debt to develop water-related infrastructure. Tex. Const. art. XVI, § 59. Since the passage of that amendment, literally thousands of such political subdivisions have been formed—from large river authorities charged with conserving, preserving, protecting, and developing the water resources within their boundaries to geographically small municipal utility districts and other water districts created primarily for supporting land development. *See, e.g.*, Sabine River Authority, Acts of 1949, 51st Leg., R.S., ch. 110; Lower Colorado River Authority, Acts of 1934, 43d Leg., 4th C.S., ch. 7; Brazos River Authority, Acts of 1929, 41st Leg., 2d C.S., ch. 13; Guadalupe River Authority, Acts of 1933, 43d Leg., 1st C.S., ch. 75; Trinity River Authority, Acts of 1955, 54th Leg., R.S., ch. 518. See Chapter 8 of this book for a discussion of the various water-related political subdivisions.

Although supplies remain available for development, much of the state's surface water has already been appropriated, and in some areas of the state groundwater resources are not readily available in significant quantities. *See* 2022 State Water Plan, at 69–76. The amount of water that can be produced under current permits, current contracts, and existing infrastructure during periods of drought is projected to decrease approximately 18 percent, from 16.8 million acre-feet in 2020 to about 13.8 million acre-feet in 2070. *See* 2022 State Water Plan, at 7. Alarmingly, the state's population is projected to grow 73 percent during the same period, but the demand for water is anticipated to grow by only 9 percent (*see* 2022 State Water Plan, at 6), and a shortfall of 6.9 million acre-feet of water is projected by 2070 (*see* 2022 State Water Plan, at 3).

Thus, for the state to successfully respond to anticipated future demand, it will have to plan, permit as necessary, and implement water supply projects and strategies—including conservation and reuse strategies—over the next several decades. This chapter provides a brief discussion of the state's current water planning protocol, an overview of some of the sources of water supplies and strategies available for meeting projected water supply demands, a brief discussion of state and federal permitting that is generally associated with the development of water supply and delivery systems, and a description of the most common means available to finance the implementation of such projects. In-depth treatment of many of these topics is included in other chapters of this book, as noted.

II. Regional and State Water Planning

§ 3.2 Introduction

In 1957, a constitutional amendment created the Texas Water Development Board (TWDB) in response to the worst drought in the state's history. Tex. Const. art. III, § 49–c. The drought lasted seven years, and by the end of 1956 all but one of the counties in the state were considered disaster areas. *See* 2022 State Water Plan, at 155. The epic drought ended in 1957 with a flood that replenished the aquifers, reservoirs, and surface water flows, but public awareness of the absence of drought protection led to the development of a structured system for water planning and strategy implementation. The TWDB was authorized in 1957 to manage and distribute a $200 million water development fund to aid communities in developing reliable water supplies. The legislature also mandated that the TWDB initiate a planning process to project future water needs and determine appropriate steps to address projected shortfalls. The TWDB has been provided with funding and other resources to assist in water supply development, maintenance, and planning from the agency's inception to the present day. *See* 2022 State Water Plan, at 141.

Over the past fifty years, the TWDB has prepared eleven state water plans. Plans were produced in 1961, 1968, 1984, 1990, 1992, 1997, 2002, 2007, 2012, 2017, and 2022. *See* Texas Water Development Board, *State Water Planning*, www.twdb.texas.gov/waterplanning/swp/. The early plans were created at a time when the primary method of water supply was the large-scale construction of reservoirs. From 1950 to 1970, more than ninety "major reservoirs" (i.e., reservoirs having a capacity of at least 5,000 acre-feet) were constructed in Texas, as compared to today, when there are a total of 187 major water-supply reservoirs across the state. *See* 2022 State Water Plan, at 66. In addition to providing a reliable source of water, these reservoirs controlled flooding, provided cheap electricity, and offered recreational opportunities. Currently, the 189 reservoirs across Texas serve as a source of water supply for the state, region, or local community. *See* 2022 State Water Plan, at 66; *see also* Texas Water Development Board, *River Basins & Reservoirs*, www.twdb.texas.gov/surfacewater/rivers/index.asp. More than half of the surface water supply in Texas comes from reservoirs, but the accumulation of sediment in reservoirs will lessen this supply over time. 2022 State Water Plan, at 68, 77; *see also* Texas Water Development Board, *Texas Lakes & Reservoirs*, www.twdb.texas.gov/surfacewater/rivers/reservoirs/index.asp. The early focus on reservoirs was reflected in the first two state water plans, but by 1980 reservoir construction had declined precipitously because of a lack of viable sites, increased difficulty in environmental permitting, and rising costs of construction.

Because of the challenges associated with reservoir development, the water plans of the 1980s and 1990s instead focused on water management and infrastructure development to best use existing water resources. For example, after 1984, the plans became increasingly more open to consider conservation, reuse, desalination, and other water supply proposals to address the growing water supply needs of Texas. The process for developing the state water plan changed over time as well. In 1992, the TWDB increased participation in the development of the water plan by including stakeholders, the Texas Parks and Wildlife Department, and the Texas Natural Resource Conservation Commission, a predecessor agency of the current Texas Commission on Environmental Quality (TCEQ). *See* 2022 State Water Plan, at 163. Even with the increased participation of other entities, the TWDB was still predominantly in charge of developing the state water plan and was required to consider the varied needs of the entire state. *See* 2022 State Water Plan, at 20.

This top-down system changed, however, after the devastating drought of 1996. The drought reminded the public of the imminent need for efficient water planning and development of dependable supplies throughout the state. The water shortage and extensive crop failures across the state spurred legislative action that has reshaped water planning in Texas. In 1997, the 75th Legislature passed Senate Bill 1 (S.B. 1), which rewrote many sections of the Texas Water Code and created a new, bottom-up approach to water planning. *See* Act of June 1, 1997, 75th Leg., R.S., ch. 1010. S.B. 1 directed the TWDB to divide the state into regional planning areas based on the agency's assessment of relevant criteria, including river basin and aquifer locations, utility development patterns, boundaries of political subdivisions, a public involvement and comment process, and existing planning area boundaries. *See* Act of June 1, 1997, 75th Leg., R.S., ch. 1010. At least once every five years, the TWDB must review the regional planning area boundaries and update them if necessary. *See* Tex. Water Code § 16.0121; 2022 State Water Plan, at 21. In response, the TWDB created sixteen regional water planning groups (RWPGs). Each region is charged with developing its own fifty-year water plan tailored to the unique needs and resources of the region. 2022 State Water Plan, at 19–27. Each RWPG is charged with developing a plan that is consistent with the guiding principles of the state water plan and that conforms to guidelines adopted by the TWDB, and is further charged with making recommendations based on data provided by or approved by the TWDB. *See* Tex. Water Code § 16.053. See Chapters 20 and 21 of this book for discussions of state water planning.

Through the regional water planning process, the state water plan is forged out of the grassroots, bottom-up assessments of water needs and supply performed by the RWPGs. The sixteen approved plans are aggregated to form the state water plan. Every five years, the RWPGs are required to prepare and adopt revised regional water plans, which again are submitted to the TWDB for approval and inclusion in the revised state water plan. Before the plan's finalization and adoption, the TWDB issues a draft version for public comment, publishes notice in the *Texas Register*, and convenes a public hearing. As outlined in the TWDB rules, each state water plan contains a wealth of information and projections of population, water demand, climate, and alternative water supplies over the next fifty years. *See* 31 Tex. Admin. Code § 358.4; 2022 State Water Plan, at 21–22.

The 2022 state water plan recommended 5,800 water supply strategies and approximately 2,400 specific projects designed to meet the need for additional water supplies to benefit Texas during severe droughts. *See* 2022 State Water Plan, at 3, 8. This would compensate for the projected shortfall of 8.9 million acre-feet by 2070 and avoid anticipated losses of approximately $153 billion annually in 2070 if drought conditions were to approach the drought of record. *See* 2022 State Water Plan, at 12. While many water supply projects or strategies are being considered, permitting processes and funding requirements often lengthen the time before a project can be implemented. Delays in the implementation of projects typically increase the total estimated capital cost.

The state water plan is a guide and is not binding on any agency, but the TCEQ is required to consider approved state and regional water plans when it makes permit decisions regarding surface water rights. *See* Tex. Water Code § 11.1501. Unless the requirement is affirmatively waived, the TCEQ can grant a permit for the appropriation of surface water only if that appropriation addresses a water supply need that is "consistent with the state water plan and the relevant approved regional water plan" in the area of appropriation. *See* Tex. Water Code § 11.134(b)(3)(E). Furthermore, the TCEQ may not issue a water right permit for municipal purposes unless the region has an approved regional water plan, but this requirement may also be waived. *See* Tex. Water Code § 11.134(c). The state water plan, even if not binding on the TCEQ, also has important implications for the funding of water supply projects; large-scale regional water supply projects are not eligible for TWDB funding unless the proposed project is consistent with state and regional water plans. *See* Tex. Water Code § 16.053(j).

III. Sources of Supply

§ 3.3 Introduction

One of the most important steps in the state water planning process is adequately identifying and considering all water supply options. There may be a number of sources, or a combination of sources, that can be used to meet projected water supply demands. Traditionally, water suppliers have focused on surface water and groundwater, but with the decreasing availability of these supplies and the increasing protection afforded such natural resources, more emphasis has been placed on nontraditional sources of supply. The following sections provide an overview of the potential sources of available water supplies identified in the state water plan.

§ 3.4 Surface Water

Surface water is a readily available and renewable source of supply. Like groundwater, however, fresh surface water is a finite resource. Within the state, twenty-three surface water basins (fifteen major river basins and eight coastal basins) produce fresh surface water. *See* 2022 State Water Plan, at 66. Regardless of the apparent supply from these basins, existing allocations of surface water will determine whether any particular river basin should be considered a viable source of supply.

For the most part, surface water is considered "state water." There are a few exemptions, such as diffused surface water runoff, but the definition of "state water" is broad and includes all "water of the ordinary flow, underflow, and tides of every flowing river, natural stream, and lake, and every bay or arm of the Gulf of Mexico, and the storm water, floodwater, and rainwater of every river, natural stream, canyon, ravine, depression, and watershed in the state." Tex. Water Code § 11.021(a). Thus, state water consists of rainfall and spring flows that have reached a watercourse or other surface water body. State water also includes water imported from outside the boundaries of the state for use in the state. Tex. Water Code § 11.021(b). State water is the property of the state and may be regulated for use by the state. *See, e.g., Texas Water Rights Commission v. Wright*, 464 S.W.2d 642, 647 (Tex. 1971). Although there are certain exemptions from permitting, the TCEQ must grant the authority to use state water. *See* Tex. Water Code § 11.121. See also Chapter 10 of this book.

When planning for the use of surface water supplies, one must first evaluate the availability and reliability of the source. The TCEQ may not issue a permit unless it has been shown that sufficient water is available for appropriation. *See* Tex. Water Code § 11.134(b)(2). In this regard, the TCEQ must review and consider an application pursuant to its rules regarding water availability. *See* 30 Tex. Admin. Code § 297.42. Assuming a sufficient supply of surface water exists for appropriation, the TCEQ may grant a permit for the diversion and use of surface water. See Chapter 10 of this book regarding surface water rights permitting.

In addition to securing the right to use surface water supplies from the TCEQ, one must consider other practical issues. The method of taking, storing, or diverting surface water may affect the yield, efficiency, and feasibility of a surface water supply project. For example, it stands to reason that surface water captured during high-flow events and stored in a reservoir will be more reliable than run-of-river or direct diversions because the latter lack a means of storage. Though reservoirs are more reliable, the cost of construction and the environmental impacts will typically be much greater for reservoir development than those associated with a direct diversion. See Chapter 27 of this book regarding reservoirs.

§ 3.5 Groundwater

Groundwater is the most-used source of water supply in rural areas of Texas and particularly in the western portion of the state, but, unlike surface water, groundwater has not been the subject of statewide regulation. See Chapters 1 and 19 of this book for discussions of the attributes of groundwater. Principles of rights to produce groundwater have been established in a series of cases dating back to the early twentieth century. In a 1904 decision, the Texas Supreme Court opined that groundwater was "secret [and] occult." *See Houston & T.C. Ry. Co. v. East*, 81 S.W. 279, 281 (Tex. 1904); *contra Sipriano v. Great Spring Waters of America, Inc.*, 1 S.W.3d 75, 77 (Tex. 1999) (citing *City of Corpus Christi v. City of Pleasanton*, 276 S.W.2d 798, 805–06 (1955) (Wilson, J., dissenting)) (advancing knowledge of geology and hydrology have made groundwater not so secret and occult); *see also City of Altus, Oklahoma v. Carr*, 255 F. Supp. 828, 833 (W.D. Tex.), *aff'd*, 385 U.S. 35 (1966) (holding that "the law of Texas is well settled that the landowner has the right to drill wells and appropriate the water beneath his land"); *see also Edwards Aquifer Authority v. Day*, 369 S.W.3d 814 (Tex. 2012) (explaining the rule of capture at length and holding that groundwater is private property, subject to "reasonable regulation"). Through these cases, the applicability of the English common-law "rule of capture" to groundwater has been confirmed by Texas courts, although in the past half century or more the legislature has embraced a system of groundwater management by groundwater conservation districts (GCDs). *See Sipriano*, 1 S.W.3d at 77; *Day*, 369 S.W.3d at 834–35. The legislature has created a number of GCDs across the state to regulate groundwater withdrawals within those GCDs' jurisdictional boundaries. Groundwater production in areas outside of GCDs is generally unregulated, and the rule of capture continues to prevail. In areas within GCDs, the type and degree of regulation vary widely. See Chapter 16 of this book for a discussion of groundwater and regulation by GCDs.

When groups plan for the use of groundwater, ample consideration must be given to the method and means of accessing the aquifer where groundwater is stored. Some of the state's most prolific aquifers cover vast geographic areas and may be accessed at various points, which provides an opportunity for many diverse water users to site wells and withdraw groundwater. Other aquifers are confined to smaller geographic areas or located far from those who would put the water to use, and thus aboveground transmission lines are required to transfer supplies from the well site to the place of use. Groundwater quality is also an important consideration. Waters in some aquifers are of a higher quality than others, and accessing pristine groundwater supplies may be impossible or more costly. Furthermore, some aquifers, like the Ogallala Aquifer in the Texas Panhandle, possess a limited ability to recharge, while others, like the Edwards Aquifer in Central Texas, are highly dependent on surface water recharge and diffused surface water runoff. When a water supply project will depend on the use of groundwater, these issues should be carefully considered. *See generally* Texas Water Development Board, *State Water Planning*, www.twdb.texas.gov/waterplanning/swp.

§ 3.6 Conjunctive Use

Conjunctive use is the concurrent use of groundwater and surface water supplies to meet demands. Conjunctive use recognizes that an entity can balance its demands by supplementing one source of supply with another. Often, alternative supplies are used to meet peak daily demands. For example, readily available groundwater supplies in rural areas of the state have enabled many utilities to meet their water needs exclusively with groundwater. The population of Texas, however, has grown rapidly over the last fifty years. Many areas that have historically relied on groundwater supplies have seen demand grow to a level that requires existing water sources to be supplemented with a renewable source of surface water supplies. *See generally* 2022 State Water Plan ch. 4. See Chapter 6 of this book regarding conjunctive management and use.

As with any project that involves blending distinct sources of supply, conjunctive use requires consideration of water quality as well as quantity. Groundwater resources may have higher levels of total dissolved solids or metals, while surface water supplies may have higher levels of nutrients or bacteria. A utility needs to carefully consider the ramifications of blending these sources. For instance, blending groundwater and surface water sources can be expected to produce water with a chemical composition different from that of either individual source. Often, this may involve a change in the overall pH of the water, resulting in the precipitation of undesirable chemical compounds into the water source.

Additionally, consideration must be given to meeting drinking water quality requirements (*see, e.g.*, 40 C.F.R. §§ 141.1–.723) when potable water is the intended end use, as well as to the potential impact that return flows resulting from such use may have on stream standards compliance. *See* 33 U.S.C. § 1313 (federal surface water standards); 30 Tex. Admin. Code §§ 307.1–.10 (Texas surface water standards). See also Chapter 30 of this book for a discussion of drinking water standards. Conjunctive use is a proven water supply management strategy that has wide support and, in some instances, has been mandated by state or federal governments. *See* 2022 State Water Plan, at 103.

§ 3.7 Reuse

Reuse is a water supply strategy that has garnered significant interest in Texas during the last several decades, but the water rights and water quality laws and regulations associated with reuse are complex. Not only are there distinctions in law between direct and indirect reuse, but there are also legal differences between the indirect reuse of surface water–based effluent and of groundwater-based effluent. *See generally* Tex. Water Code §§ 11.042, 11.046; *see also* 30 Tex. Admin. Code ch. 210 (TCEQ reclaimed water regulations). See Chapter 24 of this book for a further discussion of reuse.

In planning a reuse project, there are a number of issues to consider. The first is whether a utility desires to fully control the corpus of the water from capture to the end point of reuse (i.e., direct reuse) or whether the bed and banks of a state watercourse need to be used to convey the water to the point of reuse (i.e., indirect reuse). Second, assuming the utility seeks to use water via indirect reuse, questions related to the use of surface water for drinking water purposes arise, such as, "Where will the water be diverted?" If the water will be stored in a reservoir, there may be concerns regarding the ratio of the reuse water to natural runoff in the total volume of the reservoir as well as concerns about hydraulic detention time. These concerns regarding the end use of reclaimed water—as well as the yield of a project given special conditions that may be imposed on the authorizations and rights to use such water—can greatly influence the viability of a reuse project.

§ 3.8 Conservation

Like reuse, conservation is also a valuable water supply strategy. This is considered a supply strategy because it serves to reduce the overall demand requirements of a utility. *See* 2022 State Water Plan, at 101; *see generally* 2022 State Water Plan ch. 8. See Chapter 23 of this book regarding conservation.

The Texas legislature has recognized the need for water resource conservation. Not only is there a requirement to prepare a water conservation plan before appropriating state water (*see* Tex. Water Code § 11.1271(a)), but the legislature has also created a task force to consider and enhance conservation across the state. *See* Tex. Water Code §§ 10.001–.011 (establishing the Texas Water Conservation Advisory Council). Conservation is the first water supply strategy employed by many utilities because it is much less costly and more certain than permitting and constructing new facilities. However, conservation alone as a water supply strategy can rarely meet long-term projected demands, particularly given the population growth seen across much of Texas. Utilities should look to the regional water planning process to determine how their own conservation efforts can be improved as well as to ascertain how much of their projected future demands can be met through conservation. *See* 2022 State Water Plan, at 124; *see generally* 2022 State Water Plan ch. 8.

Conservation and drought planning are requirements for any utility that serves more than 3,300 connections. *See* 30 Tex. Admin. Code § 288.30(10)(A). Moreover, wholesale contracts are required to include language that imposes conservation planning on end users. *See* 30 Tex. Admin. Code § 288.5(1)(F). See Chapter 31 of this book for a discussion of wholesale contracts.

Reporting every five years is required to ensure that tasks are being implemented to achieve water conservation goals. *See* 30 Tex. Admin. Code § 288.30(10)(C). Oversight for water conservation activities is shared between the TCEQ and the TWDB. See Chapters 10 and 23 of this book for discussions of conservation plans.

§ 3.9 Desalination

Desalination involves the treatment and removal of dissolved solids from brackish groundwater or seawater. As noted above and further discussed in Chapter 5 of this book, groundwater is regulated differently from surface water. Seawater is considered to fall within the definition of state water. *See* Tex. Water Code § 11.021(a). Any desalination project that involves the diversion and use of brackish surface water and seawater is required to have a surface water use permit in order to use this state water, whereas desalination of groundwater may require approval by a GCD. As noted below, however, permitting for desalination projects often involves both water rights authorizations and discharge authority for sidestream wastewater. In 2015, the Texas legislature passed House Bill 2031, providing for expedited permitting for marine seawater desalination projects. *See* Act of May of 26, 2015, 84th Leg., R.S., ch. 756, § 10 (H.B. 2031). The benefits of the H.B. 2031 approach depend on the location of a planned discharge of desalination-generated wastes, and if that discharge is farther than three miles into the Gulf of Mexico, the TCEQ will not afford opportunities for hearing requests. Thus, permitting for desalination projects differs significantly depending on the source of supply and location of discharge. See Chapter 25 of this book regarding desalination.

In addition to permitting considerations, planning a desalination project raises other issues, such as the type and cost of treatment that must be used to remove dissolved solids. Membrane technology options include ultrafiltration, nanofiltration, microfiltration, and reverse osmosis, each of which involves the use of a progressively less porous membrane to remove dissolved solids. Additional treatment technologies, such as electrodialysis, can also be employed. Often, however, the limiting factor for a desalination project is how to handle the by-product waste produced from treatment. In arid portions of the state, the by-product is often disposed of via salt drying beds. In other areas of the state it may be possible to use deep-well injection to dispose of the by-product. *See* Tex. Water Code § 27.051; 30 Tex. Admin. Code §§ 331.1–.186. Where neither of these options exists or is practical, a Texas Pollutant Discharge Elimination System (TPDES) permit authorizing discharge of the by-product into a receiving water may be obtained. *See* Tex. Water Code § 26.121; see also Texas Commission on Environmental Quality, *What Is the "Texas Pollutant Discharge Elimination System (TPDES)"?*, www.tceq.texas.gov/permitting/wastewater/pretreatment/tpdes_definition.html.

§ 3.10 Aquifer Storage and Recovery

Aquifer storage and recovery (ASR) is a means by which entities construct groundwater wells that can inject water into, and subsequently extract water from, a single aquifer. ASR wells are typically used to store surface water that is available during periods of high flow for use during periods of drought. ASR wells can be used to facilitate conjunctive use, and often they assist in offsetting peak pumping demands otherwise dependent on distant or less reliable sources. See Chapter 26 of this book regarding ASR.

ASR wells are regulated under the Texas Water Code (*see, e.g.*, Tex. Water Code §§ 27.154, 36.454) and TCEQ rules. Securing the authority to operate an ASR well requires that an application be submitted to the TCEQ that includes the same information necessary to appropriate state water as well as the information necessary to demonstrate compliance with TCEQ injection wells regulations. *See* Tex. Water Code § 27.051; *see also* 30 Tex. Admin. Code ch. 331 (Underground Injection Control); *Texas Rivers Protection Ass'n v. Texas Natural Resource Conservation Commission*, 910 S.W.2d 147, 154 (Tex. App.—Austin 1995, writ denied) (holding that water diversion permits providing for storage of water for municipal use via ASR technique were permissible since water injected into an aquifer became groundwater outside state control). When reviewing an application for a permit authorizing an ASR well, the TCEQ must consider any potential impacts on water quality, whether the stored water can be successfully harvested for beneficial use, whether the project will comply with the federal Safe Drinking Water Act, 42 U.S.C. §§ 300f–300j-27, and whether the project has an effect on existing water wells. *See* Tex. Water Code § 27.153(b); *Texas Rivers Protection Ass'n*, 910 S.W.2d at 153 (holding that "beneficial use is the yardstick by which to measure legality of a permit").

ASR wells have certain unique features that differ from single-production or injection wells. Because of this, when ASR is considered, it is recommended that a three-phase approach be taken to assess the viability of any proposed well. *See generally* Edmond McCarthy, Jr., et al., *Aquifer Storage and Recovery: The Texas Perspective*, *in The Water Report* No. 19, Sept. 15, 2005, at 1. The first phase involves a preliminary feasibility study and conceptual design, which includes siting and designing certain monitoring wells. The second phase includes a field testing program to ensure that the aquifer can store the source of supply planned and that it can be secured and subsequently retrieved without excessive loss or adverse impact to the existing aquifer. The third phase involves the permitting of an

ASR well(s), which includes securing either any necessary surface water permits under Texas Water Code chapter 11 or any groundwater permits required by Texas Water Code chapter 36 (for projects located inside a GCD). Additionally, the project must be authorized by injection permits required under chapter 27 of the Texas Water Code.

§ 3.11 System Operations

To secure the right to divert and use state water for certain uses, an applicant must demonstrate that water is available for appropriation for a sufficient percentage of time. *See* 30 Tex. Admin. Code § 297.42. However, if an entity has additional, alternative supplies and can supplement its diversions with other sources, TCEQ rules allow the agency discretion regarding the necessary availability requirement. *See* 30 Tex. Admin. Code § 297.42(c). This type of supplementation is often available through the use of a "system operation" for water supplies.

A number of issues about the type of system must be considered when contemplating a system operation. One concept that may be considered is the ability to overdraft one reservoir by relying on the permitted yield of another reservoir. Another concept is the ability to operate a series of reservoirs or run-of-river rights as a system, thereby allowing diversions or releases from any one reservoir or diversion location to meet water supply obligations. For large utilities with numerous sources of supply, the concept of networking a system of supplies can lead to enhanced yield as well as redundant reliability. See Chapter 24 of this book for a discussion of water reuse, including analysis of the recent landmark issuance of the Brazos River Authority's system operations permit. See also Chapter 27 for a broader discussion of system operations.

§ 3.12 Portfolio Management

When planning and implementing water supply strategies, one must consider all available supplies. Managing a portfolio of supplies is akin to managing a portfolio of monetary investments. The goal is to provide long-term reliable water supplies at the lowest possible cost and risk. A prudent water supplier will evaluate all available water supply options, including the means for more efficient use of existing resources. This may be accomplished through reuse and conservation. A supplier should also consider ways to diversify and limit its exposure to short- and long-term water deficits. Potential causes of failure may include natural disasters such as hurricanes, source water contamination, drought, and catastrophic water supply system collapse. Not all potential disaster scenarios can be addressed, but to ensure long-term success a supplier should consider diversifying its supply portfolio. This may include entering into possible partnerships with other suppliers to gain access to additional or backup supply as well as planning for regulatory changes. *See generally* Brad B. Castleberry, *Maintaining a Diverse Water Supply*, 33 *OpFlow* No. 7, July 2007, at 14–17 (discussing portfolio management in depth).

IV. Permitting of Water Supply Projects

§ 3.13 Introduction

Once a project is identified in the state and regional water plans as a recommended strategy to meet a community's water supply needs, a water supplier can begin to work toward the realization of that project. Before construction can commence on a specific project, the water supplier may need to obtain a variety of local, state, and federal permits to gain the legal right to construct a project. Permitting a major, long-term water project is time-intensive and costly, particularly when permit applications are protested. State and federal permitting for a new reservoir, for example, may take over ten years to complete, and sometimes more if litigation occurs. Depending on the urgency with which a water supply project must be completed, many water suppliers choose to apply for and obtain all necessary permits before acquiring land for the project, obtaining additional financing, or beginning construction because of the uncertainty involved in the permitting process. Others risk this uncertainty by pursuing certain aspects of the project, such as land acquisition, in conjunction with their applications for the necessary permits. The following sections focus on how water suppliers obtain the legal right to construct and pursue a water supply project.

§ 3.14 State and Local Permitting

Surface water supply projects in Texas require authorization from the state because the state holds in trust all surface water (i.e., "state water") within the state. *See* Tex. Water Code § 11.021(a). As noted at section 3.4 above, state water is defined as all "water of the ordinary flow, underflow, and tides of every flowing river, natural stream, and lake, and of every bay or arm of the Gulf of Mexico, and the storm water, floodwater, and rainwater of every river, natural stream, canyon, ravine, depression, and watershed in the state." Tex. Water Code § 11.021(a). The TCEQ is the agency charged with regulating surface water use, including the issuance of permits to divert and use such state water and the approval of sales and transfers of water already authorized for diversion. Local entities are not typically involved in permitting surface water projects unless local regulation of real property is involved (e.g., property on which the storage or diversion facilities will be constructed). However, because groundwater is not regulated as state water, depending on the location, groundwater projects may involve the oversight and approval of local groundwater conservation districts. Thus, the regulation of a water supply project depends in large part on whether the project is based on surface water or groundwater.

§ 3.14:1 Surface Water Projects

Chapter 11 of the Texas Water Code outlines the legal and regulatory requirements to apply for a new surface water right from the TCEQ, to amend an existing surface water right, to transfer an existing surface water right to a third party, to transfer water supplies to another water basin, and to seek reuse of wastewater effluent. In allocating the right to the use of state water, Texas adheres to the doctrine of prior appropriation, where the actual "use" of water is a major element in acquiring and perfecting a water right. Texas Water Code section 11.022 provides that the "right to the use of state water may be acquired by appropriation" and, when such a right of use "is lawfully acquired, [water] may be taken or diverted from its natural channel." Tex. Water Code § 11.022. This provision, along with others in the Texas Water Code, contemplates the "use" of water within an appropriation system and also requires the taking, storage, or diversion of such water. See Chapters 4 and 10 of this book for discussions of the appropriation system and surface water permitting.

New appropriations of state water and amendments to existing authorizations are obtained through an application and permitting process with the TCEQ, which is often subject to public notice and participation requirements. See Chapter 10 of this book for a discussion of this process. When an application is submitted for a new appropriation of state water, the threshold issue that the TCEQ must address is whether unappropriated water is actually available for use at the proposed diversion point. *See* Tex. Water Code § 11.134(b)(2).

After the agency determines that water is available for appropriation, TCEQ staff focuses on other significant issues, such as environmental impacts, whether the proposed diversion will be put to a beneficial use, and whether the proposed diversion will harm the public welfare. *See* Tex. Water Code §§ 11.134, 11.147, 11.150–.152. After performing all necessary reviews, the TCEQ will prepare a draft permit that may limit the diversion allowed, include stream flow restrictions as special conditions of the permit, or include other limitations and special conditions to ensure that the water authorized for diversion will be lawfully used in a manner that addresses the requirements for permitting the use of state water that are found in the Texas Water Code. *See* Tex. Water Code § 11.134. See Chapter 10 of this book regarding surface water rights permitting.

The Texas legislature augmented the process to be used for identifying environmental flow requirements in 2007 with its passage of Senate Bill 3. *See* Act of May 28, 2007, 80th Leg., R.S., ch. 1430. These provisions require the TCEQ to adopt environmental flow regulations for certain bay and basin areas within the state, using environmental flow recommendations developed by bay and basin expert science teams and bay and basin stakeholder groups. *See* Tex. Water Code §§ 11.0235–.0237. The evaluation of environmental flow issues is key to any surface water supply project in Texas, and the implementation of environmental flow requirements may limit diversion opportunities during certain periods, depending on base, subsistence, or pulse flows, as applicable. See Chapter 11 of this book for a discussion of environmental flows.

Once issued, permits for water rights identify the date on which the permit was declared administratively complete, which is used for the purpose of setting the priority date for the water right and establishing a water right's place in the hierarchy of the prior appropriation system. Water rights also include provisions related to (1) the purpose or use for which water can be appropriated, (2) the annual diversion amount, (3) the instantaneous rate at which water can be diverted, (4) a time frame in which construction of storage and diversion facilities must commence and be completed, and (5) any special conditions the TCEQ deems necessary. *See* Tex. Water Code § 11.135.

Amendments to existing appropriative rights that seek to increase the amount of water diverted or the rate at which water is diverted are assessed by the TCEQ and noticed as would be any application for a new appropriation. *See* Tex. Water Code § 11.122(a); 30 Tex. Admin. Code § 295.158. Applications that do not request an additional appropriation of water or an increased rate of diversion may not require full notice to other water rights holders in the basin, if the amendment would authorize no greater impact on other water rights or the environment than would full use of the existing right, and in light of the terms and conditions of the existing right. *See* Tex. Water Code § 11.122(b). However, a 2006 decision by the Texas Supreme Court suggests that even minor amendments to water rights may, under certain circumstances, require notice and the opportunity for a contested case hearing. *See City of Marshall v. City of Uncertain*, 206 S.W.3d 97, 110–11 (Tex. 2006) (requiring the TCEQ to consider the impact of several limited public interest criteria when determining whether to issue notice of a water right amendment application, including whether the application is intended for a beneficial use, whether it will harm the public welfare, and any impacts on groundwater). See Chapter 10 of this book for discussions of the four corners doctrine and the *Marshall* case.

For portions of the state where surface water supplies are limited, many water supply projects focus on delivering water from a neighboring river basin to areas where such supplies can be used. Interbasin transfers of surface water are contemplated in the Texas Water Code and are an important tool for water suppliers seeking to move water resources to portions of the state where they are needed. Texas Water Code section 11.085 provides a permitting framework under which the TCEQ may authorize such transfers of water. See Chapter 10 of this book for a discussion of interbasin transfers.

The reuse of water supplies—usually in the form of discharged treated wastewater—is a viable means for water suppliers to supplement their water resources. There are, however, major legal implications for reuse projects, such as environmental sustainability concerns, water quality issues, and potential negative impacts on downstream water rights holders, some of whose rights may have been granted based on an assumption of continued municipal return flows or may have been made more reliable as a result of such discharges. Nonetheless, reuse is a key approach for many water suppliers in the state that seek to ensure that future demands will be met. Reused wastewater is considered a drought-proof supply of water, and technology now enables such water to be treated to a high level of quality before its discharge into receiving water bodies. See Chapter 24 of this book for a discussion of reuse of water.

Although most diversions of water from state watercourses require an appropriative right from the state, several exemptions from the permitting process exist in the Texas Water Code that allow the development of certain water supply projects to proceed without permit authority. See Chapter 10 of this book for a discussion of exemptions related to state water permitting and other more limited permits.

§ 3.14:2 Groundwater Projects

Texas law controlling groundwater production poses many challenges to the development of a groundwater project. First, some areas are locally regulated by GCDs, while others are unregulated. Second, each GCD develops its own plan for managing the groundwater resources within the GCD and develops its own rules to implement that plan. Third, the state established a regional groundwater management planning process wherein GCDs in a designated groundwater management area (GMA) develop planning goals and create a policy statement known as "desired future conditions" (DFC), that has the potential to affect all future groundwater projects. In evaluating a groundwater-based project, a developer must consider all of these variables.

Unlike most western states, Texas does not have a uniform, statewide system of groundwater regulation. Historically, the common-law "rule of capture" has been the governing legal principle throughout the state. *See generally Houston & T.C. Ry. Co. v. East*, 81 S.W. 279 (Tex. 1904); *Sipriano v. Great Spring Waters of America, Inc.*, 1 S.W.3d 75 (Tex. 1999); *Edwards Aquifer Authority v. Day*, 369 S.W.3d 814 (Tex. 2012) (explaining the rule of capture at length and holding that groundwater from a well became state water when it flowed into a Texas lake). Under the rule of capture, a landowner can pump as much groundwater as desired without concern for any detrimental effects on third parties as long as the pumping does not result in a wanton or wasteful use of water, the pumping landowner does not maliciously intend to harm a third party, and the pumping does not cause subsidence. *Sipriano*, 1 S.W.3d at 76. However, the rule of capture has been somewhat curtailed in recent years. *See, e.g., Day*, 369 S.W.3d at 831 (regulation of groundwater production is essential for Texas). Senate Bill 332, passed in 2011 during the 82nd legislative session, recognized that a landowner owns the groundwater below the surface of the landowner's land as "real property," but such property right does not bestow on the landowner the right to capture a specific amount. *See* Act of May 27, 2011, 82d Leg., R.S., ch. 1207. A detailed discussion of the rule of capture is provided in Chapter 5 of this book.

The legislature has expressed its clear preference for groundwater resource management by local GCDs. *See* Tex. Water Code § 36.0015. GCDs are political subdivisions and conservation and reclamation districts formed under the Conservation Amendment (Tex. Const. art. XVI, § 59) and operating pursuant to each GCD's enabling legislation as well as the general law of chapter 36 of the Texas Water Code. *See generally* Tex. Water Code ch. 36. Currently, at least 174 counties—making up more than half of the total land area in Texas—are either partially or fully within a GCD. More important, the most current TWDB data available reflect that roughly 90 percent of groundwater withdrawals and usage occur within the boundaries of a GCD. Texas Water Development Board, *Groundwater Conservation District Facts*, www.twdb.texas.gov/groundwater/conservation_districts/facts.asp [hereinafter GCD Facts]. In each legislative session since 1997 (the year in which the legislature indicated its preference for management by GCDs), the legislature created new GCDs across the state until the 85th legislative session in 2017. No new GCDs were created in the 86th legislative session in 2019. There are now a total of 99 GCDs in Texas, with the Aransas County GCD awaiting confirmation by voters through a local election. GCD Facts. See Chapter 16 of this book for a discussion of GCDs. Because most groundwater produced in Texas is located within a GCD, the remainder of this section discusses groundwater projects within GCDs.

GCDs are created "[i]n order to provide for the conservation, preservation, protection, recharging, and prevention of waste of groundwater." Tex. Water Code § 36.0015(b). These goals are reflected in a groundwater management plan developed by the district and approved by the TWDB. Tex. Water Code §§ 36.1071–.1073. See also Chapters 16 and 21 of this book. One aspect of this process that is particularly important to groundwater projects is the determination of the amount of groundwater that is available for production. See the discussion below regarding groundwater management area joint planning and the calculation of the managed available groundwater.

One of the primary tools a GCD uses to manage groundwater resources, and the tool that is of primary importance to a groundwater project, is well permitting. Texas Water Code chapter 36 gives GCDs the authority to alter the rule of capture by regulating and restricting groundwater production. *See* Tex. Water Code §§ 36.002, 36.101. Also, GCDs may restrict or limit production to protect existing wells as long as the restriction is tied to both the amount and the purpose of the prior use. *See Guitar Holding Co. v. Hudspeth County Underground Water Conservation District No. 1*, 263 S.W.3d 910, 912 (Tex. 2008). GCDs often use the permitting process to restrict or limit production from a well. For example:

- A GCD's rules may limit groundwater production based on tract size or the spacing of wells (*see* Tex. Water Code §§ 36.101(a), 36.116(a)(2)) and may regulate the spacing of wells relative to property lines or adjoining wells. *See* Tex. Water Code § 36.116(a)(1).
- Production limits may preserve historic use. *See* Tex. Water Code § 36.116(b). When issuing a permit for historic or existing use, a GCD is prohibited from discriminating between land that is irrigated for production and land that is enrolled in a federal conservation program. *See* Tex. Water Code § 36.113(h).
- Production limits may vary within different geographic areas of a GCD based on differences in the aquifer or in the use of the aquifer. *See* Tex. Water Code § 36.116(d), (e).
- A GCD may require a production permit that controls the rate and amount of withdrawal. *See* Tex. Water Code §§ 36.116(a)(2), 36.1131(b)(8). Such permits have various names, such as production permit, operating permit, high production permit, and historic use permit. A GCD may base production limits on managed depletion. *See* Tex. Water Code § 36.116(a)(2)(E).
- A GCD may base production limits on the service needs or service area of a retail water utility. *See* Tex. Water Code § 36.116(c).

In addition to evaluating the method a GCD uses to limit production, the permit term or duration of a groundwater permit is of significant importance in evaluating a groundwater-based project. GCDs set various term limits, which range from one- to ten-year terms to indefinite, renewable terms. Some GCDs provide options for temporary permits, emergency permits, and other short-term, limited permits. As discussed below, when a project involves production of groundwater inside a GCD for use outside that GCD, different rules may apply. With regard to permit duration, there is some question about how the permit term is set for projects involving the export of groundwater outside a district's boundaries, although very few projects have been implemented that would test those statutory sections. *See* Tex. Water Code § 36.122. See also Chapters 16 and 18 of this book.

A significant issue for GCDs is their authority to regulate the export of groundwater across their boundaries as concern has increased regarding water shortages. New projects to transport groundwater from one area of the state to another are a popular means for addressing such shortages. *See* Tex. Water Code § 36.122. GCDs are authorized to adopt rules requiring permits for groundwater transports (either increases of previous arrangements or new transfers) out of their boundaries occurring after March 2, 1997. *See* Tex. Water Code § 36.122(b). GCDs cannot prohibit the export of groundwater if the purchase was in effect on or before June 1, 1997. In addition to the requirements in an operating or production permit mentioned above, export permits must specify the amount of water that may be transferred out of the GCD and the period over which the water may be transferred.

When reviewing a proposed transfer, a GCD must consider (1) the availability of water in the GCD and in the proposed receiving area during the period for which the water supply is requested; (2) the projected effect of the proposed transfer on aquifer conditions, depletion, or subsidence or effects on existing permit holders or other groundwater users within the GCD; and (3) the approved regional water plan and approved management plan. Tex. Water Code § 36.122(f). Notably, a GCD is prohibited from discriminating between in-district users and transporters and may not deny a permit because the applicant seeks to transfer groundwater outside of the district. However, a GCD may limit a permit if conditions warrant the limitation, as long as it does not impose more restrictive permit conditions on transporters than on existing in-district users. *See* Tex. Water Code § 36.122(g). Groundwater export applications must be considered and processed in the same manner as in-district water use applications. *See* Tex. Water Code § 36.122(d). A GCD may not impose more restrictive permit conditions on transporters than the district imposes on existing in-district users, unless the more restrictive conditions (1) apply to all subsequent in-district and transport permit applications, (2) bear a reasonable relationship to the GCD management plan, and (3) are reasonably necessary to protect existing uses. *See* Tex. Water Code §§ 36.113(e), 36.122(c). Significantly, a GCD may periodically review the amount of water that may be transferred under a permit. *See* Tex. Water Code § 36.122(k). When determining whether to renew an export permit, a GCD must consider relevant and current data for the conservation of groundwater resources and must consider the permit in the same manner that it would consider any other permit in the GCD. *See* Tex. Water Code § 36.122(k). See also Chapter 18 of this book.

Another aspect of GCD regulation that often has an impact on a groundwater-based project is the procedure the GCD uses to process, evaluate, and issue the operating, production, and transfer permits discussed above. Chapter 36 of the Texas Water Code sets forth the minimum due-process requirements for notice and hearing for permit and permit amendment actions. *See* Tex. Water Code § 36.114. See also Chapter 16 of this book.

As mentioned above, GCDs in each GMA participate in joint planning as part of the state's overall water planning process. All the districts within a GMA must meet at least annually for joint planning. *See* Tex. Water Code § 36.108(c). The GCDs within each GMA determine how they want to manage the groundwater resources within the management area and develop the DFC of the aquifers in the area. *See* Tex. Water Code § 36.108(d). The GCDs then submit the DFC to the TWDB, which translates it into an estimate of the amount of water that could be withdrawn from the aquifers while maintaining the DFC. This water estimate is called the "modeled available groundwater" (MAG). *See* Tex. Water Code § 36.108; *see also* Tex. Water Code §§ 36.001(25), 36.1071(e)(3)(A). This, effectively, is the current term for groundwater availability. See Chapter 19 of this book regarding groundwater availability modeling.

Development of the DFC and calculation of the MAG are significant for several reasons. A GCD uses the MAG numbers in its groundwater management plan. *See* Tex. Water Code § 36.108(d–2). MAG numbers are also used in groundwater production permitting decisions. The MAG is critical because, "to the extent possible," a GCD must issue permits "up to the point that total volume of exempt and permitted groundwater production will achieve an applicable desired future condition" if applications for production are submitted. *See* Tex. Water Code § 36.1132(a). In other words, once the DFC is established and the TWDB calculates the MAG, a GCD cannot refuse to issue a production permit on the basis that no water is available if any of the MAG amount has not yet been permitted.

On the other hand, the TWDB has opined that the MAG serves as a de facto cap on permitting. *See* Robert E. Mace et al., *A Streetcar Named Desired Future Conditions: The New Groundwater Availability for Texas (Revised)* 3, *in The Changing Face of Water Rights in Texas* (State Bar of Texas 2008) [hereinafter Mace et al.] (stating that MAG numbers are a "cap on groundwater production"). Thus, it is expected that this language will be cited by GCDs that refuse to issue permits after the total volume of groundwater permitted equals the TWDB-calculated MAG.

The MAG is also used by regional water planning groups in the state water planning process. *See* Tex. Water Code § 16.053(e)(3)(A). As a result, it affects the ability of political subdivisions to obtain TWDB loans for groundwater projects. *See* Mace et al.; see also Chapter 20 of this book for a detailed discussion of state and regional water planning and Chapter 21 for joint planning.

Additionally, the MAG calculation can seriously influence planning regarding supply. Total permitted production that exceeds the MAG could result in forcing a reduction in use of an aquifer.

In summary, areas that are locally regulated by GCDs pose particular challenges to groundwater-based projects, even as they can also provide protection for the long-term viability of the project. Each GCD has a unique plan for managing the groundwater resources within the GCD and has established its own rules to implement the plan, thus increasing the complexity in evaluating the project. The regional groundwater management planning has the potential to affect all future groundwater projects. In evaluations of a groundwater-based project, it is essential to consider all these variables.

§ 3.15 Federal Permitting

Depending on the scope of a particular water supply project, federal permitting under the Clean Water Act (CWA) and assessments related to environmental impacts under the National Environmental Policy Act (NEPA) may be required and, when required, add another layer of challenges and delays to a water supply project. CWA permits and the NEPA process involve regulation by or consultation with agencies such as the Environmental Protection Agency (EPA), the U.S. Army Corps of Engineers (USACE), and the U.S. Fish and Wildlife Service. See Chapter 35 of this book for a discussion of the CWA section 404 Corps of Engineers program; Chapter 34 for a discussion of the CWA section 401 program; Chapter 32 for a discussion of the Fish and Wildlife Service and the Endangered Species Act; and Chapter 27 for a discussion of NEPA.

§ 3.15:1 Clean Water Act Section 404

The USACE CWA section 404 permit program specifically applies to the discharge of "dredged or fill material" into jurisdictional "waters of the United States." *See* 33 C.F.R. pt. 323.

Most large-scale dredge-and-fill discharges—like those associated with a water supply project—require an individual permit from the USACE. Before it can be issued, a CWA section 404 permit requires public notice and hearing, a consideration of alternatives, public interest review, and conformity with EPA guidelines. *See* 33 U.S.C. § 1344(b), (c); *see also* 40 C.F.R. pt. 230 (EPA guidelines developed with the assistance and comments of the USACE). The public interest review associated with a CWA section 404 permit involves an extensive analysis of the effects a discharge will have on the short- and long-term physical, chemical, and biological elements that make up the aquatic ecosystem. *See* 40 C.F.R. § 230.11. A CWA section 404 permit will also be subjected to the procedural requirements of NEPA, but the public interest review in the two statutes overlap significantly. *See* 40 C.F.R. § 230.10(a)(4). As mentioned earlier, securing an individual CWA section 404 permit is typically a multiyear process, and permittees usually start the CWA section 404 permitting effort early in order to minimize delays to critical water supply projects. The USACE also has the authority to issue general permits on a state, regional, or nationwide basis that exempt certain activities the agency believes have a minimal environmental impact. *See* 33 U.S.C. § 1344(e).

Before seeking individual CWA section 404 permit authorization, a water supplier must ensure that it has conducted a thorough alternatives assessment and can demonstrate that the proposed project is the least environmentally damaging practicable alternative (often referred to as a "LEDPA" analysis) and is justified economically. Such an assessment should identify the water supply project as the only practicable alternative (or as the least environmentally damaging practicable alternative) while considering environmental impacts, economics, and the overall project purpose. *See* 40 C.F.R. § 230.10(a)(2) (noting that an alternative is practicable if it is "available and capable of being done after taking into consideration cost, existing technology, and logistics in light of overall project purposes").

An individual CWA section 404 permit will not be issued if there is a practicable alternative that would have less impact on the aquatic ecosystem. *See* 40 C.F.R. § 230.10(a). Practicable alternatives include restructuring the project so that no discharge into the waters of the United States occurs or discharging at a different location than proposed by the applicant. *See* 40 C.F.R. § 230.10(a)(1); *see also Alliance to Save the Mattaponi v. U.S. Army Corps of Engineers*, 810 F. Supp. 2d 160, 163 (D.D.C. 2011). As long as the planned project requiring the dredge-and-fill operation is inherently water-dependent, this stringent consideration of alternatives typically will not require that a dramatically different alternative be considered that would effectively change the project type. In contrast, a rebuttable presumption is that practicable nonaquatic alternatives exist when a non-water-dependent activity is the subject of an individual CWA section 404 permit on a "special aquatic site." *See* 40 C.F.R. § 230.10(a)(3). Still, the USACE has an affirmative duty to consider alternatives within the framework of costs, technology, and logistics in accordance with the overall project purpose. *See* 40 C.F.R. § 230.10(a)(2); *see also Louisiana Wildlife Federation, Inc. v. York*, 761 F.2d 1044, 1048 (5th Cir. 1985); *Gouger v. U.S. Army Corps of Engineers*, 779 F. Supp. 2d 588, 603–04 (S.D. Tex. 2011). For a more detailed discussion of CWA section 404 permitting, see Chapter 35 of this book.

§ 3.15:2 Clean Water Act Section 401

Under CWA section 401, any applicant for a federal permit to conduct an activity that may cause a discharge into waters of the United States must first obtain certification that the discharge will comply with state water quality standards adopted by the state in which the discharge will originate. *See* 33 U.S.C. § 1341(a). Certification under CWA section 401 ensures that each state is involved in decisions made by the federal government that have the potential to affect its water quality. With the exception of oil and gas exploration, the TCEQ is the state agency that administers the CWA section 401 certification program. *See* 30 Tex. Admin. Code § 279.1. Certification of projects that propose a discharge resulting from oil and gas exploration is primarily the responsibility of the Railroad Commission of Texas, subject to some exceptions that fall within TCEQ's regulatory authority. *See* 16 Tex. Admin. Code § 3.93. For a detailed discussion of Clean Water Act section 401, see Chapter 34 of this book.

The TCEQ has developed a tiered system for evaluating all individual CWA section 404 permit applications based on the project size and the amount of state water affected. Tier I projects are small projects that affect less than three acres of water in the state or less than 1,500 linear feet of streams. The TCEQ has determined that incorporating certain best management practices (BMPs) and other outlined requirements into Tier I projects will sufficiently minimize impacts to water quality. Therefore, applicants that want to use the Tier I category for small projects should include a signed Tier I checklist with their application for an individual CWA section 404 permit to the USACE. *See* Texas Commission on Environmental Quality, *Tier I (Small Projects) Checklist*, TCEQ Form TCEQ-20228 (rev. Dec. 29, 2006), www.tceq.texas.gov/assets/public/permitting/assess/401cert/tier1-checklist.pdf.

Any project that requires a CWA section 404 individual permit and does not qualify for Tier I review, or for which the applicant elects not to incorporate the established Tier I criteria, is considered a Tier II project. Tier II projects are subject to an individual certification review by the TCEQ. A Certification Questionnaire and Alternatives Analysis Checklist must be submitted to the TCEQ for CWA section 401 approval. Applicants completing the Certification Questionnaire are required to provide information about the potential impacts the disposal of waste materials from a project may have on the surface water quality in the state. The Alternatives Analysis Checklist generally covers the same requirements used for determining the practicable alternatives for individual CWA section 404 permit purposes. This checklist relates to determining how project needs could be satisfied in a way that does not affect surface water, how the project could be redesigned to fit the site without affecting surface water, how the project could be minimized, what other sites were considered, and possible consequences of not building the project. An applicant is also required to compare different alternatives, to explain why the preferred alternative was selected, and to explain what will be done to minimize adverse effects on surface water. *See* Texas Commission on Environmental Quality, *Tier II 401 Certification Questionnaire and Alternative Analysis Checklist*, TCEQ Form TCEQ-20229 (rev. Apr. 4, 2004), www.tceq.texas.gov/assets/public/permitting/waterquality/forms/20229.pdf. Either the USACE district engineer or a CWA section 404 individual permit applicant may submit a request for CWA section 401 certification to the TCEQ. *See* 30 Tex. Admin. Code § 279.4(b). If the USACE requests certification, the district engineer will provide the TCEQ with a copy of the public notice, a request for certification, and a copy of the complete permit application. *See* 30 Tex. Admin. Code § 279.4(b)(1). If the permit applicant requests certification, the applicant will provide the TCEQ with a copy of the completed permit application and any amendments, a list of the names and addresses of owners of tracts of land adjacent to the site to be permitted, and a request for certification. *See* 30 Tex. Admin. Code § 279.4(b)(2). An opportunity for notice and comment on an application for certification under CWA section 401 is available to interested parties. *See* 30 Tex. Admin. Code §§ 279.5–.8. The executive director of the TCEQ will take final action on the application for certification within sixty days after receiving the certification request. 30 Tex. Admin. Code § 279.11(a). However, the executive director can elect to delay acting on a request for certification until after reviewing a CWA section 404 final permit decision document. 30 Tex. Admin. Code § 279.4(b)(3). The TCEQ will not certify a discharge under CWA section 401 if (1) there is a practicable alternative to the proposed discharge that would have less adverse impacts on the environment, (2) appropriate steps are not taken to minimize adverse impacts, (3) mitigation is not undertaken for all unavoidable adverse impacts, or (4) the executive director determines that the impacts of the project are so significant that mitigation will not compensate for the damage of the project. *See* 30 Tex. Admin. Code § 279.11(c).

The TCEQ has certified that the activities authorized by some CWA section 404 nationwide permits do not result in a violation of established Texas water quality standards and therefore do not need individual certification from the TCEQ under section 401. *See* 30 Tex. Admin. Code § 279.12. Other section 404 nationwide permits may be conditionally certified by the TCEQ. *See* 30 Tex. Admin. Code § 279.12.

§ 3.15:3 National Environmental Policy Act

NEPA is integral to many water supply projects because the issuance of federal permits under section 404 of the CWA is conditioned on NEPA compliance. NEPA requires all federal agencies to take a hard look at the potential environmental consequences of their proposed actions and to prepare a "detailed statement" regarding "major Federal actions significantly affecting the quality of the human environment." 42 U.S.C. § 4332(c). The provisions of NEPA direct that "to the fullest extent possible . . . the policies, regulations, and public laws of the United States shall be interpreted and administered in accordance with the policies set forth in this chapter." 42 U.S.C. § 4332. NEPA is a procedural statute that can influence the decision-making process of a federal agency (such as the USACE) by requiring the agency to consider environmental impacts, alternatives, and mitigation strategies for projects pursued by the federal government or projects authorized by a federal agency through the issuance of a permit.

As a procedural statute, NEPA "prohibits uninformed, not unwise, agency actions." *Stewart v. Potts*, 996 F. Supp. 668, 672 (S.D. Tex. 1998) (citing *Sabine River Authority v. U.S. Department of Interior*, 951 F.2d 669, 676 (5th Cir. 1992)). The decision-making process required by NEPA allows for public participation when major agency actions may have an adverse impact on the human environment and an injunction is appropriate to remedy an agency's failure to comply with NEPA procedures. Despite the availability of that remedy under NEPA, other statutes are the source of the substantive environmental obligations that are binding upon an agency and a permit applicant.

The NEPA process is triggered by "*major Federal actions* significantly [affecting] the quality of the human environment." 42 U.S.C. § 4332(c) (emphasis added). "Major Federal actions" include a federal agency's issuance of permits, such as CWA section 404 permits for water projects, the use of federal funds to construct projects like federal flood control projects, and the authorization of activities that occur on federal lands. *See, e.g., Maryland Conservation Council, Inc. v. Gilchrist*, 808 F.2d 1039, 1042 (4th Cir. 1986) (highway project requiring CWA section 404 permit and federal approval is a "federal" action subject to NEPA); *Crutchfield v. U.S. Army Corps of Engineers*, 192 F. Supp. 2d 444, 448 (E.D. Va. 2001) (CWA section 404 permit for wastewater treatment plant triggered NEPA procedural requirement); *Stewart*, 996 F. Supp. at 668 (municipal golf course proposal that included clearing and fragmentation of forested areas and a proposed drainage ditch that would discharge into waters of the United States was subject to USACE factual determinations under CWA section 404).

NEPA requires a consideration of the consequences of the contemplated agency action and an evaluation of possible alternatives that could be less damaging to the environment. However, NEPA compliance is not required if the agency action falls within a limited number of established categorical exclusions, which are categories of federal agency actions that have previously been determined to have no significant environmental impact either individually or cumulatively. *See* 40 C.F.R. § 1501.4. Moreover, agency actions under certain statutes will never require NEPA compliance because it has been determined that these, mostly environmental protection statutes, are the functional equivalent of NEPA. For example, the EPA is exempted from NEPA for most actions the agency takes under the Clean Air Act. *See Portland Cement Ass'n v. Ruckelshaus*, 486 F.2d 375 (D.C. Cir. 1973) (decision codified at 15 U.S.C. § 793(c)(1)); *but see American Trucking Ass'ns v. U.S. Environmental Protection Agency*, 175 F.3d 1027, 1042 (D.C. Cir. 1999), *cert. granted, cause remanded sub nom.*, *American Lung Ass'n v. American Trucking Ass'ns*, 532 U.S. 901 (2001) (only section 111 of the Clean Air Act requires the functional equivalent of a NEPA environmental impact statement, and any other EPA action under the CAA would be exempt).

When NEPA applies, however, the agency deciding whether to take the major federal action must first prepare an environmental assessment (EA). This relatively short document is issued to determine whether the action agency needs to prepare a more exhaustive environmental impact statement (EIS) or, alternatively, if that lengthy process is unnecessary because of an EA finding of no significant impact (FONSI). *See* 40 C.F.R. § 1501.5. A FONSI can be issued when a determination is made in the EA that the federal agency action will not have a significant impact on the human environment, and so an EIS is not necessary. *See* 40 C.F.R. § 1501.6(a). In order for a FONSI to be valid, the agency must prepare an adequate EA. The EA may be overturned if a reviewing court determines it to be superficial, conclusory, or flawed. Historically, such inadequacy has been evidenced by a lack of documentation, internal inconsistencies, uncertainties, or a failure to consider the cumulative impacts of a proposed action. *See* Sheldon M. Novick, *Environmental Practice Series*, *Law of Environmental Protection* § 8:49 (1987).

In an EIS, the agency must evaluate alternatives to the proposed action that might be employed to meet the stated purpose and need of the project. An alternative may be less environmentally damaging, or it may make the proposed federal action unnecessary. The courts have adopted the standard that only "feasible" and "reasonable" alternatives need to be discussed, but some deference is given to an agency's determination that an alternative need not be considered. *See Vermont Yankee Nuclear Power Corp. v. Natural Resources Defense Council*, 435 U.S. 519 (1978). See Chapter 27 of this book for further discussion of NEPA requirements for reservoir projects.

V. Funding Considerations

§ 3.16 Introduction

After a water supply project has secured the necessary permits, it may be brought online through project implementation. For the most part, large-scale water supply projects require project-specific construction methods and techniques. However, in every project, new water supplies cannot be successfully and reliably obtained without adequate funding to support the completion of the project design, site and equipment acquisition, construction, and operations and maintenance of the project once constructed. Creating a delivery system for large quantities of water also typically requires a significant expenditure of money that exceeds the existing financial capabilities of the project sponsor and the project's end users. Most projects require public funding to allow implementation of a water supply system of an adequate scale to meet present and future demands. The following sections include a brief overview of some of these funding options, and Chapter 37 of this book provides a detailed description of water supply project funding options available in Texas.

§ 3.17 Public Entity Financing Options

Many options are available to structure debt issued by a public entity for project implementation. This discussion is meant to provide only a general overview. The nuances of particular financing options vary depending on the type of entity even under the general discussions noted here. Chapter 37 of this book provides a detailed description of water supply project funding. The Conservation Amendment to the Texas Constitution authorizes conservation and reclamation districts created by the state to issue debt to further the purposes of the amendment through new water supply projects and management practices. *See* Tex. Const. art. XVI, § 59. Political subdivisions in Texas are also authorized, with approval from the state, to issue debt to supply funding for public works projects throughout the project's life cycle, including planning, land acquisition, construction, and routine maintenance phases. *See, e.g.*, Public Security Procedures Act of 1999, Tex. Gov't Code ch. 1201. A rigorous assessment of the risks and costs involved in each potential financing avenue is necessary to allow for reliable and economically sustainable water supply delivery to end users. *See generally* Michigan Water Works Association, *Water Works News* 22 (Nov. 2002); First Southwest Company, *Authorized City Debt Instruments* (Oct. 28, 1996).

§ 3.17:1 General Obligation Bonds

General obligation bonds (GOBs) are issued by a political subdivision for a specifically approved public-purpose project and are secured by the full faith and credit of the public entity through its power of ad valorem taxation. The requirement that a bond be issued for a "public purpose" means that the project must specifically benefit the entity issuing the debt and its residents. *See* Tex. Loc. Gov't Code § 374.906. Municipalities, counties, towns, and other political corporations are prohibited by the Texas Constitution from lending credit to any entity, so a GOB could not be issued to fund a project that, upon completion, is entirely privately owned. *See* Tex. Const. art. III, § 52. One exception, however, includes the funding for an economic development program. *See* Tex. Const. art. III, § 52–a. Furthermore, a project funded by GOB financing may be jointly owned or funded by another entity, as long as the political subdivision issuing the bond retains a divided or undivided interest in the project being financed.

GOBs require voter approval. The amount of GOBs that can be issued is limited by the tax revenue that can be generated at the maximum ad valorem tax rate, specified by the constitution, less taxes used to pay for other functions, including debt, of the entity. For example, a general law city may tax only up to $1.50 per $100.00 taxable assessed valuation (1.5 percent), and a home rule city may tax up to $2.50 per $100.00 taxable assessed valuation (2.5 percent). *See* Tex. Const. art. XI, §§ 4, 5. Public entities can avoid paying GOB debt through tax revenues if they are able to pay the debt from other sources.

GOBs are generally regarded as the most secure form of debt that a public entity can issue. This type of bond, like other forms of debt issued by public entities, must be reviewed by the Texas attorney general, must receive prior approval, and ultimately must be submitted to the Texas comptroller for registration in state records. *See* Tex. Gov't Code § 1202.003(a), (b). After they are approved and registered, GOBs issued by a public entity are binding obligations that are valid and incontestable in a court or other forum. Tex. Gov't Code § 1202.006(a). The only way to overturn this presumption is with a showing of fraud or forgery. *See, e.g., Leonard v. Abbott*, 171 S.W.3d 451, 460 (Tex. App.—Austin 2005, pet. denied) (bonds are generally incontestable after attorney general approval). Although the interest income earned by purchasers of some GOBs is taxable, the interest income earned by purchasers of most GOBs is tax-free, and such bonds typically have the lowest interest rate of any public securities. GOBs are a useful mechanism to finance project implementation, but voter and attorney general approval lengthens the time before funding is made available. Substantial reliance on GOBs requires planning ahead to avoid inefficient or postponed project implementation caused by delays associated with the bureaucratic system of GOB authorization.

§ 3.17:2 Revenue Bonds

Revenue bonds are issued on the foundation of a pledge of revenues that will be generated by the project through the sale of services or water generated by the project. This revenue stream may also be created by the imposition of standby fees or groundwater management fees. Debt issued by a revenue bond cannot be repaid with ad valorem taxes, but a tax may be issued to help pay for the operating expenses of the revenue-generating project.

The amount of financing for a water project available through revenue bonds is limited by the amount that rates for water services can be feasibly increased. Determining practical rate increases to secure a bond involves a technical and economic study that should be performed in coordination with a professional rate consultant trained in analyzing projected population growth, water demand, and other relevant factors. Revenue bonds typically require a higher interest rate than GOBs because of the uncertainties involved in funding the debt. The amount of interest required for a successful bond will depend, in part, on the quality of the project's financial operations and business practices.

§ 3.17:3 Certificates of Obligation/Double-Barreled Bonds

A certificate of obligation (COO) is similar to a GOB and is available for funding projects. *See generally* Tex. Loc. Gov't Code §§ 271.041–.064. Unlike GOBs, COOs do not require voter approval. A COO, however, is subject to the same referendum by voter petition as a revenue bond. If a COO is funded entirely by ad valorem taxation, it may be issued only for limited purposes, such as land acquisition. *See, e.g.*, Tex. Gov't Code § 1509.902.

COOs may be used for any lawful purpose when they are supplemented with a pledge of surplus revenue ($1,000 or more) from the project after it is implemented. A COO may also make up half of a double-barreled bond (DBB). A DBB is primarily secured by a revenue bond, but if revenue generation fails to satisfy the bond obligation over a period of time, the principal and interest payments may be satisfied by tax revenues pledged to a COO.

§ 3.17:4 Contract Revenue Bonds

A project sponsor may issue a contract revenue bond based on wholesale contracts entered into with third-party users, such as regional river authorities or entities created by a political subdivision for water services. *See generally City of Galveston v. Hill*, 519 S.W.2d 103, 106 (Tex. 1975). The contract may specify that payments are secured by taxes, revenue, or a combination of both. Depending on the terms of the contract, the public entity may or may not retain ownership over all aspects of the project. The interest rate of the contract revenue bond will be based on the strength of the project sponsor's credit.

§ 3.17:5 Anticipation Notes

Anticipation notes allow municipalities to fund water supply projects based on an ordinance passed by a city council. These bonds may be secured by a pledge of revenues, projected revenues, ad valorem taxes, or already authorized bonds that the city may issue if necessary to repay the debt. Bond anticipation notes and tax anticipation notes mature within one year of their date. Tex. Water Code § 49.154(a). Furthermore, an anticipation note issued must mature before the seventh anniversary of the date that the attorney general approves the note. *See* Tex. Gov't Code § 1431.009(a). No voter approval is necessary for anticipation notes, but these securities typically require a fairly high interest rate.

§ 3.17:6 Public Property Finance Contractual Obligations

A political subdivision or governmental agency is authorized by statute to purchase equipment or other personal property necessary for implementing a water supply project through a debt obligation contract. *See* Tex. Loc. Gov't Code § 271.005. The contract may be paid over the term of the contract with taxes, revenue from the project, or both. The term of the contract, however, cannot exceed twenty-five years. Tex. Loc. Gov't Code § 271.009.

§ 3.17:7 Commercial Paper Program

Commercial paper may be used to obtain funding for capital improvements through a short-term note program. These obligations are secured through a pledge of revenues, similar to a revenue bond, supplemented with a letter of credit from a bank guaranteeing that the purchaser will be repaid on time. These notes are used for immediate funding needs and mature in periods from one day to one year. *See* Tex. Gov't Code §§ 1371.001, 1371.059.

§ 3.17:8 Nonprofit Corporations

To avoid the constitutional prohibition against the lending of credit, political subdivisions may create nonprofit corporations to implement, finance, or operate a water supply project. *See* Tex. Transp. Code §§ 431.101–.110; *see also* Texas Development Corporation Act of 1979, Tex. Loc. Gov't Code tit. 12, subtit. C1. These corporations are specifically exempt from article III, section 52, of the Texas Constitution and are authorized to issue taxable and tax-exempt bonds. *See* Tex. Loc. Gov't Code §§ 501.055(b), 501.201; *see also* Tex. Transp. Code § 431.033 (regarding exemptions from franchise taxes). Often, nonprofit corporations are created to be used as a conduit for channeling money necessary for project implementation, and they are also used to implement water supply projects operated under a public-private partnership.

§ 3.18 Texas Funding Options

§ 3.18:1 Water Infrastructure Fund

In 2007, the 80th legislature appropriated monies to allow for deferred debt service payments to the TWDB in order to provide reduced-interest loan rates and deferral of annual principal and interest payments for state water plan projects funded through the Water Infrastructure Fund (WIF). *See* Act of May 27, 2007, 80th Leg., R.S., ch. 1428; *see generally* 31 Tex. Admin. Code §§ 363.1201–.1210. The WIF is designed to fund current water project needs and preconstruction studies. In 2009, the legislature amended WIF eligibility. Entities eligible for assistance from the WIF now include political subdivisions of the state; nonprofit water supply corporations created and operating under chapter 67 of the Texas Water Code; and certain categories of districts such as freshwater supply districts, special utility districts, and municipal utility districts. *See* Tex. Water Code § 15.971; 31 Tex. Admin. Code § 363.1202.

§ 3.18:2 Agricultural Water Conservation Grants

Agricultural Water Conservation Grants are available annually and may be issued to state agencies and political subdivisions to fund research, technical assistance, education, and technologies associated with agricultural water conservation. Funding is also available to a political subdivision for installing metering devices to quantify the impact of a water conservation strategy on irrigation.

§ 3.18:3 Agricultural Water Conservation Loans

Agricultural Water Conservation Loans are available for various public entities and individuals (if the money is routed through a bank or farm credit system) to (1) improve the efficiency of water use or delivery, (2) convert irrigated land to dryland farming, (3) improve the efficiency with which dryland farming areas use natural precipitation, (4) install devices that measure irrigation water use, (5) establish brush control activities conducted under chapter 206 of the Agriculture Code, or (6) fund other conservation projects authorized by TWDB rules. *See* 31 Tex. Admin. Code ch. 367.

§ 3.18:4 Clean Water State Revolving Fund Program

The Clean Water State Revolving Fund Program is a federal-state partnership that makes funds available to political subdivisions for planning, land acquisition, project construction, wastewater treatment, reuse projects, and nonpoint source pollution control. Individuals are also eligible to receive funding, but only for nonpoint source pollution control projects.

§ 3.18:5 Drinking Water State Revolving Fund Program

Drinking Water State Revolving Fund Program Loans are available to "eligible applicants," including all entities under the federal Safe Drinking Water Act and private individuals. *See* Tex. Water Code § 15.604. Funds may be used for all aspects of the implementation of water-related infrastructure as well as source water protection. Subsidies may be available for economically disadvantaged areas.

§ 3.18:6 Rural Water Assistance Fund Program

Political subdivisions and nonprofit water supply corporations may apply for loans from the TWDB Rural Water Assistance Fund Program to aid in the planning, acquisition, and construction of water supply infrastructure in rural areas.

§ 3.18:7 State Participation in Regional Water and Wastewater Facilities Program

Under the State Participation in Regional Water and Wastewater Facilities Program, the TWDB provides funding to political subdivisions and public entities for the construction of regional water or wastewater projects. Through this program, the state secures an ownership interest in the project that is transferred to the applicant after the customer base grows enough to allow for repayment.

§ 3.18:8 Water and Wastewater Loan Program

The federal Water and Wastewater Loan Program makes loans available to political subdivisions and nonprofit water supply corporations for, among other things, water supply projects, including reservoir construction, water storage, and agricultural water conservation.

§ 3.18:9 Economically Distressed Area Program

Grants, loans, or a combination of both may be issued under the Economically Distressed Area Program to finance water or wastewater services for economically distressed areas. In 2007, the 80th legislature provided funding for debt service payments for the State Participation and Economically Distressed Areas Programs to fund state water plan projects. Public entities, and some private entities, are eligible to receive funding from these and other TWDB programs. *See generally* Texas Water Development Board, *Financial Assistance Programs*, www.twdb.texas.gov/financial/programs/.

§ 3.18:10 State Water Implementation Fund for Texas

During the 2013 legislative session, House Bill 4 was passed to provide a fund intended to serve as a water infrastructure bank to enhance the financing capabilities of the TWDB under constitutionally created programs and revenue bond programs. The State Water Implementation Fund for Texas (SWIFT) was proposed to provide a source of revenue or security for those programs and a cash flow mechanism under which money used in TWDB programs flows back to the fund to provide protection for the fund's principal (codified at Tex. Water Code § 15.432). On November 5, 2013, voters approved amending the Texas Constitution to create two separate, constitutionally dedicated, revolving loan accounts to be managed by the TWBD and funded by a $2 billion cash infusion from the "Rainy Day Fund." At least 20 percent of the funds must be used to support water conservation programs, and at least 10 percent will be used to serve water supply infrastructure and development needs in rural Texas. In November 2014, the TWDB adopted rules to implement the SWIFT funding program and began accepting applications for the first round of SWIFT funding. As of 2018, the TWDB had approved over $1.9 billion in financial assistance from SWIFT toward twelve project sponsors identified in the 2017 State Water Plan, with a total of more than $8 billion in financial assistance under SWIFT funding since its inception. Press Release, The Texas Water Newsroom, *TWDB Approves More Than $1.9 Billion in SWIFT Financial Assistance* (July 26, 2018), https://texaswaternewsroom.org/pressreleases/2018-07-26_swift_totals.html. Chapter 37 of this book provides additional detail regarding SWIFT funding and its implementation to date to fund water projects across Texas.

VI. Conclusion

§ 3.19 Conclusion

The 2022 State Water Plan identifies the need to develop 6.9 million acre-feet of additional water supplies in order to meet the state's projected "dry year" demands in 2070, which is the planning horizon required by law. *See* 2022 State Water Plan, at 7. Further, the 2022 State Water Plan indicates that the state's population is expected to increase more than 70 percent between 2020 and 2070, from 29.7 million to 51.5 million. *See* 2022 State Water Plan, at 2. Moreover, water demands are projected to increase as well, by approximately 9 percent between 2020 and 2070, from 17.7 million to 19.2 million acre-feet per year. *See* 2022 State Water Plan, at 3. This is especially important because water user groups face a potential water shortage of 3.1 million acre-feet per year in 2020 and 6.9 million acre-feet per year in 2070 in drought-of-record conditions. *See* 2022 State Water Plan, at 3. That said, if strategies are not implemented, approximately one-third of Texas's population would have less than half the municipal water supplies it would require during a drought of record in 2070. *See* 2022 State Water Plan, at 3.

Development of these water supplies is the subject of significant planning and permitting requirements, and adequate funding is essential to project development. State law provides that water supply projects requiring state water rights permitting or state funding be consistent with approved regional and state water plans. *See* Tex. Water Code §§ 11.134(b)(3)(E), 16.053(j). Depending on the source of supply, permitting of the storage and use of water by the TCEQ or by a GCD may also be required, and federal permits are necessary for projects involving construction activities in federally regulated waters. *See* 33 U.S.C. § 1344. These activities involve compliance with state and federal procedures that often require years to complete. Finally, adequate funding for planning, permitting, site and right-of-way acquisitions, and construction of projects is necessary for new water supplies to be developed. A comprehensive consideration of each of these factors is necessary to successfully complete a water supply project in the state of Texas.

CHAPTER 4

Historical Development of Texas Surface Water Law: Background of the Appropriation and Permitting System and Management of Surface Water Resources

Glenn Jarvis[1]

I. Introduction and Overview

§ 4.1 Background of Texas Surface Water Law

Substantial modifications in Texas surface water laws have occurred more frequently than in other aspects of property law. For this reason, the Texas law of surface water rights can best be understood by reviewing its historical evolution. The evolution of surface water law in Texas is unique substantially because of the state's governmental and legal history. Politics always played a significant role motivated by social and historical events and economic considerations, which in turn were often driven by nature. Droughts and water shortages, as well as floods, often have been followed by changes in water law. This chapter traces that history and its effect on surface water law, culminating in the establishment of the prior appropriation and permitting system in effect today.

Texas was initially governed by Spanish law, then by Mexican law from 1821 until Texas achieved its independence from Mexico in 1836. Texas was a republic and sovereign nation from 1836 until it became a state in 1845. The Republic of Texas used the general laws of Mexico until 1840. The Fourth Congress of the Republic of Texas introduced the common law of England as of March 16, 1840. It preserved Spanish and Mexican mining law but notably did not preserve the water law of New Spain. *See* Act approved Jan. 20, 1840, 4th Cong., R.S., §§ 1, 2, 1840 Repub. Tex. Laws 3, 4, *reprinted in* 2 H.P.N. Gammel, *The Laws of Texas 1822–1897*, at 177, 178 (Austin, Gammel Book Co. 1898). When it became a state in 1845, Texas reserved the ownership of its public land, water, and other natural resources. *See* Ordinance adopted July 4, 1845, *reprinted in* 2 H.P.N. Gammel, *The Laws of Texas 1822–1897*, at 1228. Each of these political, legal, and historical events shaped Texas water law.

This evolution continued through the Republic period and as the new state took form. Sixteen years after the adoption of the common law in 1840, the courts adopted a version of the common-law

---

1. Glenn Jarvis has practiced law in McAllen, Texas, since 1963. He represents public and private sector clients involving water resources and law issues before regulatory agencies and courts and in various transactional settings. He has served on advisory committees of the Texas Commission on Environmental Quality and its predecessors and in an advisory capacity involving water legislation. He is a frequent writer and speaker on water resource and law topics in the United States and Mexico.

riparian rights system. *Haas v. Choussard*, 17 Tex. 588, 589 (1856); *see also* A. Dan Tarlock, *Law of Water Rights and Resources* ch. 3 (Clark Boardman Callaghan & Co. 1988) [hereinafter Tarlock]. The period from 1845 through the 1870s was politically uncertain. Texas seceded from the Union in 1861 and returned to statehood in 1870. Wells H. Hutchins, *Texas Law of Water Rights* 1–3 (1961) [hereinafter Hutchins]. Faced with public pressure to develop the state's water resources during these unstable times, the legislature passed the Irrigation Act of 1852 to encourage local private irrigation projects. *See* Act approved Feb. 10, 1852, 4th Leg., R.S., ch. 74, 1852 Tex. Gen. Laws 80, *reprinted in* 3 H.P.N. Gammel, *The Laws of Texas 1822–1897*, at 598. Thus began a divergence of water law principles: the courts followed the common-law water rights riparian system, while the legislature passed statutes regulating the use of water. This created a disconnected and confused legal water rights system. Because the period was marked by political discontent, public focus was on ensuring the stability of government rather than on regulating the state's water resources. Later, when people were free to pursue a better life and economic stability, the need for developing the state's resources gained attention, and the legislature, recognizing these needs, adopted the law of prior appropriation in the Irrigation Act of 1889. *See* Act approved Mar. 19, 1889, 21st Leg., R.S., ch. 88, 1889 Tex. Gen. Laws 100, *reprinted in* 9 H.P.N. Gammel, *The Laws of Texas 1822–1897*, at 1128.

In an effort to improve the 1889 Act, the legislature passed the 1893 Act and then the Irrigation Act of 1895, which extended the scope of the 1889 Act and confirmed the dual system of water rights: common-law riparian rights, as previously recognized by the courts, and statutory prior appropriation rights established by the legislature. *See* Act of Mar. 29, 1895, 23d Leg., R.S., ch. 44, 1895 Tex. Gen. Laws 47; Act of Mar. 9, 1895, 24th Leg., R.S., ch. 21, 1895 Tex. Gen. Laws 21, *reprinted in* 10 H.P.N. Gammel, *The Laws of Texas 1822–1897*, at 751. This legislative policy of state control of water resources, while recognizing private property rights, was reinforced by legislation passed in 1913 and 1917–18. The dual system of surface water rights and the dichotomy of the state ownership of surface water and protection of private property rights led to confusion, which was not resolved until the enactment of the Water Rights Adjudication Act in 1967. *See In re Adjudication of the Water Rights of Upper Guadalupe Segment of Guadalupe River Basin*, 642 S.W.2d 438, 439 (Tex. 1982) (noting that water law in Texas "was in a chaotic state prior to the enactment of the Water Rights Adjudication Act in 1967"). Thus, it took almost 125 years after statehood for Texas to address all water resource rights and provide a means of adjudicating the nature and extent of all surface water claims. Surface water rights were defined and quantified by the 1967 Act, with those rights claimed under both the common law and the prior appropriation statutes.

As a result of the adjudication proceedings undertaken under the 1967 Act, the common-law riparian right was converted into an appropriative right. The Act set the stage for better water management and refinement of Texas law on how surface water rights are exercised and managed. This refinement is continuing today as water managers, courts, and state water agencies, in an effort to meet the changing and increasing needs for water in a state that has a growing population and is changing from a predominantly agrarian society to a commercial and industrial society, struggle with issues such as reuse, environmental flows, interbasin transfers, the hydrologic connection between surface water and groundwater, and conjunctive use of surface water and groundwater.

II. The History of Surface Water Rights

§ 4.2 Spanish and Mexican Law and Their Influence

Before 1836, settlers from Spain and Mexico developed irrigation and municipal water systems in several areas of what is now Texas, particularly in the El Paso, San Antonio, and Laredo areas. The irrigation system in San Antonio is the best Texas example of the practical application of Spanish and Mexican water law.

The San Antonio irrigation system contained several ditches or *acequias*. Each acequia served a community of irrigators who operated their ditches within an administrative framework provided by the local government. The settlements were governed by the *alcalde* and *regimentos*, or in modern terms the mayor and the community authority, under authority granted by the king. *See San Juan Ditch Co. v. Cassin*, 141 S.W. 815 (Tex. App.—San Antonio 1911, writ ref'd). A similar system was created and maintained on the Rio Grande in the El Paso Valley on both sides of the river. These acequias also provided the Catholic missions and civil settlements with water for domestic use. *See* Betty Eakle Dobkins, *The Spanish Element in Texas Water Law* 103–13 (University of Texas Press 1959).

These water supply projects were politically, socially, and economically necessary during the Spanish colonization period and helped prevent the westward expansion of the French. In these early settlements, acequias were established to serve the missions, the presidio, domestic needs, and the limited irrigation needs of settlers' lands. *See* Hutchins, at 102–03.

Under Spanish and Mexican law, surface water was reserved to the king or the government that regulated its use, with the exception that people abutting a stream had the right to use water for basic domestic and livestock needs as a common-to-all use of water in the stream. A surface water right was gained for generally larger uses not abutting a stream—that is, not riparian to a stream—for irrigation, commercial, and industrial purposes only by a grant from the sovereign or by legal processes provided by the government. *See* Hans W. Baade, *The Historical Background of Texas Water Law—A Tribute to Jack Pope*, 18 St. Mary's L.J. 1 (1986).

As discussed below, early water law court decisions, such as *Haas v. Choussard*, 17 Tex. 588 (1856), and later *Motl v. Boyd*, 286 S.W. 458 (Tex. 1926), misunderstood these legal concepts and were later reconsidered and overturned. Later courts clarified this historical influence and relied on it to support their decisions. *See, e.g., State v. Valmont Plantations*, 346 S.W.2d 853 (Tex. App.—San Antonio 1961), *op. adopted*, 355 S.W.2d 502 (Tex. 1962), discussed below.

§ 4.3 Republic of Texas Period

When the Republic of Texas was established, it continued to be governed by Spanish and Mexican civil law during the period 1836–40. The validity and legal effect of contracts and grants of land were determined according to the civil law in effect at the time of the contract or grant. *Miller v. Letzerich*, 49 S.W.2d 404, 407–08 (Tex. 1932). Therefore, statutes in force during this period were construed in light of Mexican civil law. As noted above, the Republic adopted the English common law in 1840. At that time, embedded in English common law was a riparian right to use surface water. *See* Act approved Jan. 20, 1840, 4th Cong., R.S., §§ 1, 2, 1840 Repub. Tex. Laws 3, 4, *reprinted in* 2 H.P.N. Gammel, *The Laws of Texas 1822–1897*, at 177, 178. From 1836 through 1845, except for adoption of the English common law, there is little or no record of attention to water law. This obviously was because of other more pressing matters of the Republic. No water laws of significance were enacted until some years after Texas became a state.

§ 4.4 Early Statehood Period

The Republic of Texas became a state of the United States in 1845, and unlike other states it retained its public debt and obligations. Because of political pressures of the time and possibly because of the unknown nature of the debt, the state retained its public land and resources and debt. *See* Joint Resolution for Annexing Texas to the United States, 5 Stat. 787, 28th Cong., 2d Sess. (approved Mar. 1, 1845); Ordinance adopted July 4, 1845, *reprinted in* 2 H.P.N. Gammel, *The Laws of Texas 1822–1897*, at 1228. The result was that the United States did not initially have federal public lands in Texas as it had in other states. This fact significantly influenced the development of water law and water management in Texas in ways distinct from other states. Also, the needs of the time dictated the development of a strong agricultural economy to encourage immigration and produce food for the state's population growth.

§ 4.4:1 Irrigation Act of 1852

The first general law on the subject of water was the Irrigation Act of 1852, which was significant because irrigation enhanced agricultural production vital to the state's economy and growth. The 1852 Act authorized counties to regulate dams and distribute shares of the water. *See* Act approved Feb. 10, 1852, 4th Leg., R.S., ch. 74, 1852 Tex. Gen. Laws 80, *reprinted in* 3 H.P.N. Gammel, *The Laws of Texas 1822–1897*, at 598. Consistent with "the principles of the Mexican laws," counties were given authority to regulate the construction, operation, and maintenance of irrigation works, similar to the former regulatory power of the community alcalde system of Spanish and Mexican law. *Tolle v. Correth*, 31 Tex. 362, 364–65 (1868). It was observed that the 1852 Act was consistent with "ancient law" that regulated community irrigation. Harbert Davenport, *Development of the Texas Laws of Waters*, 21 Tex. Rev. Civ. Stat. Ann. XIII, XIX (Vernon 1954) [hereinafter Davenport]. The 1852 Act remained the law in Texas until its repeal by the so-called Water Appropriation Statute of 1913. Hutchins, at 104–05. See discussion below.

§ 4.4:2 Riparian Rights

After the adoption of the common law of England in 1840, there was embedded in Texas law an aspect of the English common law that ownership of land riparian to a stream or natural lake includes, by implication, a right to use water from the stream or lake. *See* Tarlock, ch. 3. However, it was not until sixteen years later, after the legislature's first attempt to manage the use of surface water by the Irrigation Act of 1852, discussed at section 4.4:1 above, that the courts applied English common law to Texas water law. In 1856, the Texas Supreme Court held in *Haas v. Choussard* that the "right to the use of water adjacent to one's lots, as it flowed in its natural channel was a right inherent and inseparably connected with the land itself." *Haas v. Choussard*, 17 Tex. 588, 589 (1856); *see generally* Ira P. Hilderbrand, *The Rights of Riparian Owners at Common Law in Texas*, 6 Texas L. Rev. 19 (1927). The recognition of this right was significant, especially for irrigation in the semiarid regions of Texas. *Tolle v. Correth*, 31 Tex. 362, 364–65 (1868); *Rhodes v. Whitehead*, 27 Tex. 304, 310–11, 315–16 (1863).

In *Fleming v. Davis*, 37 Tex. 173, 201–02 (1872), for example, the applicability of riparian water rights to semiarid areas was contested. The court was urged to judicially adopt the California prior appropriation system. In this case, a downstream riparian user on a stream sued an upstream user for unreasonably using water from springs, which were the headwaters of the stream. The upstream user was using the entire flow for his domestic and irrigation purposes. The court concluded, applying common-law riparian rules, that the upstream user could be enjoined from *unreasonable* detention and use of all the water while it was on his property; that without a contract or an express grant of water, the upstream user had only the right to use water co-equally with the rights of all other riparians to have the benefits of the water. Thus, the reasonable use and correlative rights concept was applied to the common-law riparian right. The court, however, advised the legislature that "the wealth and comfort of our people throughout a large portion of the State might be greatly augmented by wise legislation on this subject."

§ 4.4:3 Special Laws Creating Private Irrigation Companies

While the courts in the cases discussed at section 4.4:2 above recognized a Texas version of common-law riparian rights, between 1854 and 1879 multiple special laws were passed granting individuals, cities, and corporations the authority to construct dams and other works for the purpose of water development through irrigation enterprises. *See* 4 H.P.N. Gammel, *The Laws of Texas 1822–1897*, at 151, 400, 580, 823, 1202, 1294; 5 H.P.N. Gammel, *The Laws of Texas 1822–1897*, at 536, 789, 793–94, 1318, 1431, 1572, 1584, 1605, 1607; 6 H.P.N. Gammel, *The Laws of Texas 1822–1897*, at 712; 7 H.P.N. Gammel, *The Laws of Texas 1822–1897*, at 191. During this same period, at least fourteen of these laws granted the right to divert water from various streams for irrigation and other purposes. *See, e.g.*, 4 H.P.N. Gammel, *The Laws of Texas 1822–1897*, at 1314; 5 H.P.N. Gammel, *The Laws of Texas 1822–1897*, at 231, 302, 570, 1284, 1360, 1491, 1627; 6 H.P.N. Gammel, *The Laws of Texas 1822–1897*, at 683, 1470, 1621; 7 H.P.N. Gammel, *The Laws of Texas 1822–1897*, at 316, 1310; 9 H.P.N. Gammel, *The Laws of Texas 1822–1897*, at 14. In these special acts, the Texas legislature granted private companies the power to construct dams and divert water from a river. The grants made by these legislative acts did not take into account whether the owners owned any riparian land and contemplated use by the owner of water for irrigation purposes without restriction as to the riparian users of the water. A.W. Walker, Jr., *Legal History of the Riparian Right of Irrigation in Texas Since 1836* 41, 47, *in* Proceedings, Water Law Conference, Univ. of Texas (1959). These special acts illustrate the legislature's reliance on the legal concept that the state's land and surface waters were public waters of Texas, subject to state control within basic constitutional restraints.

For example, the Texas legislature authorized the formation of the El Paso Irrigation and Manufacturing Company for the purpose of providing irrigation to the El Paso Valley and granted to the private company the power "to divert from the channel or bed of the Rio Grande one-fourth of all the water forming said river, and apply the same to the purposes or [sic] irrigation." *See* Act approved Nov. 6, 1866, 11th Leg., R.S., ch. 157, § 10, 1866 Tex. Spec. Laws 271, 273, *reprinted in* 5 H.P.N. Gammel, *The Laws of Texas 1822–1897*, at 1491, 1493.

Water policy at that time recognized that encouraging irrigation development was important and that the state had to play a role in the development of its natural water resources. For example, a law enacted on December 20, 1861, authorized the imposition of a fine on any person who refused to work on a ditch when summoned to do so by proper authority and apparently was intended to supplement the 1852 Act. Act approved Dec. 20, 1861, 9th Leg., R.S., ch. 15, 1861 Tex. Gen. Laws 8, *reprinted in* 5 H.P.N. Gammel, *The Laws of Texas 1822–1897*, at 452.

Texas statutes relating to private corporations, however, developed more rapidly than the statutes defining the right to the water itself. This legal development added a layer of complexity to the evolving water law. For example, the Private Corporation Act was passed in 1871, which provided for the organization of canal companies for the purpose of irrigation. Act approved Dec. 2, 1871, 12th Leg., 2d C.S., ch. 74, § 2, 1871 Tex. Gen. Laws 66, 67, *reprinted in* 7 H.P.N. Gammel, *The Laws of Texas 1822–1897*, at 68, 69. Section 58 of the Private Corporation Act of April 23, 1874, made ample provision for the organization of "canal companies for the purpose of irrigation" and authorized each such corporation "to construct its canals across, along, or upon any stream of water." Act approved Apr. 23, 1874, 14th Leg., R.S., ch. 97, § 58, 1874 Tex. Gen. Laws 120, 134, *reprinted in* 8 H.P.N. Gammel, *The Laws of Texas 1822–1897*, at 122, 136. The following year, the legislature enacted a comprehensive statute to encourage the construction of canals and ditches for navigation and irrigation. It also authorized the granting of public land for each mile of canal constructed, when approved and accepted by the governor, and stated that "any such canal company *shall have the free use of the water* of the rivers and streams of this State; but in no case shall any company flow lands to the detriment of the owners without their consent, or due payment to the parties aggrieved." Act approved Mar. 10, 1875, 14th Leg., 2d C.S., ch. 62, § 7, 1875 Tex. Gen. Laws 77, 79, *reprinted in* 8 H.P.N. Gammel, *The Laws of Texas 1822–1897*, at 449, 451 (emphasis added). As discussed below, this language later proved to be insufficient to grant a private property right to actually take water from a stream where there were existing riparian claimants.

These early irrigation laws were not water rights statutes as such but were related to public regulation of commonly owned private irrigation enterprises. These statutes do, however, indicate that the legislature believed that, based on the reservation of ownership of public land and waters by the state, it was authorized to grant rights to surface waters in Texas streams. At the same time, without further constitutional authority, the courts continued to recognize a form of common-law riparian rights.

The competing interest created by this dual system was highlighted in *Mud Creek Irrigation, Agricultural & Manufacturing Co. v. Vivian*, 11 S.W. 1078 (Tex. 1889), in which a private irrigation company attempted to enforce its charter and its statutory rights. The company sought to enjoin Vivian and others from maintaining a dam on Mud Creek in Kinney County above the point where the waters of the creek entered the company's canal. The company alleged that under applicable law and its charter it had exclusive use of the waters of the stream. The court disposed of this contention by holding that "[t]he charter *conferred the right to acquire* water privileges, but it did not confer the privileges themselves." *Mud Creek Irrigation*, 11 S.W. at 1078–79 (emphasis added). The court was logical and resourceful in holding that while the company was vested with the power to *acquire*, as a private corporation, a privilege to take the waters of the creek for the purpose of irrigation, the statute did not expressly grant the right to take and use the waters. The company had to obtain this right to take water from the stream. The case left open the question of how such a company was to obtain this water right.

The court noted that canal company statutes discussed above applied to only streams on public lands, because the legislature had no power to take away or impair the *vested rights of riparian owners* without providing for the constitutional right to just compensation. This case illustrates the dilemma that existed for individuals desiring to develop their water rights. Companies, such as the plaintiff in *Mud Creek Irrigation*, had to invest relatively large amounts of capital to start and operate such enterprises, which the state encouraged by enacting statutes establishing entities to develop water resources. The legislature, however, ignored the need for laws regarding the actual right to take and use water from the state's streams. At the same time, the courts were protecting their version of common-law riparian claims as a private property right. Making the situation even more difficult was the fact that the period from 1855 to 1864 saw one of the most sustained droughts ever experienced in the state, causing water shortages lasting until 1888. *See* David W. Stahle & Malcolm K. Cleaveland, *Texas Drought History Reconstructed and Analyzed from 1698 to 1980*, 1 J. Climate 59, 66, 72 (1988) [hereinafter Stahle & Cleaveland]; Douglas Helms, *Great Plains Conservation Program, 1956–1981: A Short Administrative and Legislative History, reprinted from Great Plains Conservation Program: 25 Years of Accomplishment*, U.S. Department of Agriculture, SCS National Bulletin No. 300-2-7 (1981), www.nrcs.usda.gov/wps/portal/nrcs/detail/national/about/history/?cid=nrcs143_021382.

Responding to political and economic pressures, the legislature addressed these problems in the Irrigation Act of 1889.

§ 4.4:4 Texas Legislative Acts Adopting the Prior Appropriation Doctrine

The Irrigation Act of 1889: The purpose of the Irrigation Act of 1889 was "to encourage irrigation, and to provide for the acquisition of the right to the use of water, and for the construction and maintenance of canals, ditches, flumes, reservoirs, and wells for irrigation, and for mining, milling, and stockraising in the arid districts of Texas." Act approved Mar. 19, 1889, 21st Leg., R.S., ch. 88, 1889 Tex. Gen. Laws 100, *reprinted in* 9 H.P.N. Gammel, *The Laws of Texas 1822–1897*, at 1128.

The first four sections of the Act provided:

Section 1. Be it enacted by the Legislature of the State of Texas: That the unappropriated waters of *every river or natural stream* within *the arid portions of the state of Texas*, in which, by reason of the insufficient rainfall, irrigation is necessary for agricultural purposes, may be diverted from its natural channel for irrigation, domestic, and other beneficial uses: Provided, that said water shall not be diverted so as to deprive any person who claims, owns, or holds a possessory right or title to any land lying along the bank or margin of any river or natural stream of the use of the water thereof for *his own domestic use*.

Section 2. That *the unappropriated waters* of every river or natural stream within the arid portions of the state, as described in the preceding section of this act, are hereby declared to be the property of the public, and may be acquired by appropriation for the uses and purposes as hereinafter provided.

Section 3. The appropriation must be for the purposes named in this act, and when the appropriator, or his successor in interest, ceases to use it for such purpose the right ceases.

Section 4. As between appropriators, the one first in time is the one first in right to such quantity of the water only as is reasonably sufficient and necessary to irrigate the land susceptible of irrigation on either side of ditch or canal.

Act approved Mar. 19, 1889, 21st Leg., R.S., ch. 88, §§ 1–4, 1889 Tex. Gen. Laws 100–101, *reprinted in* 9 H.P.N. Gammel, *The Laws of Texas 1822–1897*, at 1128–29 (emphasis added).

The Act made clear that the unappropriated waters within the *arid portions* of the state were the property of the state and adopted the prior appropriation doctrine of first in time, first in right. The Act clarified the method by which irrigation ditch companies could acquire a right to take water from a stream by filing a declaration of appropriation in the office of the county clerk of the county where the headgate of the proposed canal or ditch was to be located.

The primary goal of this statute was to protect irrigation ditch companies, and its key purpose was to authorize these companies to appropriate water, urging that irrigation canals should be built "at once." Act approved Mar. 19, 1889, 21st Leg., R.S., ch. 88, §§ 1, 2, 5, 17, 1889 Tex. Gen. Laws 100–103, *reprinted in* 9 H.P.N. Gammel, *The Laws of Texas 1822–1897*, at 1128–31. The Act also protected the right of a landowner who owned property adjacent to the stream to use water of the stream "for his own domestic use," thereby statutorily confirming the state's dual system of water rights, to this extent, in the arid portions of the state.

The caption of the legislation included a reference to "wells for irrigation," which expressed an intent to include water wells and groundwater within its scope in the arid portions of the state. However, the statute itself did not address wells. From a historical perspective, it is interesting to note what would have occurred in later years with respect to groundwater law if the legislature and courts had expanded on this intent to include groundwater within the appropriation doctrine. See discussion of the Conservation Amendment below and Chapter 5 of this book for a discussion of the development of groundwater laws in Texas.

Only the riparian right aspects of the Act were interpreted by the courts. The Supreme Court of Texas, in *McGhee Irrigating Ditch Co. v. Hudson*, 22 S.W. 967 (Tex. 1893), without referring to section 1 of the Act, which protected only riparian domestic use, held:

> Section 2 of the act cannot operate, and probably was not intended to operate, on the rights of riparian owners, existing when the law was passed, but was intended to operate only on such interests as were in the state by reason of its ownership of lands bordering on rivers or natural streams, and it may be that there are some other parts of the act that would have to be so limited. . . . The word "land" includes, not only the soil, but everything attached to it, whether attached by course of nature, as trees, herbage, *and water*, or by the hand of man, as buildings and fences.

McGhee Irrigating Ditch Co., 22 S.W. at 968 (emphasis added).

The court narrowly construed section 2 of the Act, with reference to the protection of riparian rights, but did not consider section 1, which protected only domestic riparian use. The Act was later amended in 1893, addressing the manner of evidencing claims by filing declarations of appropriation in the county records, but made no other significant change and did not refer to riparian water rights claims. Act approved Mar. 29, 1893, 23d Leg., R.S., ch. 44, 1893 Tex. Gen. Laws 47, *reprinted in* 10 H.P.N. Gammel, *The Laws of Texas 1822–1897*, at 447. The 1889 and 1893 Acts were replaced by a much broader and comprehensive statute in 1895, which gave some deference to the *McGhee* court's protection of riparian claims.

The Irrigation Act of 1895: The legislature extended, and clarified to an extent, the prior appropriation doctrine in the Irrigation Act of 1895. Act of Mar. 9, 1895, 24th Leg., R.S., ch. 21, 1895 Tex. Gen. Laws 21, *reprinted in* 10 H.P.N. Gammel, *The Laws of Texas 1822–1897*, at 751. This law sought to reserve to the state stormwaters or rainwaters and, in deference to court holdings, protected the rights of riparian owners to the ordinary flow and underflow of a stream. It declared in the first five sections of the Act:

Section 1. Be it enacted by the Legislature of the State of Texas: That the unappropriated waters of the ordinary flow or underflow of every running or flowing river or natural stream, and the storm or rain waters of every river or natural stream, canyon, ravine, depression or watershed within those portions of the State of Texas *in which by reason of the insufficient rainfall or by reason of the irregularity of the rainfall*, irrigation is beneficial for agricultural purposes, are hereby declared to be the property of the public, and may be acquired by appropriation for the uses and purposes and in the manner as hereinafter provided.

Section 2. The storm or rain waters, as described in the preceding section, may be held or stored in dams, lakes or reservoirs built and constructed by a person, corporation or association of persons for irrigation, mining, milling, the construction of waterworks for cities and towns, or stockraising, within those portions of Texas described in the foregoing section; and all such waters may be diverted by the person, corporation or association of persons owning or controlling such dam, reservoir or lake for irrigation, mining, milling, the construction of waterworks for cities and towns, and stockraising.

Section 3. The ordinary flow or underflow of the running water of every natural river or stream within those portions of Texas described in section 1 of this act may be diverted from its natural channel for irrigation, mining, milling, the construction of waterworks for cities and towns, or stockraising: *Provided, that such flow or underflow of water shall not be diverted to the prejudice of the rights of the riparian owner without his consent, except after condemnation thereof in the manner as hereinafter provided.*

Section 4. The appropriation of water must be either for irrigation, mining, milling, the construction of waterworks for cities and towns, or stockraising.

Section 5. As between appropriators the first in time is the first in right.

Act of Mar. 9, 1895, 24th Leg., R.S., ch. 21, §§ 1–5, 1895 Tex. Gen. Laws 21–22, *reprinted in* 10 H.P.N. Gammel, *The Laws of Texas 1822–1897*, at 751–52 (emphasis added).

The 1895 Act not only encouraged irrigation but also addressed water for mining, milling, and stockraising uses and waterworks for cities and towns. It established the method by which irrigators and others could develop dams and take water.

By special proviso, the Act protected a riparian owner's right to the ordinary flow or underflow of water in a stream, but it failed to define "ordinary flow" or what rights a riparian owner had with respect to the remaining "unappropriated ordinary flow" in a stream. As later judicially and legislatively confirmed, the Act reserved to the state all of the unappropriated running waters, including ordinary flows, stormwater, and floodwater on a statewide basis. This means that public lands granted after July 1, 1895, the Act's effective date, do not carry with them a riparian water right claim unless expressly provided in the grant. Common-law riparian rights were limited to "ordinary flows or underflow" and to land granted or patented before July 1, 1895.

These defining dates became even more significant during the statewide adjudication of water rights undertaken under the Water Rights Adjudication Act of 1967. See discussion at section 4.6 below.

The 1895 Act also limited the ratemaking power of irrigation companies, previewing existing law with respect to regulation of rates charged by some entities for the supply or delivery of potable or nonpotable water. See Chapters 29 and 31 of this book.

In summary, the 1895 Act was primarily directed at irrigation use of water; it required irrigation ditch companies and developers of irrigation to obtain recognition for their projects by a local filing process in local county records, reminiscent of the Spanish and Mexican system of local control subject to the sovereign's control. Similar to the prior appropriation doctrine adopted in the western United States, it provided a process to obtain a legally recognized right to use water. This provided an incentive that encouraged investment in agricultural water projects by providing a process to acquire a recognized legal right to use water from a stream. It also provided the security of recognition of a water right, since the essential element of the appropriation doctrine system, "first in time is the first in right"—that is, the priority system—was made clear, and provided a means of enforcement of water rights. Nonetheless, it left much uncertainty about the nature of the riparian right and how it was to be reconciled with the appropriation doctrine of water rights.

During the period 1895–1913, knowledge of practical irrigation improved steadily, and the development of irrigation pumping converted small gravity flow irrigation systems to much larger pumping and gravity flow irrigation operations. More land was developed into large irrigated areas. *See* Davenport, XXIII. However, water rights claimants still had an incomplete system of water laws to ensure that their claims were honored.

The Dual System and Conflicts in the Courts: During this period water rights holders had to rely on the courts to resolve their disputes. This was an awkward process. It required injunction lawsuits, so that a court could exercise its equitable powers in attempting to resolve conflicts. A court could resolve only disputes between individual parties in the litigation; courts could not take into account the impact of such litigation on other water rights holders on a stream or a segment of a stream. The process also placed the courts in the difficult position of dealing with technical hydrologic and water management questions without the aid of relevant hydrologic evidence.

An example of these difficulties is an early water dispute after the 1889 and 1895 Acts but before the 1913 Act. In *Biggs v. Miller*, 147 S.W. 632 (Tex. App.—El Paso 1912, no writ), users of water from the Pecos River through one irrigation system called the "Barstow System" sought to enjoin other users through an irrigation system called the "Biggs System." Both parties claimed prior appropriation rights and riparian rights to riparian lands. The claimants sought to use an injunction to divide the waters of the stream in accordance with the parties' respective water rights.

Evidence showed that a prior federal court judgment had adjudicated to the Barstow System, whose diversion point was below the Biggs System, the prior and more senior right to use water for irrigation purposes on both its riparian and nonriparian lands. That judgment ruled that the more junior upstream Biggs System was subject to such rights as to irrigating its nonriparian lands but not its riparian lands even though the Biggs System was more senior. In other words, the first in time principal did not apply to the riparian lands.

The *Miller* court was faced with a complex record pertaining to the capacity of canals to handle water, whether rights were restricted to then-cultivated land or could include irrigable land that could later be brought under cultivation, how much water was needed to irrigate the land without waste, the capabilities of the irrigation system's headgates and other facilities, and rights to return flows. The court was also faced with procedural issues about whether all users in each of the systems were necessary parties for the adjudication of the rights for that system.

Because the suit was for an injunction, an equitable remedy could be applied. The trial court divided the flows in a detailed, practical manner, distinguishing between appropriative rights to nonriparian lands and riparian rights to riparian lands, recognizing and consistent with the dual system of water rights. The court recognized the appropriative rights under the 1895 Act and riparian rights as to riparian lands by declaring: "By our statutes, the waters of such rivers as the Pecos are the property of the public. Riparian owners have easements therein, which cannot be divested, save, perhaps, by condemnation. But statutory appropriations, when filed in compliance with law, give to such appropriators the right to take the water to non-riparian lands, there to use it for themselves or to dispose of it to water consumers." *Miller*, 147 S.W. at 637. The court disagreed with some of the equitable findings of the trial court, found procedural errors, and reversed the case for further proceedings. No resolution was achieved, and no further judicial history is available on the case.

Pending at the same time before the same court was *Biggs v. Lee*, 147 S.W. 709 (Tex. App.—El Paso 1912, writ dism'd), which involved a downstream Pecos River riparian water rights claimant's action against an upstream appropriator, seeking to enjoin him from diverting water to be used on nonriparian land. The district court's action enjoining the appropriator claimant from diverting water was reversed and remanded on appeal, without resolving the controversy.

The appellate court, on motion for rehearing, provided guidance to the district court:

> It is certain that under our laws the waters are the property of the public, subject to the easements of riparian owners. The riparian easement is the right to use an amount of water reasonably sufficient for domestic and stock-raising purposes and for irrigating the riparian lands. A statutory appropriation, under our decisions, is effective as against the waters so the property of the public, subject to the easements of the riparian owners which have the prior right.
>
> If the water is sufficient only for riparian owners using it, it must be equitably divided between them. As between the riparian owner and the statutory appropriator, the riparian owner must first have water reasonably sufficient, as indicated; but as against the excess the statutory appropriation is effective. To hold that riparian owners have the right to have all the water flow past their land as against statutory appropriations would be to destroy the appropriation statute in its entirety, for there are riparian owners on every stream, and if each had the right as against the appropriator to have all the water flow past his land, there could never be an effective appropriation anywhere. We refused to decide in the original opinion whether an appropriation is good against the water until such time as the riparian owner shall make use of it; but, as here illustrated, we very strongly incline to the opinion that this will be found to be the law. Every stream is bordered by riparian lands, even the Mississippi river, the largest stream we have. If every riparian owner had the right to have all the water, as against appropriators, flow past his land, no valid appropriation could ever be made. Again, if as we have held the riparian owner's only right is to use sufficient water for his land's purposes, still it would follow, if his right was good against appropriations, before he made use of the water, that on small streams the appropriation statute would be nullified. On the other hand, if the law is that the riparian owner can only use sufficient for his land's purposes, and if the law is that he only has the preferential right when he uses it or when in good faith he is about to use it, then there has been preserved the statutory appropriation, without, it will be noted, injuring the riparian owner; for if the water is sufficient only for the riparian owners using it, there can be no valid appropriation. If there is an excess over what the riparian owners using it need, then as to the excess the appropriation is valid. If there is a stream where none of the riparian owners care to use the water, and which flows only a small quantity, it may nevertheless be used by the appropriator, subject always to the prior right of the riparian owner to the extent of his needs.
>
> We think, however, that the point made by appellee is well taken. The riparian owner in this case is entitled to sufficient water for his land's purposes. This necessarily means sufficient usable water, and it would be proper for a decree, if he show himself entitled to one, to award sufficient water so as to avoid the mineral impregnation; but, having ascertained the

amount, as may be done, the judgment should certainly and definitely fix the same so as to make it intelligible and capable of enforcement.

Lee, 147 S.W. at 710–11.

These cases illustrate the many complex issues arising (1) in interpreting and enforcing individual water rights claimants claiming both appropriative and riparian rights; (2) against a number of parties in a single litigation without joinder of all water rights claimants on the stream or segment of a stream; and (3) without the benefit of technical definition of rates of flow, system capacities, and other relevant hydrologic evidence. They also illustrate the frustration exhibited by the courts in reconciling the dual system of law. For later litigation on the Pecos River, see the following cases: *Ward County Water Improvement District No. 2 v. Ward County Irrigation District No. 1*, 214 S.W. 490 (Tex. App.—El Paso 1919, no writ); *Hoefs v. Short*, 273 S.W. 785 (Tex. 1925); *Ward County Water Improvement District No. 3 v. Ward County Irrigation District No. 1*, 237 S.W. 584 (Tex. App.—El Paso 1922), *modified*, 295 S.W. 917 (Tex. 1927); and *Wilson v. Reeves County Water Improvement District No. 1*, 256 S.W. 346 (Tex. App.—El Paso 1923, no writ). The relative rights on the Pecos River were never fully resolved until adjudication under the Water Rights Adjudication Act of 1967 (see section 4.6:1 below). *See Borden v. Trespalacios Rice & Irrigation Co.*, 86 S.W. 11 (Tex. 1905); *City of Wichita Falls v. Bruner*, 191 S.W.2d 912 (Tex. App.—Fort Worth 1945, writ ref'd w.o.m.); Neal King, *Inadequacies of Existing Texas Procedure for Determination of Water Rights on Major Stream Segments* 66–73, *in* Proceedings, Water Law Conference, Univ. of Texas (1956).

Historically, the privately operated and financed irrigation companies that were expected to build irrigation diversion and delivery (canal) systems did not work well. Money was difficult to raise. In many instances, without further incentives other than land grants from the state, irrigation did not develop as expected after the 1895 Act. At the same time, the "filing" system provided in the 1895 Act left much to be desired. As the state grew, increased irrigation needs and population growth, and the resulting need for municipal and industrial use of water, highlighted problems with the early acts. Droughts, floods, and the need to develop agriculture and other uses constituted conditions for change.

The common-law riparian rights were yet to be defined, and the appropriation declarations filed with the county clerks required only that the amount of water to be appropriated and the area to be irrigated be stated generally as to appropriation statutory rights. This left open to conjecture many details of an appropriative statutory water right such as the specific location of use, purpose, rates, and location of diversion points. The system's lack of a manageable definition of riparian rights added to the uncertainty. This process did not create a system by which all water rights could be inventoried and managed. *See* A.P. Rollins, *The Need for a Water Inventory in Texas* 67–68, *in* Proceedings, Water Law Conference, Univ. of Texas (1952).

These circumstances led to a constitutional amendment in 1904 providing for the establishment of water districts. These political subdivisions would have the means to provide money necessary for the development of operations and facilities through assessments paid by water users and through taxation of the benefited land. The 1904 amendment did not, however, address the means of acquiring the right to take (divert) water from the state's rivers. Following another drought in 1910 and intermittent floods in the 1910–13 period, the legislature made basic changes to surface water law in 1913.

The Irrigation Act of 1913: The Irrigation Act of 1913, also known as the Burges-Glasscock Act, created the Board of Water Engineers and centralized the statutory water rights inventory process by providing that waters belonging to the state could be appropriated only pursuant to permits issued by that board through procedures provided in the Act. *See* Act of Apr. 9, 1913, 33d Leg., R.S., ch. 171. While acknowledging common-law riparian rights, it did not address their nature and extent.

The 1913 Act repealed earlier water laws, primarily those applicable to the arid regions of Texas, and adopted a uniform system of statutory water laws. "In essence the [1913 Act] declared all waters within Texas to be the property of the State, and provided means [and process] by which . . . waters could be appropriated for designated purposes, including 'waterworks for cities and towns.' (Secs. 2 and 4)." *Texas Water Rights Commission v. City of Dallas*, 591 S.W.2d 609, 613 (Tex. App.—Austin 1979, writ ref'd n.r.e.).

The Board of Water Engineers was given authority to grant permits for the statutory appropriation of the state's waters. The Act required that certified copies of all records of previous declarations of prior appropriation of water filed locally under the 1889 and 1895 Acts be filed with the board. The filings included sworn statements on the extent of work done and the amount of water that had been taken or appropriated from a stream. Some forty years later, these rights were defined as certified filings. *See* Act approved June 8, 1953, 53d Leg., R.S., ch. 352, § 2.

The 1913 Act provided that the "ordinary flow and underflow" of watercourses could not be diverted to the prejudice of the "rights of any riparian owner" without consent, but it did not define the measure or extent of a riparian right. The Act confirmed the intent of the 1895 Act's reservation of "storm waters" for later appropriation. It further cemented the dual system of water law, but in doing so clarified that nothing in the Act was to be "construed as a recognition of any riparian right in the owner of any lands the title to which . . . passed out of the state" after 1895. To this extent, the Act limited a riparian right to grants and patents issued before 1895.

The Act clarified the legislative intent in the 1895 Act with respect to the period by which the undefined riparian right could be claimed, but the extent or measure of the right was yet to be determined. The Act also made clear that the appropriation doctrine applied to the entire state, which allowed a more manageable statewide permitting system compared to the previous filing system with local county clerks. Nevertheless, the Act failed to provide a mechanism for the comprehensive inventory and adjudication of "vested" riparian rights, which would be necessary for rational allocation of the water that remained to be appropriated.

The Act did seek to clarify water rights laws with respect to irrigation use and development as well as municipal and industrial water needs. In this regard, one of the active sponsors of the Act, Rep. D. W. Glasscock, in addressing the house on behalf of the 1913 Act, stated:

> While known as the "Irrigation Bill," it is in fact much more extensive in scope than this term would indicate, and is an effort to form a comprehensive system of statutory "Water Law" for this State. It deals, not only with the important question of irrigation, in which millions of capital is now invested in this State and upon which many thousands of people are dependent; but also with every right to the use of water; from the Primary use for drinking and domestic purposes, the supply of cities and towns, the natural use for stock raising, the uses for mining, the development power, and other purposes; up to the problem of conservation of this great natural resource, and its control, application and use, to the benefit of all people of this State.

H.J. of Tex., 33d Leg., R.S. 949–50 (1913). *See Texas Water Rights Commission*, 591 S.W.2d at 613.

At the time, 90 percent or more of water was used for irrigation. Rep. Glasscock's words, when considered in light of the alternating droughts and floods and the words of the Act, show a recognition of population growth. They also show an intent to define the riparian right in terms of a natural right for domestic and livestock use, but many believed it gave protection to a riparian right to irrigation. *See* Davenport, at 1. It was not long before these issues were addressed by more legislation and another important constitutional amendment.

The Irrigation Act of 1917: A drought in 1917 increased water needs and public pressure to develop the state's water resources, culminating in the repeal of the Irrigation Act of 1913 by the 1917 Irrigation Act. *See* Act of Mar. 19, 1917, 35th Leg., R.S., ch. 88. The 1917 Act included most of the substance of the 1913 Act while clarifying the permitting process. More significantly, the Act added provisions for adjudication of water rights. Some contemporaries of the 1917 Act believed it destroyed the intent of the 1913 Act, which protected riparian rights claimants. *See* Davenport, at 1. The public's mood and the legislature's intent, however, were to give the state more control over the development of water resources. To evidence this, in the same session, a constitutional amendment was proposed to ensure legislative authority in this respect. S.J. of Tex., 35th Leg., R.S. 500 (1917).

The Conservation Amendment of 1917: On August 21, 1917, the citizens of Texas approved a constitutional amendment, Tex. Const. art. XVI, § 59, referred to as the "Conservation Amendment." The amendment enabled the legislature to create governmental entities whose purpose was to conserve water by developing the water resources. The term "conservation" meant the development of water resources through local and regional water districts, using dams, reservoir projects, and delivery systems. Water was "conserved" through use or storage for later use before it was lost to the Gulf of Mexico. The amendment provided in part:

Sec. 59(a). The conservation and development of *all* of the natural resources of this State, and development of parks and recreational facilities, including the control, storing, preservation and distribution of its storm and flood *waters*, the *waters* of its rivers and streams, for irrigation, power and all other useful purposes, the reclamation and irrigation of its arid, semi-arid and other lands needing irrigation, the reclamation and drainage of its overflowed lands, and other lands needing drainage, the conservation and development of its forests, water and hydro-electric power, navigation of its inland and coastal waters, and the *preservation and conservation of all such natural resources* of the State are each and all hereby declared public rights and duties; and the Legislature shall pass all such laws as may be appropriate thereto.

Tex. Const. art. XVI, § 59(a) (emphasis added). The Conservation Amendment covers all natural resources, including both groundwater and surface water. The Texas Supreme Court in *Sipriano v. Great Spring Waters of America, Inc.*, 1 S.W.3d 75 (Tex. 1999), stated that the Conservation Amendment passed after *Houston & T.C. Ry. Co. v. East*, 81 S.W. 279 (Tex. 1904), the seminal groundwater law case in Texas, "made clear that in Texas, responsibility for the regulation of natural resources, including groundwater, rests in the hands of the Legislature" and are "public rights and duties." 1 S.W.3d at 77. As discussed in Chapter 5 of this book, the legislature has thus far chosen regulation through local groundwater conservation districts with respect to groundwater. With respect to surface water, the governmental entities to be created were conservation and reclamation districts with such powers concerning the subject matter of the amendment as conferred by law. *See* Tex. Const. art. XVI, § 59(b).

The Conservation Amendment is important in many respects. First, it declared that all water resources were public rights and duties. Second, it empowered the legislature to pass such laws "as may be appropriate" in the conservation, development, distribution, and control of its water resources. Third, it vested lawful rights acquired before its enactment while granting authority to the legislature to pass laws appropriate to protect the public's rights. This became the legal dividing line in the development of water laws: the legislature was empowered to pass laws subject only to the test of "appropriateness" in the context of the intent expressed in the Conservation Amendment.

This constitutional authority was not self-enacting but required action by the legislature. By its very terms, the duty is placed on the legislature to execute the public policy expressed in these provisions. *City of Corpus Christi v. City of Pleasanton*, 276 S.W.2d 798 (1955). The legislature promptly acted to legally confirm the 1917 Act and its provisions.

The 1918 Act: In 1918, after passage of the Conservation Amendment, the legislature amended the 1917 Act to confirm and clarify, among other things, the extent of the power of the Board of Water Engineers to issue permits and to adjudicate existing water rights and its authority pertaining to water rates charged by suppliers for the use of water. *See* Act approved Mar. 21, 1918, 35th Leg., 4th C.S., ch. 88. This Act is sometimes called the Canales Act, after its main legislative sponsor.

In 1921, however, the Supreme Court of Texas held that the adjudication provisions in the 1917 Act were unconstitutional because they delegated judicial powers to an administrative agency. *See Board of Water Engineers v. McKnight*, 229 S.W. 301 (Tex. 1921). This was a significant decision for two reasons. On the positive side, it recognized that a vested water right is a property right. On the negative side, it delayed the proper management of surface water for many decades by dismantling the effort to adjudicate and quantify existing water rights. In the words of Chief Justice Pope, that decision "ushered in a half century interregnum during which there was no inventory of available water and no record of the extent of claims upon the dwindling supply." *In re Adjudication of the Water Rights of Upper Guadalupe Segment of Guadalupe River Basin*, 642 S.W.2d 438, 441 (Tex. 1982). See discussion of the *McKnight* case at section 4.6:1 below.

The 1925 Act: In 1925, because of the *McKnight* decision, water legislation was passed that omitted the adjudication provisions of the 1917 and 1918 Acts and thereby repealed those provisions. Act approved Mar. 28, 1925, 39th Leg., R.S., ch. 136 (article 7500a of the Texas Civil Statues). This legislation also changed the domestic and livestock reservoir exemption and the provisions regarding water districts, which are discussed more fully below.

The Dual System and Conflicts in the Courts Continue: In 1926, the Texas Supreme Court, in *Motl v. Boyd*, 286 S.W. 458 (Tex. 1926), analyzed in depth the development of water law in Texas. Simply stated, this case was brought by a riparian claimant to irrigation rights seeking to pump water from a small reservoir built and developed by an appropriator under a filing made under the 1889 Act. The riparian claimant's application for a permit was denied by the Board of Water Engineers, but the riparian continued to pump water from the reservoir. The reservoir owner sued, seeking to enjoin the riparian from diverting water. Although this case was later reversed on other grounds dealing with the nature of the riparian right, it is still an instructive case with respect to the evolution of Texas water laws as construed by a court in 1926.

In this case, the appropriator contended that the riparian right on a natural or statutory navigable stream extended only to domestic stock and household uses, and rights for other uses, including irrigation, had to be obtained by statutory appropriation. The court was urged to declare that riparian rights do not exist on natural or statutory navigable streams. Thus, the continuation of the dual system of water rights under existing statutes was squarely before the court. After an extensive analysis of Mexican laws, laws of the Republic, and later legislative acts, the court concluded that a riparian owner had the right implied in the original grant of land—to use water "not only for his domestic and household use, but for irrigation as well." *Motl*, 286 S.W. at 467 (citing *Watkins Land Co. v. Clements*, 86 S.W. 733 (Tex. 1905); *McKnight*, 229 S.W. 301; *Martin v. Burr*, 228 S.W. 543 (Tex. 1921)).

Having held that a riparian right to irrigation existed, the court recognized that a riparian right attached only to the ordinary and normal flow of a stream, not to floodwaters. The court felt compelled to legally define the water to which a riparian is entitled. The court's opinion noted that—

> riparian waters are the waters of the ordinary flow and underflow of the stream, and that the waters of the stream, when they rise above the line of highest ordinary flow, are to be regarded as flood waters or waters to which riparian rights do not attach. . . . "The line of highest ordinary flow" is the highest line of flow which the stream reached and maintains for a sufficient length of time to become characteristic when its waters are in their ordinary, normal, and usual condition, uninfluenced by recent rainfall or surface run-off.

Motl, 286 S.W. at 468–69. In applying this legal definition of flows, the court affirmed the judgment enjoining the riparian from pumping from a reservoir, *except when water was running over the appropriator's dam.* This ruling had practical results: (1) it allowed the appropriator to take as much water as desired, whether the water was ordinary or flood flow; (2) it allowed the riparian to pump water only when the reservoir was full and overflowing; and (3) regardless of the amount of ordinary flow in the stream available to the riparian at a particular point in time, it could not be taken if the water was needed to fill the reservoir, even if the appropriator was pumping at the same time. Needless to say, confusion was created as courts attempted to apply the holding in other cases.

The court's decision that a riparian right to irrigation exists and the court's perpetuation of the dual system of water rights were the significant aspects of the holding. The court's definition of "ordinary flow and underflow" and "storm flow and flood flow," normally a matter of hydrology and science rather than law, caused much uncertainty. Though considered to be dicta, the court's definition was problematic in determining water rights claims and in planning reservoir projects, which were designed to capture stormwaters and flood waters for later use but as a practical matter also captured ordinary flows, and "conserve water."

The *Motl* court made another significant though often overlooked holding. In spite of the earlier similar attack on the adjudication provisions in the 1917 and 1918 Acts in *McKnight* involving the separation-of-powers doctrine, the *Motl* court concluded that the provisions providing for the issuance of permits to appropriate waters (granting a water right) were valid and constitutional even though it was done by an administrative agency (the executive branch) instead of directly by the legislature. *Motl*, 286 S.W. at 474–75.

Another illustrative case is *Humphreys-Mexia Co. v. Arseneaux*, 297 S.W. 225 (Tex. 1927). This suit sought to enjoin the defendants from pumping, drawing off, diverting, selling, or otherwise disposing of water from a certain reservoir made by a dam across the Navasota River constructed by the plaintiff. The defendants owned land riparian to the reservoir and claimed riparian rights to water impounded by the plaintiff's dam. The defendants installed a pump on the river to divert water from impounded water constructed by the plaintiff and sold it to oil well-drilling companies in the Mexia field. The defendants claimed the rights to divert this water by virtue of their riparian rights to the land adjoining the natural stream. On the other hand, the plaintiff had obtained a permit to impound waters from the river on the dams involved. The plaintiff contended that the defendants did not have the right under their riparian rights to divert water from the impounded water and deliver it to nonriparian land.

The court noted that the plaintiff's permit authorized it to impound only public waters of the state consisting of stormwaters and floodwaters of the Navasota River and expressly prohibited it from impounding any part of the normal flow of the Navasota River. The plaintiff also constructed other dams that backed up water onto the land of other riparian owners. The court, relying on cases recognizing riparian rights, trespass laws, statutory appropriation rights, and a very complicated set of facts, determined that the injunction to prohibit the diversion of waters from the water in the flood pool would be a continuous legal wrong and trespass without just compensation and therefore denied the injunction. This case illustrates the complicated nature of the construction of dams by an appropriator faced with competing claims of riparian water rights by those owning land adjacent to the reservoir or original natural stream and how a court sitting in equity must determine the appropriate result. The court, in essence, denied the rights of the appropriator while recognizing assertable claims by a riparian. The result did not provide guidance to water rights holders in the state.

These cases illustrate the difficulties encountered in the courts when individual water rights claimants sought court enforcement of their rights against other individual water rights holders without involving all others who may be impacted on the stream or a segment of the stream. These cases were often cited as declaring the existing water law after the 1913–1925 Acts, but frustration and confusion continued among water rights claimants in efforts to enforce and protect their claims in a practical sense. This was the situation even though the courts could use their equitable powers to resolve disputes. In the 1950s, the state experienced a drought of record that resulted in litigation on a large stream segment of the Rio Grande and led to clarification and future development of Texas water law.

§ 4.5 Riparian Rights Revisited and Court Adjudication

In the years following the legislation and litigation discussed above, questions about riparian rights and an adjudication of water rights performed by the court led to the realization that a statewide legislative solution to determining existing water rights throughout the state was needed. Two of the major cases are discussed below.

§ 4.5:1 *State v. Valmont Plantations*

The decision in *Motl v. Boyd*, 286 S.W. 458 (Tex. 1926), which recognized the common-law riparian right to irrigation, remained the law until 1962, when the court decided *State v. Valmont Plantations*, 346 S.W.2d 853 (Tex. App.—San Antonio 1961), *op. adopted*, 355 S.W.2d 502 (Tex. 1962). *Valmont* was a case between appropriators and common-law riparian rights claimants on the Rio Grande, which had been severed as a separate cause arising out of *State v. Hidalgo County Water Control & Improvement District No. 18*, 443 S.W.2d 728 (Tex. App.—Corpus Christi–Edinburg 1969, writ ref'd n.r.e.). This case involved all water rights claimants on the Rio Grande below Falcon Dam, downstream of Laredo, Texas, to the Gulf of Mexico.

The *Motl* decision had been followed by the courts, and many had relied on the existence of the riparian right to irrigation in making long-range business decisions. As noted by Chief Justice Murray in his *Valmont* dissent, *Motl v. Boyd* had been cited seventy-eight times by Texas courts since 1926, and "there can be no doubt that the bench and bar of this State accepted such law as settled, and followed it up to the present time." *Valmont*, 346 S.W.2d at 883. Nonetheless, the Texas Supreme Court, having squarely before it the issue of the existence of a common-law riparian right to irrigation under Spanish and Mexican law, and having considerably more evidence and information about Spanish and Mexican law than were available to the *Motl* court, determined the law differently.

In a thoroughly considered and exhaustive study of Spanish and Mexican law, the *Valmont* court concluded that—

> (1) rights under titles from Spain, Mexico and Tamaulipas are governed by the law of the sovereigns when the grants were made, (2) those sovereigns did not have a system of riparian irrigation rights based upon or similar to the common law right to irrigate, (3) the grants involved in this suit were not made with the implied intent or agreement that the right to irrigate was appurtenant to the lands, and (4) [referring to *Motl v. Boyd*] this issue has never before been presented to a Texas Court for decision and there is no stare decisis on the subject.

Valmont, 346 S.W.2d at 881–82. The *Valmont* case clarified the classes of water rights claims in the dual system of water rights as follows: (1) rights asserted under permits and certified filings, (2) common-law riparian rights pertaining to land granted by the Republic of Texas or the state between 1840 and July 1, 1895, and (3) riparian rights to irrigation under Spanish and Mexican land grants where the right of irrigation was expressly granted.

§ 4.5:2 *State v. Hidalgo County Water Control & Improvement District No. 18*

Another important case from which *Valmont* arose is *State v. Hidalgo County Water Control & Improvement District No. 18*, 443 S.W.2d 728 (Tex. App.—Corpus Christi–Edinburg 1969, writ ref'd n.r.e.), often referred to as the *Valley Water* case. *Valley Water* emphasized the need for more efficient water rights adjudication. *Valley Water* was an injunction case, similar to earlier cases seeking clarification of water rights. This was, however, the first court adjudication among *all* water rights claimants in an independent segment of a stream, that portion of the Lower Rio Grande downstream of Falcon Reservoir. It arose during the drought of the 1950s, involved roughly three thousand parties, all potentially adverse to one another, and cost an estimated $10 million in court costs and attorney's fees. *Administrative Government in Texas—Current Problems*, 47 Texas L. Rev. 804, 875 (1969).

The background of the case involved parties who were seeking a right to a limited supply of water. It involved years of litigation between individual parties making individual claims to water rights adverse to all other party claimants. *See Hidalgo & Cameron Counties Water Control & Improvement District No. 9 v. Starley*, 373 S.W.2d 731 (Tex. 1964); *Hidalgo County Water Improvement District No. 2 v. Blalock*, 301 S.W.2d 593 (Tex. 1957); *Maverick County Water Control & Improvement District No. 1 v. City of Laredo*, 346 S.W.2d 886 (Tex. App.—San Antonio 1961, writ ref'd n.r.e.); *Hidalgo County Water Improvement District No. 2 v. Cameron County Water Control & Improvement District No. 5*, 253 S.W.2d 294 (Tex. App.—San Antonio 1952, writ ref'd n.r.e.). In this case, a streamwide approach was taken by the state's filing an injunction action against all the water rights claimants to adjudicate all water rights in the river segment below and including Falcon Reservoir.

In *Valley Water*, the trial judge took judicial custody of the water in Falcon Reservoir and the Rio Grande segment below Falcon Reservoir, to which Texas is entitled under the 1944 Treaty with Mexico. *See* Treaty Respecting Utilization of Waters of the Colorado and Tijuana Rivers and of the Rio Grande, Mexico-U.S., Feb. 3, 1944, 59 Stat. 1219, T.S. No. 994. The trial judge appointed a watermaster to allocate the available water pursuant to court orders. Recognizing the contradictory and incompatible issues resulting from the dual system of water rights, initially the court severed the riparian water rights claims from the suit and tried them separately in the *Valmont* case discussed at section 4.5:1 above. After *Valmont* was resolved, the trial court in *Valley Water* focused on appropriative rights. The trial court ultimately addressed appropriative rights and other claims. Its judgment, as modified and affirmed on appeal, (1) set aside a water reserve for municipal, industrial, and domestic and livestock uses; and (2) recognized two classes of appropriative irrigation rights: first priority for legally established statutory claims under the appropriation system and a second priority framework for equitable claims. The latter category included riparians and others who had been using water in the good-faith mistaken belief that they had riparian rights. The court justified its rejection of time priorities by observing that the existing appropriative rights in the Lower Rio Grande were to divert from a free-flowing stream. However, the Lower Rio Grande had been transformed to a controlled stream by dams built by the federal government.

A significant lesson learned during the course of these proceedings was that without some mechanism to organize the case from an evidentiary perspective, through required maps and identification of parties and land, such an adjudication was impossible. The customary evidentiary presentation by each party on an individual basis was meaningless without evidence of the technical overview of the watershed involved. In this case, the attorney general and the Texas Water Commission brought together the necessary tools by which claims could be evaluated, organized, and ultimately adjudicated. Without this assistance, the adjudication would not have been possible. The lessons learned included the need for a constitutional administrative adjudication process, without which it would be extremely difficult, or almost impossible, to quantify and adjudicate all the water rights on all the streams. *See* Garland F. Smith, *The Valley Water Suit and Its Impact on Texas Water Policy: Some Practical Advice for the Future*, 8 Tex. Tech L. Rev. 577 (1977); Corwin W. Johnson, *Adjudication of Water Rights*, 42 Texas L. Rev. 121 (1963). This experience, coupled with earlier difficulty in the court cases dealing with disputes between water rights claimants and the need to quantify and define existing water rights, led to the passage of the 1967 Adjudication Act.

§ 4.6 Water Rights Adjudication Act of 1967

The Water Rights Adjudication Act of 1967 is the underpinning of modern-day surface water rights in Texas. The state, through legislation and court decisions, attempted to tackle the complex task of untangling the various historical rights in an effort to establish a statewide water rights system that would be flexible enough to reflect changes to those rights in the future. An understanding of the background of this statute is necessary to comprehend its continuing influence today.

§ 4.6:1 Background of the Adjudication Act

To understand the impact of the Adjudication Act, one must consider the history of adjudication of water rights in Texas. The source of the Adjudication Act began with the Irrigation Act of 1917, which contained adjudication provisions that were patterned after the then-existing Wyoming system of adjudication of statutory surface water rights. Implementation of these adjudication provisions, however, was thwarted in 1921 when the Texas Supreme Court held, as discussed at section 4.4:4 above, that this statutory procedure was unconstitutional under separation-of-powers principles. *Board of Water Engineers v. McKnight*, 229 S.W. 301 (Tex. 1921).

The *McKnight* case arose from a petition filed under the 1917 Act with the Board of Water Engineers by a riparian water rights claimant alleging that he was entitled to receive water from the Pecos River from a canal company that claimed rights by appropriation. The hearing in the case was held while there was a pending suit in federal court seeking to adjudicate water rights on the Pecos involving the *McKnight* parties and other parties. Also pending at the time was another suit in district court in Reeves County by Ward County District No. 1 against the Farmers Independent Canal Company to determine the relative rights of claimants to waters of the Pecos. *See McKnight v. Pecos & Torah Lake Irrigation Co.*, 207 S.W. 599 (Tex. App.—El Paso 1918), *aff'd*, 301 S.W. 299 (Tex. 1921).

In *Board of Water Engineers v. McKnight*, the plaintiff sought an injunction, contending that sections 105–32 of the 1917 Act were unconstitutional. The trial court denied the injunction, but on appeal the injunction was granted, then affirmed by the supreme court. The supreme court found that the legislature had unconstitutionally undertaken to empower the Board of Water Engineers with judicial power to adjudicate vested water rights, except for domestic and livestock water. This power gave the same effect to the board's determination, when not appealed, as is given to a judgment of a court of competent jurisdiction, thereby violating the constitution's separation-of-powers doctrine.

The *McKnight* court did not mention or discuss the 1917 Conservation Amendment, which, in the meantime, was approved by Texas voters because the underlying adjudication proceeding was commenced before adoption of the amendment. Significantly, this constitutional amendment gave the legislature control over the development and conservation of water resources and the production of oil and gas. Later, in *Corzelius v. Harrell*, 186 S.W.2d 961 (Tex. 1945), the court recognized that the *McKnight* decision construed only the adjudication provisions of the 1917 Act, which were effective June 19, 1917. If the *McKnight* court had considered the Conservation Amendment, which applied to all natural resources of the state and made them "public rights and duties" and directed that "the Legislature shall pass all such laws as may be appropriate thereto," the decision might have been different. In *Corzelius*, the court upheld the Texas Railroad Commission's regulatory power to control drilling of oil and gas wells. In holding that the Conservation Amendment supported the legislative grant of such power to an administrative agency, the court held that the *McKnight* case was not controlling and that the separation-of-powers ruling in *McKnight* to such extent was overruled.

The *McKnight* decision undermined the authority of the Board of Water Engineers and thwarted the orderly development of the state's surface water resources, creating a desert in surface water law for some forty years. From 1921 to 1945 the board ceased to function in the role of quantifying and managing surface water rights. The Texas Supreme Court later observed that water law in Texas before 1967 "was in a chaotic state." *In re Adjudication of the Water Rights of Upper Guadalupe Segment of Guadalupe River Basin*, 642 S.W.2d 438, 439 (Tex. 1982).

While the *Valley Water* case was in progress (see section 4.5:2 above), a former attorney general and governor of Texas, sitting as a federal district judge, commented:

> [T]he Texas water laws and decisions are in hopeless confusion; . . . their application and administration would be difficult . . . ; said laws confer little, if any, real authority upon the State Board of Engineers; that the Board has granted permits on many streams . . . very few of which have been canceled, in such numbers and for such quantities that if riparian rights are given the full effect for which plaintiffs contend, practically every drop of water, normal flow, or flood, is "bespoken."

Martinez v. Maverick County Water Control & Improvement District No. 1, 219 F.2d 666, 670 (5th Cir. 1955) (quoting Judge James V. Allred's memorandum opinion from the district court). *See generally* A.A. White & Will Wilson, *The Flow and Underflow of Motl v. Boyd—The Problem*, 9 Sw. L.J. 1 (1955); *The Flow and Underflow of Motl v. Boyd—The Conclusion*, 9 Sw. L.J. 377 (1955).

Following the 1950s drought of record, the legislature again tried to delegate to the Board of Water Engineers the power to adjudicate water rights. *See* Stahle & Cleaveland, at 66. In 1953, while the *Valley Water* case was in process, article 7477 of the Texas Civil Statutes was amended. *See* Act approved June 8, 1953, 53d Leg., R.S., ch. 357, §§ 12, 13. Under article 7477, the board's determinations of water rights would not be final. Such findings could be appealed de novo, and the court could modify them. The legislature was trying to circumvent the *McKnight* ruling, which held that under the 1917 Act, because the board's findings on water rights claims were final with no right to appeal, the findings violated the separation-of-powers doctrine.

Article 7477 was, however, subsequently invalidated by the Texas Supreme Court in *Southern Canal Co. v. Texas Board of Water Engineers*, 318 S.W.2d 619 (Tex. 1958). In *Southern Canal*, the court found that the 1953 Act required application of two different but irreconcilable standards of review—that is, the preponderance of evidence standard of review in a trial de novo appeal as opposed to the substantial evidence standard of review, which is applicable to decisions by the board and other agencies of the state on appeal to the courts. Again, the legislature's attempt to quantify and evaluate water rights was frustrated.

In 1964, the Texas Water Commission requested that the Texas Research League conduct a study of the operation of the Board of Water Engineers and recommend changes to more effectively secure development of the state's water resources. Volume II of the League's study was published February 17, 1965, and dealt with water rights and water resource administration in Texas. This report was a scholarly dissertation on the problem and concluded that a water adjudication act was necessary.

A water rights adjudication bill was introduced in 1965 consistent with the Texas Research League study. It followed the Wyoming adjudication model, with appeal from the agency's determination under the substantial evidence rule. It was amended to provide for strict trial de novo appeal, but failed to pass. In 1966, interested water rights groups debated alternatives: (1) a special water court, (2) the Oregon-type approach mentioned in the *McKnight* case, and (3) the Wyoming-type adjudication act. A modified Oregon-type water rights adjudication bill was finally agreed on containing provisions for automatic appeal to court on a trial de novo basis. It was enacted by the 60th Texas Legislature and signed by Governor Connelly on April 13, 1967. *See* Act approved Apr. 13, 1967, 60th Leg., R.S., ch. 45; *see also In re Adjudication of the Water Rights of Upper Guadalupe Segment of Guadalupe River Basin*, 642 S.W.2d at 445.

§ 4.6:2 Water Rights Adjudication Act

The Water Rights Adjudication Act, codified at Texas Water Code chapter 11, subchapter G, established a statewide process. All water rights claimants, except domestic and livestock claimants (whether statutory claimants or riparian claimants), were required to file sworn claims by September 1, 1969. *See* Tex. Water Code § 11.303(c). Certain riparian claimants were required to file by July 1, 1971. *See* Tex. Water Code § 11.303(e). Nonstatutory claims were limited to maximum beneficial use between 1963 and 1967. *See* Tex. Water Code § 11.303(b). The Act did not recognize any water rights claim that did not exist before August 28, 1967, and expressly excluded claims for domestic or livestock uses. Tex. Water Code § 11.303(k), (*l*).

The Act addressed the dual system of water rights and was an improvement over previous legislation, which addressed only statutory rights. Under this new process, when a claim was filed, the then Texas Water Commission staff completed an investigative report cataloging and describing all claims previously filed. These claims were mapped by aerial photography of the river segment and surrounding areas, and all claims of water users on the segment were located on the map. When the commission completed its investigation of a stream or segment, there was notice, hearings were held, and a preliminary determination issued. The Act established the procedure for contests and exceptions to the preliminary determination, resulting in a final determination. The Act allowed for a proper initial adjudication and a narrowing of the issues by administrative determination for later court decisions only on those issues, as identified by the parties during the adjudication process. This administrative process eliminated the previous chaotic judicial process of adjudication. The final determination was automatically filed in district court, where it was considered de novo on issues defined during the administrative process and presented to the court. *See* Doug Caroom & Paul Elliott, *Water Rights Adjudication—Texas Style*, 44 Tex. B.J. 1183 (1981).

The first adjudication under the Act concerned the middle segment of the Rio Grande between Falcon Reservoir and Amistad Reservoir immediately upstream from the court-adjudicated rights in the *Valley Water* case. At the beginning, the commissioners heard these adjudication cases themselves, but because of the overwhelming tasks involved, later the cases were assigned to TWC hearing officers. The commission next conducted the Upper Rio Grande adjudication for the segment above Amistad Reservoir and below Fort Quitman, Texas, and continued by adjudicating all Texas rivers. The adjudication process was completed in 2007 with the adjudication of the Upper Rio Grande segment above Fort Quitman to the state line. *See In re Adjudication of Water Rights in the Upper Rio Grande Segment of the Rio Grande Basin*, No. 2006-3219 (327th Dist. Ct., El Paso, Tex. Oct. 30, 2006).

Upon completion of each adjudication case, which was marked by court judgment or decree, the commission issued certificates of adjudication to all parties who were adjudicated a water right in the proceedings. The certificate is required to quantify the basic extent of the right and any other findings made in the adjudication case. *See* Tex. Water Code § 11.323. A certificate evidences an existing water right in the stream segment that is adjudicated. Permits issued subsequent to an adjudication on a stream segment are now simply added to the records as a water right and are subject to the same regulation as adjudicated rights. *See* Tex. Water Code § 11.336. See Chapter 10 of this book.

§ 4.6:3 Watermasters

A significant component of the Water Rights Adjudication Act was that once rights were adjudicated, they would be enforced by a watermaster. Establishment of the watermaster program was intended to assure those holding adjudicated water rights that their rights would be enforced and protected. The watermaster concept of enforcement derived from the experiences in the *Valley Water* case (see section 4.5:2 above), wherein the court initially took judicial custody of the water in the Lower Rio Grande and appointed a watermaster to allocate and manage the distribution of the available water pursuant to court orders subject to final adjudication of the rights. This system made its way into the Adjudication Act at sections 11.325–.333, which empowered the commission, once rights were adjudicated, to appoint a watermaster to oversee water use using the regulatory tools authorized by statute.

The watermaster provisions have not been implemented statewide as provided by the Act. There is a watermaster program on the Rio Grande, implemented initially by the court in the *Valley Water* case and later by the commission in the Middle and Upper Rio Grande adjudications. The South Texas

Watermaster Program, implemented in the adjudication process, originally covered the Colorado, Guadalupe, San Antonio, and Nueces rivers. Later, the Lavaca and Navidad rivers were added by a commission order based on a petition of water rights holders on those rivers. The program was extended to the Concho Watershed pursuant to petitions filed under Texas Water Code chapter 11, subchapter I, and by legislation in 2005, adding sections 11.551–.560 to the Water Code, which established the Concho River Watermaster Program. *See* Act of May 25, 2005, 79th Leg., R.S., ch. 749; *see also City of San Angelo v. Texas Commission on Environmental Quality*, Cause No. GV4-03796 (53d Dist. Ct., Travis County, Tex. 2005); *City of San Angelo v. Texas Natural Resource Conservation Commission*, 92 S.W.3d 624 (Tex. App.—Austin 2002, no pet.).

There is a watermaster on the Lower Brazos River Basin pursuant to an April 21, 2014, commission order, which granted a petition for a watermaster there. *See* Order Granting the Petition for the Appointment of a Watermaster in the Brazos River Basin Filed by the Brazos River Coalition, TCEQ Docket No. 2013-0174-WR; SOAH Docket No. 582-13-3040 (Apr. 21, 2014).

The 82nd Legislature in 2011 addressed the potential role of watermasters in managing water rights in other river basins in the state and passed legislation amending the Adjudication Act by adding section 11.326(g), (h) to the Water Code. This provision requires, in river basins in which no watermaster has been appointed, that the executive director of the Texas Commission on Environmental Quality evaluate each river basin at least once every five years to determine whether a watermaster should be appointed, and these findings and recommendations shall be included in the commission's biennial report to the legislature. *See* Tex. Water Code § 11.326(g), (h). See Chapter 13 of this book for further discussion of watermasters.

§ 4.6:4 Cases Decided in the Adjudication Process

Most adjudication cases were resolved at the district court level and were not appealed. This shows that many complex water rights issues were resolved to the satisfaction of the claimants on a stream or segment of a stream at either the agency or district court level. However, there are a few decisions of note.

Extent of Riparian Rights: The first case under the Adjudication Act to reach the appellate courts was *In re Adjudication of Water Rights of Cibolo Creek Watershed of San Antonio River Basin*, 568 S.W.2d 155 (Tex. App.—San Antonio 1978, no writ). One water rights claimant on the Cibolo Creek, who had been recognized a right based on prescription and equity on one tract of land but denied a right on another tract, challenged the district court's decision. The appellant asserted a riparian right to the land under Spanish and successor land grant or equitable rights. He further claimed that the Adjudication Act was unconstitutional. The appellate court, citing the *Valmont* case (see section 4.5:1 above), held that the claimant did not have a riparian right because his riparian land grant did not specifically grant riparian irrigation rights. This is the first case that applied *Valmont* to a river other than the Rio Grande. The court also held that the claimant did not possess an equitable right under the *Valley Water* case (see section 4.5:2) because the unique circumstances applicable in *Valley Water* did not exist in this case. Finally, the court held that because the claimant had no vested property right, he did not have standing to raise the constitutionality of the Adjudication Act.

Four years later, the Texas Supreme Court in *In re Adjudication of Water Rights in the Llano River Watershed of Colorado River Basin*, 642 S.W.2d 446 (Tex. 1982), affirmed that riparian rights to irrigation cannot be claimed on lands granted by the state after July 1, 1895, the effective date of the Irrigation Act of 1895, in which the state reserved the ordinary flow of water in streams. The court noted:

> The act stated that the ordinary or underflow of a river or stream, as well as the storm or rain waters were the property of the public and were subject to appropriation for irrigation pur-

poses. The manner of acquiring water rights after that date was by appropriation and not by force of the riparian location of the land.

642 S.W.2d at 448. This holding finally confirmed the legislature's intent in the 1895 Act and subsequent statutes to limit riparian claims to grants or patents issued before 1895.

Subsequently, in *In re Adjudication of the Water Rights in the Medina River Watershed of the San Antonio River Basin*, 670 S.W.2d 250 (Tex. 1984), the Texas Supreme Court affirmed the commission's holding that a riparian was restricted to use during the 1963–67 period and the extended period provided in the Adjudication Act. After an extensive discussion of the *Valmont* case, court decisions since then, and Spanish and Mexican law, the court held that a riparian claimant under an 1833 Mexican grant did not own all of the waters of Medio Creek (tributary to the Medina River) and could be adjudicated only the amount of water shown to have been used during the statutory period.

Later, in *In re Adjudication of Water Rights of Lower Guadalupe River Segment*, 730 S.W.2d 64 (Tex. App.—Corpus Christi–Edinburg 1987, writ ref'd n.r.e.), the issue involved whether the water in a natural lake was public or private water. The court held that the water in the lake was public water based on the definition of the "state's water" contained in the Texas statutes beginning with the 1889 Act and statutes existing at the time the claimant acquired the land.

Merger of Riparian and Appropriative Rights: As noted at section 4.6:2 above, the purpose of the Adjudication Act was to unify the previous dual system of surface water law and to inventory and quantify the basic extent and amount of existing water rights. To quantify surface water law, the Act provided that riparian rights, other than for domestic and livestock use, be limited in amount of authorized use to historical beneficial use, and for water rights administration purposes, the commission additionally determined that merger of these riparian rights into appropriative rights was necessary to unify surface water law. Therefore, not long after the decision in the *Cibolo Creek* case, discussed above, the commission declared that the assignment of time priorities to proven riparian rights was essential to a workable scheme of proper state water rights management, and priority dates were assigned to riparian rights proved in the adjudication and included in certificates of adjudication. *See Final Determination before the Texas Water Commission in the matter of the Middle Colorado River Segment of the Colorado River Basin* (1981) (approved at the district court level).

Adjudication Act Constitutional: *In re Adjudication of the Water Rights of Upper Guadalupe Segment of Guadalupe River Basin*, 642 S.W.2d 438 (Tex. 1982), was the pivotal case that confirmed the constitutionality of the Adjudication Act. The court held that the Act did not violate the doctrine of separation of powers because the administrative determination was subject to automatic appeal and trial de novo. It further determined that riparian water rights claimants could be restricted to a defined water right based on use during a test period. Such restriction did not constitute a taking of property without just compensation because the claimants received due-process notice and hearing and there was an automatic appeal of the administrative determination and trial de novo.

Equitable and Pueblo Water Rights: The appeal in *In re Contests of the City of Laredo, to the Adjudication of Water Rights in the Middle Rio Grande Basin & Contributing Tributaries*, 675 S.W.2d 257 (Tex. App.—Austin 1984, writ ref'd n.r.e.), considered the commission decision that the equitable water rights concept adopted in the *Valley Water* case extended to rights in the Middle Rio Grande because of the unique circumstances on the Rio Grande. The court recognized that the commission lacked the equitable powers of a court to recognize an equitable right; nevertheless, on review of the commission's finding of equitable water rights on the Rio Grande it affirmed the commission's finding that the right should be recognized elsewhere in this segment of the river. The court reviewed the laws of Spain and Mexico and court decisions in California and held that the law of New Spain did not expressly create a municipal water right in the nature of a pueblo water right on the Rio Grande.

Appropriative Rights Issues: In adjudicating the basic extent and amount of an existing appropriative right, such as a certified filing or permit, the commission in its determination, and the court in considering the determination, did not make findings regarding all of the terms and conditions of a permit or certified filing. In such cases, the commission observed in a final determination that—

> the most significant terms and conditions stated in permits or amended certified filings are specifically included in the findings and/or conclusions for each rights. However, all of the terms and conditions stated in permits or amended certified filings shall continue in full force and effect, except for obsolete, irrelevant or immaterial terms and conditions which will be deleted from certificates of adjudication when they are issued.

Final Determination of All Claims of Water Rights in the Brazos III Segment of the Brazos River Basin 5 (1985) (see also para. II, pg. 11, of the *Final Determination*, regarding merger of riparian rights with appropriative rights). The final determination was affirmed in *In re Adjudication of Water Rights of the Brazos III Segment of the Brazos River Basin*, 746 S.W.2d 207 (Tex. 1988).

In *In re Contests of City of Eagle Pass, to the Adjudication of Water Rights in Middle Rio Grande Basin & Contributing Texas Tributaries*, 680 S.W.2d 853 (Tex. App.—Austin 1984, writ ref'd n.r.e.), the court affirmed the commission's adjudication involving the volume of water to which an appropriative claim is entitled. In this case, the city sought an amount of water equivalent to a water duty requirement per acre, taking into account future use and needs. The commission allowed the amount of water perfected by the city's actual maximum use before August 1967. The court applied the rules of the appropriation doctrine, which measures the extent of the right as the maximum amount beneficially used, after reasonable development, pursuant to the appropriative claim before 1967. This, the court held, is the measure of a perfected right under the prior appropriation doctrine. The effect of the court's holding restricted the water right to past beneficial use without provision for future growth and needs.

The *City of Eagle Pass* case was the only adjudication case that reached the appellate courts pertaining to basic issues involved in appropriative rights claims. All others dealt with riparian rights issues and the constitutionality of the Act in relation to riparian rights. Other than those in the *City of Eagle Pass* case, all claimants to appropriative rights were satisfied with either the commission's determination or a district court judgment. This shows that a goal of the Adjudication Act was successful: it reached an amicable resolution to many complex issues that earlier courts found difficult to resolve in a judicial setting. The Act served its purpose of establishing a statutory process that met due-process and separation-of-powers requirements to finally adjudicate existing water rights.

§ 4.6:5 Goals of the Adjudication Act

The goals of the Adjudication Act were to quantify and inventory all water rights, which were necessary for the management of water resources. Under the Act, the adjudication process assigned an acre-foot limitation and a priority date to all water rights and identified the ownership, location of diversion on the stream, diversion rate, and other details so that all water rights could be quantified and identified. The Act included both statutory and nonstatutory claims, with certain exceptions. The goals were accomplished by requiring the filing of claims and providing proof of use during the periods provided in the Act.

The Act did much more than establish a procedure for adjudication of claims. It also had the effect of limiting riparian rights, which were previously unquantified and traditionally considered not to be dependent on use, to the maximum demonstrated beneficial use during a prescribed period before the effective date of the Act. *See* Tex. Water Code § 11.303. Thus, the Act transformed riparian rights from a right to make an unquantified, reasonable use of water into a right to make a beneficial use of a specified quantity of water with a first-use priority date. The Act transformed the existing chaotic dual system of water rights to a more manageable single statutory rights system, with some exceptions discussed below and in Chapters 10 and 27 of this book. In this respect, the Act accomplished its goals.

§ 4.7 Adjudication Act: Special Issues

The Adjudication Act and the subsequent adjudication were not cure-alls. They resolved many problems caused by the dual system of water rights and paved the way for better water management, but they left some issues unaddressed. This section discusses selected statutory exemptions from the appropriation process, irrigation canal rights, the Wagstaff Act, and termination of water rights. Some of these topics have only historical significance, whereas others continue to be litigated.

§ 4.7:1 Domestic and Livestock Use

The Adjudication Act specifically excluded the adjudication of domestic and livestock use claims. Study of the historical background with specific attention to domestic and livestock use is necessary to understand the nature of these claims. As summarized below, the right to use water for domestic and livestock purposes on land that abuts a stream developed separately from the same right for other uses on land that abuts a stream and uses on land that does not abut a stream.

Spanish and Mexican Law Influence: Early Spanish and Mexican law generally provided for water use for domestic and livestock purposes in the ditch or acequias systems. Under the laws of Spain, certain common water uses did not require a grant from the sovereign. Waters in the Rio Grande could be used by all for "drinking by men and animals; as a highway, for the navigation of boats and sailing ships; for fishing; and for domestic necessities." *State v. Valmont Plantations*, 346 S.W.2d 853, 854 n.1 (Tex. App.—San Antonio 1961), *op. adopted*, 355 S.W.2d 502 (Tex. 1962). "[T]he waters of navigable rivers" could be used by all "persons in common." 346 S.W.2d at 857. Common uses included navigation, mooring of boats, making repairs on ships or sails, landing merchandise, fishing, and drying of nets. 346 S.W.2d at 857. All waters of public rivers were for public and common use, and anyone could use the water for domestic purposes. 346 S.W.2d at 860–61 (citing with approval the Spanish commentator Lasso de la Vega); *see also In re Adjudication of the Water Rights in the Medina River Watershed of the San Antonio River Basin*, 670 S.W.2d 250, 254 (Tex. 1984) (a grant from the sovereign was not "needed to take water even from a public stream for domestic or personal use," citing Lasso de la Vega, *Reglamento General De Las Medidas de Aguas*, *reprinted in* M. Galvan, *Ordenanzas de Tierras y Aguas* 155–57 (1844)).

Statutory and Common-Law Background of Domestic and Livestock Use Claims: The Irrigation Act of 1889 did not mention domestic and livestock use except to the extent that an appropriator of water "shall first make available his said land for agricultural or grazing purposes, and shall provide cisterns, wells, or storage reservoirs for water for domestic purposes." *See* Act approved Mar. 19, 1889, 21st Leg., R.S., ch. 88, § 10, 1889 Tex. Gen. Laws 100, 101–02, *reprinted in* 9 H.P.N. Gammel, *The Laws of Texas 1822–1897*, at 1128–30. This reference to domestic and livestock use is in the context of the prior appropriation doctrine and meant that the appropriator was to make water available for domestic use within the appropriator's water delivery system. The intent was to provide domestic water incident to the irrigation enterprise, which in the late 1800s and early 1900s most often included water for surrounding towns, villages, and cities.

The Irrigation Act of 1895 went further by protecting domestic drinking and livestock water use from any right acquired by an appropriation of surface water, by providing:

> Whenever any person, corporation or association of persons shall become entitled to the use of any water of any river, stream, canyon, or ravine, or the storm or rain water hereinbefore described, it shall be unlawful for any person, corporation or association of persons to appropriate or divert any such water in any way, *except that the owner whose land abuts on a running stream may use such water therefrom as may be necessary for drinking purposes for himself, family and employes* [sic], *and for drinking purposes for his and their livestock* . . . .

See Act of Mar. 9, 1895, 24th Leg., R.S., ch. 21, § 10, 1895 Tex. Gen. Laws 21, 23, *reprinted in* 10 H.P.N. Gammel, *The Laws of Texas 1822–1897*, at 751, 753 (emphasis added). This was the first legislative declaration of the rights of domestic and livestock users to surface water. Interestingly, it is stated in terms of an exception or exemption from the statute's enforcement of a lawful appropriator's rights to take water from the stream. It is a limited exemption; it applies only to those who own land that abuts a stream, the landowner's family and employees, and the landowner's livestock, and it restricts the use of water to these purposes only.

During this early period, development of the law controlling domestic and livestock use was likely influenced by how this right was recognized in arid regions in the western United States. As stated in a well-recognized 1912 water law treatise—

> In all the Western States water may be appropriated for domestic purposes. This use may be defined as a use similar to that which a riparian owner has, under the common law, to take water for himself, his family, or his stock, and the like. (Citing *Crawford v. Hathaway* (Hall), 67 Neb. 325, 93 N.W. Rep. 781, *Montrose Canal Co. v. Loutsen Leizer D. Co.*, 23 Colo. 223, 48 Pac. Rep. 53, where the Nebraska court held that the appropriation by a company of a large portion of the waters of a stream, for the purposes of supplying water to a municipality for general use, including sprinkling the streets, providing power for a light plant, for flushing sewers, is not a domestic use. This is consistent with current Texas water law requiring a municipality to acquire an appropriative right.) The right is based, however, upon the same differences, compared to the right under the common law, as are the other rights which may be acquired to the use of water under the common law and under the Arid Region Doctrine of appropriation. The first is based upon the ownership of the soil through which or adjoining which the stream flows, as an incident thereto, while the second is by virtue of an appropriation for that purpose under the doctrine of appropriation, and without regard to ownership on the stream. Even without statutory regulations, the right to appropriate water for domestic purposes is not without its limitations. The water must be used in a reasonable manner and no more can be appropriated for a purpose, even where it is prior, than will reasonably meet the demands. It is such a use as ordinarily involves but little interference with the water of a stream or its flow, and does not contemplate the diversion of large quantities of water in canals or pipe lines.

Clesson S. Kinney, *The Law of Irrigation and Water Rights* § 692 (2d ed. 1912) [hereinafter Kinney].

In speaking of domestic and livestock use, the law also makes a distinction between natural and artificial use. Natural uses are uses necessary to sustain life, as opposed to artificial uses, which do not depend on necessities but bear on the question of business, profit, pleasure, or comfort. Domestic and livestock use was given preference over artificial uses, whether from appropriative or riparian rights. This preference was based on a reasonable use rule, taking into consideration the nature and extent of the use and all the other facts surrounding the particular use involved. *See* Kinney, § 487. Many of these concepts found their way into Texas water law.

The 1925 Act authorized the appropriation of waters of the state for "[p]ublic parks, game preserves, recreation and pleasure resorts, power and water supply for industrial purposes and plants and *for domestic use*." Act approved Mar. 28, 1925, 39th Leg., R.S., ch. 136, § 1 (emphasis added).

This provision was derived from the 1913 Act and the 1917 and 1918 Acts, which later became article 7470 of the Texas Civil Statutes. These provisions allow for a permit or certified filing to appropriate water for domestic use on land that does not abut a stream and for artificial uses. These provisions have continued through codification in 1971, when they became section 5.001 and now section 11.001 of the Texas Water Code. The statutes provide for the appropriation of water for domestic use in cases in which the use of water for domestic and livestock use is not on land that abuts a stream and give natural uses the first priority in the case of competing applications for a permit.

The Texas Commission on Environmental Quality rules defined domestic and livestock use in various versions both before and after the Adjudication Act. This is notable because domestic and livestock use was excepted from adjudication. The earlier rules defined domestic and livestock use as it was traditionally understood as limited to household use and use by domestic animals, which seemingly applies to the Adjudication Act exclusion. Current rules have divided the definition of domestic use from that of livestock use consistent with statutory changes dealing with statutory permit exemptions. See discussion below. The current rules define domestic use as—

> Use of water by an individual or a household to support domestic activity. Such use may include water for drinking, washing, or culinary purposes; for irrigation of lawns, or of a family garden and/or orchard; for watering of domestic animals; and for water recreation including aquatic and wildlife enjoyment. If the water is diverted, it must be diverted solely through the efforts of the user. Domestic use does not include water used to support activities for which consideration is given or received or for which the product of the activity is sold.

30 Tex. Admin. Code § 297.1(19). Note that the first part of this definition includes the early common-law and statutory traditional definition of the domestic and livestock use, where livestock use is limited to domestic livestock and does not refer to location of use on land that abuts a stream.

The rules currently define livestock use separate from domestic livestock use as—

> The use of water for the open-range watering of livestock, exotic livestock, game animals or fur-bearing animals. For purposes of this definition, the terms livestock and exotic livestock are to be used as defined in Texas Agriculture Code, § 142.001, and the terms game animals and fur-bearing animals are to be used as defined in Texas Parks and Wildlife Code, § 63.001 and § 71.001, respectively.

30 Tex. Admin. Code § 297.1(29).

Section 297.21(a) of the rules provides that a person who owns land adjacent to a stream may directly divert and use water from the stream for domestic and livestock use without having to obtain a permit. The riparian domestic and livestock right is a vested right that predates the prior appropriation system and that is superior to appropriative rights, but it applies only to the normal flow in a stream and not to flood flows or releases from storage for downstream use. *See* 30 Tex. Admin. Code § 297.21(a). Also, section 304.21(c)(3) allows a watermaster to protect domestic and livestock uses in times of low flows. *See* 30 Tex. Admin. Code § 304.21(c)(3). These provisions deal with domestic and livestock use consistent with prior law. Additionally, permits issued after the 1913 Act are generally made subject to superior rights, and some have equated this to the exempted domestic and livestock rights on property that abuts a stream.

Domestic and Livestock Rights—Summary: The common law, state statutory law, and early Spanish and Mexican law recognize a common-to-all right, excluded from the appropriation and permitting system, to take water from a stream that abuts one's property for one's own domestic use and livestock use.

Use of water for domestic and livestock purposes on land that does not abut a stream may be appropriated from the stream pursuant to the appropriation and permitting system unless exempted by statute. See discussion below with respect to domestic and livestock reservoirs. As applied to individual fact situations, questions remain about the application of the law related to domestic and livestock use that are yet to be determined. See Chapter 27 of this book for additional discussion.

§ 4.7:2 Domestic and Livestock Reservoirs

The Adjudication Act does not cover other exempted statutory claims, such as certain reservoirs, including domestic and livestock reservoirs. This section summarizes the development of this statutory exemption.

The first clear recognition of a statutory water right outside the appropriation law requirements was a landowner's right to construct a dam and impound water on the landowner's land for a limited use of the water impounded, whether riparian or not. It was first recognized in the Irrigation Act of 1895 as an exception to the appropriation system:

> [E]xcept that the owner whose land abuts on a running stream may use such water therefrom as may be necessary for drinking purposes for himself, family and employes [sic], and for drinking purposes for his and their livestock, *and* any one whose land may be located within the area of the watershed from which the storm or rain waters are collected may construct on his land such dams, reservoirs or lakes as may be necessary for the storage of water *for drinking purposes for such owner of land, his family and employes* [sic], *and for his and their livestock* . . . .

Act of Mar. 9, 1895, 24th Leg., R.S., ch. 21, § 10, 1895 Tex. Gen. Laws 21, 23, *reprinted in* 10 H.P.N. Gammel, *The Laws of Texas 1822–1897*, at 751, 753 (emphasis added). This law recognized the common-law domestic and livestock use and exemption discussed at section 4.7:1 above and further authorized a reservoir with limited use on the landowner's land. The reservoir's use was limited to the landowner's and the landowner's livestock drinking purposes.

This provision was repealed by the 1913 Irrigation Act, but a similar right was established in the Irrigation Act of 1917. Again, the right was authorized by exemptive language. The 1917 Act included a volume of water limitation but no reference to the nature of use of the water:

> [P]rovided, however, that nothing in this Section or in this Act shall affect or restrict the right of any person or persons, owning land in this State to construct on his own property any dam or reservoir which would impound or contain less than *five hundred acre-feet of water.*

Act of Mar. 19, 1917, 35th Leg., R.S., ch. 88, § 16 (article 7496 of the Texas Civil Statutes) (emphasis added). Thus, the initial reservoir exemption in 1895 was for domestic and livestock use. It was repealed in 1913. For four years, the exemptive right did not exist. When reintroduced in 1917, it did *not* mention the purposes of use; instead, the exemption allowed a reservoir capacity of five hundred acre-feet.

In 1925, the exemption became an affirmative authorization but with a smaller volume limitation and limited purposes as follows: "Any one may construct on his own property a dam and reservoir to impound or contain not to exceed two hundred and fifty acre-feet of water for domestic and livestock purposes without the necessity of securing a permit therefor." Act approved Mar. 28, 1925, 39th Leg., R.S., ch. 136, § 5 (article 7500a of the Texas Civil Statues). The attorney general ruled the 1925 Act unconstitutional, so the nature and extent of this exemption were clouded until it was reenacted by the legislature in 1941, using the following language: "Anyone may construct on his own property a dam and reservoir to impound or contain not to exceed fifty (50) acre-feet of water for domestic and livestock purposes without the necessity of securing a permit therefor." Act of Mar. 14, 1941, 47th Leg., R.S., ch. 37, § 1.

In *City of Anson v. Arnett*, 250 S.W.2d 450 (Tex. App.—Eastland 1952, writ ref'd n.r.e.), the court was faced with interpreting these different statutes pertaining to reservoirs. A landowner constructed a dam on an unnamed watershed in 1934 and 1935 to impound one hundred acre-feet of water. Over time, the dam had fallen into disrepair and periodically could hold only fifty acre-feet. In 1951, the dam was repaired to impound about ninety acre-feet. The city sued to enjoin the landowner from pumping more than fifty acre-feet of water from the reservoir behind the dam for livestock and domestic use. The city argued that the 1925 Act was void, apparently based on the attorney general's opinion, and that any rights of the landowner before passage of the 1941 Act must be governed by article 7496, enacted in 1917.

The court did not rule on the validity of the 1925 Act because, in the court's opinion, the amount of water impounded made such a determination unnecessary. The court summarized the city's argument as follows:

> [U]nder either the 1917 Act or the Act of 1925, the only right given to a land owner was the right to construct on his land, without a permit, a dam or reservoir of the size indicated by the statute but that neither of such Acts gave him the right to use the water impounded without a permit.

City of Anson, 250 S.W.2d at 452. The court rejected this argument, saying:

> Although dams may be built without the intent to use the water impounded, such as those constructed for the purpose of flood control, it is our opinion that the usual purpose for which a land owner builds a dam of the type under consideration is to use the water. The costs of the construction of such a dam would be a needless expense to the land owner unless he could use the water impounded.

City of Anson, 250 S.W.2d at 452–53. Regardless of which statute controlled, article 7496 (enacted in 1917) or article 7500a (enacted in 1925), the capacity of the dam meant that it required no permit to construct. The court found that neither statute placed any restriction or limitation on the use of the water impounded by the dam and that even though neither statute specified that the impounded water could be used without a permit, the court held that such an intention was implied.

Because the size and purpose of use of the dam and reservoir had changed over time and the relevant statutes varied in the size and purpose of use requirements, the court also addressed the issue of which statute applied to the dam and reservoir. The court found that the 1941 Act did not apply, stating:

> The limitation of use imposed [by the 1941] Act plainly applies to dams constructed under the authority of the Act itself and not to dams which had been previously constructed. The rights of appellee Arnett were not affected by the 1941 Act since they were vested under prior laws and statutes. Under such statutes, it is our opinion that Arnett had the right to use water from his reservoir for the purposes and in the manner set out in the facts of his case. He also had the right to repair his dam to accomplish that end.

City of Anson, 250 S.W.2d at 453.

Although the applicable statutes and facts are complicated, the court's holding in the *City of Anson* case established that a water right to an exempt reservoir arises by virtue of its construction under the existing statute, within the capacity limitations and purposes of use provided by the existing statute, and that the reservoir must be constructed on land owned by the landowner, whether riparian or not.

The legislature continued to modify the reservoir exemption. The acre-feet restriction was increased to two hundred acre-feet in 1953. *See* Act approved May 27, 1953, 53d Leg., R.S., ch. 235, § 1. In 1959, the law was amended to provide: "The owner of any such dam or reservoir wishing to take water from such dam or reservoir for any beneficial purpose or purposes other than domestic or livestock use . . . can seek a permit from the State." Act approved May 8, 1959, 56th Leg., R.S., ch. 151, § 1 (amending article 7500a of the Texas Civil Statutes).

A later case that considered the reservoir exemption is *Garrison v. Bexar-Medina-Atascosa Counties Water Improvement District No. 1*, 404 S.W.2d 376 (Tex. App.—Austin 1966, writ ref'd n.r.e.). In this case, a permit authorizing a dam and reservoir on the west prong of the Medina River, a navigable stream, was invalidated. The court of appeals held that the state, not the landowner, owns the bed and banks of navigable streams. The Texas Supreme Court approved that portion of the court of appeals' opinion holding that the exemption from permitting (then article 7500a) did not apply to a navigable stream. *Garrison*, 407 S.W.2d 771 (Tex. 1966). The supreme court ruled that any exemption from permitting for a dam and reservoir would be controlled by the statute at the time of construction but that such exemptions do not apply to navigable streams. For an exemption to apply, the dam must be located on the landowner's land; if on a navigable stream, a permit is required. Thus, under the common law established by the court, the statutory exemption from permitting such a reservoir does not apply when the dam and reservoir are on a navigable stream.

The law continued to evolve. In 1971, article 7500a was repealed and recodified as sections 5.140 and 5.141 of the Texas Water Code, which are currently section 11.142. Section 11.142 allows broader uses of the water in such an exempt reservoir, but it is still subject to the earlier court decisions.

The reservoir exemption to the appropriation and permitting system was created by statute. It is considered by the courts to give a landowner who constructs a dam and reservoir on his own property, to collect diffused water, or on a nonnavigable stream the right to impound a limited amount of water. The terms that control such an exemption are those found in the law that was in effect when the dam was constructed. This exemption under common law does not apply to a navigable stream. See Chapter 27 of this book for a discussion of reservoirs, including exempt reservoirs.

§ 4.7:3 Irrigation Canal Rights

Certain other rights of landowners adjoining an appropriator's irrigation lands or facilities are of historical interest. Such claims were considered in the *Valley Water* case (see section 4.5:2 above) and possibly in adjudication cases that did not reach the appellate courts. Remnants of older statutes relating to this type of claim remain in the current statutes. The duty to provide water under reasonable terms and conditions at reasonable rates originated from these irrigation canal rights.

The early general and special legislative acts dealing with early irrigation companies, the 1889, 1895, 1913, 1917, and 1918 Acts, provided for the creation of private canal corporations to construct water diversion and distribution systems with the emphasis on delivery of water for irrigating land contiguous to the corporation's canal distribution system. *See* Hutchins, at 251. Later statutes governing the creation and operation of private canal corporations were found in article 7552 *et seq.*, *Vernon's Texas Civil Statutes*. The provisions relating to service of contiguous lands are now found in Texas Water Code sections 11.036–.041.

The court decisions that interpret and apply these statutes to claims of water rights are generally fact- and site-specific and involve questions of the relative rights of the canal company and individuals claiming the right to water from the canals. *See Borden v. Trespalacios Rice & Irrigation Co.*, 86 S.W. 11 (Tex. 1905); *Lakeside Irrigation Co. v. Buffington*, 168 S.W. 21 (Tex. App.—San Antonio 1914, writ ref'd); *American Rio Grande Land & Irrigation Co. v. Mercedes Plantation Co.*, 208 S.W. 904 (Tex. Comm'n App. 1919, judgm't adopted); *Knight v. Oldham*, 210 S.W. 567 (Tex. App.—El Paso 1919, writ ref'd); *Mudge v. Hughes*, 212 S.W. 819 (Tex. App.—San Antonio 1919, no writ); *McBride v. United Irrigation Co.*, 211 S.W. 498 (Tex. App.—San Antonio 1919, writ ref'd); *Edinburg Irrigation Co. v. Paschen*, 223 S.W. 329 (Tex. App.—San Antonio 1920), *aff'd*, 235 S.W. 1088 (Tex. Comm'n App. 1922); *Ball v. Rio Grande Canal Co.*, 256 S.W. 678 (Tex. App.—San Antonio 1923, writ ref'd);

Fairbanks v. Hidalgo County Water Improvement District No. 2, 261 S.W. 542 (Tex. App.—San Antonio 1923, writ dism'd w.o.j.); *Chapman v. American Rio Grande Land & Irrigation Co.*, 271 S.W. 392 (Tex. App.—San Antonio 1925, writ ref'd); *Edinburg Irrigation Co. v. Ledbetter*, 206 S.W. 1088 (Tex. Comm'n App. 1926); *Van Horne v. Trousdale*, 10 S.W.2d 147 (Tex. App.—El Paso 1928, no writ); *Willis v. Neches Canal Co.*, 16 S.W.2d 266 (Tex. Comm'n App. 1929, judgm't adopted). These early cases generally construed the statutes to say that all landowners contiguous to a private canal company's distribution facilities have a right to demand the use of water from the canal company (or a successor water district) and are entitled to water service on reasonable terms and rates. *See* Hutchins, at 251–52, 271–72, 279–80 (and cases cited therein).

The duty of a canal company or irrigation company to provide water on reasonable terms and rates to landowners contiguous to the company's reservoirs and distribution facilities is reflected in Texas Water Code section 11.038. This basic provision had appeared in every irrigation act since 1889 with specific reference to the content of each act. In those statutes, the duty to provide water was tied to the right of the canal or irrigation company to appropriate water and to the company's construction and maintenance of reservoir and distribution facilities as provided in each statute.

Private irrigation companies were the only facilities that were "constructed and maintained" under the statutes before 1918 and passage of the Conservation Amendment, except for early irrigation districts established after the 1904 constitutional amendments; see discussion in part III below. The facilities of water improvement districts and water control and improvement districts were constructed and maintained under later statutes after 1918. When a water district took over the facilities of a predecessor private irrigation company, these early statutes would not apply because the facilities were then maintained under post-1918 statutes, even though they may have been constructed by a private irrigation company under the pre-1918 statutes.

These historical canal corporation water service rights would appear to have limited applicability because most private canal companies in Texas have been converted into water districts; however, this is not the case, because the court in *State v. Hidalgo County Water Control & Improvement District No. 18*, 443 S.W.2d 728 (Tex. App.—Corpus Christi–Edinburg 1969, writ ref'd n.r.e.), recognized independent water rights in claimants that owned or held possessory rights to lands "adjoining or contiguous" to canals of a predecessor private irrigation company, even though their land was not later included in the boundaries of a successor water district. *Hidalgo County*, 443 S.W.2d at 748, 750–53. These landowners held permanent water supply contracts, recorded in the county records, with the predecessor private irrigation company and continued to receive deliveries of water from the successor water district. *See also Arneson v. Shary*, 32 S.W.2d 907 (Tex. App.—San Antonio 1930, writ ref'd).

As mentioned above, during codification in 1971, the provisions dealing with private irrigation companies relating to service of contiguous lands were codified into what is now Water Code sections 11.036–.041. This codification should not have changed the substantive meaning of the law it codified. Nevertheless, as codified, it appears to have changed the context and original aspect of these rights, because a court later held that these current Code provisions were not limited to irrigation uses and private irrigation companies but included other uses, including municipal use, and the court extended the provisions and the duty to serve and deliver water at reasonable rates to municipal suppliers. *See Texas Water Rights Commission v. City of Dallas*, 591 S.W.2d 609 (Tex. App.—Dallas 1979, writ ref'd n.r.e.).

The duty to serve and deliver water at reasonable rates and terms and conditions, which historically arose out of the canal company and irrigation company statutes as discussed above, has also been broadened to include other water suppliers and water usage. In *City of San Antonio v. Texas Water Commission*, 407 S.W.2d 752 (Tex. 1967), the Guadalupe-Blanco River Authority held a permit granting it "authority to appropriate, divert and use certain waters of the State as may be necessary when beneficially used for the purposes of municipal use." The court declared that the authority could not legally refuse to sell municipal water to any particular municipality. It had a duty to serve the public without discrimination and at reasonable rates. *See Allen v. Park Place Water, Light & Power Co.*, 266 S.W. 219 (Tex. App.—Galveston 1925, writ ref'd).

Thus the duty to provide water under reasonable terms and at reasonable rates found in today's Water Code chapter 11 originated historically in the state's desire to encourage agriculture and irrigation and support the construction and maintenance of irrigation waterworks designed for this purpose. See Chapter 31 of this book for a discussion of wholesale water suppliers.

§ 4.7:4 Wagstaff Act

Legislation historically referred to as the "Wagstaff Act," Act approved May 18, 1931, 42d Leg., R.S., ch. 128, § 2 (amending article 7472 of the Texas Civil Statutes), was enacted by the legislature in 1931 and later codified as Texas Water Code section 11.028. Its underlying purpose was based on a perception that upstream municipal water suppliers were threatened by major downstream senior appropriation for hydroelectric and irrigation purposes. The Act declared that it was the public policy of the state that, in the allotment and appropriation of water and issuance of permits after 1931, preference and priority were to be given to listed uses in the order provided in the statute. Domestic and municipal uses were listed first, followed by industrial, irrigation, mining, hydroelectric power, navigation, and recreation, in that order. This preferential treatment based on purpose of use was existing law and continues as law today with respect to issuance of permits, but the Act further stated—

> provided, however that all appropriations or allotments of water hereafter made for . . . any other purposes than domestic or municipal purposes, shall be granted subject to the right of any city, town or municipality of this State to make further appropriations of said water thereafter without the necessity of condemnation or paying therefor . . . .

Act approved May 18, 1931, 42d Leg., R.S., ch. 128, § 2 (amending article 7472 of the Texas Civil Statutes). This provision was highly controversial for more than fifty years because it appeared to provide a mechanism for making water available for municipal use on a watercourse (except the Rio Grande) that was otherwise fully appropriated in permits issued after 1931. No Texas court ever addressed this basic issue authoritatively. *But see City of San Antonio v. Texas Water Commission*, 407 S.W.2d 752, 764 (Tex. 1966). The uncertainties created by the Wagstaff Act were removed by the legislature in 1997 in Senate Bill 1, when it repealed Water Code section 11.028, the successor provision.

§ 4.7:5 Forfeiture and Cancellation of Water Rights

Another aspect of surface water law development that was not involved in the adjudication, but that has historical significance, concerns laws dealing with how water rights may be lost through abandonment or statutory forfeiture and cancellation. Since 1917, the legislature has provided means by which statutory water rights may be forfeited and canceled.

Forfeiture: The 1917 Irrigation Act was the first statute to provide a means by which an appropriative water right could be terminated. *See* Act of Mar. 19, 1917, 35th Leg., R.S., ch. 88. (This provision was codified as article 7544 of the Texas Revised Civil Statutes and then as section 5.030 of the Texas Water Code. The current statute on forfeiture is found at Water Code section 11.030.) Article 7544, *Vernon's Texas Civil Statutes* (1948), provided:

> Any appropriation or use of water heretofore made under any statute of this State, or hereafter made under the provisions of this Chapter, which shall be willfully abandoned during any three successive years, shall be forfeited and the water formerly so used or appropriated shall be again subject to appropriation for the purposes stated in this Act.

Former Tex. Rev. Civ. Stat. art. 7544 (1948).

Article 7544 was applied as between the water rights holders in *City of Anson v. Arnett*, where the court held that there must be clear and satisfactory evidence of an intention to abandon a water right before it will be declared forfeited. *City of Anson v. Arnett*, 250 S.W.2d 450, 454 (Tex. App.—Eastland 1952, writ ref'd n.r.e.). This is consistent with judicial disfavor of forfeiture of rights. According to the court, mere failure to repair a dam or facilities or the nonuse of water is not probative evidence of an intent to abandon a water right. *See also Lower Nueces River Water Supply District v. Cartwright*, 274 S.W.2d 199 (Tex. App.—San Antonio 1955, writ ref'd n.r.e.).

An action of forfeiture of a water right under article 7544 applied to actions between water rights holders being heard by a court rather than to cancellation of water rights by an administrative agency. *Fairbanks v. Hidalgo County Water Improvement District No. 2*, 261 S.W. 542 (Tex. App.—Austin 1923, writ dism'd w.o.j.), held that article 7544 did not give the Board of Water Engineers the power to forfeit rights because to do so would violate article I, section 1, of the state constitution by giving judicial powers to an administrative agency.

Although the 1917 Act and subsequent statutes did not give the Board of Water Engineers the authority to terminate an appropriative water right, the board did have the right to forfeit a permit, after notice, if the permitted work did not commence within ninety days, or as extended. Similar authority has been carried forward in Water Code section 11.146, which establishes procedures, including a hearing, for forfeiture proceedings.

In the codification process in 1971, the forfeiture provision in article 7544 was repealed, leaving cancellation as the only statutory means through which an appropriative right may be terminated. *See* Act approved Apr. 12, 1971, 62d Leg., R.S., ch. 58, § 2.

Cancellation: The 1953 Act, which was enacted during the historic drought of the 1950s, established another means to terminate a water right through cancellation:

> All permits or certified filings for the appropriation and use of public waters granted by the Board of Water Engineers, or filed with said Board, more than ten (10) years prior to the effective date of this Act and under which no part of the water authorized to be withdrawn and appropriated has been put to beneficial use for a period of ten (10) consecutive years next preceding the effective date of this Act are hereby canceled and shall be of no further force and effect.
>
> Provided, however, that the Board shall send notice of such pending cancellation by registered mail, return receipt requested, to the holder of any such permit or certified filing, at the last address shown by the records of the Board of Water Engineers at least ninety (90) days prior to the effective date of such cancellation. The failure of the Board of Water Engineers to cancel a permit or certified filing hereunder shall not be construed as validating any such permit or certified filing not cancelled.

Act approved June 8, 1953, 53d Leg., R.S., ch. 352, § 1.

Cancellation of water rights pursuant to statute was upheld as constitutional in *Texas Water Rights Commission v. Wright*, 464 S.W.2d 642 (Tex. 1971). The court held that the issuance of a permit authorizes the beneficial use of water and that a permittee does not acquire the right of nonuse of water. It is the duty of the appropriator to beneficially use the water. Water permits are grants of usufructuary rights to use the state's water, with the implied condition subsequent that the water is beneficially used. The cancellation statute provides a reasonable remedy for the state's enforcement of this condition subsequent after fair opportunity for notice and hearing. A permittee could reasonably have expected that his rights would be subjected to a remedy enforcing this condition, which inherently attached to the rights granted. The court concluded that the cancellation statute was not invalid even though it has retroactive effects.

III. Legislative Water Management: Water Districts and River Authorities

§ 4.8 Introduction to Legislative Water Management

As early as 1852, the legislature realized the need to manage surface water resources and to develop a system for individuals to acquire surface water rights. This effort began first in the arid portion of the state and was later extended to the entire state. The early efforts to develop water resources through private irrigation companies and privately financed projects proved less successful than was anticipated, and it was apparent that more legislation would be needed. The response was a constitutional amendment adopted on November 8, 1904. *See* Tex. Const. art. III, § 52 interp. cmt.

§ 4.9 1904 Constitutional Amendment and Legislatively Created Irrigation Districts

The 1904 constitutional amendment authorized the legislature to establish political subdivisions and districts that could issue bonds for improvements of watercourses and for the construction and maintenance of works for irrigation, drainage, navigation, and roads. Tex. Const. art. III, § 52.

This amendment, enacted when there was public concern about higher taxes, contained limitations that hampered its effectiveness. For example, it required a two-thirds majority vote of resident property owners to authorize a bond issue, prevented taxation where cities were included within the boundaries of the district, and limited the amount of bonds issued by a district.

Based on the new authority granted in the 1904 constitutional amendment, the legislature passed a statute authorizing the creation of irrigation districts. *See* Act of Apr. 15, 1905, 29th Leg., R.S., ch. 235. The legislature also passed statutes providing for the creation of drainage and levee improvement districts. A few irrigation districts were formed pursuant to these new laws, and the statutes were declared constitutional. *See, e.g., Barstow v. Ward County Irrigation District No. 1*, 177 S.W. 563 (Tex. App.—El Paso 1915, writ ref'd); *White v. Fahring*, 212 S.W. 193 (Tex. App.—Galveston 1919, writ ref'd). However, the limitations imposed by the 1904 constitutional amendment restricted the irrigation development that it was intended to encourage. This continued until the legislature responded in the 1913, 1917, and 1918 Acts.

§ 4.10 Conservation Amendment

The 1913 Act, in addition to being a comprehensive water statute relating to surface water law, authorized the creation of "irrigation districts." Act approved Apr. 9, 1913, 33d Leg., R.S., ch. 172. Questions were raised about whether the legislature, under the 1904 amendment, had sufficient authority to create water districts with the powers necessary to fully develop the state's water resources.

In 1917, the legislature passed the 1917 Act, which provided for the creation of water improvement districts. *See* Act approved Mar. 19, 1917, 35th Leg., R.S., ch. 87. The legislature also passed a joint resolution to submit to the voters of the state another and more liberal constitutional amendment with respect to, among other things, financing the operations and projects of water districts and river authorities.

The 1917 Conservation Amendment, approved by the state's electorate on August 21, 1917, authorized the legislature to establish water districts that would have more operational and financial flexibility than those authorized under the earlier amendment. *See* Tex. Const. art. XVI, § 59(b). Specifically, it authorized the creation of conservation and reclamation districts and eliminated the financing restrictions and limitations contained in the 1904 amendment (article III, section 52). *See* Tex. Const. art. XVI, § 59 interp. cmt.; Hutchins, at 12.

§ 4.11 Districts and Authorities after the Conservation Amendment

The Conservation Amendment was not self-enacting. By its terms, the legislature had the duty to implement the public policy expressed in the amendment. *See City of Corpus Christi v. City of Pleasanton*, 276 S.W.2d 798, 802–03 (Tex. 1955). At a called session of the same 35th Texas Legislature, held in 1918, legislation was passed for the purpose of implementing the Conservation Amendment. *See* Act approved Mar. 21, 1918, 35th Leg., 4th C.S., ch. 25. The 1918 Act, in addition to confirming provisions in the 1913 and 1917 Acts, provided for the creation of conservation and reclamation districts with the powers of water improvement districts. It also authorized existing water improvement districts and earlier irrigation districts to convert to conservation and reclamation districts that have the powers of such districts without having to change the district's name. Although the 1918 Act removed the limitations with regard to taxation, the process for converting to a conservation and reclamation district remained an impediment to development and use of the state's surface water. The process required a petition signed by a relatively large percentage of the owners of land in the district, confirmed by an election held in the district.

In *Trimmier v. Carlton*, 264 S.W. 253 (Tex. App.—Austin 1924), *aff'd*, 296 S.W. 1070 (Tex. 1927), the court discussed the background of these statutes and stated, without holding, that the 1917 Act dealing with water improvement districts was intended to supersede the 1913 Act because it covered the same general subject, and in many respects the two statutes were identical. However, the two statutes remained within statutory law. *See Trimmier*, 264 S.W. at 258. The court, on motion for rehearing, held that the Conservation Amendment did not supersede the 1904 amendment. To avoid the limitations imposed by the 1918 Act, special enabling legislation would be required to create a conservation and reclamation district. *Trimmier*, 264 S.W. at 262; *see also Arneson v. Shary*, 32 S.W.2d 907 (Tex. App.—San Antonio 1930, writ ref'd) (addressing the relationship between previous early irrigation canal companies and later created water districts).

Legislation passed in 1925 provided for the organization of water control and improvement districts, which were conservation and reclamation districts without the limitations created by the 1918 Act as noted in *Trimmier*. Act of Feb. 26, 1925, 39th Leg., R.S., ch. 25 (which became Tex. Rev. Civ. Stat. art. 7880–1 *et seq.* (1954) and was later codified in Texas Water Code chapter 51). Because of the uncertainty caused by the *Trimmier* decision and the subsequent 1925 Act, numerous special bills were passed to validate existing districts, convert existing districts into conservation and reclamation districts, and create new districts. *See* Tex. Rev. Civ. Stat. art. 8280–2 *et seq.* (1954); *see generally* Tex. Spec. Dist. Code.

The 1925 legislature authorized the conversion of any existing water improvement district or irrigation district into a water control and improvement district by action of its board of directors. *See* Tex. Water Code §§ 51.040–.044 (relating to water control and improvement districts). The authority to convert to a water control and improvement district was extended in 1929 to levee improvement districts or any other existing conservation and reclamation districts. *See* Tex. Rev. Civ. Stat. arts. 7880–143, 7880–143a (1954) (now included in Tex. Water Code ch. 51). Although the 1925 Act, Act of Feb. 26, 1925, 39th Leg., R.S., ch. 25, § 144, later Tex. Rev. Civ. Stat. art. 7880–144 (1954), appeared to validate that all existing water improvement districts and irrigation districts were operating under the Conservation Amendment, this issue remained uncertain with regard to existing and possible future districts and river authorities in their efforts to manage water sources within their respective jurisdictional boundaries.

The legislature also provided for other special-purpose districts, such as fresh water supply districts, Act approved July 28, 1919, 36th Leg., 2d C.S., ch. 48; municipal utility districts, Act approved Apr. 27, 1971, 62d Leg., R.S., ch. 84; and drainage districts, Act approved Mar. 23, 1907,

30th Leg., R.S., ch. 40; Act approved Mar. 28, 1911, 32d Leg., R.S., ch. 118. Many other types of districts and river authorities were created in specific watersheds—for example, the Brazos River Authority, Act of July 2, 1929, 41st Leg., 2d C.S., ch.13, 1929 Tex. Spec. Laws 22; the Guadalupe-Blanco River Authority, Act approved Oct. 25, 1933, 42d Leg., 1st C.S., ch. 75, 1933 Tex. Spec. Laws 198; and the Lower Colorado River Authority, Act approved Nov. 13, 1934, 43d Leg., 4th C.S., ch. 7, 1934 Tex. Spec. Laws 19. See Chapter 8 of this book for a discussion of water districts and Chapter 9 regarding river authorities and regional water districts.

In 1971, the legislature codified almost all water law and water district statutes. In general, it was intended that the Texas Water Code should include all general water laws of the state as well as amendments made to such laws. However, many of the general water district laws were not initially codified. Most of the provisions of the 1917, 1918, and 1925 Acts were codified, including those dealing with water improvement districts, water control and improvement districts, fresh water supply districts, and drainage districts. For example, the 1925 Act providing for water control and improvement districts is now found in Water Code chapter 51, and the statutes dealing with water improvement districts, which govern early irrigation districts under the 1905 statute, are found in chapter 55. See Chapter 8 of this book.

Significantly, in 1971 the question of the status of irrigation districts organized under the early laws pursuant to the 1904 constitutional amendment was resolved with adoption of Water Code section 55.050. Under this provision, those early irrigation districts are governed by the provisions of chapter 55 and are allowed to change their name if they desire. *See* Tex. Water Code §§ 55.050–.051. This is consistent with dicta in *Trimmier*. *See Trimmier*, 264 S.W. at 258.

In 1977, the legislature approved legislation establishing a new type of district called an irrigation district as a district separate and apart from other existing earlier water districts and irrigation water districts. Act approved June 15, 1977, 65th Leg., R.S., ch. 627. This legislation was added as chapter 58 of the Water Code. A chapter 58 irrigation district is a conservation and reclamation district pursuant to the Conservation Amendment, article XVI, section 59, of the Texas Constitution. The specific purposes of these new irrigation districts are to deliver water for irrigation, provide for drainage, and deliver untreated water to municipal suppliers. They are authorized to perform, in addition to the delivery of irrigation water, other incidental functions and may contract with municipalities, political subdivisions, water supply corporations, or other water users for the delivery of untreated water. *See* Tex. Water Code §§ 58.121–.190. See also Chapter 8 of this book.

As mentioned above, the 1925 Act authorized all existing water districts to convert to water control and improvement districts with the additional powers authorized by the Act. Similarly, chapter 58 authorizes any water improvement district (including an earlier created irrigation district operating as a water improvement district) or water control and improvement district, whose purposes were to furnish water for irrigation and delivery of untreated water, to convert to a chapter 58 irrigation district. *See* Tex. Water Code §§ 58.038–.042.

In 1995, uniform provisions dealing with water districts were enacted in chapter 49 of the Water Code. They apply to all districts, with certain exceptions for "special water authorities." Act approved June 15, 1995, 74th Leg., R.S., ch. 715 (codified at Water Code chapter 49). According to the legislature, this step was needed because of the "lack of procedural uniformity between the different types of local water district[s]" and "inconsistencies [that] lead to confusion among citizens, district board members, and state agency personnel." House Nat. Res. Comm., Bill Analysis, Tex. S.B. 626, 74th Leg., R.S. (1995). For a review of some water district organizational and operational issues, see *Ward County Irrigation District No. 1 v. Red Bluff Water Power Control District*, 170 S.W.3d 696 (Tex. App.—El Paso 2005, no pet.).

As discussed in greater detail in Chapters 8 and 9 of this book, with legal issues involving water districts and authorities, it is necessary to consider the uncodified special and general laws authorizing and governing a district or, if codified, the chapter of the Water Code covering the particular district, as well as chapter 49, which applies to all surface water districts.

IV. Conclusion

§ 4.12 Conclusion

Surface water law in Texas has evolved from a dual system of common-law riparian rights and appropriation rights granted by the state to a more uniform system based on the appropriation doctrine controlled by the constitution and legislation passed pursuant to the constitution. Within this transformation is the recognition that a perfected water right is a property right to use the state's water, which is protected by the constitution. The legislature has provided for management of its water resources through local and regional water districts and river authorities, watermaster programs, and the regulatory system within the current Texas Commission on Environmental Quality, which governs the enforcement of water rights and the granting of permits and amendments to existing water rights.

The surface water law system, as it has evolved, is not yet a perfect system. There are many legal issues and refinements yet to be considered and dealt with by the legislature, by the judiciary, and, when necessary, in amendments to the constitution. The current surface water law system has matured through this evolution and is one that can be built on to meet the state's future water resource needs.

CHAPTER 5

Groundwater Law

Susana E. Canseco[1]

I. Introduction

§ 5.1 Introduction

This chapter reviews the law of groundwater as established and applied by Texas courts. Chapter 16 of this book covers more specifically the regulation of groundwater under the Conservation Amendment, article XVI, section 59, of the Texas Constitution. Although Texas adopted the common law as a republic in 1840 (*see* Act approved Jan. 20, 1840, 4th Cong., R.S., § 1, 1840 Repub. Tex. Laws 3–6, *reprinted in* 2 H.P.N. Gammel, *The Laws of Texas 1822–1897*, at 177–78 (Austin, Gammel Book Co. 1898)), not until 1904 did Texas common law expressly address the law of groundwater. In the early 1900s, the need to use large quantities of groundwater and the ability to raise it to the surface with submersible pumps led to conflicts that required resolution by the courts. The Texas Supreme Court in *Houston & T.C. Ry. Co. v. East*, 81 S.W. 279 (Tex. 1904), commonly referred to as the "*East* case," adopted the common-law rules of capture and absolute ownership. More than one hundred years of jurisprudence have left the law little changed and much criticized. In 2012, the Texas Supreme Court thoroughly examined the nature of groundwater ownership in *Edwards Aquifer Authority v. Day*, 369 S.W.3d 814 (Tex. 2012), commonly referred to as the "*Day* case."

East and *Day* serve as "bookends" to Texas's twentieth-century groundwater law. *Day* then set the legal stage for the next century of Texas groundwater jurisprudence by leaving open the questions implied by absolute ownership, or "ownership in place," of groundwater. Since *Day*, courts have tackled ensuing questions regarding regulatory takings, the dominance of the groundwater estate over the surface estate, and whether there are implied correlative rights in groundwater under the common law.

Under the Conservation Amendment, the state has, through the creation of groundwater conservation districts (or similar governmental agencies), authorized the regulation of groundwater. *See* Tex. Const. art. XVI, § 59; Tex. Water Code ch. 36. As discussed in Chapter 16 of this book, since the late 1990s, groundwater conservation districts have been given increasing authority to regulate the use of groundwater. This increase in authority has created conflict between landowner rights in groundwater and districts' exercise of regulatory powers. This chapter reviews (1) the development of Texas groundwater law from *East* to *Day* and beyond, as well as the newest questions being presented

---

1. Susana Canseco is an attorney focusing on water rights and real estate transactions and administrative practice. She has represented land and water owners as well as groundwater conservation districts and regularly writes and speaks on water law. Susana received her BA in history from Harvard University and her JD from the University of Texas School of Law in Austin. Following law school, Susana clerked for the Honorable U.S. District Judge Lee Yeakel of the Western District of Texas. Susana would like to acknowledge the contributions of Mary Sahs and Russ Johnson in developing earlier versions of this chapter and Vanessa Puig-Williams for the *Neches & Trinity Valleys* case summary.

to the courts, and (2) the relationship between private groundwater ownership and groundwater regulation by local groundwater districts.

II. What Is Groundwater?

§ 5.2 Introduction

Although the question "What is groundwater?" seems simple, it is the critical beginning of all water law analyses in Texas. Different laws and regulations apply to "groundwater" and "state" or "surface water," which makes this categorization extremely important. In determining the legal classification of water found beneath the ground, one must first determine whether it is state water. If not, it is legally groundwater owned by the landowner and subject to regulation by groundwater conservation districts.

§ 5.3 Groundwater Is Not State Water

Because "state water" includes underground rivers and streams and the underflow of surface rivers and streams, the fact that water is found underground is not definitive proof of its character as groundwater. *See* Tex. Water Code § 11.021(a) (underflow). See also Chapter 1 of this book for a discussion of the legal distinction between state water, which is also referred to as surface water, and groundwater. The terms "state water" and "surface water" are used interchangeably in this chapter, depending on the language of the case being discussed.

Chapter 36 of the Texas Water Code, under which most groundwater is regulated, does not clarify the distinction; it defines groundwater as "water percolating below the surface of the earth." Tex. Water Code § 36.001(5). The regulations implementing the state's water rights statute add some clarity, defining groundwater as "[w]ater under the surface of the ground other than underflow of a stream and underground streams, whatever may be the geologic structure in which it is standing or moving." 30 Tex. Admin. Code § 297.1(21). Thus, the facts of each situation involving water beneath the ground's surface must be analyzed before determining whether surface water law or groundwater law applies. Several cases illustrate this analysis. *See, e.g., Texas Co. v. Burkett*, 296 S.W. 273, 278 (Tex. 1927); *Pecos County Water Control & Improvement District No. 1 v. Williams*, 271 S.W.2d 503, 506 (Tex. App.—El Paso 1954, writ ref'd n.r.e.) (underground rivers and streams); *Cantwell v. Zinser*, 208 S.W.2d 577, 579 (Tex. App.—Austin 1948, no writ).

§ 5.4 Water Discharged from Springs to Watercourses Is Not Groundwater

As early as 1927, the Texas Supreme Court recognized that spring water, which is neither surface water nor water in a subsurface stream with defined channels, was the exclusive property of the landowner. *See Texas Co. v. Burkett*, 296 S.W. 273, 278 (Tex. 1927). The first court decision directly addressing the conflict between landowners who used percolating groundwater emerging at springs and landowners who had historically benefited from and used downstream flows from a spring was *Pecos County Water Control & Improvement District No. 1 v. Williams*, 271 S.W.2d 503 (Tex. App.—El Paso 1954, writ ref'd n.r.e.) (hereinafter the "Comanche Springs case"). In that case, the defendant owned large areas of land over groundwater formations that historically provided flow to Comanche Springs. The plaintiff was the owner of state water right permits based on historic spring flows and had used and enjoyed the waters of Comanche Springs for ninety years. During the 1950s drought, the defendant's extensive groundwater use was alleged to have caused the cessation of spring flows from Comanche Springs. The downstream plaintiff, as the owner of the surface water permits, filed suit seeking an injunction and a declaration that its more senior surface water appropriative rights had priority.

The court declined to recognize the surface water rights predating the defendant's groundwater usage as justification for enjoining the groundwater use. The court held that the plaintiff had rights to the waters of Comanche Springs only after they emerged from the springs and refused to extend those rights to the water underground. *See Comanche Springs*, 271 S.W.2d at 506–07. The court also rejected as insufficiently pleaded the plaintiff's claim that, because the water supplying Comanche Springs flowed in well-defined underground channels, it was not groundwater but rather surface water. *Comanche Springs*, 271 S.W.2d at 506.

This decision was reinforced in *Denis v. Kickapoo Land Co.*, 771 S.W.2d 235 (Tex. App.—Austin 1989, writ denied), in which an upstream landowner drilled a suction well into Kickapoo Springs, metered the water before transporting it down the channel of Kickapoo Creek, and diverted it to irrigate his land. Kickapoo Springs fed Kickapoo Creek, and after the defendant's pumping, the downstream plaintiffs alleged the flow of the creek downstream of the diversion was substantially reduced. The downstream users sued, claiming unlawful diversion of state surface water. The trial court granted summary judgment for the defendant well owner, and the court of appeals affirmed, holding that "waters tributary to springs [are] treated the same as all other percolating waters" and belong absolutely to the owner of the land. *Denis*, 771 S.W.2d at 238. The landowner could do what he pleased with them, even though extracting the water dried up the springs. The court said it is immaterial that springs fed by percolating waters were the sources of a stream or surface watercourse on which rights had vested, "provided that the water was intercepted while it was still percolating through the soil before it had reached the surface of the ground at the springs." *Denis*, 771 S.W.2d at 239 (quoting Clesson S. Kinney, *A Treatise on the Law of Irrigation and Water Rights* § 1196, at 2167 (2d ed. 1912)).

§ 5.5 Groundwater Can Become State Water

Although the courts held early on that groundwater emerging from a spring and entering a watercourse loses its character as groundwater and is properly classified as surface water, only more recently has it been decided that groundwater discharged into a river, stream, or watercourse loses its status as groundwater and becomes state water. *See, e.g., City of San Marcos v. Texas Commission on Environmental Quality*, 128 S.W.3d 264, 277 (Tex. App.—Austin 2004, pet. denied).

In *Edwards Aquifer Authority v. Day*, in evaluating an Edwards Aquifer Authority (EAA) permitting decision, the court had to determine whether water from an artesian well that was allowed to flow into a lake had become state water. *Day*, 369 S.W.3d 814, 823 (Tex. 2012). The EAA had found that the artesian well water had become state water and that Day was therefore not entitled to a groundwater production permit for water withdrawn from the lake and used for irrigation. For a further discussion of this concept and related cases, see Chapter 24 of this book concerning reuse.

The supreme court affirmed the EAA's decision, finding that Day had failed to prove that water from the lake was groundwater and not state water. The court emphasized the specificity of its decision by saying, "We do not suggest that a lake can never be used to store or transport groundwater for use by its owner. We conclude only that the Authority could find from the evidence before it that that was not what had occurred on Day's property." *Day*, 369 S.W.3d at 823. The *Day* court's holding regarding groundwater turning into state water has profound implications for any landowner using groundwater to supplement water in an impoundment on a watercourse.

III. Texas Groundwater Law—the General Rule—Foundations and Exceptions

§ 5.6 The Rule of Capture: *East* to *Sipriano*

The Texas Supreme Court was presented with its first groundwater case in *Houston & T.C. Ry. Co. v. East*, 81 S.W. 279 (Tex. 1904). The plaintiff in *East* had a small well he used for household purposes. When East's new neighbor, a railroad company, moved in next door, it drilled a larger, deeper well from which it pumped a relatively large quantity of water daily for its locomotives and machine shops. After years of the railroad's pumping, East's well dried up, and he sued. The trial court rendered judgment for the defendant, which the appellate court reversed, applying the doctrine of reasonable use. *East*, 81 S.W. at 280. The Texas Supreme Court in turn reversed the appellate court's ruling and held that the plaintiff had no right to recover damages for the loss of use of his well or to prevent the railroad's groundwater pumping, even though the railroad company's use deprived the plaintiff of the use of his well.

The court chose and applied as the law of this state what is referred to as "the rule of capture." As applied, the rule of capture means that, with certain limited exceptions, a landowner may explore for water, drill a well, pump water from that well, and use any quantity he desires for any purpose he desires, on or off his land, and if in doing so he dries up his neighbor's well, the neighbor has no cause of action against him. *East*, 81 S.W. at 280–81. The court rejected a rule of reasonable use, which would have limited use of the water to the reasonable amount for the land from which it was produced. The *East* court gave two reasons for adopting the rule of capture:

> (1) Because the existence, origin, movement, and course of such waters, and the causes which govern and direct their movements, are so secret, occult, and concealed that an attempt to administer any set of legal rules in respect to them would be involved in hopeless uncertainty, and would, therefore, be practically impossible.
>
> (2) Because any such recognition of correlative rights would interfere, to the material detriment of the commonwealth, with drainage and agriculture, mining, the construction of highways and railroads, with sanitary regulations, building, and the general progress of improvement in works of embellishment and utility.

East, 81 S.W. at 281 (quoting *Frazier v. Brown*, 12 Ohio St. 294, 311 (1861)). The court further stated, "[T]he owner of land is the absolute owner of the soil and of percolating water, which is a part of, and not different from, the soil." *East*, 81 S.W. at 281 (quoting *Pixley v. Clark*, 35 N.Y. 520 (1866)). Despite this absolute-ownership language, the court recognized the common-law limitations on the exercise of the right: the groundwater must be used without waste, and the action must be without malice. *East*, 81 S.W. at 282. In quoting *Frazier*, the court also acknowledged that the rule applies only when there exists no legislation limiting the exercise of the right. *East*, 81 S.W. at 280.

As discussed below, the Texas Supreme Court repeatedly applied the rule of capture for the rest of the twentieth century, even in the face of great criticism. Finally, in 1999, the court was presented with an opportunity to abandon the rule of capture in *Sipriano v. Great Spring Waters of America, Inc.*, 1 S.W.3d 75 (Tex. 1999). It declined to do so. In *Sipriano*, the defendant purchased land, constructed wells, and produced groundwater for bottling purposes. Sipriano claimed that the wells he owned were severely depleted by the defendant's alleged nuisance, negligence, gross negligence, and malice. In the lower court, Sipriano argued that his claims fell within recognized exceptions to the rule of capture and, further, that Texas should abandon the rule of capture and replace it with the rule of reasonable use. The trial court rejected these arguments and granted summary judgment in the defendant's favor on all of the plaintiff's claims. The court of appeals affirmed. *See Fain v. Great Spring Waters of America, Inc.*, 973 S.W.2d 327 (Tex. App.—Tyler 1998). At the supreme court, Sipriano abandoned his claim of an exception to the rule of capture and argued only that the court should abandon the rule.

The court reviewed the history of the rule of capture and the cases interpreting the rule, including the common-law exceptions of waste, malice, and negligently caused subsidence. In the end, the court decided not to veer from the rule of capture and affirmed the lower court judgments.

The court emphasized that groundwater regulation was properly a legislative function, by virtue of the Conservation Amendment. *Sipriano*, 1 S.W.3d at 80. The court pointed out that only two years before, the legislature had passed Senate Bill 1 (Act of June 1, 1997, 75th Leg., R.S., ch. 1010), which had given more authority to groundwater conservation districts to manage groundwater withdrawals, streamlined the process for the Texas Commission on Environmental Quality's (TCEQ) predecessor agency to create districts in priority areas, and called for more coordinated water planning. *Sipriano*, 1 S.W.3d at 79–80. The court acknowledged that the management methods chosen by the legislature had been a matter of debate, but it also stated, "Texas voters made groundwater regulation a duty of the Legislature. And by Senate Bill 1, the Legislature has chosen a process that permits the people most affected by groundwater regulation in particular areas to participate in democratic solutions to their groundwater issues." *Sipriano*, 1 S.W.3d at 80. Therefore, the court found it improper to change the common law on which that process was intended to act. *Sipriano*, 1 S.W.3d at 80.

The court "save[d] for another day the determination of whether further revising the common law is an appropriate prerequisite to preserve Texas's natural resources and protect property owners' interests." *Sipriano*, 1 S.W.3d at 80.

The concurring opinion by Justice Hecht, joined by Justice O'Neill, presents a slightly different view. Although Justice Hecht agreed with the majority in deferring to the legislature, he pointed out that since the Texas Groundwater District Act was passed in 1949, "[N]ot much groundwater management is going on." *Sipriano*, 1 S.W.3d at 81. This concerned him, because in his words, "[I]t is not regulation that threatens progress, but the lack of it." *Sipriano*, 1 S.W.3d at 82. Accordingly, Justice Hecht concluded that "for now—but I think only for now—*East* should not be overruled." *Sipriano*, 1 S.W.3d at 83.

§ 5.7 Exceptions to the Rule of Capture

§ 5.7:1 The Waste Exception

Although the waste exception to the rule of capture has been recognized since the *East* decision in 1904, it was not until *City of Corpus Christi v. City of Pleasanton*, 276 S.W.2d 798 (Tex. 1955), that an appellate or supreme court decision addressed the waste exception. In *City of Corpus Christi*, a water company supplied the city of Corpus Christi with water by allowing groundwater to flow from the water company's artesian wells into the Nueces River, which would then transport the water 118 miles to Corpus Christi's reservoirs. The plaintiff's wells were in the vicinity of the water company's prolific pumping, and it sought to enjoin performance of the contract and prevent the "waste" of the groundwater caused by the loss of water during its transit to Corpus Christi. The claim was based on evidence that as much as 63 to 74 percent of the water discharged into the river was lost to evaporation and seepage before it was actually used by the citizens of Corpus Christi. The plaintiff relied on a 1925 statute that defined waste, in relation to artesian wells, as permitting the waters of an artesian well to run into any river without being put to lawful use.

In reversing the lower courts' decisions enjoining the transporting of water because it constituted waste, the supreme court found that it was not waste to transport water down a natural streambed with consequent loss of water by evaporation, transpiration, and seepage. Examining the limitations on the right of rule of capture, the supreme court noted, "About the only limitations applied by those jurisdictions retaining the 'English' rule [of capture] are that the owner may not maliciously take water for the sole purpose of injuring his neighbor, or wantonly and willfully waste it." *City of Corpus Christi*, 276 S.W.2d at 801 (citations omitted).

In examining whether the facts justified a finding that the water had been wasted, the court stated that it could find no common-law limitation of the means of transporting the water to the place of use and that the question whether the use to which the water is put is lawful or unlawful cannot reasonably turn on whether some of the water put into the system escapes during transportation. The plaintiff had not pleaded or claimed the water was being used for an unlawful purpose at its end destination. The court concluded that the legislature could prohibit the use of any means of transportation of groundwater that allowed the escape of excessive amounts but that it had not done so. *City of Corpus Christi*, 276 S.W.2d at 803.

Justices Griffin, Wilson, and Culver dissented. All three were troubled by the large percentage of water lost. After lamenting the majority's holding, Justice Wilson wrote on the limitations of the rule of capture: "In the field of water law, there is no consolidation to be found in the law of capture." *City of Corpus Christi*, 276 S.W.2d at 808. Portending legal battles to come, he argued that to the extent the application of the rule of capture would direct a plaintiff toward a remedy of offset, the rule's "application . . . is an extremely limited one. No one can live in a vacuum. Therefore all property rights are, to a certain extent, correlative." *City of Corpus Christi*, 276 S.W.2d at 808.

Texas courts have not considered any other cases in which a claim of waste of groundwater has been alleged or found. Similarly, there are no Texas cases addressing liability for malicious production, despite courts' continued references to the malice exception to the rule of capture.

§ 5.7:2 The Subsidence Exception

Explosive growth in the 1940s, 1950s, and 1960s in Harris and Galveston counties led to land subsidence caused by groundwater pumping. In 1973, Smith-Southwest Industries and other landowners in Harris County brought a class-action lawsuit against Friendswood Development Company alleging that Friendswood's withdrawals of large quantities of groundwater caused their land to subside.

The plaintiffs argued that the absolute-ownership rule should not insulate defendants from damages due to nuisance or negligence in the manner by which defendants made use of their property. The supreme court regarded the plaintiffs' position as effectively an argument that the reasonable-use doctrine should apply to groundwater. *Friendswood Development Co. v. Smith-Southwest Industries, Inc.*, 576 S.W.2d 21, 24 (Tex. 1978). After a careful examination of the history and background of the rule of capture in Texas and other jurisdictions, the court concluded that regarding the rule of capture (where the damage is *damnum sine injuria*), no action could lie for nuisance where there was no unlawful invasion of the right of another, and there could be no redress for negligence without the violation of a legal right and the breach of a legal duty. *Friendswood Development Co.*, 576 S.W.2d at 28. The court regarded the rule of capture as being based on inviolable property law, no matter how harsh and outmoded, upon which myriad property-based decisions had been made since *East. Friendswood Development Co.*, 576 S.W.2d at 28–29.

Because no other type of property besides groundwater could be used with such immunity from tort liability, the court held that in the future a new exception to the rule of capture would potentially apply in such circumstances. "[I]f the landowner's manner of withdrawing ground water from his land is negligent . . . and such conduct is a proximate cause of the subsidence of the land of others, he will be liable for the consequences of his conduct." *Friendswood Development Co.*, 576 S.W.2d at 30. The court also recognized that the legislature had recently created the Harris-Galveston Subsidence District to prevent future subsidence. *Friendswood Development Co.*, 576 S.W.2d at 24; *see* Harris-Galveston Coastal Subsidence District Act, 64th Leg., R.S., ch. 284. See also Chapter 16 of this book, which discusses subsidence districts.

In a dissenting opinion, Justice Pope, joined by Justice Johnson, argued that the case should have been viewed and decided based on subsidence-based damages as distinguished from a claim for damages caused by the loss of use of the water. The dissent preferred to limit the application of the rule of capture to claims for damages for loss of water but not claims for damage to the land itself. *Friendswood Development Co.*, 576 S.W.2d at 34.

IV. The Nature of Groundwater Ownership

§ 5.8 Introduction

Beginning with *Houston & T.C. Ry. Co. v. East* (see section 5.6 above), Texas courts described groundwater as real property but until recently were not called on to define whether groundwater was owned in place or if groundwater ownership vested only upon capture. As discussed more fully below, the nature of the property right in groundwater becomes especially important in the face of more rigorous groundwater regulation by groundwater conservation districts, as courts are called on to determine when regulation "goes too far" to the point of effecting a regulatory taking. The following sections summarize the history of the common law addressing groundwater ownership, the landmark case *Edwards Aquifer Authority v. Day*, and post-*Day* developments in groundwater law. Finally, the sections introduce unanswered questions resulting from these recent statements of groundwater property law.

§ 5.9 History

When the supreme court decided *East*, it described groundwater beneath a person's property as absolutely owned by the surface owners but did not clearly define whether that ownership was in place or whether ownership vested upon capture. In *East*, the Texas Supreme Court quoted a New York case, stating:

> An owner of soil may divert percolating water, consume or cut it off, with impunity. It is the same as land, and cannot be distinguished in law from land. So the owner of land is the absolute owner of the soil and of percolating water, which is a part of, and not different from, the soil.

Houston & T.C. Ry. Co. v. East, 81 S.W. 279, 281 (Tex. 1904) (quoting *Pixley v. Clark*, 35 N.Y. 520 (1866)).

In 1927, the supreme court reaffirmed the law of absolute ownership in *Texas Co. v. Burkett*, 296 S.W. 273 (Tex. 1927). The court expressly held that a landowner had the right to enter into a contract to sell groundwater, because percolating waters "were the exclusive property of [the landowner], who had all the rights incident to them one might have as to any other species of property." *Burkett*, 296 S.W. at 278.

Nearly half a century later, in the Comanche Springs case, the court stated:

> It seems clear to us that percolating or diffused and percolating waters belong to the land-owner, and may be used by him at his will. . . . These cases seem to hold that the landowner owns the percolating water under his land and that he can make a non-wasteful use thereof, and such is based on a concept of property ownership.

Pecos County Water Control & Improvement District No. 1 v. Williams, 271 S.W.2d 503, 505 (Tex. App.—El Paso 1954, writ ref'd n.r.e.).

The supreme court in *Friendswood Development Co.* refused to abandon the rule of capture, noting that it had become "an established rule of property law in this State, under which many citizens own land and water rights." *Friendswood Development Co. v. Smith-Southwest Industries, Inc.*, 576 S.W.2d 21, 29 (Tex. 1978).

In spite of these statements that seem to conclude that groundwater is owned by the landowner, none of the foregoing cases required the court to determine as a threshold issue when the property right in groundwater vested. In *Sipriano v. Great Spring Waters of America, Inc.*, 1 S.W.3d 75 (Tex. 1999), a case with a fact pattern similar to that of *East*, the supreme court focused solely on the rule of capture—a rule of nonliability for harming one's neighbor through groundwater pumping—and had no occasion to address groundwater ownership. The court's holding in *Sipriano* was based on the position that it was inappropriate for the court, given the legislature's recent efforts to expand the powers of groundwater conservation districts, "to insert itself into the regulatory mix by substituting the rule of reasonable use for the current rule of capture." *Sipriano*, 1 S.W.3d at 80.

The advent of more rigorous groundwater regulation began the era of "takings" cases pitting groundwater owners against regulatory bodies. See Chapter 38 of this book discussing governmental takings. One such case before the supreme court was *Barshop v. Medina County Underground Water Conservation District*, 925 S.W.2d 618 (Tex. 1996), in which the issue of groundwater ownership was directly relevant but was not resolved. In *Barshop*, the plaintiffs claimed that the Edwards Aquifer Authority Act (EAA Act) violated the Texas Constitution by taking their rights to withdraw Edwards Aquifer groundwater from their property. Although the plaintiffs conceded the state's right to regulate groundwater use, they nevertheless claimed that they had a vested property right in the water, which the legislation took away. The state countered that rights in groundwater were not vested until the water was actually reduced to possession, and no taking occurred by virtue of regulation of use. *Barshop*, 925 S.W.2d at 625. The court summed up the conflict by stating, "[T]he parties simply fundamentally disagree on the nature of the property rights affected by this Act." *Barshop*, 925 S.W.2d at 625.

Because the plantiffs had brought the case prior to the EAA's regulation of the aquifer, the court had before it only a facial challenge to the Act. The court therefore found it unnecessary to decide the question of groundwater ownership. The court held that the Act was not unconstitutional on its face, ruling that the plaintiffs had failed to establish that, under all circumstances, the Act would deprive landowners of their property rights. Therefore the court did not have to determine whether the Act as applied would result in a taking and saved resolution of the nature of the property right in groundwater for a future case. *Barshop*, 925 S.W.2d at 630.

§ 5.10 *Edwards Aquifer Authority v. Day:* Groundwater as Real Property

The as-applied challenge portended by *Barshop* came to the Texas Supreme Court in *Edwards Aquifer Authority v. Day*, 274 S.W.3d 742 (Tex. App.—San Antonio 2008, pet. granted). The *Day* plaintiffs before the San Antonio court of appeals, R. Burrell Day and Joel McDaniel (Day), owned a farm located over the Edwards Aquifer, within the boundaries of the EAA. Day's farm included an Edwards Aquifer well drilled in the 1950s and used for irrigation in the 1970s, but whose casing had since collapsed, the pump having been removed in 1983. After that time, the well flowed under artesian pressure, and most of the water flowed down a ditch to a lake on Day's property.

The EAA Act allowed "existing irrigation user[s] to [receive] a permit 'for not less than two acre-feet a year for each acre of land the user actually irrigated in any one calendar year during the historical period,'" and Day applied for a permit. *Day*, 274 S.W.3d at 748 (quoting the EAA Act). Day sought a permit from the Authority for use of 700 acre-feet of Edwards water per year, based on irrigation of approximately 300 acres in 1983 and 1984 from the well. The EAA denied the application. After a hearing at the State Office of Administrative Hearings, testimony showed that about 150 acres had been irrigated with water from the lake on the property, and no more than seven acres were irrigated directly from the well. The EAA therefore granted Day a permit for fourteen acre-feet of groundwater based on irrigation of land directly from the well but denied the rest of the application based on land irrigated from the lake. The EAA determined that the water historically pumped from the lake was state water and not groundwater from the Edwards Aquifer.

Day appealed the EAA's permit decision to state district court and also brought constitutional claims against the EAA, including that of a taking of property without compensation. The EAA interpleaded the state as a third-party defendant seeking contribution and indemnity from the state on the takings claims. The district court held that the lake water was groundwater and that Day was therefore entitled to a permit but granted the EAA's and state's motions for summary judgment on the constitutional claims.

Day and the EAA appealed. The appeals court agreed with the EAA's conclusion that the water used from the lake was state water and rendered judgment affirming the EAA's final order denying the bulk of Day's permit request based on water historically used from the lake. However, the court of appeals reversed the take-nothing judgment against Day on his takings claim and remanded the takings claim to the trial court for further proceedings. The court held that "landowners have some ownership rights in the groundwater beneath their property," and those rights are vested and are therefore constitutionally protected. *Day*, 274 S.W.3d at 756.

Both the state and the EAA filed petitions for review of the court of appeals' finding that the plaintiffs had a vested and constitutionally protected interest in groundwater beneath their property. Day filed a petition for review claiming error by the court of appeals in denying a permit for acres irrigated with water from the lake.

On February 24, 2012, the Texas Supreme Court issued a unanimous opinion in *Edwards Aquifer Authority v. Day*, 369 S.W.3d 814 (Tex. 2012), affirming the court of appeals' decision and finally addressing the nature of the property right in groundwater and its protection under the Texas and U.S. constitutions. In addressing the question of groundwater ownership in place, the court began by reviewing its previous decisions on the rule of capture and acknowledging that in its prior groundwater decisions it had not decided whether groundwater was owned in place.

The court stated that although it had never addressed groundwater ownership in place, it had done so long ago with respect to oil and gas, to which the rule of capture also applies and was not preclusive of ownership. The court, quoting its previous decisions, noted that the right to the oil and gas beneath a landowner's property is an exclusive and private property right inherent in land ownership, which may not be deprived without a taking of private property. *Day*, 369 S.W.3d at 829.

The supreme court concluded that there was no difference between groundwater and oil and gas with regard to common-law ownership of oil and gas in place and that of groundwater. Specifically, the court relied on *Elliff v. Texon Drilling Co.*, 210 S.W.2d 558, 562–63 (Tex. 1949), regarding the ownership of oil and gas in place:

> In our state the landowner is regarded as having absolute title in severalty to the oil and gas in place beneath his land. The only qualification of that rule of ownership is that it must be considered in connection with the law of capture and is subject to police regulations. The oil and gas beneath the soil are considered a part of the realty. Each owner of land owns separately, distinctly and exclusively all the oil and gas under his land and is accorded the usual remedies against trespassers who appropriate the minerals or destroy their market value.

Day, 369 S.W.3d at 831–32 (quoting *Elliff*, 201 S.W.2d at 561) (internal citations omitted). The court then noted, "We now hold that this correctly states the common law regarding the ownership of groundwater in place." *Day*, 369 S.W.3d at 832. The court cited the 2011 legislative revisions to Texas Water Code section 36.002 as demonstrating the legislature's understanding of the interplay between groundwater ownership and groundwater regulation.

Once the court had decided that a landowner owns groundwater in place, it analyzed whether Day had stated a viable takings claim. The court described the three categories of takings recognized by the U.S. Supreme Court and followed by the Texas Supreme Court: (1) a physical invasion of property, (2) a taking of all economically beneficial use of land, and (3) a regulatory-takings challenge analyzed under the balancing test first laid out in *Penn Central Transportation Co. v. New York City*, 438 U.S. 104 (1978). *Day*, 369 S.W.3d at 839.

In *Penn Central*, the Court identified several factors that have particular significance in determining whether the regulation rises to the level of a taking under the Constitution. Primary among those factors are the economic impact of the regulation on the claimant and the extent to which the regulation has interfered with distinct investment-backed expectations. In addition, the character of the governmental action—in essence an analysis of the reasonableness of the regulation in light of the goals to be achieved and the impacts reasonably expected—must be considered. *Day*, 369 S.W.3d at 839–40.

In applying the three categories of takings law to the case at hand, the court quickly stated that no physical invasion of property had occurred. *Day*, 369 S.W.3d at 840. It then analyzed the second and third types of takings and applied the *Penn Central* factors to Day's facts. The court found the summary judgment record lacking in evidence sufficient to illuminate the economic effect of EAA regulation on Day's operations. The court therefore agreed with the fourth court of appeals that summary judgment against Day's takings claim should be reversed and the issue remanded to the trial court. *Day*, 369 S.W.3d at 843. The case was subsequently settled.

Day's importance cannot be overstated. Just as *East* defined the first century of Texas groundwater law, *Day* will define the next. Just as it took decades for Texas oil and gas law to develop as courts worked through the implications of oil and gas ownership, market activity, and regulation, it will take decades for Texas groundwater law to do the same. Two major cases have already been decided by the courts based on the *Day* holding, and there will be many more to come. Likewise, many more questions have been raised that have yet to be definitively answered by either the appellate courts or the Texas Supreme Court.

V. Post-*Day* Cases

§ 5.11 An Extension of *Day*—Application of Oil and Gas Law to Groundwater as Real Property

In May 2016, the Texas Supreme Court issued its opinion in *Coyote Lake Ranch, LLC v. City of Lubbock*, 498 S.W.3d 53 (Tex. 2016), and in doing so seems to have indicated that as far as groundwater as real property is concerned, the court will be following oil and gas law. Coyote Lake Ranch had conveyed the groundwater estate under the ranch to the City of Lubbock in 1953. *Coyote Lake Ranch*, 498 S.W.3d at 55–56. The Ranch retained certain rights to use groundwater, but the bulk of the groundwater estate and right to develop it were conveyed to the City. Over the years, the City drilled a few wells on the Ranch, but did not begin large-scale groundwater development plans for the property until 2012. *Coyote Lake Ranch*, 498 S.W.3d at 57.

The groundwater deed gave the City expansive rights to drill "water wells and test wells" "at any time and location" on the Ranch and "'to use all that part of [the Ranch] necessary or incidental to the taking[,] production, treating[,] transmission[,] and delivery of . . . water.'" *Coyote Lake Ranch*, 498 S.W.3d at 57. The deed also gave the City rights to "construct certain specified facilities, including water lines, fuel lines, power lines, communication lines, barricades, and access roads 'on, over and under said lands necessary or incidental to any of said operations.'" *Coyote Lake Ranch*, 498 S.W.3d at 57. In 2012, the City drew up plans to drill many new wells on the property, along with constructing roads and erecting power lines. The Ranch complained that the City's proposed road construction would cause erosion on the sandy hilltops and the proposed power lines would threaten the Lesser Prairie Chicken. The Ranch sued the City to enjoin its mowing activities, arguing that the City had a duty "'to use only that amount of surface that is reasonably necessary to its operations' and that the City had a 'duty to conduct its operations with due regard for the rights of the surface owner.'" *Coyote Lake Ranch*, 498 S.W.3d at 57. The trial court granted the Ranch's request for a temporary injunction and enjoined the City from mowing grass, drilling wells without consulting the Ranch, or erecting power lines to proposed well fields. *Coyote Lake Ranch*, 498 S.W.3d at 57–58.

The City appealed, arguing that it had rights under its deed to pursue its groundwater-development plan and that the accommodation-doctrine claim brought by the Ranch did not apply to groundwater law. The Ranch responded that as a logical extension of the ownership-in-place holding in *Day*, the accommodation doctrine also applied to severed groundwater estates. The court of appeals agreed with the City and reversed the temporary injunction. *Coyote Lake Ranch*, 498 S.W.3d at 58.

On appeal to the Texas Supreme Court, the court first evaluated whether the City's deed resolved the issue between the parties, as the accommodation doctrine would apply only in the absence of an applicable agreement. The court found that "the deed leaves unclear whether the City can do everything necessary or incidental to drilling anywhere, as it claims, or only what is necessary or incidental to fully access the groundwater, as the Ranch argues." *Coyote Lake Ranch*, 498 S.W.3d at 59. The court found a similar ambiguity regarding overhead power lines and held that the deed did not resolves the parties' dispute. *Coyote Lake Ranch*, 498 S.W.3d at 59.

The court then turned to oil and gas law and explained how and why a severed mineral estate is dominant to the surface. In light of this relationship, the accommodation doctrine serves to balance the competing interests of the mineral and surface estate owners. The court analogized the groundwater estate to a mineral estate to hold that the accommodation doctrine also applies in groundwater law. In the course of reaching that holding, the court confirmed that a severed groundwater estate is dominant to the surface in the same way that a severed mineral estate is. *Coyote Lake Ranch*, 498 S.W.3d at 60–64.

In conclusion, after holding that the accommodation doctrine would apply to resolve the parties' dispute, the court analyzed the trial court's temporary injunction and found it overbroad. It therefore affirmed the judgment of the appellate court reversing the temporary injunction and remanded for further proceedings consistent with its opinion. *Coyote Lake Ranch*, 498 S.W.3d at 65.

The main result of *Coyote Lake Ranch* is that the accommodation doctrine applies as between surface and groundwater owners. Based on the dearth of accommodation-doctrine cases in oil and gas law, it seems unlikely that this will become a busy area of groundwater litigation. *See Coyote Lake Ranch*, 498 S.W.3d at 63 ("The paucity of reported cases applying the doctrine suggests that it is well-understood and not often disputed.").

Another key result is the confirmation that the groundwater estate is dominant to the surface. The court cited this dominance as a settled, uncontroversial point (*Coyote Lake Ranch*, 498 S.W.3d at 63, citing *Evans v. Ropte*, 96 S.W.2d 973, 974 (Tex. 1936)), but it took some water attorneys by surprise. In the absence of a clear statement by the supreme court to this effect in the past, transactional water lawyers had structured deals and drafted documents as though a groundwater owner would not have had the same implied rights of ingress and egress afforded mineral owners. Now the dominance of a groundwater estate to a surface estate has been clearly stated by the court, establishing that a groundwater owner does have such implied rights of ingress and egress.

§ 5.12 *Bragg*—A Groundwater Taking

Glenn and JoLynn Bragg from Medina County spent over fifteen years in litigation with the EAA, bringing various cases to defend their groundwater interests. On November 13, 2013, in *Edwards Aquifer Authority v. Bragg*, 421 S.W.3d 118 (Tex. App.—San Antonio 2013, pet. denied), the fourth court of appeals held that a regulation limiting the Braggs' use of their groundwater was a regulatory taking. A jury later awarded the Braggs over $2.5 million plus interest in compensation for that taking. This was the first time a Texas court found that a groundwater regulation resulted in a compensable taking under the Texas Constitution.

The Braggs owned two commercial pecan orchards located over the Edwards Aquifer. When they applied for initial regular permits from the EAA in 1996, the EAA granted the Braggs' permit for one of their wells, but for fewer acre-feet of water than requested, and denied the application for the Braggs' other well because it was drilled in 1995, after the end of the historical-use period. The Braggs appealed to state district court in Medina County, where the trial court found the denial of one application and shortage in the other permit were each a compensable taking entitling the Braggs to compensation. Both the EAA and the Braggs appealed to the fourth court of appeals.

Before analyzing the takings claim, the appellate court first disposed of multiple threshold issues. The court held that (1) the EAA was a proper defendant to the lawsuit, (2) a ten-year statute of limitations applied to the Braggs' takings claim, and (3) the Braggs' takings claim accrued as of the date of EAA action on their permit applications in 2004 and 2005 and were therefore not time barred. *Bragg*, 421 S.W.3d at 131, 134, 137.

The court then discussed whether a taking had, in fact, occurred. Applying *Day*, the court dismissed the EAA's arguments that no taking had occurred. The court applied the *Penn Central* test to the facts of the case. It found that the economic-impact factor weighed heavily in favor of the Braggs, because the highest and best use of the land was as commercial pecan orchards and the Braggs had invested millions of dollars in the enterprise. The court found that the second factor, evaluation of the Braggs' investment-backed expectations, also weighed heavily in favor of the Braggs, based on the Braggs' understanding of pecan crops, their understanding that they owned the water under their land, and because there was no groundwater regulatory scheme when they purchased the property. The court found that the last factor of the *Penn Central* test, regarding the nature of the regulation, heavily favored the EAA. On balance, the court held that a taking had occurred. *Bragg*, 421 S.W.3d at 146.

The court held that compensation should be determined by reference to the highest and best use of the properties, in this case as commercial pecan orchards. The court also held that "the 'property'actually taken is the unlimited use of water to irrigate a commercial-grade pecan orchard, and that 'property' should be valued with reference to the value of the commercial-grade pecan orchards immediately before and immediately after the provisions of the Act were implemented or applied." *Bragg*, 421 S.W.3d at 152.

The court concluded that the trial court properly determined that the application of the Act resulted in a taking but that it erred in calculating the compensation owed the Braggs. The appellate court reversed the trial court's judgment and remanded the case for further proceedings consistent with its opinion on the issue of compensation, and the supreme court denied review. *Bragg*, 421 S.W.3d at 152–53. On February 22, 2016, a Medina County jury returned a verdict awarding the Braggs more than $2.5 million in compensation. The EAA did not appeal the trial court's decision and in July 2016 approved a payment to the Braggs of more than $4.5 million, which included interest accruing since the taking.

The *Bragg* case is the first Texas case to apply the *Penn Central* test to determine that government regulation of groundwater actually caused a taking. It is also significant for its analysis and conclusions on the damages model established for the taking of groundwater. It remains to be seen whether the *Bragg* decision can be applied in a more widespread manner, opening the door to other takings cases.

§ 5.13 The Meaning of "Correlative Rights" and a "Fair Share" in Texas Groundwater Law

In addition to takings issues raised by the supreme court's decision in the *Day* case, when describing property rights in underlying groundwater, the court used phrases such as "correlative rights" and "fair share." *See, e.g., Edwards Aquifer Authority v. Day*, 369 S.W.3d 814, 830 (Tex. 2012). The *Day* court quoted *Elliff v. Texon Drilling Co.*, 210 S.W.2d 558, 562 (Tex. 1949), stating that—

> "correlative rights between the various landowners over a common reservoir of oil or gas" have been recognized through state regulation of oil and gas production that affords each landowner "the opportunity to produce his fair share of the recoverable oil and gas beneath his land." Similarly, one purpose of the EAAA's regulatory provisions is to afford landowners their fair share of the groundwater beneath their property. In both instances, correlative rights are a creature of regulation rather than the common law.

Day, 369 S.W.3d at 830.

The plaintiffs in *Meyer v. Lost Pines Groundwater Conservation District* attempted to test the implications of *Day*'s correlative-rights and fair-share discussion. In *Meyer*, after many years of administrative procedure, the Lost Pines Groundwater Conservation District in 2014 denied four Bastrop County landowners party status to contest the permit applications of End Op, L.P. The district adopted an administrative law judge's findings, who found that the plaintiffs, none of whom proved they owned wells completed in the same aquifer as End Op's proposed wells, had not proved a concrete, particularized injury sufficient to give them standing to contest End Op's application. The plaintiffs filed a lawsuit as a judicial appeal of the district's denial of their party status.

The plaintiffs argued aquifer drawdown caused by End Op's proposed pumping would devalue their groundwater and affect their ability to withdraw their fair share of groundwater. Under *Day*, the plaintiffs argued that injury to their property interest in groundwater was sufficient to establish a particularized injury, because Texas groundwater regulation creates correlative rights protecting the opportunity to develop groundwater, which could not be lost through nonuse. Plaintiffs' Initial Brief at 16–23, *Meyer v. Lost Pines Groundwater Conservation District*, No. 29,696 (21st Dist. Ct., Bastrop County, Tex., filed Apr. 5, 2016). The district and End Op responded that a property interest in groundwater was insufficient to show a particularized, actual, and imminent injury for standing purposes. Further, if application of correlative rights in groundwater conferred automatic standing, all landowners would have a right to a contested case hearing, because all groundwater production results in lowered water levels. End Op Response to Plaintiffs' Supplemental Brief Regarding Party Status, at 3, *Meyer v. Lost Pines Groundwater Conservation District*, No. 29,696 (21st Dist. Ct., Bastrop County, Tex., filed Sept. 5, 2017).

In January 2018, the district court in Bastrop County reversed the district's denial of the plaintiffs' requests for party status. Final Judgment, *Meyer v. Lost Pines Groundwater Conservation District*, No. 29,696 (21st Dist. Ct., Bastrop County, Tex., Jan. 4, 2018). The district and End Op appealed. The third court of appeals did not reach the standing and correlative-rights arguments, instead reversing the district court's holding regarding jurisdiction, because the plaintiffs had prematurely filed their suit for review of the district's administrative action. *End Op., L.P. v. Meyer*, No. 03-18-00049-CV, 2018 WL 4102013 (Tex. App.—Austin Aug. 29, 2018, no pet.) (mem. op.).

Despite the anticlimactic result at the appeals court, the case is important because it demonstrates the extent to which the *Day* holding can be stretched and the remaining questions about the meaning of landowner's rights to a fair share of groundwater.

VI. Recent Cases

§ 5.14 *Stratta v. Roe*

In *Stratta v. Roe*, 961 F.3d 340 (5th Cir. 2020), two landowners brought federal constitutional claims against the Brazos Valley Groundwater Conservation District (BVGCD) and its board of directors (Board), including claims for equal protection, First Amendment, and takings violations.

Plaintiff Anthony Fazzino was a Brazos County landowner who owned 26.65 acres located within 3,000 feet of a large well owned by the City of Bryan. Plaintiff David Stratta was a BVGCD director who claimed the BVGCD violated his First Amendment right of free speech by prohibiting him from speaking as a "member of the public" during an open meeting of the Board.

The plaintiffs brought suit in federal court in April 2018, and in December 2018 the federal district court in the Western District of Texas dismissed the plaintiffs' claims based on Eleventh Amendment immunity, *Burford* abstention, and qualified immunity. The Fifth Circuit affirmed the dismissal of Stratta's First Amendment claim but reversed on almost all other grounds and remanded the case to the district court. *See Stratta*, 961 F.3d at 346. In the interests of brevity and relevance, this case summary skips facts and conclusions about Stratta, as the substance of his claim is not substantive groundwater law, and he has been definitively dismissed from the case. This summary focuses on the Fifth Circuit decision on Fazzino's constitutional claims.

Fazzino's case turns on application of BVGCD rules effective as of December 2, 2004 (the Rules). The Rules established three categories of wells—existing wells, new wells, and wells with historic use. The Rules further provided a formula for calculating a production limit for a new well related to the cone of depression produced by the well. The Rules were unclear about production limits for existing wells with no historic use. *See Stratta*, 961 F.3d at 347.

Soon after the Rules took effect, the City of Bryan began drilling its Well No. 18 on a 2.7-acre tract, which it completed ten months later. The City then applied for and was conditionally granted a permit by the BVGCD to produce up to 4,838 acre-feet annually from Well No. 18 at a rate of 3,000 gallons per minute (gpm), as an existing well. The parties disputed whether the BVGCD should have classified Well No. 18 as new or existing under the Rules. *See Stratta*, 961 F.3d at 348.

The plaintiffs argued that Well No. 18 was a new well and application of the Rules' new well production-limit formula should have resulted in a permitted rate no greater than 192 gpm on the City's tract of 2.7 acres. In contrast, for a new well to produce 3,000 gpm pursuant to the formula, the well would have had to be situated on at least 649 contiguous acres. *See Stratta*, 961 F.3d at 348.

In January 2017, Fazzino filed a complaint with the BVGCD requesting that the district reduce the production limit on Well No. 18, arguing that the well should have had to comply with the new well production-limit formula. After the State Office of Administrative Hearings determined that Fazzino was not permitted to assert such a complaint, he filed an application with the BVGCD for his own 3,000 gpm permit to "offset" the production from the city's Well No. 18. The district declared the application administratively incomplete for failure to demonstrate ownership or control of sufficient acreage to meet the requirements of the production-limit formula for new wells. Fazzino requested a variance, but the district responded that it did not grant variances. The Rules did not provide for further Board action on an administratively incomplete application. *See Stratta*, 961 F.3d at 348.

Fazzino then brought equal protection and takings claims against the BVGCD. The BVGCD filed motions for dismissal under Federal Rules of Civil Procedure 12(b)(1) and 12(b)(6) for lack of jurisdiction and failure to state a claim, respectively. The district court held in favor of the BVGCD on all of its responses, including, for jurisdiction: (1) application of Eleventh Amendment immunity, (2) failure to exhaust state-court remedies, and (3) *Burford* abstention. On the BVGCD's 12(b)(6) responses, the district court agreed with the BVGCD that "Fazzino's property interest in groundwater

[was] not 'clearly established,' [and] his claims against the Directors [were] barred by qualified immunity." *See Stratta*, 961 F.3d at 349.

The Fifth Circuit reviewed *de novo* the district court's dismissal orders. The Eleventh Amendment protects states or an "arm of the state" from money judgments in federal court. Accordingly, the court first applied to the BVGCD the Eleventh Amendment immunity test delineated in *Clark v. Tarrant County*, 798 F.2d 736 (5th Cir. 1986), to determine whether the BVGCD was an "arm of the state" that warranted protection from suit. The six-factor test evaluates (1) the characterization given to the entity by state law and case law, (2) the entity's source of funding, (3) the entity's degree of autonomy, (4) the entity's scope of activity, (5) the entity's authority to sue and be sued in its own name, and (6) the entity's right to hold property. The court reviewed the factors and concluded that all weighed against the BVGCD having Eleventh Amendment immunity, except factor three regarding autonomy, which neither weighed for or against the district. The court concluded the district court had abused its discretion in dismissing the action on that basis. *See Stratta*, 961 F.3d at 350–51.

The Fifth Circuit's holding is significant on this point, because the *Clark* analysis is likely to apply similarly to all or most Texas Water Code chapter 36 GCDs. This means that another GCD sued in federal court faces an uphill battle relying on Eleventh Amendment immunity as a viable defense.

The court quickly overturned the district court decision as to ripeness of Fazzino's takings claim, based on *Knick v. Township of Scott, Pennsylvania*, 139 S. Ct. 2126 (2019). *Knick* overruled the previous requirement that a federal takings plaintiff must first seek compensation in state court. *See Stratta*, 961 F.3d at 356 (describing *Knick*'s overruling of *Williamson County Regional Planning Commission v. Hamilton Bank of Johnson City*, 473 U.S. 172 (1985)).

The Fifth Circuit then held that the district court had abused its discretion in abstaining under *Burford*. The court's most significant analysis on this issue focused on whether the case implicated "unsettled issues" of state law, and whether a federal decision would jeopardize the state's need for a coherent policy in regulating groundwater. The court found that Texas groundwater law was indeed sufficiently settled as to require a federal court to maintain its jurisdiction and decide the issues presented. *See also Edwards Aquifer Authority v. Day*, 369 S.W.3d 814 (Tex. 2012). In addressing whether the federal courts could resolve Fazzino's claims, the court found especially important the clear holding of *Day* that landowners own in place the groundwater under their land. *See Stratta*, 961 F.3d at 357.

Finally, addressing the merits, the Fifth Circuit reversed the district court's dismissal of Fazzino's takings and equal protection claims. Similar to its *Burford* abstention analysis, the court dismissed the GCD's argument that to adjudicate Fazzino's claims would require the federal courts to decide unsettled state law questions or adopt all of Texas oil and gas law for purposes of groundwater regulation. The court held that Texas law on the nature of groundwater ownership is sufficiently settled as to allow for takings claims. *See also Day*, 369 S.W.3d at 833. The court also held that Fazzino had sufficiently alleged unequal treatment by the district as compared to the district's treatment of the City as to preclude dismissal of his equal protection claim, stating the claim should be "judged . . . against the precise regulations enacted and enforced by the BVGCD in this case." *See Stratta*, 961 F.3d at 359–60.

The Fifth Circuit remanded the remaining claims to the district court, which then denied the BVGCD's motion for judgment on the pleadings based on the statute of limitations, granted the motion as to the Board members in their individual capacities, and granted the motion as to the requests for injunctive relief and punitive damages. *See Stratta v. Roe*, No. 6:18-CV-00114-ADA, 2021 WL 1199634 (W.D. Tex. Mar. 30, 2021).

§ 5.15 *Neches & Trinity Valleys Groundwater Conservation District v. Mountain Pure TX, LLC*

Neches & Trinity Valleys Groundwater Conservation District v. Mountain Pure TX, LLC, No. 12-19-00172-CV, 2019 WL 4462677 (Tex. App.—Tyler Sept. 18, 2019) (mem. op.), was an interlocutory appeal brought by the Neches and Trinity Valleys GCD to the Twelfth Court of Appeals in Tyler after the district court denied its plea to the jurisdiction that alleged governmental immunity. The groundwater district filed suit against a bottled water company, Mountain Pure TX, seeking to require Mountain Pure to comply with the Texas Water Code and GCD rules that require an entity to obtain a permit to operate a well. According to the groundwater district, Mountain Pure was pumping groundwater from an unpermitted well for its spring water bottling plant and refused to obtain a permit. Mountain Pure filed a series of counterclaims, maintaining that the water it bottled and sold did not come from a well but from an "underground formation from which water flows naturally to the surface of the earth," and arguing that the district's enforcement action against it constituted a regulatory taking. *Neches & Trinity Valleys*, 2019 WL 4462677, at *1–2.

At issue on appeal was whether the district court erred when it denied the GCD's plea to the jurisdiction alleging governmental immunity. The Texas Constitution waives governmental immunity with respect to inverse condemnation (regulatory takings) claims, but absent a properly pleaded takings claim, the government retains immunity, and a court must sustain a properly raised plea to the jurisdiction. *See Neches & Trinity Valleys*, 2019 WL 4462677, at *3 (citing *City of Houston v. Carlson*, 451 S.W.3d 828, 830 (Tex. 2014)). The Twelfth Court of Appeals reversed the district court's denial of the GCD's plea to the jurisdiction, holding that an enforcement action cannot give rise to a regulatory takings claim and that Mountain Pure had not asserted a valid takings claim. The court of appeals' decision is noteworthy because it clarified that when a GCD's rules have not yet applied restrictions to a landowner's property, "a civil enforcement action alone cannot serve as the basis of a regulatory takings claim." *See Neches & Trinity Valleys*, 2019 WL 4462677, at *5.

VII. Conclusion

§ 5.16 Conclusion

The common-law rule of capture established in *East* has been the law for more than a hundred years. Periodically over the course of the past century, the courts reaffirmed the rule, often conflating it with absolute ownership of groundwater. To provide for groundwater management, the legislature authorized creation of local groundwater conservation districts in 1949, creation of which escalated rapidly after Senate Bill 1 was passed in 1997. The conflict between property rights in groundwater and groundwater regulation finally came to a head in the 2012 landmark groundwater case *Edwards Aquifer Authority v. Day*. In *Day*, the Texas Supreme Court held that groundwater is owned in place by the surface owner unless severed and subject to constitutional protection.

One new frontier in groundwater law will be the extent to which statutory groundwater conservation districts can regulate production of groundwater without effecting a compensable governmental taking. Additionally, now that it is clear that groundwater is owned in place and it appears that Texas courts will apply oil and gas law to groundwater, questions have arisen over the best way to protect a landowner's fair share of groundwater.

CHAPTER 6

Conjunctive Management of Surface Water and Groundwater Resources

Zachary P. Sugg,[1] *Sonya Ziaja,*[2] *and Edella C. Schlager*[3]

I. Introduction

§ 6.1 Introduction

Over the last several decades, modern hydrology has greatly advanced our understanding of the interconnections between terrestrial water resources in their various forms and locations, including the complex linkages between surface water and groundwater. The more visible of the interconnections are part of what drew humans to certain areas of Texas for centuries—most notably and famously, the numerous springs that perforate the landscape in the Edwards Aquifer region of Central Texas. In the present era, naturally occurring freshwater resources are often fully allocated, or even overallocated, and are pushed beyond ecologically sustainable thresholds. As a result, the rationale for managing groundwater and surface water in an integrated fashion, that is, conjunctively, has become increasingly compelling because doing so can increase capacity to respond to hydroclimatic disturbances and achieve a variety of ecological and sustainability goals. *See* Zachary Sugg et al., *Conjunctive Groundwater Management as a Response to Socio-Ecological Disturbances: A Comparison of 4 Western U.S. States*, 7 Tex. Water J. 1 [hereinafter Sugg et al.]. But as water supply management goals and the scientific understanding of water as an indivisible, interconnected whole have advanced, laws, policies, and the integration of different water agencies have not developed in sync. Thus, the law pertaining to the conjunctive management of water is particularly dynamic in Texas as well as in other states.

---

1. Zachary Sugg is a program manager at the Babbitt Center for Land and Water Policy of the Lincoln Institute for Land Policy.

2. Sonya Ziaja is an Assistant Professor at the University of Baltimore School of Law.

3. Edella Schlager is a Professor in the School of Government and Public Policy at the University of Arizona.

II. Conjunctive Management Concepts and Terminology

§ 6.2 Terminology

The terms "conjunctive use" and "conjunctive management" are often used to signify different things. Conjunctive *use* typically refers to the strategic use of both groundwater and surface water, for example, temporarily increasing groundwater withdrawals relative to surface water during drought conditions. Conjunctive *management* is sometimes used to mean the formal integration of surface water and groundwater management and regulatory duties in a single state agency. So defined, states are either "conjunctive management states" or they are not. In this chapter, however, conjunctive management is defined more broadly as "the coordinated use of surface water supplies and storage and groundwater supplies and storage." William Blomquist et al., *Common Waters, Diverging Streams: Linking Institutions and Water Management in Arizona, California, and Colorado* 12 (Resources for the Future Press 2004). Under this definition, conjunctive management may refer to activities done at any and all administrative levels, including but not limited to various types of conjunctive use.

However defined, the salient point is that conjunctive management is not one thing, but rather an array of different practices that may be implemented to achieve different management goals. At a very basic level, the commonality among practices is that they are strategies that take advantage of the unique characteristics and functions of surface and groundwater resources—primarily the conveyance ability of the former and the storage capacity of the latter.

§ 6.3 Examples of Conjunctive Management

One of the most common kinds of conjunctive management involves the use of aquifers as natural storage reservoirs for surplus surface water, often called managed aquifer recharge (MAR). MAR systems often divert surface water from a natural channel or constructed canal into a spreading basin where it can percolate into an aquifer and be effectively stored indefinitely with minimal loss. See, for example, the discussion about the El Paso Water project in Chapter 26 of this book. MAR can also be accomplished by pumping surface water directly into an aquifer using injection wells (the reverse of a normal groundwater well). This is commonly known as aquifer storage and recovery (ASR). The typical rationale for MAR is to use the storage capability of aquifers like bank accounts for drought resilience, where recharged water functions as deposits that can be withdrawn later when reducing the use of surface water supplies becomes a high priority, as during drought.

The 2022 Texas State Water Plan estimated that the increasing use of ASR could provide up to 193,000 acre-feet (AF) of water per year by 2070. *See* Texas Water Development Board, *Water for Texas 2022* 103 (2022), www.twdb.texas.gov/waterplanning/swp/2022 [hereinafter 2022 State Water Plan]. Additionally, multiple bills pertaining to ASR were passed during the 86th legislative session. House Bill 720 incentivized aquifer recharge (AR) and ASR by authorizing the use of unappropriated storm runoff and floodwaters for aquifer recharge and by expediting the TCEQ's permitting process for surface water right applications for ASR and AR. *See* Act of May 25, 2019, 86th Leg., R.S., ch. 742 (H.B. 720), eff. June 10, 2019; House Committee on Natural Resources, *Interim Report to the 87th Texas Legislature* 21–23 (Dec. 2020), https://house.texas.gov/_media/pdf/committees/reports/86interim/Natural-Resources-Committee-Interim-Report-2020.pdf [hereinafter 2020 Interim Report]. House Bill 721 required the Texas Water Development Board (TWDB) to study the state's aquifers to identify appropriate candidates for ASR projects. *See* Act of May 27, 2019, 86th Leg., R.S., ch. 1043 (H.B. 721), eff. June 14, 2019. Senate Bill 483 clarified permitting provisions for injection wells in the Edwards Aquifer, as for ASR facilities. *See* Act of May 26, 2019, 86th Leg., R.S., ch. 583 (S.B. 483), eff. June 10, 2019. Finally, Senate Bill 520 authorized an Edwards Aquifer ASR project for the City of

New Braunfels. *See* Act of May 26, 2019, 86th Leg., R.S., ch. 585 (S.B. 520), eff. Sept. 1, 2019. See Chapter 26 of this book for further discussion of ASR.

Because of Texas's emphasis on ASR and MAR in general, the discussion below highlights examples of these forms of conjunctive management. In practice, conjunctive management in Texas tends to be limited to ASR, with only a few instances of other forms. It is nonetheless important to note that there are other types of conjunctive management, including—

- the active management of withdrawals from alluvial aquifers such that the negative impact of groundwater pumping on baseflow to connected streams is mitigated or avoided; this type of coordination can leave more surface water available in critical times for both humans and nonhumans that depend on it the most;
- the integration of treated municipal and industrial effluent into conjunctive surface and groundwater management and use systems; and
- "in-lieu" recharge, the use of alternate sources of surface water instead of normal groundwater withdrawals in such a way that the aquifer receives some recharge rather than being further depleted.

The desirability, possibility, and rationale for implementing conjunctive management are conditioned by several contextual factors. These are hydrologic conditions (the distribution and functioning of naturally occurring surface water and groundwater in an area), infrastructure (the type and extent of water conveyance systems), relevant law and policy, and the administrative context. Examples of the influence and interplay of these factors are discussed in Part III below.

III. Factors Considered in Implementing Conjunctive Management

§ 6.4 Hydrologic Conditions and Infrastructure

Hydrologic conditions influence what forms of conjunctive management are possible and which challenges may be addressed in a given location. Across Texas, the sheer variety of climatic and hydrologic conditions is enormous. See Chapters 1 and 2 of this book, which provide overviews of these conditions. Considering hydrologic conditions alone, groundwater aquifers may or may not be colocated with surface water bodies and connected to them in different ways. On the one hand, the existence of connected surface water and groundwater bodies is a necessary precondition for forms of conjunctive management, especially those that do not require major infrastructure. On the other, hydrologic conditions can preclude conjunctive management. In Texas, for example, managed recharge by irrigation districts is often inhibited by the physical availability of only one type of major water supply, either groundwater or surface water. *See* Texas Water Development Board, *Surveys of Irrigation in Texas: 1958, 1964, 1969, 1974, 1979, 1984, 1989, 1994 and 2000* (Report 347, Aug. 2001), www.twdb.texas.gov/publications/reports/numbered_reports/doc/R347/R347.pdf?d=8841.480000002775. Indirect recharge using dedicated spreading basins is possible only if there is at least one area overlying an aquifer where infiltration and percolation rates are high enough to reach the aquifer. Additionally, to be suitable for recovering recharged water, an aquifer must not be so transmissive that recharged water "escapes" downgradient before it can be withdrawn for future use.

In addition to hydrologic conditions, the presence or absence of major surface water conveyance infrastructure strongly facilitates or limits certain forms of conjunctive management. By diverting surface water from natural channels to recharge facilities located where subsurface characteristics are suitable, conveyance systems can be used to overcome certain natural hydrologic limitations. In California and central Arizona, for example, large canal systems connecting federal water providers, storage facilities, and state water users make possible conjunctive management on a vast scale. Water from distant rivers and reservoirs can be used to recharge depleted aquifers in different watersheds, river basins, and even different states. For example, the Southern Nevada Water Authority has banked over 600,000 AF of surplus Colorado River water in Arizona aquifers by using this infrastructure. *See* Arizona Water Banking Authority, *Interstate Banking*, https://waterbank.az.gov/objectives/interstate-banking. Texas, in comparison, has fewer large conveyance structures to link major irrigated agriculture regions with growing urban areas, although parts of the Lower Rio Grande, Winter Garden region, and Gulf Coast have combinations of hydrologic conditions and infrastructure amenable to certain forms of conjunctive management.

§ 6.5 Law and Policy

Even if hydrologic conditions and infrastructure are conducive, there is still the critical issue of whether and how law and policy enable, constrain, or complicate conjunctive management practices. The following sections highlight two aspects of Texas law and policy that impact conjunctive management of water resources in the state: the legal separation of surface water and groundwater and issues arising from Texas's interpretation of underflow.

§ 6.5:1 Interconnectivity of Surface Water and Groundwater in State Law

From the standpoint of conjunctive management in Texas, many or most of the salient questions and challenges flow from one basic legal and policy issue: the edifice of Texas water law is erected on a cornerstone of the legal separation of surface water and groundwater into different categories subject to different sets of rights and duties. This includes some rather arcane invented subcategories of water such as "underflow" and subterranean rivers which, although they are underground water, are not legally considered to be groundwater. See Chapter 1 of this book for further discussion of this separation.

Although these legal categories may have been useful for resolving certain problems in the past, they can be problematic for modern conjunctive management. Unhelpfully, the bifurcation of surface water and groundwater under different legal and policy regimes has been calcified by the state legislature, even as it has recently tried to encourage the use of conjunctive management. It is not controversial to say that in Texas historically, interest in conjunctive management and the hydrologic science and technology underpinning it has outpaced the development of appropriate rules and regulations. In the case of ASR, this lag has actually created a disincentive to implementation in recent years. *See* Malcolm Pirnie, Inc. et al., *An Assessment of Aquifer Storage and Recovery in Texas* 51 (Texas Water Development Board Report # 0904830940, Feb. 2011), www.edwardsaquifer.net/pdf/TWDB_2011_ASR_assessment.pdf.

One particularly acute issue stemming from the legal disconnect between surface water and groundwater in some parts of Texas—most notably the Central Texas Hill Country—is the negative impact of groundwater pumping on hydrologically connected springs. Because of the unfortunate legacy of spring flow loss in Texas (*see generally, e.g.*, Gunnar Brune & Helen C. Besse, 1 *Springs of Texas* (new ed. 2002)), in some areas of the state conjunctive management is prompted by the desire or requirement to avoid or mitigate the further degradation of remaining springs. However, Texas state courts have refused to find that groundwater pumping can be limited by the depletion of connected spring flows, even to the point that a spring is completely dried up. *See Denis v. Kickapoo Land Co.*, 771 S.W.2d 235 (Tex. App.—Austin 1989, writ denied); *Pecos County Water Control & Improvement District No. 1 v. Williams*, 271 S.W.2d 503 (Tex. App.—El Paso 1954, writ ref'd n.r.e.)). At the same time, the Texas Water Code directs groundwater conservation districts (GCDs) to address conjunctive water management issues in their management plans. *See* Tex. Water Code § 36.1071(a)(4). Consequently, since neither statutes nor case law provide protection for springs against deleterious interfering groundwater pumping, some GCDs have stepped into the breach by designing their groundwater production regulations to achieve protection of spring flows. The administrative role of GCDs related to conjunctive management is discussed further in section 6.6:4 below.

Recognition of the need to better understand the connectivity between surface water and groundwater and the challenges that the separate legal regimes pose to Texas's water supply and the use of conjunctive management has grown in recent years, as evidenced by House Bill 2652, introduced during the 87th legislative session. If passed, the bill will create a nine-person Surface Water and Groundwater Interaction Advisory Board to study and report on surface water–groundwater interaction statewide, the challenges posed by such interactions, and approaches to mitigating challenges that arise from such interactions. *See* Tex. H.B. 2652, 87th Leg., R.S. (2021), https://capitol.texas.gov/BillLookup/History.aspx?LegSess=87R&Bill=HB2652.

§ 6.5:2 Underflow and Conjunctive Management

The "underflow" of a stream is an unscientific Texas legal construct but one that potentially provides a basis for conjunctive management. It is defined simply and vaguely in the Texas Water Code as "[t]he water of the ordinary flow, underflow, and tides of every flowing river, natural stream, and lake." Tex. Water Code § 11.021(a). The Texas Commission on Environmental Quality (TCEQ) provides a more specific definition in its regulations:

> Underflow of a stream—Water in sand, soil, and gravel below the bed of the watercourse, together with the water in the lateral extensions of the water-bearing material on each side of the surface channel, such that the surface flows are in contact with the subsurface flows, the latter flows being confined within a space reasonably defined and having a direction corresponding to that of the surface flow.

30 Tex. Admin. Code § 297.1(57). Like surface water, underflow is the property of the state and therefore subject to the prior appropriation doctrine, as distinct from groundwater, which is regulated by local GCDs or not regulated at all. The potential upshot, in theory, is that this could limit groundwater users' ability to deplete surface water bodies to some extent by imposing an appropriation restriction on alluvial groundwater (underflow). In other words, to the extent that a well owner is withdrawing underground water from alluvium, that owner could be effectively infringing on state property and be required to obtain authorization from the TCEQ. The relatively peaceful coexistence of the separate regulatory regimes for groundwater and underflow could be upset if a high-capacity well or well field in an alluvial aquifer depletes the underflow such that it negatively impacts a downstream surface water right holder. *See* Ronald Kaiser, *Conjunctive Management and Use of Surface Water and Groundwater Resources*, *in Essentials of Texas Water Resources* 5-1 (Mary K. Sahs ed., 5th ed. 2018) [hereinafter Kaiser]. Such a scenario could pose additional complexities in a GCD that incorporates water withdrawals from an alluvial aquifer into its rules for granting new production permits, as the Brazos Valley GCD has done for the Brazos River Alluvium Aquifer. *See* Brazos Valley Groundwater Conservation District, *Rules of the Brazos Valley Groundwater Conservation District* 18–19 (2018), https://brazosvalleygcd.org/wp-content/uploads/2018/11/BVGCD-Rules-Adopted-11-8-18.pdf. Because underflow still lacks bright lines of demarcation, outcomes of future disputes (e.g., between river basin authorities and groundwater districts) are likely to hinge largely on particular findings of fact rather than any reliable legal concepts.

§ 6.6 Administration and Implementation of Conjunctive Management in Texas

In addition to hydrologic conditions, water infrastructure, and law and policy, administrative systems are the fourth factor determining what kinds of conjunctive management are actually practicable in a given context. See Chapters 7–9, 16, and 17 in this book regarding the various water management entities and their roles and duties in detail. The following discussion focuses on the roles of select categories of entities specifically in relation to conjunctive management practices.

§ 6.6:1 State Water Agencies

In Texas and a few other states (e.g., Arizona and California), the legal bifurcation of surface and groundwater rights and duties is mirrored by the separation of responsibilities among administrative systems. In Texas, the TCEQ regulates surface water use, and groundwater use is regulated by GCDs or is unregulated in areas without districts. This is also true when the project involves conjunctive use of both resources. Thus, a statewide agency controls the amount of surface water allocated for any purpose, while local groundwater districts, most covering only one county, control the amount of groundwater allocated within their geographic boundaries. Add to this the oversight and advisory role of the TWDB, and the conjunctive management picture becomes more complicated.

The TCEQ and the TWDB perform very different duties in relation to conjunctive management. The TWDB is involved primarily through its oversight and advisory role in the state water planning process. See Chapter 20 of this book for a discussion of state water planning. The TWDB also evaluates and recommends proposed ASR projects, plays a facilitation role, and conducts salient research. As mentioned at section 6.3 above, this research role was expanded during the 86th legislative session through passage of House Bill 721, which directed the TWDB to study the state's aquifers to determine which are conducive to development of ASR projects. *See* Act of May 27, 2019, 86th Leg., R.S., ch. 1043 (H.B. 721), eff. June 14, 2019, and study results, Texas Water Development Board, *Statewide Survey of Aquifer Suitability for Aquifer Storage and Recovery Projects or Aquifer Recharge Projects* (Dec. 2020), www.twdb.texas.gov/publications/reports/special_legislative_reports/doc/Statewide_ASR-AR_Suitability_Survey_Report_20201130.pdf. The TWDB also evaluates desired future conditions (DFCs) for groundwater, so to the extent that a conjunctive management goal is reflected in a DFC by a GCD, the TWDB conducts the technical evaluation of its feasibility. See Chapter 21 discussing the joint planning process. As a regulatory agency, the TCEQ handles permitting of ASR wells, administers water rights for regular surface water and for underflow, and deals with water quality issues (including groundwater), all of which are relevant to aspects of conjunctive management. For example, entities must obtain a right from the TCEQ to divert new surface water to store in an ASR project. Additionally, the TCEQ grants bed and banks permits to entities wishing to use natural surface waterways as a means for conveying pumped groundwater to a downstream location for conjunctive management purposes.

Some experts would say the separation of duties across this many administrative bodies is not ideal from the perspective of conjunctive management. It certainly can pose constraints. In regulatory areas that need clarification, ambiguities about which administrative entities are involved can create a barrier or disincentive to certain kinds of conjunctive management. To the extent that conjunctive management projects and practices raise new issues and identify administrative ambiguities, the separate regulatory schemes for surface water and groundwater can be problematic. Although consolidating bifurcated water agencies into one may make intuitive sense, it has almost never happened in practice. Nevertheless, in some cases conjunctive management has still developed without any major reorganization of state water agencies. Typically, this happens when legislatures pass new statutes clarifying or changing the responsibilities of existing agencies, as Texas did in 2015 with ASR project permitting in House Bill 655 (*see* Act of June 16, 2015, 84th Leg., R.S., ch. 505 (H.B. 655)), and in some cases inventing new governmental or quasi-governmental organizations to carry out new functions. Arizona is perhaps most notable in this regard, as discussed at section 6.7:1 below. See Chapter 26 of this book for a discussion of the changes made in House Bill 655.

§ 6.6:2 Municipalities

Municipalities often play major roles in conjunctive management in Texas. All three full-scale ASR projects currently in operation are operated by municipalities: San Antonio, Kerrville, and El Paso's hybrid system. Thirty-four municipalities sponsored ASR-related projects recommended by the TWDB in the 2022 State Water Plan, including more than half of the projects to establish ASR systems or pilot projects. *See* Texas Water Development Board, *2022 State Water Plan Documents*, https://2022.texasstatewaterplan.org/wmstype/AQUIFER%20STORAGE%20&%20RECOVERY. Further, a number of water providers in Texas rely on multiple sources of surface and groundwater, for example, the cities of El Paso, Midland, Round Rock, San Marcos, Tyler, and Victoria. *See* Kaiser, at 5-9–5-11. City water utilities tend to try to maximize their portfolios of surface supplies in order to reduce groundwater depletion when hydrologic conditions are relatively good, though this varies depending on the reliability of those surface supplies. For example, the Canadian River Municipal Water Authority has blended together water from Lake Meredith with groundwater for domestic supply in the past, but in recent years this has been impossible due to poor reservoir conditions during drought. *See* Kaiser, at 5-9.

§ 6.6:3 River Basin Organizations

River basin organizations may also be involved in conjunctive use and management indirectly by providing water to operators implementing projects such as the cities mentioned above. They also become involved more directly in ASR through the regional water planning process. The Brazos River Authority, Guadalupe-Blanco River Authority, Lower Colorado River Authority, and San Jacinto River Authority each sponsored ASR projects recommended by the TWDB in the 2022 State Water Plan. *See* Texas Water Development Board, 2022 State Water Plan, https://2022.texasstatewaterplan.org/wmstype/AQUIFER%20STORAGE%20&%20RECOVERY. River authorities may implement their own conjunctive management projects to increase their flexibility to provide water from different sources to their customers under different conditions. For example, as part of its Mid-Basin Water Supply Project, in 2020 the Guadalupe-Blanco River Authority obtained a right to divert 75,000 AF of surface water per year from the Guadalupe River. *See* Guadalupe-Blanco River Authority, *GBRA Advances Mid-Basin Water Supply Project*, www.gbra.org/news/2020/08/gbra-advances-mid-basin-water-supply-project/. Water that is not distributed to customers will be stored in the Carrizo Aquifer through an ASR project using injection wells. *See* South Central Texas Regional Water Planning Group, 2 *2021 South Central Texas Regional Water Plan* 5.2.15-1–5.2.15-29, www.twdb.texas.gov/waterplanning/rwp/plans/2021/L/RegionL_2021RWP_V2.pdf?d=13261.98499999009.

§ 6.6:4 Groundwater Conservation Districts

Finally, GCDs may play different roles in relation to conjunctive management. What kind of role they actually play, if any, is highly dependent on the particularities of a given district's rules, management approach, and the water use issues that are salient at the local and regional levels. GCDs are relevant to conjunctive management in one capacity as regulatory and permitting entities. Questions exist about whether pumping restrictions could limit the ability of an ASR operator to withdraw large amounts of groundwater during dry times. The San Antonio Water System purposely located its ASR system outside of GCD jurisdiction in part to avoid GCD regulations that would pertain in addition to existing regulation by the TCEQ. This issue has been clarified more recently through legislation, as discussed previously. See Chapter 26 of this book discussing ASR.

GCDs can also potentially play a role as conjunctive managers themselves in their capacity as planning and management entities. As noted at section 6.5:1 above, this is because the Texas Water Code mandates that GCDs, in consultation with regional surface water management entities, address conjunctive surface water management issues in their management plans (*see* Tex. Water Code § 36.1071(a)(4)) and directs them to consider "environmental impacts, including impacts on spring flow and other interactions between groundwater and surface water" in reviewing these plans in the joint planning process. *See* Tex. Water Code § 36.108(d)(4). See Chapter 16 of this book discussing GCD management plans and Chapter 21 covering the joint planning process. Thus, GCDs are able to conduct one form of conjunctive management: the curtailment of groundwater pumping specifically to reduce impacts on connected surface water flows. The lack of specificity about how to implement these statutory requirements has meant that in practice GCDs satisfy them through a wide range of actions, from simply acknowledging the existence of groundwater-surface water interactions to incorporating them into DFCs, which are actual management goals. *See generally* Kaiser.

Once joint planning efforts result in the adoption of a DFC that is based on maintaining minimum flows for streams or springs within a prescribed area, an individual GCD in the prescribed area may design its permitting policies to achieve that goal. For example, the Barton Springs Edwards Aquifer Conservation District in groundwater management area (GMA) 10 actually implements two DFCs for Barton Springs, one for extreme drought and one for "all conditions." The minimum discharge threshold of the "all conditions" DFC functions as a permitting cap for the district, and the extreme drought minimum discharge rate provides the basis for drought management practices. *See* Barton Springs/Edwards Aquifer Conservation District, *DFCs for District Aquifers Adopted*, https://bseacd.org/uploads/DFCs_for_District_Aquifers_Adopted.pdf. In Bell County, the Clearwater Underground Water Conservation District implements the GMA 8 DFC pertaining to the protection of flows from Salado Springs into Salado Creek during a repeat of the drought of record by using the TWDB's modeled available groundwater volume for the Edwards Aquifer (Balcones Fault Zone) within Bell County as a permitting cap. *See* Clearwater Underground Water Conservation District, *District Management Plan* 9 (rev. Jan. 9, 2019), www.cuwcd.org/wp-content/uploads/2012/11/Final_CUWCD_MP_09JAN19.pdf.

GCDs can also designate management zones where different pumping curtailment thresholds apply based on index wells and spring flows. This is how the Hays Trinity GCD manages pumping of Jacob's Well, a hydrologically sensitive natural spring located near Wimberley, Texas. Jacob's Well provides an estimated 20 percent of the base flow to the Blanco River, and the spring is also economically and culturally important to the local area. Jacob's Well is sensitive to drought and pumping from the Middle Trinity Aquifer. The first known occurrence of zero flow at Jacob's Well was in 2000, and the spring has stopped flowing in several years since. *See* Hays Trinity Groundwater Conservation District, *Management Zones*, http://haysgroundwater.com/management-zones-draft-rules. After several years of community action to protect the spring, the Hays Trinity GCD adopted a rule in March 2020 that created the Jacob's Well Groundwater Management Zone, a 39-square-mile area where different degrees of groundwater pumping cutbacks for permitted users are triggered when there is a ten-day average spring flow of 6, 5, or 3 cubic feet per second (cfs). While pumping reductions in the vicinity of Jacob's Well during drought may mitigate spring flow declines, the rule's stated purpose is to protect the aquifer and wells, not to maintain minimum flows. Implementation of voluntary curtailments of 20 percent in August 2020 and then 30 percent in November 2020 did not prevent spring flow from dropping to 0 cfs briefly in January 2021. *See* Dalton Sweat, *Jacob's Well Worries*, *San Marcos Daily Record*, Jan. 31, 2021, www.sanmarcosrecord.com/news/jacobs-well-worries.

A related example is Val Verde County, which, without a GCD, has neither representation in GMA 7 nor the authority and capacity to conduct management activities to implement the GMA 7 DFCs that are tied to flows at San Felipe Springs. Further, existing DFCs may be insufficient to address all of the groundwater management concerns in the county, which include threatened and endangered species that depend on spring flows. Texas Water Development Board, *Overview of Groundwater Conditions in Val Verde County, Texas* (Dec. 2018), www.twdb.texas.gov/groundwater/special_projects/valverde/docs/Groundwater-Resources-of-Val-Verde-County-86th-legislature.pdf. Val Verde County unsuccessfully pursued a bill in the 86th legislative session that would have created a GCD with three management zones based on hydrologic features and the authority to implement pumping curtailments to protect spring flow and base flow. *See* H.B. 3781, Sec. 8872.111(a), 86th Leg., R.S. (2019).

Additionally, the Edwards Aquifer Authority (EAA) is required by its enabling legislation to limit groundwater pumping from the Edwards Aquifer to maintain spring flows. *See* Act of May 30, 1993, 73d Leg., R.S., ch. 626, § 1.14(a)(2), as amended (EAA Act). The EAA has also sought to prevent harm to vulnerable streams within its jurisdiction by prohibiting certain forms of groundwater transfers. However, as with all groundwater districts, water regulation within the area regulated by the EAA is split between the EAA (groundwater) and the TCEQ (surface water). This distinction was the basis of the *Day* case discussed below. After groundwater from the aquifer is discharged through a spring, the EAA loses jurisdiction over the water. Groundwater from the aquifer, upon arising to the surface through a spring, is no longer located "within" the aquifer. *See* EAA Act § 1.08(b). The text of the EAA Act is uncodified, but an unofficial compilation is available at www.edwardsaquifer.org/eaa/legislation-rules/eaa-rules. Upon discharge from the springs into a watercourse, the water becomes state surface water and is regulated by the TCEQ. *See Edwards Aquifer Authority v. Day*, 369 S.W.3d 814, 822–23 (Tex. 2012). The EAA has no power to regulate the appropriation of surface water. *See* EAA Act § 1.08(b); *Edwards Aquifer Authority v. Day*, 274 S.W.3d 742, 752 (Tex. App.—San Antonio 2008), *aff'd*, 369 S.W.3d 814 (Tex. 2012). Therefore, the EAA has no continuing jurisdiction over discharges from springs hydrologically connected to the aquifer. *See* EAA Act § 1.08(b). See Chapter 17 of this book for an in-depth discussion of the EAA.

These examples notwithstanding, relatively few GCDs have adopted pumping production limits specifically in order to reduce impacts on connected surface water and spring flows. Only about 2 percent of all DFCs are expressed in terms of spring flow rates. *See* 2020 Interim Report, at 49. It is not yet clear how much of a role GCDs will play in this type of conjunctive management.

Finally, GCDs may find opportunities to be part of evolving partnerships spearheaded by other kinds of organizations that involve conjunctive management. The Middle Pecos GCD is working with the City of Fort Stockton on an effort spearheaded by the nonprofit Texas Water Trade to restore Comanche Springs that, in addition to a market-based pilot for voluntary irrigation reductions, will evaluate the potential for conjunctive water management options to revive the springs while meeting users' water needs. *See* 2020 Interim Report, at 61; *see also* Robert E. Mace et al., *Bringing Back Comanche Springs: An Analysis of the History, Hydrogeology, Policy, and Economics* (Report 2020-08, Dec. 2020), https://texaswatertrade.org/wp-content/uploads/2020/12/Bringing-Back-Comanche-Springs-12102020_v2.pdf.

IV. Examples of Conjunctive Management in Texas and the Western States

§ 6.7 Conjunctive Management Cases and Conflicts in Texas and the Western United States

As noted in the discussion at Part III above, conjunctive management in Texas has generally been limited to ASR projects, a few instances of the adoption of goals of limiting groundwater pumping to protect springs, and the simple use of both groundwater and surface water (i.e., portfolio strategies) by a number of entities. To broaden this discussion, Part IV highlights several cases from other states and one binational dispute that involves Texas. The selection of cases is by no means comprehensive; rather, it is intended to capture a relatively high amount of diversity using a small number of examples, which illustrate an important management or policy challenge, are notable for being longstanding and emblematic, illustrate the variety of conjunctive management practices, or exhibit an interesting legal issue.

§ 6.7:1 Regional-Scale Recharge in Central Arizona

Regarding conjunctive management, Arizona has some interesting commonalities with Texas: surface and groundwater are legally bifurcated; there is a legal concept of "subflow" similar to Texas's underflow (*see* Robert Jerome Glennon & Thomas Maddock, III, *In Search of Subflow: Arizona's Futile Effort to Separate Groundwater from Surface Water*, 36 Ariz. L. Rev. 567); and there are separate state agencies with jurisdiction over water quantity and quality. Key distinctions include (1) a very different groundwater regulation and administration system for its five Active Management Areas (which do not cover the entire nontribal areas of the state) pursuant to the 1980 Groundwater Management Act, codified at Ariz. Rev. Stat. §§ 45-401 to -704; and (2) its access to the region's "fuel for growth" (*see* Douglas E. Kupel, *Fuel for Growth: Water and Arizona's Urban Environment* (University of Arizona Press 2003))—the Colorado River—via the Central Arizona Project (CAP) canal, which moves water hundreds of miles uphill from the Colorado River to metro Phoenix and Tucson.

Despite the legal and administrative separation of groundwater and surface water, during the 1980s and especially the 1990s Arizona evolved a robust and innovative set of statutes (*see, e.g.*, Arizona Department of Water Resources, *Underground Water Storage, Savings and Replenishment*, https://new.azwater.gov/recharge/statutes-and-policies) and new organizations that today govern a regional-scale system of recharge and recovery credits and permits. *See* Sharon B. Megdal, *Arizona's Recharge and Recovery Programs* 188, *in Arizona Water Policy: Management Innovations in an Urbanizing, Arid Region* (Bonnie G. Colby & Katharine L. Jacobs eds., Resources for the Future Press 2007) [hereinafter Megdal]. Certainly one primary goal for developing rules and organizations for recharge for Arizona, as a junior appropriator to California on the Colorado River, was to devise a way to beneficially use the unused portion of its river allotment that could otherwise potentially be diverted by California. To date, over 4 million AF of water, mostly from the CAP, has been "banked" underground, about 14 percent of which has been stored for Nevada. *See* Arizona Water Banking Authority, https://.waterbank.az.gov/.

Recharge in Central Arizona has been done through a mixture of regional MAR facilities, some of which operate by recharge basins and others indirectly via facilitating in-lieu recharge. Funding for the construction of recharge facilities was originally generated by a property tax levied by the Central Arizona Water Conservation District (the organization that manages the CAP), a power granted it by the legislature in 1990. *See* Megdal, at 193; Central Arizona Project, *Annual Report* (2000), https://library.cap-az.com/documents/departments/finance/2020-Comprehensive-Annual-Financial-Report.pdf; Ariz. Rev. Stat. §§ 45-895.01, 45-897.01, 48-3715.02.

At various times, the Arizona legislature has created various new governmental and quasi-governmental entities for the financial, administrative, and managerial capacity to meet particular recharge-related goals. For example, the Arizona Water Banking Authority (AWBA) was legislated into existence in 1996 to use tax revenues to manage the regional water bank and its system of credits. It is run by a governor-appointed board chaired by the director of the Arizona Department of Water Resources and relies on several funding streams for its operation. *See* Megdal, at 200. The AWBA's water banking activities generate a number of benefits salient to state and regional water management goals, including reducing the impact of drought-related curtailments to surface water supplies; furthering groundwater management goals such as ameliorating long-term groundwater mining;

creating a pool of water to be used to settle tribal water claims; and meeting interstate water storage agreements with Nevada. *See* Arizona Water Banking Authority, *About Us*, https://waterbank.az.gov/about-us/benefits.

Besides the creation of an intricate finance and administrative apparatus, conjunctive management in Central Arizona is largely possible because of the combination of (1) the existence of large surface water conveyance infrastructure (primarily the CAP system) that can route water to regional recharge facilities, and (2) the colocation of that infrastructure with aquifers suitable for recharge and recovery. From a Texas perspective, the substantial conjunctive management practices in Central Arizona are perhaps noteworthy because they were executed without definitively resolving the issue of the legal and administrative bifurcation of surface and groundwater. Arizona exemplifies how states can work around these potential challenges through clever legislative and regulatory development and implementation.

Since the 1990s, Arizona has been primarily in a recharging mode. In more recent years, however, the amount of unused Colorado River water available for banking has shrunk as demands in Central Arizona have increased. Given this and the near-certainty of official shortages on the Colorado River in the near future, it may be interesting to observe how the system functions if and when it shifts into a recovery mode.

§ 6.7:2 Conjunctive Management Practices and Issues in California

Conjunctive management in California depends on its hydrologic conditions, built infrastructure, and law. Like Texas, California has a variety of alluvial groundwater basins, with differing means for recharge. The physical conditions for conjunctive management in California differ from Texas in that California has a large centrally controlled conveyance system for surface water. The federal Central Valley Project (CVP) is linked to the state-controlled State Water Project (SWP). Those two projects allow for the large scale diversion of major rivers and open options for cross-basin conjunctive management.

The goals of conjunctive management in California vary across jurisdictions. In the interior of the state, conjunctive management is used to augment freshwater for agriculture and environmental purposes; for saltwater intrusion on the coasts; and for increasing the flexibility of local management throughout the state. *See* Sugg et al., at 6. The SWP and CVP are critical to many of these projects. Although centralized statewide data on conjunctive management is sparse, a voluntary survey from the California Department of Water Resources found that 71 percent of respondents relied on the SWP with another 24 percent relying on the CVP (these figures are not mutually exclusive).

The relationship between large-scale surface water conveyance infrastructure and groundwater is not one-way, however. During the 2007–2010 and 2012–2017 droughts in California, agriculture's increased dependence on groundwater pumping accelerated land subsidence and compaction in the Central Valley. *See* Claudia C. Faunt et al., *Water Availability and Land Subsidence in the Central Valley, California, USA*, 24 Hydrogeol. J. 675, 679–80 [hereinafter Faunt]. Over time, subsidence and compaction have reduced the overall flow capacity of the Delta-Mendota Canal, a key feature of the CVP, by 20 percent. *See* Michelle Sneed et al., *Land Subsidence along the Delta-Mendota Canal in the Northern Part of the San Joaquin Valley, California, 2003–10*, U.S. Geological Survey Scientific Investigations Report 2013-5142 (2013), https://pubs.usgs.gov/sir/2013/5142/. Radar measurements suggest that portions of the California Aqueduct, the principal feature of the SWP, have subsided up to twenty-five feet, causing difficulties in service and maintenance. *See* Tom G. Farr et al., *Progress Report: Subsidence in California, March 2015–September 2016* 14 fig. 8; Faunt, at 679–80. In other words, the absence of effective groundwater management in the Central Valley eventually led to distressing and costly consequences for surface water management. *See* Brett Walton, Circle of Blue, *Sinking Land Causes California Water Chokepoint* (Feb. 10, 2017), www.circleofblue.org/2017/water-management/infrastructure/sinking-land-causes-california-water-chokepoint/. Highlighting the importance of conjunctive management, agricultural areas that imported surface water to use for aquifer recharge had lower rates of subsidence. *See* Pierre Jeanne et al., *Role of Agricultural Activity on Land Subsidence in the San Joaquin Valley, California*, 569 J. Hydro. 462 (2019).

Traditionally, conjunctive management in California has been complicated by its water rights system. As in Texas, state law treats rights to groundwater as distinct from rights to surface water. Initially, California followed the English common-law rule of capture. *See Gould v. Eaton*, 111 Cal. 639, 644–45 (Cal. 1896); *Hanson v. McCue*, 42 Cal. 303, 309–10 (Cal. 1871). At the turn of the twentieth century, the California Supreme Court replaced the rule of capture for groundwater with the rule of "correlative rights," providing that landowners had rights to the groundwater beneath their properties that were analogous to the correlative rights of riparian landowners to surface water. *See Hudson v. Dailey*, 156 Cal. 617 (Cal. 1909); *Katz v. Walkinshaw*, 141 Cal. 116, 121–36 (Cal. 1903) (extending "correlative rights" doctrine to groundwater connected to streamflow as well as percolating groundwater). Appropriative rights to groundwater can be gained by diverting groundwater for out-of-basin use. *See City of Barstow v. Mojave Water Agency*, 23 Cal. 4th 1224, 1240 (Cal. 2000); *see also Katz*, 141 Cal. at 135–36. Prescriptive rights to groundwater can also be gained in limited circumstances. *See City of Los Angeles v. City of San Fernando*, 14 Cal. 3d 199, 270–86 (Cal. 1975). All of these ways of acquiring and implementing property rights to groundwater are different from the riparian and appropriative rights systems to surface water in the state. *See Lux v. Haggin*, 69 Cal. 255 (Cal. 1886). The legal separation of groundwater and surface water has made conjunctive management and conjunctive use challenging. *See* Theodore E. Grantham & Joshua H. Viers, *100 Years of California's Water Rights System: Patterns, Trends and Uncertainty*, 9 Envtl. Res. Lett. 084012 (2014).

Two twenty-first-century developments in California water law are bringing the necessity of conjunctive management to the fore. These are the enactment of the Sustainable Groundwater Management Act of 2014 (SGMA) and the common-law application of the public-trust doctrine to some groundwater.

The SGMA requires that groundwater sustainability agencies (GSAs) consider and address groundwater–surface water interaction through Groundwater Sustainability Plans (GSPs). *See* Cal. Water Code §§ 10727, 10727.2. "Sustainable groundwater management" is defined by statute as "the management and use of groundwater in a manner that can be maintained . . . without causing [six] undesirable results," including the requirement that groundwater withdrawals not result in "significant and unreasonable adverse impacts on beneficial uses of the surface water." Cal. Water Code § 10721(v), (x). The SGMA has heightened interest among districts in managed aquifer recharge and water trading. *See* Debra Perrone & Melissa Merri Rohde, *Benefits and Economic Costs of Managed Aquifer Recharge in California*, 14 San Francisco Estuary & Watershed Sci. 1 (2016); Nell Green Nylen et al., Wheeler Water Institute, Center for Law, Energy & the Environment, *Trading Sustainably: Critical Considerations for Local Groundwater Markets under the Sustainable Groundwater Management Act* (U.C. Berkeley School of Law 2017), www.law.berkeley.edu/wp-content/uploads/2017/06/CLEE_Trading-Sustainably_2017-06-21.pdf. The characteristics of aquifers and overlying land vary; not all districts have territory that is well suited to managed aquifer recharge. *See* A. T. O'Geen et al., *Soil Suitability Index Identifies Potential Areas for Groundwater Banking on Agricultural Lands*, 69 Cal. Agric. 75 (2015). Trading water-use rights or contracts across basins takes advantage of that variation in capacity to engage in aquifer recharge. The SGMA allows newly developed GSAs to import surface water in exchange for agreements to reduce or stop groundwater extraction. *See* Cal. Water Code § 10726.2(b), (d), (e). Rather than import surface water, some GSAs, like the Pajaro Valley Water Management Agency, provide recycled water to agricultural users to decrease groundwater pumping. *See* Pajaro Valley Water Management Agency, *Basin Management Plan Update* 4, 17, 19 (Feb. 2014), www.pvwater.org/images/about-pvwma/assets/bmp_update_eir_final_2014/BMP_Update_Final_February_2014_(screen).pdf. However, groundwater trading is relatively new in California, and although the state allows for surface water transfers, the SGMA provides for groundwater transfers only within the same basin. *See* Cal. Water Code § 10726.4(a)(2), (a)(3).

In 2018, the Court of Appeals for the Third Appellate District ruled that the public-trust doctrine applies to groundwater resources that feed streams and that the SGMA does not supersede the public trust doctrine. *See Environmental Law Foundation v. State Water Resources Control Board*, 237 Cal. Rptr. 3d 393 (Cal. Ct. App. 2018) (the *Scott River* case). The public-trust doctrine's application to water was established in California in *National Audubon Society v. Superior Court*, requiring that the state hold in trust and protect navigable waters and their tributaries for the benefit of the people of the state. *National Audubon Society v. Superior Court*, 33 Cal. 3d 410, 441 (Cal. 1983) ("[T]he public trust is more than an affirmation of state power to use public property for public purposes. It is an affirmation of the duty of the state to protect the people's common heritage of streams, lakes, marshlands and tidelands, surrendering that right of protection only in rare cases when the abandonment of that right is consistent with the purposes of the trust."); *see El Dorado Irrigation District v. State Water Resources Control Board*, 142 Cal. App. 4th 937, 965–66 (2006); *see also* Alida Cantor, *The Public Trust Doctrine and Critical Legal Geographies of Water in California*, 72 Geoforum 49 (2016); Erin Ryan, *The Public Trust Doctrine, Private Water Allocation, and Mono Lake: The Historic Saga of* National Audubon Society v. Superior, 45 Envtl. L. 561 (2015); Richard M. Frank, *The Public Trust Doctrine: Assessing Its Recent Past & Charting Its Future*, 45 U.C. Davis L. Rev. 665 (2011); Joseph L. Sax, *The Public Trust Doctrine in Natural Resource Law: Effective Judicial Intervention*, 68 Mich. L. Rev. 471 (1970). The *Scott River* case originated from a dispute in Siskiyou County about whether aquifers abutting the Scott River are hydrologically connected to the surface flows of that river. Groundwater pumping in the region intensified, leading to dramatic reductions in surface flows—including to the point of dewatering. The effect on aquatic habitat was devastating. *See* Richard Frank, *California Court Finds Public Trust Doctrine Applies to State Groundwater Resources*, Legal Planet (Aug. 29, 2018), http://legal-planet.org/2018/08/29/california-court-finds-public-trust-doctrine-applies-to-state-groundwater-resources/.

Relying on the National Audubon Society, environmental groups and the Pacific Coast Federation of Fishermen's Associations petitioned the State Water Resources Control Board (SWRCB) and the county to limit groundwater pumping to preserve the surface river. The plaintiffs filed suit after the SWRCB and county declined to act, asserting that groundwater interconnected with surface flows is subject to the public-trust doctrine. Although the county maintained that the public-trust doctrine does not apply, the SWRCB eventually sided with the plaintiffs, contrary to its initial position. The trial court found for the plaintiffs on summary judgment. *See* Michael C. Blumm & Aurora Paulsen Moses, *The Public Trust as an Antimonopoly Doctrine*, B.C. Envtl. Aff. L. Rev. 1, 34–35 (2017).

The court of appeals likewise held for the plaintiffs. They reasoned that because "*National Audubon* and its progeny recognize that government has a duty to consider the public trust interest when making decisions impacting water that is imbued with the public trust" and the Scott River is subject to the public-trust doctrine, the county and the SWRCB have a duty to regulate hydrologically connected groundwater to preserve the flow of the Scott River. *See Environmental Law Foundation*, 237 Cal. Rptr. 3d at 404. Furthermore, the court of appeals rejected the county's argument that the SGMA preempts the public-trust doctrine. In doing so, the court stressed the preeminence of the public-trust doctrine, regardless of state water legislation, stating:

> We reject . . . the County's position that because SGMA is comprehensive it occupies the field and supplants the common law. But even if the legislation was deemed comprehensive, *National Audubon* teaches the two systems can live in harmony. If the expansive and historically rooted appropriative rights system in California did not subsume or eliminate the public trust doctrine in the state, then certainly SGMA, a more narrowly tailored piece of legislation, can also accommodate the perpetuation of the public trust doctrine.

Environmental Law Foundation, 237 Cal. Rptr. 3d at 408. In short, the *Scott River* case suggests that where navigable streams are concerned, conjunctive management is the rule. *See also* Alida Cantor et al., UC Water, *Navigating Groundwater-Surface Water Interactions under the Sustainable Groundwater Management Act* 19–20, https://escholarship.org/content/qt720033b2/qt720033b2.pdf.

§ 6.7:3 Conjunctive Management Practices in Nebraska

Historically, Nebraska administered surface water and groundwater separately. *See* J. David Aiken, *The Western Common Law of Tributary Groundwater: Implications for Nebraska*, 83 Neb. L. Rev. 541 (2005). Natural resource districts (NRDs), created in 1972, were granted exclusive authority to govern groundwater, both quality and quantity. *See* Neb. Rev. Stat. § 2-3201. The NRDs were organized by river basin, with some basins, such as the Platte and Republican, containing multiple districts. The Nebraska Department of Water Resources (NeDWR) exercised exclusive control over surface waters, issuing and administering water rights under the prior appropriation system. The limitations of separate systems of water governance and administration emerged with interstate water conflicts beginning in the 1990s, highlighting the hydrologic connection between groundwater and surface water. Groundwater pumping in the Platte and Republican river basins impacted surface water flows, threatening endangered species in the Platte and moving Nebraska out of compliance with its surface water allocation commitments under the Republican Interstate River Compact. The Platte and Republican NRDs were reluctant to actively limit groundwater pumping to protect surface water flows, and the NeDWR, under state law, did not have the authority to require active regulation of groundwater pumping. The Nebraska legislature created a Water Policy Task Force in 2002 with participants representing diverse water user types from across the state. *See* Water Policy Task Force, *Report of the Nebraska Water Policy Task Force to the 2003 Nebraska Legislature* (Dec. 2003), http://govdocs.nebraska.gov/epubs/N1500/B003-2003.pdf.

Following multiple meetings, the Task Force made recommendations to the legislature, which led to the adoption of Legislative Bill 962 in 2004. L.B. 962, 98th Leg., Session Two, 2004, www.nebraskalegislature.gov/FloorDocs/98/PDF/Slip/LB962.pdf. The law recognized the hydrologic connection between ground and surface waters and gave the NeDWR the authority to limit groundwater use and to work with NRDs to develop integrated water management plans. Specifically, the NeDWR received the authority to declare basins fully or overappropriated, resulting in a moratorium on high capacity wells and surface water rights. *See* 457 Neb. Admin. Code ch. 24. Furthermore, "The objective of an integrated management plan . . . is to manage such river basin, subbasin, or reach to achieve and sustain a balance between water uses and water supplies for the long term." Neb. Rev. Stat. § 46-715(1)(b). The 2004 Act put in place the laws, regulations, and rules necessary to engage in conjunctive water management. Other laws, such as the Nebraska Water Resources Cash Fund, provided additional support for actively coordinating groundwater and surface water use. *See* Neb. Rev. Stat. § 61-218(3).

All NRDs located in basins declared fully or overappropriated have developed integrated water management plans. Of these NRDs, those located in the Republican and Platte river basins have begun to experiment with and adopt conjunctive water management; that is, they actively recharge groundwater basins in order to support surface water flows, and they pump groundwater to place in a river to augment surface flows. For instance, the four NRDs located in the Republican River basin developed the Nebraska Cooperative Republican Platte Enhancement Project, involving the retirement of irrigated acreage and the use of the groundwater rights to augment the Republican River as necessary so that Nebraska remains in compliance with the interstate compact. *See* Upper Republican Natural Resources District, *Republican River Compact Compliance*, www.urnrd.org/programs-regulations/republican-river-compact-compliance. In contrast, the Central Platte NRD has invested in capturing excess river flows and flood flows in irrigation canals, recharging the groundwater aquifer, and augmenting river flows. *See* Central Platte Natural Resources District, *Putting Water Back to the Platte River*, http://cpnrd.org/water-resources/recharge-canals/.

Over the course of twenty years, Nebraska has substantially revised its water administration system, moving from a highly fragmented system in which NRDs and the NeDWR managed groundwater and surface water in isolation, to an integrated water management system. The NRDs in conjunction with the NeDWR develop integrated water management plans that consist of a variety of rules, regulations, and best management practices that conserve water and limit water withdrawals. In addition, NRDs engage in conjunctive water management in order to reduce overappropriation and achieve or maintain compliance with interstate agreements by enhancing river flows.

§ 6.7:4 Conjunctive Management Practices in Colorado

Colorado water law has long recognized the hydrologic connection between groundwater and surface water, as both are covered by the prior appropriation system. However, not until the 1960s after conflict between well owners and surface water rights holders emerged did the state actively attempt integrated management of ground and surface waters. *See* Lawrence J. MacDonnell, *Colorado's Law of "Underground Water": A Look at the South Platte Basin and Beyond*, 59 U. Colo. L. Rev. 579 (1988) [hereinafter MacDonnell]. The 1950s brought a historic drought, and farmers invested in high-capacity wells. *See* Lain Strawn, *The Last GASP: The Conflict over the Management of Replacement Water in the South Platte River Basin*, 75 U. Colo. L. Rev. 597 (2004). By the 1960s the effects of groundwater pumping on surface water flows, especially in the South Platte and Arkansas river basins, became apparent. Irrigation organizations reliant on surface water diversions demanded that groundwater be brought within the prior appropriation system, as it was patently unfair for surface water users to reduce their diversions of water during a drought while groundwater pumpers faced no such reductions. *See* MacDonnell, at 582–90. In 1969, the Colorado legislature adopted the Water Rights Determination and Administration Act, Colo. Rev. Stat. §§ 37-92-101 to -602, a far-reaching law requiring all water rights, surface and groundwater, to be adjudicated and assigned a priority date. In addition, the law allowed for augmentation and substitute supply plans. These plans represent the most common form of conjunctive water management in Colorado. They are primarily used to mitigate the impact of groundwater pumping on surface water flows. *See* William Blomquist et al., *Common Waters, Diverging Streams: Linking Institutions and Water Management in Arizona, California, and Colorado* 94–101 (Resources for the Future Press 2004). In other words, well owners are allowed to divert water out of priority as long as they replace that water and make senior water rights holders whole. Well associations and irrigation organizations acquire surface water rights and either make the water available to the State Engineer to return to the stream or river or recharge the water underground through ponds or ditches with the water seeping back to the river. The difference between the two types of plans is permanency. Augmentation plans have been approved by a water court and are recognized and incorporated into the prior appropriation system. Substitute supply plans are approved by the State Engineer's Office and are temporary. They are typically used to replace an out-of-priority water use while waiting for a water court to approve an augmentation plan. *See* Colorado Division of Water Resources, *Synopsis of Colorado Water Law* 27 (7th ed. 2016). Since 1969 Colorado has realized its goal of incorporating groundwater into its prior appropriation system and has provided tools for groundwater users that allow out-of-priority pumping while protecting surface water flows.

As discussed above regarding Nebraska, Colorado is also a party to recovering endangered species on the Platte River and in addressing compliance issues with the Republican Interstate River Compact. In both instances, Colorado has turned to conjunctive water management as the preferred means of addressing its commitments. The Northern Colorado Water Conservancy District operates the Tamarck Project, which consists of a series of ponds located at different distances from the South

Platte River. Water is diverted from the river when there is excess water (i.e., no one claims the water) and placed in ponds. The water seeps into the aquifer and migrates to the river, retiming river flows to better correspond to water demands of species in the Platte River in Nebraska and helping to meet Colorado's commitment to species recovery. *See* Northern Colorado Water Conservancy District, *Platte River Recovery*, https://www.northernwater.org/what-we-do/protect-the-environment/environmental-collaboratives/platte-river-recovery. Also, in 2004 the Colorado legislature created the Republican River Water Conservation District (RRWCD). *See* Colo. Rev. Stat. §§ 37-50-101 to -142. The RRWCD, in addition to purchasing and retiring irrigated acreage and purchasing and leasing surface water rights to use to meet compact requirements, has developed a project to place groundwater in the North Fork of the Republican River near the state line with Nebraska. The RRWCD purchased groundwater rights and uses them to provide additional flows to the river as needed. *See* Colorado Division of Water Resources, *State Engineer's Statement of Basis and Purpose for Rules and Regulations Governing the Diversion and Use of Water Resources in the Republican River Compact Administration Groundwater Model Domain for Compliance with the Republican River Compact*, https://dnrweblink.state.co.us/dwr/0/edoc/3376857/DWR_3376857.pdf?searchid=0e52d7cf-5a7a-4196-a30b-05d6d29461fc. Conjunctive water use is an important management approach for Colorado. It is used to maintain stream flows so as to protect senior water rights holders under the prior appropriation doctrine and to allow Colorado to meet its interstate water delivery requirements.

§ 6.7:5 Rio Grande Compact Interstate Dispute

The dispute between Texas and New Mexico under the Rio Grande Compact indicates that the rationale offered for the intrastate separation of property rights to groundwater and surface water may not apply to interstate water disputes. In its filings to the U.S. Supreme Court in *Texas v. New Mexico*, 138 S. Ct. 954 (2018) (the *Rio Grande* case), Texas takes the position that the quantity of surface water in the Rio Grande depends on groundwater use and that New Mexico has a duty to engage in conjunctive management. Specifically, Texas claims that New Mexico has failed to maintain compact conditions on the Rio Grande by allowing groundwater pumping from approximately 2,500 new wells. In the shadow of litigation, "[f]armers, water policy experts, municipal officials and others have been working behind the scenes to build a framework for a possible settlement." Michael Coleman, *Supreme Court Hears NM-Texas Water Dispute*, Albuquerque J. (Jan. 9, 2018), www.abqjournal.com/1116605/supreme-court-hears-nmtexas-water-dispute.html.

Interstate river and groundwater conflicts are not new to the Supreme Court. Beginning with litigation over the Pecos Interstate River Compact, *Texas v. New Mexico*, 482 U.S. 124 (1987), as a matter of equitable apportionment, the Court has required groundwater regulation to limit impacts on surface water flows, even where groundwater has not been explicitly mentioned in the compact. *See* Burke W. Griggs, *Interstate Water Litigation in the West: A Fifty-Year Retrospective*, 20 U. Denv. Water L. Rev. 153 (2017); Barton H. Thompson, Jr., *Beyond Connections: Pursuing Multidimensional Conjunctive Management*, 47 Idaho L. Rev. 273, 282 (2011); *see, e.g., Montana v. Wyoming*, 138 S. Ct. 758 (2018); *Kansas v. Nebraska*, 538 U.S. 720 (2003); *Kansas v. Colorado*, 514 U.S. 673, 694 (1995); *Arizona v. California*, 376 U.S. 340, 341 (1964). That groundwater extraction in New Mexico would have implications for its delivery of surface water to Texas is not novel. See Chapter 14 of this book for additional discussion of the Rio Grande and Pecos River Compacts. *See also* Tylynn R. Payne, *Comment, in (Not So) Deep Water: The Texas–New Mexico Water War and the Unworkable Provisions of the Rio Grande Compact*, 52 Tex. Tech L. Rev. 669 (2020).

However, Texas's theory—that groundwater management needs to be developed and implemented in a way that is aligned with surface water management goals—has not been applied to Texas's own water management. The *Rio Grande* case, alongside the *Scott River* case in California, reinforce decades of conjunctive management case law. When rivers run low, the reality that water in the ground and water on the ground are part of the same resource can overturn presumptions of legal separateness.

V. Conclusion

§ 6.8 Conclusion

Conjunctive management is not a single thing but an array of management practices based on the fundamental notions that surface water and groundwater (and, increasingly, treated effluent) are a single resource that should be managed holistically rather than in a fragmented manner. At a basic level, the idea is to leverage the natural advantages of different kinds of water sources—e.g., the renewability of surface water sources and the storage reservoir capacity of certain kinds of aquifers—to increase water flexibility, security, and resilience to disturbances. As the case studies discussed above show, conjunctive management strategies may be conducted for a variety of purposes and can generate multiple benefits at different scales, such as increasing resilience to drought, mitigating groundwater overdraft, and maintaining minimum stream flows where groundwater and surface water are interconnected.

The concepts of conjunctive management are consistent with recent advances in modern hydrology and hydrogeology, but policy and especially legal developments have been slow compared to the sciences. In some states, and especially Texas, where groundwater can be literally owned in place as real property, water rights systems rest on an unscientific nineteenth-century presumption that surface water and groundwater are two separate things and can be controlled, apportioned, and managed as such. This is also reflected in the bifurcation of administrative and regulatory responsibilities among different agencies. Unsurprisingly, such fragmented legal and administrative systems have turned out to be not very conducive to enacting shifting social and environmental priorities that favor conjunctive management. Rather than undertake the herculean political task of reforming these systems, states such as Texas and especially Arizona have opted for legislative workarounds to create functioning permitting and regulatory systems to remove certain historical disincentives to some forms of conjunctive management. This is illustrated by the several bills passed in the Texas legislature in recent years to encourage the adoption of ASR.

In Texas, innovators in conjunctive management include larger cities in the drier parts of the state, such as El Paso and San Antonio, where real water supply challenges have fostered innovation in forms of managed aquifer recovery. As of 2022 state water planning, conjunctive management strategies were of increasing interest among water management entities in the state, and new projects are expected in the coming years. Clearly there is interest in ASR projects; less certain is the extent to which forms of conjunctive management that do not require major infrastructure or that limit withdrawals will be implemented, such as the curtailment of groundwater pumping by groundwater management districts to reduce impacts to connected surface water bodies. This is important given the many parts of the state where groundwater and surface water are connected.

Given the more recent development of the regulatory regime in Texas, legal professionals may do well to become educated on subjects such as state permitting requirements and processes and the financing of ASR projects. Although recently passed statutes have clarified previously ambiguous aspects, some disincentives still remain. Some of them are tied to live legal questions that seem likely to arise in Texas courts in the coming years, such as the legal vulnerability of recharged water to interference from other groundwater pumpers. Absent future legislation, it may be some time before issues and disputes intensify and, consequently, reliable precedents are worked out by the courts.

CHAPTER 7

State and Federal Governmental Entities with Water Resource Jurisdiction

Ross Crow[1]
Update by Kathy J. Humphreys[2]

I. Introduction

§ 7.1 Introduction

This chapter provides an overview of the major state and federal authorities with jurisdiction over water resources. It focuses primarily on the water resource jurisdiction of such governmental entities and does not attempt to summarize the overall jurisdiction, function, and mission, except to provide context to the water resource discussion. The chapter identifies the source of each state or federal governmental entity's authority, delineates the scope of jurisdiction, and describes generally how each functions to accomplish its mission. Details on many of the programs discussed in this chapter are contained in other chapters of this book, as noted. For discussion of local governmental entities with jurisdiction over water resources, see Chapters 8, 9, 16, and 17.

II. State Governmental Entities with Water Resource Jurisdiction

§ 7.2 Introduction

The population of the state of Texas continues to grow each year. According to the Texas Demographic Center, Texas has in recent years added hundreds of thousands of new residents each year through migration and natural increase, and the state population is projected to increase from approximately 30 million in 2020 to more than 47 million by 2050. *See* Texas Demographics Center, *Texas Population Projections 2010 to 2050* (Sept. 25, 2019), https://demographics.texas.gov/

---

1. Ross Crow is an attorney with the City of Austin Law Department where he practices environmental and administrative law with an emphasis on matters relating to surface water, groundwater, wastewater, public drinking water, and water supply. Mr. Crow often presents papers at Texas water law conferences and has contributed lead articles on water issues to the *Texas Environmental Law Journal.* He is the recent recipient of the Texas City Attorneys Association's Galen Sparks Award for Outstanding Public Service by an Assistant City Attorney. Mr. Crow is grateful for the assistance of attorneys and staff at several state agencies and other entities for their review of and contributions to this chapter.

2. Kathy Humphreys has been an attorney with the Texas Commission on Environmental Quality for over twenty years. Ms. Humphreys primarily supports clients in the Water Quality Division and Waste Permits Division, focusing on issues relating to permitting.

Resources/publications/2019/20190925_PopProjectionsBrief.pdf. To meet the needs of our growing population for access to safe, clean, plentiful water, the state must manage its water carefully. Many state agencies play a role in protecting and conserving the state's precious water resources for the benefit of its current and future citizens.

§ 7.3 Texas Commission on Environmental Quality

The Texas Commission on Environmental Quality (TCEQ) is the primary environmental agency in the state of Texas. Its mission is to protect the state's public health and natural resources consistent with sustainable economic development. Its goal is clean air, clean water, and the safe management of waste. *See* Texas Commission on Environmental Quality, *Mission Statement and Agency Philosophy*, www.tceq.texas.gov/agency/mission.html. The commission is the agency of the state given primary responsibility for implementing the state constitution and laws relating to the conservation of natural resources and the protection of the environment. Tex. Water Code § 5.012.

The pursuit of this broad goal in a state the size of Texas requires an agency of similar scope. The TCEQ is one of the largest environmental agencies in the world, with approximately 2,800 employees, a central office in Austin and sixteen regional offices, and a $378 million operating budget for the 2021 fiscal year. *See* Texas Commission on Environmental Quality, *About Us*, www.tceq.texas.gov/agency/about-the-tceq. The TCEQ's water programs include those that maintain the quality and prevent pollution of water in the state, ensure that water for human consumption meets standards designed to protect health, and mete out the supply of state water so that sources of supply are not overdrawn.

Texas has been granted primacy by the federal government to implement within the state a key component of the federal Clean Water Act (CWA) relating to the National Pollutant Discharge Elimination System (NPDES) program. *See* 40 C.F.R. pt. 123. The NPDES is a federal regulatory program to control discharges of pollutants to surface waters of the United States. To earn and maintain primacy, the state must adopt a regulatory scheme that is at least as stringent as the CWA. *See* 40 C.F.R. § 123.25. The state assumed the authority to administer the NPDES program on September 14, 1998. *See* U.S. Environmental Protection Agency, *NPDES State Program Information*, www.epa.gov/npdes/npdes-state-program-information. The TCEQ's Texas Pollutant Discharge Elimination System (TPDES) program now has delegated federal regulatory authority over discharges of pollutants to Texas surface water, with the exception of discharges associated with oil, gas, and geothermal exploration and development activities, which are regulated by the Railroad Commission of Texas. *See* Texas Commission on Environmental Quality, *What Is the "Texas Pollutant Discharge Elimination System (TPDES)"?*, www.tceq.texas.gov/permitting/wastewater/pretreatment/tpdes_definition.html. Accordingly, a person may be required to obtain a federal permit and a state permit to discharge oil and gas wastes to surface water in the state. *See* Railroad Commission of Texas, *Discharges*, www.rrc.state.tx.us/oil-gas/applications-and-permits/environmental-permit-types-information/discharges/. Texas has also been granted primacy with respect to the Safe Drinking Water Act (SDWA). *See* 40 C.F.R. pts. 141, 142; *see also* Tex. Health & Safety Code ch. 341 (state standards for drinking water). The grants of primacy to the state for these two bodies of law provide a primary basis for the TCEQ's legal authority in these areas of water regulation.

Legislation effective September 1, 2019, transferred authority from the Railroad Commission of Texas (RRC) to the Texas Commission on Environmental Quality (TCEQ) to issue certain discharge permits for the discharge of produced water, hydrostatic test water, and gas plant effluent resulting from certain oil and gas activities by amending section 26.131 of the Texas Water Code. Pursuant to the legislation, the TCEQ sought federal delegation from the Environmental Protection Agency (EPA) to supplement or amend the Texas Pollutant Discharge Elimination System (TPDES) program to include delegation of the National Pollutant Discharge Elimination System (NPDES) permit authority for these discharges. The EPA announced January 15, 2021, that it approved Texas's request to administer the NPDES program for discharges from produced water, hydrostatic test water, and gas plant effluent or oil and gas discharges within the state of Texas. The TCEQ will take over responsibility of permitting authority for the discharges of oil and gas activities, pipelines, and natural gas processing plants that formerly were under RRC jurisdiction. *See* U.S. Environmental Protection Agency, *EPA approves Clean Water Program to Texas Commission on Environmental Quality* (Jan. 15, 2021), www.epa.gov/newsreleases/epa-approves-clean-water-program-texas-commission-environmental-quality.

The TCEQ also has legal authority to regulate the use of water through its water rights permitting program. This authority, codified in the Texas Water Code, provides that state water in Texas is the property of the state, which holds it in trust. "State water" is defined at section 11.021 and essentially includes surface water in a watercourse. *See* Tex. Water Code § 11.021. Because of its ownership of water, the state holds the legal authority over the right to use state water. For further discussion of state water and the state's legal authority over the right to use state water, see Chapters 1, 4, and 10 of this book.

The TCEQ was created by the legislature as an agency of the executive branch of Texas state government. Tex. Water Code § 5.051. The TCEQ was preceded by several agencies with the same functions, including most recently the Texas Natural Resource Conservation Commission (TNRCC), and the agency provides details of its earlier history on its website at www.tceq.texas.gov/agency/organization/tceqhistory.html. References to these predecessor agencies are found in older case law as well as in statutes and rules that have not been updated to reflect the current agency name. The TCEQ may only exercise authority granted by the legislature. *See, e.g., Cities of Austin, Dallas, Fort Worth & Hereford v. Southwestern Bell Telephone Co.*, 92 S.W.3d 434, 441–42 (Tex. 2002); *Public Utility Commission of Texas v. City Public Service Board of San Antonio*, 53 S.W.3d 310, 315–16 (Tex. 2001); *State v. Public Utility Commission of Texas*, 883 S.W.2d 190, 194 (Tex. 1994); *Martinez v. Texas Employment Commission*, 570 S.W.2d 28, 31 (Tex. 1978). General powers and duties are contained in chapter 5 of the Water Code, which provides that the commission has general jurisdiction over water and water rights including, among other things—

- the issuance of water rights permits, water rights adjudication, cancellation of water rights, and enforcement of water rights (see Chapters, 4, 10, and 13 of this book);
- continuing supervision over districts created under article III, section 52(b)(1) and (b)(2), and article XVI, section 59, of the Texas Constitution (see Chapters 8, 9, and 16);
- the state's water quality program, including issuance of permits; enforcement of water quality rules, standards, orders, and permits; and water quality planning (see Chapters 33 and 34);
- the adoption and enforcement of rules and performance of other acts relating to the safe construction, maintenance, and removal of dams (see Chapters 39 and 27); and
- the administration of the state's limited programs involving underground water and water wells (although the Water Code gives the TCEQ jurisdiction in this area, local groundwater conservation districts are the preferred method for regulating groundwater (*see* Tex. Water Code § 36.0015)).

See Tex. Water Code § 5.013.

Chapter 7 of the Water Code provides the TCEQ with the authority to enforce the provisions of the Water Code and the Health and Safety Code within the commission's jurisdiction under section 5.013 and rules adopted under those provisions. Tex. Water Code § 7.002. The TCEQ, referring to the three-member governing commission, or the executive director of the agency may institute legal proceedings to compel compliance with the relevant provisions of the Water Code and Health and Safety Code as well as rules, orders, permits, or other decisions of the commission. Tex. Water Code § 7.002. The commission may delegate its enforcement authority to its executive director. Tex. Water Code § 7.002. See Chapter 13 of this book for further discussion of water rights enforcement.

Some of the key chapters of the Water Code related to the TCEQ's jurisdiction over water resources include—

- chapter 5, Texas Commission on Environmental Quality, which provides general authority;
- chapter 7, Enforcement (see Chapter 13 of this book); and
- chapter 11, Water Rights (see Chapters 4, 10, and 11).

The TCEQ also has broad rulemaking authority; that is, the commission can adopt rules to implement the statutes enacted by the legislature. The Water Code provides that the commission shall adopt any rules necessary to carry out its powers and duties under the Code and other laws of this state. Tex. Water Code § 5.103. The commission's rules are contained in title 30 of the Texas Administrative Code. Rule chapters specific to water rights and water supply include—

- chapter 288, Water Conservations Plans and Drought Contingency Plans;
- chapter 290, Public Drinking Water (see Chapters 29 and 30 of this book);
- chapter 292, Special Requirements for Certain Districts and Authorities (see Chapter 9);
- chapter 293, Water Districts (see Chapters 8, 9, and 16);
- chapters 295 and 297, Water Rights, Procedural and Substantive, respectively (see Chapters 4, 10, and 11);
- chapter 298, Environmental Flow Standards; and
- chapter 20, Rulemaking.

The commission must adopt its rules in accordance with the rulemaking requirements of Texas Government Code chapter 2001, commonly referred to as the Administrative Procedure Act (APA). Tex. Water Code § 5.103(c); 30 Tex. Admin. Code § 20.3. In 2021, the Texas legislature adopted Senate Bill 3 to address the impacts of Winter Storm Uri on electric and water service in the state. Senate Bill 3, Act of June 8, 2021, 87th Leg., R.S. ch. 426 (S.B. 3), eff. Sept. 1, 2021. Included in S.B. 3 is a requirement that not later than March 1, 2022, affected utilities must submit to TCEQ an emergency preparedness plan, and not later than July 1, 2022, or upon final approval by TCEQ, must implement the approved plan.

§ 7.3:1 Decision-Making Body

The commission itself is made up of three members, appointed by the governor with the advice and consent of the senate. Tex. Water Code § 5.052. The members of the commission serve on a full-time basis; hold office for staggered terms of six years, with the term of one member expiring every two years; and may not serve more than two terms. Tex. Water Code §§ 5.056, 5.057. The governor appoints one member of the commission to serve as its chair to preside over meetings. Tex. Water Code § 5.058. The commissioners are charged with establishing overall agency direction and policy and with making final determinations on contested permitting and enforcement matters. *See* Texas Commission on Environmental Quality, *Office of the Commissioners*, www.tceq.texas.gov/agency/organization/commissioner.html [hereinafter TCEQ Commissioners]. Four TCEQ Offices report directly to the TCEQ Commissioners: General Counsel, Chief Auditor, Chief Clerk, and Public Interest Counsel. *See* TCEQ Commissioners.

The commission is subject to the Open Meetings Act, Texas Government Code chapter 551, which requires its members to have all of their discussions and decisions conducted in a forum open to the public, with some limited exceptions. *See* Tex. Gov't Code § 551.002; *see also* Tex. Gov't Code §§ 551.071–.090. This open meeting is commonly referred to as the "commission agenda" or simply "agenda." It is held relatively regularly, usually every other Wednesday morning, at the TCEQ central offices in North Austin. Notice must be given about the items that will be considered on any agenda. *See* Tex. Gov't Code § 551.041. The commission posts its agenda on the TCEQ's website in advance of the meeting. *See* Texas Commission on Environmental Quality, *Commissioners' Agendas*, www.tceq.texas.gov/agency/decisions/agendas/comm. Links on the site lead to all documents provided to the commissioners for consideration on each agenda item. Additionally, TCEQ agenda meetings are webcast, with a live video feed from the meeting broadcast to the public over the Internet. *See* TexasAdmin.com, www.texasadmin.com/tx/tceq/. The agenda may also be viewed at www.youtube.com/user/TCEQNews.

The Texas Water Code authorizes the commission to delegate to the executive director its authority to act on an application or other request to issue, renew, reopen, transfer, amend, extend, withdraw, revoke, terminate, or modify a permit, license, certificate, registration, or other authorization or approval under the following circumstances:

1. required notice has been given;

2. the applicant agrees in writing to the action to be taken by the executive director; and

3. the application is uncontested.

Tex. Water Code § 5.122.

An application is uncontested if no party protests the application, if all parties have settled and withdrawn their protests to the application, or if all parties agree to the action to be taken by the executive director. The ability to delegate decisions on uncontested matters to the executive director means that the commission does not have to hear and decide on every permit application and enforcement action. This delegation authority is essential to the efficient execution of the commission's duties. Before taking action on a delegated matter, the executive director posts the proposed action on the executive director's searchable agenda for at least three days. *See* Texas Commission on Environmental Quality, *Executive Director's Agenda and Marked Agenda*, www.tceq.texas.gov/agency/decisions/cc/eda.html.

§ 7.3:2 Office of Water

The TCEQ is composed of several "Offices," which are further divided into "Divisions" and then "Sections." *See* Texas Commission on Environmental Quality, *TCEQ Organization Map*, www.tceq.texas.gov/agency/organization/index.html. The Office of Water contains the Water Quality, Water Quality Planning, Water Supply, and Water Availability divisions.

The Water Supply division is responsible for programs that "ensure the production, treatment, delivery and protection of safe and adequate drinking water." *See* Texas Commission on Environmental Quality, *Office of Water*, www.tceq.texas.gov/agency/organization/water.html [hereinafter TCEQ Office of Water].

The Water Supply division performs the following functions:

- oversees the production, treatment, quality, and delivery of drinking water for the public by implementation of the SDWA;
- assesses and protects sources of public drinking water;
- offers technical assistance on operating public water systems;
- reviews engineering plans for new or significantly modified public water systems or exceptions to TCEQ rules;
- assesses the financial, managerial, and technical capabilities of public water systems; and

- manages the Water District Database and the Safe Drinking Water Information System (SDWIS).

See TCEQ Office of Water. Before the enactment of House Bill 1600 (H.B. 1600) (83rd Legislature, 2013), the Water Supply division was also responsible for ensuring provision of safe and adequate water and sewer utility services at fair rates. H.B. 1600 transferred this duty to the Public Utility Commission beginning September 1, 2014. *See* Act of May 13, 2013, 83d Leg., R.S., ch. 170, § 2.96, eff. Sept. 1, 2013. See section 7.4 below for further discussion regarding this function.

The Water Availability division manages the diversion, storage, and use of surface water and protects groundwater through planning and pollution prevention programs. This is the primary division responsible for responding to drought conditions to ensure adequate water supplies. It is also responsible for the development of water availability models (WAMs), the primary tools used to determine whether and how much of the state's surface water is available for water rights permits. See Chapter 12 of this book for more information regarding WAMs.

The division performs the following functions:

- processes applications for water rights permits and amendments;
- maintains WAMs for all river basins;
- reviews water conservation plans and drought contingency plans;
- performs groundwater quality planning and assessments;
- supports the interagency Texas Groundwater Protection Committee and the Texas Groundwater Protection Strategy;
- manages the state's plan for preventing groundwater pollution from pesticides and the state's program for the identification of priority groundwater management areas;
- ensures compliance, through the watermaster programs, with water rights by monitoring stream flows, reservoir levels, and water use (the TCEQ Office of Compliance and Enforcement is responsible for enforcement of water rights in areas that do not have watermasters; see Chapter 13 of this book for discussion of enforcement of water rights); and
- supports interstate river compacts.

See TCEQ Office of Water.

§ 7.3:3 Watermasters

The TCEQ employs watermasters in some parts of the state to ensure compliance with water rights rules and permits in certain designated geographic areas. *See, e.g.*, Tex. Water Code § 11.326. The TCEQ watermasters allocate water between users and ensure compliance with water rights by monitoring streamflows, reservoir levels, and water use; coordinate diversions in the basins managed by their programs; and regulating reservoirs as needed to prevent waste of water or the use of water in quantities in excess of a user's water right. *See* Texas Commission on Environmental Quality, *Watermasters*, www.tceq.texas.gov/permitting/water_rights/wmaster.

Currently, watermasters operate in four large areas: the Rio Grande Basin (*see* Tex. Water Code § 11.3271; 30 Tex. Admin. Code ch. 303); the South Texas Watermaster Region (*see* Tex. Water Code §§ 11.326–.333; 30 Tex. Admin. Code ch. 304); the Concho River Basin (*see* Tex. Water Code §§ 11.551–.561; 30 Tex. Admin. Code ch. 304); and part of the Brazos River Basin (*see* Tex. Water Code §§ 11.326–.333; 30 Tex. Admin. Code ch. 304). The watermaster for the South Texas Watermaster Program serves as the watermaster for the Concho River Watermaster Program. Tex. Water Code § 11.554(a). The Brazos watermaster was added in 2014 after a contested case hearing process in which the TCEQ ordered that a watermaster be appointed to help regulate diversions in a portion of the Brazos River basin, including the Possum Kingdom Reservoir and the rest of the basin downstream from it. For a water basin in which a watermaster is not appointed, the executive director must evaluate the water basin at least once every five years to determine whether a watermaster should be appointed. Tex. Water Code § 11.326(g)(1). See Chapter 13 of this book for further discussion of the watermaster program.

§ 7.3:4 Attorneys

The TCEQ's attorneys are primarily assigned to three offices: the Office of General Counsel, the Office of Legal Services, and the Office of Public Interest Counsel. The general counsel is the chief advisor to the commissioners on questions of law and ethics. The general counsel and assistant general counsel attorneys provide legal assistance to the commissioners for their review of permits, proposed enforcement actions, rules, and other matters, in addition to managing the administrative affairs of the commissioners' office. *See* TCEQ Commissioners. One of their primary functions is briefing the commissioners on agenda items before each commission meeting.

In addition to its role as advisor to the commission, the Office of General Counsel houses alternative dispute resolution (ADR) staff to assist permit applicants and persons opposed to the applications in resolving their differences informally, to avoid the time and expense of contested case hearings. *See* TCEQ Commissioners.

While the general counsel's office works for the commissioners, the attorneys in the Office of Legal Services represent the agency's executive director and staff, which includes staff in the Office of Water. This office manages legal services for the agency in environmental law, enforcement litigation, bankruptcy, the RESTORE Act program, and general agency operations. The Office of Legal Services is divided into three divisions, two of which provide legal counsel and representation related to water resource issues and program areas: the Environmental Law Division (ELD) and the Litigation Division (LD). Attorneys in the ELD provide legal counsel to the agency in all areas of permitting and rulemaking and represent the executive director in contested permitting matters. The division's functions also include legal support related to federal program delegation, interpretation of environmental statutes and rules, and support for the Office of the Attorney General in state and federal court litigation. Within the ELD, the Water Section is composed of attorneys who work with legal issues related to water resources, including water use permit and permit amendment applications. *See* Texas Commission on Environmental Quality, *Office of Legal Services*, www.tceq.texas.gov/agency/organization/ols.html [hereinafter TCEQ Office of Legal Services].

The LD provides legal representation and support to the Enforcement, Field Operations, and Remediation divisions of the Office of Compliance and Enforcement. These are the attorneys who prosecute alleged violations of the commission's rules. The division negotiates agreed enforcement orders, represents the executive director in enforcement actions, advises the agency concerning cleanup standards and recovery of cleanup costs, and coordinates other related programs. Through the Environmental Crimes Section, the LD also investigates and gathers evidence on environmental crimes for prosecution in state and federal courts. *See* TCEQ Office of Legal Services.

The Office of Public Interest Counsel (OPIC) represents the public interest in matters considered by the TCEQ to ensure that the commission is responsive to citizens' concerns regarding environmental quality and consumer protection. The OPIC does not formally represent individuals at TCEQ proceedings; however, it is a statutory party in all contested case hearings. *See* Tex. Water Code § 5.273. Additionally, citizens who have questions about the legal aspects of dealing with the TCEQ, its hearing process, and its rules can obtain help from this office. Assistance is available to anyone who is affected by a particular permit application or other agency authorization. The staff of the OPIC also assists people with questions about enforcement proceedings. *See* Texas Commission on

Environmental Quality, *Office of the Public Interest Counsel*, www.tceq.texas.gov/agency/decisions/participation/public_interest/index.html.

§ 7.4 Public Utility Commission

The Public Utility Commission of Texas (PUC) regulates the state's electric, telecommunication, and water and sewer utilities, implements respective legislation, and offers customer assistance in resolving consumer complaints. *See* Public Utility Commission of Texas, *About the PUCT, Mission & History*, www.puc.texas.gov/agency/about/mission.aspx. The PUC was given jurisdiction over water and sewer utilities on September 1, 2014. *See* Act of May 13, 2013, 83d Leg., R.S., ch. 170, § 2.96(a). The agency is now responsible for the economic regulation of water and sewer service, including the issuance and transfer of certificates of convenience and necessity (CCNs) designating service areas, the determination of water and sewer utility rates, and the administration of hearings and proceedings regarding CCNs and rates. *See* Act of May 13, 2013, 83d Leg., R.S., ch. 170, § 2.96(a).

From its creation by the legislature in 1975 until 1986, the PUC was responsible for the oversight of water and sewer utilities. In 1986, those functions were transferred to the Texas Water Commission, a TCEQ predecessor agency. In 2013, in connection with the Sunset Advisory Commission's review of the PUC, the Texas legislature transferred responsibilities related to the regulation of water and sewer utility service areas and rates from the TCEQ back to the PUC. Regarding the transfer, the Sunset Advisory Commission found that "PUC's staff and its Commission are geared toward overseeing utilities and ensuring that regulated utility rates are just and reasonable." Sunset Advisory Commission, *Final Report with Legislative Action, Public Utility Commission of Texas* 27 (July 2013), www.sunset.texas.gov/public/uploads/files/reports/Public%20Utility%20Commission%20Staff%20Report%202013%2083rd%20Leg.pdf [hereinafter Sunset Staff Report]. Further, it found that "[t]ransfer offers potential benefits by aligning most State utility regulation within one agency." Sunset Staff Report, at 27.

Water resource functions taken over by the PUC include—

- administering the state's water and sewer utility rates under chapter 13 of the Texas Water Code (see Chapters 29 and 31 of this book for further discussion of retail and wholesale rates);
- regulating service areas of retail public utilities through the administration of CCNs;
- determining reasonable rates for the furnishing of raw or treated water;
- reviewing applications for utility sales, transfers, and mergers;
- assessing the financial, managerial, and technical capabilities of public water systems; and
- referring failing or abandoned water and sewer utilities to the Office of the Attorney General for the appointment of a receiver.

Key Water Code chapters pertaining to the PUC's water resource jurisdiction include chapters 11, 12, and 13. See also Chapters 29, 30, and 31 of this book (regulation of retail and wholesale water rates and services). The PUC's rules are divided into procedural rules and substantive rules. The PUC's procedural rules, which apply to electric, telecommunications, and water and sewer utilities, are located in 16 Texas Administrative Code chapter 22. The PUC's substantive rules applicable to water and sewer utilities are located in 16 Texas Administrative Code chapter 24.

The PUC used a two-phase approach to adopting rules to accomplish the transfer of jurisdiction from the TCEQ over the economic regulation of water and sewer utilities. The first phase involved moving the TCEQ's rules (formerly 30 Texas Administrative Code chapter 291), with minor changes, to 16 Texas Administrative Code chapter 24. 39 Tex. Reg. 5920 (Aug. 1, 2014). The phase 1 rules became effective September 1, 2014, the same date that jurisdiction transferred to the PUC. On December 16, 2016, the PUC adopted phase 2 rules with substantive revisions. 41 Tex. Reg. 9895

(Dec. 16, 2016). The phase 2 rules include amendments to implement the legislature's creation of a new classification system for water and sewer utilities into Class A, Class B, and Class C utilities depending on the utility's number of water or sewer taps or connections. In addition to the rule changes, the PUC updated the rate filing package forms and information that a utility must submit as part of a rate change application. In 2019, the Legislature added a fourth class for water and sewer utilities, Class D, while also amending the definition of Class B and C utilities. The Commission further amended its rules and rate filing packages to reflect this change. *See* 45 Tex. Reg. 2845 (May 1, 2020).

In 2021, the Legislature adopted Senate Bill 997 related to PUC review of a contractual rate charged for furnishing raw or treated water, or water or sewer service. *See* Act of June 4, 2021, 87th Leg., R.S., ch. 307 (S.B. 997), eff. Sept. 1, 2021. S.B. 977 prohibits the PUC from holding a hearing or prescribing just and reasonable amounts to be charged under a contract unless the PUC determines that the amount charged under the contract harms the public interest. The bill provides for judicial review of the PUC's public interest determination by trial de novo and in the event of such appeal requires abatement of PUC proceedings on the contract until entry of a final judicial determination that a rate charged under the contract harms the public interest. To facilitate dispute resolution, after a final judicial determination, the law allows parties to amend a contract before the PUC begins rate proceedings.

§ 7.4:1 Decision-Making Body

The commission has traditionally been composed of three commissioners appointed by the governor with the advice and consent of the senate. Tex. Util. Code § 12.051(a). Senate Bill 2154 increases the PUC from three to five members. At least two commissioners must be qualified in the field of public utilities and utility regulation. The bill prohibits a former commissioner from lobbying for one year after ceasing to be a commissioner. Under the legislation the Governor is to appoint the chair of the commission within thirty days of the effective date of the legislation (Sept. 1, 2021) and to set staggered terms for the remaining terms of the existing commissioners. *See* Act June 18, 2021, 87th Leg., R.S., ch.1052 (S.B. 2154), eff. Sept. 1, 2021. Commissioners serve staggered six-year terms. Tex. Util. Code § 12.051(c). One commissioner is designated by the governor as the presiding officer. Tex. Util. Code § 12.052(a). The executive director is responsible for the day-to-day operations of the PUC. *See* Tex. Util. Code § 12.103.

§ 7.4:2 Office of Public Utility Counsel

The PUC's Office of Public Utility Counsel (OPUC) is an independent state agency created in 1983 that represents the interests of residential and small commercial consumers in PUC proceedings. *See* Tex. Util. Code § 13.001. The OPUC is headed by a public counsel appointed by the governor with the advice and consent of the senate. *See* Tex. Util. Code § 13.021. OPUC gained authority to intervene on behalf of water and sewer utility customers on September 1, 2013. *See* Act of May 13, 2013, 83d Leg., R.S., ch. 170, § 2.96(g).

Powers and duties of the OPUC include that the office—

1. must assess the effect of utility rate changes and other regulatory actions on residential consumers in Texas;

2. must advocate in the office's own name a position determined by the public counsel to be most advantageous to a substantial number of residential consumers;

3. may appear or intervene, as a party or otherwise, as a matter of right on behalf of residential

consumers, as a class, in any proceeding before the PUC, including an alternative dispute resolution proceeding, and small commercial consumers, as a class, in any proceeding in which the public counsel determines that small commercial consumers are in need of representation, including an alternative dispute resolution proceeding;

4. may initiate or intervene as a matter of right or otherwise appear in a judicial proceeding that involves an action taken by an administrative agency in a proceeding, including an alternative dispute resolution proceeding, in which the public counsel is authorized to appear, or in which the public counsel determines that residential consumers or small commercial consumers are in need of representation; and

5. may recommend legislation to the legislature that the office determines would positively affect the interests of residential and small commercial consumers.

See Tex. Water Code § 13.017(b).

Importantly, the appearance of OPUC in a proceeding does not preclude the appearance of other parties on behalf of residential or small commercial consumers. Tex. Water Code § 13.017(d).

§ 7.5 Texas Water Development Board

Created in 1957 by legislative act and constitutional amendment, the Texas Water Development Board (TWDB) is the state agency primarily responsible for water planning and for administering water financing for the state. Tex. Water Code § 6.011. The board's mission is to lead the state's efforts in ensuring a secure water future for Texas. In this regard, TWDB provides water planning, data collection and dissemination, financial assistance, and technical assistance services. *See* Texas Water Development Board, *About the Texas Water Development Board*, www.twdb.texas.gov/about/ [hereinafter About the TWDB].

The board has general jurisdiction over—

- the development and implementation of a statewide water plan;
- the administration of the state's various water assistance and financing programs, including those created by the constitution;
- the administration of the National Flood Insurance Program; and
- other areas specifically assigned to the board by the Texas Water Code or other law.

Tex. Water Code § 6.012(a).

The key chapters in the Water Code related to the TWDB's jurisdiction include—

- chapter 6, Texas Water Development Board;
- chapter 15, Texas Water Assistance Program;
- chapter 16, Provisions Generally Applicable to Water Development; and
- chapter 17, Water Development, Public Funding.

Like the TCEQ, the TWDB has the authority to adopt rules necessary to carry out its powers and duties. Tex. Water Code § 6.101(a). Its rulemaking process is also governed by the Administrative Procedure Act. *See* Tex. Water Code § 6.101(c). The rules of the TWDB are contained in 31 Texas Administrative Code chapters 353 through 384.

§ 7.5:1 Decision-Making Body

The board is made up of three members, appointed by the governor with the advice and consent of the senate. Tex. Water Code § 6.052(a). The chair of the board is designated by the governor. Tex. Water Code § 6.059. Members serve on a full-time basis. Tex. Water Code § 6.061. The members of the board hold office for staggered terms of six years, with the terms of one member expiring each odd-numbered year. Tex. Water Code § 6.056(a). An appointee may not serve more than two six-year terms. Tex. Water Code § 6.056(b). The executive administrator is the chief executive officer of the TWDB, who oversees the day-to-day functions of the agency.

§ 7.5:2 Programs

Although the TWDB is not regulatory in nature, the agency nonetheless plays a crucial role in evaluating and prioritizing water-related infrastructure projects for state funding, and whether a project is contained in a regional or state water plan can affect its ability to obtain state financing or permits. *See* Tex. Water Code §§ 11.134(b)(3), 16.053(j)(1). See Chapters 10 and 20 of this book. Moreover, the agency has taken on a greater role in the area of groundwater management in recent years, having responsibility for approval of groundwater conservation districts' groundwater management plans and serving as the key resource to local groundwater districts and groundwater management areas. *See* Tex. Water Code § 36.1072; 31 Tex. Admin. Code ch. 356. See Chapter 21 of this book regarding groundwater management area joint planning.

The TWDB—

- supports the development of regional water plans and incorporates them into a state water plan for the orderly and responsible development, management, and conservation of the state's water resources;
- supports the development of regional flood plans and incorporates them into the state flood plan, the first of which is due September 1, 2024;
- provides loans to local governments for water supply projects; water quality projects including wastewater treatment, municipal solid waste management, and nonpoint source pollution control; flood control projects; agricultural water conservation projects; rural and small community water and wastewater projects; and groundwater district creation expenses;
- provides grants and loans for the water and wastewater needs of the state's economically distressed areas;
- provides agricultural water conservation funding and water-related research and planning grants;
- conducts studies of the occurrence, quantity, quality, and availability of the state's surface water and groundwater;
- collects data and conducts studies concerning the freshwater needs of the state's bays and estuaries;
- administers the Texas Water Bank, which facilitates the transfer, sale, or lease of water and water rights throughout the state, and administers the Texas Water Trust, where water rights are held for environmental flow purposes (note that in H.B. 2225, the legislature in 2021 gave the Texas Parks and Wildlife Department certain authority to manage rights in the Texas Water Trust, as further discussed below); and
- maintains a centralized data bank of information on the state's natural resources, called the Texas Natural Resources Information System, and manages the Strategic Mapping Program, a

> Texas-based, public and private sector cost-sharing program to develop consistent, large-scale computerized base maps describing basic geographic features of Texas.

See About the TWDB.

The TWDB's water planning function involves a continuous process that responds to changing environmental, socioeconomic, and demographic conditions. To address these changes, Texas law requires that the board develop and adopt a new state water plan every five years. Tex. Water Code § 16.051(a). This state water plan must incorporate regional water plans developed every five years by regional water planning groups. Tex. Water Code § 16.051(a). Water plans provide for—

> the orderly development, management, and conservation of water resources and preparation for and response to drought conditions, in order that sufficient water will be available at a reasonable cost to ensure public health, safety, and welfare; further economic development; and protect the agricultural and natural resources of the entire state.

Tex. Water Code § 16.051(a). The state water plan also acts as a guide to state water policy, which the TCEQ must take into consideration in matters coming before it. Tex. Water Code § 16.051(b). Thus, the TWDB's role in the water planning process is fourfold: it reviews regional water plans in accordance with agency rules and guidelines and resolves interregional conflicts; approves regional water planning groups' plans; develops the state water plan; and provides funding for implementation. *See* House Committee on Natural Resources, *Interim Report to the 82nd Texas Legislature* 16–17 (Dec. 2010), www.house.state.tx.us/_media/pdf/committees/reports/82interim/House-Committee-on-Natural-Resources-Interim-Report-2010.pdf [hereinafter 2010 Interim Report]. The TWDB manages the Strategic Mapping (StratMap) Initiative, which is available at https://tnris.org/stratmap/. See also Chapter 20 of this book discussing state water planning and Chapter 37 on financing water projects.

Partly in response to the extraordinary flooding in Texas caused by Hurricane Harvey in 2017, the Texas legislature in 2019 adopted significant flood-related legislation, including Senate Bill 7, Senate Bill 8, Senate Bill 500, and House Joint Resolution 4. *See* Texas Water Development Board, *Implementation of Flood Legislation from the 86th Legislative Session*, www.twdb.texas.gov/flood/doc/Flood_Implementation_Issues_for_Stakeholder_Consideration.pdf. The legislation greatly expanded the TWDB's role in flood planning and financing. In addition to existing programs, the TWDB now administers a new state and regional flood planning process with flood planning regions based on river basins. *See* Texas Water Development Board, *Flood Planning*, www.twdb.texas.gov/flood/planning/index.asp. The first regional flood plans will be due in 2023, and the first state flood plan will be due September 1, 2024. The legislature also made a one-time transfer of $793 million from the state's Economic Stabilization ("Rainy Day") Fund to create a flood financial assistance program administered by the TWDB. The legislature additionally provided the TWDB with funds to collect more flood-related data, advance its river and coastal modeling capabilities, and distribute critical flood information through an online dashboard. *See* Texas Water Development Board, *TWDB Flood Programs*, www.twdb.texas.gov/flood/index.asp. For further discussion of the developments, see Chapter 39 of this book.

The TWDB also performs functions essential to the development and conservation of groundwater resources. The TWDB develops groundwater availability models (GAMs) for the state's aquifers. *See* Tex. Water Code § 16.012(l). These computer models include comprehensive information about the aquifers that is critical to groundwater resource management. Local groundwater conservation districts are required to use GAM information, if available, in the development of their groundwater management plans. *See* Tex. Water Code § 36.1071(h). The GAMs also serve a key role in TWDB's verification of groundwater availability in the state and regional water planning process. This vital information is used in the groundwater management area joint planning process to determine desired future conditions (DFCs) of groundwater aquifers. *See* Tex. Water Code § 36.108(d). See Chapter 19 of this book for a detailed discussion of development of GAMs and Chapter 21 for a discussion of the joint groundwater planning process. In addition to providing technical and administrative assistance in the adoption of DFCs and developing the GAMs, the board also conducts administrative reviews and develops a study of DFC submissions in the instance that an affected person timely files a petition with the groundwater district requiring the district to contract with the State Office of Administrative Hearings for a hearing on the reasonableness of the DFC. *See* Tex. Water Code § 36.1083.

The board conducts studies and is an important repository for data regarding the state's water resources, such as location, quantity, and quality. These studies and data are used to inform water planning and development. For example, at the request of the 84th Legislature in 2015, the board studied the hydrology and geology of the state's aquifers to determine the quality and quantity of groundwater in the aquifers (specifically regarding salinity), how water moves between aquifers, and the contributions of aquifers to surface water flows. *See* Act of May 18, 2015, 84th Leg., R.S., ch. 159, § 1 (H.B. 1232), eff. May 28, 2015. The resulting study is available at www.twdb.texas.gov/groundwater/docs/studies/TexasAquifersStudy_2016.pdf. The legislature has also required the TWDB to provide biennial reports on key water issues prior to each legislative session. For instance, in 2003, the 78th Texas Legislature passed House Bill 1370, Act of May 15, 2003, 78th Leg., R.S., ch. 49, eff. May 15, 2003, adding Texas Water Code section 16.060, which directs the TWDB to pursue seawater desalination and to report progress in a biennial report due December 1 of each even-numbered year. In 2015, the legislature further amended section 16.060 to require updates on brackish groundwater desalination and designation of brackish groundwater production zones. *See e.g.*, Texas Water Development Board, *The Future of Desalination in Texas: 2020 Biennial Report on Seawater and Brackish Groundwater Desalination* (87th legislature, Dec. 1, 2020), www.twdb.texas.gov/innovativewater/desal/doc/2020_TheFutureofDesalinationinTexas.pdf.

In another of its key functions, the TWDB administers several loan programs for financing the planning, design, construction, improvement, or expansion of water and wastewater facilities. TWDB financial assistance programs are funded through state-backed bonds, a combination of state bond proceeds and federal grant funds, or limited appropriated funds and are often provided at interest rates lower than the current market rate. These programs include—

- the State Water Implementation Fund of Texas,
- the Drinking Water State Revolving Fund,
- the Clean Water State Revolving Fund,
- the Texas Water Development Fund,
- the Flood Infrastructure Fund,
- FEMA Flood Mitigation Assistance,
- the Agricultural Water Conservation Grant and Loan Program,
- the Groundwater Conservation District Loan Program,
- the State Participation Program, and
- the Regional Water Planning Group Grant Program.

See generally Texas Water Development Board, *Financial Assistance Programs*, www.twdb.texas.gov/financial/programs/index.asp.

The State Water Implementation Fund of Texas, commonly known as SWIFT, was created by the Texas legislature in 2013 as a means to provide an additional funding source for water development projects in the state water plan. *See* Act of May 20, 2013, 83d Leg., R.S., ch. 207, § 2.01 (H.B. 4); Act of May 26, 2013, 83d Leg., R.S., ch. 836, § 33 (H.B. 1025); Tex. S.J. Res. 1, 83d Leg., L.S. (2013); Tex. Water Code ch. 15, subchs. G, H. The legislation provided for the use of $2 billion from the state's Economic Stabilization Fund, also known as the Rainy Day Fund, to support loans for projects contained in the state water plan. Texas voters overwhelmingly approved the constitutional amendment necessary to fund SWIFT in November 2013. The TWDB regulations implementing SWIFT, which were adopted in November 2014, are found at 31 Tex. Admin. Code ch. 363, subchapter M. See also Chapter 37 of this book on financing water projects.

§ 7.6 Texas Parks and Wildlife Department

The Texas Parks and Wildlife Department (TPWD) is an executive agency formed in 1963 by merging the State Parks Board and Game and Fish Commission. *See* Tex. Parks & Wild. Code § 11.011. The TPWD's mission is to manage and conserve the natural and cultural resources of Texas and to provide hunting, fishing, and outdoor recreation opportunities for the use and enjoyment of present and future generations. Texas Parks and Wildlife Department, *Mission & Philosophy*, https://tpwd.texas.gov/about/mission-philosophy.

The TPWD derives its authority over state water resources from various statutes in the Texas Parks and Wildlife Code and the Texas Water Code. The TPWD has primary responsibility for protecting the state's fish and wildlife resources. The agency regulates the taking and conservation of marine life and sand, gravel, and mud shell and protects fish in public waters. *See* Tex. Parks & Wild. Code §§ 1.011(d), 1.012. Resource protection activities include investigating fish kills and seeking restoration of lost resources; providing recommendations for protecting fish and wildlife resources to local, state, and federal agencies; and providing recommendations to the TCEQ on scheduling instream flows and freshwater inflows to Texas estuaries for the management of fish and wildlife resources. *See* Tex. Parks & Wild. Code § 12.0011; *see also* Texas Parks and Wildlife Department, *Statutory Authority*, https://tpwd.texas.gov/landwater/water/conservation/water_resources/legal/. The rules of the TPWD are contained in 31 Texas Administrative Code chapters 51 through 69.

The TPWD's direct regulation of water resources includes issuing approval for the removal of sand and gravel from riverbeds (*see* Tex. Parks & Wild. Code ch. 86; 31 Tex. Admin. Code §§ 69.101–.121), the enforcement of prohibitions against operation of vehicles in riverbeds (*see* Tex. Parks & Wild. Code ch. 90), and the issuance of permits for the placing of any species of fish, shellfish, or aquatic plant into public waters of the state (*see* Tex. Parks & Wild. Code § 66.015).

The TPWD also has authority to enforce prohibitions against unauthorized discharges of waste into or adjacent to state waters and TCEQ rules, orders, or permits regulating discharges when such violations "affect aquatic life and wildlife." Tex. Water Code § 26.129. In such instances, the TPWD is authorized to bring suit to recover natural resource damages.

In 2021, the legislature adopted House Bill 2225, requiring TPWD to encourage and facilitate the dedication of water rights in the Texas Water Trust for environmental needs. House Bill 2225, Act of June 15, 2021, 87th Leg., R.S., ch. 689 (H.B. 2225), eff. Sept. 1, 2021. The legislature clarified that this law may not be construed to authorize TPWD to exercise any authority expressly granted to TWDB or TCEQ under Water Code chapter 15, subchapter K. The agency's major influence over water resources comes from its role as an advisor to the TCEQ and other state regulators, in the following ways:

- Through its mission of conserving the state's wildlife and wildlife habitats, the TPWD can employ voluntary programs or interagency agreements to attempt to increase water yield. This often occurs through private landowner watershed management programs that are administered by other agencies or river authorities. *See* Texas Parks and Wildlife Department, *Landowner Incentive Program (LIP)*, https://tpwd.texas.gov/landwater/land/private/lip/.
- TPWD provides input to regional water planning groups and the TWDB during the development of state and regional water plans. *See* Tex. Water Code §§ 16.051, 16.053.

- In conjunction with the TWDB, the TPWD established and maintains a bay and estuary data collection and evaluation program and conducts studies to determine bay conditions necessary to support a sound ecological environment. *See* Tex. Water Code § 16.058.
- With the TCEQ and the TWDB, the TPWD established and maintains an instream flow data collection and evaluation program. *See* Tex. Water Code § 16.059.

§ 7.6:1 Decision-Making Body

The Texas Parks and Wildlife Commission consists of nine members of the public who are appointed by the governor with the advice and consent of the senate, one of whom is appointed to preside over the commission. Tex. Parks & Wild. Code §§ 11.012(a), 11.014(a). The members of the commission hold office for staggered terms of six years, with the terms of three members expiring every two years. Tex. Parks & Wild. Code § 11.013. The commission is required to meet quarterly and have an annual public meeting. Tex. Parks & Wild. Code § 11.015. The chief operating officer of the TPWD is its executive director, who is appointed by the commission. Tex. Parks & Wild. Code § 11.017.

The TPWD is currently organized into thirteen divisions: Wildlife, Coastal Fisheries, Inland Fisheries, Law Enforcement, State Parks, Infrastructure, Legal, Support Resources, Communications, Human Resources, Executive Office, Financial Resources, and Information Technology. *See* Texas Parks and Wildlife Department, *Administration & Divisions*, https://tpwd.texas.gov/about/administration-divisions.

§ 7.6:2 Influence on Water Resources

Regulatory Function: As stated above, the TPWD regulates the removal of sediment from riverbeds. *See* Tex. Parks & Wild. Code ch. 86; 31 Tex. Admin. Code §§ 69.101–.121. The sediments include marl, sand, mud shell, gravel, or a combination of such materials. 31 Tex. Admin. Code § 69.102(9). Before disturbing or taking sediment from state water, a person must obtain a permit from the TPWD. *See* 31 Tex. Admin. Code § 69.104. Projects to restore or maintain the storage capacity of existing public water supplies, maintenance projects carried out by public utilities for noncommercial purposes, and public road projects of the Texas Department of Transportation are exempt from these permitting requirements. 31 Tex. Admin. Code § 69.120. The TPWD may issue general or individual permits. *See* 31 Tex. Admin. Code § 69.104. A general permit may be issued for a project that involves an insignificant disturbance or removal of sedimentary materials from the public waters of the state. 31 Tex. Admin. Code § 69.102(5). Such projects include pipeline construction and maintenance and other activities that necessitate the disturbance or removal of less than one thousand cubic yards of sedimentary material and that are not likely to affect a natural resource. 31 Tex. Admin. Code § 69.115(a). An application for an individual permit is more complex, requiring both a mailed and published notice. *See* 31 Tex. Admin. Code § 69.105(b). The applicant or a person with a "justifiable interest" may request a contested case hearing, which is referred to the State Office of Administrative Hearings. 31 Tex. Admin. Code § 69.107. The TPWD also issues permits for dredging in coastal waters. *See* 31 Tex. Admin. Code §§ 69.201–.209.

In addition to its regulatory function, the TPWD influences state water resource decisions by actively participating in decision-making processes at the TCEQ and providing support to it and other state agencies with water resource jurisdiction. The TPWD also monitors rulemaking actions and regularly provides comments and suggestions for TCEQ rules.

Water Rights: In regard to water rights permitting, the TCEQ must send the TPWD a copy of all permit applications to store, take, or divert water. The TPWD must make recommendations to the TCEQ to protect fish and wildlife resources. The TPWD may be a full party in any hearing on an application to store, take, or divert water, and the TCEQ must consider information, evidence, and testimony offered by the TPWD. *See* Tex. Parks & Wild. Code § 12.024; Tex. Water Code § 11.147(f). Note, however, that the TCEQ takes the position that as a result of changes to Texas Water Code section 5.115(b) in 2011, the TPWD may not contest the issuance of a permit or license by the TCEQ.

The TPWD has played a strong role in the arena of water rights through its participation in the development of environmental flow requirements pursuant to Senate Bill 3. *See* Act of May 28, 2007, 80th Leg., R.S., ch. 1430, § 1.13. The TPWD provided many of the tools used to determine instream flows and provides valuable technical experience. See Chapter 11 of this book for a discussion of the Senate Bill 3 instream flows requirements. Also, under the Water Code, 5 percent of the annual firm yield of water in any reservoir and associated works constructed with state financial participation that is within two hundred river miles of the coast is appropriated to the TPWD for use to make releases to bays and estuaries and for instream uses, and the TCEQ is required to issue permits for this water to the TPWD under procedures adopted by the TCEQ. *See* Tex. Water Code §§ 15.3041(a), 16.1331(a).

The Water Code contains several requirements for the TPWD's participation in the environmental flows process. The TPWD, the TWDB, and the TCEQ have joint responsibility for establishing and maintaining an instream flow data collection and evaluation program. *See* Tex. Water Code § 16.059(d). A Texas Parks and Wildlife Commission member must serve on the Environmental Flows Advisory Group. Tex. Water Code § 11.0236(c)(3). The TPWD, the TWDB, and the TCEQ are required to provide written reports to the Environmental Flows Advisory Group describing agency responses to recommendations of the Science Advisory Committee of the Group. *See* Tex. Water Code § 11.02361(f). The staffs of the TPWD, the TWDB, and the TCEQ are required to provide technical assistance to each basin and bay expert science team and may serve as nonvoting members of the science teams. *See* Tex. Water Code § 11.02362(k).

State Water Planning: The TPWD also plays a role in the development of the state water plan and assists regional water planning groups in creating regional water plans. *See* 31 Tex. Admin. Code § 357.11(e)(2). See Chapter 20 of this book for more on the state water planning process. Often, the TPWD can assist regional water planning groups with an accurate description of a natural resource, as required for regional water plans.

Estuary Program: The TPWD works with other agencies to ensure the health of the state's bays and estuaries. It is required to participate and provide assistance in estuary programs. *See* Tex. Water Code § 5.605(a)(2). The TPWD and the TCEQ are required to review bay and estuary studies prepared by the TPWD and the TWDB to determine inflow conditions necessary for the bays and estuaries. *See* Tex. Water Code § 11.1491(a). The TPWD and the TWDB have joint responsibility for establishing and maintaining a bay and estuary data collection and evaluation program. Tex. Water Code § 16.058(a).

Water Quality: The TPWD also influences water resources in the area of water quality. The TPWD has been active in the TCEQ process for developing total maximum daily loads (TMDLs) for state waters. The TCEQ must develop and set water quality standards based on all quality-assured data obtained by the TCEQ, including the local watershed and river basin database, which is to be composed of data obtained from river authorities, wastewater discharge permit holders, state and federal agencies, and other relevant sources. *See* Tex. Water Code §§ 26.023, 26.0135. The TPWD plays a large role in periodic revisions of these standards, including formation of policy and development of rules and guidance. Texas Parks and Wildlife Department, *Statutory Authority*, *Texas Parks and Wildlife Department Involvement in Water Issues*, https://tpwd.texas.gov/landwater/water/conservation/water_

resources/legal/. (Other agencies' roles in the TMDL process are briefly discussed at section 7.10:2 below.) See Chapter 33 of this book for further discussion of TMDLs. The TPWD also has authority concurrent with the TCEQ to enforce water quality violations when violations may impact fish and wildlife. *See* Tex. Water Code §§ 7.109, 26.129. Additionally, the TPWD has statewide responsibility for the Natural Resource Damage Assessment (NRDA) Program, as a cotrustee of the state's natural resources (the NRDA Program is discussed in more detail at section 7.8:2 below). Texas Parks and Wildlife Department, *Natural Resource Trustee Agencies*, https://tpwd.texas.gov/landwater/water/environconcerns/damage_assessment/trustees.phtml.

State Scientific Areas: As a unique tool for protecting a particular water resource, the TPWD is authorized to create state scientific areas for the purposes of education, scientific research, and preservation of flora and fauna of scientific or educational value. *See* Tex. Parks & Wild. Code § 81.501. There are two state scientific areas: Redfish Bay, established to protect seagrass, and the San Marcos River State Scientific Area, which was created in 2012 to protect Texas wild rice during low water flow periods as part of a larger habitat conservation plan for protection of all the Edwards Aquifer–related endangered species. 31 Tex. Admin. Code §§ 57.910, 57.921.

§ 7.7 Railroad Commission of Texas

The Railroad Commission of Texas (RRC) was established in 1891, pursuant to a constitutional amendment to regulate the railroads. Railroad Commission of Texas, *About RRC*, www.rrc.texas.gov/about-us/. Over time, the commission has been given responsibility to oversee the activities of many different industries. Railroad Commission of Texas, *History of the Railroad Commission*, www.rrc.texas.gov/about-us/history/. The RRC has primary regulatory jurisdiction over the oil and natural gas industry, pipeline transporters, the natural gas and hazardous liquid pipeline industry, natural gas utilities, the liquefied petroleum gas (LP-gas) industry, and coal and uranium surface mining operations. With regard to uranium exploration activities, the RRC, the TCEQ, and groundwater conservation districts may all have regulatory jurisdiction. *See* Tex. Nat. Res. Code § 131.354. The primary statutes under which the RRC operates are the Texas Natural Resources Code, the Texas Water Code, the Texas Health and Safety Code, and the Texas Utilities Code. The commission also has regulatory and enforcement responsibilities under federal law, including the Surface Coal Mining Control and Reclamation Act, the Safe Drinking Water Act, the Pipeline Safety Act, the Resource Conservation Recovery Act, and the Clean Water Act. *See* Railroad Commission of Texas, *RRC's Authority and Jurisdiction*, www.rrc.texas.gov/about-us/faqs/rrc-authority-and-jurisdiction/. The RRC's implementing regulations are in 16 Texas Administrative Code part 1.

The RRC plays an important role in water resources. RRC rules provide that "[n]o person conducting activities subject to regulation by the commission may cause or allow pollution of surface or subsurface water in the state." 16 Tex. Admin. Code § 3.8(b). Generally, under the memorandum of understanding (MOU) between the TCEQ and the RRC, where an activity would otherwise be regulated by the TCEQ, the RRC has jurisdiction if that activity is associated with the exploration, development, or production of oil, gas, or geothermal resources, including transportation of crude oil and natural gas by pipeline, and from solution brine mining activities. *See* 16 Tex. Admin. Code § 3.30(b)(2)(B)(i). Note, however, as stated in the section above for the TCEQ, responsibility for regulating certain discharges has been transferred from the RRC to the TCEQ. Regulation of some discharges remains with the RRC. A revised MOU explains:

> Under Texas Natural Resources Code, Title 3, and Texas Water Code, Chapter 26, the RRC regulates discharges from activities associated with the exploration, development, or production of oil, gas, or geothermal resources, including transportation of crude oil and natural gas by pipeline, and from solution brine mining activities, except that on delegation to

> the TCEQ of NPDES authority for discharges into surface water in the state of produced water, hydrostatic test water, and gas plant effluent resulting from the activities described in Texas Water Code §26.131(a), the TCEQ has sole authority to issue permits for those discharges.

16 Tex. Admin. Code § 3.30(b)(2)(B)(i). The EPA announced the delegation on January 15, 2021. *See* U.S. Environmental Protection Agency, *EPA approves Clean Water Program to Texas Commission on Environmental Quality* (Jan. 15, 2021), www.epa.gov/newsreleases/epa-approves-clean-water-program-texas-commission-environmental-quality.

The RRC also has jurisdiction over drilling, construction, operation, and closure of many injection wells, including those used for disposal of oil and gas waste and those used for enhanced recovery of oil or natural gas. The RRC implements and enforces rules related to the proper well spacing, drilling, cementing, casing, and plugging of these wells to protect groundwater resources. *See* 16 Tex. Admin. Code §§ 3.9, 3.13, 3.46, 3.95–.97.

Additionally, the RRC grants uranium exploration permits. *See* Railroad Commission of Texas, *Uranium Exploration*, www.rrc.texas.gov/surface-mining/programs/uranium-exploration/. Uranium is found in a soluble form in aquifers in south Texas. The uranium exploration process involves drilling a number of exploration holes or wells into aquifer formations. Permits are required to protect groundwater from contamination during this process. The RRC retains jurisdiction over the exploration holes and wells until they are plugged, registered with the TCEQ, or included in a TCEQ production area authorization. *See* Tex. Nat. Res. Code § 131.354(a); *see also* Tex. Water Code § 27.0513 (regarding production area authorizations). Statutes and rules under the RRC's uranium exploration program are contained in Natural Resources Code chapter 131 and 16 Texas Administrative Code chapter 11.

§ 7.7:1 Decision-Making Body

There are three commissioners; each is elected statewide for a six-year term, with one commissioner seeking election every two years. When a commissioner is appointed by the governor to fill an unexpired term, the appointee serves until the next general election, at which time the appointee may run for the remainder of the unexpired term. Railroad Commission of Texas, *Commissioners,* www.rrc.texas.gov/about-us/commissioners/. The executive director, appointed by the commissioners, serves as the commission's chief administrative officer and is responsible for the overall operation of the commission.

§ 7.7:2 Influence on Water Resources

Groundwater Production: Importantly, while groundwater conservation districts have broad authority over the production of groundwater within their local jurisdictions, their authority may be limited when the groundwater production is associated with the exploration, development, or production of oil or gas or with mining operations because of the RRC's jurisdiction over water used for those purposes. *See* Tex. Water Code § 36.117; *see also* Tex. Nat. Res. Code ch. 131 (uranium exploration), § 91.101(a)(2)(A) (regarding activities associated with certain injection water source wells).

Uranium Mining: The RRC shares jurisdiction with the TCEQ over uranium mining projects. Uranium is a naturally occurring element that exists in commercially viable quantities in only a few places in the United States; one of those places is south Texas. In situ uranium mining, which involves injection of fluid into wells, is primarily regulated by the TCEQ; however, the RRC regulates the initial exploration phase in which the regulated entity drills numerous boreholes into the underground formation to attempt to locate uranium deposits. *See* Tex. Nat. Res. Code ch. 131. As with any drilling into a groundwater-bearing formation, this exploration must be carefully regulated to ensure contaminants are not introduced into freshwater. RRC regulations related to uranium mining projects are designed to protect fresh groundwater from contamination from exploration activities. *See* Tex. Nat. Res. Code ch. 131; 16 Tex. Admin. Code ch. 11.

"Frac Water": Management of water used for fracturing gas wells, or "frac water," has come under increasing scrutiny because of a dramatic increase in oil and gas production through the use of horizontal drilling and hydraulic fracturing. Hydraulic fracturing, or "fracking," allows oil and gas production from the dense shale that otherwise is unrecoverable through conventional means. Water mixed with sand and small amounts of other chemicals is pumped in large volumes at high pressure into the shale formation, forcing its way into tiny cracks and spaces to extract the trapped oil and gas. This area of regulation is evolving as lawmakers and regulators address concerns related to the volume of water used in the process, the effects of the process on groundwater quality, and reuse or disposal of frac water. For example, during the 2011 legislative session, the Texas Natural Resources Code was amended to require disclosure to the RRC and on the Internet of the quantity and composition of hydraulic fracturing fluids, and it establishes a complex disclosure process. *See* Tex. Nat. Res. Code § 91.851. For additional discussion of hydraulic fracturing, see Chapter 41 of this book.

§ 7.8 General Land Office

Formed by the Republic of Texas in 1836, the Texas General Land Office (GLO) is the oldest state agency. Part of the GLO's mission is to protect the environmental health of the state's coasts, including beaches, wetlands, and coastal preserves, and it is the lead agency for responding to coastal oil spills. *See* Texas General Land Office, *Environmental Protection*, www.glo.texas.gov/coast/coastal-management/environmental-protection/index.html.

§ 7.8:1 Decision-Making Body

The commissioner of the GLO serves a four-year term and is elected statewide. *See* Texas General Land Office, *Overview*, www.glo.texas.gov/the-glo/about/overview/index.html. The day-to-day operation of the agency is managed by the chief clerk.

§ 7.8:2 Influence on Water Resources

Coastal Spill Response, Cleanup, and the NRDA: The GLO administers and directs all coastal discharge response and cleanup operations resulting from unauthorized discharges of oil pursuant to the Oil Spill Prevention and Response Act of 1991. *See* Tex. Nat. Res. Code ch. 40. As part of its responsibility for handling unauthorized oil spills, the GLO registers terminal facilities, establishes standards for discharge prevention and spill response capabilities for terminal facilities and vessels, certifies discharge cleanup organizations, and defines spill cleanup standards. The GLO also has authority to remove and dispose of wrecked, derelict, or substantially dismantled vessels from coastal waters. *See* Tex. Nat. Res. Code ch. 40. As a cotrustee of the state's natural resources, the GLO also has statewide responsibility for the Natural Resources Damage Assessment (NRDA) Program. *See* Texas General Land Office, *Environmental Protection*, www.glo.texas.gov/coast/coastal-management/environmental-protection/index.html [hereinafter GLO Environmental Protection].

The NRDA Program is the legal and technical process designed to restore areas damaged by releases and ensure that responsible parties pay for restoring the affected areas. The GLO works with other members of the NRDA Trustees Council to act on behalf of the public to identify the injured natural resources and determine the extent of the impact. They also negotiate with responsible parties to obtain restoration of damaged resources or will recover damages from responsible parties to plan and carry out restoration activities. *See* GLO Environmental Protection. The GLO's NRDA rules are located in 31 Texas Administrative Code chapter 20.

Nonpoint Source Pollution Control Program: The GLO's Nonpoint Source Pollution Control Program, dealing with stormwater runoff, floodplain management, and related critical water quality issues, is designed to reduce and enhance management of polluted runoff from activities related to forestry, agriculture, urban areas, marinas, shoreline and stream channel modification, and wetlands and vegetated shorelines, or riparian areas. The GLO works with the TCEQ and the Texas State Soil and Water Conservation Board (TSSWCB) to develop, fund, and implement nonpoint source pollution control projects. Other collaborating partners include municipalities, counties, the TPWD, the RRC, and the Texas Department of Transportation.

Coastal Management Program: The GLO is also responsible for the administration of the Texas Coastal Management Program (CMP). The CMP is based on the Coastal Coordination Act of 1991. *See generally* Tex. Nat. Res. Code ch. 33. The boundaries of the coastal zone are set out in 31 Texas Administrative Code section 503.1. The Texas coastal zone is generally the area seaward of the Texas coastal facility designation line, up to three marine leagues into the Gulf of Mexico. *See* National Oceanic and Atmospheric Administration, Office for Coastal Management, *Coastal Zone Management Programs: Texas*, https://coast.noaa.gov/czm/mystate/#texas. The National Oceanic and Atmospheric Administration approved Texas's CMP in 1996. The CMP links federal, state, and local activities along the coast pursuant to the federal Coastal Zone Management Program, discussed at section 7.17:2 below. *See* Texas General Land Office, *Coastal Management Program*, www.glo.texas.gov/coast/grant-projects/cmp/. The GLO administers the CMP in conjunction with the Coastal Coordination Advisory Committee, also discussed at section 7.11:2 below. The GLO acts as the lead agency to coordinate and implement the CMP for the management of uses affecting coastal natural resource areas, in cooperation with other state agencies that have duties relating to coastal matters such as the TCEQ and the TPWD. *See* Tex. Nat. Res. Code § 33.052. Originally another state agency, the Coastal Coordination Council, administered the CMP. As a result of the sunset process, the Texas legislature in 2011 transferred this responsibility to the GLO, abolished the Coastal Coordination Council, and established the Coastal Coordination Advisory Committee, discussed at section 7.11:2 below. *See* Texas General Land Office, *Coastal Coordination Advisory Committee*, www.glo.texas.gov/the-glo/boards-commissions/coastal-coordination/index.html. In addition to the GLO, the TPWD, and the TCEQ, the following state agencies implement the goals and policies of the CMP through their statutory authorities: the RRC, the Texas Department of Transportation, the Texas Historical Commission, the PUC, the TSSWCB, and the TWDB. *See* Texas General Land Office, *Texas Coastal Management Program Biennial Report* 2017–2018 16 (Dec. 2018), www.glo.texas.gov/coast/coastal-management/forms/files/cmp-biennial-report-2017-2018.pdf.

Some of the elements included in the CMP are—

- identification of the boundaries of the coastal zone subject to the CMP;
- a continuous analysis of the potential uses for the land and water within the coastal zone, and recommendations about which configurations of uses maximize the benefits conferred on citizens;
- guidelines on the priority of uses within the coastal zone and a list of the uses of the land and water within the coastal zone that are permissible under state law and that would have a direct and significant impact on the coastal waters; and

- a procedure for determining the consistency of an agency or subdivision action or a federal agency action or activity or outer continental shelf plan with the goals and policies of the CMP.

See, e.g., Tex. Nat. Res. Code § 33.053(a)(1)–(3), (a)(11).

In administering the CMP, the GLO—

- may review an agency action, such as a proposed rule, or a permit for consistency with the goals and policies of the CMP if the agency's consistency determination is contested, including holding a hearing and making findings necessary to a complete and thorough review;
- must, in coordination with other agencies and subdivisions, prepare a biennial report on the effectiveness of the CMP; and
- may award grants to projects that further the goals and policies of the CMP.

See Tex. Nat. Res. Code §§ 33.204, 33.205.

If an agency permit or action is determined to be inconsistent with the CMP, the commissioner of the GLO must report his findings to the agency. Tex. Nat. Res. Code § 33.206(b). If the agency does not modify or amend the proposed permit or action to be consistent with the goals and policies of the CMP, the commissioner must request an attorney general opinion on the consistency of the proposed permit or action with the CMP. Tex. Nat. Res. Code § 33.206(c). If the attorney general finds that the proposed permit or action is inconsistent and the agency still declines to modify or amend it, the attorney general must file suit against the agency in a Travis County district court. *See* Tex. Nat. Res. Code § 33.208(b).

§ 7.9 Department of Licensing and Regulation

The Texas Department of Licensing and Regulation (TDLR) is the state's umbrella occupational agency. *See* Tex. Occ. Code § 51.051(a). The TDLR regulates occupations that include water well drillers and water well pump installers. *See* Tex. Occ. Code chs. 1901, 1902. In this regard, the Water Well Drillers Advisory Council advises the department. *See* Tex. Occ. Code § 1901.109.

§ 7.9:1 Decision-Making Body

The TDLR Commission has seven members, appointed by the governor for staggered six-year terms. *See* Tex. Occ. Code §§ 51.052(a), 51.055(a). In turn, the nine members of the Water Well Drillers Advisory Council are appointed by the presiding officer of the Texas Commission of Licensing and Regulation, with the commission's approval. Tex. Occ. Code § 1901.101(a). A member of the advisory council serves a six-year term, with the term expiring September 15. Tex. Occ. Code § 1901.104. The executive director of the TDLR, in addition to performing any duties assigned by the commission, administers and enforces the department's programs and issues the licenses. Tex. Occ. Code § 51.103(a).

§ 7.9:2 Influence on Water Resources

The TDLR helps protect the state's water resources through its jurisdiction over water well drillers and water well pump installers. The purpose of the TDLR's rules is to provide procedural and substantive requirements for the licensing, complaint procedures, continuing education, and technical standards for well drillers and pump installers and to ensure the quality of the state's groundwater for the safety and welfare of the public. 16 Tex. Admin. Code § 76.1. A person may not drill a water well or install a pump without a license from the TDLR. *See* 16 Tex. Admin. Code § 76.20. The TDLR issues well driller and pump installer licenses pursuant to chapters 1901 and 1902 of the Texas

Occupations Code and its rules in 16 Texas Administrative Code chapter 76. To obtain a license, an applicant must meet experience requirements and pass an examination. *See* 16 Tex. Admin. Code §§ 76.21, 76.23. Licensees must also complete continuing education requirements in order to renew their licenses. 16 Tex. Admin. Code § 76.25. The TDLR rules are designed to ensure that water well drillers and pump installers will not present a serious risk of pollution to a groundwater source. By ensuring that only qualified persons drill water wells into groundwater-bearing formations or install pumps, the TDLR serves an important role in protecting groundwater quality.

The TDLR's rules also include notification requirements for instances when a driller or pump installer encounters water injurious to vegetation, land, or other water. In such cases, the well must be plugged, repaired, or properly completed to avoid injury or pollution. *See* 16 Tex. Admin. Code §§ 76.71, 76.101, 76.104. This, along with other reporting requirements, helps the agencies with water resource jurisdiction develop information about water wells and groundwater quality. The TDLR has authority to enforce its rules for licensees using administrative penalties. *See* 16 Tex. Admin. Code § 76.90. The TDLR's rules also contain specific technical requirements for drilling, cementing, casing, and capping wells. These rules help protect groundwater from contamination that could be introduced through the well if proper procedures are not followed.

The TDLR and the TWDB maintain a cooperative database for well reports called the Texas Well Report Submission and Retrieval System. This database contains all well reports for water wells drilled since 2003, with the exception of reports made confidential by the well owners in accordance with state law. *See* Texas Water Development Board, Submitted Drillers Reports (SDR) Database, www.twdb.texas.gov/groundwater/data/drillersdb.asp; *see also* Tex. Occ. Code § 1901.251(c).

Another function of the TDLR is to assist in the location and remediation of abandoned or deteriorated wells. There are water wells on private property all over the state that were drilled before regulation. Many have not been used or maintained. When such a well is identified, such as by a complaint, the TDLR works with the TCEQ and local groundwater conservation districts to investigate and bring the landowner into compliance. *See* 16 Tex. Admin. Code § 76.111 (MOU between the TDLR, the TCEQ, and groundwater conservation districts).

The TDLR plays a role in regulating water resources through its jurisdiction over weather modification activities, sometimes referred to as "cloud seeding." The term "weather modification and control" is defined by TDLR rules as "[c]hanging or controlling, or attempting to change or control, by artificial methods the natural development of atmospheric cloud forms or precipitation forms that occur in the troposphere." 16 Tex. Admin. Code § 79.10(7). A person must obtain a license from the TDLR before beginning any weather modification project. 16 Tex. Admin. Code § 79.11(a). Before issuing a permit, the TDLR must find that "the operation proposed in the application will not significantly dissipate the clouds and prevent their natural course of developing rain in the area where the operation is to be conducted to the material detriment of persons or property in that area." 16 Tex. Admin. Code § 79.21(a)(1). In 2019, the TDLR made changes to its weather modification rules that limit current requirements to weather modification conducted by aircraft, add a subsection for use of ground-based equipment with less stringent reporting requirements, and as an option, allow for reporting of both on a publicly accessible website. *See* 16 Tex. Admin. Code § 79.33. Note that in its staff report for 2020–21 the Sunset Advisory Commission (SAC) recommended for elimination as unnecessary the licensing program for weather modification, however, the staff's recommendation was not adopted by the SAC. *See* Sunset Advisory Commission, *Staff Report with Commission Decisions*, Texas Department of Licensing and Regulation, (87th legislature, 2020–21), www.sunset.texas.gov/public/uploads/files/reports/Texas%20Department%20of%20Licensing%20and%20Regulation%20Staff%20Report%20with%20Commission%20Decisions.pdf.

§ 7.10 Texas State Soil and Water Conservation Board

The Texas State Soil and Water Conservation Board (TSSWCB) is the state agency "that administers Texas' soil and water conservation law and coordinates conservation and nonpoint source pollution abatement programs throughout the State." Texas State Soil and Water Conservation Board, *About the Texas State Soil and Water Conservation Board*, www.tsswcb.texas.gov/about [hereinafter About the TSSWCB]. In reaction to the Dust Bowl of the 1930s, the Texas legislature created the TSSWCB in 1939 to organize the state into soil and water conservation districts (SWCDs). *See* About the TSSWCB; *see also* Texas State Soil and Water Conservation Board, *Texas Soil and Water Conservation Districts*, www.tsswcb.texas.gov/swcds [hereinafter *Texas Soil and Water Conservation Districts*]. The mission of the TSSWCB is "working in conjunction with local SWCDs, to encourage the wise and productive use of natural resources." About the TSSWCB; *see also* Tex. Agric. Code § 201.001(d). The bulk of the TSSWCB's activities "involve making grants of state funds, on a cost-share basis, to landowners to address water quality issues and public safety concerns about flood control structures throughout the state." Sunset Advisory Commission, *Report to the 82nd Legislature* 140 (Feb. 2011), www.sunset.texas.gov/public/uploads/files/reports/Report%20to%20the%2082%20 Leg%202011.pdf. Rules related to the TSSWCB are contained in 31 Texas Administrative Code chapters 517 through 530.

§ 7.10:1 Decision-Making Body

The TSSWCB is governed by a seven-member board. Five board members are elected by soil and water conservation district directors in the state district they represent. *See About the TSSWCB*; Tex. Agric. Code § 201.011(1). These board members serve two-year staggered terms. Tex. Agric. Code § 201.015(a). Two board members are appointed by the governor. Tex. Agric. Code § 201.011(2). The executive director of the TSSWCB, appointed by the board, oversees the day-to-day functions of the agency. The TSSWCB is headquartered in Temple and has five district offices.

The TSSWCB provides assistance to the state's 216 SWCDs. Each SWCD is an independent political subdivision of the state government, brought into existence by a vote of the landowners within the boundaries of the district. An SWCD is governed by a board of five directors who are elected by rural landowners in the district. The SWCDs are actively involved in soil and water conservation activities, such as operation and maintenance of flood control structures. The SWCDs do not have taxing authority and rely on funds from the TSSWCB. The SWCDs can be contacted through their local U.S. Department of Agriculture (USDA) Natural Resources Conservation Service or USDA Service Center. *See Texas Soil and Water Conservation Districts.*

§ 7.10:2 Influence on Water Resources

Flood Control Program: Water management is an integral part of soil conservation. The SWCDs play a vital role in one of the earliest federal programs, the Watershed Protection and Flood Prevention Program, which is administered by the NRCS. The NRCS, over the course of sixty years, has designed and constructed nearly two thousand floodwater retarding structures, or dams, in Texas. *See* Texas State Soil and Water Conservation Board, *Flood Control Program*, www.tsswcb.texas.gov/programs/flood-control-program [hereinafter *Flood Control Program*]. In addition, the NRCS has assisted watershed sponsors in the installation of land treatment practices, channel improvements, and dikes for watershed protection. *See* U.S. Department of Agriculture, Natural Resources Conservation Service, *Watershed Protection and Flood Prevention Program*, www.nrcs.usda.gov/wps/portal/nrcs/main/tx/programs/planning/wpfp/. These structures are built with the understanding that the private property owner provides the land, the federal government provides the technical design expertise and the funding to construct them, and then units of local government (local sponsors) are responsible for maintenance. See the discussion of NRCS dams in Chapter 39 of this book. The SWCDs, along with a "taxing" partner (e.g., county, water control and improvement district), are the local sponsors. The TSS-WCB administers the Operation and Maintenance Grant and Structural Repair Grant Programs to assist the SWCDs and certain other cosponsors in meeting their obligations. *See Flood Control Program*; *see also* 31 Tex. Admin. Code ch. 529.

NPS Management: The TSSWCB, along with the SWCDs, is instrumental in meeting the environmental mandates in the Clean Water Act and the Safe Drinking Water Act. The TSSWCB is the lead state agency for planning, implementing, and managing programs and practices for abating agricultural and silvicultural nonpoint source (NPS) pollution. Tex. Agric. Code § 201.026(a), (b). Responsibilities of the TCEQ and the TSSWCB related to point and NPS pollution are contained in an MOU at 30 Tex. Admin. Code § 7.102. Correspondingly, the TSSWCB manages the agricultural and silvicultural portions of the Coastal Coordination Advisory Committee, discussed at section 7.11:2 below. *See* Texas State Soil and Water Conservation Board, *Coastal Nonpoint Source Pollution Control Program*, www.tsswcb.texas.gov/programs/texas-nonpoint-source-management-program/coastal-nonpoint-source-pollution-control-program.

The CWA requires states to have an NPS management program. *See* 33 U.S.C. § 1329. The Environmental Protection Agency (EPA), through CWA section 319 grants, provides federal funding that is equally split between the TCEQ and the TSSWCB to implement the Texas NPS management program. Texas State Soil and Water Conservation Board, *Texas Nonpoint Source Management Program*, www.tsswcb.texas.gov/programs/texas-nonpoint-source-management-program [hereinafter *Texas Nonpoint Source Management Program*].

To address NPS pollution, Texas uses a "watershed" approach. *See Texas Nonpoint Source Management Program*. The TSSWCB focuses its efforts on a subset of the CWA section 303(d) impaired waters where agricultural or silvicultural NPS pollution is contributing to water quality impairment. A list of watersheds is available at www.tsswcb.texas.gov/programs/texas-nonpoint-source-management-program/watershed-protection-plan-program. The TSSWCB applies the watershed approach through the Total Maximum Daily Load (TMDL) Program and the Watershed Protection Plan (WPP) Program.

TMDLs are an estimate by the state of the pollutants that an impaired water body can receive. TMDLs are discussed at sections 7.6:2 above and 7.14:2 below and also in Chapter 33 of this book. The TSSWCB and the TCEQ share responsibility for developing and implementing TMDLs and have entered into an MOU, which may be found at www.tceq.texas.gov/assets/public/waterquality/tmdl/moa_sept2006.pdf. The agencies, through a public stakeholder process, develop an Implementation Plan (I-Plan) to achieve the goals of the TMDL in the watershed. The I-Plan recommends best management practices for nonpoint sources. Texas State Soil and Water Conservation Board, *Total Maximum Daily Load Program*, www.tsswcb.texas.gov/programs/texas-nonpoint-source-management-program/total-maximum-daily-load-program.

A WPP is "a coordinated framework for implementing prioritized and integrated water quality protection and restoration strategies driven by environmental objectives." Texas State Soil and Water Conservation Board, *Watershed Protection Plan Program*, www.tsswcb.texas.gov/en/wpp [hereinafter WPP Program]. Through this program, the state encourages stakeholders to "holistically address all of the sources and causes of impairments and threats to both surface and groundwater resources within a watershed." WPP Program. The TCEQ and the TSSWCB provide technical and financial assistance to develop the WPPs, which follow EPA guidance. *See* U.S. Environmental Protection Agency, *Nonpoint Source Program and Grants Guidelines for States and Territories* (issued Apr. 12, 2013), www.epa.gov/sites/production/files/2015-10/documents/319-guidelines-fy14.pdf. The WPP must coordinate with the development of a TMDL and the I-Plan; however, in some instances, a WPP may be used in lieu of a TMDL. *See* WPP Program.

The main mechanism for implementing these TMDLs and WPPs is Water Quality Management Plans (WQMPs). The TSSWCB, through the local SWCDs, develops, supervises, and monitors individual WQMPs for agricultural and silvicultural lands. Through the WQMPs, which are voluntary and incentive-based, agricultural producers and other rural landowners implement best management practices. *See* Texas State Soil and Water Conservation Board, *Water Quality Management Plan*, www.tsswcb.texas.gov/programs/water-quality-management-plan. There are specific requirements for poultry WQMPs. *See* Texas State Soil and Water Conservation Board, *Poultry Water Quality Management Program*, www.tsswcb.texas.gov/programs/water-quality-management-plan/poultry-water-quality-management-program. The TSSWCB and SWCDs work closely with the federal NRCS on WQMPs, which are certified by the SWCD, local NRCS, and the TSSWCB.

Rio Grande Carrizo Cane Eradication Program: In order to help achieve the Governor's border security priorities, the Texas Legislature, in 2015, directed the TSSWCB to develop and implement a Rio Grande Carrizo Cane Eradication Program (RGCCEP). Comprehensively addressing the impacts of carrizo cane on border security is paramount to the program, while also accruing benefits to the ecosystem health of the Rio Grande and water user groups in south Texas. Due to the diversity of biological, legal, and cultural issues associated with control of carrizo cane along the 1,255-mile Rio Grande international border, the RGCCEP takes an ecosystem-based approach that integrates the use of biological, chemical, and mechanical controls to manage carrizo cane along the Rio Grande. This approach promotes restoration of treated areas with beneficial native plants and necessitates a long-term maintenance and monitoring program to ensure control is successful. *See* Texas State Soil and Water Conservation Board, *Rio Grande Carrizo Cane Eradication Program,* www.tsswcb.texas.gov/programs/rio-grande-carrizo-cane-eradication-program.

§ 7.11 Coordination between State Agencies with Memoranda of Understanding

Because each of the agencies discussed above has some jurisdiction over water in the state, it is sometimes difficult to draw the jurisdictional lines between them. In some cases, more than one agency has jurisdiction over the same subject matter. Memoranda of understanding (MOUs) between the agencies regarding agency roles and responsibilities, as well as interagency communication in committees and councils made up of representatives of multiple agencies, help coordinate management of water resources by various state agencies. MOUs are used to clarify and provide for the respective duties, responsibilities, or functions on any matter under either agency's jurisdiction that is not otherwise expressly assigned. MOUs between the TCEQ and other state agencies are adopted by rule. *See* Tex. Water Code § 5.104(b).

As the primary state-level environmental agency, the TCEQ has MOUs with several other state agencies, including the TWDB, the TPWD, the RRC, the TSSWCB, and the TDLR. These MOUs or references to their location are found in the TCEQ's rules at 30 Texas Administrative Code chapter 7. Reading the appropriate MOU may be beneficial when questions of regulatory jurisdiction arise.

§ 7.11:1 Water Conservation Advisory Council

Water conservation is essential to management of scarce water resources. A new emphasis was placed on conservation in 2007 when Senate Bill 3 created the Water Conservation Advisory Council and directed the TWDB to appoint the members. *See* Water Conservation Advisory Council, *About Us*, www.savetexaswater.org/about/index.html. The council was created to provide to lawmakers, policymakers, and the public a water conservation resource. Tex. Water Code § 10.002. The council is composed of twenty-three members appointed by the TWDB who represent different entities and interest groups, including the TCEQ, the Texas Department of Agriculture, the TPWD, the TSSWCB, the TWDB, regional water planning groups, federal agencies, groundwater conservation districts, river authorities, and environmental groups. *See* Tex. Water Code § 10.003(a).

The council's powers and duties are—

1. monitoring trends in water conservation implementation;
2. monitoring new technologies for possible inclusion in the TWDB's best management practices guide;
3. monitoring the effectiveness of the state and local water conservation public awareness programs;
4. establishing a state water management resource library;
5. establishing a public recognition program for water conservation;
6. monitoring the implementation of regional water plan water conservation strategies; and
7. monitoring water conservation target and goal guidelines to be considered by the TWDB and the TCEQ.

See Tex. Water Code § 10.010.

By December 1 of each even-numbered year, the council submits a report on progress made in water conservation and recommendations for legislation to the governor, lieutenant governor, and speaker of the house of representatives. Tex. Water Code § 10.011. See Chapter 23 of this book for further discussion of water conservation.

§ 7.11:2 Coastal Coordination Advisory Committee

The Coastal Coordination Advisory Committee (CCAC), established in 2011 as part of the legislation abolishing the Coastal Coordination Council, advises the GLO on matters related to the Texas Coastal Management Program (CMP). The twelve-member committee is composed of one member from each of the seven state natural resource agencies, including the GLO, the TCEQ, the TWDB, the TPWD, the RRC, the TSSWCB, and the Texas Transportation Commission; four members appointed by the land commissioner who represent specific coastal interests; and one nonvoting member representing the Texas Sea Grant College Program. *See* Tex. Nat. Res. Code § 33.2041.

As discussed above, the GLO is responsible for reviewing agency actions that may adversely affect a coastal natural resource area to ensure that they comply with the goals and policies of the CMP. The land commissioner will review an agency action if a member of the CCAC, or certain agencies or persons, contests the consistency determination for the proposed action in an administrative hearing; one of these persons files a request for referral; and three voting members of the CCAC agree that there is a significant unresolved dispute regarding the proposed action's consistency with the goals and policies of the CMP. Additionally, the CCAC must refer the matter to the land commissioner for review. *See* Tex. Nat. Res. Code § 33.205(c). CCAC members may also be involved in a preliminary review of a permit or proposed action for consistency with the CMP. *See* Tex. Nat. Res. Code § 33.205(f)(1). CCAC members may request additional information from a federal agency or request that the land commissioner review a federal action, activity, or outer continental shelf plan because of concerns about consistency with the CMP. *See* Tex. Nat. Res. Code § 33.206(d), (e).

§ 7.11:3 Drought Preparedness Council

The Drought Preparedness Council is composed of representatives from fourteen agencies or groups, including the TCEQ, the TWDB, the TPWD, and the TSSWCB. *See* Tex. Water Code § 16.055(b). It is responsible for—

1. assessing and public reporting of drought and water supply conditions;
2. advising the governor on significant drought conditions;
3. making recommendations for the state's response to drought-related disasters for inclusion in the state emergency management plan and the state water plan;
4. advising the regional water planning groups on drought-related issues;
5. ensuring effective coordination among state, local, and federal agencies in drought-response planning; and
6. reporting to the legislature, not later than January 15 of each odd-numbered year, regarding significant drought conditions in the state.

Tex. Water Code § 16.055(e).

The council is required to develop and implement a comprehensive state drought preparedness plan for mitigating the effects of drought and to periodically update the plan. Tex. Water Code § 16.0551(a). The plan is designed to facilitate the flow of information between agencies, define duties and responsibilities of various players in responding to drought conditions, and ensure coordination between the state and federal governments regarding drought policy. *See* Tex. Water Code § 16.0551(b). See Chapter 22 of this book for further discussion of drought planning and response.

§ 7.12 Texas Legislature

The Texas legislature meets for 140 days every two years. Each legislative session, hundreds of bills are filed that have the potential to affect the law of water resources. After being filed, these bills may be assigned to certain standing committees for consideration and possible action. Bills related to water resources are generally assigned to certain standing committees in the Senate and certain standing committees in the House, as discussed below. Although these are not state agencies, they are state-level committees that influence the development of the body of law used by the state agencies that regulate water resources.

§ 7.12:1 House Committees

In the Texas House of Representatives, water-related bills are primarily referred to the eleven-member Natural Resources Committee. A water-related bill may also be referred to the Environmental Regulation Committee, the Land and Resource Management Committee, the Appropriations Committee (if it concerns funding), or the State Affairs Committee (if it involves matters of state policy, the administration of state government, or other high-profile or big-picture issues). Each session the House adopts a resolution setting out its rules, including the jurisdiction of each of its standing committees. *See, e.g.*, Tex. H.R. 4, 86th Leg., R.S. (2019).

The House Natural Resources Committee has jurisdiction over all matters pertaining to—

- natural resources conservation;

- appropriation, allocation, control and development of land and water resources;
- groundwater conservation districts, irrigation districts, water supply districts and other types of water-related districts, and authorities not otherwise assigned to another standing committee;
- the TCEQ's regulation of water resources; and
- river compacts, the Southwestern States Water Commission, and the TWDB.

See Texas House of Representatives, Natural Resources Committee, https://house.texas.gov/committees/committee/?committee=C390.

The Land and Resource Management Committee handles the creation, modification, and regulation of municipal utility districts and the power of eminent domain. *See* Texas House of Representatives, Land & Resource Management Committee, https://house.texas.gov/committees/committee/?committee=C360. Among other issues, the Environmental Regulation Committee has jurisdiction over water pollution, including the environmental regulation of industrial development, environmental matters that are regulated by the Department of State Health Services or the TCEQ, and oversight of the TCEQ as it relates to environmental regulation. *See* Texas House of Representatives, Environmental Regulation Committee, https://house.texas.gov/committees/committee/?committee=C260.

§ 7.12:2 Senate Committees

At the beginning of each session, the Senate adopts a resolution laying out its rules. This resolution includes a list of the standing committees and the number of members on each. *See, e.g.*, Tex. S.R. 2, 87th Leg., R.S. (Tex. 2021). Through the 83rd legislative session in 2013, bills related to water resources were referred primarily to the eleven-member Senate Natural Resources Committee. However, with the 84th legislative session in 2015, the Senate Committee on Agriculture, Water, and Rural Affairs was created, and the Senate Natural Resources Committee was renamed the Senate Natural Resources and Economic Development Committee. The Agriculture, Water, and Rural Affairs committee heard most water-related bills. In 2019, the Senate rules split this committee into two committees: the Senate Committee on Agriculture, with five members, and the Senate Committee on Water and Rural Affairs, with seven members. In 2021, however, the Senate rules recombined these committees creating a nine-member Water, Agriculture, and Rural Affairs committee. The Senate also formed a new nine-member Local Government Committee in 2021 that will be hearing bills regarding water districts. Some water-related bills are heard by the Senate Natural Resources and Economic Development Committee. For example, items related to the economic regulation of water and sewer service and the use of groundwater for power generation and mining, as well as bills related to environmental permitting procedures, were referred to the Senate Natural Resources and Economic Development Committee during the 2019 legislative sessions. Unlike the House committees, there is no written delineation of the jurisdiction of each Senate committee.

III. Federal Regulatory Authorities with Jurisdiction over Water Resources

§ 7.13 Introduction

The interplay between the state and federal government is an important consideration in the water resource arena. Texas avoids the tussles over ownership of lake- and streambeds that occur between the federal government and the western states because Texas retained its public lands when it entered the Union. The federal government controls so few lands within the state that its role is limited in water supply and water rights matters. *See* Anthony S. Corbett, *The Players—Who's Who in Water Rights* 1, *in Water Rights Boot Camp* (State Bar of Texas 2006). See also Chapter 4 of this book. This is not to say, however, that the federal government is without influence over Texas's water resources. The federal government has the authority to apportion interstate waters and sets national standards for a variety of water-related environmental programs. Federal agencies also affect water conservation, storage, development, control, and supply. *See* Corbett, at 1. The following sections provide a brief summary of a variety of the main federal regulatory authorities with jurisdiction over water resource issues.

§ 7.14 U.S. Environmental Protection Agency

Established in 1970, the U.S. Environmental Protection Agency (EPA) conducts federal research, monitoring, standard-setting, and enforcement activities to ensure environmental protection. The mission of the EPA includes the protection of the nation's waters, and it carries out both regulatory and voluntary programs to fulfill this mission. *See* U.S. Environmental Protection Agency, *EPA History*, www.epa.gov/history.

§ 7.14:1 Organizational Structure

The EPA is an independent agency of the Executive Branch, headed by an administrator who is appointed by the President with the advice and consent of the Senate. In addition to the Office of the Administrator, there are eleven headquarters offices and ten regional offices. U.S. Environmental Protection Agency, *EPA Organization Chart Leadership*, www.epa.gov/aboutepa/epa-organization-chart. The headquarters' Office of Water is responsible for the agency's water quality activities. The Office of Water—

> is responsible for implementing the Clean Water Act and Safe Drinking Water Act, and portions of the Coastal Zone Act Reauthorization Amendments of 1990, Resource Conservation and Recovery Act, Ocean Dumping Ban Act, Marine Protection, Research and Sanctuaries Act, Shore Protection Act, Marine Plastics Pollution Research and Control Act, London Dumping Convention, the International Convention for the Prevention of Pollution from Ships and several other statutes.

U.S. Environmental Protection Agency, *About the Office of Water*, www.epa.gov/aboutepa/about-office-water. Within the Office of Water are the Office of Ground Water and Drinking Water, the Office of Science and Technology, the Office of Wastewater Management, and the Office of Wetlands, Oceans and Watersheds.

Texas is part of the EPA's Region 6, which is headquartered in Dallas, EPA Region 6 serves Arkansas, Louisiana, New Mexico, and Oklahoma and sixty-six Tribal Nations. Region 6 is headed by a regional administrator who is appointed by the President. Within EPA Region 6, the Water Division and the Enforcement and Compliance Assurance Division deal most directly with water issues. The Water Division provides oversight of the water programs. *See* U.S. Environmental Protection Agency, *Organization of EPA's Region 6 Office* in Dallas, www.epa.gov/aboutepa/organization-chart-epas-region-6-office-dallas#water. Other areas within EPA Region 6, such as the Superfund Division, which includes the spill response program, also address the quality of water resources. Attorneys in the Office of Regional Counsel assist on the legal aspects of the water programs.

The jurisdiction of the EPA is derived from statute. *See National Pork Producers Council v. U.S. Environmental Protection Agency*, 635 F.3d 738 (5th Cir. 2011) (EPA regulations found to exceed statutory authority). The EPA's rules are contained in title 40 of the Code of Federal Regulations.

§ 7.14:2 Influence on Water Resources

As mentioned in the discussion of the EPA's Office of Water above, the EPA has a role under a number of statutes and treaties. A full discussion of the EPA's programs is beyond the scope of this chapter, but a few of the more significant programs are briefly summarized. In the area of water resources, the EPA's responsibilities include the regulation of discharges of pollutants into waters of the United States, addressing nonpoint sources, setting drinking water standards, and regulation and protection of wetlands. The EPA obtains its authority for these duties under the Clean Water Act (CWA), 33 U.S.C. §§ 1251–1387 (see Chapters 3, 33, 34, and 35 of this book) and the Safe Drinking Water Act (SDWA), 42 U.S.C. §§ 300f–300j-27 (see Chapter 30 of this book). A number of duties established by the CWA and the SDWA may be delegated to a state, and in such instances the EPA plays a lesser role. See discussion at section 7.3 above regarding delegation of authority to Texas.

Clean Water Act: Key to the EPA's jurisdiction under the CWA is whether the water body is considered "waters of the United States." The determination of whether a particular water body is part of the "waters of the United States" is often hotly contested. On April 21, 2020, the Department of the Army and the EPA published a final rule defining "waters of the United States." *See* 85 Fed. Reg 22340. The revised definition is found at 40 Code of Federal Regulations section 120.2 and includes definitions for both jurisdictional waters and nonjurisdictional waters. On June 9, 2021, the EPA and the Department of the Army announced their intention to "revise the definition of 'waters of the United States' (WOTUS) to better protect our nation's vital water resources that support public health, environmental protection, agricultural activity, and economic growth." U.S. Environmental Protection Agency, News Release, *EPA, Army Announce Intent to Revise Definition of WOTUS* (June 9, 2021), www.epa.gov/newsreleases/epa-army-announce-intent-revise-definition-wotus. (The U.S. Army Corp of Engineers' role is discussed at section 7.15:2 below.) See Chapter 35 of this book for further discussion of "waters of the United States."

The CWA was enacted to "restore and maintain the chemical, physical, and biological integrity of the Nation's waters." 33 U.S.C. § 1251(a). There are three CWA permitting programs that regulate point sources that discharge pollutants into the waters of the United States: the section 402 National Pollutant Discharge Elimination System (NPDES) permits program, the section 404 dredge and fill permits, and the section 401 state certification program. *See* 33 U.S.C. §§ 1341, 1342(a), 1344; *see also* 33 U.S.C. § 1311(a) (prohibiting unauthorized discharge of oil or hazardous substances).

National Pollutant Discharge Elimination System Program: Section 402 of the CWA authorizes the EPA to issue NPDES permits to control water pollution by regulating point sources that discharge pollutants into the waters of the United States, along with the state pretreatment program, the general permits program, and the biosolids program. *See* 33 U.S.C. § 1342. The EPA may delegate the NPDES program to the states to administer. *See* 33 U.S.C. § 1342(b). This authority was delegated to the Texas Natural Resource Conservation Commission (the predecessor to the Texas Commission on Environmental Quality (TCEQ)) in 1998. As discussed in section 7.3 of this chapter, in January 2021, the TCEQ received authorization from the EPA to issue permits for produced water, hydrostatic test water, and gas plant effluent discharges resulting from certain oil and gas activities. *See* 86 Fed. Reg. 9332 (Feb. 12, 2021). The EPA retains oversight of the program and has the authority, in certain circumstances, to object to the NPDES permit. *See* 33 U.S.C. § 1342(c), (d).

The NPDES program is the key means by which the EPA implements the CWA's two fundamental approaches to control water pollution: technology-based regulations and water quality standards. *See* 33 U.S.C. §§ 1311, 1312, 1313, 1316, 1317. Technology-based regulations (effluent limitations) seek to reduce pollution by requiring a discharger to effectuate equipment or process changes, without reference to the effect on the receiving water; state-adopted water quality standards define the permissible level of pollution in a specific body of water regardless of the source of pollution. *See* 33 U.S.C. §§ 1311, 1312, 1313, 1316, 1317.

There are a number of technology standards, including the best practicable control technology currently available (BPT), applicable to discharges of conventional pollutants to surface water by existing sources (and the baseline for control applicable in all circumstances); best available technology economically achievable (BAT), applicable to toxic and nonconventional pollutants by existing sources; and new source performance standards (NSPS), applicable to new sources discharging into surface waters. *See* U.S. Environmental Protection Agency, *Learn about Effluent Guidelines*, www.epa.gov/eg/learn-about-effluent-guidelines. The EPA promulgates technology effluent limitations on an industry-by-industry basis. *See* 40 C.F.R. pts. 401–471. For a discussion of the TCEQ's use of these standards, see Chapter 34 of this book.

As for the water quality component, the CWA provides for the states to establish the water quality standards that consist of (1) the designated use(s) of a water body, (2) the water quality criteria necessary to protect the use(s), and (3) an antidegradation policy. *See* 33 U.S.C. §§ 1311(b)(1)(C), 1313. See also Chapter 33 of this book. The designated use(s) (e.g., public water supply, recreation, agriculture) should allow for "the protection and propagation of fish, shellfish and wildlife and for recreation in and on the water" (fishable/swimmable standard). 40 C.F.R. § 131.2. If a water body does not meet the fishable/swimmable standard, the state must submit a use attainability analysis to demonstrate that obtaining that standard is not feasible. *See* 40 C.F.R. § 131.10(g), (j); U.S. Environmental Protection Agency, *Use Attainability Analysis (UAA)*, www.epa.gov/wqs-tech/use-attainability-analysis-uaa. The designated use(s) and the use attainability analysis are subject to the EPA's review and approval, as discussed below. For the specifics on use designations in Texas, see Chapter 33 of this book.

The water quality criteria, either numeric or narrative, are then derived by the state from the designated use(s)—the maximum concentrations of pollutants that could occur without jeopardizing the use. *See* 33 U.S.C. § 1313. For narrative statements, states must develop a mechanism for translating or interpreting them into numeric limits. *See* 40 C.F.R. § 122.44(d)(1)(vi). The EPA, under CWA section 304, periodically publishes documents "reflecting the latest scientific knowledge" to assist the states in selecting appropriate criteria. *See* 33 U.S.C. § 1314(a)(1). These water quality-based effluent limitations (WQBELs) are required when the technology-based effluent limits (TBELs) will not assure compliance with applicable water quality standards for the particular receiving stream. *See* 33 U.S.C. § 1312; 40 C.F.R. § 122.44(d). See Chapters 33 and 34 of this book for details on the Texas water quality standards.

As for the antidegradation component, the state must ensure that the existing water quality is protected, even though water quality criteria and uses are met and maintained. 40 C.F.R. § 131.12; *see* Lauren Kalisek, *The Principle of Antidegradation and Its Place in Texas Water Quality Permitting*, 41 Texas Envtl. L.J. 1, 3 (2010) ("Antidegradation can easily be described as the next frontier in setting permit discharge limits."). Different types of waters have different levels of antidegradation protection. Tier 1 applies to all waters—existing uses criteria must be maintained. Tier 2 applies to high-quality waters that exceed fishable/swimmable criteria—degradation will be allowed only on a showing that it is necessary to accommodate important social or economic development in the region. Tier 3 applies to outstanding national resource waters (e.g., national parks and wildlife refuges)—degradation is strictly prohibited. *See* Kalisek, at 9.

A state may adopt variances to its water quality standards through policies "generally affecting their application and implementation, such as mixing zones, low flows, and variances." 40 C.F.R. § 131.13. These policies are subject to EPA review and approval. *See* 40 C.F.R. § 131.13. See Chapter 21 of this book for a discussion of the specifics of the Texas program.

The states submit their water quality standards to the EPA for its review. *See* 33 U.S.C. § 1313(c); 40 C.F.R. § 131.5. If the agency disapproves a state water quality standard, and the state does not make appropriate changes, the EPA must propose and promulgate revised standards. *See* 33 U.S.C.

§ 1313(c)(3), (c)(4); 40 C.F.R. §§ 131.5, 131.21. The water quality standards are effective only when they have been approved by the EPA (or, if the standards were disapproved, when the EPA adopts federal standards). *See* 40 C.F.R. § 131.21. The EPA approval of a new or revised water quality standard is considered a federal action, which may be subject to the section 7 consultation requirements of the Endangered Species Act. Consultation with the U.S. Fish and Wildlife Service (FWS) and the National Marine Fisheries Service is part of the EPA's water quality standards approval process. *See* U.S. Environmental Protection Agency, *How are Water Quality Standards Developed?*, www.epa.gov/standards-water-body-health/how-are-water-quality-standards-developed.

Once the water quality standards have been finalized, they are used in determining NPDES permit limits, impairment status, total maximum daily loads (TMDLs) endpoints, and the issuance of section 404 permit applications and section 402 certifications. *See* 40 C.F.R. § 131.21(d). A critical element of the water quality standards is periodically assessing the waters to determine the degree to which these standards are being met. *See* 40 C.F.R. § 130.4. To that end, on a biennial basis a state submits to the EPA a list (the 303(d) list) of water bodies, with a priority ranking, for which TBELs are (or are threatened to be) insufficient to achieve the water quality standards. *See* 33 U.S.C. §§ 1315(b)(1), 1313(d); *see also* 33 U.S.C. § 1313(c) (triennial state water quality standard review). As discussed earlier in this chapter, the state also must estimate the TMDL that the impaired water body can receive and still attain its use designation. *See* 33 U.S.C. § 1313(d). A TMDL is composed of a wasteload allocation (for existing and future point sources) and a load allocation (for existing and future nonpoint sources), "with seasonal variations and a margin of safety." 33 U.S.C. § 1313(d)(1)(C). States must develop an implementation plan for the TMDL. (As discussed earlier in this chapter, the TCEQ and the Texas State Soil and Water Conservation Board share this responsibility.) See also discussion in Chapter 33 of this book. The EPA must approve the 303(d) list and the TMDLs or propose its own. *See* 33 U.S.C. § 1313(d)(2). In practice, the EPA rarely prepares an entirely new list but partially disapproves a list because of an omission and then adds to the list. *See* U.S. Environmental Protection Agency, Office of Water, *303(d) Listed Impaired Waters: State, Watershed and National Geospatial Datasets* (Jan. 2010), www.epa.gov/tmdl/303d-listed-impaired-waters-state-watershed-and-national-geospatial-data. The EPA does not approve the implementation plans. *See* U.S. Environmental Protection Agency, *Guidelines for Reviewing TMDLs Under Existing Regulations Issued in 1992*, www.epa.gov/tmdl/guidelines-reviewing-tmdls-under-existing-regulations-issued-1992.

Nonpoint Source Management: Nonpoint source pollution (NPS) is pollution that "does not result from a discharge at a specific, single location (such as single pipe) but generally results from land runoff, precipitation, atmospheric deposition, or percolation." U.S. Environmental Protection Agency, Office of Water Regulations and Standards, *Nonpoint Source Guidance* 3 (1987); see also U.S. Environmental Protection Agency, *Basic Information about Nonpoint Source (NPS) Pollution*, www.epa.gov/nps/basic-information-about-nonpoint-source-nps-pollution. The CWA requires states to submit an NPS management program to the EPA. *See* 33 U.S.C. § 1329(d); *see also* 33 U.S.C. § 1288(b). An integral element of an approvable program is its identification of best management practices (BMPs) to reduce nonpoint runoff. 33 U.S.C. § 1329(b)(2)(a); *see also* 33 U.S.C. § 1342(p) (use of BMPs in NPDES stormwater permits).

Once approved, the state is eligible for section 319 grants to assist in the implementation of the program, such as lake protection and restoration activities. *See* 33 U.S.C. § 1329(h); U.S. Environmental Protection Agency, *319 Grant Program for States and Territories,* www.epa.gov/nps/319-grant-program-states-and-territories. (As mentioned at section 7.10:2 above, the TCEQ and the TSSWCB equally split these monies in Texas.) Other agencies may supplement these funds, such as the NRCS through its EQIP program.

The reauthorization of the Coastal Zone Management Act also focused on NPS by requiring coastal states to submit a Coastal Nonpoint Program to the EPA and the National Oceanic and Atmospheric Agency (NOAA) for approval. *See* 16 U.S.C. § 1455b(a); National Oceanic and Atmospheric Administration, Office for Coastal Management, *Coastal Nonpoint Pollution Control Program*, http://coast.noaa.gov/czm/pollutioncontrol/#Texas; *see also* Texas State Soil and Water Conservation Board, *Coastal Nonpoint Source Pollution Control Program*, www.tsswcb.texas.gov/programs/texas-nonpoint-source-management-program/coastal-nonpoint-source-pollution-control-program. The state must identify land uses that contribute to degradation of coastal areas, identify critical coastal areas, and implement management measures to achieve the CWA water quality standards. *See* 16 U.S.C. § 1455b(b). The Texas CMP is discussed at section 7.8:2 above.

Section 401 Certification: Section 401 of the CWA requires an applicant for a federal permit or license for any activity that may result in any discharge to waters of the United States to obtain a certification from the state. *See* 33 U.S.C. § 1341; U.S. Environmental Protection Agency, *Clean Water Act Section 401 Guidance for Federal Agencies, States and Authorized Tribes* (June 2019), www.epa.gov/cwa-401/clean-water-act-section-401-guidance-federal-agencies-states-and-authorized-tribes [hereinafter CWA Section 401 Guidance]. Examples of federal licenses and permits subject to section 401 certification include CWA section 404 permits, Federal Energy Regulatory Commission (FERC) hydropower licenses, and Rivers and Harbors Act section 9 and section 10 permits. CWA Section 401 Guidance. The state reviews and certifies that the federal permit or license will comply with the CWA effluent and water quality standards, or else the federal authority cannot issue the permit or license. *See* 33 U.S.C. § 1341. The Texas 401 certification program is discussed in Chapter 34 of this book. Most certifications in Texas are issued in connection with section 404 dredge and fill permits.

Section 404: The CWA is also the source for the EPA's authority to regulate and protect wetlands. Section 404 of the CWA establishes a permitting program to regulate the discharge of dredged or fill material into waters of the United States, including wetlands. For example, a person who wishes to build a dam or levee may need to get a section 404 permit under this program. The EPA and the U.S. Army Corps of Engineers (Corps) each administer specific aspects of this program, with the Corps in charge of the day-to-day program implementation, including permit decisions and enforcement. As mentioned above, the EPA determines the scope of geographical jurisdiction ("waters of the United States"). U.S. Environmental Protection Agency, *Memorandum of Agreement: Exemptions Under Section 404(f) of the Clean Water Act*, www.epa.gov/cwa-404/memorandum-agreement-exemptions-under-section-404f-clean-water-act. Additionally, the EPA identifies activities that are exempt from permitting, develops and interprets environmental criteria used in evaluating permit applications, reviews and comments on individual permit applications, enforces section 404 provisions, and has authority to veto the Corps' permit decisions. *See* U.S. Environmental Protection Agency, *Wetland Regulatory Authority,* www.epa.gov/sites/production/files/2015-03/documents/404_reg_authority_fact_sheet.pdf [hereinafter *Wetland Regulatory Authority*]; 33 U.S.C. § 1344(b), (c); *Mingo Logan Coal Co. v. U.S. Environmental Protection Agency*, 714 F.3d 608 (D.C. Cir. 2013) (EPA veto of section 404 permit). See also Chapter 35 of this book.

Safe Drinking Water Act: The SDWA, codified at 42 U.S.C. §§ 300f–300j-27, is the main federal law that ensures the quality of drinking water, and it applies to every public water system. See discussion in Chapter 30 of this book. Texas has received "primacy" to implement and enforce the SDWA drinking water quality standards. *See* U.S. Environmental Protection Agency, *Water Enforcement in Texas*, www.epa.gov/tx/compliance-assurance-and-enforcement-texas#3. The standards to ensure healthy, safe water for human consumption are set at the federal level by the EPA. *See* 42 U.S.C. § 300f(3). Texas's standards must be at least as restrictive as the federal standards for the state to maintain primacy over this program. *See* 40 C.F.R. § 142.10. A state is allowed to make its rules more restrictive (i.e., a lower allowable level of a certain constituent), but not less. For example, when the EPA adopted revisions to its drinking water standards for lead and copper, Texas was then required to adopt equally restrictive standards to maintain primacy of its drinking water program. *See, e.g.*, 30 Tex. Admin. Code § 290.117. As a primacy state, Texas has two years to adopt its rules, which can be extended for an additional two years if approved by the EPA. *See* 40 C.F.R. § 142.12. Rules governing drinking water that are adopted by a state are reviewed by the EPA to ensure that the state rules are no less stringent than the federal rules.

§ 7.15 U.S. Army Corps of Engineers

The U.S. Army Corps of Engineers is a federal agency and a combat arms branch of the U.S. Army that traces its roots back to the American Revolution. U.S. Army Corps of Engineers, *The U.S. Army Corps of Engineers: A Brief History*, www.usace.army.mil/About/History/Brief-History-of-the-Corps/Introduction/. The mission of the Corps is to provide vital public engineering services in peace and war to strengthen the "Nation's security, energize the economy and reduce risks from disasters." U.S. Army Corps of Engineers, *Mission and Vision*, www.usace.army.mil/About/Mission-and-Vision/. The Corps employs approximately 37,000 civilians and soldiers who provide engineering services within the United States and in foreign countries. U.S. Army Corps of Engineers, *About Us*, www.usace.army.mil/About/.

§ 7.15:1 Organizational Structure

The Corps is led by the commanding general and chief of engineers. It is organized geographically into nine divisions. Far west Texas is in the South Pacific Division, while the rest of Texas is in the Southwestern Division. Within the Southwestern Division, there is a Fort Worth District, Galveston District, Tulsa District, and Little Rock District. The Southwestern Division is headquartered in Dallas. U.S. Army Corps of Engineers, *Where We Are*, www.usace.army.mil/Locations/.

§ 7.15:2 Influence on Water Resources

The Corps engages in a wide spectrum of activities supporting its civilian and military mission. This section generally discusses the Corps' water resource-related activities. The Corps' duties include keeping channels open for navigation; protecting against floods; safeguarding the environment; generating clean, reliable hydropower; providing water to communities; managing recreation areas; and responding to disasters. *See* U.S. Army Corps of Engineers, *Civil Works*, www.usace.army.mil/Missions/CivilWorks/. The Corps builds and maintains infrastructure projects, including dredging waterways and the construction, operation, and maintenance of multipurpose reservoirs. The Corps operates approximately twenty-five surface water supply reservoirs within the state of Texas. *See* U.S. Army Corps of Engineers, Institute for Water Resources, *2011 M&I Water Supply Database* 6 (Apr. 2012), www.iwr.usace.army.mil/Portals/70/docs/iwrreports/2012-R-02.pdf. As a result, a person who wishes to divert or use water from one of these reservoirs will often be required to obtain a permit or contract rights from the Corps for use of the water supply. *See* Anthony S. Corbett, *The Players—Who's Who in Water Rights* 2, *in Water Rights Boot Camp* (State Bar of Texas 2006). See Chapters 3, 35, and 27 of this book. The Corps' water supply contracts do not guarantee quantity or quality of the water—only the storage space.

The Corps runs the regulatory programs, under the Rivers and Harbors Act and CWA section 404, requiring permits for most activities that occur in the federal waters and wetlands, including construction or renovation of dams, dikes, piers, and jetties; dredging; discharges of dredged or fill material; and commercial and residential development. *See* U.S. Army Corps of Engineers, *Regulatory Program Overview*, https://usace.contentdm.oclc.org/utils/getfile/collection/p16021coll6/id/2058. The Corps is also responsible for permitting ocean disposal of dredged material under the Marine Protection, Research, and Sanctuaries Act, also known as the Ocean Dumping Act. *See* 33 U.S.C. § 1413. Similar to the Section 404 program, the Corps uses the EPA's environmental criteria, and permit issuance is subject to EPA concurrence. *See* 33 U.S.C. § 1413. The Corps' rules are contained in title 33 of the Code of Federal Regulations parts 203–385.

As discussed earlier in this chapter, the Corps' jurisdiction under section 404 is limited to "waters of the United States." The scope of the Corps' authority under the Rivers and Harbors Act is narrower—truly "navigable waters"—which is defined as "those waters that are subject to the ebb and flow of the tide and/or are presently used, or have been used in the past, or may be susceptible to use to transport interstate or foreign commerce." 33 C.F.R. § 329.4; *see also* 33 U.S.C. §§ 401, 403.

Under section 404, the Corps has the authority to designate disposal areas and issue specific disposal permits for dredged or fill material. 33 U.S.C. § 1344(a); J. Gordon Arbuckle, *Environmental Law Handbook* 198 (12th ed. 1993). Additionally, the Corps shares enforcement powers of the CWA with the EPA. Arbuckle, at 199. The Corps has the power to issue cease and desist orders, levy administrative penalties, and resolve violations through the use of permits to authorize illegal fill activities that have already occurred. Arbuckle, at 199–200. The Corps primarily issues three types of section 404 permits: standard, general, and letters of permission. See Chapter 35 of this book, which discusses permits under section 404 of the CWA. The premise of the section 404 permitting program is that "no discharge of dredged or fill material may be permitted if: (1) a practicable alternative exists that is less damaging to the aquatic environment or (2) the nation's waters would be significantly degraded." 40 C.F.R. § 230.10. If a discharge is unavoidable, compensatory mitigation may be required as a condition of a 404 permit. Compensatory mitigation includes restoration, establishment, enhancement and, in certain circumstances, preservation of wetlands, streams, and other aquatic resources. *See* U.S. Environmental Protection Agency, *Background about Compensatory Mitigation Requirements under CWA Section 404*, www.epa.gov/cwa-404/background-about-compensatory-mitigation-requirements-under-cwa-section-404; *see also* 40 C.F.R. §§ 230.91–.98. See discussions in Chapters 3, 35, and 27 of this book regarding wetlands mitigation.

§ 7.16 U.S. Department of the Interior

The U.S. Department of the Interior (DOI), a cabinet-level agency, was created in 1849 to handle federal domestic matters. U.S. Department of the Interior, *History of the Interior*, www.doi.gov/whoweare/history. The DOI is charged with managing and protecting America's natural and cultural resources. Employing 70,000 people, the DOI has 11 technical bureaus:

- U.S. Fish and Wildlife Service
- Bureau of Reclamation
- U.S. Geological Survey
- Bureau of Ocean Energy Management
- Bureau of Safety and Environmental Enforcement
- Bureau of Land Management
- National Park Service
- Office of Surface Mining, Reclamation and Enforcement
- Bureau of Indian Affairs

- Bureau of Indian Education
- Bureau of Trust Funds Administration

U.S. Department of the Interior, *Bureaus*, www.doi.gov/bureaus.

As discussed earlier in this chapter, Texas has few federal lands, and thsu the DOI's involvement within Texas is more limited than it is in some other states. The bureaus and offices with potential to affect Texas water resources are the U.S. Fish and Wildlife Service, the Bureau of Reclamation, the U.S. Geological Survey, the Bureau of Ocean Energy Management, and the Bureau of Safety and Environmental Enforcement, which are discussed briefly below. In addition, the DOI's Office of Environmental Policy and Compliance plays a coordinating role. *See* U.S. Department of the Interior, *Office of Environmental Policy & Compliance*, www.doi.gov/oepc.

§ 7.16:1 U.S. Fish and Wildlife Service

The U.S. Fish and Wildlife Service (FWS) is the result of the consolidation of the Bureau of Fisheries and the Bureau of Biological Survey in 1940. U.S. Fish and Wildlife Service, *Creation, Authority, and Function* 022 FW 1 (Mar. 6, 1998) www.fws.gov/policy/022fw1.html. The FWS cites as its mission "working with others to conserve, protect, and enhance fish, wildlife, plants, and their habitats for the continuing benefit of the American people." U.S. Fish and Wildlife Service, *FWS Fundamentals*, www.fws.gov/info/pocketguide/fundamentals.html.

Organizational Structure: The director is head of the FWS and is appointed by the President with the advice and consent of the Senate. The FWS has more than 8,00 employees. *See* U.S. Fish and Wildlife Service, *About Us*, www.fws.gov/help/about_us.html. The employees are located at facilities across the country, including a headquarters office in Falls Church, Virginia, and twelve Unified Interior Regions. Texas is part of the Region 6 (Arkansas-Rio Grande-Texas-Gulf), headquartered in Albuquerque, New Mexico. *See* U.S. Department of the Interior, *Unified Interior Regional Boundaries*, www.doi.gov/employees/reorg/unified-regional-boundaries/.

Influence on Water Resources: The FWS is responsible for implementing and enforcing federal wildlife laws such as the Endangered Species Act (ESA), 16 U.S.C. §§ 1531–1544; the Migratory Bird Treaty Act, 16 U.S.C. §§ 703–712; the Marine Mammal Protection Act, 16 U.S.C. §§ 1361–1412h; and the Lacey Act, 16 U.S.C. §§ 3371–3378 (relating to the control of illegally taken fish and wildlife). The FWS also manages the National Wildlife Refuge System and the National Fish Hatchery System. Texas has nineteen National Wildlife Refuges, the oldest of which is located near Muleshoe (established in 1935). *See* U.S. Fish and Wildlife Service, *Texas*, www.fws.gov/refuges/profiles/ByState.cfm?state=TX. There are three National Fish Hatcheries in Texas, located near Burnett, San Marcos, and Uvalde. *See* U.S. Fish and Wildlife Service, Texas *National Fish Hatcheries*, www.fws.gov/fisheries/hatcheries/texas.html.

This section briefly discusses some of the FWS authorities that affect Texas water resources. One of the significant responsibilities of the FWS, which continues to have far-reaching effects on Texas water resources, is the administration of the ESA with respect to terrestrial and freshwater organisms. *See* U.S. Fish & Wildlife Service, *Endangered Species Act: Overview*, www.fws.gov/endangered/laws-policies/index.html. The FWS decides which species are listed as endangered or threatened.

The ESA makes it unlawful for a person to take a listed animal without a permit. *See* 16 U.S.C. § 1538(a)(1)(B). "Take" is defined as "to harass, harm, pursue, hunt, shoot, wound, kill, trap, capture, or collect or attempt to engage in any such conduct." 16 U.S.C. § 1532(19). The term "harm" is defined by regulation as "an act which actually kills or injures wildlife. *See* 50 C.F.R. § 17.3 Such an act may include significant habitat modification or degradation where it actually kills or injures wildlife by significantly impairing essential behavioral patterns, including breeding, feeding or sheltering." The FWS issues permits for the "incidental taking" of a listed animal if the take is mitigated with a conservation plan. *See* 16 U.S.C. § 1539(a)(1)(B), (a)(2). The FWS also has the power to issue civil and criminal penalties for violations of the ESA. *See* 16 U.S.C. § 1540. The ESA and its impact on water resources in Texas is discussed in Chapter 32 of this book.

The FWS also plays an important role in permitting. The Fish and Wildlife Coordination Act (FWCA), which predates the National Environmental Policy Act (NEPA) and the ESA, provides the basic authority for the FWS's involvement in evaluating impacts to fish and wildlife from proposed water resource development projects. *See* 16 U.S.C. §§ 661–667e. The FWCA requires that fish and wildlife resources "receive equal consideration and be coordinated with other features of water-resource development programs." 16 U.S.C. § 661. Federal agencies that construct, license, or permit water resource development projects, such as the Corps, the Bureau of Reclamation, the NRCS, or FERC, must first consult with the FWS (and the National Marine Fisheries Service in some instances) and state fish and wildlife agencies regarding the impacts on fish and wildlife resources and measures to mitigate these impacts. *See* 16 U.S.C. § 662. The FWCA, NEPA, ESA, CWA, and, in FERC projects, the Federal Power Act, work together to ensure that fish and wildlife values are fully and equally considered in water resource development planning but have different legislative requirements. *See* U.S. Fish and Wildlife Service, *Water Resources Development under the Fish and Wildlife Coordination Act* III–5 (Nov. 2004), www.fws.gov/habitatconservation/fwca.pdf. The FWS provides comments on section 404 permit applications, as discussed in Chapter 35 of this book. In the FERC licensing process, as discussed at section 7.18 below, FERC is required to impose conditions to protect fish and wildlife, which are based on recommendations from the FWS. See Chapter 27 of this book.

Additionally, the FWS implements the North American Wetlands Conservation Act, 16 U.S.C. §§ 4401–4414 (matching grants for wetlands conservation projects benefiting migratory birds) and assists in other voluntary habitat conservation and restoration programs such as Partners for Fish and Wildlife, which "provides technical and financial assistance to landowners interested in restoring and enhancing wildlife habitat on their land." *See* U.S. Fish and Wildlife Service, *Partners for Fish & Wildlife*, www.fws.gov/partners/. The FWS's duties include maintaining the National Wetlands Inventory, a series of topical maps that show wetlands and deepwater habitats. *See* U.S. Fish and Wildlife Service, *National Wetlands Inventory*, www.fws.gov/wetlands/. The FWS is also the repository for Coastal Barriers Resources Act maps and advises federal agencies, landowners, and Congress regarding whether properties are in or out of the Coastal Barrier Resources System (CBRS) and what kind of federal expenditures (e.g., flood insurance) are allowed in the CBRS. *See* 16 U.S.C. §§ 3501–3510; U.S. Fish and Wildlife Service, *Coastal Barriers Resources System*, www.fws.gov/cbra/Act.html.

§ 7.16:2 Bureau of Reclamation

The Bureau of Reclamation was established to construct dams and aqueducts in the West pursuant to the Reclamation Act of 1902. As discussed in Chapter 14 of this book, Congress made the Reclamation Act applicable to Texas in 1906. The Bureau of Reclamation's most famous project is Hoover Dam. The bureau is the largest wholesaler of water in the country, bringing water to more than 31 million people. With fifty-three power plants, the bureau is also the second largest producer of hydroelectric power in the western United States. *See* Bureau of Reclamation, *Bureau of Reclamation—About Us*, www.usbr.gov/main/about/. The bureau's mission is to manage, develop, and protect water and related resources in an environmentally and economically sound manner in the interest of the American public. Bureau of Reclamation, *About Us—Mission*, www.usbr.gov/main/about/mission.html.

Organizational Structure: The head of the Bureau of Reclamation is the commissioner, who is appointed by the President with the advice and consent of the Senate. There are five regional offices; far west Texas is included within the Upper Colorado Region. *See* Bureau of Reclamation, *Upper Colorado Region*, www.usbr.gov/uc/aboutus/index.html. The remainder of Texas is in the Great Plains Region. *See* Bureau of Reclamation, *Great Plains Regional Organization*, www.usbr.gov/gp/about_us/.

Influence on Water Resources: The bureau's role in developing, organizing, and orchestrating the creation of dams and reservoirs in Texas, such as the Rio Grande Project, is discussed in Chapter 14 of this book.

§ 7.16:3 U.S. Geological Survey

The U.S. Geological Survey (USGS) was created in 1879 and was charged with "classification of the public lands, and examination of the geological structure, mineral resources and products of the national domain." U.S. Geological Survey, *Introduction*, https://pubs.usgs.gov/circ/c1050/intro.htm. Today the USGS' mission is "to monitor, analyze, and predict current and evolving dynamics of complex human and natural Earth-system interactions and to deliver actionable intelligence at scales and timeframes relevant to decision makers." *See* U.S. Geological Survey, *Who We Are*, www.usgs.gov/about/about-us/who-we-are. The USGS is the nation's largest water, earth, and biological science and civilian mapping agency.

Organizational Structure: The USGS is headed by a director who is appointed by the President with the advice and consent of the Senate. The USGS has several program offices located throughout the state. *See* U.S. Geological Survey, *Oklahoma-Texas Water Science Center*, www.usgs.gov/centers/ot-water/locations.

Influence on Water Resources: The Oklahoma-Texas Water Science Center (Center) obtains information regarding streamflow, water quality, groundwater levels, and water use and availability in Texas and Oklahoma. U.S. Geological Survey, *Oklahoma-Texas Water Science Center*, www.usgs.gov/centers/ot-water. To evaluate current conditions, the Center has over 850 real-time stream, lake, reservoir, precipitation, water quality, and groundwater stations in Texas and Oklahoma. *See* U.S. Geological Survey, National Water Dashboard, https://dashboard.waterdata.usgs.gov/app/nwd/?aoi=wsc-oktx. USGS maps have been used in determining whether the EPA has jurisdiction under the CWA. *See United States v. Chevron Pipe Line Co.*, 437 F. Supp. 2d 605 (N.D. Tex 2006).

§ 7.16:4 Bureau of Ocean Energy Management (formerly Bureau of Ocean Energy Management, Regulation, and Enforcement and Minerals Management Service)

The Minerals Management Service was established in 1982 to facilitate mineral revenue collection and manage the outer continental shelf offshore lands. The agency was renamed in 2010 to the Bureau of Ocean Energy Management, Regulation, and Enforcement (BOEMRE). U.S. Department of the Interior, *History of the Interior*, www.doi.gov/whoweare/history/. In response to the *Deepwater Horizon* explosion and resulting oil spill in the Gulf of Mexico, the agency underwent comprehensive regulatory reforms relating to offshore oil and gas regulation. Bureau of Ocean Energy Management, *Regulatory Reforms*, www.boem.gov/About-BOEM/Reforms/Reforms.aspx. In 2011, the duties of BOEMRE were split between the Bureau of Ocean Energy Management and the Bureau of Safety and Environmental Enforcement. Bureau of Ocean Energy Management, *Reorganization of the Former MMS*, www.boem.gov/Reorganization/. The Bureau of Safety and Environmental Enforcement is discussed at section 7.16:5 below.

The Bureau of Ocean Energy Management (BOEM) is responsible for developing the Five Year Outer Continental Shelf Oil and Natural Gas Leasing Program, developing renewable energy activities on the Outer Continental Shelf, and providing access to marine mineral resources on the Outer Continental Shelf. *See* U.S. Department of the Interior, *About BOEM—Fact Sheet*, www.boem.gov/sites/default/files/documents/newsroom/fact-sheets/BOEM-FactSheet-About.pdf.

Organizational Structure: The BOEM is led by a director appointed by the DOI secretary. Three regional directors are responsible for management and program implementation. Bureau of Ocean Energy Management, *BOEM Leadership*, www.boem.gov/Leadership/. Texas is in the Gulf of Mexico Region. Bureau of Ocean Energy Management, *BOEM Regions*, www.boem.gov/BOEM-Regions.

Influence on Water Resources: The BOEM's influence on water resources is indirect through its regulation of drilling activities in the Gulf of Mexico. According to the DOI's website, the Gulf Coast is home to one of the most ecologically complex regions in the country and the site of a number of National Wildlife Refuges, National Parks, and National Seashores, including Padre Islands National Seashore. *See* U.S. Department of the Interior, *Interior Fact Sheet—BP Deepwater Horizon Response*, www.doi.gov/deepwaterhorizon/Interior-Fact-Sheet-BP-Deepwater-Horizon-Response.

§ 7.16:5 Bureau of Safety and Environmental Enforcement

As discussed at section 7.16:4 above, the Bureau of Safety and Environmental Enforcement (BSEE) was created in 2011 in the wake of the *Deepwater Horizon* spill. The BSEE's mission is to "promote safety, protect the environment, and conserve resources offshore through vigorous regulatory oversight and enforcement." Bureau of Safety and Environmental Enforcement, *About Us*, www.bsee.gov/About-BSEE/index/.

Organizational Structure: The BSEE is led by a director appointed by the DOI secretary. Bureau of Safety and Environmental Enforcement, *Leadership*, www.bsee.gov/who-we-are/our-organization/leadership. The BSEE is supported by three regional offices: New Orleans, Louisiana (Gulf of Mexico Region), Camarillo, California (Pacific Region), and Anchorage, Alaska (Alaska Region). Bureau of Safety and Environmental Enforcement, *Regional Offices*, www.bsee.gov/who-we-are/our-organization/regional-offices. Texas is in the Gulf of Mexico Region.

Influence on Water Resources: Like the BOEM, the BSEE's influence on water resources is through its regulation of drilling activities in the Gulf of Mexico. The BSEE is to protect the environment and promote conservation and safety of offshore resources through its regulatory oversight and enforcement of outer continental shelf oil and gas drilling, production, and inspection operations. The BSEE also is responsible for oil spill response, including developing standards and guidelines for offshore operators. Bureau of Safety and Environmental Enforcement, *About Us*, www.bsee.gov/About-BSEE/index/.

The BSEE operates the National Offshore Training and Learning Center to secure proper training and up-to-date knowledge for its offshore inspectors. Bureau of Safety and Environmental Enforcement, *National Offshore Training Program*, www.bsee.gov/who-we-are/our-organization/national-programs/national-offshore-training-program.

§ 7.16:6 Office of Environmental Policy and Compliance

The DOI's Office of Environmental Policy and Compliance (OEPC) coordinates and develops environmental policy and program evaluations. It provides "for a coordinated and unified approach and response to environmental issues that affect multiple bureaus in order to ensure that the Department of the Interior speaks as one entity with respect to those issues." U.S. Department of the Interior, Office of Environmental Policy & Compliance, *Director's Office*, www.doi.gov/oepc/director-office. Within the OEPC are interdepartmental teams such as the Environmental Review Team (NEPA compliance), the Environmental Response and Recovery Team (natural resource damages), and the Environmental Cleanup and Liability Management Team (Superfund liability). *See* U.S. Department of the Interior, Office of Environmental Policy & Compliance, *Office of Environmental Policy & Compliance*, www.doi.gov/oepc.

§ 7.17 National Oceanic and Atmospheric Administration

The National Oceanic and Atmospheric Administration (NOAA) was formed in 1970, consolidating some of the oldest federal agencies at that time: the United States Coast and Geodetic Survey (whose roots date back to the Jefferson administration), the Weather Bureau, and the Bureau of Commercial Fisheries. *See* National Oceanic and Atmospheric Administration, *NOAA Heritage Legacy*, www.noaa.gov/heritage. Today, NOAA is composed of the National Marine Fisheries Service (NMFS, also known as NOAA Fisheries); the National Ocean Service (NOS); the National Environmental Satellite, Data, and Information Service (NESDIS); the Office of Oceanic and Atmospheric Research; the National Weather Service; and the Office of Marine and Aviation Operations & NOAA Corps. *See* National Oceanic and Atmospheric Administration, *NOAA Organization* Chart, www.noaa.gov/about/organization/noaa-organization-chart. The mission of NOAA is "to understand and predict changes in climate, weather, oceans, and coasts, to share that knowledge and information with others, and to conserve and manage coastal and marine ecosystems and resources." National Oceanic and Atmospheric Administration, *About Our Agency*, www.noaa.gov/about-our-agency.

§ 7.17:1 Organizational Structure

NOAA is an agency of the U.S. Department of Commerce. The Under Secretary of Commerce for Oceans and Atmosphere serves as the administrator of NOAA. There are two deputy administrators: the Assistant Secretary for Commerce for Oceans and Atmosphere and the Assistant Secretary for Environmental Observation and Prediction. The Chief Scientist advises the administrator and the deputies. All of these are appointed by the President with the advice and consent of the Senate. *See* U.S. Department of Commerce, Office of Privacy and Open Government, *Under Secretary of Commerce for Oceans and Atmosphere and Administrator of the National Oceanic and Atmospheric Administration* (Directive No. DOO 10–15, Dec. 12, 2011), www.osec.doc.gov/opog/dmp/doos/doo10_15.html.

§ 7.17:2 Influence on Water Resources

NOAA is instrumental in providing data regarding Texas water resources through, for instance, the National Weather Service, the NESDIS, and the NOS. NOAA is the lead federal agency for the National Integrated Drought Information System. *See* National Oceanic and Atmospheric Administration, National Centers for Environmental Information, *Drought: History of the U.S. Monitoring System*, www.ncdc.noaa.gov/news/drought-history-and-function-monitoring-system-united-states. See Chapter 22 of this book. NOAA monitors river, lake, and tidal levels and models hydrologic flow. The NOS, by way of example, operates twelve tide stations in Texas. *See* National Oceanic and Atmospheric Administration, *Tides and Currents*, https://tidesandcurrents.noaa.gov/stations.html?type=Water+Levels.

Besides its scientific support, NOAA also serves as the natural resource damage trustee for natural resources managed or controlled by the Department of Commerce and for natural resources managed or controlled by other federal agencies, if those resources are in "or using waters navigable by deep draft vessels, tidally influenced waters, or waters of the contiguous zone, the exclusive economic zone, and the outer continental shelf." 40 C.F.R. § 300.600(b)(1). Within NOAA's NOS is the Office of Response and Restoration (OR&R). The OR&R has three divisions and one program: the Emergency Response Division, the Assessment and Restoration Division, the Marine Debris Division, and the Disaster Preparedness Program. The Emergency Response Division provides scientific support to those responding to oil and chemical spills and assesses environmental injury. The Assessment and Restoration works with the Coast Guard, the EPA, and state environmental agencies to help protect and restore NOAA's trust resources. The Marine Debris Division coordinates marine debris management activities with the agency, as well as with its partners and the public. The Disaster Preparedness Program focuses on providing disaster response and recovery training. *See* National Oceanic and Atmospheric Administration, Office of Response and Restoration, *About*, http://response.restoration.noaa.gov/about. Texas water resources, such as Lavaca Bay, have been subject to NOAA's Damage Assessment, Remediation, and Restoration Program. This program's most high-profile project is the *Deepwater Horizon*/BP oil spill. *See* National Oceanic and Atmospheric Administration, *Gulf Spill Restoration*, www.gulfspillrestoration.noaa.gov/.

The Office for Coastal Management administers the Coastal Zone Management Act (CZMA). *See* National Oceanic and Atmospheric Administration, Office for Coastal Management, *Coastal Zone Management Act*, https://coast.noaa.gov/czm/act/ [hereinafter About the CZMA].

The CZMA outlines three national programs: the National Coastal Zone Management Program, the National Estuarine Research Reserve System, and the Coastal and Estuarine Land Conservation Program (CELCP). The CELCP provides matching funds to state and local governments to purchase threatened coastal and estuarine lands or obtain conservation easements. *See* National Oceanic and Atmospheric Administration, Office for Coastal Management, *The Coastal and Estuarine Land Conservation Program*, https://coast.noaa.gov/czm/landconservation/. Under the Coastal Zone Management Program, the states develop and implement coastal zone management plans in accordance with guidance developed by NOAA. *See* 16 U.S.C. § 1455. To be eligible for NOAA approval, each state's plan is required to define boundaries of the coastal zone, to identify uses of the area to be regulated by the state, the mechanism (criteria, standards, or regulations) for controlling such uses, and broad guidelines for priorities of uses within the coastal zone. *See* 15 C.F.R. § 923.1(c). Once a state's program is approved, the state is eligible for grants to implement the program. *See* 16 U.S.C. § 1455. The Texas Coastal Program was approved in 1996 and is administered by the Texas General Land Office in conjunction with the Coastal Coordination Advisory Committee, which are discussed at sections 7.8:2 and 7.11:2 above. *See* National Oceanic and Atmospheric Administration, Office for Coastal Management, *Coastal Zone Management Programs: Texas*, https://coast.noaa.gov/czm/mystate/#texas. Each state participating in this program is to evaluate its coastal management program (also known as section 309 assessment) in nine coastal zone enhancement areas every five years. *See* 16 U.S.C. § 1456b. The nine enhancement objectives include: wetlands, hazard management, public access, reduction of marine debris, assessment of coastal growth and development, management plans for important coastal areas, use of ocean resources, facilitation of appropriate sites for energy facilities and government facilities, and facilitation of the siting of public and private aquaculture facilities. *See* 16 U.S.C. § 1456b(a). Furthermore, the CZMA provides that federal actions (e.g., permits, licenses, and financial assistance) must be conducted in a manner consistent with the federally approved plans. *See* 16 U.S.C. § 1456.

The National Estuarine Research Reserve System, established by the CZMA, is a network of coastal sites "designated to protect and study estuarine systems." National Oceanic and Atmospheric Administration, Office of Coastal Management, National Estuarine Research Reserves, https://coast.noaa.gov/nerrs/. Texas has one reserve, the Mission-Aransas Estuary, and the University of Texas is the lead state agency for the reserve. *See* Mission-Aransas National Estuarine Research Reserve, *About: Mission-Aransas National Estuarine Research Reserve*, http://missionaransas.org/about.

The National Marine Protected Areas Center, located within NOAA's Office of National Marine Sanctuaries, was established in 2000 to "strengthen and connect the nation's marine protected areas." The National Marine Protected Areas Center "is a partnership between NOAA and the Department of the Interior to serve as a resource to all federal, state, territorial and tribal programs responsible for the health of the nation's oceans." National Marine Protected Areas, National MPA Center, https://marineprotectedareas.noaa.gov/aboutmpas/mpacenter/. Texas has several Marine Protected Areas; see http://marineprotectedareas.noaa.gov/nationalsystem/nationalsystemlist/ for the full list.

The National Marine Sanctuaries Act provides protection of marine environments that have "special national significance due to the conservation, recreational, ecological, historical, scientific, cultural, archeological, educational, or esthetic qualities." 16 U.S.C. §§ 1431–1447f; *see also* National Marine Sanctuaries, Legislation, https://sanctuaries.noaa.gov/about/legislation/. The Office of National Marine Sanctuaries makes designations to comprehensively protect designated areas of the marine environment. *See* 16 U.S.C. §§ 1431–1447f; *see also* National Marine Sanctuaries, Designations, https://sanctuaries.noaa.gov/management/designations.html. Texas has one national marine sanctuary, the Flower Garden Banks National Marine Sanctuary. *See* National Oceanic and Atmospheric Administration, National Marine Sanctuaries, *Flower Garden Banks*, http://flowergarden.noaa.gov/welcome.html.

While providing scientific support, the NMFS (also known as NOAA Fisheries), in conjunction with other law enforcement agencies, enforces more than forty domestic laws and international treaties in the two-hundred-mile-wide U.S. Fishery Conservation Zone. *See* National Oceanic and Atmospheric Administration, NOAA Fisheries, *Enforcement*, www.fisheries.noaa.gov/topic/enforcement. The NMFS plays a complementary role to the Fish and Wildlife Service under the Endangered Species Act. The FWS deals with terrestrial and freshwater species, and the NMFS administers the program for marine and anadromous species. See Chapters 17, 32, and 27 of this book for more information regarding the specifics of the ESA and its impact on water resources. The NMFS shares enforcement authority with the FWS under the Marine Mammal Protection Act, with responsibility for dolphins, porpoises, whales, and seals. *See* 16 U.S.C. §§ 1361–1423h. Also, as discussed in Chapter 35 of this book, the NMFS has the opportunity to comment on all individual and some general 404 permits. Additionally, the NMFS plays an important role in the FERC licensing process. See Chapter 27 of this book. The NMFS has six regional offices; Texas is in the Southeast region, which has its headquarters in St. Petersburg, Florida. *See* National Oceanic and Atmospheric Administration, *NOAA Fisheries, Southeast Regional Office*, www.fisheries.noaa.gov/about/southeast-regional-office. The NMFS also maintains a laboratory in Galveston, Texas. *See* National Oceanic and Atmospheric Administration, *Southeast Fisheries Science Center*, www.sefsc.noaa.gov/.

§ 7.18 Federal Energy Regulatory Commission

The Federal Energy Regulatory Commission (FERC) regulates the interstate transmission of electricity, natural gas, and oil. It reviews proposals to build liquefied natural gas terminals and interstate natural gas pipelines as well as licenses hydropower projects. Federal Energy Regulatory Commission, What is FERC?, *Overview of FERC*, www.ferc.gov/about/what-ferc/about/overview-ferc. The statutes under which FERC derives its authority include the Federal Power Act, 16 U.S.C. §§ 791a–828c; Natural Gas Act, 15 U.S.C. §§ 717–717z; Public Utility Regulatory Policies Act of 1978, 16 U.S.C. §§ 2601–2645; and the Energy Policy Act of 2005, 42 U.S.C. §§ 13201–13574.

§ 7.18:1 Organizational Structure

FERC is composed of up to five commissioners who are appointed by the President with the advice and consent of the Senate. Commissioners serve five-year terms and have an equal vote on regulatory matters. *See* Federal Energy Regulatory Commission, Meet the Commissioners, www.ferc.gov/about/commission-members. The FERC has regional offices in New York, Atlanta, Chicago, Portland, and San Francisco, which deal primarily with hydropower projects. Texas is served by the Atlanta office. *See* Federal Energy Regulatory Commission, Key *Contacts*, www.ferc.gov/about/contact-us/key-contacts. On June 24, 2021, the FERC announced the establishment of the Office of Public Participation, which will help members of the public to learn about and participate in FERC proceedings. Federal Energy Regulatory Commission, News Release, *FERC Establishes Office of Public Participation* (June 24, 2021), www.ferc.gov/news-events/news/ferc-establishes-office-public-participation.

§ 7.18:2 Influence on Water Resources

As discussed in Chapters 3 and 27 of this book, FERC may have jurisdiction over the construction of a dam if it includes hydroelectric facilities. FERC is required to impose conditions on hydroelectric facilities to protect fish and wildlife. *See* 16 U.S.C. § 803(j). These conditions may be based on recommendations from the Fish and Wildlife Service and the National Marine Fisheries Service.

§ 7.19 U.S. Department of Agriculture

The U.S. Department of Agriculture (USDA), originally established in 1862 by President Lincoln, was elevated to a cabinet-level agency in 1889. *See* 7 U.S.C. § 2201; Act of Feb. 9, 1889, 25 Stat. 659. The mission of the USDA is to "provide leadership on food, agriculture, natural resources, rural development, nutrition, and related issues based on public policy, the best available science, and effective management." U.S. Department of Agriculture, *About the U.S. Department of Agriculture*, www.usda.gov/our-agency/about-usda. The involvement of the USDA in Texas water resources is mostly indirect. For instance, as discussed in Chapter 32 of this book, the USDA has been required under the Endangered Species Act to adopt or develop conservation programs regarding the Edwards Aquifer. This section focuses on the USDA's Farm Service Agency (FSA) and Rural Development, both of which provide water-related loans (see Chapters 22 and 29, respectively), and the Natural Resources Conservation Service (NRCS), formerly the Soil Conservation Service, which administers the "Swampbuster" program (see Chapter 35).

§ 7.19:1 Organizational Structure

The head of the USDA is the Secretary of Agriculture. The day-to-day activities are handled by the Deputy Secretary. There are eight Under Secretaries, including the Under Secretary for Rural Development, the Under Secretary for Natural Resources and Environment, and the Under Secretary for Trade and Foreign Agricultural Services. *See* U.S. Department of Agriculture, *USDA Organization Chart*, www.usda.gov/sites/default/files/documents/usda-organization-chart.pdf. All these positions are appointed by the President with the advice and consent of the Senate.

Rural Development: The Under Secretary for Rural Development is assisted by a Deputy Under Secretary. *See* U.S. Department of Agriculture, Rural Development, *Leadership*, www.rd.usda.gov/about-rd/leadership. Three administrators answer to the Rural Development leadership: the Administrator for Rural Housing, the Administrator for Business-Cooperative Service, and the Administrator for Rural Utilities Service. *See* U.S. Department of Agriculture, Rural Development, *Leadership*, www.rd.usda.gov/about-rd/leadership. The Rural Utility Service programs are discussed in Chapter 29 of this book.

Farm Service Agency (FSA): The FSA is led by the administrator who reports to the Under Secretary for Farm Production and Conservation. Three deputies report to the administrator, including the Deputy Administrator for Field Operations, who oversees state and county offices. *See* U.S. Department of Agriculture, Farm Service Agency, *Structure and Organization*, www.fsa.usda.gov/about-fsa/structure-and-organization/index.

Natural Resources Conservation Service (NRCS): The Under Secretary for Natural Resources and the Environment oversees the NRCS. The Chief provides overall leadership for the activities of the NRCS. *See* U.S. Department of Agriculture, Natural Resources Conservation Service, *NRCS Leadership*, www.nrcs.usda.gov/wps/portal/nrcs/main/national/about/leadership/.

§ 7.19:2 Influence on Water Resources

As discussed above, the involvement of the USDA in Texas water resources is mostly indirect. This section focuses on the USDA's FSA and Rural Development, both of which provide water-related loans (see Chapters 22 and 29 of this book, respectively), and the NRCS, formerly the Soil Conservation Service, which administers the "Swampbuster" program (see Chapter 35).

United States Department of Agriculture—Rural Development: The role of the United States Department of Agriculture–Rural Development (USDA–RD) is to "improve the economy and quality of life in rural America." U.S. Department of Agriculture, Rural Development, *About RD*, www.rd.usda.gov/about-rd/. The USDA–RD is primarily a grant and loan agency for rural housing and development projects. *See* Anthony S. Corbett, *The Players—Who's Who in Water Rights* 2, *in Water Rights Boot Camp* (State Bar of Texas 2006). It serves as a critical source of financing of utility infrastructure that would not otherwise be available in rural communities. Corbett, at 2. For example, the USDA–RD administers Resource Conservation and Development loans and Watershed loans. *See* 7 C.F.R. pt. 1781. These loans can be used for many water development and conservation programs, including—

1. water development, storage, treatment, and conveyance for agricultural irrigation;
2. drainage systems and facilities to sustain agricultural production or protect farmers and rural residents from water damage. These can include soil conservation and water control facilities such as dikes, terraces, detention reservoirs, stream channels, ditches, and other special land treatment and stabilization measures; and
3. management and control of vegetation along waterways and in drainage basins to stabilize streamflow, recharge groundwater, and conserve water supplies.

See 7 C.F.R. § 1781.6(a)

The USDA–RD also administers Emergency Community Water Assistance Grants to assist certain residents of rural areas to obtain or maintain adequate quantities of water that meet the standards set by the Safe Drinking Water Act. *See* 7 C.F.R. § 1778.3; *see also* U.S. Department of Agriculture, Rural Development, *Emergency Community Water Assistance Grants*, www.rd.usda.gov/

programs-services/emergency-community-water-assistance-grants. See Chapter 29 of this book, which discusses rural utilities and USDA–RD financial assistance.

Farm Service Agency: The mission of the FSA is to equitably serve all farmers, ranchers, and agricultural partners through the delivery of effective, efficient agricultural programs for all Americans." U.S. Department of Agriculture, Farm Service Agency, *Mission*, www.fsa.usda.gov/about-fsa/history-and-mission/index. The FSA implements agricultural policy, administers credit and loan programs, and manages conservation, commodity, disaster, and farm marketing programs through a national network of offices. *See* U.S. Department of Agriculture, Farm Service Agency, *State Offices*, www.fsa.usda.gov/state-offices/index.

In addition to providing low-interest loans for drought disaster relief (see Chapter 22 of this book), the FSA implements the Farmable Wetlands Program to restore wetlands in order to reduce downstream flood damage, improve surface water and groundwater quality, and recharge groundwater supplies. *See* U.S. Department of Agriculture, Farm Service Agency, *Farmable Wetlands Program*, www.fsa.usda.gov/programs-and-services/conservation-programs/farmable-wetlands/index. Another FSA program, the Source Water Protection Program, is "designed to help prevent pollution of surface and ground water used as the primary source of drinking water by rural residents." *See* U.S. Department of Agriculture, Farm Service Agency, *"Grassroots" Source Water Protection Program*, www.fsa.usda.gov/programs-and-services/conservation-programs/source-water-protection/index.

Natural Resources Conservation Service: The NRCS, which traces its origin from efforts to combat the Dust Bowl of the 1930s, "helps America's farmers, ranchers, and forest landowners conserve the nation's soil, water, air and other natural resources." U.S. Department of Agriculture, Natural Resources Conservation Service, *About NRCS*, www.nrcs.usda.gov/wps/portal/nrcs/main/national/about/. Like the FSA and the USDA–RD, the NRCS works at the local level, in field offices at USDA service centers in nearly every county in the United States. *See* U.S. Department of Agriculture, Natural Resources Conservation Service, Local *Service Centers Directory*, www.nrcs.usda.gov/wps/portal/nrcs/main/national/contact/local/.

As discussed in Chapter 35 of this book, the NRCS administers the Swampbuster program. Generally, this program removes "certain incentives to produce agricultural commodities on converted wetlands or highly erodible land, unless the highly erodible land is protected from excessive soil erosion." U.S. Department of Agriculture, Natural Resources Conservation Service, *Wetland Conservation Provisions (Swampbuster)*, www.nrcs.usda.gov/wps/portal/nrcs/detailfull/national/water/wetlands/?&cid=stelprdb1043554. The NRCS is responsible for making wetlands determinations which are depicted on FSA maps. There is an MOU regarding the delineation of wetlands between the USDA, the DOI, the EPA, and the U.S. Army. *See Memorandum of Agreement Among the Department of Agriculture, the Environmental Protection Agency, the Department of the Interior, and the Department of the Army Concerning the Delineation of Wetlands for Purposes of Section 404 of the Clean Water Act and Subtitle B of the Food Security Act* (Jan. 1994). The NRCS maintains a list of hydric soils occurring in U.S. wetlands, which assists in determining wetlands status. *See* U.S. Department of Agriculture, Natural Resources Conservation Service, *Hydric Soils*, www.nrcs.usda.gov/wps/portal/nrcs/main/soils/use/hydric.

The NRCS administers the Watershed Protection and Flood Prevention Program, which provides local government sponsors (such as the soil and water conservation districts discussed earlier in this chapter) with technical and financial support to implement conservation practices and improvements, including floodwater-retarding dams and reservoirs. *See* 16 U.S.C. §§ 1001–1012. This program is detailed in Chapter 39 of this book, and, as noted therein, the focus is generally on small projects in upstream tributary watersheds.

As discussed at section 7.10:2 above, the NRCS provides assistance regarding Water Quality Management Plans (WQMPs). Funding is provided for water resource-related projects through such programs as the Environmental Quality Incentives Program. *See* U.S. Department of Agriculture, Natural Resources Conservation Service, *Environmental Quality Incentives Program*, www.nrcs.usda.gov/wps/portal/nrcs/main/tx/programs/financial/eqip/.

§ 7.20 U.S. Coast Guard

The U.S. Coast Guard (USCG) is a branch of the United States Armed Forces. The USCG's workforce includes over 51,000 active duty and civilian workers and "is the principal federal agency responsible for maritime safety, security, and environmental stewardship in U.S. ports and inland waterways, along more than 95,000 miles of U.S. coastline, throughout the 4.5 million square miles of U.S. Exclusive Economic Zone (EEZ), and on the high seas." United States Coast Guard, Organizational Overview, www.uscg.mil/About/.

§ 7.20:1 Organizational Structure

The head of the Coast Guard is the Commandant. United States Coast Guard, *Senior Coast Guard Leadership*, www.uscg.mil/seniorleadership/. There are nine USCG districts, divided between the Atlantic Area and the Pacific Area. United States Coast Guard, *United States Coast Guard Organization Chart*, www.uscg.mil/units/Organization/. Texas is in the Eighth Coast Guard District, which is headquartered in New Orleans. United States Coast Guard, *8th Coast Guard District*, www.uscg.mil/units/Organization/#d8.

§ 7.20:2 Influence on Water Resources

The USCG is the federal counterpart to the Texas General Land Office in responding to coastal spills. EPA Region 6 and the USCG have entered into an MOU to delineate roles in pollution response. *See* Texas General Land Office, *Memorandum of Agreement between U.S. Environmental Protection Agency Region 6, and U.S. Coast Guard Eighth Coast Guard District, New Orleans, LA Regarding Response Boundaries for Oil and Hazardous Substances Pollution Incidents on Scene Coordinator Responsibilities* (Revised Feb. 12 2010), www.glo.texas.gov/ost/spill-response-resources/rrtvi/d8r6moacorrected.pdf. Similarly, the EPA, the USCG, the Fish and Wildlife Service, the National Marine Fisheries Service, the National Ocean Service, and the DOI's Office of Environmental Policy and Compliance signed an interagency memorandum of agreement. *See* U.S. National Response Team, *Inter-agency Memorandum of Agreement Regarding Oil Spill Planning and Response Activities Under the Federal Water Pollution Control Act's National Oil and Hazardous Substances Pollution Contingency Plan and the Endangered Species Act* (renewed July 2014), www.nrt.org/sites/2/files/ESAMOA.pdf.

The USCG's mission also includes enforcement of fisheries laws at sea and regulation to prevent the introduction of invasive species into the maritime environment and unauthorized ocean dumping. *See* 6 U.S.C. § 468.

§ 7.21 Council on Environmental Quality

As discussed in Chapters 3 and 27 of this book, water projects may trigger the applicability of NEPA. Generally, NEPA procedures involve the oversight of or consultation with the federal agencies. The Council on Environmental Quality (CEQ) is part of the executive office of the President and "coordinates the federal government's efforts to improve, preserve, and protect America's public health and environment." *See* The White House, Council on Environmental Quality, www.whitehouse.gov/ceq/.

§ 7.21:1 Organizational Structure

The CEQ was established within the Executive Office of the President by Congress as part of NEPA in 1969. *See* The White House, Council on Environmental Quality, www.whitehouse.gov/ceq/. The chair of the CEQ is appointed by the President with the advice and consent of the Senate.

§ 7.21:2 Influence on Water Resources

Under NEPA, the CEQ works to balance environmental, economic, and social objectives in pursuit of NEPA's goal of "productive harmony" between humans and the natural environment. 42 U.S.C. § 4331(a). Under NEPA, the CEQ is tasked with ensuring that federal agencies meet their obligations under the Act. The CEQ has issued guidance to assist the federal agencies in their review. *See* Office of NEPA Policy and Compliance, *History of CEQ NEPA Regulations and Guidance*, www.energy.gov/nepa/nepa-guidance-requirements/history-ceq-nepa-regulations-and-guidance.
NEPA review adds complexity and often delay to water resource projects. See Chapters 3 and 27 of this book.

§ 7.22 Interstate Compacts

As discussed in more detail in Chapter 14 of this book, interstate stream compacts, such as the Red River Compact, the Pecos River Compact, and the Rio Grande Compact, are administered by a commission. Generally, there is a representative from each state, plus a nonvoting federal commissioner. *See, e.g.*, Red River Compact Commission, www.owrb.ok.gov/rrccommission/rrccommission.html. The federal agencies that support these compacts are the Corps, the Bureau of Reclamation, the USGS, and the NRCS.

§ 7.23 Congressional Committees

Various congressional standing committees exercise jurisdiction over water or water-related entities. For example, the Senate has standing committees for Energy and Natural Resources and the Environment and Public Works. The Subcommittee on Water and Power, a subcommittee of the Committee on Energy and Natural Resources, oversees and has legislative responsibilities for irrigation; reclamation projects, including related flood control purposes; power marketing administrations; energy development impacts on water resources; groundwater resources and management; hydroelectric power; low head hydropower; and energy-related aspects of deepwater ports. *See* U.S. Senate Committee on Energy & Natural Resources, Subcommittee on Water and Power, www.energy.senate.gov/water-power.

The Senate Committee on the Environment and Public Works includes oversight of regulations from drinking water to wastewater systems to public infrastructure. The Fisheries, Water, and Wildlife Subcommittee has jurisdiction over a variety of issues, including the CWA, (including wetlands), water pollution, ocean dumping, SDWA, CZMA, invasive species, fisheries and wildlife, ESA, national wildlife refuges, and outer continental shelf lands. *See* U.S. Senate Committee on Environment and Public Works, *Subcommittees—Fisheries, Water, and Wildlife*, www.epw.senate.gov/public/index.cfm/fisheries-water-and-wildlife. Moreover, the Senate Committee on Commerce, Science and Transportation, including the Subcommittee on Oceans, Fisheries, Climate Change and Manufacturing has jurisdiction over matters that impact our oceans, coasts and inland waterways including: coastal zone management, marine fisheries; marine mammals;

and ocean, weather, and atmospheric activities. The subcommittee is responsible for overseeing the National Oceanic and Atmospheric Administration (NOAA), the U.S. Coast Guard, the Marine Mammal Commission, the U.S. Global Change Research Program, the Department of Commerce manufacturing bureaus, the Minority Business Development Agency (MBDA), and workforce development matters. *U.S. Senate Committee on Commerce, Science, and Transportation*, www.commerce.senate.gov/oceans-fisheries-climate-change-and-manufacturing-subcommittee.

The House has similar, but not identical, committees with jurisdiction over water issues. The Natural Resources Committee has jurisdiction over, among other things, creating new water supplies for communities affected by drought and preparing communities for climate change-related impacts on water supplies. The Subcommittee on Water, Oceans, and Wildlife is responsible for "overseeing the agencies that manage America's water resources, hydropower development, and federal transmission lines." *See, U.S. House Committee on Natural Resources, Natural Resources Committee, Water, Oceans, and Wildlife*, https://naturalresources.house.gov/subcommittees/water-oceans-and-wildlife. Likewise, the Transportation and Infrastructure Committee includes the Water Resources and Environment Subcommittee, which deals with matters relating to water resources development, conservation and management, water pollution control and water infrastructure, and hazardous waste cleanup. U.S. House Transportation and Infrastructure Committee, *Subcommittees—Water Resources and Environment*, https://transportation.house.gov/subcommittees/water-resources-and-environment-116th-congress. The House Energy and Commerce Committee and, more specifically, the Subcommittee on Environment and Climate Change also exercises jurisdiction over all matters relating to water contamination. *See* U.S. House Committee on Energy & Commerce, *Subcommittees—Environment & Climate Change*, https://energycommerce.house.gov/subcommittees/environment-and-climate-change-117th-congress.

IV. Conclusion

§ 7.24 Conclusion

It takes many state and federal agencies, working together, to protect and sustain our vital water resources. The TCEQ acts as the primary regulatory authority with water resource jurisdiction in Texas. The TWDB is responsible for water planning and for administering water financing, while the PUC governs the economic regulation of water and sewer service. Although the RRC is not a water resource agency, due to the nature of the activities it regulates its jurisdiction often overlaps with the TCEQ. There are many more state agencies with jurisdiction over water resource matters, whether in a regulatory, research and advisory, or funding role. The federal government's authority over Texas's state waters is more limited, but the EPA, FWS, and others at the federal level also play their part in regulating water resources.

CHAPTER 8

Water Districts

Trey Lary[1]

I. Introduction

§ 8.1 Definition

A water district is a local government entity that has specified powers and encompasses a specified geographic area. Water districts have existed in Texas in various forms since the early 1900s. Current Texas law provides for more than a dozen different types of districts. This chapter addresses the constitutional basis for water districts, the general powers and duties applicable to them by statute, and the creation process and powers of the most common types of districts.

II. Constitutional Provisions

§ 8.2 Introduction

Two provisions in the Texas Constitution provide the authority under which water districts, both general law and special law, are created. See Chapter 4 of this book for a discussion of the history of these provisions.

§ 8.3 Article III, Section 52

Article III, section 52, of the Texas Constitution provides that the Texas legislature may authorize a political subdivision or a "defined district" to issue debt in an amount "not to exceed one-fourth of the assessed valuation of the real property of such district" for the following purposes:

1. the improvement of rivers, creeks, and streams to prevent overflows and to permit navigation or irrigation thereof or in aid of such purposes;
2. the construction and maintenance of pools, lakes, reservoirs, dams, canals, and waterways for the purposes of irrigation, drainage, or navigation or in aid thereof; and
3. the construction, maintenance, and operation of macadamized, graveled, or paved roads and turnpikes or in aid thereof.

---

1. Trey Lary is a partner at Allen Boone Humphries Robinson LLP, where he practices public finance, water district, land development, and local government law. Trey also represents clients before state agencies and the Texas legislature.

The author gratefully acknowledges the contributions of the late Angela M. Stepherson for her excellent work in drafting the original and updating previous editions of this chapter.

See Tex. Const. art. III, § 52(b). The issuance of debt payable from taxes must be approved at an election by a two-thirds majority of those voting.

§ 8.4 Article XVI, Section 59

Article XVI, section 59, of the Texas Constitution provides that conservation and reclamation districts may be created and may be authorized by the legislature to issue debt and levy a maintenance and operations tax for various purposes related to "[t]he conservation and development of all the natural resources of this State." *See* Tex. Const. art. XVI, § 59(a), (b). Debt payable from taxes must be approved at an election by a simple majority of those voting. *See* Tex. Const. art. XVI, § 59(c). Subsections (d) and (e) of article XVI, section 59, set out the procedural requirements for passage of special law district legislation. Those requirements are discussed at section 8.48 below.

§ 8.5 Amendments

In the Texas Supreme Court's decision in *Deason v. Orange County Water Control & Improvement District No. One*, 244 S.W.2d 981 (Tex. 1952), the court held that neither article III, section 52, nor article XVI, section 59, as then worded, authorized the legislature to grant a water control and improvement district the power to finance and operate firefighting equipment. *Deason*, 244 S.W.2d at 984; *see also* Tex. Att'y Gen. Op. Nos. H-28 (1973), M-76 (1967). That case was addressed by a 1978 amendment to article III, section 52, and by a similar amendment to article XVI, section 59. Both sections now explicitly allow districts to provide firefighting services and to issue debt for the purpose. *See* Tex. Const. art. III, § 52(d), art. XVI, § 59(f).

Article XVI, section 59, was also amended in 2003 to include the development of parks and recreational facilities as an explicit constitutional purpose and to allow the legislature to authorize districts in certain counties (Bexar, Bastrop, Waller, Travis, Williamson, Harris, Galveston, Brazoria, Fort Bend, and Montgomery) and the Tarrant Regional Water District to issue debt payable from taxes (upon voter authorization) and to levy an operations and maintenance tax for the purpose of developing parks and recreational facilities. *See* Tex. Const. art. XVI, § 59(a), (c–1). This amendment was the culmination of a series of court cases, attorney general opinions, and statutory enactments that addressed the authority of districts to provide such facilities and the means by which they could be financed. *See, e.g., Harris County Water Control & Improvement District No. 110 v. Texas Water Rights Commission*, 593 S.W.2d 852 (Tex. App.—Austin 1980, no writ); Tex. Att'y Gen. Op. Nos. DM-420 (1996), JM-1259 (1990), JM-1173 (1990), MW-313 (1981), H-491 (1975). The currently applicable statutory provisions are found in chapter 49, subchapter N, of the Texas Water Code; those provisions are discussed in detail at section 8.15:7 below.

III. Texas Water Code Chapter 49: General Provisions

§ 8.6 Applicability

Chapter 49 of the Texas Water Code establishes uniform administrative provisions applicable to all types of districts defined in section 49.001 and discussed in this chapter, generally referred to as water districts. Before the enactment of chapter 49, chapter 50 of the Water Code had contained some administrative provisions generally applicable to all such districts, but for the most part each chapter of the Water Code included sometimes varying administrative provisions applicable to only the particular type of district covered by that chapter, such as municipal utility districts under chapter 54; most of these provisions were repealed in 1995.

The provisions in chapter 49 generally apply to a "district," which is defined by section 49.001(a)(1) to be—

> any district or authority created by authority of either Sections 52(b)(1) and (2), Article III, or Section 59, Article XVI, Texas Constitution, regardless of how created. The term "district" shall not include any navigation district or port authority created under general or special law, any conservation and reclamation district created pursuant to Chapter 62, Acts of the 52nd Legislature, 1951 (Article 8280–141, Vernon's Texas Civil Statutes), or any conservation and reclamation district governed by Chapter 36 unless a special law creating the district or amending the law creating the district states that this chapter applies to that district.

Tex. Water Code § 49.001(a)(1).

Under this definition, chapter 49 does not apply to navigation districts, port authorities, or groundwater conservation districts. As discussed below, specific sections in chapter 49 may also provide that they apply or do not apply to districts that meet particular criteria.

The definition of "district" in section 49.001(a)(1) includes districts "regardless of how created." Section 49.002(a) provides that—

> [chapter 49] applies to all general and special law districts to the extent that the provisions of this chapter do not directly conflict with a provision in any other chapter of this code or any Act creating or affecting a special law district. In the event of such conflict, the specific provisions in such other chapter or Act shall control.

Tex. Water Code § 49.002(a).

A "general law district" is one created by the county or by the Texas Commission on Environmental Quality (TCEQ) under the general procedures set out in the chapter of the Water Code applicable to that type of district. The procedures for creating the different types of general law districts are described below. A "special law district" is one created through the passage of particular local legislation; that process is discussed at sections 8.47–8.49 below. For a special law district, the specific language of the creation legislation and any amendments that conflict with any provisions in chapter 49 control over chapter 49.

Section 49.002(b) reiterates that chapter 49 generally does *not* apply to groundwater conservation districts governed by chapter 36 of the Water Code, "unless a special law creating the district or amending the law creating the district states that this chapter applies to that district." Tex. Water Code § 49.002(b). Chapter 36 of the Water Code sets out the administrative provisions applicable to groundwater conservation districts; see Chapter 16 of this book for detailed information regarding those districts.

Water districts are subject to many of the same statutes in the Texas Government Code and the Texas Local Government Code that apply to other types of local government entities, such as cities and counties. For example, districts must comply with the Open Meetings Act, the Public Information Act, and the Local Government Records Act. *See* Tex. Gov't Code §§ 551.001(3)(H), 552.003(1)(A)(viii); Tex. Loc. Gov't Code § 201.003(7). In addition, districts may be subject to certain federal laws such as the Safe Drinking Water Act or federal regulations governing municipal bonds.

§ 8.7 Directors

The chapter of the Texas Water Code applicable to a type of district establishes the specific qualifications a person must meet to serve on the board of directors for each particular type of district. Chapter 49, however, contains administrative provisions that generally apply to directors for all types of districts. In addition to the provisions discussed in detail in the following sections, chapter 49 addresses the election of board officers, the oath of office and bond required for directors, and the fees of office paid to directors. *See* Tex. Water Code §§ 49.054, 49.055, 49.060. Of particular note, a majority of a district board is the quorum required to hold a board meeting, and a majority of the total number on the board is needed to approve an action item, rather than only a majority of those present. *See* Tex. Water Code § 49.053. In other words, if a district's board is made up of five members, three members are needed for a quorum to hold a board meeting. If only three members are present, all three must vote in favor of an item for it to pass.

§ 8.7:1 Disqualification

Section 49.052 of the Texas Water Code sets out the circumstances under which a person is prohibited from serving on the board of directors. This section applies to any district "that includes less than all the territory in at least one county and which, if located within the corporate area of a city or cities, includes within its boundaries less than 75 percent of the incorporated area of the city or cities." Tex. Water Code § 49.052(a). Section 49.052(f) provides that the section does not apply to special water authorities, as that term is defined in section 49.001(a)(8); certain districts that are not required to obtain TCEQ approval of their bonds under section 49.181(h)(1)(D); or districts whose main function is to provide irrigation for agricultural purposes or to provide nonpotable water. *See* Tex. Water Code § 49.052(f).

A person is disqualified from serving or continuing to serve on a board if that person is related within the third degree of affinity or consanguinity to or employed by a developer of property in the district, another board member, or a person who provides professional services to the district. *See* Tex. Water Code § 49.052(a)(1), (2); *see also* Tex. Gov't Code ch. 573, subch. B (computing degrees of relationship by affinity and consanguinity). A person is also disqualified if that person is a developer of property in the district, as defined by section 49.052(d); is providing professional services to the district; is a party to a contract with the district, except for services provided by the district to the general public; or is a party to a contract with a developer of property in the district, except for the purpose of acquiring property to establish a residence or a business in the district or to qualify to serve as a director. *See* Tex. Water Code § 49.052(a)(3)–(5).

If the board determines that a director is disqualified, it must replace that director within sixty days. *See* Tex. Water Code § 49.052(b). Willfully continuing to serve as a board member when disqualified is a misdemeanor. *See* Tex. Water Code § 49.052(c). The presence of a disqualified member on a board, however, does not affect any rights obtained by a third party through board action as long as the third party was unaware of the disqualification. *See* Tex. Water Code § 49.052(e).

In addition to disqualification, section 49.052(g) provides that a board, by unanimous vote of the other members, may remove a director who has missed at least half of the regularly scheduled meetings during the preceding twelve-month period. *See* Tex. Water Code § 49.052(g). A director removed under this section may appeal the removal to the TCEQ, which may reinstate the director for good cause. *See* 30 Tex. Admin. Code § 293.35 (reinstatement of board member).

Finally, a person may be prohibited from holding more than one governmental office under the "dual office holding" provisions of the Texas Constitution or under the common-law doctrine of incompatibility. An examination of those topics is beyond the scope of this chapter.

§ 8.7:2 Election of Directors and Terms of Office

Under section 49.103 of the Texas Water Code, directors serve four-year terms, and, as a general rule, director elections are held on the uniform election date in May of even-numbered years. Tex. Water Code § 49.103(a), (b); *see also* Tex. Elec. Code § 41.001 (uniform election dates). Section 41.0052 of the Texas Election Code authorized political subdivisions, including water districts, not later than December 31, 2016, to change the date of director elections to another uniform election date.

See Tex. Elec. Code § 41.0052. Section 49.103(e) specifically provides that these requirements "take precedence over all prior statutory enactments." Tex. Water Code § 49.103(e). Section 49.103 as a whole, however, does not apply to special law districts that do not have elected directors or to special utility districts operating under chapter 65 of the Water Code. *See* Tex. Water Code § 49.103(f); *see also* Tex. Water Code § 65.103 (election and terms of office of special utility district directors).

Directors are required to serve staggered terms. When a district is first organized under section 49.102 of the Water Code (discussed at section 8.8 below), the permanent directors must agree or draw lots to determine which directors will come up for election first. *See* Tex. Water Code § 49.102(h). A district may determine that directors will be elected by position number, at large, or from single-member districts. *See* Tex. Water Code § 49.103(c), (d). Most districts elect directors at large. Districts must generally comply with the Election Code unless otherwise provided. *See* Tex. Water Code § 49.101. Director candidates often run unopposed, and in that case, chapter 2, subchapter C, of the Election Code allows a district to cancel an election if each candidate is unopposed and no propositions appear on the ballot.

§ 8.7:3 Vacancies

A board may appoint a new director to fill a vacancy. *See* Tex. Water Code § 49.105(a). If the board does not fill a vacancy within sixty days after the position becomes vacant, 10 percent of the registered voters in the district may petition the board to fill the vacancy. *See* Tex. Water Code § 49.105(b). If the board has multiple vacancies and cannot act because it no longer has a quorum as required by section 49.053, or if a position is vacant for more than ninety days, regardless of whether a voter petition has been presented, the vacancy may be filled by either the TCEQ or the county commissioners court, as applicable. *See* Tex. Water Code § 49.105(c). The commissioners court fills the vacancy if the district was created by the county—for example, a fresh water supply district. Otherwise, the TCEQ fills the vacancy if the district is required to obtain TCEQ approval of its bonds under section 49.181. *See* 30 Tex. Admin. Code §§ 293.31–.34.

§ 8.7:4 Conflicts of Interest; Ethics Disclosures

District directors must comply with chapter 171 of the Texas Local Government Code, which generally regulates conflicts of interest of local public officials. *See* Tex. Water Code § 49.058; *see also* Tex. Loc. Gov't Code § 171.001(1) (defining "local public official"). Chapter 171 requires officials to disclose certain interests in matters that come before them for a vote and to abstain from participating in the matters under certain conditions. *See* Tex. Loc. Gov't Code §§ 171.002 (types of interests covered), 171.004 (disclosure and abstention), 171.005 (voting on budget). Failure to comply with these requirements is a misdemeanor. *See* Tex. Loc. Gov't Code § 171.003. A violation, however, does not affect the action taken unless it would not have passed without the vote of the person who had the conflict. *See* Tex. Loc. Gov't Code § 171.006.

Chapter 176 of the Local Government Code also applies to district directors. *See* Tex. Loc. Gov't Code § 176.001(3) (defining "local government entity"), (4) (defining "local government officer"). This chapter requires that a local government officer disclose certain relationships with persons who enter into or seek to enter into contracts with the local government entity. Unlike chapter 171, chapter 176 does not require any abstention from voting. Depending on the circumstances, however, abstention may be required under chapter 171. Chapter 176 further requires that local government officers and persons who enter into or seek to enter into contracts with the local government entity disclose certain gifts, as defined by section 176.001(2–b). *See* Tex. Loc. Gov't Code § 176.001(2–b). A local government officer is required to file a disclosure statement if a vendor "has given to the local government officer or a family member of the officer one or more gifts that have an aggregate value of more than $100" in a twelve-month period. Tex. Loc. Gov't Code § 176.003(a)(2)(B). Certain exceptions apply; most notably, a disclosure statement is not required for a gift of food accepted as a guest. *See* Tex. Loc. Gov't Code § 176.003(a–1). Failure to file required disclosure statements with the local government entity is a misdemeanor. *See* Tex. Loc. Gov't Code § 176.003.

§ 8.8 Confirmation Elections

Section 49.102 of the Texas Water Code generally requires an election to confirm the creation of a district and to elect permanent directors. A confirmation election is not required for a special law district if it is not required by the creation legislation. *See* Tex. Water Code § 49.102(j). The vast majority of special law districts are required to have a confirmation election. *See, e.g.*, Tex. Spec. Dist. Code §§ 8138.023, 8203.023. The board's order canvassing the results of the election must include the district's boundaries and must be filed with the TCEQ and recorded in the deed records. *See* Tex. Water Code § 49.102(f). In most districts, an election to authorize the future issuance of bonds and the levy of a maintenance tax is held at the same time as the confirmation election. An election to approve a plan to provide firefighting services may also be held simultaneously with the confirmation election. *See* Tex. Water Code § 49.102(i); see also section 8.15:6 below.

Section 49.1025 of the Water Code provides qualifications for a voter in a confirmation election or an election held in conjunction with the confirmation election to authorize taxes and bonds. *See* Tex. Water Code § 49.1025. A person is not a qualified voter if the person, on the date of the election, is a developer of property in the district, as defined by section 49.052(d) of the Water Code; is related within the third degree of affinity or consanguinity to a developer of property in the district; is an employee of a developer of property in the district; or has resided in the district less than thirty days. *See* Tex. Water Code §§ 49.052(d), 49.1025(b)(1). Further, a person is not a qualified voter if the person has "received monetary consideration from a developer of property in the district in exchange for the person's vote." *See* Tex. Water Code § 49.1025(b)(2). A voter is required to complete and submit a voter affidavit, the form of which is prescribed by the office of the attorney general. *See* Tex. Water Code § 49.1025(c), (e). The voter affidavit must require the voter to state under oath the address of the voter and that the voter resides in the territory of the district; the date the voter changed the voter's residence to such address; and that the voter's registration is effective on the date of the election. *See* Tex. Water Code § 49.1025(f).

§ 8.9 Bond Elections

As discussed at section 8.3 above, the Texas Constitution requires that the voters of a district authorize the issuance of bonds payable from taxes. A bond election may be held at the same time as any other election held by the district. *See* Tex. Water Code § 49.106(c); *but see* Tex. Water Code § 53.172 (requiring a bond election for a fresh water supply district to be held separately from other elections). As noted at section 8.8 above, most districts hold their initial bond election at the same time as their confirmation election. Before a bond election may be held, the district must obtain and make available to the public an engineer's report describing the type and cost of the facilities and other items to be financed by the bonds. *See* Tex. Water Code § 49.106(a). Similarly, before a park bond election may be held, the district must develop and make available to the public a park plan describing the park and recreational facilities to be developed and the cost of such facilities. *See* Tex. Water Code § 49.4645(b). Typically, the amount to be authorized covers the full amount of the bonds that are estimated to be needed over the life of the district. The actual issuance of bonds generally occurs in phases as the district develops.

§ 8.10 Management of a District

The board of directors is responsible for the management of the district but may hire employees or consultants as necessary to conduct the business of the district. *See* Tex. Water Code § 49.057(a). The needed employees or consultants will vary depending on the level of activity in the district. The majority of water districts do not have employees but contract with consultants to provide services. Officers, employees, or consultants who routinely handle district funds must provide a bond or insurance to protect against theft of funds. *See* Tex. Water Code § 49.057(e), (i). The district may provide health, retirement, and other benefits to its employees. *See* Tex. Water Code § 49.069. When hiring professional consultants such as attorneys, engineers, accountants, or financial advisors, a district must comply with the Professional Services Procurement Act, chapter 2254, subchapter A, of the Texas Government Code. *See* Tex. Water Code § 49.057(d). That act provides that professional consultants may not be hired based on competitive bids; they must be hired based on "demonstrated competence and qualifications" and "for a fair and reasonable price." Tex. Gov't Code § 2254.003(a).

The board of a district must establish a fiscal year for the district and adopt an annual budget. *See* Tex. Water Code §§ 49.057(b), 49.158. The board may change the fiscal year, but not more than once in any two-year period. *See* Tex. Water Code § 49.158. The board must designate one or more banks to serve as the depository for district funds; any funds that are not insured by the Federal Deposit Insurance Corporation must be secured as provided by the Public Funds Collateral Act, chapter 2257 of the Government Code. *See* Tex. Water Code § 49.156(a), (b). Investment of district funds must comply with the Public Funds Investment Act, chapter 2256 of the Government Code. *See* Tex. Water Code § 49.157(a).

§ 8.11 Sources of District Revenues

Districts may receive revenue from a variety of sources to pay for and finance district facilities and services. Districts may levy ad valorem taxes, components of which may include operation and maintenance taxes, debt service taxes, and contract taxes. Districts also have broad authority to impose fees and charges, including fees for services such as water and sewer service, impact fees, and standby fees.

§ 8.11:1 Operation and Maintenance Tax

If authorized by the voters, a district may levy an ad valorem tax to cover expenses associated with administration of the district and operation and maintenance of its facilities. *See* Tex. Water Code § 49.107(a), (b). The election to authorize an operation and maintenance tax may be held at the same time as any election held by the district and is generally held at the same time as the confirmation election. *See* Tex. Water Code § 49.107(c). The election may authorize a tax "for a specific maximum rate or for an unlimited rate." Tex. Water Code § 49.107(d). A district located in one of the counties listed in article XVI, section 59(c–1), of the Texas Constitution may levy a maintenance tax for parks and recreational facilities. If the district is located in Harris County or an adjacent county, a maintenance tax levied for that purpose may not exceed ten cents per $100 assessed valuation. *See* Tex. Water Code § 49.107(h).

All ad valorem taxes, including operation and maintenance taxes, levied by districts are subject to the "truth in taxation" provisions of sections 49.236 through 49.23603 of the Texas Water Code, which requires the board to publish notice and hold a public hearing before establishing the district's tax rate. Under certain circumstances, if a board approves a tax rate that exceeds certain limits, the voters may petition the district to hold an election to roll back a portion of the operation and maintenance tax. *See* Act of May 27, 2019, 86th Leg., R.S., ch 944, § 89 (S.B. 2), eff. Jan. 1, 2020 (adding Tex. Water Code § 49.23603). Under other circumstances, if a board approves a tax rate that exceeds certain limits, an automatic election to approve the tax rate is triggered. *See* Act of May 27, 2019, 86th Leg., R.S., ch. 944, § 89 (S.B. 2), eff. Jan. 1, 2020 (adding Tex. Water Code §§ 49.23601, 49.23602). Only the operation and maintenance tax portion of the total tax may be decreased as a result of an election; an election does not affect taxes required to pay the debt service on bonds or to pay contractual obligations. *See* Tex. Water Code §§ 49.236–.23603.

§ 8.11:2 Debt Service Tax

For certain types of water districts (such as municipal utility districts, water control and improvement districts, fresh water supply districts, and levee improvement districts), most bonds issued are payable in whole or in part from ad valorem taxes. The individual chapters of the Texas Water Code pertaining to each type of district provide authority to issue bonds and to levy a debt service tax to pay unlimited tax bonds.

Section 54.601 of the Water Code provides that "[a]t the time bonds payable in whole or in part from taxes are issued," the board of directors of a municipal utility district shall levy "a continuing direct annual ad valorem tax for each year while all or part of the bonds are outstanding on all taxable property within the district in sufficient amount to pay" the interest on and the principal of the bonds. *See* Tex. Water Code § 54.601. Section 54.602 of the Water Code prescribes the method of determining the tax rate to be levied in each year. *See* Tex. Water Code § 54.602. There are similar statutory provisions for water control and improvement districts (*see* Tex. Water Code § 51.433), fresh water supply districts (*see* Tex. Water Code § 53.188), and levee improvement districts (*see* Tex. Water Code § 57.251).

§ 8.11:3 Contract Tax

A district may enter into a contract that requires the district to make payments from any income of the district, including bond or note proceeds or taxes. *See* Tex. Water Code § 49.108(a). A contract that requires a district to make payments from taxes must be approved by the district's voters, although the contract may authorize the board to later amend the contract without further voter approval. *See* Tex. Water Code § 49.108(b). With certain exceptions, if a district is required to obtain the TCEQ's approval of its bonds under section 49.181 of the Texas Water Code, the district must also obtain the approval of the TCEQ's executive director before entering into a contract tax obligation that is longer than three years. *See* Tex. Water Code § 49.108(e); *see also* 30 Tex. Admin. Code § 293.89 (requirements for approval of contract tax). The TCEQ's rules are designed to ensure that a district has the financial means to fulfill a contract tax obligation. As with other types of district taxes, a district board must follow the procedures in section 49.236 of the Water Code before setting a contract tax rate. *See* Tex. Water Code § 49.236.

§ 8.11:4 Rates and Fees

Under section 49.212 of the Texas Water Code, districts have broad authority to establish and enforce fees and charges for district facilities and services. To enforce the payment of fees and charges as well as taxes that have been unpaid for more than six months, a district may discontinue any facility or service. *See* Tex. Water Code § 49.212(c); *see also* Tex. Water Code §§ 49.351(j) (allowing a district to discontinue any service to enforce payment of fire services fee), 49.464(c) (providing that a district may not refuse the use of any facility or service other than recreational facilities to enforce payment of fees for recreational facilities). The customers of a district that provides water or sewer service to household users may appeal a board decision affecting water, sewer, or drainage rates to the Public Utility Commission of Texas. *See* Tex. Water Code § 13.043(b)(4), (c)–(e).

Districts may levy impact fees as provided by chapter 395 of the Texas Local Government Code. *See* Tex. Water Code § 49.212(d). An impact fee is a charge "against new development in order to generate revenue for funding or recouping the costs of capital improvements or facility expansions necessitated by and attributable to the new development." Tex. Loc. Gov't Code § 395.001(4). In lieu of following the procedural requirements in chapter 395 for adopting impact fees, a district may obtain the TCEQ's approval. *See* Tex. Loc. Gov't Code § 395.080; *see also* 30 Tex. Admin. Code ch. 293, Subch. N (approval of impact fees). Section 49.212(d) provides that certain charges and fees are not considered impact fees and can be imposed without following the procedural requirements of chapter 395. *See* Tex. Water Code § 49.212(d).

Districts that propose to or actually do provide retail water or sewer or drainage services may charge standby fees as provided by section 49.231 of the Water Code. A standby fee is "a charge, other than a tax, imposed on undeveloped property for the availability of potable water, sanitary sewer, or drainage facilities and services." Tex. Water Code § 49.231(a)(1). A standby fee may be charged to recoup debt service or operation and maintenance costs for facilities made available to but not used by undeveloped property. *See* Tex. Water Code § 49.231(b). A district must obtain TCEQ approval to impose standby fees. *See* Tex. Water Code § 49.231(c); *see also* 30 Tex. Admin. Code ch. 293, subch. M (approval of standby fees); *McMillan v. Texas Natural Resources Conservation Commission*, 983 S.W.2d 359 (Tex. App.—Austin 1998, pet. denied) (interpreting the standby fee statute and rules).

Certain property owned by electric and gas utilities, carbon dioxide pipelines, and telecommunications and cable providers is exempt from district impact fees and standby fees. *See* Tex. Water Code § 49.212(f)–(i).

§ 8.12 Issuance of Bonds and Other Obligations

Districts are authorized to issue bonds, bond anticipation notes, tax anticipation notes, and revenue notes to finance district improvements. Water district bonds may be issued as revenue bonds but are most often issued as unlimited tax (or general obligation) bonds. Water district bonds are typically tax-exempt.

§ 8.12:1 Bonds

The individual chapters of the Texas Water Code pertaining to each type of district provide authority to issue bonds. Bond authority varies by type of district. *See, e.g.*, Tex. Water Code §§ 51.401, 51.402 (authority of water control and improvement districts to issue bonds), 53.171 (authority of fresh water supply districts to issue bonds), 54.501 (authority of municipal utility districts to issue bonds), 57.201 (authority of levee improvement districts to issue bonds).

With certain exceptions, districts are required to obtain TCEQ approval to issue bonds. *See* Tex. Water Code §§ 49.181–.182; *see also* Tex. Water Code § 49.181(a) (TCEQ approval is not required for refunding bonds or for bonds issued to and approved by certain entities), (h) (listing districts not required to obtain TCEQ approval of bonds). Under current TCEQ rules, TCEQ approval is not required for bonds issued for road purposes. However, TCEQ approval is currently required for bonds issued for the purpose of providing water, wastewater, and drainage facilities and services as well as parks and recreational facilities. The TCEQ has developed detailed rules designed to ensure that district bonds are financially feasible and are used only to finance district projects. *See* 30 Tex. Admin. Code ch. 293, subchs. E–G.

Except for refunding bonds or bonds sold to certain entities, a district must sell its bonds through competitive sealed bids; notice of the sale must be published in a newspaper of general circulation in the county where the district is located and also in a financial publication. *See* Tex. Water Code § 49.183(a), (b).

Even if TCEQ approval is not required, all district bonds must be approved by the Texas attorney general. *See* Tex. Water Code § 49.184; Tex. Gov't Code § 1202.003 (requiring attorney general review and approval of all public securities); *see also* 1 Tex. Admin. Code ch. 53, subchs. A, F (rules for attorney general approval of district bonds). Over the years, the attorney general has issued a number of "All Bond Counsel Letters," reflecting the attorney general's position on bond-related issues. These letters may be viewed at the Texas attorney general website, www.texasattorneygeneral.gov/public-finance/all-bond-counsel-letters. After bonds are approved by the attorney general, they are registered by the comptroller and are "incontestable in any court or other forum, for any reason." *See* Tex. Water Code § 49.184(d); *see also* Tex. Gov't Code § 1202.006.

§ 8.12:2 Bond Anticipation and Tax Anticipation Notes

A district may issue bond anticipation notes and tax anticipation notes with a term of not more than one year in anticipation of receiving bond proceeds or tax revenues. *See* Tex. Water Code § 49.154. If a district is required to obtain TCEQ approval of its bonds, it must have a bond application on file with the commission before issuing a bond anticipation note. Tex. Water Code § 49.154(d); *see also* 30 Tex. Admin. Code § 293.54 (requirements for approval of bond anticipation notes; limitation on use of proceeds).

§ 8.12:3 Revenue Notes

Unlike debt payable from taxes, a district may issue notes payable from system revenues without first holding an election. *See* Tex. Water Code § 49.153(a). Such notes may not place a lien on district property or taxes. *See* Tex. Water Code § 49.153(b). With certain exceptions, a district must obtain TCEQ approval before issuing a revenue note with a term of more than three years. *See* Tex. Water Code § 49.153(c), (d) (providing that section 49.153 does not apply to special water authorities), (e) (listing exceptions to the requirement to obtain TCEQ approval); *see also* 30 Tex. Admin. Code § 293.80 (detailing TCEQ rules for the approval of revenue notes).

§ 8.13 Financial Oversight

Unless its financial activity falls below certain thresholds, a district is required to have an independent annual audit of its finances. *See* Tex. Water Code § 49.191; *see also* Tex. Water Code §§ 49.198 (listing criteria under which a district may prepare an annual financial report instead of an audit), 49.197 (giving exemptions for financially dormant districts); 30 Tex. Admin. Code § 293.94 (describing TCEQ rules regarding annual financial reporting requirements); Texas Commission on Environmental Quality, *Water District Financial Management Guide* (RG-080, Mar. 2004), www.tceq.texas.gov/publications. For most districts, the audit must be submitted to the TCEQ executive director within 135 days after the district's fiscal year ends. *See* Tex. Water Code §§ 49.191(d), 49.194(a), (h) (requiring special water authorities to submit audit within 160 days after fiscal year ends).

If a district meets the criteria to prepare a financial report instead of an audit, it must file the financial report with the TCEQ executive director within forty-five days after the district's fiscal year ends. *See* Tex. Water Code § 49.198(c). If a district meets the criteria for financial dormancy, it must file a financial dormancy affidavit with the TCEQ executive director by January 31 of each year as long as the district is financially dormant. *See* Tex. Water Code § 49.197(d). A district must make all of its fiscal records available to the public. *See* Tex. Water Code § 49.196(b).

The Texas Comptroller of Public Accounts maintains a "Special Purpose District Public Information Database" on its website. *See* Texas Comptroller of Public Accounts, *Special Purpose*

District Public Information Database, https://spdpid.comptroller.texas.gov/. Section 403.0241 of the Texas Government Code, as amended in 2019, requires certain special purpose districts, including certain water districts, to annually provide certain financial and operating information to the comptroller for inclusion in the database. *See* Act of May 25, 2019, 86th Leg., R.S., ch. 868, § 1 (H.B. 3001), eff. Sept. 1, 2019 (amending Tex. Gov't Code § 403.0241).

§ 8.14 Notice to Purchasers

Under section 49.455 of the Texas Water Code, certain districts that meet the criteria set out in section 49.452 are required to file in the county deed records and with the TCEQ information concerning the district in a prescribed form. *See* Tex. Water Code § 49.455(a), (j). The information that must be filed includes the name of the district, a map and boundary description of the district, the district's tax rate, the amount of bonds authorized and issued, the amount of any standby fee imposed by the district, the date of the district's confirmation election, the functions of the district, and a notice to purchasers in the form required by section 49.452. *See* Tex. Water Code § 49.455(b). The district is also required to make the notice to purchasers available in its office. *See* Tex. Water Code § 49.453. Under section 49.452, anyone who proposes to sell property in a district subject to that section must first give the notice obtained from the district to the purchaser. *See* Tex. Water Code § 49.452. The purpose of these sections is to ensure that buyers are aware that they are purchasing property in a district and the potential impact of the district on their property.

§ 8.15 General Powers

In addition to those discussed below, a number of general powers are granted to districts under chapter 49 of the Texas Water Code. *See, e.g.*, Tex. Water Code §§ 49.004 (authority to establish civil penalties for breach of district rules), 49.211(b) (purchase of land, facilities, and equipment), 49.213 (contracting authority), 49.218 (acquisition of property), 49.220 (use of rights-of-way), 49.225 (leases), 49.226 (sale or exchange or property), 49.234 (authority to prohibit septic tanks).

§ 8.15:1 Solid Waste

Section 49.213(c)(6) of the Texas Water Code authorizes districts to contract for municipal solid waste services. *See* Tex. Water Code § 49.213(c)(6); *see also* Tex. Water Code § 54.203 (authority of municipal utility districts to provide solid waste services). Some districts contract for trash collection and bill customers for this service along with other district services.

§ 8.15:2 Peace Officers

Under section 49.216 of the Texas Water Code, districts may contract for or hire their own peace officers, who have the authority to make arrests for offenses related to district property or any offense under state law. *See* Tex. Water Code § 49.216(a). Some districts contract with the county or a nearby city to provide extra patrol services in the district.

§ 8.15:3 Eminent Domain

A district may condemn land or easements within or outside its boundaries "necessary for water, sanitary sewer, storm drainage, or flood drainage or control purposes or for any other of its projects or purposes, and may elect to condemn either the fee simple title or a lesser property interest." Tex. Water Code § 49.222(a); *but see* Tex. Water Code § 54.209 (limiting authority of municipal utility districts to condemn outside their boundaries). The procedures in chapter 21 of the Texas Property Code generally apply to district condemnations. *See* Tex. Water Code § 49.222(b). A district may not condemn land to obtain "rights to underground water or of water or water rights." Tex. Water Code § 49.222(c).

If a district, through the exercise of eminent domain or other powers, makes necessary the relocation of roads, railroads, electric or telephone lines, or pipelines, section 49.223 of the Texas Water Code requires that the relocation be done at the sole expense of the district. *See Southwestern Bell Telephone, L.P. v. Emmett*, 459 S.W.3d 578 (Tex. 2015) (interpreting when a district's action "makes necessary" a relocation).

§ 8.15:4 Water Rights

Although a district may not acquire water rights by condemnation, section 49.2261(1) of the Texas Water Code gives districts broad authority to "purchase, acquire, sell, transfer, lease, or otherwise exchange water or water rights under an agreement between the district and a person or entity that contains terms that are considered advantageous to the district." Tex. Water Code § 49.2261(1).

§ 8.15:5 Annexation and Exclusion of Land

Districts may annex land into or exclude land from their boundaries as provided in chapter 49, subchapter J, of the Texas Water Code. Other chapters of the Water Code authorize particular types of districts to annex or exclude land under certain conditions. *See, e.g.*, Tex. Water Code § 54.739 (municipal utility districts). Districts do not have the power to unilaterally annex land; they may annex land only upon petition by the landowner. *See* Tex. Water Code §§ 49.301, 49.302. If the land proposed for annexation by the district is located in the extraterritorial jurisdiction of a city (or, for some types of districts like municipal utility districts, in the corporate limits of a city), the city must consent to its being annexed into the district. *See* Tex. Loc. Gov't Code § 42.0425; *see also* Tex. Water Code § 54.016 (inclusion of land in municipal utility district).

A district board may call a hearing on the exclusion of land either on its own motion or if petitioned by a landowner. *See* Tex. Water Code §§ 49.303(b), (c), 49.306 (grounds for exclusion); *see also* Tex. Water Code § 49.3075 (exclusion of certain land not served by district upon petition of landowner). To prevent impairing the security of district bonds, a district generally may exclude land only if it does not have any bonds payable from taxes outstanding. *See* Tex. Water Code §§ 49.303(a), 49.3075(a); *but see* Tex. Water Code §§ 49.3076, 49.3077 (excluding land from certain districts), 49.309, 49.314 (excluding nonirrigated land). Further, if a district has already held an election to approve bonds, the district may not rely on that election if property is excluded from the district. *See* Tex. Water Code § 49.303(d). In such instances, a new bond election is required.

A municipal utility district is authorized to substitute land of equal value after it has obtained voter approval for the issuance of bonds or has sold bonds, without requiring a new bond election or impairing the security of already issued bonds. *See* Tex. Water Code §§ 54.739–.747.

§ 8.15:6 Fire Departments

Section 49.351 of the Texas Water Code allows a district that provides potable water or sewer services or facilities to household customers to provide firefighting services. "Firefighting services" is defined as "all of the customary and usual services of a fire department, including fire suppression, fire prevention, training, safety education, maintenance, communications, medical emergency services, photography, and administration." Tex. Water Code § 49.351(k). A district may provide its own fire department, may contract with other districts to operate a joint fire department, or may contract with an existing department to provide firefighting services in the district. *See* Tex. Water Code § 49.351(a), (d), (e). Most districts that provide firefighting services do so through a contract. A district may levy taxes, issue bonds, or charge residents a fee to fund firefighting services. *See* Tex. Water Code § 49.351(a).

Before a district "imposes an ad valorem tax or issues bonds payable wholly or partly from ad valorem taxes to finance the establishment of a fire department, contracts to operate a joint fire department, or contracts with another person to perform firefighting services," it must have a detailed plan prepared and approved by its board of directors, obtain TCEQ approval of the plan, and then hold an election to allow voters in the district to approve or disapprove the plan. Tex. Water Code § 49.351(g)–(i); *see also* 30 Tex. Admin. Code ch. 293, subch. K (TCEQ approval of fire plans and bonds). For districts created by the TCEQ, a fire plan may also be submitted for approval as part of a creation application. *See* Tex. Water Code § 49.351(g); *see, e.g.*, 30 Tex. Admin. Code § 293.11(c)(8) (creation requirements for water control and improvement district), (d)(10) (municipal utility district), (e)(6) (water improvement district), (h)(12) (special utility district).

Additionally, a district may collect from its customers a voluntary contribution on behalf of organizations providing firefighting services to the district. Water and sewer service may not be terminated for failure to pay a voluntary contribution. *See* Tex. Water Code § 49.351(l).

§ 8.15:7 Recreational Facilities

In addition to other services, districts may finance, develop, and maintain recreational facilities, defined as "parks, landscaping, parkways, greenbelts, sidewalks, trails, public right-of-way beautification projects, and recreational equipment and facilities. The term includes associated street and security lighting." Tex. Water Code § 49.462(1). A district may develop recreational facilities on a site also used for utility facilities. *See* Tex. Water Code § 49.463. A district may charge fees to pay for recreational facilities. *See* Tex. Water Code § 49.464(b), (c). Districts in most counties are prohibited from using tax funds to finance recreational facilities, although they may issue revenue bonds. *See* Tex. Water Code § 49.464(d).

Pursuant to the 2003 constitutional change discussed at section 8.5 above, districts in certain counties (Bexar, Bastrop, Waller, Travis, Williamson, Harris, Galveston, Brazoria, Fort Bend, and Montgomery) may, upon voter approval, issue bonds payable from taxes or levy an operation and maintenance tax to finance recreational facilities. Section 49.4645 of the Texas Water Code limits the amount and uses of such bonds. *See* Tex. Water Code § 49.4645; *see also* 30 Tex. Admin. Code § 293.41(e).

§ 8.16 Contracts and Competitive Bidding

Chapter 49, subchapter I, of the Texas Water Code establishes requirements and procedures for district construction contracts. In particular, competitive bidding requirements apply to contracts "for construction and repair and renovation of district facilities and for the purchase of equipment, materials, machinery, and all things that constitute or will constitute the plant, works, facilities, or improvements of the district." Tex. Water Code § 49.273(a). For contracts greater than $75,000, the district must advertise for bids. Contracts for more than $25,000 up to $75,000 must be let on the basis of at least three solicited written bids. Bids are not required for contracts up to $25,000. *See* Tex. Water Code § 49.273(d)–(f). Certain types of contracts are also excepted from the bidding requirements. *See* Tex. Water Code §§ 49.273(j) (exception for certain repair work), 49.274 (emergency projects), 49.278. District contractors must provide performance and payment bonds as required by chapter 2253 of the Texas Government Code. *See* Tex. Water Code § 49.275. The TCEQ has also adopted rules regarding district contracts. *See* 30 Tex. Admin. Code §§ 293.63, 293.64.

§ 8.17 Dissolution

Under chapter 49, subchapter K, of the Texas Water Code, the TCEQ may dissolve a district that has been inactive for five years and has no bonds outstanding. The TCEQ must give notice and hold a hearing regarding a proposed dissolution, unless the board of directors of the district or the owners of a majority in value of the land in the district execute the petition for dissolution. *See* Tex. Water Code §§ 49.322, 49.3225, 49.324; *see also* 30 Tex. Admin. Code ch. 293, subch. L (commission procedure for dissolution of district). Upon dissolution of a district, its assets escheat to the state and are disposed of by the comptroller as provided in chapter 74 of the Texas Property Code. *See* Tex. Water Code § 49.327. Other chapters of the Water Code may allow for the dissolution of particular types of districts under certain circumstances. *See, e.g.*, Tex. Water Code §§ 54.734 (municipal utility districts), 57.3295 (dissolution of certain levee improvement districts by the commissioners court of a county).

Section 49.3225(e) of the Water Code prohibits the dissolution of a district under any provision of law if the district (1) has bonds outstanding, (2) has a contractual obligation to pay money, or (3) owns, operates, or maintains public works, facilities, or improvements. *See* Act of May 24, 2019, 86th Leg., R.S., ch. 539, § 1 (H.B. 2914), eff. Sept. 1, 2019 (adding Tex. Water Code § 49.3225).

§ 8.18 Specific Types of Districts

Although chapter 49 of the Texas Water Code sets out administrative provisions applicable to most types of districts, to understand fully the workings of a particular district it is always necessary to review the history of that district, the specific chapter of the Water Code under which the district operates, and, if the district is a special law district, the creation legislation and any amendments. In addition, legislation may be enacted that alters the powers and duties of a previously created general law district. Finally, if a district has been converted to a different type of district under one of the provisions discussed below, its name may not reflect its actual powers. Basic information regarding existing districts is available through the TCEQ's Water District Database, www.tceq.texas.gov/waterdistricts/iwdd.html.

IV. Water Control and Improvement Districts (Texas Water Code Chapter 51)

§ 8.19 Specific Powers

A water control and improvement district (WCID) has the basic powers provided in Texas Water Code section 51.121. *See* Tex. Water Code § 51.121. Those powers vary somewhat depending on the provision of the Texas Constitution under which the district was created but in essence encompass water and irrigation services. A WCID may also obtain the power to provide sewer and drainage services through application to the TCEQ. *See* Tex. Water Code §§ 51.331–.334; 30 Tex. Admin. Code § 293.15.

§ 8.20 Creation Process

A WCID may be created either by the applicable county commissioners court or by the TCEQ.

§ 8.20:1 Creation by a County

After notice and a hearing, the county commissioners court may create a WCID located in that county only. *See* Tex. Water Code §§ 51.016–.021. The creation process is initiated by a petition filed by a majority of the persons owning land that represents more than a majority in value of the land in the proposed district. If there are more than fifty landowners in the proposed district, the petition may be signed by fifty landowners. *See* Tex. Water Code § 51.013(a). Section 51.014 of the Texas Water Code sets out the required contents of the petition, which include the provision of the Texas Constitution under which the district is proposed to be created. *See* Tex. Water Code § 51.014; *see also* Tex. Water Code § 51.011 (WCID may be created under either article III, section 52, or article XVI, section 59). Under section 42.042 of the Texas Local Government Code, city consent to the creation must be obtained if some or all of the proposed district is located in a city's extraterritorial jurisdiction. *See* Tex. Loc. Gov't Code § 42.042. If the commissioners court approves the creation, it must appoint five temporary directors who will serve until the election required under section 49.102 of the Water Code. *See* Tex. Water Code § 51.026; *see also* section 8.8 above.

§ 8.20:2 Creation by the Texas Commission on Environmental Quality

The TCEQ has exclusive jurisdiction to create WCIDs that are located in two or more counties. *See* Tex. Water Code § 51.027. The petition requirements are the same as for a WCID created by a county. The TCEQ is required to give notice of an application to create a WCID, but it is required to hold a hearing only if it determines to do so under section 49.011 of the Texas Water Code. *See* Tex. Water Code § 51.028; *see also* 30 Tex. Admin. Code §§ 293.11(c) (TCEQ requirements for application to create WCID), 293.12 (notice procedures).

The TCEQ also has jurisdiction under section 51.333 of the Water Code to create a WCID that will be located in one county if it is proposed to have the power to provide sewer and drainage services.

§ 8.21 Conversion

Upon notice and a hearing, another type of district may be converted to a WCID through action of the district's board of directors. *See* Tex. Water Code §§ 51.040–.044.

§ 8.22 Division

Through an election, a WCID that does not have any outstanding debt may be divided one time into two or more separate districts. *See* Tex. Water Code §§ 51.748–.753. The resulting districts have the same powers as any other WCID. *See* Tex. Water Code § 51.752.

Chapter 51A of the Texas Water Code applies to a specific subset of WCIDs, those that contain at least 10,000 acres. Chapter 51A provides for the creation and exclusion of subdistricts from such WCIDs.

§ 8.23 Governing Body

A WCID is governed by a five-member board of directors. *See* Tex. Water Code § 51.071. To serve on the board, a person must be a Texas resident, "own land subject to taxation in the district or be a qualified voter in the district," and be eighteen or older. Tex. Water Code § 51.072.

V. Fresh Water Supply Districts (Texas Water Code Chapter 53)

§ 8.24 Specific Powers

A fresh water supply district (FWSD) may be created to conserve, transport, and distribute freshwater from any sources for domestic and commercial purposes. *See* Tex. Water Code § 53.101. Through an election, a FWSD may obtain the power to provide sewer service. *See* Tex. Water Code § 53.121. A FWSD located in a county that meets certain population criteria may hold an election to assume the powers of a county road district operating under chapter 257 of the Texas Transportation Code. Currently, this provision applies to districts located in Bexar, Dallas, and Harris counties or counties adjacent to them. *See* Tex. Water Code § 53.029(c)–(e). Under Texas Water Code chapter 53, FWSDs have no means to obtain the power to provide general drainage services, but the attorney general has allowed FWSDs that assume road district powers to provide drainage facilities necessary to serve the roads.

§ 8.25 Creation Process

A FWSD may be created only by the applicable county commissioners court. *See* Tex. Water Code § 53.061. The creation process begins with the presentation of a petition. *See* Tex. Water Code § 53.013. The petition must include the information described in section 53.014 of the Texas Water Code and must "be signed by a majority of the persons who hold title to land in the proposed district that represents a total value of more than 50 percent of the value of all the land in the proposed district." Tex. Water Code § 53.014(1). As with other types of districts, city consent is required under section 42.042 of the Texas Local Government Code if a FWSD is proposed to be created in the extraterritorial jurisdiction of a city. If the commissioners court approves the creation after holding a public hearing pursuant to Water Code section 53.016, it must appoint five temporary supervisors to serve on the district's board until a confirmation election is held under section 49.102 of the Water Code. *See* Tex. Water Code § 53.020(a).

§ 8.26 Division

A FWSD that has no outstanding bonds, is not levying taxes, and is located in a county that meets certain population criteria may, upon election, be divided into two separate districts. *See* Tex. Water Code § 53.029(b); *see also* Tex. Water Code §§ 53.030–.043 (division procedures). Currently, this provision applies to districts located in Bexar, Dallas, and Harris counties or counties adjacent to them.

§ 8.27 Governing Body

A FWSD is governed by a five-member board of elected supervisors. *See* Tex. Water Code § 53.062. Except for FWSDs located in Denton County, to serve on a FWSD board a person must be a registered voter of the district or be a Texas resident, own property subject to taxation in the district, and be eighteen years old or older. *See* Tex. Water Code § 53.063(a). To be a supervisor for a FWSD located in whole or in part in Denton County, a person must be registered to vote in the district. *See* Tex. Water Code § 53.063(b).

VI. Municipal Utility Districts (Texas Water Code Chapter 54)

§ 8.28 Specific Powers

Municipal utility districts (MUDs) are the most common type of district in Texas, and the Texas Water Code grants them a wide variety of powers. Under section 54.201 of the Water Code, MUDs may provide water, sewer, and drainage services and facilities. *See* Tex. Water Code § 54.201. Through application to the TCEQ, either as part of a creation application or later, a MUD may acquire the power under article III, section 52, of the Texas Constitution, to design, construct, and finance roads or improvements in aid of roads. *See* Tex. Water Code § 54.234; 30 Tex. Admin. Code ch. 293, subch. P. A MUD may also provide street or security lighting within the district, although it may not issue bonds payable from taxes for that purpose unless the district is able to issue park bonds for such facilities or has obtained road powers. *See* Tex. Water Code § 54.236. A MUD that has been in existence for at least ten years may repair and maintain streets in the district and may issue bonds for that purpose, if authorized by the voters. *See* Tex. Water Code §§ 54.242, 54.522.

§ 8.29 Creation Process

A MUD may be created only by the TCEQ. Creation of a MUD is initiated by a petition that must be signed by the majority in value of landowners in the proposed district as required by section 54.014 of the Texas Water Code and that includes the information listed in section 54.015 of the Water Code. *See* Tex. Water Code § 54.015; *see also* 30 Tex. Admin. Code § 293.11(d) (TCEQ requirements for MUD creation application). If the district is proposed to be located within the corporate limits or extraterritorial jurisdiction of a city, the city must consent to the creation. *See* Tex. Water Code § 54.016; *see also* Tex. Loc. Gov't Code § 42.042. If the district is proposed to be located outside the corporate limits of a city, the county commissioners court may review the proposed creation and submit information to the TCEQ, which the TCEQ must consider. *See* Tex. Water Code § 54.0161. The TCEQ must give notice of a proposed MUD creation and may hold a hearing as provided by section 49.011 of the Water Code. *See* Tex. Water Code §§ 54.018, 54.020; *see also* 30 Tex. Admin. Code § 293.12 (notice procedures). If the TCEQ approves the creation under the criteria in section 54.021, it must appoint five temporary directors to serve on the board until the confirmation election is held under section 49.102. *See* Tex. Water Code § 54.022.

§ 8.30 Conversion

Any district created pursuant to article XVI, section 59, of the Texas Constitution may be converted to a MUD through application to the TCEQ. *See* Tex. Water Code §§ 54.030–.036; 30 Tex. Admin. Code § 293.15 (TCEQ application requirements for conversion). The board of directors of a district must give notice and hold a hearing before submitting an application to the TCEQ for conversion of the district to a MUD. *See* Act of May 27, 2019, 86th Leg., R.S., ch. 539, § 5 (H.B. 2914), eff. Sept. 1, 2019 (amending Tex. Water Code § 54.030).

§ 8.31 Governing Body

A MUD is governed by a five-member board of directors. To serve as a director, a person must be a Texas resident, be at least eighteen years old, and either own taxable land in the district or be a qualified voter in the district. *See* Tex. Water Code §§ 54.101, 54.102; *see also* Tex. Water Code § 54.103 (prohibiting certain persons from being appointed to fill vacancies on a MUD board).

VII. Drainage Districts (Texas Water Code Chapter 56)

§ 8.32 Specific Powers

A drainage district may construct and maintain "canals, drains, ditches and levees, and other improvements of the district" and may make changes and additions to the system as needed. *See* Tex. Water Code §§ 56.111, 56.126.

§ 8.33 Creation Process

A drainage district may be created by the county commissioners court. *See* Tex. Water Code § 56.082. The process is initiated under section 56.014 of the Texas Water Code by a petition that must contain the listed information and be signed by at least twenty-five resident freehold taxpayers in the proposed district or by at least one-third of those taxpayers if there are fewer than seventy-five of them. *See* Tex. Water Code § 56.014. If the commissioners court makes the findings required by section 56.019 at a public hearing, it must appoint an engineer to prepare and present to the court a report concerning the drainage needs of the land in the district. *See* Tex. Water Code §§ 56.016–.026. The commissioners court must also appoint temporary directors to serve until the creation of the district is confirmed. *See* Tex. Water Code § 56.061(b).

As an alternative, a drainage district may be created through the election process set out in section 56.033 of the Water Code. *See* Tex. Water Code § 56.033.

§ 8.34 Governing Body

A drainage district is generally governed by a three-member board of directors. *See* Tex. Water Code § 56.061(a). To serve on the board, a person must meet the eligibility requirements for public office set out in section 141.001(a) of the Texas Election Code. *See* Tex. Water Code § 56.062. Under the procedures set out in section 56.069 of the Texas Water Code, the board's powers and functions may be transferred to the county commissioners court. *See* Tex. Water Code § 56.069.

VIII. Levee Improvement Districts (Texas Water Code Chapter 57)

§ 8.35 Specific Powers

Under section 57.091 of the Texas Water Code, a levee improvement district (LID) may provide all works and facilities necessary to serve the following purposes:

1. to construct and maintain levees and other improvements on, along, and contiguous to rivers, creeks, and streams;
2. to reclaim lands from overflow from these streams;
3. to control and distribute the waters of rivers and streams by straightening and otherwise improving them; and
4. to provide for the proper drainage and other improvement of the reclaimed land.

Tex. Water Code §§ 57.091–.092.

§ 8.36 Creation Process

A LID is created by the county commissioners court. *See* Tex. Water Code § 57.017(a). The process is initiated by a petition containing the information listed in section 57.012 of the Texas Water Code and signed by the landowners of a majority of the acreage in the proposed district. *See* Tex. Water Code § 57.012. The commissioners court must set a hearing between fifteen and thirty days after receiving the petition. In addition to posting notice of the hearing, notice must be provided to the TCEQ executive director, who must file a report with the court concerning the proposed district and also attend the hearing. *See* Tex. Water Code §§ 57.014–.017. If the court makes the findings set out in section 57.019, the LID is created. *See* Tex. Water Code § 57.019.

§ 8.37 Governing Body

After creating a LID, the county commissioners court must appoint three directors to serve on the board of directors. In a district with a population of 2,000 or more, the commissioners court may increase the total number of directors to five. The court appoints directors to fill vacancies on the board, and it may remove directors. *See* Tex. Water Code §§ 57.051, 57.053. Alternatively, voters in the district may petition the board to hold an election to determine whether directors should be elected rather than appointed. *See* Tex. Water Code §§ 57.057, 57.060, 57.061. If directors are elected, the board consists of five members who must be "qualified property taxpaying elector[s]." *See* Tex. Water Code §§ 57.058–.059. A vacancy on an elected board is filled by appointment of the board. *See* Tex. Water Code § 57.053.

IX. Irrigation Districts (Texas Water Code Chapter 58)

§ 8.38 Specific Powers

Irrigation districts serve the limited purpose of providing untreated water for irrigation and drainage services. Irrigation districts are specifically prohibited from providing treated water, sewer services, or "other similar municipal services." *See* Tex. Water Code § 58.121.

§ 8.39 Creation Process

An irrigation district may be created either by the applicable county commissioners court or by the TCEQ. In either case, the creation process begins with a petition signed by a majority of the persons owning land that represents more than a majority of the property by value in the proposed district (or fifty landowners if there are more than fifty), as required by section 58.013 of the Texas Water Code; the petition must contain the information described in Code section 58.014. *See* Tex. Water Code §§ 58.013–.014. If the proposed district is in the extraterritorial jurisdiction of a city, consent is required under section 42.042 of the Texas Local Government Code.

§ 8.39:1 County

After notice and a hearing, the county commissioners court has the authority to create an irrigation district located in one county. *See* Tex. Water Code §§ 58.017–.021. If the commissioners court approves the creation, it must appoint temporary directors to serve on the board. *See* Tex. Water Code § 58.026(a).

§ 8.39:2 Texas Commission on Environmental Quality

The TCEQ has the authority under section 58.027 of the Texas Water Code to create an irrigation district located in two or more counties. *See* Tex. Water Code § 58.027. The creation process is similar to the one for other types of districts created by the TCEQ. *See* Tex. Water Code §§ 58.028, 58.030; 30 Tex. Admin. Code §§ 293.11(f), 293.12.

§ 8.40 Governing Body

Section 58.071 of the Texas Water Code provides that an irrigation district is governed by a five-member board of directors. *See* Tex. Water Code § 58.071. To serve as a director, a person must be a Texas resident, be at least eighteen years old, own land in the district, and not owe any taxes or assessments to the district. *See* Tex. Water Code § 58.072. The disqualification provisions in section 49.052 of the Water Code, discussed at section 8.7:1 above, do not apply to irrigation district directors.

X. Other Types of General Law Districts

§ 8.41 Groundwater Conservation Districts

Groundwater conservation districts are created and operate under chapter 36 of the Texas Water Code. See Chapter 16 of this book for discussion of these districts.

§ 8.42 Water Improvement Districts

Under chapter 55 of the Texas Water Code, a water improvement district may be created by the county if located in one county or by the TCEQ if located in two or more counties. A water improvement district may provide irrigation and water services. *See* Tex. Water Code §§ 55.161, 55.163.

§ 8.43 Regional Districts

The TCEQ may create regional districts over land located in Harris County or an adjacent county. *See* Tex. Water Code §§ 59.001, 59.003. The creation process may be initiated by existing districts that will be included in the regional district, a landowner of at least two thousand contiguous acres, one or more county commissioners courts, or a city. *See* Tex. Water Code § 59.003(a). The general purposes of a regional district are to provide water, sewer, and drainage facilities and services, including on a wholesale basis. *See* Tex. Water Code § 59.004.

§ 8.44 Navigation Districts

Counties may create various types of navigation districts. These districts are governed by chapters 60–63 of the Texas Water Code. Further discussion is beyond the scope of this book.

§ 8.45 Special Utility Districts

The TCEQ creates special utility districts under chapter 65 of the Texas Water Code by converting nonprofit water supply corporations created and operating under chapter 67 of the Water Code. *See* 30 Tex. Admin. Code § 293.11(h) (application requirements for creation of special utility district). These districts are authorized to provide water, sewer, and drainage services under section 65.201 of the Water Code, but the majority provide water service only. *See* Tex. Water Code § 65.201. Unlike other types of districts, special utility districts may not levy taxes. *See* Tex. Water Code §§ 65.235 (stating that a special utility district may not levy maintenance tax), 65.503 (authorizing issuance of only revenue bonds).

§ 8.46 Stormwater Control Districts

The TCEQ creates stormwater control districts under chapter 66 of the Texas Water Code. *See* 30 Tex. Admin. Code § 293.11(i) (requirements for stormwater district creation application). As the name implies, the purpose of these districts is to provide facilities for the control of stormwater. *See* Tex. Water Code § 66.201.

XI. Special Law Districts

§ 8.47 Introduction

The Texas legislature has latitude to create districts to serve any of the purposes provided by the Texas Constitution. In recent legislative sessions, an increasing number of districts have been created through legislation. If the legislature is in session (regular sessions occur only in odd-numbered years), a creation through this process may be faster and less expensive than the TCEQ process and may provide a more desirable combination of powers for the district. As with any type of legislation, these creation bills must sometimes run a political gantlet to be passed, and sometimes they do not pass at all.

§ 8.48 Process

Legislation to create or amend the powers of a water district is a type of local or special law in that it does not have general applicability. Under article XVI, section 59(d), of the Texas Constitution, notice of the intent to introduce legislation creating a district or altering the powers or boundaries of an existing district must be published at least thirty days and not more than ninety days before the legislation is filed. Notice and a copy of the legislation must also be sent to the governor, who must in turn submit it to the TCEQ for preparation of a report on the legislation to the governor, the lieutenant governor, and the speaker of the house. A copy of proposed creation legislation must also be provided to the county and to any city with jurisdiction; city consent requirements under general law apply to the creation of special law districts. *See* Tex. Const. art. XVI, § 59(e). Once filed, special district legislation proceeds through the legislative process in the same manner as other legislation. Special district legislation is codified in the Texas Special District Local Laws Code. *See* Tex. Spec. Dist. Code § 1.001.

§ 8.49 Powers

As noted above, districts created by the legislature are not subject to the constraints of general law; they may have any purpose allowed by the constitution and often have a set of powers customized to fit their particular circumstances. The committees of the legislature with jurisdiction often recommend or require the use of standard language in bills that create new or amend existing water districts. In general, legislative committees recommend or require bills creating special law districts to conform to the general law; however, there are certain additional powers that are routinely included in such bills. For example, in recent legislative sessions, numerous municipal utility districts have been created with the addition of division powers (*see, e.g.*, Tex. Spec. Dist. Code §§ 8492.151–.157). Also, legislation is commonly pursued to give existing districts certain additional powers. For example, districts originally created without road powers often subsequently acquire road powers (*see, e.g.*, Tex. Spec. Dist. Code §§ 7993.053–.054) or districts acquire powers to designate defined areas (*see, e.g.*, Tex. Spec. Dist. Code § 7993.055).

River authorities, such as the Lower Colorado River Authority, and districts that function as regional service providers, such as the Upper Trinity Regional Water District and the North Texas Municipal Water District, are generally created through legislation. These entities usually encompass a larger geographic area and have powers tailored to the particular purposes they are intended to serve. The Texas Water Development Board has produced a map showing the location of river authorities. See Plate 5. The enabling legislation for many of these authorities has not yet been codified, so it is necessary to check the session laws or *Vernon's Water Auxiliary Pamphlet* to locate the creation legislation and any amendments. See Chapter 9 of this book regarding river authorities and regional water districts.

River authorities are perhaps the best-known special law districts. Although the general public may view "river authorities" as having extraordinary power and authority, in fact "[t]here is no general purpose definition of a 'river authority.'" 35 David B. Brooks, *Texas Practice Series: County and Special District Law* § 46.29 (2d ed. 2019). Although the Texas Water Code defines river authorities for specific statutory purposes not relevant to this discussion, it contains no general purpose definition. *See, e.g.*, Tex. Water Code §§ 26.0135, 30.003(4), 49.001. River authorities "are authorized under the same constitutional provision which authorizes the various types of water conservation districts." Brooks, at § 46.29.

The two existing subsidence districts, the Harris-Galveston Subsidence District and the Fort Bend Subsidence District, are also legislatively created and have been designated as "conservation and reclamation" districts under article XVI, section 59, of the Texas Constitution, effective September 1, 2005. *See* Tex. Spec. Dist. Code §§ 8801.002, 8834.002. Although these districts have some powers similar to groundwater conservation districts, they are no longer subject to chapter 36 of the Water Code, and the general law provisions in chapter 49 of the Water Code also do not apply to the subsidence districts. *See* Tex. Spec. Dist. Code §§ 8801.102, 8834.006. The primary purpose of the subsidence districts is to prevent subsidence. *See* Tex. Spec. Dist. Code §§ 8801.003, 8834.003. See also Chapter 16 of this book for a discussion of subsidence districts.

XII. Conclusion

§ 8.50 Conclusion

For a century, water districts have been created in Texas to provide various types of services to the public. Some districts serve only the area within their boundaries, while others provide wholesale and other services to large areas. Different types of districts may be created through different processes and have different powers and duties, although they generally have in common the administrative provisions in chapter 49 of the Texas Water Code. Whatever the type, districts occupy a unique position in the landscape of Texas government.

CHAPTER 9

River Authorities and Regional Water Districts

Lyn Clancy[1] and Emily Rogers[2]

I. Introduction

§ 9.1 Introduction

The legislature has long recognized that regional water problems are often best addressed by regional entities rather than by more localized districts. *See* Water District and River Authority Study Committee, 1 *Report to the 70th Texas Legislature* 3–4 (Dec. 1986), https://lrl.texas.gov/scanned/interim/69/w291r_1.pdf [hereinafter 70th Committee Report]. River authorities and other regional water districts have long played a vital role in water resources management across the state. They regularly take the lead in water planning, financing, and construction of water projects needed to meet the long-term needs of Texas for water supply, wastewater treatment, and flood control. They also perform many other needed functions such as water quality monitoring, septic tank regulation, operation of parks and recreation facilities, and policing water bodies to ensure public safety.

Regional water districts and river authorities are created by the legislature pursuant to the same constitutional provisions authorizing creation of other water districts. *See* Tex. Const. art. III, § 52; art. XVI, § 59. See Chapter 8 of this book for a discussion of water districts. The regional entities' unique importance to the state water supply is recognized primarily because their boundaries and service areas generally cover extended multicounty areas, often encompassing an entire river basin. The specific powers and duties established by their enabling acts can vary significantly, depending on their history and purpose. In other words, as creatures of statute, there is no "one-size-fits-all" definition or description of a "regional water district" or "river authority." River authorities are perhaps the best-known special law districts. Although the general public may view river authorities as having extraordinary power and authority, in fact "[t]here is no general purpose definition of a 'river authority.'" 35 David B. Brooks, *Texas Practice Series: County and Special District Law* § 46.29 (2d

---

1. Lyn Clancy is a Managing Associate General Counsel and Senior Water Policy Advisor with the Lower Colorado River Authority (LCRA). She has worked for LCRA since 2000, focusing on water rights, water supply, and river management. Lyn worked on environmental and utility litigation as an associate at Fulbright & Jaworski prior to joining the LCRA and as a briefing attorney for the Texas Supreme Court upon graduating from the University of Texas School of Law. Lyn has master's degrees in water chemistry and water resources management from the University of Wisconsin–Madison.

2. Emily Rogers is the managing partner at Bickerstaff Heath Delgado Acosta L.L.P. She joined Bickerstaff in 2000 after working as a staff attorney for the Texas Natural Resources Conservation Commission. Emily represents river authorities, water districts, cities, and others on water rights and water supply related issues. She received her BA in history from the University of Texas at Austin in 1992 and her MA in history from Southwest Texas State University in 1994. After graduate school, Emily attended the University of Houston Law Center, where she received her JD in 1997.

ed. 2018). Although the Texas Water Code defines river authorities for specific statutory purposes, it contains no general-purpose definition. *See, e.g.*, Tex. Water Code §§ 26.0135, 30.003(4), 49.001.

As summarized in part II below, the continuing study, analysis, and discussion of special law water districts with regional scope reflect the state's continued interest in regional management of surface water resources and oversight by the legislature and state agencies. The term "river authorities" has come to include most special law districts whose names include the term, as well as other types of regional water districts. This chapter focuses on the "certain districts and authorities" covered by 30 Texas Administrative Code chapter 292 and listed in section 292.1. With one addition, Titus County Fresh Water Supply District No. 1, the list is based on Senate Bill 2. See discussion at section 9.4 below. This chapter also provides citations to the enabling legislation of fourteen additional special law districts that have been deemed important in one or another of the various agency and legislative studies.

II. Oversight of Regional Water Districts and River Authorities

§ 9.2 Introduction

Similar to all water districts, as discussed in Chapter 8 of this book, regional water districts and river authorities as political subdivisions of the state are subject to Texas open government laws related to open meetings and public records, Tex. Gov't Code §§ 551.001(3)(H), 552.003(1)(A)(viii), and financial accountability requirements, Tex. Water Code §§ 49.191–49.200. Many are subject to continuing supervision and rate review by the Texas Commission on Environmental Quality (TCEQ). *See, e.g.*, Tex. Water Code §§ 11.036–.041, 12.013, 12.081, 13.043(b), 49.002; 30 Tex. Admin. Code ch. 291. These regional entities continue to be subject to periodic scrutiny by the Texas legislature in its efforts to ensure proper management of the state's water resources, particularly surface water.

§ 9.3 Legislative Oversight

The lack of uniformity among river authorities and regional water districts and a lack of formal legislative oversight have given rise to a series of legislative initiatives to study and, in some cases, more directly regulate authorities and districts.

In 1985, legislation was enacted that required nineteen specifically named river authorities to be reviewed by the Sunset Advisory Committee under the Sunset Act. Act of May 26, 1985, 69th Leg., R.S., ch. 238, §§ 3–4. Those entities were scheduled for review in 1991. Act of May 26, 1985, 69th Leg., R.S., ch. 238, § 4. That law provided that unless the board directors of a river authority were continued in office, their membership would expire and the governor would appoint a new board. Act of May 26, 1985, 69th Leg., R.S., ch. 238, § 4. Another bill required the state auditor to annually audit twenty-three specifically named "river authorities and certain districts." Act of May 26, 1985, 69th Leg., R.S., ch. 795, § 2.008. The bill also created a study committee "to study water districts and river authorities . . . to determine if their powers and duties are appropriate for management of the state's water resources." Act of May 26, 1985, 69th Leg., R.S., ch. 795, § 2.001.

In December 1986, the Water District and River Authority Study Committee issued its two-volume report to the 70th Legislature. *See* 70th Committee Report, https://lrl.texas.gov/scanned/interim/69/w291r_1.pdf (Vol. I); https://lrl.texas.gov/scanned/interim/69/w291r_2.pdf (Vol. II). Declaring that the "era of water development" had ended in Texas, the committee recommended a focus on water management, with a significant expansion of state regulatory authority. 70th Committee Report, Vol. I, at 9. The committee found that the existing water resource management structure should be changed to establish a "Texas Water Resources Management Oversight Committee" with supervisory authority over all districts and authorities. 70th Committee Report, Vol. 1, at 19. The report recommended repeal of the state audit and sunset requirements passed in 1985. 70th Committee Report, Vol. 1, at 20–22. That report also addressed many other issues still being debated today, such as water conservation, water planning, and groundwater management.

In 1989, the 1985 audit and sunset requirements for river authorities and districts were repealed. The bill also amended Texas Water Code section 12.081(a), under which the TCEQ had the continuing right of supervision over districts and authorities created under Texas Constitution article III, section 52, and article XVI, section 59. The amendment made clear that the provisions regarding districts also applied to river authorities, unless otherwise stated. *See* Act of May 10, 1989, 71st Leg., R.S., ch. 196.

Another evaluation of river authorities and selected districts occurred in 2000, this time by the Senate Interim Committee on Natural Resources. That committee was charged with reviewing "the missions and roles of all Texas river authorities, including their powers and duties, financing, fee structures, service areas, board composition, relationships with other river authorities, competition with private sector service providers, communities they serve, and roles in and contributions to the state's water plan." Senate Interim Committee on Natural Resources, *Interim Report to the 77th Legislature, Missions and Roles of Texas River Authorities* 9 (Nov. 2000), https://lrl.texas.gov/scanned/interim/76/n219r.pdf. Noting that the term "river authority" has no statutory definition, the committee studied the twenty river authorities that were covered by 30 Texas Administrative Code chapter 292 as well as an additional twenty select special law districts. The report to the Texas legislature identified a number of mechanisms for increased oversight but did not make any specific recommendations.

In 2001, as part of Senate Bill 2, the legislature created the Texas Water Advisory Council to, among other things, provide additional oversight of river authorities. Act of May 27, 2001, 77th Leg., R.S., ch. 966, art. 1 (adding Tex. Water Code ch. 9 (since repealed)). This council consisted of legislators, other state officials, and public members. Act of May 27, 2001, 77th Leg., R.S., ch. 966, § 1. The duties of the council included a periodic review of thirty districts and authorities named in the bill and required the entities to provide a variety of information, including a self-assessment and the results of a management audit. Act of May 27, 2001, 77th Leg., R.S., ch. 966, § 1. Over the next two years, the council received written reports and heard testimony from entities scheduled for review. Testimony was also encouraged from others, such as customers of the entities under review. The legislature repealed the review process in 2003 (Act of May 30, 2003, 78th Leg., R.S., ch. 1057, § 1), and the council was abolished in 2007 (Act of May 28, 2007, 80th Leg., R.S., ch. 1430, § 2.36).

The issue of river authority oversight was revisited again in 2007 as part of an interim study by the Senate Natural Resources Committee. The committee studied nineteen river authorities and select districts listed by the TCEQ during testimony. Senate Committee on Natural Resources, *Interim Report to the 81st Legislature, Texas River Authorities* (Mar. 2009), https://senate.texas.gov/cmtes/80/c580/c580.RiverAuthorityReport80.pdf [hereinafter 81st Interim Report]. The committee was charged with reviewing all state-created river authorities, "including the powers exercised by each authority and the advisability of subjecting these authorities to legislative review." 81st Interim Report, at 1. The committee was also charged with considering "options for ensuring adequate protection of public assets, improving transparency of operations, enhancing appropriate access to financial and management records, and authorizing audits by the State Auditor's office." 81st Interim Report, at 1. That committee concluded that no major reforms to the structure of river authorities were necessary at that time but recommended continued efforts of river authorities to improve their operations and activities. 81st Interim Report, at 5. During the 81st legislative session, bills were introduced that once again would have placed certain river authorities under sunset review and a higher level of scrutiny by the state auditor; however, these bills did not pass. *E.g.*, Tex. S.B. 725, 81st Leg., R.S. (2009); Tex. S.B. 795, 81st Leg., R.S. (2009).

The 83rd regular legislative session again saw river authorities and districts subject to proposed additional oversight. With the addition of Texas Water Code section 49.1991 and Texas Government Code section 322.0171, river authorities are now subject to periodic efficiency review by the Legislative Budget Board (LBB). *See* Act of May 23, 2013, 83d Leg., R.S., ch. 1293, § 1 (H.B. 2362). The LBB is charged with review of the effectiveness and efficiency of the policies, management, fiscal affairs, and operations of river authorities. *See* Tex. Water Code § 49.1991; Tex. Gov't Code § 322.0171(a). Several additional bills failed that would have mandated periodic self-evaluation by river authorities and districts. *E.g.*, Tex. H.B. 14, 83d Leg., R.S. (2013); Tex. H.B. 3397, 83d Leg., R.S. (2013); Tex. S.B. 14, 83d Leg., R.S. (2013); Tex. S.B. 867, 83d Leg., R.S. (2013).

In 2015, "sunset review," without the threat of abolition that usually accompanies review by the Sunset Commission, became a reality for several river authorities. Act of May 31, 2015, 84th Leg., R.S., ch. 1148, § 1 (S.B. 523) (adding Tex. Gov't Code § 325.025).

Each river authority subject to sunset review undergoes a review of the entity's governance, management, operating structure, and compliance with legislative requirements, and the expense of the review will be paid by the river authority. Tex. Gov't Code § 325.025(c), (d). An entity that is reviewed pursuant to this section is not required to conduct a management audit under the TCEQ's rules. Tex. Gov't Code § 325.025(e); *see also* 30 Tex. Admin. Code § 292.13(6)(A).

In 2017, sunset review of river authorities once again came before the legislature during the 85th legislative session. House Bill 2802 would have abolished sunset review of river authorities by repealing section 325.025 of the Government Code. In addition to its abolition of sunset review of river authorities, the bill also included a provision that would have repealed Legislative Budget Board review of the Lower Colorado River Authority. *See* H.B. 2802, 85th Leg., R.S (2017). The bill passed the house but failed to pass the senate.

Sunset review of the first four river authorities was considered by the legislature in 2017 and included reviews of the Central Colorado River Authority (CCRA), the Palo Duro River Authority (PDRA), the Sulphur River Basin Authority, and the Upper Colorado River Authority. In its report to the legislature, dated February 10, 2017, the Sunset Advisory Commission found that "the small size and limited resources of the four river authorities [the Central Colorado River Authority, the Palo Duro River Authority, the Sulphur River Basin Authority, and the Upper Colorado River Authority] under sunset review this cycle directly affects their capacity to carry out their missions and raises questions about their ability to solve local water needs or make a real impact on their watersheds." Sunset Advisory Commission, *Report to the 85th Legislature* 55 (Feb. 2017), www.sunset.texas.gov/public/uploads/u64/Report%20to%20the%2085th%20Legislature_Revised%20June%202017.pdf [hereinafter 85th Report]. As a result, the commission made several recommendations regarding the governance of both the Central Colorado River Authority and Sulphur River Basin Authority, discussed just above and in section 9.6:22.

Although the legislation requiring sunset review expressly stated that it was sunset without abolition, the commission found that the CCRA "ha[d] outlived its relevance as a river authority." 85th Report, at 55. Because the commission did not have the statutory authority to abolish the CCRA, it instead "recommend[ed] the Legislature transfer through separate, non-Sunset legislation CCRA's only ongoing responsibility, maintaining three small dams, to its neighboring river authority, the Upper Colorado River Authority." 85th Report, at 55. The legislature followed this recommendation, in part, by enacting Senate Bill 2262, which gave the CCRA until December 31, 2018, to complete the transfer of its assets to Coleman County (rather than the Upper Colorado River Authority). *See* Act of May 24, 2017, 85th Leg., R.S., ch. 975 (S.B. 2262). Upon the transfer to Coleman County, the CCRA ceased to exist.

Further, regarding its review of the PDRA, the commission recommended that the PDRA be reclassified as a local water district and that the authority be removed from sunset review. 85th Report, at 56. With the passage of House Bill 1920, the PDRA was renamed the Palo Duro Water District and is no longer subject to sunset review. *See* Act of May 26, 2017, 85th Leg., R.S., ch. 1046 (H.B. 1920), eff. Sept. 1, 2017.

In 2019, the legislature once again considered the sunset reports of several larger river authorities: the Guadalupe-Blanco River Authority, the Lower Colorado River Authority, the Nueces River Authority, and the Red River Authority of Texas. In large part, this review resulted in minimal changes to the enabling acts of these entities and some management recommendations, primarily aimed at reinforcing good government practices and improving transparency, similar to those that had been implemented for the entities reviewed in 2017. *See* Sunset Advisory Commision, *Staff Report with Final Results: Guadalupe-Blanco River Authority, Red River Authority of Texas, Nueces River Authority* (2019), www.sunset.texas.gov/public/uploads/files/reports/River%20Authorities%20Staff%20Report%20with%20Final%20Results_0.pdf; Sunset Advisory Commission, *Staff Report with Commission Decisions: Lower Colorado River Authority* (Jan. 2019), www.sunset.texas.gov/public/uploads/files/reports/Lower%20Colorado%20River%20Authority%20Staff%20Report%20with%20Commission%20Decisions_1-17-19_0.pdf. These are discussed in more detail at sections 9.6:7, 9.6:10, 9.6:17, and 9.6:18 below, respectively.

More recently, the Sunset Commission completed reports on the San Jacinto River Authority and Brazos River Authority in early 2021. *See* Sunset Advisory Commission, *Staff Report with Commission Decisions: Brazos River Authority* (Nov. 2020), www.sunset.texas.gov/public/uploads/files/reports/Brazos%20River%20Authority%20Staff%20Report%20with%20Commission%20Decisions_1-21-21.pdf; Sunset Advisory Commission, *Staff Report with Commission Decisions: San Jacinto River Authority* (Jan. 2021), www.sunset.texas.gov/public/uploads/files/reports/San%20Jacinto%20River%20Authority%20Staff%20Report%20with%20Commission%20Decisions_1-21-21.pdf. The legislature passed House Bill 1570, adopting various Sunset Commission recommendations regarding the Brazos River Authority. Act of May 21, 2021, 87th Leg., R.S., ch. 664, § 1 (H.B. 1570), eff. Sept. 1, 2021 (discussed in section 9.6:3 below). However, the legislature failed to act on Senate Bill 716, which would have implemented various Sunset Commission recommendations for the San Jacinto River Authority, leaving open the possibility for action next in 2023, according to revised schedule adopted by Senate Bill 713.

The legislature has amended the list and schedule for sunset review of river authorities, both in 2019 and 2021. See Act of May 27, 2019, 86th Leg., R.S., ch. 596, §§ 2.08, 3.05, 3.06, 3.09, 3.10, 7.07 (S.B. 619), eff. June 10, 2019; Act of May 24, 2019, 86th Leg., R.S., ch. 467, § 8.008 (H.B. 4170), eff. Sept. 1, 2019; Act of May 31, 2021, 87th Leg., R.S. ch. 850, § 8.01 (S.B. 713), eff. June 16, 2021.

The current schedule and list of river authorities subject to sunset includes:

Sept. 1, 2023

- Bandera County River Authority and Groundwater district
- Upper Guadalupe River Authority
- Lavaca-Navidad River Authority
- San Antonio River Authority
- San Jacinto River Authority

Sept. 1, 2025

- Angelina and Neches River Authority
- Lower Neches Valley Authority
- Sabine River Authority of Texas
- Trinity River Authority

Sept. 1, 2029 (initial review completed 2017)

- Upper Colorado River Authority
- Sulphur River Basin

Sept. 1, 2031 (initial review completed 2019)

- Guadalupe-Blanco River Authority
- Lower Colorado River Authority
- Nueces River Authority
- Red River Authority of Texas

§ 9.4 TCEQ Oversight

The TCEQ has a continuing right of supervision over districts and authorities created under article III, section 52, and article XVI, section 59, of the Texas Constitution and has an obligation to report all findings to the governor, lieutenant governor, and speaker of the house. *See* Tex. Water Code § 12.081. Except for matters relating to an authority's or a district's electric utility operations, supervision may include (1) inquiry into the qualifications of the officers and directors of any district or authority; (2) requiring audits or other financial information, inspections, evaluations, and engineering reports; (3) issuance of witness subpoenas to carry out its authority; (4) investigations and hearings using commission-appointed examiners; (5) issuance of rules necessary to supervise the districts and authorities (except for water quality ordinances adopted by any river authority that meet or exceed minimum requirements established by the commission); and (6) issuance of permits under Texas Health and Safety Code chapter 361. Tex. Water Code § 12.081(a)(1)–(7) (as amended by Act of May 27, 2019, 86th Leg., R.S., ch. 608, § 1 (S.B. 911), eff. Sept. 1, 2019). In addition, river authorities required to undergo sunset review must provide information related to the operation and maintenance of dams under their control, which TCEQ must then post to an Internet website. Act of May 29, 2021, 87th R.S., ch. 574, § 1 (S.B. 600), eff. Sept. 1, 2021.

Moreover, if a district provides wholesale potable water and wastewater services, it must adopt a program that provides customers an opportunity to review and comment on the district's annual budget before that budget is adopted by the board. Tex. Water Code § 49.200.

The TCEQ has adopted rules that apply to thirty-one specific water districts and river authorities identified by name. *See* 30 Tex. Admin. Code ch. 292, § 292.1(a). (Although section 292.1 refers to the source of the list as being Texas Water Code section 9.010, section 9.010 was repealed in 2003 and did not include Titus County Fresh Water Supply District No.1). In addition to the administrative policies required by Water Code sections 49.199 and 49.200, these specific entities are required to adopt standards for conduct and activities that meet the minimum requirements set forth in the rules. 30 Tex. Admin. Code §§ 292.11(a), 292.13. Any district or authority subject to chapter 292 may adopt policies that address other administrative matters or that are more specific about the interpretation and implementation of the minimum requirements. 30 Tex. Admin. Code § 292.11(b). All administrative policies and amendments must be submitted to the TCEQ executive director. 30 Tex. Admin. Code § 292.12(a). These policies are on file at the TCEQ and available to the public for review. 30 Tex. Admin. Code § 292.12(b). To determine whether a covered district or authority is in compliance with its adopted administrative policies, the executive director may request additional documents from the entity or inspect records at the entity's office. 30 Tex. Admin. Code § 292.12(c). In addition to the TCEQ oversight of these entities authorized by chapters 292 and 293, the activities of most are controlled by water rights and other regulatory authorizations, such as wastewater discharge permits, issued and administered by the TCEQ.

The "certain districts and authorities" subject to these requirements are—

- Angelina and Neches River Authority
- Bexar-Medina-Atascosa Counties Water Control and Improvement District No. 1
- Brazos River Authority
- Canadian River Municipal Water Authority
- Colorado River Municipal Water District
- Dallas County Utility and Reclamation District
- Guadalupe-Blanco River Authority
- Gulf Coast Water Authority
- Lavaca-Navidad River Authority
- Lower Colorado River Authority
- Lower Neches Valley Authority
- Mackenzie Municipal Water Authority
- North Central Texas Municipal Water Authority
- North Harris County Regional Water Authority
- North Texas Municipal Water District
- Northeast Texas Municipal Water District
- Nueces River Authority
- Red River Authority of Texas
- Sabine River Authority
- San Antonio River Authority
- San Jacinto River Authority
- Sulphur River Basin Authority
- Sulphur River Municipal Water District
- Tarrant Regional Water District
- Titus County Fresh Water Supply District No. 1
- Trinity River Authority
- Upper Colorado River Authority
- Upper Guadalupe River Authority
- Upper Neches River Municipal Water Authority
- West Central Texas Municipal Water District

§ 9.5 General Powers and Duties of Regional Water Districts and River Authorities

A regional water district or river authority has only those powers expressly granted by statute or implied as an incident to express powers. *Franklin County Water District v. Majors*, 476 S.W.2d 371, 373 (Tex. App.—Texarkana 1972, writ ref'd n.r.e.); *Harris County Water Control & Improvement District No. 58 v. City of Houston*, 357 S.W.2d 789, 795 (Tex. App.—Houston 1962, writ ref'd n.r.e.). Language in an enabling act that provides "[e]xcept as expressly limited by this Act, the District shall have and is hereby authorized to exercise all powers, rights, privileges, and functions conferred by General Law upon any District or Districts created pursuant to Section 59, of Article 16, of the Constitution of the State of Texas" constitutes a general grant of power to exercise any powers conferred by general law on any district created pursuant to article 16, section 59(a). *See City of San Antonio v. Texas Water Commission*, 392 S.W.2d 200, 213 (Tex. App.—Austin 1965), *aff'd*, 407 S.W.2d 752 (Tex. 1966). This type of language is found in many enabling acts, and, today, many of the powers conferred by general law on water districts are embodied in chapter 49 of the Texas Water Code. Unless excluded by the enabling statute of a particular entity, chapter 49 provides regional water suppliers, including river authorities, the authority to—

- acquire property through eminent domain, within and outside the district
- construct, operate, and maintain works necessary to accomplish the purposes assigned by general or special law
- contract for or employ peace officers
- coordinate and contract with governments and entities
- install and maintain parks
- issue contract bonds, property tax bonds, and revenue bonds
- levy an operation and maintenance tax
- regulate irrigation

Further, chapter 49 allows an entity with raw water pipelines conveying any water through more than ten counties to own or operate electric generation or transmission facilities and to sell electricity within the district. Tex. Water Code § 49.233. An entity that operates wastewater collection systems may also regulate private sewage and on-site sewage facilities, Tex. Water Code § 49.234, and entities that provide potable water or sewer service are also authorized to provide firefighting services, Tex. Water Code § 49.351.

In many instances, an entity's enabling act will provide statutory authority to sell water and condemn land outside its limits. However, courts have held that this seemingly broad grant of authority does not separately empower an entity to operate an autonomous water system wholly outside its boundaries. *See Harris County Water Control & Improvement District No. 58*, 357 S.W.2d 789. Unless express authority is granted to provide service outside the district boundaries, the "overriding purpose is service within the district," and thus statutes authorizing acquisition of properties outside the district must be relied on primarily in developing the area within the district. 357 S.W.2d at 796; *see also* Tex. Att'y Gen. Op. No. H-1195 (1978) (concluding that the Upper Colorado River Authority's enabling act, which allowed the authority "to acquire by . . . lease . . . and to maintain, use and operate any and all property . . . within or without the boundaries of the District, necessary or convenient to the exercise of the powers, rights, privileges, and functions conferred upon it by this Act [Act of May 29, 1935, 44th Leg., ch. 126, § 2(f), 1935 Tex. Gen. Laws 336, 338]" was sufficient to authorize use of the Stacy Reservoir for impoundment of purchased water before distribution to users within the district, even though the reservoir was located outside the district).

§ 9.6 Specific River Authority and Regional Water District Information

As discussed above, river authorities and regional water districts generally have only those powers expressly granted by statute. The practitioner should review the enabling acts of each of these entities, which are often tailored to the unique needs of their respective regions. The following sections provide more details about the establishment, powers, duties, and legislative history of the river authorities and special water districts in Texas identified in 30 Texas Administrative Code chapter 292.

§ 9.6:1 Angelina & Neches River Authority

History

The Angelina & Neches River Authority (ANRA) was originally established in 1935 as the Sabine-Neches Conservation District (SNCD). *See* Angelina & Neches River Authority, *Comprehensive Annual Financial Report, Fiscal Year 2017* 13 (Feb. 2018), www.anra.org/about/public_information/pdfs/ANRA_CAFR_FY2017.pdf [hereinafter ANRA Annual Report]. In 1949 the Texas legislature divided the district into the Sabine River Authority (SRA) and the Neches River Conservation District (NRCD). The NRCD was inactive until 1971, when Governor Preston Smith appointed nine members to the Board of Directors. In 1977, the district's name was changed to the Angelina & Neches River Authority. ANRA Annual Report, at 14.

The ANRA's central office is located in Lufkin, Texas. The authority's territorial jurisdiction of 8,500 square miles lies wholly or in part of the following seventeen counties: Van Zandt, Smith, Henderson, Newton, Cherokee, Anderson, Rusk, Houston, Nacogdoches, San Augustine, Shelby, Angelina, Trinity, Sabine, Polk, Jasper, and Orange. The ANRA is recognized as an independent governmental agency authorized to construct, maintain, and operate any and all works necessary for the purpose of controlling, storing, and preserving water resources in the Neches River Basin. The ANRA receives no tax revenues from the state, nor can it levy any taxes. ANRA revenues are derived solely from services provided. It is authorized to issue revenue bonds for the purpose of financing projects to be paid by and through customer contracts that obligate the customer to pay its share of the debt obligation. *See* ANRA Annual Report, at 6.

In the early 1970s, the ANRA began providing water and wastewater utility operational assistance to cities, industries, school districts, and other governmental agencies in the region by providing laboratory services for regulatory compliance. In 1972, the ANRA was assigned responsibility for private on-site sewage facility regulation around Sam Rayburn Reservoir, and the authority continues to manage this regulatory program today. See ANRA Annual Report, at 14. The on-site sewage facility program was expanded in 2009 to include the portion of San Augustine County within the Neches River Basin, and in 2015 it was expanded once again to include the entirety of Angelina County. *See Order Adopting Rules of the Angelina & Neches River Authority for On-Site Sewage Facilities* (issued Oct. 19, 2015), www.anra.org/divisions/wastewater/ossf/pdfs/TCEQ_Certified_Order_2015-10-19.pdf.

Currently, the ANRA administers several water quality–related environmental programs including the Upper Neches basin surface water quality monitoring programs (through the TCEQ's Texas Clean Rivers Program), the Attoyac Watershed Protection Plan, a permit compliance monitoring program, an industrial pretreatment program, and a water/wastewater sample collection and testing program. *See* ANRA Annual Report, at 30. The ANRA also owns and operates a regional wastewater facility, a regional compost facility, and a retail water and wastewater utility and is engaged in obtaining the federal permit that would authorize the impoundment of Lake Columbia.

Structure

The ANRA is governed by a nine-member board of directors appointed by the governor to staggered six-year terms. Tex. Spec. Dist. Code § 8501.102. The directors are residents of the Neches River basin, and one-third of the board is appointed every two years. Tex. Spec. Dist. Code § 8501.101.

The board sets policy, provides oversight, and employs a general manager to ensure compliance with state and federal law and board-approved policies and directives. See ANRA Annual Report, at 30.

Powers and Duties

- Bonding authority: revenue bonds
- Chapter 49 duties
- Conservation of water and soil
- Coordinate/contract with governments/entities
- Dams and reservoirs
- Drainage and flood control
- Hydroelectric generation facilities
- Property acquisition through eminent domain, within and outside district
- Purchase/construct works to carry out district purposes
- Water quality
- Water supply: irrigation, municipal, retail, and wholesale

Citations to Special Law or Codes

Tex. Spec. Dist. Code §§ 8501.001–.901
S.B. 523, Act of May 31, 2015, 84th Leg., R.S., ch. 1148, § 2
S.B. 619, Act of May 27, 2019, 86th Leg., R.S., ch. 596, § 3.05

§ 9.6:2 Bexar-Medina-Atascosa Counties Water Control and Improvement District No. 1

History

The Bexar-Medina-Atascosa Counties Water Control and Improvement District No. 1 (BMA) was created in 1993, though its roots can be traced back to the early 1900s, when some of its system canals were initially constructed. The BMA's service area covers portions of three counties west of San Antonio, serving a primarily rural population and seven communities: Castroville, Devine, La Coste, Lytle, Natalia, Pearson, and Rio Medina. The BMA must follow specific procedures to exclude land within its service area. *See* Tex. Spec. Dist. Code ch. 9007. The BMA supplies water via gravity flow through releases from Medina Lake through Diversion Lake into more than 250 miles of irrigation canals. Over the last twenty years, the BMA has focused considerable effort on improvements to its delivery system to reduce system loss. *See* Bexar-Medina-Atascosa Counties Water Control and Improvement District No. 1, *Natural Resource Plan—Conveyance System Efficiency, Water Quality, and Municipal Water Demand* 1 (1995), www.twdb.texas.gov/publications/reports/contracted_reports/doc/95483071.pdf.

Structure

The BMA is governed by a seven-member board of directors elected to staggered four-year terms. Five of the directors are elected from single-member precincts in which they must reside, and two are elected at large. *See* Tex. Spec. Dist. Code § 9001.051.

Powers and Duties

Chapter 49 duties.

Citations to Special Law or Codes

Tex. Spec. Dist. Code ch. 9007
H.B. 2460, Act of May 19, 1993, 73d Leg., R.S., ch. 370
S.B. 1647, Act of May 24, 1995, 74th Leg., R.S., ch. 544

§ 9.6:3 Brazos River Authority

History

The Brazos River Authority (BRA) began as the Brazos River Conservation and Reclamation District, created by act of the Texas legislature in 1929. Texas State Historical ASsociation, Handbook of Texas, www.tshaonline.org/handbook/entries/brazos-river-authority [hereinafter Brazos River Authority Online]. In 1953, its name was changed to the Brazos River Authority. Brazos River Authority Online. It is the first and the oldest river authority in the United States and has the duty to develop, conserve, and make available for beneficial use the surface waters of the Brazos River basin. Brazos River Authority Online. As part of this duty, it built the Lake Possum Kingdom Reservoir in 1941. Brazos River Authority Online. The Lake Granbury Reservoir followed in 1968, and the Lake Limestone Reservoir in 1978. Brazos River Authority Online. At the same time, the BRA began working closely with the U.S. Army Corps of Engineers for water supply and flood control purposes. As a result, the following federal reservoirs were integrated into the BRA's water storage system: lakes Aquilla, Belton, Georgetown, Granger, Proctor, Somerville, Stillhouse Hollow, Waco, and Whitney.

Brazos River Authority Online. Subsequently, the BRA's interests in Lake Waco were transferred to the city of Waco. In 1967, the BRA acquired two canal systems along the Gulf coast, providing water to Brazoria, Fort Bend, and Galveston counties for rice irrigation and industrial and municipal uses. Brazos River Authority Online. The canal system was sold to the Gulf Coast Water Authority in 1988. Brazos River Authority Online. The BRA also holds the water rights permit for Allens Creek Reservoir, which is under development.

Today, the BRA covers approximately 42,000 square miles and all or part of seventy Texas counties, reaching from the New Mexico border to Freeport on the Gulf coast. In addition to its reservoirs, it manages two potable-water treatment facilities and eight sewerage treatment facilities, seventeen recreational parks, and more than one hundred water quality test sites. Memorandum from the BRA to Lyn Clancy, Managing Assoc. Gen. Counsel, Lower Colorado River Authority (Dec. 22, 2010) (on file with author).

In 2013, the 83rd Legislature enacted H.B. 2362, which required the BRA and the Lower Colorado River Authority to undergo an efficiency review by the Legislative Budget Board (LBB) before the LBB conducts a review of any other river authority. *See* Act of May 23, 2013, 83d Leg., R.S., ch. 1293, §§ 1, 3 (H.B. 2362). The LBB assessed the BRA's financial affairs and operations and reported its findings to the governor and the legislature. *See* Legislative Budget Board, *Brazos River Authority—Management and Performance Review* (Feb. 2015), www.lbb.state.tx.us/Documents/Publications/Other/1860_BrazozRiverAuthority.pdf.

In 2021, the 87th legislature enacted House Bill 1570, which adopted several Sunset Commission recommendations, including establishing grounds for removal of directors and director training requirements, requiring the board to distinguish between policy-making responsibilities of the board and management responsibilities of the general manager, and directing the BRA to maintain a system to act on complaints. Act of May 21, 2021, 87th Leg., R.S., ch. 664, § 1 (H.B. 1570), eff. Sept. 1, 2021.

Structure

The BRA is governed by a board of twenty-one directors appointed by the governor and confirmed by the Texas senate. The directors serve staggered six-year terms in which seven seats come open every February 1 of each odd-numbered year. The presiding officer is also appointed by the governor. *See* Tex. Spec. Dist. Code § 8502.009(a)–(b), (e).

Powers and Duties

- Bonding authority: contract bonds, property tax bonds with election, and revenue bonds
- Chapter 49 duties
- Conservation of water and soil
- Coordinate/contract with governments/entities
- Dams and reservoirs
- Drainage and flood control
- Hydroelectric generation facilities
- Property acquisition through eminent domain, within and outside district
- Purchase/construct works to carry out district purposes
- Wastewater
- Water quality
- Water supply: industrial, irrigation, mining, municipal, steam-electric generation, and wholesale

Citations to Special Law or Codes

Tex. Spec. Dist. Code § 8502.001
S.B. 1593, Act of June 18, 1999, 76th Leg., R.S., ch. 1291
H.B. 2362, Act of May 23, 2013, 83d Leg., R.S., ch. 1293, § 3
S.B. 523, Act of May 31, 2015, 84th Leg., R.S., ch. 1148, § 14
H.B. 2846, Act of May 16, 2019, 86th Leg., R.S., ch. 380

§ 9.6:4 Canadian River Municipal Water Authority

History

The Canadian River Municipal Water Authority (CRMWA) is a conservation and reclamation district created by special act of the Texas legislature in 1953, pursuant to section 59 of article XVI of the Texas Constitution. The territory of the district consists of the cities of Amarillo, Borger, Brownfield, Lamesa, Levelland, Lubbock, O'Donnell, Pampa, Plainview, Slaton, and Tahoka, as well as any territory annexed to any of the cities. Act of Apr. 22, 1953, 53d Leg., R.S., ch. 243, § 2; *see* www.crmwa.com/resources/CRMWA-Enabling-Act-RVSD-2009.pdf.

In addition to the powers and duties outlined below in this section, the CRMWA is best known for operating the Sanford Dam and Lake Meredith. Although the U.S. Congress had authorized construction of the Canadian River Project in 1949, it was not until 1962 that construction actually started. 43 U.S.C. § 600b. Canadian River Municipal Water Authority, *History of CRMWA*, www.crmwa.com/history-of-crmwa [hereinafter CRMWA History]. Congress required the states of Texas, New Mexico, and Colorado to enact the Canadian River Compact before the project could be constructed. The compact was ratified by the Texas legislature in 1951. Tex. Water Code § 43.001. See Chapter 14 of this book regarding multijurisdictional compacts. By 1965, Sanford Dam was completed, creating the new Lake Meredith. CRMWA History. Starting in 1968, a 322-mile aqueduct carried Lake Meredith's waters to the member cities. CRMWA History. Because of the high salinity of Lake Meredith, the CRMWA, the state of Texas, and the federal Bureau of Reclamation joined to create the Lake Meredith Salinity Control Project near Logan, New Mexico. Canadian River Municipal Water Authority, *Lake Meredith Salinity Control Project*, www.crmwa.com/lake-meredith-salinity-control-project. In 2001, the CRMWA began blending groundwater and surface water to increase supplies and improve water quality. Email from John Williams, Special Advisor, CRMWA, to Lyn Clancy, Managing Assoc. Gen. Counsel, Lower Colorado River Authority (Nov. 30, 2010, 01:53 CST) (on file with author). Lake Meredith became unusable during 2012 and 2013 due to lack of inflow. The CRMWA currently supplies a blend of groundwater and surface water that varies based on the salinity level in the lake. The blend goal is to meet state drinking water standards while trying to maximize the use of the renewable surface water. Email from John Williams, Special Advisor, CRMWA, to Lyn Clancy, Managing Assoc. Gen. Counsel, Lower Colorado River Authority (May 14, 2013, 14:06 CST) (on file with author) [hereinafter Williams 2013 email]. From 2005 through 2011, the CRMWA's groundwater resources underwent major expansions by bringing its total holding of groundwater rights to over 460,000 acres providing 70,000 acre-feet of water per year. Williams 2013 email.

Today, in addition to operating Lake Meredith, the Sanford Dam, and the associated aqueduct, the CRMWA also pays for operation of the Lake Meredith Salinity Control Project and the Conjunctive Use Groundwater Supply Project. Canadian River Municipal Water Authority, *John C. Williams Aqueduct & Wellfield—Phase I & II*, www.crmwa.com/john-c-williams-aqueduct-wellfield-phase-i-ii. Right-of-way is being purchased to prepare for the expansion of its groundwater delivery infrastructure because aqueducts to transport the groundwater are of limited capacity.

No taxes are levied. All revenue is derived from sale of water to the member cities.

Structure

The CRMWA is currently governed by a seventeen-member board of directors, each of which serves a two-year term. The number of board members can change over time based on population. Two directors are elected by the governing body of each member city with a population of more than ten thousand. Smaller cities can elect only a single director. The board meets once every quarter and for special meetings as needed. Each director must be a qualified voter and property-owning taxpayer in the city from which elected and cannot be an employee or member of the governing body of the city. Act of Apr. 22, 1953, 53d Leg., R.S., ch. 243, § 3.

Powers and Duties

- Bonding authority: contract bonds, property tax bonds, and revenue bonds
- Chapter 49 duties
- Conservation of water and soil
- Coordinate/contract with governments/entities
- Dams and reservoirs
- Drainage and flood control
- Parks
- Property acquisition through eminent domain, within and outside district
- Purchase/construct works to carry out district purposes
- Taxes: operation and maintenance expenses
- Water quality
- Water supply: municipal, wholesale, and out-of-district

Citations to Special Law or Codes

S.B. 126, Act of Apr. 22, 1953, 53d Leg., R.S., ch. 243
S.B. 339, Act of Apr. 29, 1955, 54th Leg., R.S., ch. 196
H.B. 914, Act of May 8, 1957, 55th Leg., R.S., ch. 204
H.B. 56, Act of Mar. 30, 1961, 57th Leg., R.S., ch. 67
H.B. 134, Act of Mar. 27, 1969, 61st Leg., R.S., ch. 63
S.B. 201, Act of Apr. 6, 1981, 67th Leg., R.S., ch. 42
H.B. 2131, Act of May 14, 1987, 70th Leg., R.S., ch. 251
H.B. 1285, Act of May 29, 1989, 71st Leg., R.S., ch. 1248, § 81
H.B. 2642, Act of May 10, 1995, 74th Leg., R.S., ch. 220
S.B. 1833, Act of May 26, 2007, 80th Leg., R.S., ch. 1339
S.B. 1040, Act of Apr. 30, 2009, 81st Leg., R.S., ch. 24

§ 9.6:5 Colorado River Municipal Water District

History

The Colorado River Municipal Water District (CRMWD) is a conservation district created in 1949 pursuant to article XVI, section 59, of the Texas Constitution to satisfy the growing water supply needs of the Midland-Odessa area. Act of May 31, 1949, 51st Leg., R.S., ch. 340; Colorado River Municipal Water District, *CRMWD's History*, www.crmwd.org/about/history/ [hereinafter CRMWD History]. The water-supply work truly began in 1951 with the construction of the Colorado River Dam and the creation of the surface reservoir Lake J. B. Thomas. Soon after, the Martin County Well Field was created to provide groundwater to a growing population. As the need for water increased, the CRMWD completed the E. V. Spence Reservoir in 1969. Unfortunately, drought conditions brought increasing difficulty to the region and rendered the reservoir unusable. By 1971, the CRMWD had been forced to dramatically expand its groundwater pumping. CRMWD History.

Although a third lake, the O.H. Ivie Reservoir, was constructed in 1990, it has not been full to capacity since June 1997. The twenty-five-year drought in the region has ensured that the O. H. Ivie reservoir is never more than 55 percent full. To better address customers' water needs during drought, the CRMWD dramatically expanded its diversion system in the 1980s and 1990s. Today, it can impound more than 100,000 acre-feet of water in its diversion system. CRMWD History. In 2010, the CRMWD further expanded its water supply efforts by acquiring additional groundwater and moved forward on construction of a water reclamation project. Press Release, Colorado River Municipal Water District, *CRMWD Takes Steps to Provide Additional Water for the Region* (June 3, 2010). The reclamation project, which began operations in May 2013, is the first direct potable reuse system in the country. Laura Martin, *Texas Leads the Way with First Direct Potable Reuse Facilities in U.S.*, Water-Online.com (Sept. 16, 2014), www.wateronline.com/doc/texas-leads-the-way-with-first-direct-potable-reuse-facilities-in-u-s-0001. In the fall of 2014, Lake J. B. Thomas received heavy inflow and went from 1.44 percent capacity to 46.95 percent capacity. Then in the summer of 2015, heavy rains allowed J. B. Thomas to reach its highest capacity since the 1950s, topping out at 78.66 percent capacity.

Protection of water quality is also an active concern of the district. In 1961, the legislature amended the CRMWD's enabling act to provide the district with the power and authority to study, correct, prevent, control, regulate, and eliminate artificial and natural pollution, including oil field brine pollution of the Colorado River and its tributaries upstream from the north boundary line of Coke County, Texas. In addition, the district was granted the authority to acquire sources of saltwater by any means and to sell saltwater and freshwater for mining, oil field flooding and repressuring, industrial, manufacturing, or other purposes. Act of Aug. 3, 1961, 57th Leg., 1st C.S., ch. 4.

Structure

The CRMWD is governed by a twelve-member board of directors to which the city councils of each member city appoint four directors to serve staggered two-year terms. Act of May 31, 1949, 51st Leg., R.S., ch. 340.

Powers and Duties

- Air quality control
- Bonding authority: contract bonds, property tax bonds, and revenue bonds
- Chapter 49 duties
- Conservation of water and soil
- Coordinate/contract with governments/entities
- Dams and reservoirs
- Drainage and flood control
- Electric generation and transmission facilities
- Parks
- Police and security services
- Property acquisition through eminent domain, within and outside district
- Purchase/construct works to carry out district purposes
- Solid waste disposal
- Wastewater
- Water quality
- Water supply: municipal and wholesale

Citations to Special Law or Codes

H.B. 757, Act of May 31, 1949, 51st Leg., R.S., ch. 340
S.B. 31, Act of Aug. 3, 1961, 57th Leg., 1st C.S., ch. 4
H.B. 1801, Act of May 22, 1981, 67th Leg., R.S., ch. 621

§ 9.6:6 Dallas County Utility and Reclamation District

History

The Dallas County Utility and Reclamation District (DCURD) was created by a 1983 special act of the Texas legislature that became effective on February 1, 1984. Act of May 23, 1983, 68th Leg., R.S., ch. 628. The DCURD is the successor to Dallas County Municipal Utility District No. 1, which was created in 1972 by the Texas Water Commission. The DCURD was created to construct and operate certain infrastructure and amenity elements within the Las Colinas development in Irving, Texas. Major projects of the DCURD reach well beyond water resources and include reclamation projects, raw water and flood control systems, and mass transit and road construction projects. DCURD activities are supported in part by the City of Irving Tax Increment Finance District No. 1, created to accelerate economic development in Las Colinas through various means, including advancement of infrastructure construction, of which the DCURD is a beneficiary. *See* Dallas County Utility and Reclamation District, www.dcurd.org/.

Structure

The DCURD is governed by a board of five directors appointed by the Irving, Texas, city council. A board member serves a four-year term, unless removed for cause.

Powers and Duties

- Bonding authority: property tax bonds and revenue bonds
- Chapter 49 duties
- Chapter 54 district powers and duties, including street lighting, roads (inside and outside district), electricity, navigation, parks, and raw and treated water supply
- Conservation of water and soil
- Coordinate/contract with governments/entities
- Dams and reservoirs
- Drainage and flood control
- Police and security services
- Property acquisition through eminent domain, within and outside district
- Purchase/construct works to carry out district purposes
- Solid waste disposal
- Taxes: operation and maintenance expenses
- Wastewater
- Water quality
- Water supply: irrigation, out-of-district, retail, and wholesale

Citations to Special Law or Codes

S.B. 963, Act of May 23, 1983, 68th Leg., R.S., ch. 628
H.B. 2421, Act of June 11, 1985, 69th Leg., R.S., ch. 475

§ 9.6:7 Guadalupe-Blanco River Authority

History

The Guadalupe River Authority was created in 1933 as a water conservation and reclamation district. In 1935, it was reauthorized as the Guadalupe-Blanco River Authority (GBRA). The GBRA's statutory district includes ten counties: Caldwell, Calhoun, Comal, DeWitt, Gonzales, Guadalupe, Hays, Kendall, Refugio, and Victoria. *See* Guadalupe-Blanco River Authority, *About GBRA*, www.gbra.org/about/default.aspx; *see also* Judy Gardner, Texas State Historical Association, *Guadalupe-Blanco River Authority*, www.tshaonline.org/handbook/entries/guadalupe-blanco-river-authority.

Throughout its statutory district, the GBRA owns and operates several hydroelectric generation facilities and associated reservoirs, wastewater collection and treatment systems, and water treatment and delivery systems. Additionally, the GBRA operates the Calhoun Canal System, which diverts and delivers water from the Guadalupe River to industrial, municipal, and agricultural customers along the canal system. The GBRA also operates the water storage portion of the Canyon Reservoir through its cooperative project with the U.S. Army Corps of Engineers. *See* Guadalupe-Blanco River Authority, *Canyon Reservoir*, www.gbra.org/operations/canyon-reservoir.

Groundwater has always been of great importance to the GBRA because approximately a third of the water in the Guadalupe basin derives from the Edwards Aquifer. Guadalupe-Blanco River Authority, *Edwards Aquifer and the Guadalupe River*, www.gbra.org/drought/edwardsaquifer.aspx. It is for this reason the GBRA acted to safeguard its water sources and joined as a plaintiff in the 1991 *Sierra Club v. Babbitt* case, which ultimately mandated a minimum discharge below which the Edwards Aquifer could not go. Since that time, the GBRA participated in the development and implementation of the Edwards Aquifer Recovery Implementation Program (EARIP), which is designed to protect endangered species and their habitats in Comal Springs and San Marcos Springs, which emanate from the Edwards Aquifer. *See* LaMarriol Smith, *Building a Habitat Conservation Plan*, GBRA River Run 8 (Winter/Spring 2012), www.gbra.org/wp-content/uploads/2021/05/riverrun-2012winterspring.pdf. See Chapter 32 of this book for discussion of the EARIP.

More recently, the GBRA has expanded its groundwater resources with the acquisition of Carrizo Aquifer water in Caldwell and Gonzales counties. The GBRA, through its joint project with the Alliance Regional Water Authority, will treat and deliver this groundwater to municipal users in Hays, Caldwell, and Comal counties. *See* Katerina Barton, *Alliance Water Project to Save $60M, Hays Free Press*, July 11, 2018, https://haysfreepress.com/2018/07/11/alliance-water-project-to-save-60m/; Alliance Water, Frequently Asked Questions, www.alliancewater.org/faqs.

In 2019, the GBRA underwent sunset review. In response to the recommendations by the Sunset Advisory Commission, the GBRA's enabling act was amended to require the governor to appoint the board president, require training of its board members, separate policymaking and management functions, create a process for handling complaints, adopt an asset management plan, and develop and implement alternative dispute resolution procedures to assist with internal and external disputes under GBRA's jurisdiction. The GBRA will undergo sunset review again in 2031. *See* Act of Apr. 30, 2019, 86th Leg., R.S., ch. 22 (S.B. 626), eff. Sept. 1, 2019.

Structure

The GBRA is governed by a nine-member board of directors. Each director must be a property taxpayer in Texas and reside in a county within the authority's boundaries. Only one director may come from any one county. All directors are appointed by the governor to six-year terms. Act of May 27, 1969, 61st Leg., R.S., ch. 432, § 4.

Powers and Duties

- Bonding authority: revenue bonds
- Conservation of water and soil
- Coordinate/contract with governments/ entities
- Dams and reservoirs
- Drainage and flood control
- Electric generation and transmission facilities
- Forestry
- General powers and duties of any district created by Tex. Const. art. XVI, § 59
- Groundwater management
- Navigation
- Property acquisition through eminent domain, within and outside district
- Purchase/construct works to carry out district purposes
- Wastewater
- Water supply: irrigation, out-of-district, retail, and wholesale

Citations to Special Law or Codes

S.B. 97, Act of Oct. 12, 1933, 43d Leg., 1st C.S., ch. 75
H.B. 138, Act of Oct. 11, 1935, 44th Leg., 1st C.S., ch. 410
H.B. 294, Act of Mar. 28, 1963, 58th Leg., R.S., ch. 45
H.B. 1416, Act of May 27, 1969, 61st Leg., R.S., ch. 432
S.B. 1028, Act of May 22, 1975, 64th Leg., R.S., ch. 433
S.B. 1477, Act of May 30, 1993, 73d Leg., R.S., ch. 626
S.B. 361, Act of May 17, 1995, 74th Leg., R.S., ch. 524
S.B. 523, Act of May 31, 2015, 84th Leg., R.S., ch. 1148, § 5
S.B. 626, Act of Apr. 30, 2019, 86th Leg., R.S., ch. 22

§ 9.6:8 Gulf Coast Water Authority

History

Before World War II, areas with large industrial and petrochemical development, including Baytown and Texas City, experienced significant localized subsidence. This trend continued during and after the war, when rapid industrial and municipal growth began to create broad regional patterns of subsidence, raising serious concerns over flooding. The Industrial Water Company, founded in 1946, used surface water from the Brazos River as a substitute for the groundwater supply for industries in Texas City. In 1965, the Texas legislature created the Galveston County Water Authority (GCWA) to provide an adequate water supply for municipal, domestic, manufacturing, irrigation, and other useful purposes for the inhabitants and water users of Galveston County. Act of May 26, 1965, 59th Leg., R.S., ch. 712. The GCWA purchased the assets of the Industrial Water Company in 1971. Also in 1971, the cities of Galveston and League City contracted with the GCWA to deliver up to 30 million gallons per day (MGD) of potable water purchased from the City of Houston. The acquisition of a surface water supply by the GCWA for these cities further reduced reliance on groundwater. In 1981, the GCWA purchased an 18 MGD surface-water treatment plant from Texas City. In 1987, the GCWA purchased a 25 percent interest in the new City of Houston Southeast Water Purification Plant for the cities of Galveston and League City. In 1988, the GCWA purchased the Brazos River Authority Canal Division, which included three pump stations and 150 miles of canals across Brazoria, Fort

Bend, and Galveston counties. The purchase included 225,000 acre-feet of water rights in the Brazos River. In 1991, the name was changed to the Gulf Coast Water Authority to reflect its service to a broader area. Act of May 23, 1991, 72d Leg., R.S., ch. 818. In 1999, the surface-water treatment plant was expanded to 50 MGD. In 2006, the GCWA purchased the assets of Chocolate Bayou Water Company, which included two pump stations, several reservoirs, and an extensive canal system. This purchase included an additional 175,000 acre-feet of water rights in the Brazos River.

In 2019, the GCWA's territory was formally expanded beyond Galveston County and is coextensive with the boundaries of Brazoria, Fort Bend, and Galveston Counties. *See* Act of May 20, 2019, 86th Leg., R.S., ch. 390, § 2 (H.B. 4690), eff. June 2, 2019. The GCWA is the major provider of surface water to the Texas City Industrial Complex and the cities and water districts in Galveston County; of surface water to the southern Brazoria County Industrial Complex and 18,000 acres of agricultural land in Brazoria and Galveston counties; and of surface water to the cities of Missouri City, Pearland, and Sugarland and water districts serving Pecan Grove and Stafford. In 2015, the 84th Legislature granted express authority to the GCWA, in connection with the acquisition of water or the treatment, storage, or transportation of water, to enter into retail service agreements within the boundaries of the Electric Reliability Council of Texas (ERCOT), which covers much of Texas, for sale of electricity under certain limited circumstances. *See* Act of May 27, 2015, 84th Leg., R.S., ch. 943, § 1 (H.B. 4168), eff. Sept. 1, 2015. The GCWA may enter into contracts related to water projects located outside of its territory. *See* Act of May 20, 2019, 86th Leg., R.S., ch. 390, § 5 (H.B. 4690).

Measurements by the Harris-Galveston Subsidence District in Galveston County indicate that conversion from groundwater to surface water has completely arrested subsidence in that county. *See* Gulf Coast Water Authority, *GCWA History and Timeline*, www.gulfcoastwaterauthoritytx.gov/gcwa-history-and-timeline.

Structure

The GCWA is governed by a ten-member board of directors, each of which serves a two-year staggered term, representing municipal, industrial, agricultural, and general interests. All directors must be residents of the state. Five members are appointed by the Galveston County Commissioners Court, two by the Fort Bend County Commissioners Court, and three by the Brazoria County Commissioners Court.

Powers and Duties

- Bonding authority: revenue bonds
- Chapter 49 duties (no taxes)
- Chapter 54 district powers and duties, including drainage and flood control, irrigation, navigation, solid waste disposal, and wastewater treatment
- Coordinate/contract with governments/entities
- Dams and reservoirs
- Electricity sales (limited)
- General powers and duties of any district created by Tex. Const. art. XVI, § 59
- Oil and gas leases
- Property acquisition through eminent domain, within and outside district
- Purchase/construct works to carry out district purposes
- Water quality
- Water supply: irrigation, municipal, out-of-district, retail, and wholesale

Citations to Special Law or Codes

H.B. 1127, Act of May 26, 1965, 59th Leg., R.S., ch. 712
H.B. 1383, Act of May 19, 1969, 61st Leg., R.S., ch. 399
H.B. 165, Act of May 27, 1979, 66th Leg., R.S., ch. 708
H.B. 2343, Act of May 23, 1983, 68th Leg., R.S., ch. 1049
H.B. 2837, Act of May 23, 1991, 72d Leg., R.S., ch. 818
H.B. 2177, Act of May 27, 1993, 73d Leg., R.S., ch. 683
S.B. 683, Act of May 18, 2011, 82d Leg., R.S., ch. 1259
H.B. 4168, Act of May 27, 2015, 84th Leg., R.S., ch. 943
H.B. 4690, Act of May 20, 2019, 86th Leg., R.S., ch. 390

§ 9.6:9 Lavaca-Navidad River Authority

History

The Jackson County Flood Control District was created by the Texas legislature in August 1941 to store, preserve, and distribute the surface and flood waters of Jackson County, Texas. The district's name was changed to the Lavaca-Navidad River Authority (LNRA) in 1969. *See* Christopher Long, Texas State Historical Association, Handbook of Texas, *Lavaca-Navidad River Authority*, www.tshaonline.org/handbook/entries/lavaca-navidad-river-authority [hereinafter About the LNRA].

Once created, the Flood Control District quickly provided local sponsorship for the Bureau of Reclamation's Palmetto Bend Reclamation Project (also known as Lake Texana), but the work was not finally authorized by Congress until 1968. In 1978, the U.S. Bureau of Reclamation and the authority executed a lease agreement by which the authority assumed greater control of operations and maintenance for the project. Although the Palmetto Bend Dam was completed in 1979, creating Lake Texana, the LNRA did not assume full responsibility for operations and maintenance until 1985, when the project finally neared substantial completion. Texas state Historical ASsociation, Handbook of Texas, *Lake Texana*, www.tshaonline.org/handbook/entries/lake-texana; About the LNRA.

With a completed reservoir, the LNRA spent much of the 1990s expanding its customer base. Currently, the LNRA holds water supply contracts with the Formosa Plastics Corporation, The Interplast Group, the cities of Corpus Christi and Point Comfort, and the Calhoun County Navigation District. See About the LNRA.

Also in the early 1990s, the LNRA, along with the TWDB, began efforts to obtain fee title to the federal interest in the Palmetto Bend Project. On November 13, 2000, the Palmetto Bend Conveyance Act, Pub. L. No. 106-512, 114 Stat. 2378, was approved, conveying title from the United States to the state of Texas acting through the TWDB or the LNRA or both. In May 2001, approximately six months after the initial transaction, the LNRA secured the necessary financing and assumed the TWDB's remaining interest in the project and became sole proprietor of Lake Texana and the associated properties.

In 2003, in an effort to assist newly formed groundwater conservation districts (GCDs) in the Lavaca basin, the LNRA was granted express authority to discover, develop, and produce groundwater for local use within the Lavaca River basin and to coordinate and contract with GCDs to engage in conjunctive use of groundwater and surface water management. *See* Act of May 30, 2003, 78th Leg., R.S., ch. 1224. The legislation also gave the LNRA authority for desalination projects and ancillary facilities, including an electric power generation facility, and augmented the types of facilities the LNRA may own, construct, operate, and maintain and the purposes for which it is created.

Today, in addition to its reservoir operations, the authority operates and maintains three raw water delivery systems consisting of nearly 170 miles of large-diameter pipeline and multiple pump stations, four public parks and campgrounds, and an event complex in and around the Lake Texana

Reservoir. Of the nearly 8,000 acres surrounding Lake Texana, approximately 5,000 acres are managed as wildlife habitat, and the balance is leased and managed for hay production. Although expansion of the Palmetto Bend Project was authorized by Congress and the Texas Water Commission after decades of review and scrutiny, the LNRA is actively pursuing a new appropriation on the Lavaca River for an off-channel storage alternative that would include cancellation of the authorized expansion of the on-channel impoundment. *See* March 29, 2021 Email from Patrick Brzozowski to Lyn Clancy; *see also* About the LNRA.

Structure

The LNRA is governed by a nine-member board of directors appointed by the governor to staggered six-year terms. The directors must reside within the LNRA's jurisdiction and be property taxpayers as well as legal voters of the state of Texas.

Powers and Duties

- Bonding authority: contract bonds, property tax bonds, and revenue bonds
- Chapter 49 duties
- Conservation of water
- Coordinate/contract with governments/entities
- Dams and reservoirs
- Drainage and flood control
- Electric generation and transmission facilities
- Forestry
- Navigation
- Other: all powers and duties conferred by general or special law on any other district not contravened by enabling legislation
- Parks
- Property acquisition through eminent domain, within and outside district
- Purchase/construct works to carry out district purposes
- Solid waste disposal
- Taxes: operation and maintenance expenses; special taxes for pollution control and district master plan
- Wastewater
- Water quality
- Water supply: irrigation, municipal, out-of-district, and wholesale

Citations to Special Law or Codes

H.B. 362, Act of May 14, 1941, 47th Leg., R.S., ch. 361, art. II
H.B. 516, Act of May 10, 1947, 50th Leg., R.S., ch. 186
H.B. 836, Act of May 14, 1953, 53d Leg., R.S., ch. 383
H.B. 676, Act of May 10, 1955, 54th Leg., R.S., ch. 313
S.B. 11, Act of Aug. 6, 1959, 56th Leg., 3d C.S., ch. 22
S.B. 62, Act of Feb. 28, 1963, 58th Leg., R.S., ch. 14
S.B. 808, Act of June 2, 1969, 61st Leg., R.S., ch. 417
H.B. 2305, Act of May 23, 1983, 68th Leg., R.S., ch. 1035
H.B. 228, Act of May 17, 1989, 71st Leg., R.S., ch. 956
S.B. 1276, Act of May 30, 2003, 78th Leg., R.S., ch. 1224
S.B. 580, Act of May 30, 2011, 82d Leg., R.S., ch. 616
S.B. 523, Act of May 31, 2015, 84th Leg., R.S., ch. 1148, § 6

§ 9.6:10 Lower Colorado River Authority

History

The Lower Colorado River Authority (LCRA) was created in 1934 as a conservation and reclamation district with a statutory authority covering ten counties encompassing the lower Colorado River, including Bastrop, Blanco, Burnet, Colorado, Fayette, Llano, Matagorda, San Saba, Travis, and Wharton counties. *See* S.B. 2, Act of Nov. 10, 1934, 43d Leg., 4th C.S., ch. 7; Tex. Spec. Dist. Code § 8503.003. Between 1935 and 1951 the LCRA built six dams along the Colorado River above Austin, including Tom Miller Dam, which is owned by the city of Austin. Lower Colorado River Authority. John Williams & William McCann, Texas State Historical ASsociation, Handbook of Texas, *Lower Colorado River Authority*, www.tshaonline.org/handbook/entries/lower-colorado-river-authority [hereinafter Williams & McCann]; *see also* John A. Adams, Jr., *Damming the Colorado: The Rise of the Lower Colorado River Authority, 1933–1939* (Texas A&M University Press 1990); James H. Banks & John E. Babcock, *Corralling the Colorado: The First Fifty Years of the Lower Colorado River Authority* (Eakin Press 1988).

These dams help control the river in floods and provide a reliable supply of water by forming the chain called the Highland Lakes. *See* Lower Colorado River Authority, *The Colorado River and Highland Lakes*, www.lcra.org/water/highland-lakes-overview/ [hereinafter LCRA Lakes]. The LCRA also operates hydroelectric facilities at the six dams. LCRA Lakes. Two of the Highland Lakes, Buchanan and Travis, provide water supplies for communities throughout its service area as well as businesses, power plants, and agriculture. *See* Lower Colorado River Authority, *Water Supply Operations*, www.lcra.org/water/water-supply-planning/water-supply-operations/ [hereinafter LCRA Water Supply]. The LCRA also supplies water for irrigated agriculture in Colorado, Matagorda, and Wharton counties; however, these supplies can be reduced or suspended altogether during certain drought conditions. *See* LCRA Water Supply. In the mid-1990s, the LCRA began operating several potable water and wastewater systems; however, it has since divested itself of these facilities. The LCRA is now focused on expanding its water supply, with specific projects to develop groundwater on LCRA property in Bastrop County and an off-channel reservoir in Wharton County. *See* Lower Colorado River Authority, *New Water Supply Projects*, www.lcra.org/water/water-supply-planning/new-water/.

In addition to its water-related responsibilities, the LCRA also supplies wholesale electricity throughout central Texas to several electric cooperatives and cities. The LCRA operates fossil-fueled power plants in Bastrop, Fayette, and Llano counties, in addition to its six hydroelectric facilities on the Colorado River. *See* Lower Colorado River Authority, *Powering Texas*, www.lcra.org/energy/electric-power/ [hereinafter *Powering Texas*]; *see also* Tex. Spec. Dist. Code § 8503.004(t); Act of Apr. 22, 1965, 59th Leg., R.S., ch. 124. The LCRA Transmission Services Corporation, which is an instrumentality of LCRA, owns, operates, and maintains several thousand miles of power lines and hundreds of electric substations. *See* Lower Colorado River Authority, *LCRA Transmission Services Corporation*. www.lcra.org/energy/electric-transmission/. In support of renewable energy development, LCRA has diversified its energy sources to include wind and solar power, and LCRA Transmission Services Corporation joined other transmission service providers to construct infrastructure to bring wind power from West Texas to more densely populated areas through the Competitive Renewable Energy Zones. Lower Colorado River Authority, *Renewable Energy*, www.lcra.org/energy/electric-power/renewable-energy/; *see also* Tex. Spec. Dist. Code § 8503.004(c).

Amendments to the LCRA's enabling act have added to the LCRA's responsibilities and authority. The legislature provided the LCRA authority over pollution control of ground and surface waters and water quality monitoring in 1971. *See* Tex. Spec. Dist. Code § 8503.004(q). Since 1988, the LCRA has sponsored the Colorado River Watch Network, a volunteer-based environmental-education and data collection program along the Colorado River and its tributaries. *See* Lower Colorado River

Authority, *Colorado River Watch Network*, www.lcra.org/water/quality/colorado-river-watch-network/Pages/default.aspx [hereinafter *Colorado River Watch*]. More than five hundred volunteers take part in the program. Under the Clean Rivers Act of 1991, the LCRA conducts a comprehensive assessment of the region's water quality. *Colorado River Watch*; *see also* Act of May 31, 1971, 62d Leg., R.S., ch. 820. Most recently, with the passage of Senate Bill 632 in 2021, the legislature granted the LCRA authority to provide certain fiber capacity and facilities for the purpose of facilitating broadband service connectivity. Act of April 30, 2021, 87th Leg., R.S., ch. 3, § 1 (S.B. 632), eff. April 30, 2021; Tex. Spec. Dist. Code § 8502.032.

The LCRA also operates more than twenty-five parks and recreational facilities along the Colorado River, at the Highland Lakes, and at downstream lakes with power plants. *See* Lower Colorado River Authority, *Parks*, www.lcra.org/parks/land-business-development/about-us/. The LCRA also works with local communities to bring new businesses and to help existing businesses expand. Between 1990 and 1995 the LCRA helped add more than $23 million in capital investment in and around Central Texas. *See* Williams & McCann. Like many other river authorities, the LCRA receives no state tax money and cannot levy taxes. The LCRA operates on revenues from wholesale electricity and water sales and other services.

House Bill 2362, enacted by the 83rd Legislature, required the LCRA and Brazos River Authority to undergo an efficiency review by the Legislative Budget Board (LBB) before the LBB conducted a review of any other river authority. The LBB completed its review of the Brazos River Authority in 2015 but has not yet begun its assessment of the LCRA. *See* Act of May 23, 2013, 83d Leg., R.S., ch. 1293, §§ 1, 3 (H.B. 2362). In 2015, the 84th Legislature amended the LCRA's enabling act to provide the state auditor with the authority to audit the LCRA, which was completed in 2016. *See* Act of May 31, 2015, 84th Leg., R.S., ch. 1148, §§ 7, 8 (S.B. 523). While the same legislation excluded from sunset review the LCRA's management of generation or transmission of electricity through the LCRA or its nonprofit affiliates, the state auditor may make recommendations regarding such review in the future. *See* Act of May 31, 2015, 84th Leg., R.S., ch. 1148, § 7.

In 2019, the LCRA underwent sunset review. In response to the recommendations by the Sunset Advisory Commission, the LCRA's enabling act was amended to require enhanced training of its board members, create a process for handling public complaints and provide for public testimony at all board meetings, develop and implement alternative dispute resolution procedures to assist with internal and external disputes under the LCRA's jurisdiction, and implement a public engagement process for water supply projects. See Act of May 30, 2019, 86th Leg., R.S., ch. 18, § 2 (S.B. 606), eff. Sept. 1, 2019 (adding Tex. Spec. Dist. Code §§ 8503.0065, 8503.0105–.0108). The LCRA will undergo sunset review again in 2031. *See* Tex. Spec. Dist. Code § 8503.0021(a).

Structure

The LCRA board has fifteen directors appointed by the governor for staggered six-year terms. See Tex. Spec. Dist. Code § 8503.006(a), (c). The chair of the board is also appointed by the governor. Tex. Spec. Dist. Code § 8503.007. Twelve of the LCRA's fifteen directors represent the LCRA's ten-county statutory district. Each county has one director, except for Travis, which has two. The remaining director's seat is an at-large position that rotates among the remaining nine counties. Three directors represent the LCRA's electric service area outside the statutory district. These are at-large positions that rotate among the counties in the LCRA's electric service area. Tex. Spec. Dist. Code § 8503.006(a), (b).

Powers and Duties

- Bonding authority: revenue bonds
- Chapters 49, 51, and 152 duties
- Conservation of water and soil
- Coordinate/contract with governments/entities
- Dams and reservoirs
- Drainage and flood control
- Electric generation and transmission facilities
- Forestry
- Hydroelectric generation facilities
- Oil and gas leases
- Parks
- Police and security services
- Property acquisition through eminent domain, within and outside district
- Purchase/construct works to carry out district purposes
- Regulate private sewage, on-site sewage facilities
- Rural middle mile broadband services
- Solid waste disposal
- Wastewater
- Water quality
- Water supply: industrial, irrigation, mining, municipal (and other beneficial uses), out-of-district (limited), retail, and wholesale

Citations to Special Law or Codes

Tex. Spec. Dist. Code ch. 8503
S.B. 2, Act of Nov. 10, 1934, 43d Leg., 4th C.S., ch. 7
H.B. 2362, Act of May 23, 2013, 83d Leg., R.S., ch. 1293, § 3
H.B. 2000, Act of May 22, 2015, 84th Leg., R.S., ch. 547
H.B. 910, Act of May 29, 2015, 84th Leg., R.S., ch. 437, § 38
S.B. 523, Act of May 31, 2015, 84th Leg., R.S., ch. 1148, §§ 7, 8
S.B. 606, Act of May 7, 2019, 86th Leg., R.S., ch. 18
H.B. 2325, Act of June 14, 2019, 86th Leg., R.S., ch. 1116, § 5
Act of April 30, 2021, 87th Leg., R.S., ch. 3

§ 9.6:11 Lower Neches Valley Authority

History

The Lower Neches Valley Authority (LNVA) was created in 1933 as the second river authority in the state, pursuant to article III, section 52, and article XVI, section 59, of the Texas Constitution. Act of Oct. 23, 1933, 43d Leg., 1st C.S., ch. 63. The authority's primary boundaries encompass all of Hardin, Jefferson, and Tyler counties and eastern Chambers and Liberty counties, but the LNVA has power to act inside or outside the boundaries of the authority within the Neches River basin or the adjacent Neches-Trinity coastal basin. *See* Tex. Spec. Dist. Code §§ 8504.003, 8504.103. A primary purpose of the LNVA is to supply water to municipalities, industry, and agriculture and to protect the freshwater intakes of cities, industries, and farms along the lower Neches River that were threatened by saltwater intrusion from the Gulf of Mexico. *See* Lower Neches Valley Authority, *About*, https://lnva.dst.tx.us/about/ [hereinafter About the LNVA]. Originally, most of the LNVA's customers were rice farmers; however, industrial growth has surpassed that historical use. The lower part of the Neches River has been deepened and straightened to provide access for large ocean-going vessels serving the oil refining industry within Jefferson County, thus the need for saltwater protection. To accomplish this, the LNVA owns and operates a saltwater barrier and navigation lock near the mouth of Pine Island Bayou. *See* About the LNVA.

Initially, the LNVA planned construction of a large reservoir on the Neches River near Rockland for the purpose of storing water. However, the U.S. Army Corps of Engineers' planned construction of four reservoirs (two major reservoirs, one at Rockland on the Neches and the other at McGee Bend on the Angelina River, and two regulating reservoirs downstream of the major reservoirs) superseded the LNVA's plans. The LNVA was named the local sponsor of the Neches River basin reservoirs and furnished $15,000,000 of the construction costs of McGee Bend Reservoir (now Sam Rayburn Reservoir, completed in 1965), as well as Town Bluff Dam and B. A. Steinhagen Reservoir, completed in 1951. The other two reservoirs, Rockland and Dam A, were deferred until needed and have since been deauthorized by Congress. *See* About the LNVA.

The Sam Rayburn and Steinhagen reservoirs are owned by the U.S. government and operated by the U.S. Army Corps of Engineers, Fort Worth District. The LNVA provides local financial sponsorship. The LNVA has state-approved water rights to use essentially the entire dependable freshwater yield of the Sam Rayburn Reservoir, approximately 820,000 acre-feet (or 267 trillion gallons) a year. Water releases through Rayburn's and Steinhagen's powerhouses generate electrical power for use in homes and industries within the area. *See* About the LNVA.

The LNVA delivers fresh surface water to its customers using a pumping and distribution system comprising twenty-one pumps capable of pumping more than 1 billion gallons of water a day. The LNVA supplies water to nine cities and water districts, twenty-six industries, and over one hundred irrigated farms. The water is lifted into a canal system and then delivered by gravity flow throughout most of the four-hundred-mile canal system that covers an area of approximately seven hundred square miles, principally in Jefferson, Liberty, and Chambers counties. *See* About the LNVA.

In 1997, the LNVA's enabling legislation was amended to expand its economic development program throughout the basin to include education, transportation, public safety, recreation, health care, water and wastewater treatment, and rural water and sewer development. Act of May 26, 1997, 75th Leg., R.S., ch. 1263; Tex. Spec. Dist. Code § 8504.201(5). The LNVA's Economic Development Assistance Program consists of low-interest loans or local matching grants for water/wastewater infrastructure improvements and private enterprise projects that improve water availability, water quality, and water management or that enhance economic growth both within and without the LNVA's service area. As an economic development project, the LNVA supplies the Bolivar Peninsula in Galveston County up to five million gallons per day of treated freshwater from its West Treatment Plant in Winnie, Chambers County, built in 2004.

Since 2008, the LNVA has operated and now owns the Devers Canal System in Chambers and Liberty counties. Additionally, the LNVA operates the North Regional Treatment plant that treats the industrial effluent from four refineries and chemical plants south of Beaumont, Texas.

The LNVA has no power to levy taxes.

Structure

The LNVA is governed by a board of nine directors, two of whom reside in Tyler County, two from Hardin County, and five from Jefferson County. They are appointed to six-year terms by the governor.

Powers and Duties

- Bonding authority: revenue bonds
- Chapter 49 duties (no taxes)
- Conservation of water and soil
- Coordinate/contract with governments/entities
- Dams and reservoirs
- Drainage and flood control
- Electric generation and transmission facilities
- Forestry
- Industrial development corporation
- Navigation
- Oil and gas leases
- Other: all powers and duties conferred by general or special law on any other district, not contravened by enabling legislation
- Parks
- Property acquisition through eminent domain, within and outside district
- Purchase/construct works to carry out district purposes
- Wastewater
- Water quality
- Water supply: industrial, irrigation, mining, municipal, out-of-district, retail, and wholesale

Citations to Special Law or Codes

Tex. Spec. Dist. Code ch. 8504
S.B. 38, Act of Oct. 23, 1933, 43d Leg., 1st C.S., ch. 63
H.B. 2919, Act of May 26, 1997, 75th Leg., R.S., ch. 1263
S.B. 523, Act of May 31, 2015, 84th Leg., R.S., ch. 1148, § 9
S.B. 619, Act of May 27, 2019, 86th Leg., R.S., ch. 596, § 3.06

§ 9.6:12 Mackenzie Municipal Water Authority

History

The Mackenzie Municipal Water Authority (MMWA) was created in 1965. Act of May 13, 1965, 59th Leg., R.S., ch. 277. The MMWA's boundaries encompass the city of Tulia in Swisher County, the city of Silverton in Briscoe County, and the cities of Floydada and Lockney in Floyd County. The primary purpose of the MMWA is to furnish water to these municipalities. Dam construction on Lake Mackenzie was completed in 1974 and opened to the public in 1976. All facilities, including the land, dam, water treatment plant, pipelines, and pump stations were financed by the four cities and the taxpayers. *See* Lake Mackenzie, *Who We Are*, http://lakemackenzie.com/general-info.html.

Structure

The MMWA is governed by an eight-member board of directors. The governing body of each of the four customer cities appoints two board members each, who serve two-year staggered terms. Board members must reside in the cities from which they are appointed. Act of May 13, 1965, 59th Leg., R.S., ch. 277.

Powers and Duties

- Bonding authority: contract bonds, property tax bonds, and revenue bonds
- Chapter 49 duties
- Conservation of water
- Dams and reservoirs
- Groundwater development and use (limited)
- Parks
- Police and security services
- Property acquisition through eminent domain, within and outside district
- Purchase/construct works to carry out district purposes
- Water quality
- Water supply: out-of-district, retail, and wholesale

Citations to Special Law or Codes

H.B. 622, Act of May 13, 1965, 59th Leg., R.S., ch. 277

§ 9.6:13 North Central Texas Municipal Water Authority

History

The North Central Texas Municipal Water Authority (NCTMWA) was created in 1957 as a conservation and reclamation district comprising the territory contained within the cities of Goree, Haskell, Knox City, Munday, Rule, Rochester, and Seymour (in Baylor, Haskell, and Knox counties). The district was created to provide, process, and transport water for municipal, domestic, industrial, and mining uses. Act of April 9, 1957, 55th Leg., R.S., ch. 86. Today, the NCTMWA provides treated water to the cities of Aspermont, Benjamin, Goree, Haskell, Knox City, Munday, O'Brien, Rochester, Rule, and Weinert; to the Paint Creek and Rhineland Water Supply Corporations; and to the Knox County Special Utility District. The 86th legislature, in 2019, passed H.B. 3663, which allows NCTMWA to acquire groundwater sources. H.B. 3663, Act of May 21, 2019, 86th Leg., R.S., ch. 546.

Structure

The NCTMWA is governed by a board composed of two directors appointed by the head of governing bodies of the cities of Goree, Haskell, Knox City, and Munday. Each board member must reside in and own taxable property within the city from which he is appointed. Directors serve two-year staggered terms. Act of April 10, 1969, 61st Leg., R.S., ch. 77.

Powers and Duties

- Bonding authority: property tax bonds and revenue bonds
- Coordinate/contract with governments/entities
- Dams and reservoirs (in Baylor, Haskell, Knox, and Throckmorton counties)
- Groundwater development
- Parks
- Police and security services
- Property acquisition through eminent domain within Baylor, Haskell, Knox, and Throckmorton counties and outside district
- Purchase/construct works to carry out district purposes
- Water quality
- Water supply: municipal, out-of-district, retail, and wholesale

Citations to Special Law or Codes

H.B. 494, Act of Apr. 9, 1957, 55th Leg., R.S., ch. 86
S.B. 257, Act of Apr. 10, 1969, 61st Leg., R.S., ch. 77
S.B. 1027, Act of May 31, 1971, 62d Leg., R.S., ch. 849
H.B. 3663, Act of May 21, 2019, 86th Leg., R.S., ch. 546

§ 9.6:14 North Harris County Regional Water Authority

History

On June 18, 1999, the bill that created the North Harris County Regional Water Authority (NHCRWA) was signed into law, and a special election was called for January 15, 2000, at which voters confirmed the creation of the new authority and elected directors to lead it. The boundaries of the authority are essentially US Highway 290 on the west, the Harris County line on the north (Spring Creek), FM Road 1960 and Bammel-North Houston on the south, and the western shores of Lake Houston on the east. The NHCRWA comprises 335 square miles and includes approximately 460,000 residents. *See* Act of May 20, 1999, 76th Leg., R.S., ch. 1029; *see also* North Harris County Regional Water Authority, *North Harris County Regional Water Authority*, www.nhcrwa.com/ [hereinafter About the NHCRWA].

Following the January 2000 election, the NHCRWA became the single entity empowered to negotiate for a secure, long-term, reliable, quality supply of wholesale drinking water for all the independent neighborhoods, municipal utility districts, small municipalities, and permitted well owners within its boundaries. A primary charge of the NHCRWA is to develop and implement a strategy for complying with the Harris-Galveston Subsidence District's Regulatory Plan that requires a reduction in groundwater usage to no more than 20 percent of total water demand by the year 2030. *See* About the NHCRWA. See Chapter 16 of this book for a discussion of subsidence districts.

Since the authority is not a taxing entity, funding for future water supply and the infrastructure through which to deliver it is accomplished through the sale of revenue bonds paid for by groundwater pumpage fees. *See* About the NHCRWA.

Structure

The NHCRWA is governed by a five-member board of directors. One director is elected from each of the five single-member voting districts by the qualified voters of the district. The directors serve staggered four-year terms and must be qualified voters in the voting district they represent. *See* Act of May 20, 1999, 76th Leg., R.S., ch. 1029.

Powers and Duties

- Bonding authority: revenue bonds
- Chapter 49 (does not apply)
- Conservation of water
- Coordinate/contract with governments/entities
- Groundwater (regulation of pumping)
- Property acquisition through eminent domain, within and outside district
- Purchase/construct works to carry out district purposes
- Water quality
- Water supply: municipal, out-of-district, and wholesale

Citations to Special Law or Codes

H.B. 2965, Act of May 20, 1999, 76th Leg., R.S., ch. 1029
S.B. 270, Act of May 9, 2001, 77th Leg., R.S., ch. 232
H.B. 1110, Act of May 17, 2001, 77th Leg., R.S., ch. 1296
S.B. 1444, Act of May 26, 2001, 77th Leg., R.S., ch. 1423
S.B. 2, Act of May 28, 2001, 77th Leg., R.S., ch. 966
S.B. 1725, Act of May 30, 2003, 78th Leg., R.S., ch. 381
H.B. 1208, Act of May 26, 2005, 79th Leg., R.S., ch. 271
S.B. 331, Act of May 28, 2005, 79th Leg., R.S., ch. 1343

§ 9.6:15 North Texas Municipal Water District

History

The North Texas Municipal Water District (NTMWD) is a conservation and reclamation district created in 1951. Local interests saw a need to finance, construct, and operate facilities to meet the water needs of the North Texas and Dallas areas. Act of Apr. 4, 1951, 52d Leg., R.S., ch. 62; *see* North Texas Municipal Water District, *History*, www.ntmwd.com/history [hereinafter NTMWD History].

In 1956, the NTMWD delivered treated water to approximately 32,000 citizens. Today, the NTMWD meets the daily water needs of more than 1.6 million people in Collin, Rockwall, and portions of Dallas, Denton, Fannin, Grayson, Hunt, Hopkins, Kaufman, and Van Zandt counties. NTMWD History. In addition, the NTMWD provides wastewater treatment and solid waste disposal services. All services are provided through contracts in which municipalities pledge revenues received from water, sewer, and solid waste customers. NTMWD History. The NTMWD's three systems are completely separate financially; systems may neither subsidize nor draw revenue from each other. Personal Communication from Jim Parks, NTMWD, to Lyn Clancy, Managing Assoc. Gen. Counsel, Lower Colorado River Authority (Apr. 15, 2011) (on file with author) [hereinafter Parks Personal Communication].

Lake Lavon serves as the NTMWD's main raw water supply. The NTMWD holds all of the water rights in the reservoir. The reservoir also serves as temporary storage for additional supplies that are transferred into Lake Lavon from other sources, to augment supplies. Parks Personal Communication; *see also* Texas State Historical Association, *Lavon Lake*, www.tshaonline.org/handbook/entries/lavon-lake. The NTMWD also holds water rights for raw water supplies from the East Fork Raw Water Supply Project (i.e., the East Fork Wetland), Jim Chapman Lake, Lake Bonham, and Lake Texoma.

Additional supplies are also available through a contract with the Sabine River Authority (SRA) providing for water transfer to Lake Lavon from Lake Tawakoni, and from a contract with Greater Texoma Utility Authority for additional supplies from Lake Texoma. *See* North Texas Municipal Water District, *Our Water System*, www.ntmwd.com/our-water-system/ [hereinafter Waste Water]. The NTMWD has recognized its role in developing future water supplies that are needed to meet the water demands of a population expected to exceed 3.8 million by 2060.

As mentioned, the NTMWD provides wastewater treatment services to cities and communities within its service area. *See* Waste Water. Additionally, the NTMWD provides municipal solid waste services for five member cities and residents of Collin County. The NTMWD owns and operates the 121 Regional Disposal Facility (121 RDF) in Melissa, which is expected to meet the needs of its customers for the next forty years. The NTMWD also operates three solid waste transfer stations. *See* Parks Personal Communication.

Structure

The NTMWD is currently governed by a twenty-five-member board of directors appointed to two-year staggered terms by the city councils of the NTMWD member cities of Allen, Farmersville, Forney, Frisco, Garland, McKinney, Mesquite, Plano, Princeton, Richardson, Rockwall, Royse City, and Wylie. The size of the board can change as population increases; member cities with a population of five thousand or more appoint two directors; cities with a population of less than five thousand appoint only one director. Each director must reside and own taxable property in the represented city. *See* Act of Apr. 4, 1951, 52d Leg., R.S., ch. 62.

Powers and Duties

- Air quality control
- Bonding authority: contract bonds and revenue bonds
- Conservation of water and soil
- Coordinate/contract with governments/entities
- Dams and reservoirs
- Drainage and flood control
- Electric generation and transmission facilities
- Parks
- Police and security services
- Property acquisition through eminent domain, within and outside district
- Purchase/construct works to carry out district purposes
- Regulate private sewage, on-site sewage facilities
- Solid waste disposal
- Wastewater
- Water quality
- Water supply: irrigation, municipal, out-of-district, retail, and wholesale

Citations to Special Law or Codes

S.B. 141, Act of Apr. 4, 1951, 52d Leg., R.S., ch. 62
H.B. 654, Act of Apr. 28, 1969, 61st Leg., R.S., ch. 122
S.B. 640, Act of Apr. 23, 1975, 64th Leg., R.S., ch. 90
S.B. 715, Act of Apr. 29, 2009, 81st Leg., R.S., ch. 20

§ 9.6:16 Northeast Texas Municipal Water District

History

The Northeast Texas Municipal Water District (NETMWD) was formed in 1953 to be the local sponsor of Lake O' the Pines in the Cypress basin. Wright Patman and Lyndon B. Johnson were instrumental in arranging for federal participation in creating Lake O' the Pines, which was constructed to reduce flooding of the city of Jefferson and is the primary source of the NETMWD's water. The district territory covers portions of fifty-nine east Texas counties. *See* Northeast Texas Municipal Water District, *About Us*, www.netmwd.com/about-us [hereinafter *About Us*].

In 1957, the NETMWD obtained the right to divert and consume 203,800 acre-feet annually from the lake. The NETMWD had no financial resources and was dependent on contributions from a local property tax from member cities and sales of raw water. The NETMWD was able to discontinue assessing taxes by 1977 due to the growth of raw water sales. *See About Us*.

The NETMWD constructed its first water treatment plant in 1984. In 1995, a contract was signed with the city of Longview to provide a long-term water supply from Lake O' the Pines. In 1998, the NETMWD acquired its second water treatment plant, which provides treated water to the city of Pittsburg. The NETMWD's facilities have a combined water treatment capacity of 9.2 million gallons per day and serve the communities of Avinger, Daingerfield, Diana, Harleton, Hughes Springs, Jefferson, Lone Star, Mims, Ore City, Pittsburg, and Tryon Road. In addition, the NETMWD provides water for key industrial facilities in its service area. *See About Us*.

The NETMWD's mission is to protect the water quality in the Cypress basin and to provide a sufficient supply of water to Northeast Texas. *See* Northeast Texas Municipal Water District, *Our Mission*, www.netmwd.com/home.

Structure

The NETMWD is governed by a seven-member board of directors selected by the city councils of the seven member cities of Lone Star, Jefferson, Avinger, Pittsburg, Daingerfield, Ore City, and Hughes Springs. Northeast Texas Municipal Water District, *About Us*, https://netmwd.com/about-us. The directors are elected for a two-year term and must be residents of the city from which they are elected. Act of Apr. 23, 1953, 53d Leg., R.S., ch. 78.

Powers and Duties

- Bonding authority: tax bonds and revenue bonds
- Conservation of water
- Coordinate/contract with governments/entities
- Dams and reservoirs
- Parks
- Property acquisition through eminent domain, within and outside district
- Purchase/construct works to carry out district purposes
- Taxes: operation and maintenance expenses
- Wastewater
- Water quality
- Water supply: irrigation, municipal, and wholesale

Citations to Special Law or Codes

S.B. 130, Act of Apr. 23, 1953, 53d Leg., R.S., ch. 78
S.B. 395, Act of May 4, 1959, 56th Leg., R.S., ch. 375
S.B. 36, Act of July 14, 1959, 56th Leg., 2d C.S., ch. 28
S.B. 63, Act of Aug. 2, 1961, 57th Leg., 1st C.S., ch. 16
H.B. 1598, Act of May 8, 1975, 64th Leg., R.S., ch. 193

§ 9.6:17 Nueces River Authority

History

The Nueces River Authority (NRA) was created in 1935 to conserve and develop water resources in the Nueces River basin. Act of Oct. 14, 1935, 44th Leg., 1st C.S., ch. 427. The NRA's service area covers more than 17,000 square miles in South Texas, including all or part of twenty-two counties, from Rocksprings to the Gulf of Mexico. *See* Act of May 21, 1985, 69th Leg., R.S., ch. 665, § 1; *see also* Nueces River Authority, *Water for the Future—Developing and Protecting Water Resources in South Texas Since 1935*, www.nueces-ra.org/NRA/pdfs/brochure.pdf [hereinafter NRA Brochure]. The Nueces River basin is about 235 miles long and 115 miles wide and is divided into three segments.

For its first thirty-five years, the NRA functioned solely through its board of directors, having no staff and only those funds it could realize from contributions. Email from Con Mims, Gen. Mgr., to Lyn Clancy, Managing Assoc. Gen. Counsel, Lower Colorado River Authority (Nov. 12, 2010) [hereinafter Mims email]. For several years, NRA directors promoted reservoir development projects, but none were affordable. The small rural communities in the Nueces basin had adequate groundwater supplies for municipal purposes; industrial water use was practically nonexistent except in the lower basin, and projects strictly for agricultural use were cost-prohibitive. The board hired its first employee—a part-time executive director—in 1970. Mims email. In 1973, the NRA secured a contract with the Texas Water Quality Board (now the TCEQ) to study municipal wastewater treatment needs in the Nueces basin. With this contract, the NRA was able to hire its first secretary and a full-time employee, in addition to its part-time executive director.

In 1974, the NRA began to issue tax-exempt revenue bonds to finance construction of air and water pollution control equipment for various industries. Mims email. During the 1970s and early 1980s, the NRA and the city of Corpus Christi cosponsored development of Choke Canyon Reservoir, which was constructed by the U.S. Bureau of Reclamation on the lower Frio River, to serve as a municipal and industrial water supply for the Coastal Bend region. Although the NRA owns 20 percent of the water rights associated with the Choke Canyon Reservoir, Corpus Christi retains all operation and maintenance responsibilities and all rights to sell the water supply because it is solely responsible for all project costs and liabilities. *See* NRA Brochure.

The NRA responded to record-breaking drought conditions in 1996 by financing and participating in construction of the Mary Rhodes pipeline for the city of Corpus Christi, which transports 41,840 acre-feet of the city's water from Lake Texana in Jackson County to the city's treatment facilities in Nueces County. The Lavaca-Navidad River Authority, owner of Lake Texana, issued bonds and constructed the primary pump station at the lake. *See* NRA Brochure; Mims email.

The NRA is an active participant in the regional water planning effort, serving as the administrator for the Coastal Bend Regional Water Planning Group (Region N) and providing two voting members to that group. *See* NRA Brochure; Mims email. The NRA also has a voting member in the South Central Texas Regional Water Planning Group (Region L—San Antonio region). *See* NRA Brochure; Mims email. During the 84th legislative session on behalf of the South Central Texas Regional Water Planning Group, the NRA succeeded in passage of legislation designating sections of the Upper Nueces, Frio, Sabinal, Comal, and San Marcos rivers as ecologically unique stream segments. *See* Act of May 7, 2015, 84th Leg., R.S., ch. 86 (H.B. 1016).

The NRA has focused on protection of limited water resources, contracting for the last twenty-five years with the TCEQ to carry out the state's Clean Rivers Program in the Nueces and its adjoining coastal basins. In an effort to protect the quality of the upper Frio River, the NRA is constructing a $30 million wastewater collection and treatment system to replace deteriorating septic systems in the City of Leakey and nearby subdivisions.

The NRA supported the establishment of a watermaster to enforce water rights permits in the Nueces, San Antonio, and Guadalupe River basins. The NRA is represented on the South Texas Watermaster Advisory Committee. The NRA also serves as an active member of the Nueces Estuary Advisory Council. *See* NRA Brochure; Mims email. The NRA chaired the Nueces River and Corpus Christi and Baffin Bays Basin and Bay Area Stakeholder Committee and the Edwards Aquifer Habitat Conservation Plan Stakeholders Committee. The NRA successfully advocated for a legislative ban on off-road vehicles in state-owned riverbeds. *See* Act of June 20, 2003, 78th Leg., R.S., ch. 800.

The NRA levies no taxes and receives no state or federal appropriations.

In 2019, the NRA underwent sunset review. In response to the recommendations by the Sunset Advisory Commission, the NRA's enabling act was amended to require the governor to appoint the board president, require training of its board members, separate policymaking and management functions, create a process for handling complaints and for allowing public testimony at board meetings, and develop and implement alternative dispute resolution procedures to assist with internal and external disputes under the NRA's jurisdiction. The NRA will undergo sunset review again in 2031. *See* Act of Apr. 30, 2019, 86th Leg., R.S., ch. 21, § 2 (S.B. 625), eff. Sept. 1, 2019.

In 2021, the NRA's enabling legislation was codified at Tex. Special Dist. Local Laws Code ch. 8511 (Act of May 27, 2021, 87th Leg, R.S., ch. 914, §§ 1.03, 2.01, 3.04 (H.B. 3530)).

Structure

The NRA is governed by a board of twenty-one directors who serve six-year staggered terms, all appointed by the governor with the advice and consent of the senate. Board members must be residents and property taxpayers within the district. Nueces County must have four members, with Jim Wells and San Patricio counties each having two representatives. Act of May 26, 1971, 62d Leg., R.S., ch. 695.

Powers and Duties

- Bonding authority: contract bonds, property tax bonds, and revenue bonds
- Conservation of water and soil
- Coordinate/contract with governments/entities
- Dams and reservoirs
- Drainage and flood control
- Electric generation and transmission facilities
- Navigation
- Parks
- Police and security services
- Property acquisition through eminent domain, within and outside district
- Purchase/construct works to carry out district purposes
- Regulate private sewage, on-site sewage facilities
- Solid waste disposal
- Taxes: operation and maintenance expenses; special taxes for pollution control
- Wastewater
- Water quality
- Water supply: irrigation, municipal, out-of-district (surplus), retail, and wholesale

Citations to Special Law or Codes

H.B. 141, Act of Oct. 14, 1935, 44th Leg., 1st C.S., ch. 42
H.B. 358, Act of Feb. 24, 1937, 45th Leg., R.S., ch. 21
H.B. 38, Act of Oct. 25, 1937, 45th Leg., 2d C.S., ch. 20
S.B. 329, Act of Apr. 13, 1939, 46th Leg., R.S., Spec. L., ch. 7
S.B. 320, Act of June 15, 1939, 46th Leg., R.S., ch.27
H.B. 83, Act of Apr. 9, 1941, 47th Leg., R.S., ch. 144
H.B. 560, Act of May 7, 1943, 48th Leg., R.S., ch. 390
H.B. 813, Act of May 16, 1945, 49th Leg., R.S., ch. 305
H.B. 1832, Act of May 26, 1971, 62d Leg., R.S., ch. 695
S.B. 437, Act of May 21, 1975, 64th Leg., R.S., ch. 699
H.B. 467, Act of May 20, 1977, 65th Leg., R.S., ch. 565
H.B. 1006, Act of Apr. 26, 1979, 66th Leg., R.S., ch. 138
S.B. 1254, Act of May 17, 1985, 69th Leg., R.S., ch. 844
S.B. 1245, Act of May 21, 1985, 69th Leg., R.S., ch. 665
H.B. 1820, Act of May 29, 2005, 79th Leg., R.S., ch. 977
S.B. 523, Act of May 31, 2015, 84th Leg., R.S., ch. 1148, § 10
S.B. 625, Act of Apr. 30, 2019, 86th Leg., R.S., ch. 21
H.B. 3530, Act of May 27, 2021, 87th Leg., R.S., ch. 914, §§ 1.03, 2.01, 3.04

§ 9.6:18 Red River Authority of Texas

History

The Red River Authority (RRA) was created in 1959 as a conservation and reclamation district. Act of May 8, 1959, 56th Leg., R.S., ch. 279. The RRA's territorial jurisdiction encompasses all Texas counties lying wholly or partly within the watershed of the Red River and its tributaries upstream from the northeast corner of Bowie County as well as Hartley, Hutchinson, and Lipscomb counties. Act of

May 8, 1959, 56th Leg., R.S., ch. 279; Act of May 26, 1977, 65th Leg., R.S., ch. 529; Act of May 15, 1975, 64th Leg., R.S., ch. 217. In 1981, the legislature added Lamar and Red River counties, and Bowie County for limited purposes, and divided the authority's territorial jurisdiction into three geographical regions. Act of May 25, 1981, 67th Leg., R.S., ch. 870.

The RRA provides public services in the areas of research, planning, design, permit acquisition, development, treatment and distribution of surface water and groundwater, treatment and disposal of municipal and industrial wastewater, and environmental protection through pollution abatement and control. The authority has issued millions of tax-exempt contract revenue bonds to provide financial assistance to public entities throughout the Red River basin. The RRA currently provides expert assistance and services related to water resource management to more than sixty-five towns, communities, and cities throughout the basin. *See* Red River Authority of Texas, *About Us*, *Scope of Services*, www.rra.texas.gov/?dhp=/scope_of_services.htm. See also Chapter 14 of this book regarding multijurisdictional issues.

In 2019, the RRA underwent sunset review. In response to the recommendations by the Sunset Advisory Commission, the RRA's enabling act was amended to require the governor to appoint the board president, require training of its board members, add grounds for removal of a director on the board, prohibit a director from serving as the general manager of the RRA, separate policymaking and management functions, create a process for handling complaints, adopt an asset management plan, develop and implement alternative dispute resolution procedures to assist with internal and external disputes under the RRA's jurisdiction, and establish procedures to ensure affected persons are notified and provided an opportunity to comment on significant water rate changes and inform those affected persons of the appeals process. The RRA will undergo sunset review again in 2031. *See* Act of Apr. 30, 2019, 86th Leg., R.S., ch. 23 (S.B. 627), eff. Sept. 1, 2019.

The RRA was also tasked by the 86th Legislature to study the feasibility of increasing navigation on the Red River between Texarkana and Denison by completing the navigation system of locks and dams. The study must be submitted to the standing committees of the legislature by January 1, 2021. *See* Act of May 27, 2019, 86th Leg., R.S., ch. 1192 (H.B. 4166), eff. Sept. 1, 2019.

In 2021, the Texas legislature codified the RRA's enabling legislation in Chapter 8510 of the Special District Local Laws Code. H.B. No. 3530, Act of May 27, 2021, 87th Leg., R.S., ch. 914.

Structure

The RRA's governing body is composed of a nine-member board of directors, all of whom are appointed by the governor and confirmed by the senate. A board member must be a legal voter, a property taxpayer, and a resident within the RRA's jurisdiction. Three directors come from each of the three geographic regions. Each director serves a six-year staggered term. One director from each of the three geographical regions, along with the board president, serve on the RRA's executive committee. The executive committee functions as a policy and administrative oversight committee for all agency-related functions. Act of May 27, 1969, 61st Leg., R.S., ch. 856; Act of May 25, 1981, 67th Leg., R.S., ch. 870; *see* also Red River Authority of Texas, *About Us*, *Governing Body*, www.rra.texas.gov/?dhp=/governing_body.htm.

Powers and Duties

- Air quality control
- Bonding authority: contract bonds, property tax bonds, and revenue bonds
- Chapter 49 duties
- Conservation of water and soil
- Coordinate/contract with governments/entities
- Drainage and flood control
- Electric generation and transmission facilities
- Navigation
- Other: any powers conveyed to navigation districts by general law and all powers and rights conferred by general law on any district created by Tex. Const. art. XVI, § 59
- Parks
- Police and security services
- Property acquisition through eminent domain, within and outside district
- Purchase/construct works to carry out district purposes
- Solid waste disposal
- Wastewater
- Water quality
- Water supply: irrigation, retail, and wholesale

Citations to Special Law or Codes

Tex. Spec. Dist. Code ch. 8510
S.B. 419, Act of May 8, 1959, 56th Leg., R.S., ch. 279
H.B. 800, Act of May 24, 1961, 57th Leg., R.S., ch. 504
S.B. 296, Act of May 25, 1967, 60th Leg., R.S., ch. 570
S.B. 710, Act of May 15, 1969, 61st Leg., R.S., ch. 715
H.B. 1399, Act of May 27, 1969, 61st Leg., R.S., ch. 856
H.B. 2165, Act of May 15, 1975, 64th Leg., R.S., ch. 217
S.B. 1282, Act of May 26, 1977, 65th Leg., R.S., ch. 529
S.B. 490, Act of Apr. 16, 1981, 67th Leg., R.S., ch. 86
H.B. 1549, Act of May 25, 1981, 67th Leg., R.S., ch. 870
S.B. 1348, Act of May 27, 1983, 68th Leg., R.S., ch. 696
H.B. 1285, Act of May 29, 1989, 71st Leg., R.S., ch. 1248, § 83
S.B. 281, Act of May 25, 2013, 83d Leg., R.S., ch. 1156
S.B. 523, Act of May 31, 2015, 84th Leg., R.S., ch. 1148, § 12
S.B. 627, Act of Apr. 30, 2019, 86th Leg., R.S., ch. 23
H.B. 3530, Act of May 27, 2021, 87th Leg., R.S., ch. 914, §§ 1.03, 3.03

§ 9.6:19 Sabine River Authority

History

The Sabine River Authority (SRA) was created by the Texas legislature in 1949 as a conservation and reclamation district with broad powers to control, store, preserve, and distribute the waters of the Sabine River and its tributaries for useful purposes. The service area of the SRA includes all or parts of twenty-one counties, including Collin, Rockwall, Kaufman, Hunt, Hopkins, Rains, Van Zandt, Franklin, Wood, Smith, Upshur, Gregg, Rusk, Harrison, Panola, Shelby, Sabine, San Augustine,

Newton, Jasper, and Orange. Act of Apr. 27, 1949, 51st Leg., R.S., ch. 110, 1949 Tex. Gen. Laws 193; *see* Sabine River Authority of Texas, *About the Authority*, www.sratx.org/aboutsra/history.asp [hereinafter SRA History]. The SRA is headquartered in Orange, Texas, and has five operational divisions located throughout the Sabine River basin and environmental services located in the upper and lower basin.

The primary activities of the SRA include municipal, industrial, and agricultural raw water supply; hydroelectric power generation; water quality and pollution control activities; management of three major reservoirs (Lake Tawakoni, Lake Fork, and joint ownership of Toledo Bend Reservoir) and the John Simmons Gulf Coast Canal System (serving primarily Orange County customers); recreational facilities; and an economic development initiative to enhance economic growth in the Sabine River basin. The SRA also provides an extensive water quality monitoring program throughout the basin. *See* SRA History.

The SRA purchased the Orange County Water Company in 1954. The newly acquired canal system, now known as the John Simmons Gulf Coast Canal System, provided the catalyst for the operations of the SRA. Lake Tawakoni, a 927,440 acre-foot water supply reservoir about eighty miles east of Dallas, was permitted in 1955 and completed in 1960. The project was funded through a water supply agreement with the city of Dallas to provide water for municipal and industrial purposes. Toledo Bend Reservoir, which forms a portion of the Texas-Louisiana border, was initiated in 1955 and constructed by the SRA and the Sabine River Authority of Louisiana, primarily for the purposes of water supply, hydroelectric power generation, and recreation. The reservoir, one the nation's largest at sixty-five miles long, inundating 185,000 surface acres, and impounding 4,477,000 acre-feet of water, was completed in 1966. Hydroelectric revenues and expenses are shared equally between Texas and Louisiana. The Lake Fork Reservoir, the most recent project undertaken by the SRA, is a 27,690 surface-acre reserve, begun in 1972 and completed in 1980. Lake Fork impounds 675,819 acre-feet and has a firm yield of 188,660 acre-feet per year. *See* Christopher Long, Texas State Historical Association, Handbook of Texas, *Sabine River Authority*, www.tshaonline.org/handbook/entries/sabine-river-authority [hereinafter Long]. See Chapter 14 of this book regarding multijurisdictional issues.

The SRA does not receive funds from local, state, or federal governments and does not have the authority to levy taxes. As a matter of policy, the SRA has limited its activities to major projects beyond the financial means of local interests. *See* Long. Operating revenues are primarily derived from the sale of raw water, hydroelectric power, water quality services, and recreational and land use permit fees. The SRA provides tax-exempt bond financing to industries and municipalities for water supply, wastewater, and air quality programs. The SRA has also issued pollution control bonds; these are the liability of the firms for whom they were issued. *See* Long.

Structure

The SRA is governed by a nine-member board of directors appointed by the governor with the consent of the senate for staggered six-year terms. Board representation consists of four members who reside in the upper basin, four members who reside in the lower basin, and one at-large member. At the close of fiscal year 2013, the SRA had 103 full-time employees throughout the basin. *See* Act of May 27, 1999, 76th Leg., R.S. ch. 1496.

Powers and Duties

- Bonding authority: contract bonds and revenue bonds
- Chapters 49, 51, and 54 powers and duties
- Conservation of water and soil
- Coordinate/contract with governments/entities
- Dams and reservoirs
- Drainage and flood control
- Hydroelectric generation facilities
- Navigation
- Parks
- Police and security services
- Property acquisition through eminent domain, within and outside district
- Purchase/construct works to carry out district purposes
- Solid waste disposal
- Toll bridges and ferries: contract for and regulate
- Wastewater
- Water quality
- Water supply: irrigation, municipal, wholesale

Citations to Special Law or Codes

H.B. 467, Act of Apr. 27, 1949, 51st Leg., R.S., ch. 110
H.B. 145, Act of Apr. 6, 1955, 54th Leg., R.S., ch. 101
H.B. 551, Act of Apr. 7, 1955, 54th Leg., R.S., ch. 93
S.B. 298, Act of May 22, 1973, 63d Leg., R.S., ch. 238
H.B. 1285, Act of May 29, 1989, 71st Leg., R.S., ch. 1248, § 79
S.B. 1120, Act of May 2, 1991, 72d Leg., R.S., ch. 100
H.B. 3846, Act of May 27, 1999, 76th Leg., R.S., ch. 1496
S.B. 1162, Act of May 27, 2015, 84th Leg., R.S., ch. 855, § 1.06 (adding Tex. Spec. Dist. Code ch. 9063)
S.B. 523, Act of May 31, 2015, 84th Leg., R.S., ch. 1148, § 13
S.B. 619, Act of May 27, 2019, 86th Leg., R.S., ch. 596, § 3.09

§ 9.6:20 San Antonio River Authority

History

The San Antonio River Authority (SARA), created in 1937 as the San Antonio River Canal and Conservancy District, is charged with preserving, protecting, and managing the resources and environment of the San Antonio River and its tributaries over a 3,658-square-mile service area within Bexar, Goliad, Karnes, and Wilson counties. Act of May 12, 1961, 57th Leg., R.S., ch. 233, 1961 Tex. Gen. Laws 466; *see also* San Antonio River Authority, *About SARA*, www.sariverauthority.org/about. The San Antonio River Improvements Project (SARIP) was one of SARA's largest recent projects; it was a $384.1 million joint investment by Bexar County, the city of San Antonio, the U.S. Army Corps of Engineers, SARA, and the San Antonio River Foundation in flood control, amenities, ecosystem restoration, and recreational improvements to the San Antonio River. San Antonio River Authority, *San Antonio River Improvements Project Fact Sheet*, www.sariverauthority.org/about/history/san-antonio-river-improvements-project [hereinafter SARIP]. SARA serves as project manager for all sections of the SARIP and as local sponsor with the Corps of Engineers for one reach of the project (the Mission Reach). Portions of the SARIP include the restored portions of the original San Antonio River Walk. SARIP.

Currently, SARA is serving as the project manager for the San Pedro Creek Culture Park in which Bexar County, in coordination with the City of San Antonio, is making significant investments to transform the creek from a concrete-lined drainage ditch into a natural creek habitat and world-class linear park. *See* San Pedro Creek Culture Park, The Project, https://spcculturepark.com/the-project/.

SARA has worked on a variety of flood control projects, has developed watershed master plans for the watersheds within its district, and serves as local sponsor for the maintenance and repair of twenty-seven flood dams in Bexar County and thirteen in Karnes County. San Antonio River Authority, *Flood Risk Mitigation*, www.sariverauthority.org/public-services/flood-risk-mitigation. SARA also administers the Federal Emergency Management Agency (FEMA) buy-out programs throughout the San Antonio River Basin. Additionally, during FEMA's Map Modernization Program, SARA decided to not only digitize flood risk maps but also update them with the most up-to-date and accurate flood models and terrain mapping. The result is a more accurate depiction of flood risk throughout SARA's jurisdiction. SARA is now leading the development of FEMA's Risk Map products within its jurisdiction. San Antonio River Authority, *Risk MAP*, www.sariverauthority.org/services/flood-management/engineering-projects/san-antonio-river-authority-risk-map [hereinafter SARA Fact Sheet]. SARA operates an accredited Environmental Sciences Department Laboratory and conducts weekly tests of stormwater and wastewater for cities within its service area. *See* San Antonio River Authority, *Laboratory Services*, www.sariverauthority.org/public-services/laboratory-services. As with many other river authorities, SARA provides significant support to the state's Clean Rivers Program and supports additional water quality sampling in the San Antonio River and its tributaries through the SARA Water Monitoring Data Program. *See* San Antonio River Authority, *Clean Rivers Program*, www.sariverauthority.org/public-services/environmental-sciences/clean-rivers-program.

Located within an area that has a history of water conflicts and endangered species issues, SARA has been an active participant in the Region L water planning group and was active in the development of the Edwards Aquifer Recovery Implementation Plan (EARIP). SARA Fact Sheet. SARA is the administrator of the Regional Water Resources Development Group (RWRDG), which is a coalition of Edwards Aquifer communities and water systems that have come together to jointly acquire withdrawal permits, as well as administrator of the Regional Water Alliance, a group of Region L water purveyors and regional water entities working together to seek and implement solutions to meet the region's water needs. SARA Fact Sheet.

SARA also operates and maintains three wastewater treatment plants and collection systems in northeast Bexar County and a wastewater system at Randolph Air Force Base and contracts to provide wastewater services to the cities of La Vernia and Somerset. SARA contracts with the Goliad County Water Supply Corporation to provide operation and maintenance services for water systems in the Goliad County communities of Berclair and Fannin. In addition to water/wastewater services, SARA owns and operates nature-based parks and paddling trails in communities within its service area. *See* SARA Fact Sheet.

Structure

A twelve-member elected board of directors governs SARA; six directors are elected from Bexar County, two are at large, and four are from single-member districts that are coterminous with Bexar County commissioner precincts. Two directors are elected at large from each of the three downstream counties. Each member serves a staggered six-year term. Policies established by the board are executed by the management organization under the direction of a general manager appointed by the board. *See* Act of May 12, 1961, 57th Leg., R.S., ch. 233; Act of May 27, 1987, 70th Leg., R.S., ch. 701.

Powers and Duties

- Bonding authority: contract bonds and revenue bonds
- Conservation of water and soil
- Coordinate/contract with government and entities
- Dams and reservoirs
- Drainage and flood control
- Navigation
- Oil and gas leases
- Parks
- Pollution control districts (establish)
- Property acquisition through eminent domain, within and outside district
- Purchase/construct works to carry out district purposes
- Sewage treatment
- Solid waste disposal
- Taxes: limited rights to levy ad valorem taxes for planning operation and maintenance expenses
- Wastewater
- Water quality
- Water supply: irrigation, municipal, retail, and wholesale

Citations to Special Law or Codes

H.B. 726, Act of May 3, 1937, 45th Leg., R.S., ch. 276
H.B. 542, Act of Mar. 24, 1939, 46th Leg., R.S., ch. 9
H.B. 64, Act of Mar. 30, 1953, 53d Leg., R.S., ch. 60
H.B. 317, Act of May 16, 1957, 55th Leg., R.S., ch. 504
S.B. 55, Act of Mar. 18, 1959, 56th Leg., R.S., ch. 37
H.B. 83, Act of May 12, 1961, 57th Leg., R.S., ch. 233
S.B. 704, Act of May 19, 1969, 61st Leg., R.S. ch. 836
S.B. 452, Act of May 17, 1975, 64th Leg., R.S. ch. 301
H.B. 1643, Act of May 30, 1975, 64th Leg., R.S., ch. 604
S.B. 741, Act of Apr. 18, 1981, 67th Leg., R.S., ch. 60
S.B. 1437, Act of May 27, 1987, 70th Leg., R.S., ch. 701
S.B. 523, Act of May 31, 2015, 84th Leg., R.S., ch. 1148, § 15

§ 9.6:21 San Jacinto River Authority

History

The San Jacinto River Authority (SJRA) was part of the larger group of regional water providers created by special act of the legislature in the 1930s. In 1937, the San Jacinto River Conservation and Reclamation District (whose name was changed in 1951 to the San Jacinto River Authority) was charged with developing, conserving, and protecting the water resources of the San Jacinto River basin. The SJRA boundaries include the entire watershed of the San Jacinto River and its tributaries, excluding Harris County. This includes all of Montgomery County and parts of Fort Bend, Grimes, Liberty, San Jacinto, Walker, and Waller counties. Act of May 12, 1937, 45th Leg., R.S., ch. 426; Act of May 14, 1951, 52d Leg., R.S., ch. 366. The SJRA serves many customers in the Houston area and is authorized to operate in East Harris County through an agreement with the city of Houston, which gives the SJRA the exclusive right to sell water east of the San Jacinto River. San Jacinto River Authority, *About*, www.sjra.net/about [hereinafter About the SJRA].

The SJRA is responsible for municipal and industrial raw water supply, wholesale treated water supply, water quality management, wastewater treatment, and water and soil conservation. To provide these services, the SJRA uses income primarily derived from the sale and distribution of water and treatment of wastewater, as it has no taxing authority. This revenue covers the cost of operation and maintenance as well as retirement of outstanding debt. Revenue bonds are sold to finance projects. *See* About the SJRA. In its early years, from 1939 to 1949, the SJRA received a portion of state ad valorem taxes from Montgomery, Walker, San Jacinto, and part of Liberty counties. Act of June 13, 1939, 46th Leg., R.S., ch. 10.

The SJRA is organized into five operational divisions: the Lake Conroe Division, Woodlands Division, Highlands Division, GRP Division, and Flood Management Division. *See* About the SJRA. The SJRA operates and maintains the dam, spillway structure, and service outlet at Lake Conroe, which was completed by the SJRA in 1973 as a water supply reservoir through a joint venture with the city of Houston, which owns two-thirds of the water rights in the reservoir. *See* About the SJRA. Within the Woodlands Division, the SJRA provides wholesale water supply (from forty groundwater wells and a surface water treatment plant at Lake conroe) and operates three regional wastewater systems within The Woodlands Township. *See* About the SJRA. Within the Highlands Division, the SJRA delivers water from Lake Houston through canals to a number of large industrial, municipal, and agricultural customers in East Harris County. *See* About the SJRA.

Finally, the SJRA has been closely involved in efforts to reduce reliance on groundwater within the region to address issues of subsidence. Through its Groundwater Reduction Plan (GRP) Division, the SJRA is responsible for implementing a countywide surface water program that will meet the groundwater reduction requirements of the Lone Star Groundwater Conservation District and ensure reliable long-term water supplies for all of Montgomery County. *See* About the SJRA. The GRP Division designed, constructed, and now operates, maintains, and administers a water treatment plant and transmission lines that withdraw raw surface water from Lake Conroe, treat it to meet or exceed drinking water standards, and then transmit it to customer cities and utilities within Montgomery County. *See* About the SJRA; *see also* Lone Star Groundwater Conservation District *Rules of the Lone Stare Groundwater Conservation District*, (as amended, eff. Sept.. 8, 2020) www.lonestargcd.org/s/LSGCD-Rules-final-Adopted-Sept-8-20202582.pdf; *see also* Carolyn Ahrens & Jace A. Houston, *Groundwater Reduction Plans: A Case Study from the Lone Star GCD, in The Changing Face of Water Rights in Texas* (State Bar of Texas 2011).

Structure

The SJRA is governed by a seven-member board of directors appointed by the governor to six-year staggered terms. Four of the directors must be residents of a county wholly within the SJRA's territory. Act of May 23, 2003, 78th Leg., R.S., ch. 847.

Powers and Duties

- Air quality control
- Bonding authority: revenue bonds
- Conservation of water and soil
- Coordinate/contract with governments/entities
- Dams and reservoirs
- Drainage and flood control
- Hydroelectric generation facilities
- Navigation
- Oil and gas leases
- Parks
- Police and security services
- Property acquisition through eminent domain, within and outside district
- Purchase/construct works to carry out district purposes
- Regulate private sewage, on-site sewage facilities
- Solid waste disposal
- Wastewater
- Water quality
- Water supply: irrigation, municipal, and wholesale

Citations to Special Law or Codes

H.B. 832, Act of May 12, 1937, 45th Leg., R.S., ch. 426
H.B. 941, Act of May 1, 1939, 46th Leg., R.S., ch. 10
H.B. 1079, Act of June 13, 1939, 46th Leg., R.S., ch. 10
H.B. 828, Act of June 3, 1941, 47th Leg., R.S., ch. 480
H.B.1094, Act of July 2, 1941, 47th Leg., R.S., ch. 613
H.B. 696, Act of May 10, 1943, 48th Leg., R.S., ch. 371
S.B. 224, Act of May 14, 1951, 52d Leg., R.S., ch. 366
H.B. 1282, Act of May 25, 1967, 60th Leg., R.S., ch. 547
H.B. 1683, Act of May 21, 1991, 72d Leg., R.S., ch. 698
S.B. 526, Act of May 23, 2003, 78th Leg., R.S., ch. 847
S.B. 523, Act of May 31, 2015, 84th Leg., R.S., ch. 1148, § 16
H.B. 1824, Act of May 27, 2019, 86th Leg., R.S., ch. 1286, § 2 (adding Tex. Parks & Wild. Code § 86.0192)

§ 9.6:22 Sulphur River Basin Authority

History

The Sulphur River Basin Authority (SRBA) was created in 1985. *See* Act of May 29, 1985, 69th Leg., 1st C.S., ch. 3. The SRBA helps protect the water quality of the Sulphur River basin by serving as the designated partner agency for the Texas Clean Rivers Program within the basin. *See* Sulphur River Basin Authority, *Clean Rivers Program*, http://srbatx.org/clean-rivers.html.

The Sulphur River basin is in the northeast corner of Texas and includes all or part of Bowie, Cass, Delta, Fannin, Franklin, Hopkins, Hunt, Lamar, Morris, Red River, and Titus counties. The headwater streams are the North and South Sulphur Rivers, which originate in Fannin County. The Middle Sulphur converges with the South Sulphur at Cooper Lake. These rivers all converge and flow eastward into Wright Patman Lake and exit Texas south of the city of Texarkana. The Sulphur River basin drainage area is approximately 3,558 square miles. *See* Sulphur River Basin Authority, *About Us*, http://srbatx.org/aboutus.html.

Four of the sixteen unique reservoir sites designated by the 2007 State Water Plan are located within the Sulphur River basin, including various stages of the Marvin Nichols Reservoir. *See* Texas Water Development Board, 2 *Water for Texas 2007* 265–68, www.twdb.texas.gov/waterplanning/swp/2007/. The reservoir is also included in the 2012 State Water Plan. *See* Texas Water Development Board, *Water for Texas 2012* 193, www.twdb.texas.gov/waterplanning/swp/2012/. See also Chapter 27 of this book regarding reservoirs. After a lengthy legal challenge brought by the Region D water planning group, the Texas Water Development Board decided in early 2015 to retain the Marvin Nichols Reservoir within the Region C plan. News Release, Texas Water Development Board, *TWDB votes on the Interregional Conflict between Region C and Region D* (Jan. 8, 2015), www.twdb.texas.gov/waterplanning/rwp/regions/RegionCandDConflict2016.asp; *see also Texas Water Development Board v. Ward Timber, Ltd.*, 411 S.W.3d 554 (Tex. App.—Eastland 2013, no pet.).

In 2013, the 83rd Legislature passed House Bill 1675, subjecting the SRBA to sunset review with the potential for abolition. *See* Act of May 26, 2013, 83d Leg., R.S., ch. 1279, § 2.03, eff. June 14, 2013. However, in 2015 the 84th Legislature repealed and replaced this law with sunset review without abolition when it enacted sunset review for several river authorities. *See* Act of May 31, 2015, 84th Leg., R.S., ch. 1148, § 17 (S.B. 523); Act of May 31, 2015, 84th Leg., R.S., ch. 938, § 4.01 (H.B. 3123).

In 2017, the SRBA underwent sunset review. "[T]o allow SRBA and its stakeholders to reestablish the working relationships and trust needed to best meet the needs of the Sulphur River basin," the Sunset Advisory Commission made several specific recommendations to the legislature to overhaul the SRBA's leadership and operations. Sunset Advisory Commission, *Report to the 85th Legislature* 55 (Feb. 2017), www.sunset.texas.gov/public/uploads/u64/Report%20to%20the%2085th%20Legislature_Revised%20June%202017.pdf. In response to the recommendation, the SRBA's enabling act was amended to alter its board structure, require training of its board members, separate policymaking and management functions, create a process for handling complaints, and require the board to seek advice on a proposed permitted project from the relevant county judge. The act also removed the authority's power to develop hydroelectric power. *See* Act of May 19th, 2017, 85th Leg., R.S., ch. 276, § 9 (H.B. 2180), eff. Sept. 1, 2017. The SRBA will undergo sunset review again in 2029.

Structure

The SRBA is governed by a seven-member board of directors, serving staggered six-year terms, appointed by the governor. Two members of the board must be appointed from each of three regions specifically identified in the enabling legislation, and one member must be appointed to represent the authority at large. The board meets monthly. *See* Tex. Spec. Dist. Code § 8508.0051.

Powers and Duties

- Air quality control
- Bonding authority: revenue bonds
- Conservation of water and soil
- Coordinate/contract with governments/entities
- Dams and reservoirs
- Drainage and flood control
- Irrigation
- Parks
- Police and security services
- Property acquisition through eminent domain, within and outside district
- Purchase/construct works to carry out district purposes
- Solid waste disposal
- Taxes: no taxing authority or debt payable by taxes

Citations to Special Law or Codes

H.B. 1675, Act of May 26, 2013, 83d Leg., R.S., ch. 1279, § 2.03
S.B. 523, Act of May 31, 2015, 84th Leg., R.S., ch. 1148, § 17
H.B. 3123, Act of May 31, 2015, 84th Leg., R.S., ch. 938, § 4.01
H.B. 2180, Act of May 19th, 2017, 85th Leg., R.S., ch. 276, §§ 5, 9
H.B. 4172, Act of May 24, 2019, 86th Leg., R.S., ch. 468, § 1.03 (adding Tex. Spec. Dist. Code ch. 8508)

§ 9.6:23 Sulphur River Municipal Water District

History

The Sulphur River Municipal Water District (SRMWD) was created in 1955 and initially comprised the territory within the cities of Cooper, Commerce, and Sulphur Springs. It primarily provides water for domestic, municipal, and industrial purposes from its primary source of supply, Jim Chapman Lake, but may also provide water for irrigation when supplies are plentiful. Act of Apr. 28, 1955, 54th Leg., R.S., ch. 212. The district owns rights to divert 38,520 acre-feet per year from the lake. *See* Certificate of Adjudication No. 03-4797. It has contracted much of this supply to the Upper Trinity Regional Water District and the North Texas Municipal Water District. *See* Certificate of Adjudication Nos. 03-4797A, 03-4797B. The remaining SRMWD supply is divided between the city of Cooper (1,072 acre-feet per year) and the city of Sulphur Springs (18,128 acre-feet per year). *See also* Texas Water Development Board, Region C Water Planning Group, *1 2011 Region C Water Plan* 1.53 tbl. 3.8, www.twdb.texas.gov/waterplanning/rwp/plans/2011/. Jim Chapman Lake (also known as Cooper Lake), a U.S. Army Corps of Engineers–constructed facility, also provides water supply for the North Texas Municipal Water District and the city of Irving. *See* U.S. Army Corps of Engineers, *Welcome to Jim Chapman Lake/Cooper Dam*, www.swf-wc.usace.army.mil/cooper/. Other territory within Delta, Franklin, Hopkins, and Hunt counties can be annexed into the district. Act of Apr. 28, 1955, 54th Leg., R.S., ch. 212.

Structure

The SRMWD is governed by a board of directors, each of whom is appointed by a majority vote of the governing body of each city within the district for staggered two-year terms. A director must reside and own taxable property in the city from which appointed. No city employee or member of the city governing body may serve as a director. Any annexed city with a population of 5,000 or more may appoint a board member. Act of April 28, 1955, 54th Leg., R.S., ch. 212.

Powers and Duties

- Bonding authority: contract bonds, property tax bonds, and revenue bonds
- Conservation of water
- Coordinate/contract with governments/entities
- Dams and reservoirs
- Fishing, hunting, and boating regulation
- Groundwater purchase
- Property acquisition through eminent domain (limited), within Delta, Franklin, Hopkins, and Hunt counties
- Purchase/construct works to carry out district purposes
- Taxes: operation and maintenance expenses
- Wastewater
- Water quality
- Water supply: irrigation (surplus), municipal, retail, and wholesale

Citations to Special Law or Codes

H.B. 713, Act of Apr. 28, 1955, 54th Leg., R.S., ch. 212

§ 9.6:24 Tarrant Regional Water District

History

In 1922, a massive flood along the Trinity River killed ten people and resulted in more than $1 million in damages. Tarrant Regional Water District, *How was TRWD founded?*, www.trwd.com/how-was-trwd-founded/ [hereinafter *TRWD History*]. As a result, in 1924 the Tarrant Regional Water District was established originally as the Tarrant County Water Improvement District No. 1. *See* Email from Chad Lorance, Tarrant Regional Water District, to Lyn Clancy, LCRA Managing Assoc. Gen. Counsel (Dec. 9, 2010) (on file with author) [hereinafter Lorance email]. The name was changed to the Tarrant County Water Control and Improvement District No. 1 in 1926 when the district was charged with providing adequate water supply to the citizens of Tarrant County, and again in 1996 to the Tarrant Regional Water District (TRWD). *See TRWD History*; Lorance email.

The TRWD completed construction of the Lake Bridgeport and Eagle Mountain Lake dams in 1931 and 1932, respectively. After another disastrous flood damaged large portions of Fort Worth in 1949, the TRWD worked in conjunction with the U.S. Army Corp of Engineers to implement extensive improvements to the city's levee system. *See* Tarrant Regional Water District, *Flood Protection*; www.trwd.com/flood-protection/ [hereinafter TRWD Flood]. The TRWD completed the construction of the Cedar Creek Reservoir dam in 1964 and the Richland-Chambers dam in 1987. Water transport pipelines were completed from the Cedar Creek and Richland-Chambers reservoirs in 1973 and 1988, respectively, to bring water to Tarrant County. Construction was completed on the $62 million Benbrook Lake pipeline in 1998. *See* TRWD Flood.

The TRWD currently owns and operates four major reservoirs in Texas—Cedar Creek, Eagle Mountain Lake, Lake Bridgeport, and Richland-Chambers—that are used for water supply purposes. The district also delivers water via a pipeline to Lakes Arlington and Benbrook, which serve as terminal storage reservoirs for the district. *See generally* Tarrant Regional Water District, *FAQs*, www.trwd.com/about-trwd/faqs [hereinafter TRWD FAQs]. The TRWD is one of the largest raw water suppliers in Texas, providing water to more than two million people in the North Central Texas area and serving more than thirty wholesale customers, including the cities of Arlington, Fort Worth, and Mansfield as well as the Trinity River Authority. *See* TRWD FAQs.

Structure

The TRWD is governed by a five-member publicly elected board. Members serve staggered four-year terms and must own land subject to taxation within the district, which includes much of the city of Fort Worth and areas surrounding Eagle Mountain Lake. Board meetings are generally held monthly.

Powers and Duties

- Bonding authority: contract bonds, property tax bonds, and revenue bonds
- Chapters 49, 50, and 51 duties
- Conservation of water
- Coordinate/contract with governments/entities
- Dams and reservoirs
- Drainage and flood control
- Oil and gas leases
- Parks
- Police and security services
- Property acquisition through eminent domain, within and outside district
- Purchase/construct works to carry out district purposes
- Regulate private sewage, on-site sewage facilities adjacent to reservoirs via TCEQ order
- Taxes: operation and maintenance expenses (flood control only)
- Wastewater
- Water quality
- Water supply: irrigation, municipal, and wholesale (raw surface water only)

Citations to Special Law or Codes

H.B. 921, Act of May 9, 1957, 55th Leg., R.S., ch. 268
H.B. 1071, Act of May 24, 1961, 57th Leg., R.S., ch. 352
S.B. 294, Act of May 27, 1961, 57th Leg., R.S., ch. 414
H.B. 807, Act of May 20, 1965, 59th Leg., R.S., ch. 601
S.B. 1674, Act of May 24, 1995, 74th Leg., R.S., ch. 592
H.B. 3636, Act of May 15, 2001, 77th Leg., R.S., ch. 433
H.B. 2639, Act of May 28, 2005, 79th Leg., R.S., ch. 1363

§ 9.6:25 Titus County Fresh Water Supply District No. 1

History

The Titus County Fresh Water Supply District No. 1 was created by an election of Titus County voters in 1966 and validated by an act of the legislature in 1967. Act of May 4, 1967, 60th Leg., R.S., ch. 221. By countywide election in August 1966, Titus County voters authorized the issuance of over $2 million in tax and revenue bonds to be used for the construction of what is now known as Lake Bob Sandlin, on the Cypress River. The district was converted into a municipal utility district by the Texas Water Rights Commission (now the TCEQ) in 1974. The TWDB was a co-owner in the lake, furnishing approximately 60 percent of the finances. The city of Mt. Pleasant and the Industrial Generating Company (now Luminant) contracted for the purchase of water from the lake, and certainly these contracts were a big factor in getting the lake built. The city of Pittsburg may take water from the lake under an agreement between the district and the Northeast Texas Municipal Water District. Titus County Fresh Water Supply District No. 1, *Brief History of the District*, www.tcfreshwater.com/information/.

Structure

The Titus County Fresh Water Supply District No. 1 is governed by a five-member elected board of supervisors. Board members serve staggered two-year terms. Act of May 4, 1967, 60th Leg., R.S., ch. 221.

Powers and Duties

- Bonding authority: contract bonds, property tax bonds, and revenue bonds
- Chapters 53 and 54 powers
- Conservation of water and soil
- Coordinate/contract with governments/entities
- Dams and reservoirs
- Police and security services
- Property acquisition through eminent domain, within and outside district
- Purchase/construct works to carry out district purposes
- Regulate private sewage, on-site sewage facilities
- Solid waste disposal
- Taxes: special taxes for pollution control
- Water quality
- Water supply: municipal, retail, and wholesale

Citations to Special Law or Codes

H.B. 601, Act of May 4, 1967, 60th Leg., R.S., ch. 221

§ 9.6:26 Trinity River Authority

History

The Trinity River Authority (TRA) was created in 1955 and charged with maintaining a master plan for basinwide development, serving as local sponsor for federal water projects, and providing services authorized by the Texas legislature within the TRA's territory. *See* Act of June 6, 1955, 54th Leg., R.S., ch. 518.

The TRA provides water and wastewater treatment, along with recreation and reservoir facilities, for municipalities within the 17,000-square-mile Trinity River basin. The TRA also serves as a conduit for tax-exempt financing for municipal water and wastewater facilities and industrial air- and water-pollution control facilities. The TRA receives no state appropriations, and although its enabling act authorizes the imposition of a tax, it has never exercised this authority. Personal Communication from Howard Slobodin, TRA Attorney, and Michelle Clark, TRA's Public Information Mgr., to Lyn Clancy, LCRA Managing Assoc. Gen. Counsel (Nov. 16, 2010) (on file with author) [hereinafter Slobodin & Clark].

The TRA operates five wastewater treatment facilities and one regional treated water system in the Dallas–Fort Worth Metroplex. It operates three treated water systems in the vicinity of Lake Livingston, which it also owns and operates for its benefit and for the benefit of the City of Houston. The TRA pioneered the concept of regional systems with its Central Regional Wastewater System, established in 1957, which now serves all or part of twenty-one contracting parties and approximately 1.2 million people in the Metroplex. Trinity River Authority of Texas, *Central Regional Wastewater System*, www.trinityra.org/services/wastewater_treatment_facilities/central_regional_wastewater_system/index.php. The TRA serves as local sponsor for several federal water projects. Most are multipurpose U.S. Army Corps of Engineers projects that provide water supply and recreational opportunities. TRA-sponsored projects include the following: Bardwell Lake, Joe Pool Lake, Navarro Mills Lake, and the Wallisville Saltwater Barrier. The TRA operates recreational facilities at Lake Livingston. *See* Trinity River Authority of Texas, *Wolf Creek Park*, www.trinityra.org/recreation/wolf_creek_park.php.

The TRA is an active participant in regional water planning, with the majority (81 percent) of the Trinity River basin falling within the Region C regional planning group (which includes Dallas–Fort Worth) and the remainder falling within the Region H regional planning group (which includes the Houston metropolitan area). *See* Trinity River Authority of Texas, *Basin Planning*, www.trinityra.org/basin_planning/index.php. In addition, the TRA actively participated in the development of environmental flow standards for watersheds draining to Galveston Bay as part of the Senate Bill 3 process. See Chapter 11 of this book for a more detailed discussion of environmental flows. The TRA also actively participates in regional flood planning, and serves as the administrator of the Trinity Regional Flood Planning Group (Region 3).

Structure

The TRA is governed by a twenty-five-member board of directors, who are appointed for staggered six-year terms by the governor. The TRA's statute specifies that three of the board members be appointed from within Tarrant County, four from Dallas County, one from each of the remaining fifteen counties within its geographical jurisdiction, and the remaining three at large. Board members must reside and own taxable property in the area from which they are appointed. Act of June 6, 1955, 54th Leg., R.S., ch. 518.

Powers and Duties

- Bonding authority: contract bonds, property tax bonds, and revenue bonds
- Conservation of water and soil
- Coordinate/contract with governments/utilities
- Dams and reservoirs
- Drainage and flood control
- Forestry
- General powers and duties of any district created by Tex. Const. art. XVI, § 59
- Hydroelectric generation facilities
- Industrial development corporation
- Navigation
- Oil and gas leases
- Other: all powers and duties conferred by general or special law on any other district, not contravened by enabling legislation
- Parks
- Property acquisition through eminent domain, within and outside district
- Purchase/construct works to carry out district purposes
- Regulate private sewage, on-site sewage facilities
- Solid waste disposal
- Taxes: special taxes for pollution control
- Wastewater
- Water quality
- Water supply: industrial, irrigation, municipal, and wholesale

Citations to Special Law or Codes

H.B. 20, Act of June 6, 1955, 54th Leg., R.S., ch. 518
S.B. 463, Act of May 15, 1957, 55th Leg. R.S., ch. 256
S.B. 22, Act of Nov. 11, 1957, 55th Leg., 1st C.S., ch. 22
S.B. 45, Act of July 14, 1959, 56th Leg., 2d C.S., ch. 29
S.B. 360, Act of Apr. 29, 1965, 59th Leg., R.S., ch. 173
S.B. 579, Act of May 15, 1967, 60th Leg., R.S., ch. 273
S.B. 333, Act of Apr. 24, 1969, 61st Leg., R.S., ch. 155
S.B. 334, Act of Apr. 24, 1969, 61st Leg., R.S., ch. 156
S.B. 332, Act of May 8, 1969, 61st Leg., R.S., ch. 193
S.B. 542, Act of May 8, 1969, 61st Leg., R.S., ch. 198
S.B. 708, Act of May 15, 1969, 61st Leg., R.S., ch. 364
S.B. 993, Act of Apr. 12, 1979, 66th Leg., R.S., ch. 87
S.B. 994, Act of May 26, 1979, 66th Leg., R.S., ch. 674
S.B. 1543, Act of May 26, 1991, 72d Leg., R.S., ch. 858
S.B. 792, Act of Apr. 28, 1995, 74th Leg., R.S., ch. 74
S.B. 523, Act of May 31, 2015, 84th Leg., R.S., ch. 1148, § 18
S.B. 619, Act of May 27, 2019, 86th Leg., R.S., ch. 596, § 3.10

§ 9.6:27 Upper Colorado River Authority

History

The Upper Colorado River Authority (UCRA) was chartered in 1935 to protect the watersheds of Coke, Tom Green, and contiguous counties. *See* Act of May 1, 1935, 44th Leg., R.S., ch. 126. The UCRA received initial funding through a grant of ad valorem taxes from Coke and Tom Green counties. *See* Act of Oct. 23, 1936, 44th Leg., 3d C.S., ch. 505; Act of June 21, 1939, 46th Leg., R.S., ch. 4; Act of Apr. 23, 1941, 47th Leg., R.S., ch. 174; Act of Apr. 21, 1943, 48th Leg., R.S., ch. 170. Although the UCRA's enabling act provides it with fairly broad powers related to water sales, it does not directly manage or operate any dams. Instead, up through the 1990s, it provided funding to local communities for water supply improvements. Since that time, its efforts have focused on water quality protection (the Texas Clean Rivers Program and nonpoint source abatement), brush control for water conservation, public education and outreach, and urban storm water management. *See* Upper Colorado River Authority, *About Us*, www.ucratx.org/about-us [hereinafter *About Us*].

As a consequence of sunset review, and with the enactment of House Bill 1921 in 2017, the 85th Legislature amended specific sections of the UCRA's enabling legislation (Special District Local Laws Code sections 8506.003, 8506.051, and 8506.056) to clarify its territory and boundaries. Act of May 19, 2017, 85th Leg., R.S., ch. 269, § 1 (H.B. 1921), eff. Sept. 1, 2017; Sunset Advisory Commission, *Report to the 85th Legislature* (Feb. 2017), www.sunset.texas.gov/public/uploads/u64/Report%20to%20the%2085th%20Legislature_Revised%20June%202017.pdf [hereinafter 85th Report]. The UCRA's territory now includes Concho, Crockett, Glasscock, Irion, Menard, Mitchell, Nolan, Reagan, Runnels, Schleicher, Sterling, and Taylor counties, in addition to Coke and Tom Green. To more accurately reflect this territory, H.B. 1921 specifies that each director of the UCRA must reside in a county located in the authority's territory and that the directors should evenly represent all counties within the authority's jurisdiction.

The Sunset Advisory Commission also recommended to the legislature that it "[d]irect UCRA to work with local partners to identify priorities and develop strategies to meet changing watershed needs." 85th Report, at 56. Responding to that recommendation, the legislature required the UCRA to implement a process for complaints, separate its policymaking and management functions, provide an opportunity for alternative dispute resolution, conduct board training, and adopt a public comment policy. Act of May 19, 2017, 85th Leg., R.S., ch. 269, §§ 5, 6 (H.B. 1921), eff. Sept. 1, 2017. The LCRA will undergo sunset review again in 2029.

Structure

The UCRA is governed by a nine-member board of directors, each appointed by the governor for staggered six-year terms. See Tex. Spec. Dist. Code § 8506.051. The governor designates the presiding officer of the board, who serves at the governor's pleasure. The board elects a secretary and treasurer. As of 2019, the UCRA had a limited staff of three full-time employees. *See About Us*. In 2021, the legislature specifically authorized the board to employ a general manager, and placed the general manager, rather than the presiding officer, in charge of the UCRA's general office. Act of May 19, 2021, 87th Leg., R.S., ch. 332, §1 (H.B. 2083), eff. Sept. 1, 2021.

Powers and Duties

- Bonding authority: revenue bonds
- Conservation of water
- Coordinate/contract with governments/entities
- Dams and reservoirs
- Drainage and flood control
- Forestry
- Hydroelectric generation facilities (subordinate to irrigation and municipal use)
- Parks
- Police and security services
- Property acquisition through eminent domain, within and outside district
- Purchase/construct works to carry out district purposes
- Water and soil quality
- Water supply: irrigation, municipal, out-of-district, retail, and wholesale

Citations to Special Law or Codes

Tex. Spec. Dist. Code ch. 8506
H.B. 77, Act of May 1, 1935, 44th Leg., R.S., ch.126
S.B. 21, Act of Oct. 23, 1936, 44th Leg., 3d C.S., ch. 505
S.B. 493, Act of June 21, 1939, 46th Leg., R.S., ch. 4
S.B. 65, Act of Apr. 23, 1941, 47th Leg., R.S., ch. 174
S.B. 93, Act of Apr. 21, 1943, 48th Leg., R.S., ch. 170
H.B. 511, Act of Apr. 9, 1947, 50th Leg., R.S., ch. 484
H.B. 858, Act of May 19, 1973, 63d Leg., R.S., ch. 268
S.B. 194, Act of May 30, 1983, 68th Leg., R.S., ch. 484, art. IV
H.B. 3053, Act of May 24, 1995, 74th Leg., R.S., ch. 516
S.B. 523, Act of May 31, 2015, 84th Leg., R.S., ch. 1148, § 19
S.B. 1162, Act of May 27, 2015, 84th Leg., R.S., ch. 855, § 1.05
H.B. 1921, Act of May 19, 2017, 85th Leg., R.S., ch. 269, §§ 1, 3, 5, 6
H.B. 2083, Act of May 19, 2021, 87th Leg., R.S., ch. 332, §1

§ 9.6:28 Upper Guadalupe River Authority

History

The Upper Guadalupe River Authority (UGRA) was created as a conservation and reclamation district in 1939. Act of Apr. 19, 1939, 46th Leg., R.S., ch. 5; *see also* Act of May 26, 1965, 59th Leg., R.S., ch. 632. The UGRA's territory comprises Kerr County. The mission of the UGRA is to protect, develop, and manage the water quantity, quality, and sustainability in the Guadalupe River watershed in Kerr County. *See* Upper Guadalupe River Authority, *About UGRA*, www.ugra.org/public-information/about-ugra. In 1971, the legislature broadened the UGRA's authority to allow it to control waters and floodwaters of the Upper Guadalupe River and its tributaries within and outside of Kerr County for the benefit of its district and to provide wastewater services to municipalities and others. Act of May 13, 1971, 62d Leg., R.S., ch. 430.

In fulfilling the role of steward of the Upper Guadalupe River and its tributaries for Kerr County, the UGRA has initiated programs that focus on stewardship, public awareness, and planning.

The UGRA's extensive water quality monitoring program includes routine sample collection at over forty sites and is supported by the UGRA Environmental Laboratory, which is nationally accredited by the NELAC Institute. The UGRA also offers several programs for citizens to be involved in protecting water quality through volunteer monitoring and river cleanups.

A portion of the Guadalupe River in Kerrville was designated as impaired due to *Escherichia coli (E. coli)* bacteria levels that did not meet state surface water quality standards. In 2011, the UGRA was selected by the TCEQ to receive grant funding to put bacteria reduction strategies in place with the assistance of the City of Kerrville, the Texas Department of Transportation, and Kerr County. Over the next three years, the UGRA and the other local partners implemented strategies to reduce the primary sources of bacterial pollution that were identified in the Guadalupe River in Kerrville. In December 2014, for the first time in twelve years, the TCEQ listed the portion of the Guadalupe River in Kerrville flowing through the city of Kerrville as fully supporting recreational use. *See* Guadalupe-Blanco River Authority, *2015 Clean Rivers Program Basin Highlights Report: Guadalupe River and Lavaca-Guadalupe Coastal Basins*, www.gbra.org/wp-content/uploads/2021/04/basinhighlights2015.pdf. See Chapter 33 of this book for a discussion of water quality standards.

The UGRA's outreach and education programs focus on engaging the public in demonstrations, activities, and presentations on water quality, pollution, conservation, riparian management, and water supply planning. Each year, dozens of programs are presented to school groups, civic groups, and other organizations.

The UGRA has adopted an incremental approach to water supply enhancement, which includes a rebate and cost assistance program for rainwater catchment systems, participation in federal and state programs to assist landowners with brush management and control of *Arundo donax*, and the construction of water and sediment control basins. The UGRA is an active member in the Plateau Water Planning Group and other initiatives to manage future water supplies. In addition, the UGRA is a partner in the Guadalupe-Blanco River Trust, which encourages the voluntary conservation, stewardship, and enjoyment of the land and water resources of the Upper Guadalupe River watershed. *See* Guadalupe-Blanco River Trust, http://gbrtrust.org/.

Structure

The UGRA is governed by a nine-member board of directors appointed by the governor to serve staggered six-year terms, all of whom must be residents and property owners within Kerr County and over the age of twenty-one. Act of May 26, 1965, 59th Leg., R.S., ch. 632.

Powers and Duties

- Bonding authority: tax bonds (limited) and revenue bonds
- Chapters 51 and 54 powers and duties
- Conservation of water and soil
- Coordinate/contract with governments/entities
- Dams and reservoirs
- Drainage and flood control
- Forestry
- Parks
- Police and security services
- Property acquisition through eminent domain, within and outside district
- Purchase/construct works to carry out district purposes
- Solid waste disposal
- Taxes: operation and maintenance expenses
- Wastewater
- Water quality
- Water regulation and control of the Upper Guadalupe River and its tributaries within and outside Kerr County
- Water supply: irrigation and wholesale

Citations to Special Law or Codes

S.B. 303, Act of Apr. 19, 1939, 46th Leg., R.S., ch. 5
H.B. 428, Act of Apr. 9, 1957, 55th Leg., R.S., ch. 83
H.B. 865, Act of Apr. 29, 1965, 59th Leg., R.S., ch. 193
H.B. 1058, Act of May 26, 1965, 59th Leg., R.S., ch. 632
H.B. 989, Act of May 13, 1971, 62d Leg., R.S., ch. 430
H.B. 2368, Act of May 26, 1983, 68th Leg., R.S., ch. 1059
S.B. 194, Act of May 30, 1983, 68th Leg., R.S., ch. 484, art. IV
S.B. 1793, Act of May 22, 1997, 75th Leg., R.S., ch. 830
S.B. 1171, Act of May 28, 1999, 76th Leg., R.S., ch. 1544
S.B. 523, Act of May 31, 2015, 84th Leg., R.S., ch. 1148, § 20
S.B. 619, Act of May 27, 2019, 86th Leg., R.S., ch. 596, § 2.08

§ 9.6:29 Upper Neches River Municipal Water Authority

History

Created in 1953, the Upper Neches River Municipal Water Authority (UNRMWA) is charged with controlling, storing, conserving, protecting, distributing, and utilizing storm and floodwaters and unappropriated flows of the Neches River and its tributaries in Anderson, Cherokee, Henderson, and Smith counties, for domestic, municipal, industrial, irrigation, and other useful purposes. Act of May 13, 1953, 53d Leg., R.S., ch. 412; *see also Owens v. Upper Neches Municipal Water Authority*, 514 S.W.2d 58, 60 (Tex. App.—Tyler 1974, writ ref'd n.r.e.). The UNRMWA is a wholesale water provider to the cities of Palestine and Tyler and to lakeside domestic and irrigation systems. It is also contracted to provide water to the city of Dallas. *See* Texas Water Development Board, *East Texas Regional Water Planning Area—2011 Update of the Regional Water Plan, Final Plan* (Sept. 1, 2010), www.twdb.texas.gov/waterplanning/rwp/plans/2011/.

The UNRMWA owns and operates Lake Palestine, outside Tyler. This 25,600-acre lake on the Neches River provides one of the major recreational opportunities in the region and is well known for its largemouth bass fishing. The lake also serves as a water supply for industrial and municipal purposes. Construction of the original dam was started in 1960, completed in 1962, and enlarged in 1972. The drainage area above the dam is about 839 square miles. *See* LakePalestine.com, *Lake Palestine Information*, www.lakepalestine.com/information.

Structure

The UNRMWA is governed by a three-member board of directors, who are appointed by the governor. The board members serve six-year terms and must be residents of the city of Palestine. Act of July 6, 1959, 56th Leg., 2d C.S., ch. 9.

Powers and Duties

- Bonding authority: contract bonds and revenue bonds
- Chapters 51 and 55 powers and duties
- Conservation of water and soil
- Coordinate/contract with governments/entities
- Drainage and flood control
- Hydroelectric generation facilities
- Oil and gas leases
- Parks
- Police and security services
- Property acquisition through eminent domain, within and outside district
- Purchase/construct works to carry out district purposes
- Regulate private sewage, on-site sewage facilities
- Taxes: operation and maintenance expenses, special taxes for pollution control
- Water quality
- Water supply: irrigation, municipal, and wholesale

Citations to Special Law or Codes

H.B. 579, Act of May 13, 1953, 53d Leg., R.S., ch. 412
H.B. 405, Act of Apr. 26, 1955, 54th Leg., R.S., ch. 193
S.B. 14, Act of Nov. 11, 1957, 55th Leg., 2d C.S., ch. 31
S.B. 23, Act of July 6, 1959, 56th Leg., 2d C.S., ch. 9
S.B. 8, Act of Aug. 5, 1959, 56th Leg., 3d C.S., ch. 3
S.B. 194, Act of May 30, 1983, 68th Leg., R.S., ch. 484
H.B. 1285, Act of May 29, 1989, 71st Leg., R.S., ch. 1248, § 82

§ 9.6:30 Upper Trinity Regional Water District

History

Created in 1989, the Upper Trinity Regional Water District (UTRWD) is a conservation and reclamation district with the authority to finance, construct, and operate regional facilities to meet the water needs of the Denton County area. Act of June 16, 1989, 71 Leg., R.S., ch. 1053 (H.B. 3112); see Upper Trinity Regional Water District, Our History, www.utrwd.com/about-us/who-we-are/history [hereinafter UTRWD History].

Today, the UTRWD meets the daily water needs of more than 300,000 people in Denton and Collin counties. The UTRWD has a comprehensive and diversified portfolio of water supply sources. Under contracts with the cities of Dallas and Denton, the UTRWD purchases raw water from

Lewisville Lake and Ray Roberts Lake. Additional supplies are also available from Jim Chapman Lake pursuant to a contract with the city of Commerce. In addition, the UTRWD reuses a large portion of the water imported from Chapman Lake. Recognizing its role in developing the future water supplies needed to meet the water demands for a rapidly growing service area, the UTRWD began construction of Lake Ralph Hall in the summer of 2021, with an expected in-service date in 2026. Through the state regional water planning process, the UTRWD has identified numerous water management strategies, including conservation, reuse, and additional reservoirs.

The UTRWD separately provides wholesale wastewater treatment services to twelve cities and communities within its service area. UTRWD owns and operates four regional water reclamation plants.

Structure

UTRWD is governed by a twenty-five member board of directors appointed to two-year staggered terms by governing bodies of UTRWD's members, which include Argyle, Aubrey, Bartonville, Celina, Copper Canyon, Corinth, Castle Hills (Denton County Fresh Water Supply District No. 1A), Lantana (Denton County Fresh Water Supply District No.7), Denton, Double Oak, Flower Mound, Highland Village, Irving, Justin, Krum, Lake Cities Municipal Utility Authority, Lewisville, Mustang Special Utility District, Northlake, Pilot Point, Ponder, Prosper, and Sanger. Denton County also appoints two representatives.

Powers and Duties

- Bonding authority: contract bonds and revenue bonds
- Conservation of water and soil
- Coordinate/contract with governments/entities
- Dams and reservoirs
- Property acquisition through eminent domain, within and outside the district
- Purchase/construct works to carry out district purposes
- Regulate private sewage, on-site sewage facilities
- Solid waste disposal
- Wastewater
- Water quality
- Water supply: irrigation, out-of-district, and wholesale

Citations to Special Law or Codes

H.B. 3112, Act of June 16,1989, 71st Leg., R.S. ch. 1053
S.B. 1657, Act of August 28,1995, 74th Leg., R.S. ch. 494
S.B. 835, Act of May 3, 2001, 77th Leg., R.S., ch. 46

§ 9.6:31 West Central Texas Municipal Water District

History

Formation of the West Central Texas Municipal Water District (WCTMWD) was the result of a cooperative effort by the district's four member cities—Abilene, Albany, Anson, and Breckenridge—in response to prolonged drought conditions in West Central Texas during the 1950s. West Central Texas Municipal Water District, Response to Tex. Sen. Comm. Nat. Resource Committee Questionnaire (Nov. 1999) (on file with author) [hereinafter Questionnaire]. The WCTMWD was created to provide a source of water supply for municipal, domestic, industrial, and mining uses. Act of Mar. 30, 1955, 54th Leg., R.S., ch. 66. The WCTMWD constructed, operates, manages, and maintains the Hubbard Creek Reservoir, which has a capacity of 324,000 acre-feet. *See* Questionnaire. The WCTMWD also constructed and maintains one hundred miles of raw water pipelines and pump stations. *See* Questionnaire.

The WCTMWD's enabling legislation was substantially amended in 1985 to provide the district with increased water-related powers. Act of May 9, 1985, 69th Leg., R.S., ch. 167. As a result of the amendment, an additional pipeline from Hubbard Creek Reservoir to Abilene was constructed and the WCTMWD also contracted for access to water in the O. H. Ivie Reservoir. *See* Questionnaire.

Structure

The WCTMWD is governed by a board of directors currently composed of twelve members who are appointed by the city council or commission of each member city. The number of board members for each city is determined by the city's population, but each city is guaranteed at least two directors. Act of Mar. 30, 1955, 54th Leg., R.S., ch. 66. The board meets at least three times a year and schedules additional meetings as necessary. *See* Questionnaire.

Powers and Duties

- Air quality and water pollution control facilities (acquire, construct, and finance)
- Bonding authority: contract bonds and revenue bonds
- Conservation of water and soil
- Coordinate/contract with governments/entities
- Dams and reservoirs
- Drainage and flood control
- Electric generation and transmission facilities
- Groundwater regulation (pumping/well spacing)
- Parks
- Police and security services
- Property acquisition through eminent domain, within and outside district
- Purchase/construct works to carry out district purposes
- Regulate private sewage, on-site sewage facilities
- Solid waste disposal
- Wastewater
- Water quality
- Water supply: industrial, irrigation, municipal, and wholesale

Citations to Special Law or Codes

H.B. 407, Act of Mar. 30, 1955, 54th Leg., R.S., ch. 66
H.B. 911, Act of May 10, 1955, 54th Leg., R.S., ch. 349
S.B. 9, Act of Nov. 11, 1957, 55th Leg., R.S., ch. 13
S.B. 16, Act of Feb. 25, 1959, 56th Leg., R.S., ch. 14
S.B. 144, Act of Mar. 14, 1961, 57th Leg., R.S., ch. 32
S.B. 308, Act of May 11, 1961, 57th Leg., R.S., ch. 194
H.B. 685, Act of Apr. 18, 1963, 58th Leg., R.S., ch. 100
S.B. 315, Act of May 9, 1985, 69th Leg., R.S., ch. 167

§ 9.7 Additional Districts and Authorities

Authority and special district enabling legislation and its amendments for many years were published by West Publishing Company in a "Water Auxiliary Laws" pamphlet as part of its Vernon's Texas Civil Statutes publication. Some law libraries still maintain the pamphlet, but it has not been updated for many years. Without such a publication, it is extremely difficult to find and track such legislation. A Special District Local Laws Code was created for purposes of codifying these acts into one readily accessible place, Act of May 20, 2003, 78th Leg., R.S., ch. 1277, but only a handful of the acts have been added to date.

As discussed in the introduction to this chapter, different legislative studies and legislation have focused on a variety of special law water districts and authorities thought to merit particular scrutiny because of their perceived importance in the management of the state's water resources. In addition to the water districts and authorities summarized in the main body of this chapter, the following sections list the additional districts and authorities that are included in the TWDB map of regional water providers and special water districts and provides citations to their enabling legislation.

§ 9.7:1 Bandera County River Authority and Groundwater District

Citations to Special Law or Codes

H.B. 988, Act of May 31, 1971, 62d Leg., R.S., ch. 629
S.B. 1636, Act of May 27, 1989, 71st Leg., R.S., ch. 654
S.B. 363, Act of May 19, 2015, 84th Leg., R.S., ch. 302
S.B. 523, Act of May 31, 2015, 84th Leg., R.S., ch. 1148, § 3
S.B. 2068, Act of June 12, 2017, 85th Leg., R.S. ch. 763

§ 9.7:2 Bistone Municipal Water Supply District

Citations to Special Law or Codes

H.B. 899, Act of May 14, 1957, 55th Leg., R.S., ch. 368
H.B. 685, Act of May 8, 1959, 56th Leg., R.S., ch. 258
H.B. 975, Act of May 24, 1961, 57th Leg., R.S., ch. 258
S.B. 862, Act of May 18, 1981, 67th Leg., R.S., ch. 234
H.B. 3166, Act of May 15, 2007, 80th Leg., R.S., ch. 920 (nonsubstantive revisions)

§ 9.7:3 Cibolo Creek Municipal Authority

Citations to Special Law or Codes

H.B. 1399, Act of May 13, 1971, 62d Leg., R.S., ch. 347
S.B. 137, Act of Mar. 28, 1977, 65th Leg., R.S., ch. 44
S.B. 452, Act of Mar. 30, 1983, 68th Leg., R.S., ch. 31
H.B. 2906, Act of May 26, 2009, 76th Leg., R.S., ch. 715

§ 9.7:4 Franklin County Water Improvement District

Citations to Special Law or Codes

H.B. 1161, Act of May 26, 1965, 59th Leg., R.S., ch. 719

H.B. 1256, Act of May 17, 1967, 60th Leg., R.S., ch. 308
H.B. 2469, Act of May 26, 1985, 69th Leg., R.S., ch. 412
H.B. 717, Act of Apr. 18, 1991, 72d Leg., R.S., ch. 59
H.B. 338, Act of Apr. 2, 1997, 75th Leg., R.S., ch. 3

§ 9.7:5 Greater Texoma Utility Authority

Citations to Special Law or Codes

Tex. Spec. Dist. Code ch. 8283
H.B. 976, Act of Apr. 19, 1979, 66th Leg., R.S., ch. 97
S.B. 1270, Act of June 17, 1983, 68th Leg., R.S., ch. 398
H.B. 1120, Act of June 20, 2003, 78th Leg., R.S., ch. 509

§ 9.7:6 Gulf Coast Waste Disposal Authority

Citations to Special Law or Codes

S.B. 225, Act of May 23, 1969, 61st Leg., R.S., ch. 409
H.B. 1035, Act of May 6, 1971, 62d Leg., R.S., ch. 202
S.B. 722, Act of May 21, 1973, 63d Leg., R.S., ch. 258
H.B. 705, Act of May 26, 1973, 63d Leg., R.S., ch. 466
S.B. 1054, Act of May 30, 1975, 64th Leg., R.S., ch. 443
S.B. 621, Act of May 27, 1979, 66th Leg., R.S., ch. 841
S.B. 666, Act of May 28, 1979, 66th Leg., R.S., ch. 630
H.B. 1697, Act of May 13, 1985, 69th Leg., R.S., ch. 202
S.B. 561, Act of May 19, 1987, 70th Leg., R.S., ch. 209
S.B. 34, Act of June 6, 1990, 71st Leg., 6th C.S., ch. 24
H.B. 2049, Act of Apr. 10, 1995, 74th Leg., R.S., ch. 47
H.B. 2050, Act of Apr. 25, 1995, 74th Leg., R.S., ch. 48

§ 9.7:7 Lubbock County Water Control and Improvement District No. 1

Citations to Special Law or Codes

S.B. 1715, Act of May 29, 1989, 71st Leg., R.S., ch. 1149

§ 9.7:8 Palo Duro Water District (Formerly Palo Duro River Authority)

Citations to Special Law or Codes

S.B. 523, Act of May 31, 2015, 84th Leg., R.S., ch. 1148, § 11
H.B. 1920, Act of May 26, 2017, 85th Leg., R.S., ch. 1046
H.B. 4172, Act of June 7, 2019, 86th Leg., R.S., ch. 468, § 1.03 (adding Tex. Spec. Dist. Code ch. 8509)

§ 9.7:9 Palo Pinto County Water Control and Improvement District No. 1

Citations to Special Law or Codes

S.B. 303, Act of May 23, 1961, 57th Leg., R.S., ch. 416
S.B. 706, Act of May 22, 1969, 61st Leg., R.S., ch. 837
H.B. 1630, Act of May 20, 1971, 63d Leg., R.S., ch. 450

§ 9.7:10 Riverbend Water Resources District

Citations to Special Law or Codes

Tex. Spec. Dist. Code ch. 9601

§ 9.7:11 Sulphur Springs Water District

Citations to Special Law or Codes

H.B. 1379, Act of May 15, 1969, 61st Leg., R.S., ch. 310

§ 9.7:12 White River Municipal Water District

Citations to Special Law or Codes

H.B. 468, Act of Apr. 26, 1957, 55th Leg., R.S., ch. 221
S.B. 42, Act of Aug. 2, 1961, 57th Leg., 1st C.S., ch. 34
S.B. 43, Act of Aug. 2, 1961, 57th Leg., 1st C.S., ch. 35
H.B. 3096, Act of May 17, 2001, 77th Leg., ch. 1506, art. 2

CHAPTER 10

Surface Water Rights Permitting

Susan M. Maxwell[1] and Doug Caroom[2]

I. Overview

§ 10.1 Statutory Framework

As discussed more fully in Chapter 4 of this book, surface water is owned by the state and available for use pursuant to the statutory appropriation process. The statute defines "state water" as follows:

> The water of the ordinary flow, underflow, and tides of every flowing river, natural stream, and lake, and of every bay or arm of the Gulf of Mexico, and the storm water, floodwater, and rainwater of every river, natural stream, canyon, ravine, depression, and watershed in the state is the property of the state.

Tex. Water Code § 11.021(a).

Appropriative surface water rights in Texas are usufructuary—that is, a right to use the water, not ownership of the corpus. The appropriative system provides for precisely defined water rights, authorizing the use of water in a specific amount, by diversion at a definite location (diversion point(s) or reach(es)), for a particular purpose, and for use at a particular location. It is unlawful to willfully take, divert, or appropriate any state water for any purpose without first complying with all applicable requirements of chapter 11 of the Texas Water Code. Tex. Water Code § 11.081. Violators are also subject to civil and administrative penalties. *See* Tex. Water Code §§ 11.082, 11.0842–.0843. Once put to beneficial use according to its terms, a water rights permit is "perfected" and becomes a vested property right. Tex. Water Code §§ 11.025–.026. Under certain circumstances, however, a vested water right may be abandoned or totally or partially canceled for nonuse.

---

1. Susan M. Maxwell is a partner at Bickerstaff Heath Delgado Acosta L.L.P., where she practices primarily in water law, including representation of cities, water districts, river authorities, and other local governmental entities and private parties in litigation, permitting, and other administrative proceedings, and transactional work involving surface water and groundwater rights. A graduate of the University of Texas School of Law and the LBJ School of Public Affairs, Ms. Maxwell is a former judicial law clerk to the late Honorable Barefoot Sanders, Senior District Judge, U.S. District Court for the Northern District of Texas. She recently served as chair of the State Bar of Texas Environmental and Natural Resources Law Section.

2. Doug Caroom is a partner at Bickerstaff Heath Delgado Acosta L.L.P., whose practice specializes in the areas of water and environmental law. In the past, Mr. Caroom has served as Chief of the Texas Attorney General's Environmental Protection Division and President of the State Bar of Texas Environmental Law Section, and has been an Adjunct Professor of Water Law at the University of Texas School of Law. He regularly represents river authorities, cities, and water districts in matters involving both surface water and groundwater supply.

The authors would like to acknowledge the indirect contribution to this chapter in the current edition of some excerpted content authored by Robin Smith in a different chapter of prior editions, particularly on the topics of cancellation, interbasin transfers, the public welfare requirement, and the "four corners" doctrine.

Under the doctrine of seniority or "first in time, first in right," each water right is assigned a specific priority date. During times of shortage, this system determines the allocation of water among appropriators from the same source of supply. A senior right holder is entitled to fully exercise his right before junior right holders receive any water. *See* Tex. Water Code § 11.027; 30 Tex. Admin. Code § 297.44; *see also* Tex. Water Code § 11.053 (TCEQ authority to temporarily suspend or adjust water rights in times of drought or other emergency shortage, in accordance with priority system); *Texas Commission on Environmental Quality v. Texas Farm Bureau*, 460 S.W.3d 264 (Tex. App.—Corpus Christi–Edinburg 2015, pet. denied) (affirming declaratory judgment that invalidated TCEQ's drought rules for violating prior appropriation doctrine).

Different uses of water are ranked preferentially by statute. The preferences apply for purposes of permit issuance, as between competing applications to appropriate water, and rank uses in the following order: domestic and municipal, agricultural and industrial, mining, hydroelectric power, navigation, recreation, and "other beneficial uses." Tex. Water Code § 11.024. However, once a water right has been granted, the statutory preferences play no role. Instead, the priority or seniority of the water rights governs. *See* 30 Tex. Admin. Code § 297.43(d).

A person who desires to permanently appropriate water must obtain a permit from the Texas Commission on Environmental Quality (TCEQ). *See* Tex. Water Code § 11.121. The permit may be granted in whole or in part only if, after filing a proper application, paying the required fees, and having notice and opportunity for a hearing, the applicant shows that—

1. unappropriated water is available in the source of supply;
2. the proposed appropriation—
    a. is intended for a beneficial use,
    b. does not impair existing water rights or vested riparian rights,
    c. is not detrimental to the public welfare,
    d. considers the applicable environmental and water quality assessments required by statute, and
    e. addresses a water supply need in a manner consistent with the state water plan and the relevant approved regional plan(s); and
3. reasonable diligence will be used to avoid waste and achieve water conservation.

Tex. Water Code § 11.134(b); *see* 30 Tex. Admin. Code §§ 297.41–.50, 297.53–.56. Other standards apply to the various types of temporary or limited permits discussed in part V below.

§ 10.2 Administrative Process

The TCEQ is subject to the requirements of the Administrative Procedure Act. *See generally* Tex. Gov't Code §§ 2001.001–.903. Thus, notice by mail (by the TCEQ) and publication (by the applicant) are required for applications to appropriate water and for amendments and other applications that may affect other existing water rights. This notice begins a period, generally thirty days or fewer, during which others may file comments or request a hearing on the application. For any application seeking a new appropriation of water, individual notice is mailed to all water rights holders located in the river basin involved. *See* Tex. Water Code § 11.132; 30 Tex. Admin. Code §§ 295.151–.153, 295.157. The notice requirements under section 11.132 now include identification of any proposed alternative source of water, other than state (surface) water, with direct mailed notice to be provided to each groundwater conservation district with jurisdiction over a proposed alternative groundwater source. *See* Tex. Water Code §§ 11.132(c)(5), 11.132(d)(2)(B).

In 2009, the TCEQ changed its previous practice of issuing notice of an application following its determination of administrative completeness. Under the current rules, notice is mailed after TCEQ staff have completed their technical review of the application and prepared a draft permit. *See* 30 Tex.

Admin. Code § 295.151(a). The TCEQ regularly updates its web page of all water rights applications that have reached the "at notice" stage with copies of the notice, draft permit, and TCEQ staff's underlying technical memos. *See* www.tceq.texas.gov/permitting/water_rights/wr-permitting/wr-apps-pub-notice. Under this procedure, water rights holders (and their attorneys) are better positioned to evaluate whether a protest of the application is warranted, rather than filing a protest based only on the application notice in order to preserve the future ability to challenge the application. Special notice rules apply to other types of water rights described in part V below. *See* 30 Tex. Admin. Code §§ 295.154 (temporary permit), 295.156 (emergency permit). Part III below further addresses notice and hearing requirements applicable to permit amendments. Additionally, prior to filing an application to construct a storage reservoir, preapplication written notice must be provided to the governing body of each county and municipality in which all or part of the reservoir will be located. *See* Tex. Water Code § 11.124(f); 30 Tex. Admin. Code § 295.42.

The commission will hold a public hearing on the application on the motion of a commissioner or on the request of the TCEQ's executive director or any "affected person." *See* Tex. Water Code §§ 11.132(a), 11.133; 30 Tex. Admin. Code § 295.171. If the notice period passes without receipt of a timely hearing request, the TCEQ may act on the application without holding a public hearing or referring it for a contested case hearing by the State Office of Administrative Hearings (SOAH). *See* Tex. Water Code § 11.132(d); 30 Tex. Admin. Code § 295.173. In several cases, the appellate courts have affirmed that, where the statutory notice is adequate, the would-be protestant fails to exhaust administrative remedies by not requesting a hearing within the identified time frame. *See Chocolate Bayou Water Co. & Sand Supply v. Texas Natural Resource Conservation Commission*, 124 S.W.3d 844, 853–54 (Tex. App.—Austin 2003, pet. denied); *Friends of Canyon Lake, Inc. v. Guadalupe-Blanco River Authority*, 96 S.W.3d 519, 525 (Tex. App.—Austin 2002, pet. denied). The commission also may delegate to its executive director its authority to act on a water right application in cases where the required notice has been given, the water right holder or applicant agrees to the action to be taken by the executive director, and the application is uncontested and does not require an evidentiary hearing or has become uncontested, by either the subsequent withdrawal of all timely hearing requests or the written agreement by all parties to the action to be taken by the executive director. *See* Tex. Water Code § 5.122(a); 30 Tex. Admin. Code § 50.133(a).

To qualify as an affected person to obtain a contested case hearing on a water right application, a person must have a "personal justiciable interest" in the application that is different from that of the public generally. *See* 30 Tex. Admin. Code §§ 55.251, 55.256(a). Generally, holders of other water rights and water right claimants in the same source of supply qualify as affected persons, as do environmental and recreational users of the water and often nearby property owners. Governmental entities with state law authority over "issues contemplated by the application" may also be affected persons. *See* 30 Tex. Admin. Code § 55.256(b). A state agency (not including a river authority) receiving notice of an application may submit comments to the TCEQ regarding the notice but may not contest issuance of the permit. *See* Tex. Water Code § 5.115(b). The TCEQ's executive director is a statutory party to a water right permit contested case hearing and participates in order to provide information to complete the administrative record and to support the executive director's position developed in the underlying proceeding, unless the executive director has revised or reversed that position. *See* Tex. Water Code § 5.228(c). The TCEQ's Office of Public Interest Counsel (OPIC) is also a statutory, independent party to all proceedings before the commission, representing the public interest, and is thus a party to every contested case hearing. *See* Tex. Water Code § 5.273(a).

A contested case hearing before a SOAH administrative law judge is in many ways comparable to a nonjury trial to the court. A limited motions practice is possible, prehearing discovery is available, and rules of evidence are generally applied. *See* 30 Tex. Admin. Code §§ 80.1–.155; *see generally* 30 Tex. Admin. Code ch. 80 (TCEQ contested case rules). The product of the contested case hearing, however, is normally a proposal for decision that is presented to the TCEQ commissioners for consideration and action. *See* 30 Tex. Admin. Code §§ 80.252, 80.255–.267. Following action by the commission, including action on a properly filed motion for rehearing, an appeal for judicial review is possible. *See* Tex. Water Code § 5.351(a); 30 Tex. Admin. Code §§ 80.272–.276; *see also* Acts 2021, 87th Leg., R.S., ch. 174, § 1 (S.B. 211), eff. Sept. 1, 2021.

§ 10.3 Types of Water Rights

This chapter deals primarily with the acquisition and amendment of permanent surface water rights. However, several other types of water rights may be obtained from the TCEQ to address specific situations. These rights include term permits, temporary permits, seasonal permits, emergency permits, interbasin transfer permits, and bed and banks permits, which are discussed at sections 10.6 and 10.7 and part V below.

II. Permanent Water Right Appropriation

§ 10.4 Application and Administrative Completeness

Texas Water Code section 11.124 sets out requirements for an application to appropriate state water. Application forms and instructions are available from the TCEQ and online at www.tceq.texas.gov/permitting/water_rights/wr-permitting/wr_applications.html. TCEQ staff assigned to the Water Rights Permitting Team are helpful and well informed, and it is generally advisable for a permit applicant to confer with staff before filing an appropriation or amendment application. Subchapter A of the TCEQ's Procedural Water Rights rules establishes the requirements for completing the application. Division 1 of subchapter A sets out the general requirements (*see* 30 Tex. Admin. Code §§ 295.1–.17), and subsequent divisions of subchapter A set out requirements applicable to various particular types of applications (*see* 30 Tex. Admin. Code §§ 295.21–.114). There are also specific requirements for maps, plats, and drawings to accompany the application (*see* 30 Tex. Admin. Code §§ 295.121–.122) and various types of filing fees and other fees applicable to water use applications (*see* 30 Tex. Admin. Code §§ 295.131–.140). Current TCEQ practice requires submission of water right applications in two parts: an electronic copy filed through WRPT@tceq.texas.gov and one hard copy submitted to the TCEQ's Central Office with the accompanying fees.

Guidelines for application processing are provided by 30 Texas Administrative Code sections 281.1–.4, 281.17–.20, and 281.22–.24. In 2017, the TCEQ's Water Availability Division completed an overhaul of the application forms and accompanying detailed instructions used for new and amended water rights and for bed and banks authorizations. These revised forms and instructions, which include an Administrative Information Report (and accompanying checklist) and a separate Technical Information Report with components and worksheets specific to various types of applications, can be found at the website referenced above. TCEQ staff reviews applications within ten days following receipt to determine whether appropriate fees have been paid and all the information required to process the application has been provided. If so, the TCEQ declares the application "administratively complete" and initiates technical review of the application; if not, the agency staff sends a letter to the applicant requesting additional information. The applicant is required to submit "any other information as the executive director . . . may reasonably require." 30 Tex. Admin. Code § 281.4(7). As a practical matter, additional information is virtually always requested, under this provision or others. During this initial review, a project manager is assigned to each application as a single point of contact and coordination for all TCEQ legal and technical staff working on the application.

Upon receipt of the executive director's letter requesting additional information, the applicant has thirty days to supply the requested information, or else the application may be returned. *See* 30 Tex. Admin. Code §§ 281.18(a), 281.19(b). When all the information requested has been supplied, TCEQ staff will declare the application to be administratively complete, which triggers initiation of the technical review period. This date of administrative completeness also becomes the permit's priority date.

TCEQ rules call for completion of the technical review within seventy-five working days following the declaration of administrative completeness, plus any extensions of time needed for the applicant to respond to requests for additional information. *See* 30 Tex. Admin. Code § 281.19(a). However, based on the staff's determination, the executive director may approve an extension of this time period for technical review. *See* 30 Tex. Admin. Code § 281.20.

§ 10.5 Technical Review

TCEQ staff performs its technical review by preparing three memoranda evaluating the criteria: a hydrology memorandum, an environmental memorandum, and a conservation memorandum. (For applications that involve storage rights, the TCEQ's dam safety team prepares a fourth memorandum on storage facility issues.) The hydrology memorandum evaluates the availability of unappropriated water and the impact of the proposed appropriation on existing water rights. The staff incorporates recommended special conditions for compliance with adopted environmental flow standards, if applicable, and may also recommend other requirements as part of the water availability analysis, based on the environmental review. The hydrology analysis may also recommend special conditions for the protection of existing water rights.

The environmental memorandum evaluates the impacts of the proposed appropriation on instream uses, recreational uses, aquatic and riparian habitat, water quality, and bay and estuary freshwater inflows. If necessary, the staff will recommend stream flow limitations or other conditions to protect any applicable environmental flow standards and to avoid or mitigate unacceptable environmental impacts under any other applicable statutes. *See generally* 30 Tex. Admin. Code § 297.42(b). However, for applications for a new appropriation in a basin for which the TCEQ has adopted environmental flow standards through the Senate Bill 3 (S.B. 3) process, TCEQ staff evaluates the environmental and water quality parameters of the application in terms of its compliance with those adopted standards. The TCEQ is still undergoing a process of developing guidelines for the implementation of its S.B. 3 rules in water rights permitting. See Chapter 11 of this book for further discussion of environmental flows and water rights permitting.

The conservation team evaluates the applicant's water conservation plan and drought contingency plan, if appropriate. If necessary, the team recommends permit conditions to assure compliance with applicable requirements. The conservation memorandum also evaluates the consistency of the application with the most recently adopted state and regional water plans.

§ 10.5:1 Hydrology Review

The availability of the unappropriated water requirement has been, and continues to be, a key source of controversy in contested permit applications. *See* Tex. Water Code § 11.134(b)(2). One aspect of the controversy has centered around the legal definition of unappropriated water—that is, what standard is used to measure it. The Texas Supreme Court addressed the question of what constitutes unappropriated water in the *Stacy Dam* decision, *Lower Colorado River Authority v. Texas Department of Water Resources*, 689 S.W.2d 873 (Tex. 1984). The lower courts held that the Texas Water Commission could find unappropriated water based on the fact that the existing water rights were not being fully used and were unlikely to be fully used, even though full use of existing permits would show the water to be completely appropriated. The supreme court reversed and expressly held that unappropriated water means the amount of water that remains after taking into account complete satisfaction of all existing uncanceled permits and filings valued at their recorded levels. *Lower Colorado River Authority*, 689 S.W.2d at 874. Even if historical use data indicate that the maximum amount claimed under senior water rights has never actually been used, the commission's analysis must account for all existing senior rights at face value. This is known as the "four corners doctrine" and is discussed further at section 10.9 below.

The availability of unappropriated water is determined by TCEQ staff using water availability models (WAMs), which have been developed for each river basin in the state pursuant to Senate Bill 1 (S.B. 1). In 2019, legislation passed that requires the TCEQ to obtain or develop updated WAMs for the Brazos, Neches, Red, and Rio Grande river basins by December 1, 2022. *See* Tex. Water Code § 16.012(h–1). This legislation and the nature and use of these WAMs are discussed in more detail in Chapter 12 of this book. Water right applicants can now access various tools to utilize the basin WAM models through TCEQ's website. *See* www.tceq.texas.gov/permitting/water_rights/wr_technical-resources/wam.html.

The version of the WAM (Run 3) used to determine the availability of unappropriated water operates generally as follows: (1) historic stream flow records are "naturalized" or adjusted to remove the impact of diversions, return flows, and major reservoirs; (2) existing water rights in the basin are satisfied to the full extent authorized in order of seniority, taking into account various losses and gains in each river segment and honoring stream flow restrictions and other conditions in each water right; (3) full consumptive use of the authorized diversion of each water right is assumed, unless the water right contains express requirements regarding return flows; (4) any instream flow requirements established in adopted S.B. 3 rules, associated with any particular water right, or otherwise established to protect downstream senior rights must be satisfied; and (5) water remaining in the model following this process is considered to be available for appropriation. The appropriation requested by the application is then inserted into the WAM as the most junior priority right in the model. The model is run, and it produces output reflecting how frequently and to what extent water is available to satisfy the requested right if all existing rights are fully exercised.

The model nearly always indicates that some amount of water is available for appropriation. During periods of flooding or high flows, virtually every river basin will have some unappropriated water at some locations. The question is whether that water is available with sufficient reliability to support the issuance of a new water right. For example, if an application was made for 1,000 acre-feet of water annually, and the WAM showed that 250 acre-feet per year were available on a reliable basis (100 percent of the time), but 1,000 acre-feet were available only 10 percent of the time, it would not generally make sense to grant the 1,000 acre-feet water right as requested. That would simply be setting up potential enforcement problems, with an authorized diversion but water not legally available at times and in sufficient quantities to satisfy the demand. This is when the TCEQ water availability rule (30 Tex. Admin. Code § 297.42) comes into play.

With the exception of term permits, the rule states that "an application for a new or increased appropriation will be denied unless there is a sufficient amount of unappropriated water available for a sufficient amount of the time to make the proposed project viable and ensure the beneficial use of water without waste." 30 Tex. Admin. Code § 297.42(a). Differing uses and types of water rights are analyzed under different standards. Under subsection (i), the TCEQ may require construction of sufficient storage to yield the requested annual diversion at all times under conditions no more severe than the worst drought of record. *See* 30 Tex. Admin. Code § 297.42(i). Under subsection (c), the TCEQ's "75% Rule" applicable to direct diversions for irrigation, a less demanding standard, is applied: 75 percent of the water requested must be available 75 percent of the time to authorize a new appropriation. *See* 30 Tex. Admin. Code § 297.42(c). Regarding appropriations for municipal use, 100 percent reliability is typically required.

Subsection (h) states that an appropriation for an on-channel reservoir for municipal use will normally be limited to its "firm yield," which is the supply that a reservoir could have produced annually if it had been in place during the worst drought of historical record. *See* 30 Tex. Admin. Code §§ 297.1(21) (definition of "firm yield"), 297.42(h). Additionally the rule contains several exceptions for situations when otherwise required reliability is not necessary—for example, a groundwater recharge project, an aquifer storage and recovery project, a conjunctive surface water/groundwater project, a project that "scalps" flood flows, nonconsumptive instream uses not dedicated to environmental needs or bay and estuary inflows, or a system operation in conjunction with other water rights. *See* 30 Tex. Admin. Code § 297.42(d). In such instances the TCEQ determines the reliability required for authorization of the requested appropriation on a case-by-case basis, based on whether the proposed project will be viable for its intended purpose and water will be put to beneficial use without waste. Similarly, the TCEQ has adopted different water availability requirements governing new types of water projects involving aquifer storage and recharge. *See* 30 Tex. Admin. Code § 297.42(e), (g). See Chapter 27 of this book regarding reservoirs.

Use of water in excess of the firm yield or firm supply is considered "overdrafting." The TCEQ's water availability rule allows approval of water rights that may involve overdrafting if the applicant has a drought management plan or reliable alternative sources of supply sufficient to meet demands during drought periods. *See* 30 Tex. Admin. Code § 297.42(h).

The TCEQ's predecessor agencies have not always used the availability standard reflected by 30 Texas Administrative Code section 297.42. Many of the older reservoirs in Texas are authorized to use the entire storage capacity of the reservoir annually. Additionally, water rights quantified through the water rights adjudication process are not based on a determination of water availability. *See* Tex. Water Code §§ 11.301–.341.

Closely parallel to the determination of availability of unappropriated water is the requirement that the TCEQ must grant a water right application only if the proposed appropriation does not impair existing water rights or vested riparian rights. *See* Tex. Water Code § 11.134(b)(3)(B). Although the WAM prevents impairment of existing water rights in determining the availability of unappropriated water, TCEQ staff frequently imposes operational constraints to provide real-world protection for downstream water rights. A typical provision of this nature is a "stream flow restriction," which restricts diversion or impoundment under the new appropriation when the flow of the stream at an identified reference point (often the diversion point) is less than a specified number of cubic feet per second, thus ensuring that a known amount of water will pass to downstream users. Such stream flow restrictions or "instream flow requirements" are most commonly imposed to ensure that water remains available for environmental purposes. The TCEQ may also require various forms of "special condition" as part of the permit—for example, in the form of accounting or return flow requirements. *See generally* 30 Tex. Admin. Code §§ 297.45(e), 297.59(a); *see also* TCEQ Form 10214c, Worksheet 7.0 (information worksheet outlining the types of applications for which an accounting plan is generally required). Provisions designed to protect other water rights may also be included—for example, by reducing the amount of water permitted or assigning a junior priority date to the new appropriation.

After the executive director issues the final draft permit, the appropriation is incorporated into the basin WAM so that it will be protected in future water availability determinations. In so doing, the stream flow requirements, whether for the protection of senior water rights or environmental flows, are incorporated as part of the right to be protected. As a practical matter, due to the requirements of modeling water availability and potential impairment for most water right applications, the commission generally must proceed sequentially with pending applications within a given basin, and thus a complicated or contested application can sometimes delay approval of later priority applications in that basin.

§ 10.5:2 Environmental Review

The Texas Water Code requires the TCEQ to consider various types of environmental impacts of any application to store, take, or divert surface water. These other requirements include the following:

- The TCEQ must assess the effects, if any, of the issuance of the permit on the bays and estuaries of Texas, paying particular attention to appropriations within two hundred river miles of the coast. *See* Tex. Water Code § 11.147(b); 30 Tex. Admin. Code § 297.55. Additionally, 5 percent of the annual firm yield of any reservoir project within that range of the coast constructed with state participation funds is dedicated to the Texas Parks and Wildlife Department (TPWD) for environmental purposes. *See* Tex. Water Code § 16.1331(a); 30 Tex. Admin. Code § 297.55(c).
- To the extent practicable in light of all public interests, the commission must include permit conditions that it considers necessary to maintain existing instream uses, fish and wildlife habitats, and the water quality of the river or stream. Tex. Water Code § 11.147(d), (e); *see also* Tex. Water Code § 11.150 (required assessment of effects on water quality in the state); 30 Tex. Admin. Code §§ 297.54, 297.56. See Chapter 33 of this book for a detailed discussion of water quality issues.
- For a proposed water right in excess of five thousand acre-feet per year, the TCEQ may require the applicant to take reasonable actions to mitigate adverse impacts on fish and wildlife habitat. *See* Tex. Water Code § 11.152; 30 Tex. Admin. Code § 297.53.
- The commission must consider the effects, if any, on groundwater or groundwater recharge. Tex. Water Code § 11.151. If the commission determines that granting an appropriation could significantly impair existing groundwater uses, groundwater quality, or spring flow, it may deny or place restrictions on the water right to prevent or mitigate such impacts. 30 Tex. Admin. Code § 297.47(b).

As part of S.B. 3 and H.B. 3, in 2007 the legislature amended various provisions in chapter 11 of the Water Code to set out the state's policy regarding "environmental flows" to maintain the biological soundness of the state's rivers, lakes, bays, and estuaries. *See* Tex. Water Code § 11.0235. For now, although the TCEQ may not issue new permits for instream flows dedicated to environmental needs or bay and estuary inflows, it may approve an application to amend an existing water right to change the use or add such a use. *See* Tex. Water Code § 11.0237. Prospectively, any new or amended water right that increases the amount of water authorized must include a provision allowing the TCEQ to adjust conditions in the water right to provide for the protection of instream flows or freshwater flows in compliance with applicable flow standards. *See* Tex. Water Code §§ 11.147(e–1)–(e–3), 11.1471(d); see also Chapter 11 of this book.

The TCEQ has developed rules for adopting environmental flow standards (a schedule of flow quantities) for most of the river basin and bay systems in Texas, as the basis for determining the amount of unappropriated water to be set aside (with an assigned priority date) to satisfy downstream instream flow needs or freshwater inflow needs for affected bays and estuaries (essentially, a "floor" below which water should not be appropriated). *See* Tex. Water Code § 11.1471. These adopted basin-specific standards are often referred to as the "S.B. 3 rules." Thereafter, the TCEQ must consider the applicable environmental flow standards in its water rights permitting and include any necessary protective conditions. *See* Tex. Water Code §§ 11.134(b)(3)(D), 11.023(a) (qualifying the provision on purposes of appropriation of state water), 11.147(b)–(e). For basins with adopted S.B. 3 rules, TCEQ staff have taken the approach that compliance with these rules is the relevant environmental and water quality analysis for an application seeking a new appropriation, and thus review under the various other statutes described above is not also necessary. See Chapter 11 of this book for further discussion of environmental flows permitting requirements.

The TPWD has significant authority relating to certain environmental aspects of water rights applications. The TCEQ must provide a copy of every application for a permit to store, take, or divert water to the TPWD, which is entitled to comment and to participate in hearings on such applications but may not contest permit issuance. The TCEQ, in making a final decision on a water rights application, must consider all information and evidence that the TPWD may present. *See* Tex. Water Code § 11.147(f).

§ 10.5:3 Conservation Review

The third form of technical review performed by TCEQ staff addresses a variety of conservation-oriented issues, including the applicant's intended use of the water, the applicant's planning for water conservation and drought contingency, and the relationship of the application to the state's larger scale water planning.

See also Chapter 23 of this book regarding conservation and Chapter 20 regarding state and regional water planning.

Beneficial Use: The Texas Water Code recognizes various purposes for which state water may be appropriated, stored, or diverted: domestic and municipal, agricultural and industrial, mining and mineral recovery, hydroelectric power, navigation, recreation, public parks, game preserves, certain types of aquifer recharge, and "any other beneficial use." *See* Tex. Water Code § 11.023(a), (b); *see also* Tex. Water Code § 11.024 (public policy on appropriation preferences); 30 Tex. Admin. Code § 297.43(a). The TCEQ can grant a water rights application only if the proposed appropriation is "intended for a beneficial use." Tex. Water Code § 11.134(b)(3)(A). An irrigator, industrial user, or municipality that has definite plans to put the water to use after obtaining the permit normally meets this standard. In such cases, the commission may also inquire whether the volume of water requested is excessive in light of the use intended.

For water supply projects constructed in advance of current need, particularly reservoirs, this issue can be somewhat more complex. Commitments from future water supply customers would certainly satisfy the requirement. The S.B. 1 water planning process also identifies projected water needs and water supply strategies that have been approved in order to meet those needs. Such evidence will normally satisfy the "intended for a beneficial use" requirement. In most instances this will be a fact issue that is not seriously contested.

The commission has not yet ruled on whether a speculative appropriation application by a public entity satisfies the statutory requirement. Certainly a private party seeking to appropriate water for subsequent sale *intends* to see that the water is put to beneficial use. The same is arguably the case for a governmental entity that serves as a regional wholesale water supplier and seeks to develop new water supplies for current and/or prospective customers. Other western states, however, have sometimes applied a higher standard when the private entity is not the end user and has no contract in hand to assure the water's beneficial use. *See, e.g.*, Colo. Rev. Stat. § 37-92-103(3)(a); *Jaeger v. Colorado Ground Water Commission*, 746 P.2d 515 (Colo. 1987) (en banc).

Conservation and Drought Contingency: As defined in the Water Code, "conservation" means the development of water resources and those practices, techniques, and technologies that reduce consumption, reduce loss or waste, improve efficiency in use, increase recycling and reuse, or prevent pollution of water so that supplies are available for future or alternative uses. Tex. Water Code § 11.002(8); *see also* 30 Tex. Admin. Code § 297.1(14). The TCEQ may grant a water right application only if the applicant has provided evidence that reasonable diligence will be used to avoid waste and achieve water conservation under the latter part of that definition. *See* Tex. Water Code § 11.134(b)(4); *see also* 30 Tex. Admin. Code §§ 297.48 (waste prevention), 297.50 (water conservation plan requirement).

All applicants for new or amended water rights must now develop and submit a water conservation plan and adopt reasonable conservation measures, with different TCEQ rules governing plans for different types of water users, e.g., municipal use by public water suppliers, industrial or mining use, agricultural use, or wholesale water suppliers. *See* Tex. Water Code § 11.1271(a); 30 Tex. Admin. Code §§ 288.1–.7, 288.30, 295.9. An application to appropriate water submitted without a conservation plan is administratively incomplete, and the TCEQ is prohibited from considering the application until the plan is submitted. 30 Tex. Admin. Code § 295.9. Only the following types of applications are exempt from the conservation plan requirement: (1) applications to impound water solely for in-place use, (2) applications for emergency use, and (3) applications for temporary use. 30 Tex. Admin. Code § 295.9(5).

Depending on the specified type of use and volume of water appropriated, a holder of *existing* appropriative rights also must develop, submit, and implement a water conservation plan that is consistent with the appropriate approved regional water plan and that adopts reasonable water conservation measures. This requirement for a water conservation plan does not result in the need for amending existing water rights. *See* Tex. Water Code § 11.1271(b); 30 Tex. Admin. Code § 288.30. An entity required to submit a water conservation plan to the TCEQ is now also required to submit a copy of its plan to the Texas Water Development Board (TWDB) and to report annually to the TWDB on its progress in implementing the plan. *See* Tex. Water Code §§ 16.402–.404, 11.1271(g).

An applicant for appropriation of new or additional state water has the burden of showing that the proposed appropriation is necessary and reasonable for the proposed use and must include information that supports the proposed use and evaluates conservation and other feasible alternatives to new water development. 30 Tex. Admin. Code § 297.50(b). Based on its review of the conservation plan, the commission may prescribe in the permit the implementation of reasonable water conservation measures. *See* 30 Tex. Admin. Code § 297.50(c).

In addition to conservation plans, wholesale and retail public water suppliers and irrigation districts applying for or holding an existing water right must develop and submit drought contingency plans consistent with the appropriate approved regional water plan, to be implemented during periods of water shortages and drought. Tex. Water Code § 11.1272(a). As with conservation plans, an application submitted without a required drought contingency plan is administratively incomplete, and the TCEQ is prohibited from considering the application until the plan is submitted. *See* 30 Tex. Admin. Code § 295.9. The commission has promulgated separate rules describing the requirements of drought contingency plans for municipal uses by public water suppliers, for irrigation use, and for wholesale water suppliers. *See* 30 Tex. Admin. Code §§ 288.20–.22. See Chapter 22 of this book for further discussion of drought contingency planning.

Consistency with State and Regional Water Plans: The legislature's emphasis on effective water planning is reflected in the requirement that the TCEQ may grant a water rights application only if the proposed appropriation addresses a water supply need in a manner consistent with the state water plan and any relevant approved regional water plans, unless the commission waives this consistency requirement. *See* Tex. Water Code § 11.134(b)(3)(E). The commission must consider these plans in its review of any application to store, take, or divert surface water or for a permit amendment. Tex. Water Code § 11.1501.

In theory this consistency requirement could be problematic for many small and private water use projects because they are not specifically addressed in or contemplated by the state water plan or regional water plans. In practice, however, TCEQ staff considers the statutory consistency requirement satisfied if the application is "not inconsistent" with the relevant plans. Thus, many smaller applications are considered "not inconsistent" because one would not anticipate that the regional plan would address water rights that do not have a significant impact on the regional planning effort. For major projects, the consistency requirement is applied more rigorously, and the project's inclusion in the regional and state plans is desirable. See Chapter 20 of this book for further discussion of Texas water planning at the state and regional levels.

§ 10.5:4 Dam Safety

Additional requirements apply to water right applications involving storage facilities. *See generally* TCEQ Form 10214c, Worksheet 2.0 (required to be completed for any application including impoundment authorization, reservoir, or dam facilities). If the application proposes construction of a dam higher than six feet for either storage or diversion of water, the application must provide additional information showing the location, profile (height, length, etc.), cross sections, layout of the dam and appurtenant structures, such as spillways, and the basis for hydraulic design. *See* Tex. Water Code § 11.126(c); *see also* 30 Tex. Admin. Code §§ 295.122, 299.3(b). Plans for reservoir projects, as well as plats and reports associated with the application, must be prepared by a professional engineer. *See* 30 Tex. Admin. Code §§ 295.41, 299.4; *but see* 30 Tex. Admin. Code § 299.5 (authority of executive director to approve exceptions to certain requirements). However, there are now statutory exemptions from safety requirements for dams located on private property, with a maximum impoundment capacity of less than five hundred acre-feet, classified as low or significant hazard, and located in a less-populated county and outside municipal limits. *See* Tex. Water Code § 12.052(e–1).

Plans submitted at the application stage are preliminary in nature. After the permit is issued, detailed construction plans must be filed with, and approved by, the TCEQ's executive director before construction begins. 30 Tex. Admin. Code § 299.22; *see also* 30 Tex. Admin. Code § 299.16. The commission's dam safety rules address many aspects of the hydrologic and structural adequacy of the dam as well as the dam's downstream hazard potential. The TCEQ has published a document entitled *Guidelines for Operation and Maintenance of Dams in Texas* (TCEQ Pub. No. GI-357, Nov. 2006, available at www.tceq.texas.gov/publications/gi/gi_357) that contains more detailed information about dam safety requirements. TCEQ supervision continues through the construction of the dam and after construction pursuant to the agency's dam safety authority. *See* Tex. Water Code § 12.052; 30 Tex. Admin. Code §§ 299.3, 299.16–.17, 299.25–.30, 299.51, 299.61, 299.71–.72. See Chapter 39 of this book regarding regulation of dams.

§ 10.5:5 Public Welfare

The commission may grant a water right only if it finds that it will not be "detrimental to the public welfare." Tex. Water Code § 11.134(b)(3)(C). This provision allows the TCEQ to balance other impacts of the water project against the benefits of the project. There is no definition of "public welfare" or "detrimental to the public welfare" in chapter 11 of the Texas Water Code or in TCEQ rules. However, in 2017 the legislature enacted a new provision clarifying that under the section 11.134(b)(3)(C) requirement the commission "may consider only the factors that are within the jurisdiction and expertise of the commission as established by [Water Code chapter 11]." *See* Tex. Water Code § 11.134(b–1). The revised TCEQ rule on consideration of public welfare uses this same language. *See* 30 Tex. Admin. Code § 297.46. A recent decision by the Texas Supreme Court provides similar guidance on "public interest" requirements. *See Railroad Commission of Texas v. Texas Citizens for a Safe Future & Clean Water*, 336 S.W.3d 619 (Tex. 2011) (the "*Popp* case") (holding, with respect to a Water Code provision regarding "public interest" findings to be made by the Texas Railroad Commission on applications for commercial injection wells, that the agency's construction of "public interest" was reasonable and entitled to deference). Under the *Popp* case analysis, the TCEQ need only consider public welfare factors that are related to its own regulatory authority in water rights permitting. As a practical matter, this has generally meant that TCEQ staff have concluded that the section 11.134(b)(3)(C) requirement is satisfied if the applicant has met the other applicable statutory criteria under chapter 11 and there are no other facts raising an issue of detriment, within the scope of the TCEQ's regulatory authority.

Although extremely broad, the public welfare issue normally is not the basis for denial of an application. Several factors contribute to this conclusion: (1) use and development of the state's natural resources is constitutionally determined to be in the public interest by the "Conservation Amendment" (Tex. Const. art. XVI, § 59); (2) the statute requires an affirmative finding of detriment; and (3) the most frequently raised issues relating to public welfare, such as environmental impacts, are addressed by more specific statutory requirements. Nonetheless, in *City of Marshall v. City of Uncertain*, 206 S.W.3d 97 (Tex. 2006), the supreme court made a point of emphasizing that the legislature's intent in enacting Water Code section 11.122(b) and other portions of S.B. 1 was to "make the amendment process less cumbersome" but "also to protect the public welfare by otherwise ensuring protection of this valuable resource." *City of Marshall*, 206 S.W.3d at 107. An applicant for a water right appropriation or amendment must take care to satisfy this criterion and be aware that it has implications for determining whether notice of the application is required.

§ 10.6 Interbasin Transfers

Section 11.085 of the Texas Water Code requires special TCEQ authorization for permits to take or divert water from one river basin to another. At least conceptually, such transfers provide a means for water-scarce areas of the state to obtain water from areas with more water resources. The applicant must obtain a permit or amendment from the TCEQ to authorize any such interbasin transfer. *See* Tex. Water Code § 11.085(a); 30 Tex. Admin. Code §§ 295.13, 297.18. Because this water is permanently taken out of the basin of origin, procedures considerably more burdensome than those involved for the appropriation of water are imposed in order to ensure full notice to, and protection of, basin-of-origin interests.

Besides publication requirements, notice of an application for interbasin transfer must be mailed to each mayor, county judge, groundwater conservation district, and legislator in the basin of origin and to legislators in the receiving basin. Tex. Water Code § 11.085(f)–(h). The TCEQ, before taking any action on an application for an interbasin transfer, must hold at least one public meeting in the basin of origin as well as in the recipient basin.

In weighing the effects of a proposed transfer, the TCEQ must consider several factors, including (1) the fifty-year needs of both basins and guidance from any relevant regional water plan(s) regarding feasible and practicable alternative supplies, (2) the amount and purposes of use, (3) water conservation and drought contingency measures, (4) the economic impact on both basins, (5) impacts on environmental concerns, (6) compensation or mitigation to the basin of origin, and (7) the information submitted by the applicant. *See* Tex. Water Code § 11.085(k); *see also City of San Antonio v. Texas Water Commission*, 407 S.W.2d 752, 758–59 (Tex. 1966) (requiring the commission to balance future benefits and detriments of the two competing basins before authorizing an interbasin transfer). The TCEQ may grant the application, in whole or in part, only to the extent that the detriments to the basin of origin during the proposed transfer period are less than the benefits to the receiving basin during that period, and only if the applicant has prepared a drought contingency plan and has developed and implemented water conservation measures that will result in the "highest practicable levels" of conservation and efficiency achievable within the applicant's jurisdiction. *See* Tex. Water Code § 11.085(*l*); *see, e.g., Upper Trinity Regional Water District v. National Wildlife Federation*, 514 S.W.3d 855 (Tex. App.—Houston [1st Dist.] 2017, no pet.) (affirming TCEQ's approval of water conservation plan for interbasin reservoir project).

Newly authorized interbasin transfers become junior in priority to all other water rights in the receiving basin granted before the transfer application was filed. *See* Tex. Water Code § 11.085(s). Although this provision may not prevent outright new interbasin transfer projects, it can severely limit the feasibility of an interbasin transfer from an existing senior water right, at least in river basins that are fully appropriated, because it could significantly affect the reliability of the water right during times of drought.

Although an interbasin transfer permit is required, the remaining requirements of Water Code section 11.085 do not apply to a limited group of exempt interbasin transfers. The exempt interbasin transfers include transfers of three thousand acre-feet or less; emergency transfers; transfers to adjoining coastal basins; transfers from the part of the geographic area of a county, city, or retail public utility's retail service area that is within the basin of origin for use in that part of the county, city, or utility's retail service area not within the basin of origin; and transfers imported from a source located wholly outside the boundaries of Texas, except water that is imported from a source located in the United Mexican States, for use in Texas, and transported by using the bed and banks of any flowing natural stream located in Texas. Tex. Water Code § 11.085(v). Most interbasin transfers authorized to date fall within one of these statutory exemptions.

§ 10.7 Bed and Banks Permits

Use of the "bed and banks" of state watercourses, pursuant to procedures approved by the TCEQ and its predecessors, to convey stored or conserved water for downstream use has long been authorized. *See* Tex. Water Code § 11.042(a). This authorization includes the reuse of return flows derived from either privately owned groundwater or previously appropriated state water. *See* Tex. Water Code § 11.042(b), (c). Such authorization is obtained pursuant to the provisions of 30 Texas Administrative Code section 297.16. *See also* 30 Tex. Admin. Code § 295.161 (notice requirements for bed and banks applications). The point of discharge and the point of diversion are identified, as well as the authorized quantity of water to be discharged and diverted. Such authorization is limited to the amount of water discharged less transmission losses. Special conditions, usually including an accounting plan, may be imposed to protect existing water rights as well as environmental needs for instream flows and the bays and estuaries. *See* Tex. Water Code § 11.042(c). See Chapter 27 of this book for additional discussion of bed and banks authorizations in the context of the reuse of surface water.

III. Amendments to Surface Water Rights

§ 10.8 General Considerations

Alteration of an existing surface water right, in virtually any respect other than a simple change of ownership, must be authorized by the TCEQ as an amendment. The executive director also may initiate amendment of water rights to correct errors, protect senior water rights, require reporting, or assist with enforcement of the terms and conditions of the water right. *See* 30 Tex. Admin. Code § 297.61. Otherwise, amendments are normally initiated by the owners of the water right. A water right must be amended to authorize a change in the place of use, purpose of use, point of diversion, rate of diversion, acreage to be irrigated, or any other alteration in the water right. *See* Tex. Water Code § 11.122(a). If the water right is governed by a TCEQ-approved accounting plan, subsequent modifications to such an accounting plan must also be submitted for approval by TCEQ staff, though these types of modifications are generally not subject to notice and hearing requirements.

TCEQ staff review of an amendment application is similar to that provided for a permit application. If the application involves a request for an additional appropriation, the full review described in part II above is required. If a new appropriation is not involved, the analysis focuses on whether the requested changes affect other water right holders or the environment. Most other requirements are applicable to amendments, although many would have already been considered in authorization of the initial appropriation.

The TCEQ's standard of review is reflected in the "no injury" rule, which states that amendments (1) to increase the appropriative amount, (2) to change the point of diversion or return flow, (3) to increase the consumptive use of water, (4) to increase the rate of diversion, or (5) to change from direct diversion to on-channel storage will not be authorized unless it is determined that the change has no adverse impact on other appropriators. *See* 30 Tex. Admin. Code § 297.45(a). The adverse impact can take the form of making less water available than would have been available with full exercise of the right before amendment, increasing another appropriator's obligation to pass water for other senior water rights, or substantially affecting stream flow conditions as they would have existed before amendment of the water right. *See* 30 Tex. Admin. Code § 297.45(a).

The applicant has the burden of showing that there are no adverse impacts on other water right holders or the environment. 30 Tex. Admin. Code § 297.45(d). The TCEQ may impose conditions such as stream flow restrictions or return flow requirements and may require subordination of the amended water right in order to avoid adverse impacts on other rights or the environment. *See* 30 Tex. Admin. Code §§ 297.45(c) (subordination of a water right based on a change in diversion point), 297.45(e) (other types of conditions or restrictions designed to protect senior water rights).

§ 10.9 Four Corners

Under Texas Water Code section 11.122(b), often referred to as the "four corners rule," TCEQ staff determines, from the terms of the existing water right (within the "four corners" of the document) and the nature of the requested amendments, whether there is any potential for adverse impacts and thus whether notice is required. Section 11.122(b) provides:

> Subject to meeting all other applicable requirements of this chapter [Texas Water Code chapter 11] for the approval of an application, an amendment, except an amendment to a water right that increases the amount of water authorized to be diverted or the authorized rate of diversion, shall be authorized if the requested change will not cause adverse impact on other water right holders or the environment on the stream of greater magnitude than under circumstances in which the permit, certified filing, or certificate of adjudication that is sought to be amended was fully exercised according to its terms and conditions as they existed before the requested amendment.

Tex. Water Code § 11.122(b). In essence, this is the converse of the commission's "no injury" rule; instead of directing that an amendment not be authorized unless it can be shown that there is no adverse effect on other water rights or the environment, it directs that the amendment be granted if it is shown that the adverse effects do not occur. *See also* 30 Tex. Admin. Code § 297.45(b).

The four corners rule codified in section 11.122(b) is itself an application of the *Stacy Dam* decision, with the commission considering the full appropriation amount of the water right in determining whether an amendment to the water right could cause harm. *See City of Marshall v. City of Uncertain*, 206 S.W.3d 97, 105–06 (Tex. 2006); *Lower Colorado River Authority v. Texas Department of Water Resources*, 689 S.W.2d 873, 873–74, 880–82 (Tex. 1984).

The precise parameters of section 11.122(b), particularly in those instances in which an amendment can be granted without notice and the opportunity for a contested case hearing, were litigated in *City of Marshall*, 206 S.W.3d 97. Generally, the court had ruled that the provision does not preclude contested hearings on amendments, but it significantly narrowed the issues that could be raised. In some cases, a hearing might be necessary to assess the impact of the amendment on other water rights and environmental flow requirements, as well as other public interest issues such as adequacy of water conservation plans, consistency with state and regional water plans, and effects on groundwater. However, the court stated that the TCEQ, under the full-use assumption, might be able to make the necessary determinations from the face of the application; in those cases, notice and hearing would not be required. *City of Marshall*, 206 S.W.3d at 111.

Even after the supreme court's decision, the TCEQ's application of the section 11.122(b) requirements to new amendment applications is still evolving. In most cases, permit amendment applicants are required to address TCEQ staff's "*Marshall* criteria"—a series of questions now included in the TCEQ's updated application forms (Worksheet 1.2) and designed to assist staff in assessing the potential impacts under limited public interest criteria and notice requirements for each application, discussed at section 10.10 below. Generally, TCEQ staff and the commission have decided that no notice is required for applications to amend only the type or place of use. To date, there have been few cases decided by the appellate courts under the *City of Marshall* analysis, and these have generally upheld the TCEQ's actions under section 11.122(b). *See R.E. Janes Gravel Co. v. Texas Commission on Environmental Quality*, 522 S.W.3d 506 (Tex. App.—Houston [14th Dist.] 2016, pet. denied); *Concho River Basin Water Conservancy Ass'n v. Texas Commission on Environmental Quality*, No. 07-12-00302-CV, 2013 WL 6254910 (Tex. App.—Amarillo Dec. 3, 2013, pet. denied) (mem. op.).

Even beyond the existing section 11.122(b) parameters, certain types of pending and future water right amendment applications not otherwise requiring notice or a hearing opportunity will be exempt from those requirements and from technical review by TCEQ staff and may not be referred to SOAH for a contested hearing. These exemptions, however, will be available only for amendments that (1) add a purpose of use that does not substantially alter the existing use right, (2) add a place of use in the same basin as currently authorized, or (3) change the diversion point, subject to various limitations designed to protect other existing water rights and environmental flows. *See* Tex. Water Code § 11.122(b–3).

§ 10.10 Notice Requirements

Water rights amendment applications are generally subject to the same notice requirements applicable to water use permit applications. *See* 30 Tex. Admin. Code § 295.158(b). Whether notice is required for an amendment application depends on the sort of amendment(s) being requested. Amendments that do not involve additional consumptive use or an increased rate or period of diversion and, in the judgment of the executive director, have no possibility of harming existing water rights or the public interest are processed without providing notice to other water right holders or the public. *See* 30 Tex. Admin. Code § 295.158(c)(1). Various types of amendments, evaluated on a case-by-case basis, may not require such additional notice, including a clarification of existing terms of the water right, a reduction in the appropriation or the diversion rate, a change in the location of use, a change in diversion point or addition of diversion point when there are no water rights in the intervening distance between the old and new diversion points, an increase in the rate of diversion from storage, or the removal of storage authorization for an unconstructed reservoir if the authorized diversion will be stored in an aquifer storage and recovery project for later retrieval and use. 30 Tex. Admin. Code § 295.158(c)(3); Tex. Water Code § 11.158(b). Finally, based on the inclusion of Water Code section 11.122(b–3), a limited category of minor amendments is now expressly exempted from both notice and technical review. *See* 30 Tex. Admin. Code § 295.158(c)(2).

Notice (both mailed and published) is typically required for amendments to (1) increase the appropriation or rate/period of diversion, (2) change the place of use that may affect other water right holders, (3) change the purpose of use that would materially change the period of time that water could be diverted or increase the authorized consumptive use of water, (4) change the diversion point that could affect other water right holders, or (5) relocate or enlarge an existing reservoir. *See* 30 Tex. Admin. Code § 295.158(b).

As with notice for an application for a new water right, notice of the amendment application is issued following TCEQ staff's completion of its technical review and preparation of the draft amended permit. *See* 30 Tex. Admin. Code §§ 295.151(a), 295.158(b).

The executive director's evaluation of these factors and decision whether to require publication of notice are influenced by the framework resulting from the *City of Marshall* decision, discussed at section 10.9 above.

IV. Cancellation of Water Rights

§ 10.11 General Provisions

Texas Water Code chapter 11, subchapter E, establishes the state's water rights cancellation process. Under these provisions, water rights (permits or certificates of adjudication) may be totally or partially canceled based on ten consecutive years of nonuse. Tex. Water Code § 11.172. The original statute enacted in 1957 was held constitutional by the Texas Supreme Court. *Texas Water Rights Commission v. Wright*, 464 S.W.2d 642 (Tex. 1971) (ruling that this vested property right nonetheless has an implied condition subsequent of continued beneficial use).

After satisfaction of all notice and hearing requirements, the TCEQ may cancel in whole or in part a water right if it has not been put to beneficial use at any time for a ten-year period immediately before the cancellation proceeding. Tex. Water Code § 11.173(a). The executive director may initiate a proceeding for cancellation of a water right, pursuant to Water Code section 11.174, with direct mail notice before the hearing to the water right holder and other water right holders in the same watershed and published notice in a newspaper in each county in which water from the source of supply was authorized for diversion and use. *See* Tex. Water Code §§ 11.174, 11.175.

The statute expressly exempts from cancellation water rights dedicated to certain conservation programs and water use consistent with long-term water planning. If the nonuse results from (1) the implementation of water conservation measures under the water right holder's submitted water conservation plan, (2) some restriction on use of the water under an order issued by the executive director, or (3) an inability to obtain water authorized because of drought conditions, the water right is exempt from cancellation. *See* Tex. Water Code § 11.173(b). Under Water Code section 11.183, the TCEQ may allow a water right holder with reservoir storage to retain the impoundment to the extent of the reservoir's conservation storage capacity for domestic, livestock, or recreational purposes. Tex. Water Code § 11.183. Section 11.184 prohibits the cancellation of water rights authorizing the use of water for municipal purposes if water has been put to use for such purpose at any time during the relevant ten-year period. *See* Tex. Water Code § 11.184.

There are two exceptions to the mandatory requirement of a hearing before cancellation. The first exception applies when the right to a hearing is expressly waived by the affected water right holder. The second exception relates to water rights granted for a term. Because these "term permits" do not vest any water rights in the permit holder for longer than the stated term, they automatically expire and are canceled in accordance with their terms without further need for notice or hearing. *See* Tex. Water Code § 11.176(b), (c). In making its required findings regarding "reasonable diligence" and "justified nonuse," the commission must consider, among other factors, certain conservation measures by the water right holder and whether the water right is being made available for private marketing or is reserved for environmental use. *See* Tex. Water Code § 11.177(b). Once a cancellation proceeding has been brought against a water right holder, no further such proceedings may be brought during the five years following the hearing. Tex. Water Code § 11.186.

Although available for many years as a potential mechanism to address the problem of overappropriated watercourses, the cancellation provisions have rarely been used.

§ 10.12 Abandonment and Forfeiture

Water rights can also be lost through abandonment and forfeiture. If a lawful appropriation of state water is willfully abandoned during any three successive years, the right to use the water is forfeited and the water is subject to appropriation by another. Tex. Water Code § 11.030. The water right holder must have the intent to knowingly relinquish the water right. If TCEQ records indicate that the water is not being used, the executive director may contact the water right holder regarding intent to cancel the water right. If the water right holder does not so intend, the commission uses the same procedure for an abandonment case as it does for a cancellation. *See* 30 Tex. Admin. Code § 297.75.

If a permit contemplates construction of a storage reservoir or construction of diversion facilities, construction must begin within the time fixed by the commission but no more than two years after the date the permit is issued. The permittee must work diligently and continuously to complete the work. *See* Tex. Water Code § 11.145(a); *see also* 30 Tex. Admin. Code §§ 297.51, 297.74(a). However, the permittee may, before the expiration of current commencement or completion deadlines, apply for an extension of time to preserve the permit by showing reasonable diligence and reasonable cause for failure to meet the authorized time limits. 30 Tex. Admin. Code § 295.72. If the permittee fails to begin or complete construction within the time limits in the permit, the water right is subject to cancellation in whole or part, after notice and an opportunity for hearing. *See* Tex. Water Code § 11.146(b), (d). Forfeiture under section 11.146 does not apply to construction of a reservoir designed for the storage of more than 50,000 acre-feet of water. Tex. Water Code § 11.146(g).

A temporary or term permit may be revoked or suspended upon written or verbal notice by the executive director or the basin watermaster, if any, without hearing, if necessary to protect senior or vested water rights or instream uses and freshwater inflow needs for bays and estuaries. 30 Tex. Admin. Code § 297.74(b).

V. Exceptions from Permitting and Limited Permits

§ 10.13 Introduction

Certain types of surface water use are exempt from permitting by the TCEQ. Also, in addition to the regular appropriation permit issued under section 11.121 of the Texas Water Code, the TCEQ issues several types of more restrictive permits authorized by the Code.

§ 10.14 Exemptions

The use of water for domestic and livestock purposes is generally exempt from state water rights administration. Without obtaining a permit, a person (but not a commercial operation) may construct on his or her own property a dam or reservoir up to two hundred acre-feet in capacity for domestic and livestock purposes. Tex. Water Code § 11.142(a); 30 Tex. Admin. Code § 297.21. Similarly, a person, other than a commercial enterprise, may construct a reservoir of this size without a permit for fish and wildlife purposes. Tex. Water Code § 11.142(b). Statutory law expressly exempts *storage* of water for domestic and livestock uses, but not the use itself, from the state water rights appropriation process. As a practical matter, however, this exemption for domestic and livestock *use* is the established existing law and practice. *Cf. City of Anson v. Arnett*, 250 S.W.2d 450 (Tex. App.—Eastland 1952, writ ref'd n.r.e.) (discussing the statute as a limitation on the type of water use allowable without a permit).

The Texas Water Code also authorizes the conversion of an exempt domestic and livestock or fish and wildlife reservoir to other beneficial uses, through a permit issued by the TCEQ. *See* Tex. Water Code § 11.143; 30 Tex. Admin. Code § 297.15. See Chapter 27 of this book for further discussion of these exempt and nonexempt distinctions and other issues relating to reservoirs.

§ 10.15 Term Permits and Temporary Permits

The TCEQ may issue a permit for a term of years based on the availability of water that has been appropriated to others but is not yet being used. *See* Tex. Water Code § 11.1381(a); 30 Tex. Admin. Code § 297.19(a). For example, water appropriated to a reservoir that is constructed to meet future water needs might be available for term permits until the future need develops. Term permits automatically expire and are canceled in accordance with their terms without further need for notice or hearing. *See* Tex. Water Code § 11.176(b), (c).

The commission may also issue a temporary permit for a duration of up to three years. Notice and hearing are not required for temporary permits authorizing the use of ten acre-feet or less for a duration of less than one year. Temporary permits are junior to all other appropriations in the watercourse and are designed for activities such as highway construction or oil and gas well drilling projects. *See* Tex. Water Code § 11.138; 30 Tex. Admin. Code § 297.13. In recent years, the TCEQ has granted some temporary permits to allow water right holders to mitigate drought impacts, such as by allowing movement of authorized diversion points.

§ 10.16 Emergency Permits

The TCEQ has substantial authority to address emergency conditions by authorizations to appropriate or use state water on an emergency basis or to use water appropriated to another, if emergency conditions present an imminent threat to public health and safety and there are no feasible, practicable alternatives. *See* Tex. Water Code § 11.139; 30 Tex. Admin. Code § 297.17. Such authorizations are for a limited duration (an initial period of not more than 120 days) and, if granted without notice and hearing, must be followed by a hearing as soon as practicable. In drought conditions, the TCEQ can mandate without notice or hearing the temporary transfer and use of surface water from a permittee holding a water right for a nonmunicipal use to a city or supplier of water for domestic or municipal use, for public health and safety purposes. *See* Tex. Water Code § 11.139(h); 30 Tex. Admin. Code § 297.17(g). However, for emergency transfers authorized under these provisions, the person granted the transfer authorization is liable, to the affected water right holder(s) from whom use is transferred, for the fair market value of the water transferred as well as for damages caused by the transfer of use. 30 Tex. Admin. Code § 297.17(*l*).

Relatedly, drought conditions may sometimes also be the basis for the TCEQ to approve emergency amendments to a permittee's water management plan.

§ 10.17 Seasonal Permits

The TCEQ may grant seasonal permits, which are typically used for irrigation only to fill an off-channel reservoir during the wet season. *See* Tex. Water Code § 11.137; 30 Tex. Admin. Code § 297.12.

§ 10.18 Contractual Permits

The TCEQ has also issued contractual permits (these are no longer issued) or contractual amendments to authorize use, pursuant to a contract, by a third party not expressly authorized under the base permit. The owner of the base permit obtains a "contractual amendment" to the permit, authorizing use by the third party. 30 Tex. Admin. Code §§ 297.14 (contractual permit), 297.101–.108 (water supply contracts and amendments).

Contractual permits or amendments are not usually necessary if the diversion and use are authorized under the supplier's water right or if the new use involves only an addition of a diversion point or a change in the location of use of a water right that authorizes storage. In such instances, a water supply contract that meets the TCEQ's requirements may be filed with the executive director. 30 Tex. Admin. Code §§ 295.101, 295.183, 297.101–.108. However, the TCEQ requires an amendment if the added diversion point is not part of a bed and banks authorization, and for new places of use, if the seller's water right does not contain those authorizations. See Chapter 31 of this book for further discussion of wholesale water suppliers.

§ 10.19 New Forms of TCEQ Permit Authority

Under a statute passed during the 2015 legislative session, the TCEQ has new authority to issue permits for certain diversions of state water from the Gulf of Mexico (or a bay or arm of the Gulf) for desalination and industrial purposes. For these permits, the commission is not required to make a finding of water availability. *See* Tex. Water Code § 11.1405. Once these marine seawater permits are granted, a permit holder can obtain certain types of permit amendments (e.g., a change or addition of diversion point, with no increase in diversion amount) on an expedited basis and with priority technical review by TCEQ staff. *See* Tex. Water Code § 11.122(b–1), (b–2). Other 2015 legislation exempts from permitting requirements the diversion and use of marine seawater that has a total dissolved solids concentration of less than 20,000 milligrams per liter, and provides for bed and banks authorization for such sufficiently treated marine seawater. *See* Tex. Water Code ch. 18. The TCEQ has recently adopted rules for marine seawater desalination projects under these statutes. *See generally* 30 Tex. Admin. Code ch. 318; ch. 295, subch. G. See also Chapter 25 of this book.

Under a statute passed during the 2019 legislative session, the TCEQ has express authority to authorize the appropriation of water, including stormwater and floodwater, for aquifer recharge. *See* Tex. Water Code § 11.157. The TCEQ must adopt rules addressing the required frequency of availability of such appropriations. The TCEQ may now also grant (1) an application to convert an existing reservoir storage water right to an authorization for aquifer storage and recovery or (2) an application to amend an existing reservoir storage right to authorize storage as part of an aquifer storage and recovery project in an amount equal to all or part of the documented amount of reservoir yield lost to sedimentation. *See* Tex. Water Code § 11.158. For further discussion of aquifer storage and recharge projects, see Chapter 26 of this book. For further discussion of reservoir rights, see Chapter 27.

VI. Conclusion

§ 10.20 Conclusion

This chapter provides an overview of the permitting and amendment of surface water rights. The process is largely dictated by the statutes of chapter 11 of the Texas Water Code and implemented under chapters 295 and 297 of the TCEQ's rules. Several evolving and controversial issues involved in surface water rights permitting and amendments are addressed in more detail in other chapters of this book.

CHAPTER 11

Environmental Flows in Water Rights

Jason Godeaux[1] *and Todd Galiga*[2]

I. Protecting Environmental Flows

§ 11.1 Introduction

The consideration and protection of instream flows—that is, water within rivers, streams, and lakes—and of freshwater inflows into bays and estuaries are important components of water management, water rights permitting, and water development and planning. This chapter addresses primarily the protection of environmental flows through the water rights permitting process. Historically, the term "environmental flows" encompassed instream flows and "freshwater inflows," referred to as "inflows," into bays and estuaries. Under current general practice, environmental flows refers to the amount of water necessary to sustain a broad range of biological needs and aquatic system functions in rivers and bays. Rivers moderate floods and droughts, renew soil fertility, help recharge certain aquifers, and provide habitat and breeding sites for fish and wildlife. Sandra Postel & Brian Richter, *Rivers for Life: Managing Water for People and Nature* 2 (Island Press 2003). Wetlands and flowing streams act as natural filters, absorbing pollutants, decomposing waste, and churning out freshwater. Postel & Richter, at 3. Simply put, river and bay systems require flowing water to maintain their functions, uses, and benefits to people, fish, and wildlife. Assessing and addressing the impacts of water projects on the needs of these natural systems are increasingly complex undertakings, and Texas law has correspondingly evolved in acknowledgement of such complexity. This chapter provides context for how environmental flows are addressed in the state's quest to balance the needs of a growing population with protection of environmental flows to sustain both the economy and the quality of life in Texas.

Regulatory actions such as Federal Energy Regulatory Commission hydropower licensing, Clean Water Act water quality certification and dredge and fill permitting, and the application of the Endangered Species Act may consider and affect environmental flows (see Chapters 7, 34, 35, and 32 of this book, respectively). In Texas, however, the regulation of surface water rights is the primary body of law that specifically addresses environmental flow needs. Thus, this chapter presents the legal

---

1. Jason Godeaux is the supervisor of the Resource Protection Team at the Texas Commission on Environmental Quality. A graduate of Sam Houston State University with a BS in biology, he has worked with the agency for over fifteen years. His previous role with the agency was as an aquatic scientist developing revisions to the Texas Surface Water Quality Standards.

2. Todd Galiga is the Senior Attorney for the Water section in the Environmental Law Division at the Texas Commission on Environmental Quality. He has worked on surface water and groundwater issues at the TCEQ for almost twenty-five years.

The authors would like to acknowledge the authors of this chapter in earlier editions of this book: Hope Wells and Collette Barron Bradsby. This seventh edition update is based largely on their work.

framework for the protection of environmental flows in water rights permitting. Some water rights matters continue under a historic regulatory framework. Since the 2007 enactment of a new statutory scheme for incorporating environmental flows into water rights permitting actions for new appropriations of water, however, practitioners are likely to encounter the newer regulatory framework when handling a water rights matter.

§ 11.2 Historical Overview

The Texas Constitution provides that the preservation and conservation of all natural resources of the state, including the waters of its rivers and streams, are public rights and duties and that the legislature shall pass such laws as may be appropriate to effect such preservation and conservation. *See* Tex. Const. art. XVI, § 59; *City of Corpus Christi v. City of Pleasanton*, 276 S.W.2d 798, 803 (Tex. 1955) (noting that it is the legislature's duty to protect and preserve natural resources). Constitutional authority to preserve water resources has been in place since 1917, but during most of Texas history, state law did not require the consideration of environmental flows.

The first appearance of statutory environmental flow consideration in water rights permitting came in 1975, as the health of the state's bays and estuaries, including related freshwater inflows, were given legislative attention. *See* Act of June 2, 1975, 64th Leg., R.S., ch. 344, § 2. Environmental flow protection progressed with a suite of provisions added to the Texas Water Code in 1985. *See* Act of May 26, 1985, 69th Leg., R.S., ch. 795, §§ 1.047–10.012. In 2003, broad authority for this practice was added to Water Code section 11.147, which requires water rights permits to include, to the extent practicable when considering all public interests, conditions to maintain existing instream uses and water quality as well as fish and wildlife habitats. Tex. Water Code § 11.147(d), (e). The Texas Commission on Environmental Quality (TCEQ, which will be used to denote the agency and any predecessor agencies, unless otherwise noted) adopted implementing regulations not long after. *See* 36 Tex. Reg. 2908 (May 6, 2011).

§ 11.3 Using Permit Conditions in Individual Water Rights to Protect Environmental Flows

§ 11.3:1 New Proposed Surface Water Appropriation

Starting with the 1985 statutory changes and resulting regulations, the commission considered the potential effect on environmental flows of each new proposed permit to store, take, or divert surface water (new appropriation). These considerations included the following:

- Texas Water Code section 11.147(b) and 30 Texas Administrative Code section 297.55: the commission must assess effects on bays and estuaries, particularly for appropriations within 200 river miles of the coast.
- Texas Water Code section 11.147(d), (e) and 30 Texas Administrative Code sections 297.54 and 297.56: the commission must include permit conditions needed to maintain existing instream uses, fish and wildlife habitats, and the water quality of the river or stream to the extent practicable in light of all public interests.
- Texas Water Code section 11.152 and 30 Texas Administrative Code section 297.53: if the application seeks more than 5,000 acre-feet per year (AF/year), the commission may add conditions to the permit to mitigate adverse impacts on fish and wildlife habitat.
- Texas Water Code section 11.151 and 30 Texas Administrative Code section 297.47(b): if the proposed permit could significantly impair existing groundwater uses, groundwater quality, or

> spring flow, the commission may deny the application or include special conditions designed to prevent or mitigate such impacts.

See Douglas G. Caroom & Susan M. Maxwell, *Surface Water Rights Permitting, in Essentials of Texas Water Resources* 152, 158 (Mary K. Sahs ed., 1st ed. 2009).

As part of the commission's technical review of each water rights permit application, the commission staff prepared several memoranda evaluating the statutory criteria as applied to the application. An environmental memorandum was prepared to evaluate "the impacts of the proposed appropriation on instream uses, recreational uses, aquatic and riparian habitat, water quality, and bay and estuary freshwater inflows. [If impairment was expected, the staff could] recommend stream flow limitations or other conditions to avoid or mitigate unacceptable environmental impacts." Caroom & Maxwell, at 155.

The purpose of the hydrology memorandum was to evaluate the availability of unappropriated water and the impact of the proposed appropriation on existing water rights. If the environmental memorandum recommended instream flow or other requirements, those were incorporated into the water availability analysis. *See* Caroom & Maxwell, at 155. After 1999, the commission's hydrology review used the current water availability models (WAMs). See Chapter 12 of this book for the history of WAMs. Instream flow requirements associated with the proposed water rights have to be satisfied when running the WAM for a proposed water right. *See* Caroom & Maxwell, at 156.

A permit provision typical for protecting environmental flows is a "streamflow restriction" that "restricts diversion or impoundment under the new appropriation when the flow of the stream at an identified reference point (often the diversion point) is less than a specified number of cubic feet per second." Caroom & Maxwell, at 157. Such a restriction would ensure that a known amount of water would be downstream of the diversion point. Additionally, the commission staff could also recommend inclusion of a "special condition" in the form of accounting or return flow requirements. *See generally* 30 Tex. Admin. Code §§ 297.45(e), 297.59(a); *see* Caroom & Maxwell, at 157–58.

§ 11.3:2 Permit Amendments Subject to Special Conditions

Certain water rights amendments trigger an assessment of environmental impacts and the possible imposition of permit special conditions to protect the environment. The Texas Water Code provides that a water rights application for a new appropriation can be approved only if it does not impair existing water rights or the environment. *See* Tex. Water Code § 11.134(b)(3)(B), (b)(3)(D); 30 Tex. Admin. Code § 297.45. See also Chapter 10 of this book. This requirement is limited for amendments to water rights by Water Code section 11.122(b). *See also* 30 Tex. Admin. Code § 297.56(b). Water Code section 11.122(b) provides:

> (b) Subject to meeting all other applicable requirements of this chapter for the approval of an application, an amendment, except an amendment to a water right that increases the amount of water authorized to be diverted or the authorized rate of diversion, shall be authorized if the requested change will not cause adverse impact on other water right holders or the environment on the stream of greater magnitude than under circumstances in which the permit, certified filing, or certificate of adjudication that is sought to be amended was fully exercised according to its terms and conditions as they existed before the requested amendment.

Tex. Water Code § 11.122(b).

Under section 11.122(b) (often called the "four corners doctrine"), amendments that increase the amount of water authorized to be diverted or increase the rate of diversion should be assessed differently from other types of amendments and are subject to the same assessment as new permit applications. For other amendment applications, the commission is directed to issue the amendments after finding that the proposed amendment will not cause adverse impacts to other water right holders or the environment of a greater magnitude than those impacts that would be experienced under the full exercise of the original right. *See* Tex. Water Code § 11.122(b). The level of consideration of applications for amendments that do not increase the appropriated amount or diversion rate was the subject of *City of Marshall v. City of Uncertain*, 206 S.W.3d 97 (Tex. 2006).

The City of Marshall's amendment application requested permission to add industrial purposes to its municipal water use permit and to use the water in the Sabine River Basin as well as continuing use in the Cypress Creek Basin. The commission, relying on section 11.122(b), issued the amendment without performing an environmental analysis and without providing notice to the public or an opportunity for a hearing. The City of Uncertain, the Caddo Lake Institute, the Caddo Lake Area Chamber of Commerce and Tourism, and several other affected parties appealed the commission decision.

The Texas Supreme Court remanded the city's application back to the commission. The court found that section 11.122(b) required the commission to consider not only the effects of the proposed amendment on other water rights and the environment but also the impacts of the application on the other factors, the "public interest criteria," in section 11.134. *See City of Marshall*, 206 S.W.3d at 110–12. The court stated that the record in the case was devoid of any commission factual inquiry regarding environmental impacts or impacts on other water right holders and whether the other factors in section 11.134 could be adversely affected by the amendment. *See City of Marshall*, 206 S.W.3d at 109–11.

§ 11.3:3 Suspension of Permit Conditions

Before the enactment of Senate Bill 3 in 2007, permit conditions relating to freshwater inflows and instream uses could be suspended if the commission determined an emergency existed that could not practically be resolved in other ways. *See* Tex. Water Code § 11.148(a). In these circumstances, the Texas Parks and Wildlife Department must be provided notice and an opportunity to comment. *See* Tex. Water Code § 11.148(b). Although the Parks and Wildlife Department is the only party entitled to notice of the initial emergency suspension, all affected persons are notified by publication immediately after the suspension, and a hearing to determine whether the suspension should be continued must be held within fifteen days of the order to suspend. *See* Tex. Water Code § 11.148(c). The commission's adopted rules implementing these provisions can be found in 30 Texas Administrative Code chapter 35.

§ 11.3:4 Limitations on the Effectiveness of Permit Conditions in Protecting Environmental Flows

Permit conditions in individual water rights for protecting environmental flows, as mentioned above, were directed at the subject river or stream segment and thus their effectiveness was limited. This limitation was one of the drivers for the enactment of Senate Bill 3 in 2007. For example, environmental protection gained through individual permit restrictions depends on someone's decision to file a water right application; environmental flow protection was considered only in the context of applications for new appropriations. The review of such an application could result in addressing environmental needs by stream segment or river basin but only to the extent that a particular water project's diversion affected a defined reach of the affected stream. *See generally* Joint Committee on the Study Commission on Water for Environmental Flows, *Interim Report to the 79th Legislature* 11–17 (Dec. 2004), https://texaswater.tamu.edu/readings/ef_plicy/txstudycomm.pdf.

Another shortcoming of relying on permit conditions is that not until 1985 was the commission required to consider the protection of environmental flows when it issued a water right. Almost a hundred years of water right authorizations by the state preceded the consideration of any environmental flow needs. Full appropriation of water occurred in some basins such as the Colorado without any consideration or reservation of water for the protection of instream uses and freshwater inflows to bays and estuaries.

For example, with the exception of the Lower Colorado River Authority's water rights for Lakes Buchanan and Travis, none of the adjudicated water rights in the Colorado Basin included consideration of environmental flows. Although special permit conditions provide some environmental protection, even without such conditions, instream uses have a passive support system in the form of (1) water passed to meet the needs of downstream senior water rights, (2) water released from a reservoir for downstream diversion, (3) appropriated but unused water, and (4) return flows, those flows that are returned to the stream after an original diversion and use. Unused water rights and return flows generally make up a significant portion of the water currently available to meet environmental needs. In most fully appropriated streams, the *only* remaining sources of additional water available to meet environmental needs are appropriated but unused water left in the stream and return flows. *See* 30 Tex. Admin. Code § 297.1(43). In some river basins, water released for downstream diversion plays a major role in supporting environmental flow needs.

As the state's population increases and water demands rise, less permitted water will remain instream, thus creating the potential for adverse environmental impacts in areas that previously had not experienced such impacts. The availability of return flows to continue contributing to environmental needs may be less in the future. See Chapter 24 of this book. In essence, reuse water rights divert discharged return flows from a watercourse. Depending on the circumstances, the reuse of return flows may or may not provide some environmental protection; in some cases, it may replace the need to develop additional sources, but it may have the potential to disrupt ecosystems dependent on historically discharged return flows.

Thus, since 1985, instream flows and freshwater inflows to bays and estuaries were considered on a case-by-case basis in individual permits. In 2000, the San Marcos River Foundation filed an application for Permit No. 5724 with the Texas Natural Resource Conservation Commission on July 10, 2000, for 1.3 million AF/year for instream flows. Several other applications were filed for instream flows. These cases were an impetus for the later legislation. By 2003, interest in a more holistic approach was increasing, culminating in the passage of House and Senate Bills 3 in 2007. *See* Act of June 15, 2007, 80th Leg., R.S., ch. 1351 (H.B. 3); Act of May 28, 2007, 80th Leg., R.S., ch. 1430 (S.B. 3). These bills contained almost identical environmental flow provisions, but the general practice is to refer to S.B. 3 when describing the framework.

§ 11.4 Senate Bill 3: A Paradigm for Environmental Flow Protection

The S.B. 3 framework for the protection of environmental flows is based on the evaluated needs of a complete river and bay system. *See* S.B. 3, § 1.13. Under S.B. 3, environmental requirements in water rights are no longer based on the site-specific and case-by-case determinations under Texas Water Code sections 11.147(b)–(e), 11.150, 11.151, and 11.152, which usually evaluated a single stream or river or a stream segment. *See* Tex. Water Code § 11.147(e–3). Instead, S.B. 3 implements protection through environmental flow standards and environmental flow set-aside rules adopted by the commission. Whether a water right application for a new appropriation of water or an amendment that increases the amount of water authorized to be stored, taken, or diverted will be processed using the environmental flow standards depends on whether standards have been adopted for the river basin where the water project is located. Environmental flow standards have been adopted for all the major Texas river basins except for the Cypress, Red, Sulphur, and Canadian. *See* 30 Tex. Admin. Code ch. 298. See Figure 1, showing the major Texas river basins.

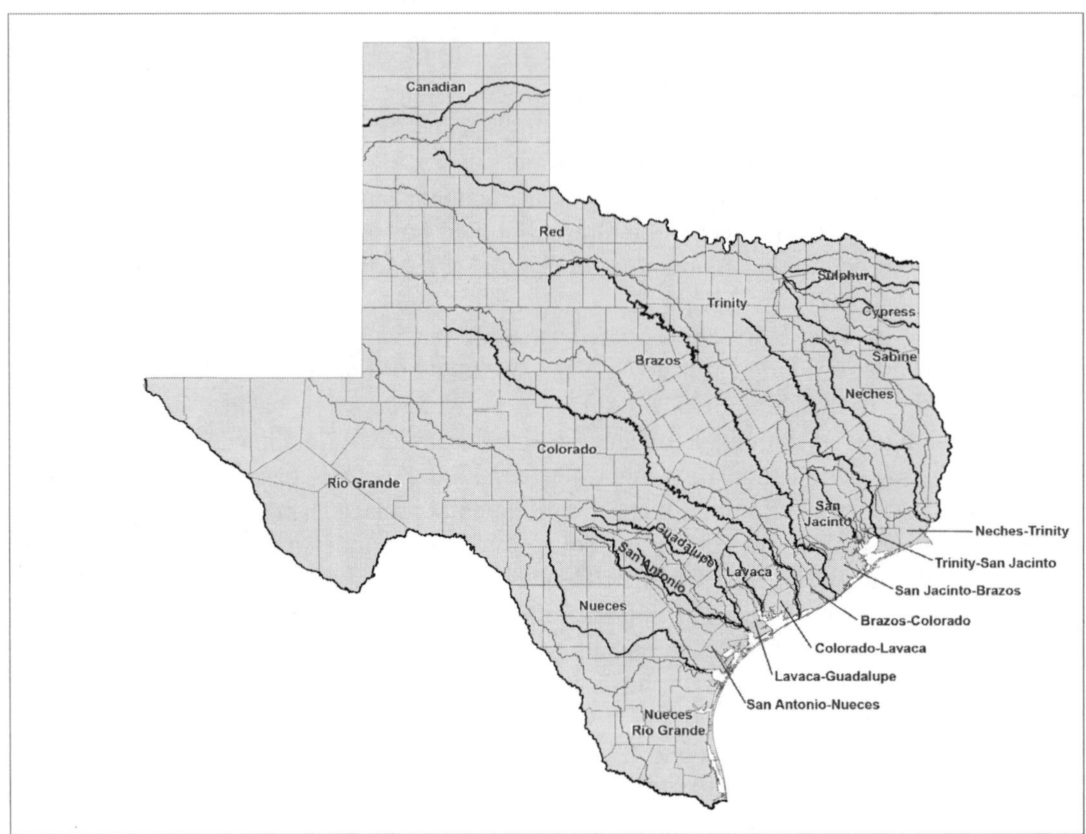

Figure 1. Texas River Basins. Texas Water Development Board, River Basins, www.twdb.texas.gov/surfacewater/rivers/river_basins/index.asp.

To develop these standards and set-asides, local science teams with expertise regarding each particular basin considered all reasonably available science and developed environmental flow regimes for that basin. These were recommended to a local stakeholder group and to the commission. This was performed for the basins identified in S.B. 3. The entire process was overseen by the Environmental Flows Advisory Group and coordinated by a statewide science committee, with the goal of ensuring consistency in environmental flow activities throughout the state.

The legislation established a priority order and time frame for considering specific groups of river basin and bay systems. The historic permit-by-permit consideration of flow conditions in a river basin, as summarized above, continued to be applied until S.B. 3–required standards for that basin were in place. Any permit or permit amendment that increased the amount of water authorized to be stored, taken, or diverted, beginning September 1, 2007 (the effective date of the legislation), was subject to a limited re-opener allowing the commission to adjust any flow conditions in the permit once the environmental flow standards for the subject basin were adopted.

Environmental flow standards have been adopted for all Texas river basins and associated bay and estuary systems prioritized in S.B. 3. *See* 30 Tex. Admin. Code ch. 298. Specifically, rules for environmental flow standards have been adopted for the following: the Sabine and Neches Rivers and Sabine Lake Bay; the Trinity and San Jacinto Rivers and Galveston Bay; the Colorado and Lavaca Rivers and Matagorda and Lavaca Bays; the Guadalupe, San Antonio, Mission, and Aransas Rivers and Mission, Copano, Aransas, and San Antonio Bays; the Nueces River and Corpus Christi and Baffin Bays; the Brazos River and its associated bay and estuary system; and the Rio Grande, the Rio Grande estuary, and the Lower Laguna Madre. There is no statutory deadline for adoption of environmental flow standards for the state's other basins.

§ 11.5 Details of the Senate Bill 3 Framework

§ 11.5:1 Introduction

The details of the S.B. 3 framework are primarily of historical interest now that the environmental flow standards have been adopted for all Texas river basins and associated bay and estuary systems prioritized in S.B. 3. Nevertheless, because of the importance of environmental flows to the water rights permitting scheme, a rudimentary understanding of development of the standards and set-asides is helpful and is provided in the following sections. For a more detailed discussion, see Hope Wells & Colette Barron Bradsby, *Environmental Flows*, *in Essentials of Texas Water Resources* ch. 11 (Mary K. Sahs ed., 5th ed. 2018).

§ 11.5:2 Policy Statements

S.B. 3 amended Texas Water Code section 11.0235 to encourage voluntary water and land stewardship. *See* Tex. Water Code § 11.0235(b). Amended section 11.0235(c) requires the commission to consider and "to the extent practicable" provide for freshwater inflows and instream flows necessary to maintain the viability of the state's streams, rivers, and bay and estuary systems in the commission's regular granting of permits for the use of state waters. *See* Tex. Water Code § 11.0235(c). It also states that, as an essential part of the state's environmental flow policy, all permit conditions relating to freshwater inflows to bays and estuaries and instream flow needs must be subject to temporary suspension if necessary for water to be applied to essential beneficial uses during emergencies. *See* Tex. Water Code § 11.0235(c). This policy includes permit conditions based on the adopted environmental flow standards as permit conditions that could be suspended, in addition to permit conditions in water rights granted prior to S.B. 3, as discussed at section 11.3:3 above. Numerous policy directives were added to Water Code chapter 11, including a statement of the need for specific time frames and prompt action to protect environmental flows, enforcement and more effective water rights administration, improved science and adaptive management, and a consensus-based regional approach throughout the state. *See* Tex. Water Code § 11.0235(d–1), (d–2), (d–4)–(d–6), (f). In addition, section 11.0235(e) was amended, noting how environmental flow standards are to be developed and how those standards will be integrated into the regional water planning and water permitting process. *See* Tex. Water Code § 11.0235(e). Finally, section 11.0235(d–3) states that in those basins in which water is available for appropriation, the commission should establish set-asides below which water will not be available for appropriation. In those basins in which unappropriated water is not sufficient to meet environmental flow standards established by the commission, "a variety of market approaches, both public and private, for filling the gap must be explored and pursued." Tex. Water Code § 11.0235(d–3).

§ 11.5:3 Environmental Flows Advisory Group and Environmental Flows Science Advisory Committee

To oversee the process of developing flow standards, S.B. 3 established the Environmental Flows Advisory Group of nine members: three members of the Texas House of Representatives appointed by the speaker; three members of the Texas Senate appointed by the lieutenant governor; and three appointed by the governor. *See* Texas Commission on Environmental Quality, *Environmental Flows Advisory Group*, www.tceq.texas.gov/permitting/water_rights/wr_technical-resources/eflows/group.html. Of the members appointed by the governor, one must come from the Texas Parks and Wildlife Commission, one from the Texas Water Development Board (TWDB), and one from the TCEQ.

The advisory group was required to submit a report to the governor and legislature not later than December 1, 2008, and every two years thereafter, summarizing hearings and studies, legislative recommendations, and progress on the development of flow recommendations. *See* Tex. Water Code § 11.0236(*l*). The reports from 2010 and 2013, primarily of historic interest, are available at the TCEQ website referenced above. The legislation also established a statewide Environmental Flows Science Advisory Committee composed of between five and nine members. The science committee provided the advisory group with scientific expertise and made recommendations for environmental flow protection. *See* Tex. Water Code § 11.02361; *see also* Texas Commission on Environmental Quality, *Texas Environmental Flows Science Advisory Committee*, www.tceq.texas.gov/permitting/water_rights/wr_technical-resources/eflows/txenvironmentalflowssac.html.

§ 11.5:4 Priority of Systems and the Development of Environmental Flow Regime Recommendations

S.B. 3 established a priority order for developing environmental flow regime recommendations and adopting environmental flow standards by the commission. In descending order, the priority is as follows:

> Group 1: The river basin and bay systems of the Trinity and San Jacinto Rivers and Galveston Bay, and the Sabine and Neches Rivers and Sabine Lake Bay.
>
> Group 2: The river basin and bay systems of the Colorado and Lavaca Rivers and Matagorda and Lavaca Bays, and the Guadalupe, San Antonio, Mission, and Aransas Rivers and Mission, Copano, Aransas, and San Antonio Bays.
>
> Group 3: The river basin and bay systems of the Nueces River and Corpus Christi and Baffin Bays; the Rio Grande, the Rio Grande estuary, and the Lower Laguna Madre; and the Brazos River and its associated bay and estuary system.

See Tex. Water Code § 11.02362(b).

With respect to each river basin and bay system in the priority groups, the advisory group appointed a basin and bay area stakeholder committee that in turn established a basin and bay expert science team. *See* Tex. Water Code § 11.02362(f), (i). Each stakeholder committee had at least seventeen members. The goal was for the membership to reflect a fair and equitable balance of interest groups concerned about each river basin and bay system. The legislation enumerated certain interest groups to be represented. *See* Tex. Water Code § 11.02362(f); *see also* Texas Commission on Environmental Quality, *Environmental Flows*, www.tceq.texas.gov/permitting/water_rights/wr_technical-resources/eflows/ [hereinafter *Environmental Flows*] (committee membership and information).

Each science team included technical experts with special expertise regarding the river basin and bay system being considered or having expertise about the development of environmental flow conditions in general. *See* Tex. Water Code § 11.02362(i); *see also Environmental Flows*. Each science team developed environmental flow analyses, defined in the legislation as "the application of a scientifically derived process for predicting the response of an ecosystem to changes in instream flows or freshwater inflows." Tex. Water Code § 11.002(15). Each science team recommended an environmental flow regime for the river basin and bay system for which the team was established. *See* Tex. Water Code § 11.02362(m). Environmental flow regimes are defined as—

> a schedule of flow quantities that reflects seasonal and yearly fluctuations that typically would vary geographically, by specific location in a watershed, and that are shown to be adequate to support a sound ecological environment and to maintain the productivity, extent, and persistence of key aquatic habitats in and along the affected water bodies.

Tex. Water Code § 11.002(16). "In developing the analyses and recommendations, the science team must consider all reasonably available science, without regard to the need for water for other uses, and the science team's recommendations must be based solely on the best science available." Tex. Water Code § 11.02362(m).

Each science team submitted its analyses and flow regime recommendations to the stakeholder committee, the advisory group, and the commission. The stakeholder committee and the advisory group were prohibited from changing the analyses or recommendations of the science team. *See* Tex. Water Code § 11.02362(n). The stakeholder committee reviewed the analyses and recommendations, considering them with other factors such as present and future water needs, and submitted recommendations to the commission and advisory group. *See* Tex. Water Code § 11.02362(o). The advisory group, when appropriate, also submitted comments on the science teams' analyses and recommendations to the commission. *See* Tex. Water Code § 11.02362(q).

S.B. 3 provided that if the commission established an estuary advisory council for a particular basin with specific duties related to implementing permit conditions for environmental flows, the council would act as the stakeholder committee for that basin and be subject to the same operational and membership requirements as other stakeholder committees. *See* Tex. Water Code § 11.02362(r). The Nueces Estuary Advisory Council is the only estuary advisory council in existence in Texas and was created by an Agreed Order issued by the Texas Water Commission (predecessor agency to the TCEQ) in 1992. The council is charged with assessing the effectiveness of water management strategies, including freshwater inflow requirements relating to Choke Canyon Reservoir, Lake Corpus Christi, and associated estuary systems. In accordance with S.B. 3, the Nueces River and Corpus Christi and Baffin Bays Stakeholder Committee is composed of members of the Nueces Estuary Advisory Council along with additional stakeholders meeting the interests required by the statute. *See* Tex. Water Code § 11.02362(f).

For the Rio Grande Basin and bay system, the flow regime was required to exclude uses attributable to Mexican water flows for the Rio Grande below Fort Quitman and to comply with all relevant treaties and court decisions. *See* Tex. Water Code § 11.02362(n), (o). In developing its recommendations, the Rio Grande stakeholder committee was required to consider the water accounting requirements of any international water sharing treaty, minutes, and agreements applicable to the Rio Grande and the effects of allocation of water on the Rio Grande watermaster in the middle and lower Rio Grande. *See* Tex. Water Code § 11.02362(o). The Rio Grande stakeholder committee did not submit recommendations. See Chapter 14 of this book regarding multijurisdictional water rights to the Rio Grande.

§ 11.5:5 Adoption of Environmental Flow Standards and Set-Asides

As previously discussed, S.B. 3 set deadlines for each step of the process resulting in adoption of environmental flow standards (rules) for each of the prioritized river basins and bay systems. Generally, the time frame provided that once a stakeholder committee established a science team, the science team was given one year to submit its analyses and flow regime recommendations. The stakeholder committee was then given six months to submit its recommendations on the work of the science team. Once the commission received recommendations from both the science team and stakeholder committee, the commission had one year to adopt flow standards for the basin and bay system.

Under S.B. 3, the advisory group could also establish a schedule for developing environmental flow regime recommendations and adopting flow standards for river basins and bay systems not listed in the priority groups. *See* Tex. Water Code § 11.02362(e). According to the legislation, requiring the advisory group to establish a schedule for all other basins in the state in no way prohibits "an effort to develop information on environmental flow needs and ways in which those needs can be met by a voluntary consensus-building process" in those basins. Tex. Water Code § 11.02362(e). For example, the Caddo Lake Institute, a nonprofit scientific and educational corporation, in partnership with the Nature Conservancy, has been working with multiple agencies, universities, and other interested stakeholders to assess and develop the flow needs of Caddo Lake in the Cypress Creek Basin. *See* Caddo Lake Institute, *Environmental Flows Project*, https://caddolakeinstitute.org/flows-project/.

S.B. 3 requires the commission, by rule, to adopt environmental flow standards for each river basin and bay system in this state "that are adequate to support a sound ecological environment, to the maximum extent reasonable considering other public interests and other relevant factors." Tex. Water Code § 11.1471(a)(1). Section 11.1471 requires the commission to establish an amount of unappropriated water, if available, to be set aside to satisfy the environmental flow standards "to the maximum extent reasonable when considering human water needs." Tex. Water Code § 11.1471(a)(2). The commission is also required to create procedures for implementing adjustments of permit conditions. *See* Tex. Water Code § 11.1471(a)(3).

In adopting flow standards, the commission must consider the following: the geographical extent of the river basins and bay systems as adopted by the advisory group and the TWDB, schedules established by the advisory group, environmental flow analyses and recommended flow regimes developed by the science team, stakeholder committee recommendations regarding the suggested flow regime, comments submitted by the advisory group, specific characteristics of the system, economic factors, human and other competing water needs, all reasonably available science, and any other appropriate information. *See* Tex. Water Code § 11.1471(b). Environmental flow standards adopted by the commission must consist of "a schedule of flow quantities, reflecting seasonal and yearly fluctuations that may vary geographically by specific location in a river basin and bay system." Tex. Water Code § 11.1471(c). As mentioned above, the commission has, by rule, adopted flow standards for each of the priority basins after considering recommendations made by the various stakeholder committees and science teams established by S.B. 3. Table 1 summarizes this rulemaking.

Table 1: TCEQ Rulemaking for Priority Basin and Bay Systems

River Basin and Bay System	Rule Citation	Date of Adoption
Trinity and San Jacinto Rivers and Galveston Bay	30 Tex. Admin Code ch. 298, subch. B, §§ 298.200–.240	April 20, 2011
Sabine and Neches Rivers and Sabine Lake Bay	30 Tex. Admin. Code ch. 298, subch. C, §§ 298.250–.290	April 20, 2011
Colorado and Lavaca Rivers and Matagorda and Lavaca Bays	30 Tex. Admin Code ch. 298, subch. D, §§ 298.300–.340	August 8, 2012
Guadalupe, San Antonio, Mission, and Aransas Rivers and Mission, Copano, Aransas, and San Antonio Bays	30 Tex. Admin Code ch. 298, subch. E, §§ 298.350–.390	August 8, 2012
Nueces River and Corpus Christi and Baffin Bays	30 Tex. Admin Code ch. 298, subch. F, §§ 298.400–.440	February 12, 2013
Brazos River and its associated bay and estuary system	30 Tex. Admin Code ch. 298, subch. G, §§ 298.450–.490	February 12, 2013
Rio Grande, Rio Grande Estuary, and Lower Laguna Madre	30 Tex. Admin Code ch. 298, subch. H, §§ 298.500–.540	February 12, 2013

§ 11.5:6 Periodic Review of Flow Standards and Abolishment of Advisory Group and Local Committees

After submitting its environmental flow standard recommendation to the commission, each stakeholder committee, in consultation with its science team, submitted a work plan for advisory group approval. *See* Tex. Water Code § 11.02362(p). The work plan establishes a schedule for periodic review of environmental flow analyses, regime recommendations, and flow standards; recommends specific monitoring and studies; and establishes a schedule for validation and refinement of flow standards and strategies to achieve those standards. *See* Tex. Water Code § 11.02362(p)(1)–(3). The statute requires that the periodic review occur at least once every ten years; however, some stakeholder groups adopted a shorter review period in their work plans. Work plans for each of the priority basins have been prepared by the applicable stakeholder committees with the exception of the Rio Grande stakeholder committee. *See Environmental Flows* (links to individual stakeholder committee work plans).

Information regarding specific work plan studies funded by the legislature and completed as part of the adaptive management phase of S.B. 3 can be found at Texas Water Development Board, *Statewide Environmental Flows (S.B. 3)*, www.twdb.texas.gov/surfacewater/flows/environmental/index.asp. Over twenty studies were completed across five basin-bay areas.

The TCEQ may alter an environmental flow standard or set-aside in a rulemaking process undertaken in accordance with a schedule established by the commission and involving stakeholder participants from the basin. In establishing a schedule, the commission is required to consider the work plan submitted by the applicable stakeholders committee. The rulemaking process may not occur more frequently than once every ten years, unless the stakeholder's work plan provides for periodic review to occur more frequently and the work plan is adopted by the advisory group. In that case, if the commission finds the schedule appropriate, the review and rulemaking may be undertaken together. *See* Tex. Water Code § 11.1471(f). In a second rulemaking, the time frame for the adaptive management process for the Sabine and Neches Basins was reduced to a five-year cycle, based on an approved work plan. *See* 37 Tex. Reg. 6629 (Aug. 24, 2012) (amending 30 Tex. Admin. Code § 298.90 (eff. Aug. 30, 2012)).

After the commission adopted flow standards for all the river basin and bay systems in the state, the advisory group, science advisory committee, and all stakeholder committees and science teams were to be abolished. *See* Tex. Water Code §§ 11.0236(m), 11.02361(g), 11.02362(s). The abolishment date is unknown at this time, since the advisory group has not adopted a schedule for developing environmental flow standards for the remaining river basin and bay systems in the state.

II. Environmental Flow Standards and Set-Asides in Water Rights Permitting

§ 11.6 Water Rights Permitting after Senate Bill 3

§ 11.6:1 Amended Water Rights Permitting Provisions

In addition to instituting a robust science-driven process for determining the environmental needs of river basins and bay systems, S.B. 3 amended various permitting provisions of the Texas Water Code to integrate requirements relating to environmental flow standards and set-asides into water rights appropriations. Specifically, amended Water Code section 11.023 provides that state water may be appropriated for certain enumerated purposes, only to the extent that such water has not been set aside by the commission to meet environmental flow needs. *See* Tex. Water Code § 11.023(a).

Amended section 11.134 provides that the commission can grant an application for a new appropriation or amendment of a permit that increases the appropriation only if the permit includes consideration of the environmental flow standards, and, if applicable, the assessments under Water Code sections 11.147(b)–(e), 11.150, 11.151, and 11.152. *See* Tex. Water Code § 11.134(b)(3)(D).

Amended section 11.147 requires the commission to apply environmental flow standards, including any set-asides, for the purpose of determining the environmental flow conditions necessary to maintain freshwater inflows, existing instream uses and water quality, or fish and aquatic wildlife habitat in the permitting process instead of the factors in section 11.147(b)–(e). *See* Tex. Water Code § 11.147(e–3).

The commission is prohibited from issuing a permit for a new appropriation or an amendment to an existing water right that increases the amount of water authorized to be stored, taken, or diverted if the permit or amendment would impair any flow set-aside established by the commission. *See* Tex. Water Code § 11.1471(d). Permits or amendments to existing water rights that increase the amount of water authorized to be stored, taken, or diverted issued after adoption of flow set-asides must contain provisions to ensure protection of the set-aside. *See* Tex. Water Code § 11.1405(f), (g).

With respect to an environmental flow set-aside or environmental flow standard (for a river basin other than the middle and lower Rio Grande), the priority date assigned to a set-aside or standard is the date that the commission receives environmental flow regime recommendations from the applicable science team. Tex. Water Code § 11.1471(e). The adopted set-asides must be included in the WAMs with that priority date. This priority date has no other purpose. *See* 30 Tex. Admin. Code § 298.20; *see also* Texas Commission on Environmental Quality, *Draft Senate Bill 3 Permitting Guidelines* 3, www.tceq.texas.gov/assets/public/permitting/watersupply/water_rights/eflowsrevised_draft_sb3 _implementation_guidelines.pdf [hereinafter *Draft Senate Bill 3 Permitting Guidelines*]. It is important to note that the commission did not adopt any set-asides in the first round of rulemakings. See Chapter 12 of this book relating to the commission's use of water availability models in the evaluation of water rights.

§ 11.6:2 The Use of Environmental Flow Standards and Set-Asides in Permitting Decisions

Under S.B. 3, river basin and bay system environmental flow standards adopted by the commission will be implemented through water right permit conditions. The flow standards consist of a schedule of flow quantities, reflecting seasonal and yearly fluctuations that may vary geographically by specific location in a river basin and bay system. *See* Tex. Water Code § 11.1471(c). The commission has adjusted its technical review process to ensure that permits protect, to the extent practicable, the required range of variable flow distribution needs in specific locations within an affected water body. Thus, permit conditions in S.B. 3 basins are based on the adopted standards found in the commission's chapter 298 rules, which apply only to new appropriations of water or an amendment to an existing water right that increases the amount of water authorized to be stored, taken, or diverted. *See* 30 Tex. Admin. Code § 298.10. The environmental flow standards for each basin and bay system include measurement points, specific flow values for different flow levels (subsistence, base, high flow pulses), and freshwater inflow standards, where applicable. *See* 30 Tex. Admin. Code ch. 298. The adopted rules for each basin and bay system also include provisions describing how these standards will be included and protected in water right permit conditions. *See* 30 Tex. Admin. Code §§ 298.230, 298.285, 298.335, 298.385, 298.435, 298.485, 298.535.

The commission has adjusted its technical review process to ensure that special conditions in water rights requesting new or increased appropriations protect, to the extent practicable, the adopted standards in accordance with chapter 298 of the commission rules. Guidelines explaining how environmental flow standards will be applied in water rights permits are found in *Draft Senate Bill 3 Permitting Guidelines*.

Generally, the draft guidelines describe how commission staff intend to formulate recommendations for flow restriction special conditions for permits or amendments that request new appropriations of water using adopted S.B. 3 standards. In addition, the guidelines describe how the commission intends to make adjustments pursuant to the re-opener provisions of S.B. 3, as well as the consideration of voluntary contributions when determining adjustments to permits. In response to public comment received in relation to the drafts, the March 2016 document also includes a specific example of applying S.B. 3 standards to a new appropriation and identifies circumstances under which the commission proposes to use S.B. 3 standards to develop special conditions in applications that do not include a new appropriation of water.

As illustrated in the draft guidelines, the commission's evaluation of a proposed water right's impacts to bays and estuaries and the method of addressing freshwater inflow protection through the permitting process is markedly different from the agency's historical approach. Although the TCEQ had authority to include these types of conditions, they were rarely included in water rights permits. Rather than implement freshwater inflow standards as special conditions in new water rights, staff instead considers whether a new application impairs freshwater inflow standards as part of the water availability determination for new appropriations of water as required in the TCEQ's adopted environmental flow standards. The TCEQ recently has considered two major water rights applications that included environmental flow issues. These were the application by the Brazos River Authority for Water Use Permit No. 5851, TCEQ Docket No. 2005-1490-WR; and the application by the Guadalupe-Blanco River Authority for Water Use Permit No. 12378, TCEQ Docket No. 2014-1658-WR. The Commission Orders for these cases are available on the TCEQ's website. The Commission Order for the GBRA case was appealed to the district court in 2020 in *National Wildlife Federation v. Texas Commission on Environmental Quality*, No. D-1-GN-20-007096 (98th Dist. Ct., Travis County, Tex. Nov. 21, 2020).

§ 11.6:3 Re-Opener Provisions in Permits Issued Pending Adoption of Environmental Flow Standards

S.B. 3 established a re-opener for permits issued after September 1, 2007, but before adoption of environmental flow standards for the subject basin. Such permits for a new appropriation or an amendment to an existing water right that increases the amount of water authorized to be stored, taken, or diverted must include a provision allowing the commission to adjust the conditions included in the permit or amended water right to provide for protection of instream flows or freshwater inflows if needed to achieve compliance with applicable environmental flow standards when those standards are adopted. *See* Tex. Water Code § 11.147(e–1). With respect to an amended water right, the commission may adjust only conditions that related to the increase in the amount of water to be stored, taken, or diverted. *See* Tex. Water Code § 11.147(e–1). Permits in existence before the effective date of S.B. 3 (September 1, 2007) were not affected by this requirement. *See* Tex. Water Code § 11.147(e–1). With respect to permits subject to this re-opener, in order to make an adjustment in the environmental conditions once the environmental flow standards are adopted for the subject basin, the commission must determine through an expedited public comment period whether an adjustment is appropriate. Such an adjustment must (1) not increase the amount of the pass-through or release requirement for the protection of instream flows or freshwater inflows by more than 12.5 percent of the annualized total of the requirement; (2) be based on consideration of priority dates and diversion points of other water rights in the basin subject to adjustment; and (3) be based on consideration of any contributions to the Texas Water Trust or voluntary amendments to existing water rights for environmental flows that contribute to meeting the applicable flow standards. *See* Tex. Water Code § 11.147(e–1)(1)–(3). Any water rights holder who makes a contribution or amends a water right for environmental flows is entitled to credit for the benefits of the contribution or amendment against any required permit adjustment. *See* Tex. Water Code § 11.147(e–2). The commission's adopted rules include a specific process for adjustments and methods for calculating the adjustments. *See* 30 Tex. Admin. Code § 298.25.

§ 11.7 Set-Asides Used for Other Beneficial Uses in Emergency Situations

A set-aside could temporarily be made available for other beneficial uses in emergency situations. *See* Tex. Water Code §§ 5.506(a–1), 11.148(a–1). Suspension of a set-aside is subject to the same process provided for the suspension of permit conditions. *See* Tex. Water Code § 11.147(b), (c). See section 11.3:3 above relating to procedures for the suspension of special permit conditions. The commission's adopted rules implementing these provisions can be found in 30 Texas Administrative Code chapter 35.

§ 11.8 Environmental Flow Protection and Permitting in Non-S.B. 3 River Basins

In river basins without adopted environmental flow standards (Cypress, Red, Canadian, and Sulphur), the commission's review of an application for a new appropriation of water considers environmental impacts in accordance with the requirements in Texas Water Code sections 11.147(b)–(e), 11.150, 11.151, and 11.152 and TCEQ rules. As with historical permits, discussed at section 11.3 above, the technical review may rely on existing data, studies, and literature, or the commission may require site-specific studies. Where applicable and available, instream flow studies and water quality assessments must be considered during this technical review. *See* Tex. Water Code § 11.147(b), (d). Based on this review, a streamflow restriction may be included as a permit special condition for the storage or diversion of water. A streamflow restriction special condition would require that a certain amount of flow be passed downstream before the water right holder may divert or store water. Factors that might lead to a streamflow restriction include the perennial nature of the stream, aquatic life uses and biological integrity, water quality, threatened or endangered species, and existing recreational use. *See* 30 Tex. Admin. Code §§ 297.54, 297.56.

As was the case before the enactment of S.B. 3, applications supported by site-specific studies are rare; the majority of streamflow restrictions in special conditions for permits not subject to S.B. 3 are derived using desktop methodologies. The desktop methodology most commonly employed is the "Lyons method," which determines instream flow values based on 40–60 percent of the monthly median flow. Robert L. Bounds & Barry Lyons, Texas Parks and Wildlife Department, *Existing Reservoir and Stream Management Recommendations Statewide Minimum Streamflow Recommendation* (Oct. 16, 1979). The Lyons method provides a schedule of minimum monthly flows that must be present in the stream before diversion is authorized. Permit special conditions are tailored to the specific impacts of the water project. Beyond streamflow restrictions, other types of special conditions, depending on the type of project, may include a requirement for protective intake screens to limit fish injuries, a mitigation plan for habitat or species loss, a requirement to protect water quality, and seasonal limits on diversion rates. *See* 30 Tex. Admin. Code § 297.53. The assessment of water quality impacts must consider the applicable Texas surface water quality standards. *See* 30 Tex. Admin. Code § 297.54; *see also* 30 Tex. Admin. Code §§ 307.1–.10. See Chapter 33 of this book for a general discussion of Texas surface water quality standards.

III. Appropriating Water Specifically for Instream Uses

§ 11.9 General Appropriation of Water for Instream Uses

§ 11.9:1 New Appropriations Specifically for Instream Uses

Instead of adding special conditions to an underlying permit to protect environmental flows, the state has, in limited circumstances, allowed for water to be used for instream purposes by amending an existing water right to add such uses. Water deposited in the Texas Water Trust likewise may be designated for instream uses. *See* Tex. Water Code § 15.7031. In the early 2000s, several applicants sought entirely new appropriations of water for environmental flow purposes. These applications triggered years of litigation and culminated with the legislature taking action through S.B. 3 to prohibit new appropriations for instream uses while simultaneously enacting new regulatory consideration of environmental flow needs and clarifying that existing water rights may be amended to include instream uses as an authorized use of water. *See* Tex. Water Code § 11.0237.

Beginning in 2000, several applications were filed seeking new appropriations of water to protect instream uses. Although issuing new permits for "instream flows dedicated to environmental needs or bay and estuary inflows" is now prohibited, the history of these instream flow applications is important because the applications served as an additional catalyst for legislation to protect environmental flows. Table 2 provides basic information about these cases. For a more detailed discussion, see Hope Wells & Colette Barron Bradsby, *Environmental Flows*, *in Essentials of Texas Water Resources* ch. 11 (Mary K. Sahs ed., 5th ed. 2018).

Table 2: Historic Applications for Instream Flows

Permit Applicant	Application	Filing Date	Appropriation Amount	Basin	Appeals
San Marcos River Foundation	Application of the San Marcos River Foundation for Permit No. 5724, filed with the Texas Natural Resource Conservation Commission on July 10, 2000	July 10, 2000	Approx. 1.3 million AF/year	San Marcos and Guadalupe rivers and the San Antonio Bay and Estuary	*San Marcos River Foundation v. TCEQ*, No. GN3-01251; *Texas Commission on Environmental Quality v. San Marcos River Foundation*, 267 S.W.3d 356, 360 (Tex. App.—Corpus Christi–Edinburg 2008, pet. denied)

Table 2: Historic Applications for Instream Flows					
Caddo Lake Institute, Inc.	Application No. 5787		2.15 million AF/year of state water for nonconsumptive instream uses to be measured at six references points on the following streams in the Cypress Creek Basin: Big Cypress Creek, Little Cypress Creek, Black Cypress Bayou, James Bayou, Harrison Bayou, and Kitchen Creek		*Caddo Lake Institute, Inc. v. TCEQ*, No. GN4-00132
Lower Colorado River Authority (LCRA)		October 30, 2002	All the remaining unappropriated state water in the Colorado River Basin downstream of a reference point at O.H. Ivie Reservoir, Coleman County, and downstream of a reference point at Lake Brownwood, Brown County, an amount in excess of five million AF, for instream uses	Colorado River Basin	TCEQ Docket No. 2003-0731-WR, dismissed by TCEQ on Nov. 19, 2003
Matagorda Bay Foundation		November 8, 2002	663,774 AF for nonconsumptive instream use and freshwater inflow into Matagorda Bay	Lavaca River Basin; the Colorado-Lavaca Coastal Basin; and the Lavaca-Guadalupe Coastal Basin	TCEQ Docket No. 2003-0732-WR, dismissed by TCEQ on Nov. 19, 2003

Table 2: Historic Applications for Instream Flows					
Galveston Bay Conservation and Preservation Association (GBCPA) and Galveston Bay Foundation (GBF)		November 12, 2002	3.8 million AF for instream uses and freshwater inflows	Trinity River Basin and the Trinity-San Jacinto Estuary and Galveston Bay	*Galveston Bay Conservation & Preservation Ass'n, Galveston Bay Foundation & Matagorda Bay Foundation v. TCEQ,* No. GN4-00160; *Texas Commission on Environmental Quality v. Galveston Bay Conservation & Preservation Ass'n,* 267 S.W.3d 361, 366 (Tex. App.—Corpus Christi–Edinburg 2008, no pet.)
Lavaca-Navidad River Authority		December 30, 2002	346,300 AF to be measured at a reference point in the Lavaca River Basin; 153,902 AF at a reference point in the Colorado-Lavaca Coastal Basin; and 163,572 AF at a reference point in the Lavaca-Guadalupe Coastal Basin	Lavaca River Basin; Colorado-Lavaca Coastal Basin; Lavaca-Guadalupe Coastal Basin	TCEQ Docket No. 2003-0719-WR, dismissed by TCEQ on Nov. 19, 2003

§ 11.9:2 Permits Amended to Include Instream Uses

Before 2007, ten water rights were amended to authorize instream use purposes to meet instream flow needs or freshwater inflows to bays and estuaries. For example, the Lower Colorado River Authority's water rights for Lake Travis and Lake Buchanan authorize the use of appropriated water for the needs of both the Colorado River and Matagorda Bay. *See* Certificates of Adjudication No. 14-5478A and No. 14-5482A (1989). The common element to these water rights is that instream use was not part of the original appropriation; existing water rights were amended to add instream uses.

Under Texas Water Code section 11.134, all appropriated water must be intended for a beneficial use. *See* Tex. Water Code § 11.134(b)(3)(A). "Beneficial use" is defined as "that amount of water which is economically necessary for a purpose authorized by [chapter 11], when reasonable intelligence and reasonable diligence are used in applying the water to that purpose and shall include conserved water." Tex. Water Code § 11.002(4); 30 Tex. Admin. Code § 297.1(8). Water Code section 11.023 lists the categories of uses for which state water may be appropriated. The list identifies eight specific uses and one broad category of "any other beneficial use." *See* Tex. Water Code § 11.023(a), (b).

In 1993, the TCEQ amended 30 Texas Administrative Code chapter 297 by adding a definition for "instream use":

> The beneficial use of instream flows for such purposes including, but not limited to, navigation, recreation, hydropower, fisheries, game preserves, stock raising, park purposes, aesthetics, water quality protection, aquatic and riparian wildlife habitat, freshwater inflows for bays and estuaries, and any other instream use recognized by law. An instream use is a beneficial use of water. Water necessary to protect instream uses for water quality, aquatic and riparian wildlife habitat, recreation, navigation, bays and estuaries, and other public purposes may be reserved from appropriation by the commission.

30 Tex. Admin. Code § 297.1(25). The rules were further amended in 1999 by including instream use in the list of purposes for which state water may be appropriated, stored, or diverted. *See* 30 Tex. Admin. Code § 297.43(a)(10). The TCEQ has issued amended permits for purposes that provide water for environmental needs such as wetland enhancement, waterfowl management, wildlife propagation and preservation, and stream quality control. *See, e.g.*, Permit No. 5736, City of Corpus Christi (2001); Certificate of Adjudication No. 7-4493, Texas Parks and Wildlife Department (1986); Certificate of Adjudication No. 22-4539, U.S. Department of Interior (1986); Certificate of Adjudication No. 22-4543, Thomas H. Sweeney Jr., et al. (1986); Certificate of Adjudication No. 7-4296, U.S. Anahuac Wildlife Refuge (1986); Certificate of Adjudication No. 12-5328, Contract No. 1895-9, Dow Chemical Company (1994).

The practice of amending water rights to change the use or to add a use of instream flows dedicated to environmental needs or bay and estuary inflows was confirmed by S.B. 3, and the commission has continued to issue amended permits that authorize instream uses. *See* Tex. Water Code § 11.0237(a).

§ 11.9:3 The Texas Water Trust

The Texas Water Trust was established within the Texas Water Bank to hold water rights dedicated to environmental needs, including instream flows, water quality, fish and wildlife habitat, and bay and estuary inflows. Water rights may be held in trust for a term specified by contract or in perpetuity. *See* Tex. Water Code § 15.7031. S.B. 3 provided additional authority to the Texas Parks and Wildlife Department to protect and enforce Texas Water Trust deposits. Under Texas Water Code section 11.0841(c), the department has "the rights of a holder of a water right" held in the trust, including the right to file suit to prevent the unlawful use of the right. *See* Tex. Water Code § 11.0841(c)(1).

The trust currently contains three water rights in perpetuity. Two are Rio Grande rights totaling approximately 1,200 AF. These are senior irrigation rights donated to the Parks and Wildlife Department with the express requirement that they be deposited in the trust. *See* Certificate of Adjudication No. 23-914 (2003); Water Use Permit No. 3041 (2003). Texas State University provided the third trust deposit in the form of 33,108 AF of former hydroelectric rights. *See* Certificate of Adjudication No. 18-3865D (2006). Each deposited right has been amended to expressly authorize a change in use to allow the affected water right or portion of water right to be used to provide water for instream uses. The statute's use of the phrase "water rights dedicated to" environmental needs has been interpreted as an acknowledgment that existing water rights may be converted to instream use purposes. *See* Tex. Water Code § 15.7031(a). The commission, when authorizing deposits into the trust, has required that the water right to be deposited be amended to include instream use as a purpose of use.

Private water trusts also exist in the state and may become a more common tool to provide water for environmental flows through water rights management, habitat restoration, or watershed protection. Many land trust activities also benefit both the water quality and quantity of Texas rivers, streams, bays, and estuaries. For more information on land trusts, *see* www.texaslandtrustcouncil.org/.

IV. Conclusion

§ 11.10 Conclusion

Maintaining the fishery and aquatic wildlife resources and the ecological processes of riverine and bay systems is an increasingly important and complex task as the demands on finite water sources rise with the needs of a fast-growing state. With the transition from case-by-case protection of environmental flows to the imposition of environmental flow standards and establishment of set-asides for complete river and bay systems, the practitioner must carefully navigate the Texas Water Code and commission rules to determine how a water project will be evaluated in water rights permitting. In addition, environmental flow standards for nonpriority basins have yet to be adopted. Thus, today's practitioner must remain aware of both pre- and post-S.B. 3 procedure as well as the history behind the legislation.

CHAPTER 12

Determining Surface Water Availability

Kathy Alexander-Martin[1] and Ruth Ann Takeda[2]

§ 12.1 Introduction

When the Texas Commission on Environmental Quality (TCEQ) considers an application for an appropriation of surface water, it must consider, among other factors, whether the permit will impair either existing water rights or vested riparian rights, and whether "unappropriated water is available in the source of supply." *See* Tex. Water Code § 11.134(b)(2); see also Chapter 10 of this book for a discussion of water rights applications. This chapter describes the water availability models (WAMs) and the hydrologic analysis that the TCEQ executive director uses to support these required findings. This chapter begins with a discussion of Texas court decisions that have had an impact on the way the TCEQ determines water availability.

§ 12.2 Court Decisions about Water Availability

The *Stacy Dam* (or *Stacy*) case was an important decision of the Texas Supreme Court regarding how the state should determine water availability for new appropriations. *Lower Colorado River Authority v. Texas Department of Water Resources*, 689 S.W.2d 873 (Tex. 1984). In *Stacy*, the court reviewed a challenge of a finding of water availability made by the Texas Department of Water Resources, a predecessor agency to the TCEQ. The Colorado River Municipal Water District (CRMWD) applied for a permit to appropriate water from the Colorado River. Under state law, the department could not issue a permit for a new appropriation of water unless water remained available in the source of supply after considering senior water rights at their maximum authorized amounts. 689 S.W.2d at 875. The CRMWD contended that the estimated amount of permitted but unused water, when subtracted from the maximum authorized amounts, yielded sufficient "unappropriated water" to support its permit request. Some water rights holders were not fully using their appropriated rights at the time the appropriation was made; for example, municipalities were allowed to appropriate for future needs. Therefore, the CRMWD concluded that it should be allowed to appropriate the unused water and put it to immediate beneficial use. 689 S.W.2d at 874–75. The court disagreed. Discussing its 1926 opinion in *Motl v. Boyd*, 286 S.W. 458 (Tex. 1926), the court held that "the term 'unappropriated water' means the amount of water remaining after taking into account all existing uncancelled permits and filings *valued at their recorded levels*." 689 S.W.2d at 874 (emphasis added).

---

1. Kathy Alexander-Martin, PhD, is a Technical Specialist for the Water Availability Division, Texas Commission on Environmental Quality, and has worked with water rights at the agency for more than twenty years.

2. Ruth Ann Takeda, JD, is an attorney with the Environmental Law Division, Texas Commission on Environmental Quality, who has provided legal services to the Water Availability Division at the agency for approximately seven years.

Contrary to the CRMWD's arguments, in the court's view, the calculation was a simple matter of taking the amount of state water that the agency had previously determined the stream furnished and subtracting from that the amount of state water already appropriated to others. Any amount of water left over is water available for appropriation. 689 S.W.2d at 880. The court further held that, in this calculation, "the amount of state water already appropriated to others" is the full paper amount of issued water rights, not just the amount of water historically diverted or forecast to be diverted in the future. 689 S.W.2d at 880.

Taken together, the *Stacy* and *Motl* decisions are the foundation of the TCEQ's water availability analysis. In practice, the calculation is more complex than the court's language suggests. At the heart of the complexity are the hydrologic facts that both the amount of state water that a stream furnishes and the amount of that water needed to satisfy all existing water rights vary depending on the specific location in the river basin under consideration. Adding to the complexity is that the amount of state water that a stream furnishes, which TCEQ staff refers to as the *naturalized flow*, cannot be directly measured. Naturalized flow has to be calculated from a number of different sources of data. These and other complexities of the availability analysis are discussed in the description of the WAM below.

§ 12.3 Development of the Texas Water Availability Modeling System

The TCEQ's predecessor agencies developed models for eight of the twenty-three river basins in Texas during the 1970s and 1980s. *See* Texas Natural Resource Conservation Commission (TNRCC), *Documentation for Legacy Water Availability Models Used for Water Rights Permitting* (June 25, 1998), on file with the author [hereinafter Documentation for Legacy Models]. The purpose of the modeling tools used by the TCEQ and its predecessor agencies was to "allow the staff to obtain a reasonably accurate scientific estimate whether there was 'unappropriated water' at points along the river." *Lower Colorado River Authority v. Texas Department of Water Resources*, 689 S.W.2d 873, 875 (Tex. 1984). By the mid-1990s, the models were outdated and many of the underlying calculations used to support the modeling assumptions were not available. *See* TNRCC, Draft Technical Paper #2, *Evaluation of Existing Water Availability Models* (1997), on file with the author [hereinafter Technical Paper #2]. In 1997, the Texas legislature authorized funding for the development of modern modeling capability for twenty-two of the twenty-three river basins. Act of June 1, 1997, 75th Leg., R.S., ch. 1010, § 2.08; Act of May 25, 1999, 76th Leg., R.S., ch. 518. The legislation provided funding for the construction of the models and required the agency to provide information to all water rights holders. The models developed as a result of this legislation provided an updated and uniform suite of modeling tools for planning purposes and also for water rights permitting.

Owing to the complexity associated with accurate calculations of physical stream flow and increasingly complex water management strategies and associated permits, the initial development phase of the Texas WAMs began with a series of technical meetings among agency staff of the TNRCC (now the TCEQ), the Texas Water Development Board (TWDB), the Texas Parks and Wildlife Department, and outside consultants. These technical meetings resolved fundamental issues related to the choice of the model to use and attendant technical issues related to model construction and assumptions. The meetings also resulted in documentation of WAM technical issues and the underlying assumptions of TCEQ's WAM data sets. *See* Texas Commission on Environmental Quality, *WAM Resolved Technical Issues 1999–2000*, on file with author [hereinafter *WAM Resolved Technical Issues 1999–2000*]. The *WAM Resolved Technical Issues 1999–2000* document was originally prepared to provide a means for memorializing decisions regarding how water rights and related issues were addressed during the initial development of the WAMs for each basin in the state. Development of the WAM data sets was completed in 2003; however, the TCEQ continues to fund development efforts for the Water Rights Analysis Package (WRAP) simulation programs. As a result, some issues in the original document were relevant only during the initial model development process; other issues were superseded by more advanced modeling techniques, or the WAMs were modified by the TCEQ as it processed water rights permit applications. In 2015, the TCEQ, in collaboration with its modeling stakeholders, updated the *WAM Resolved Technical Issues* document through 2015. *See* Texas Commission on Environmental Quality, *WAM Technical Issues 2015*, www.tceq.texas.gov/assets/public/permitting/watersupply/water_rights/20190805wrap_resolved_issues.pdf [hereinafter *WAM Technical Issues 2015*]. The subsequent development of the Texas WAM System consists of five phases; the first two, discussed in the next section, relate to the development of naturalized flows for each river system. *See* Technical Paper #2.

As discussed above, the current WAMs were created in the early 2000s. A statewide extreme drought during 2011 heightened concerns about whether the state had experienced a new drought of record that would require updates to the naturalized flows in the WAMs. During the 85th legislative session in 2017, Senate Bill 696 was introduced to update the naturalized flows in priority basins; however, this bill did not pass the House. Issues related to WAM updates were considered again after the 85th legislative session and included a charge from the Texas speaker of the house to the House Committee on Natural Resources to "[a]nalyze the need to update Water Availability Models for the river basins in this state." *See* Speaker Joe Strauss, *Interim Committee Charges, Texas House of Representatives, 85th Legislature* 30 (Oct. 2017), https://house.texas.gov/_media/pdf/interim-charges-85th.pdf (House Committee on Natural Resources Interim Charge 7). The House Committee on Natural Resources held a hearing on this charge, and the Interim Report recommended a state-supported revenue source for WAM updates. (*See* House Committee on Natural Resources, *Interim Report to the 86th Legislature* 127, 134 (Dec. 2018), https://house.texas.gov/_media/pdf/committees/reports/85interim/Natural-Resources-Committee-Interim-Report-2018.pdf. Bills were filed during the 86th legislative session to begin the WAM update process, including House Bill 723, which was signed by the governor on May 24, 2019, and requires the TCEQ to update the naturalized flows for the Brazos River, Red River, Neches River, and Rio Grande basins by December 1, 2022, if the legislature appropriates money specifically for that purpose. *See* Act of May 24, 2019, 86th Leg., R.S., ch. 164 (H.B. 723), eff. Sept. 1, 2019. Soon thereafter, House Bill 1 was signed by the governor on June 15, 2019, which appropriated $2,162,000 for WAM updates for the four basins. *See* Act of May 25, 2019, 86th Leg., R.S., ch. 1353, § 18.48 (H.B. 1), eff. Sept. 1, 2019.

§ 12.4 Naturalized Flows

Naturalized stream flow represents the flow in a river that would have occurred without human impacts, such as reservoir construction, diversions, and return flows. Naturalized stream flow is the baseline condition for water availability accounting. It is the amount of water that the stream furnishes. *See Lower Colorado River Authority v. Texas Department of Water Resources*, 689 S.W.2d 873, 880 (Tex. 1984). The naturalized flows are determined over a time period known as the "period of record." For most Texas river systems, the naturalized flow encompasses at least a fifty-year period of record that includes the drought of the 1950s, recognized as an extremely severe drought throughout much of the state. The period of record also includes major floods and less severe droughts, thereby representing an approximation of historic hydrologic variability.

Naturalized stream flows are calculated by first identifying all U.S. Geological Survey (USGS) gages in a river basin and then selecting a subset of those gages that meet the requirements for having a sufficient period of record and having no known major issues with the gage flow data. Development of the naturalized flows consists of two parts: adjusting the gaged flows to approximate predevelopment conditions and filling in or extending the period of record for a gaging station. Gaged flows are adjusted using the following equation:

$$NF = GF + \Sigma D - \Sigma RF + \Sigma E + \Sigma\Delta S$$

where NF is the naturalized flow, GF is the gaged flow, D is all diversions upstream of the gage, RF is all return flows upstream of the gage, E is the net reservoir evaporation for all reservoirs upstream of the gage, and S is the change in content for all reservoirs upstream of the gage. *See* TNRCC, Draft Technical Paper #1, *Evaluation of Naturalized Streamflow Methodologies* (1997), on file with the author [hereinafter Technical Paper #1]. Note that this procedure may vary. Some coastal basins have few or no USGS gages. For example, in the Nueces–Rio Grande Coastal Basin, a rainfall-runoff model was used to estimate stream flow.

A Geographical Information System (GIS) is then used to identify water rights locations, reservoirs, and return flow locations. Next, these locations are grouped within an incremental watershed. An incremental watershed is the area between a downstream gage and the upstream gages that contributes flow to that gage. For gages at the top of watersheds, the incremental area is simply the watershed area that contributes runoff to that gage. The naturalized flow adjustments are performed for incremental watersheds. The incremental flow, or the difference between the flows at the downstream gage and the upstream gage, is added to the flow at the upstream gage, and the simulation uses this total flow to determine water availability for water rights.

Data availability determines the level of detail for the adjustments described above. In general, data on the end-of-month content for reservoirs, evaporation rates, and storage/volume/surface area relationships are available for most large reservoirs in Texas. These data are generally unavailable for smaller reservoirs, so they are usually not included in the adjustments. Excluding the smaller permitted reservoirs from the flow naturalization process has little effect on the estimates of naturalized flow. *See* Technical Paper #1. Domestic and livestock uses are also not part of the adjustments. There are no reporting requirements for these users; therefore, quantification of domestic and livestock use is not practical. *See* David Klein & Robin Smith, *Exploring the Scope of Landowner Water Rights for Domestic and Livestock Purposes*, 7 Tex. Tech Admin. L.J. 119, 141 (2007). In addition, domestic and livestock uses are considered to be superior to other uses. Therefore, the naturalized flows, which represent the starting point for water availability determinations for permitted users, are already reduced by the amount of domestic and livestock use and support the superior status of these uses. See also Chapter 4 of this book.

Other issues related to data availability include the accuracy and availability of diversion and return flow data for permitted water rights. For example, some water rights owners may overestimate self-reported water use to avoid cancellation for nonuse. *See* Tex. Water Code § 11.173. Another example is that some municipal rights have missing data. For these rights, diversions are estimated using a statistical correlation with population. Lastly, for water rights with questionable self-reported use for irrigation purposes, the diversions are estimated based on available information or are assumed to be zero. This avoids overestimating the naturalized flow and subsequent water availability. The TCEQ uses this conservative approach to determine the amount of water the stream furnishes to prevent "double permitting" or the stacking of permits or grants of a new appropriation that overlays existing permits. *See Stacy*, 689 S.W.2d at 876.

Surface water and groundwater are interconnected. See Chapter 1 of this book regarding water and the hydrologic cycle. An evaluation of an appropriation of state water must consider effects of the proposed permit on groundwater or groundwater recharge. *See* Tex. Water Code § 11.151. The WAMs include both implicit and explicit consideration of groundwater–surface water interaction depending on whether data exists to quantify the interaction. The naturalized flows that are the basis for the WAM account for both contribution to river flow caused by groundwater coming to the surface in the river or its banks and decreases in river flow caused by the river flowing over recharge features or losing surface water to groundwater recharge. Any unquantified groundwater–surface water interaction that occurs above a USGS gage is recorded at that gage to the extent the interaction historically occurred.

To the extent groundwater–surface water interaction can be quantified through appropriate channel loss studies or by spring flow measurements, the WAM naturalized flows and the simulation explicitly take these quantified values into account. Channel losses represent the amount of water available at an upstream point that may not reach the downstream point due to seepage, evapotranspiration, infiltration, or unaccounted-for diversions. The naturalized flow, computed as described above, already includes natural losses. In river basins, where appropriate studies have been performed, specific channel loss adjustments are included in the flow naturalization process. This is because a quantified portion of the water diverted at an upstream point would not reach the downstream point. In some basins, such as the Guadalupe, San Antonio, Colorado, and Rio Grande, the effects of groundwater pumpage and variable spring flows are calculated and removed from the gaged flows so that the gaged flows represent only watershed runoff. Adjustments are performed and the spring flows are added back to the naturalized flow during the simulation.

§ 12.5 Other Hydrologic and Spatial Data

In addition to the naturalized flow, water availability simulations require evaporation rates for each basin. The U.S. Army Corps of Engineers (USACE) maintains precipitation and evaporation data for major reservoirs. *See* U.S. Army Corps of Engineers, *Query Hydrologic Data on Ft Worth District Lakes*, www.swf-wc.usace.army.mil/cgi-bin/rcshtml.pl?page=Hydrologic. Both the stream flow naturalization process and the water availability simulation use this reservoir-specific information. For all other reservoirs, in particular those that impound less than five thousand acre-feet of water, if specific information is unknown, the TWDB data sets of precipitation and monthly gross evaporation rates for the entire state for each one-degree quadrangle of latitude and longitude are used. *See* Texas Water Development Board, *Lake Evaporation and Precipitation*, https://waterdatafortexas.org/lake-evaporation-rainfall. Net evaporation rates are derived by subtracting precipitation from evaporation, and they are then used in the simulation for small reservoirs.

Individual water rights are represented spatially at a specific location, known as a *control point*. The simulation requires information including the drainage area of the control point, the relationship between the control point and other control points, and the relationship between the control point and the next upstream and downstream gaged control points. Drainage area information and control point connectivity are derived from the TCEQ's GIS database for each basin. This information is used during the simulation to distribute flows from gaged to ungaged control points so that the model can then calculate the amount of flow available to each water right. Additional information for water rights includes the amount of water authorized for storage and diversion, the associated priority dates, the pattern of monthly water use, and any instream flow requirements or other special conditions that affect water availability.

§ 12.6 WRAP and Prior Appropriation Accounting

During the development phase of the Texas WAM System, the Water Rights Analysis Package (WRAP) was selected to model prior appropriation accounting. *See* Technical Paper #2. "Prior appropriation accounting" means that water rights are processed in the order of their priority dates, with senior water rights being fully satisfied before junior rights can divert. *See* Tex. Water Code § 11.027. See also Chapter 4 of this book. WRAP includes three component models: the simulation model SIM, a postprocessing application TAB, and a program to facilitate development of naturalized flows HYD. The WAM System also includes developmental versions of daily WAMs for six river basins. *See* Texas A&M University, *Water Rights Analysis Package (WRAP) Modeling System*, https://wrap.engr.tamu.edu.

The monthly simulation model SIM is used to determine water availability for water rights applications. SIM reads the water rights, ranks the rights in priority order, and then reads the parameter information for each control point in preparation for flow distribution. SIM executes an annual loop in which naturalized stream flow and evaporation for each month of the year are read. SIM distributes naturalized flow from gaged control points to ungaged control points using a drainage area ratio between the ungaged and gaged control points. SIM then executes a monthly loop. This loop is the basis for calculating the amount of water that each water right can store and divert, the remaining amount available to other rights, and the amount of water available for appropriation to new permits.

In the monthly loop, during each month of the period of record, SIM processes water rights in priority order, with senior water rights processed first. The target stream flow depletion is the amount of water needed by an individual water right in any month. Target stream flow depletion is determined from the authorized diversion amount and the end-of-month reservoir storage from the preceding month and is limited by any instream flow requirements or other special conditions. The end-of-month content is used to calculate reservoir drawdown and determine the amount of water a reservoir would need to fill completely. SIM assumes that a senior reservoir may fill completely before any water is available to downstream rights. *See WAM Technical Issues 2015*, Issue #3 Conservation Storage Protection.

After computing the target stream flow depletion, SIM determines the amount of stream flow available to meet the target. Upstream junior rights do not have access to water needed to meet the depletion needs of downstream senior rights because WRAP incorporates a strict interpretation of the prior appropriation doctrine. In other words, in the water availability simulation, junior rights do not have access to all of the flow at their control point. Any water necessary to meet the demands of a senior right is passed downstream. This includes any water needed to satisfy fully the storage rights of downstream senior reservoirs. *See WAM Technical Issues 2015*, Issue #3 Conservation Storage Protection.

As each water right is processed in turn, SIM performs a water balance to determine the stream flow depletion, reservoir evaporation, end-of-month storage, diversion and diversion shortage, instream flow requirement, and instream flow shortage. SIM attempts to meet all or any portion of the water right's depletion demand and then adjusts the stream flow availability at the control point of the water right and all downstream control points. This is accomplished by subtracting stream flow depletions, adding return flows, and adjusting for channel losses, if any. The result is the amount of water remaining to satisfy the needs of junior water rights; any water left over would be available for appropriation to others.

When all basin water rights are processed, SIM computes the regulated, available, and unappropriated flows. The regulated flow is the stream flow at a control point after accounting for all water rights. This is the "actual" physical stream flow and includes water flowing past a point that would be needed by downstream senior water rights. Thus, not all of the regulated flow at a control point may be available to water rights at that point. The available flow is the amount of water a water right can use to meet its target stream flow depletion. The unappropriated flow is the amount of stream flow that is not needed by existing basin water rights and may be available for appropriation to others.

§ 12.7 Water Availability Analysis

The TCEQ uses the WAMs to process applications that request new appropriations of state water, to analyze the effects of amendment applications on existing water rights, to process requests for term water (diversion permits for a limited duration or "term"), and to analyze reuse applications. See Chapter 10 of this book for a discussion of these applications. The TCEQ currently maintains two different versions of the input data sets for each river basin. The full authorization simulation (Run 3) is used to evaluate requests for new appropriations of water and amendments that could potentially affect senior water rights. *See WAM Technical Issues 2015*, Appendix A, Issue #19 RUN3 and RUN8 of the New WAMs Relating to the Review of New Perpetual Water Right Applications and Term Water Right Applications. The full authorization data set for each river basin assumes that all water rights holders divert their entire authorized amount and that reservoirs are included at their as-built capacity. *See WAM Technical Issues 2015*, Appendix A, Issue #10 Model Runs. This ensures that the actual recorded values of all water rights are deducted from the physical stream flow, as required by *Stacy*.

Term water rights are not included in this data set. Term water rights are based on appropriated but unused water and are subordinate to senior appropriative rights. *See* Tex. Water Code § 11.1381(a), (d). See also Chapter 10 of this book. Return flows are also not included in the full authorization data set because these flows are potentially interruptible. *See* 30 Tex. Admin. Code § 297.42(g). Earlier agency models did include return flows. *See* Documentation for Legacy Models. Therefore, some or all of the return flows in the river may have been appropriated to others in past agency permitting actions. Excluding return flows from current permitting decisions for perpetual water rights lessens uncertainty in permitting actions by ensuring that actual physical stream flows do not include flows that could be removed from the stream at any time.

For applications requesting a new appropriation of state water, TCEQ staff first compiles parameter information for the diversion point for the new application—that is, the drainage area and location of the point with respect to gages and other water rights. This information is then inserted into the full authorization data set, along with the priority date of the application and the type of use requested by the applicant. Any instream flow requirements are also included, modeled at the priority date of the application. *See WAM Technical Issues 2015*, Issue #2 Streamflow Restrictions Associated with Permits. Since instream flow requirements are modeled using a priority date, they are treated like an additional water right. This means that a downstream senior instream flow requirement could limit diversions and impoundment by an upstream junior water right. Instream flow requirements are usually based on the regulated flow computed at the priority date of the underlying water right, unless the model user specifies otherwise.

After the requested appropriation in the new application is entered into the WAM, SIM is executed and an output file is generated. The output file contains the diversion amount and any shortage, monthly reservoir storage and evaporation, and instream flow information. Additionally, regulated flow, available flow, unappropriated flow, and naturalized flow are written into the output files. The post-processing application, TAB, is used to generate statistical information for the period of record. For water rights diversions, TAB computes the reliability of the diversion. Volume reliability is the percentage of the diversion demand that is actually satisfied, computed for the entire period of record. Period reliability is the percentage of months during the period of record that either the diversion demand is fully met or a specified percentage of the demand is equaled or exceeded.

For applications requesting water for municipal use, an application will not be granted unless the water requested for appropriation is shown to be equal to the firm yield, which means the water is available 100 percent of the time. *See* 30 Tex. Admin. Code § 297.42(h). That is, the volume reliability and period reliability must both equal 100 percent. For applications requesting a direct diversion from a stream for irrigation use, 75 percent of the requested demand must be available 75 percent of the time. *See* 30 Tex. Admin. Code § 297.42(c). The percentage of months that 75 percent of the request is available is used to determine whether the "75/75" criterion is met. If the applicant indicates that a reliable alternative source of water is available to avoid impacts on stream flow, the TCEQ may grant a request that does not meet the "75/75" criterion if the request would not affect existing water rights. The TCEQ evaluates the availability of the alternative source, in particular its availability during drought times when unappropriated water may be unavailable, the reliability of the source, and its quantity and quality to ensure that any water rights granted will be beneficially used without waste. *See* 30 Tex. Admin. Code § 297.42(c). For certain applications, such as system operations, scalping (diversions during times of high stream flows), and diversions for aquifer storage and recovery or aquifer recharge, availability is determined on a case-by-case basis. *See* 30 Tex. Admin. Code § 297.42(d)–(g). For these types of applications, the maximum amount of water that could be granted is the maximum amount of unappropriated water available in any given year as determined by the simulation. The TCEQ cannot grant an application for more water than the agency determines the stream furnishes.

If water is unavailable to meet the requested demand, TCEQ staff executes iterative simulations with reduced demands to determine whether any amount of water is available to the applicant. For applications requesting storage of state water, staff performs a simulation to determine whether there is sufficient unappropriated water to refill the reservoir if there are extended periods of time during which the reservoir is empty because there is no available unappropriated water. If unappropriated water is available to refill the reservoir, staff recommends granting the application. An underlying assumption of a water availability simulation is that reservoirs are assumed full at the start of the simulation. This is because the period of record for most basins begins in 1940, generally a wet year in most parts of the state. (Note that WRAP allows the user to specify the storage capacity at the beginning of the simulation as a specified percentage of total reservoir capacity.) If a reservoir cannot refill during the period of record, the assumption is that insufficient water is available for appropriation. In addition, if the reservoir is not full a percentage of the time, inflows of state water appropriated to other water rights could not pass downstream and those water rights could be affected by the application. If the reservoir does not refill, TCEQ staff recommends denial of the application unless the applicant can demonstrate that an alternative source is available that is reliable and of sufficient quantity and quality to make the proposed project viable and ensure that, if a permit is granted, it will be protective of senior water rights and the environment. *See* 30 Tex. Admin. Code §§ 297.42(a), (b), 297.45.

For amendments to existing water rights, TCEQ staff must evaluate whether the proposed change harms other water rights in the basin. *See* Tex. Water Code § 11.122. The evaluation is conducted by running two simulations using the full authorization data set. The first simulation does not include the new application and represents a baseline condition. The application information is then added to the input data set and a second simulation is performed. TAB is used to calculate volume reliabilities for both simulations, and the results are compared. Volume reliability is used because most water rights authorize an annual amount of water and the TCEQ's rules require consideration of effects on water quantity. *See* 30 Tex. Admin. Code § 297.45(a). If the analysis demonstrates effects on the reliabilities of basin rights senior to the amendment application, the TCEQ may recommend that the authorization include special conditions to mitigate these effects. *See* 30 Tex. Admin. Code § 297.45(c), (e). In certain cases, TCEQ staff may also evaluate changes in reservoir storage for downstream reservoirs to ensure that senior storage rights are not impaired by the amendment application. *See* 30 Tex. Admin. Code § 297.42(a).

The current conditions data set for each river basin includes (1) reported actual diversions for each water right, (2) current capacity for reservoirs, (3) recent return flows, and (4) term water rights. The TCEQ conservatively uses the highest annual self-reported use for each water right for a ten-year period to determine the diversion target for each water right in the current conditions data set. This allows the TCEQ to determine whether water that is permitted but unused is available for appropriation for a term of years. *See* Tex. Water Code § 11.1381(a). Requests for term water are processed in a similar manner as those for a new appropriation, as explained above. The only difference is that the current conditions data sets are used in the simulation. When no water is available for appropriation in the full authorization simulation, the current conditions simulation is used to determine whether term water may be available. In other words, an application for a perpetual water right may be denied and the applicant may instead be allowed to use water for a specified period of time, usually ten years.

Return flows are included in the current conditions simulation; therefore, applications for indirect reuse of treated effluent are also represented in this simulation. See Chapter 24 of this book for a discussion of reuse. The amount of return flows included in the WAM is the minimum reported monthly discharge for each month. *See WAM Technical Issues 2015*, Issue #10 Return Flows. The target diversion for a reuse water right is developed based on the actual volume of the return flows that are represented in the WAM. Including reuse diversions in the WAM ensures that water available to a water right, based on an authorization to divert discharged return flows, is not allocated to more junior water rights on a term basis. This prevents harm to existing reuse water rights in future agency permitting actions.

The TCEQ has adopted environmental flow standards for all river basins directly draining to the Gulf of Mexico. See Chapter 11 of this book.

§ 12.8 Administrative Findings on the WAM

There are no reported court decisions in which the TCEQ's use of the WRAP model, or the modeling assumptions incorporated in that model, have been at issue. However, applications of the WRAP model and WAM data sets, and underlying modeling assumptions, have been issues in administrative proceedings. Issues in these cases have ranged from the accuracy of data inputs to the methods used to determine water availability, compliance with the TCEQ's adopted freshwater inflows standards, and injury to other water rights. While such administrative decisions have no precedential value, they can be of persuasive value in later cases.

In the first case to address issues related to the water availability models, protestants to a water rights application asserted that the TCEQ's model did not properly account for channel losses and that the model was not used correctly. *See* Application of Southerland Properties, Inc. for Permit No. 5647 to Appropriate Water, TNRCC Docket No. 2000-1230-WR; SOAH Docket No. 582-01-1272 (final order issued May 16, 2002). The administrative law judge (ALJ) found that although the model might be considered a "black box" with respect to the complex nature of the input data, TCEQ staff experience with the model proved compelling and the ALJ agreed with the TCEQ that the WRAP was useful in the determination of water availability. *See* Proposal for Decision, SOAH Docket No. 582-01-1272, at 24–25.

In a second case, the TCEQ's use of the WAM to determine injury to other water rights as a result of an amendment was addressed. The City of San Angelo applied to amend its water right to add a downstream diversion point. An issue in this case was whether the move of a diversion point could affect other water rights. The executive director performed an analysis using the WAM and determined that other water rights would not be affected. *See* Application No. 1298B by the City of San Angelo for Amendment to Certificate of Adjudication 14-1298, TCEQ Docket No. 2009-0815-WR; SOAH Docket No. 582-10-0292 (final order issued Mar. 24, 2011). In this case the ALJ found that the WAM is the best hydrologic model available to the TCEQ to assess potential impacts from water rights amendments. *See* Findings of Fact and Conclusions of Law, SOAH Docket No. 582-10-0292, at 6, available in the TCEQ's Central Records.

Use of the WAMs to determine water availability for term permits was addressed in the application of Bradley B. Ware for an extension of his term permit. *See* Application of Bradley B. Ware to Amend Water Use Permit No. 5594, TCEQ Docket No. 2008-0181-WR; SOAH Docket No. 582-08-1698. Ware filed an application to extend or delete the term on his existing term water use permit. The executive director determined, based on the WAM, that no water was available for a either a term permit or a perpetual permit. The ALJ found that the WAM is designed to be the most accurate method available to determine water availability without regard to the amount of water requested by an application but that the TCEQ is not required by law to use the WAM in this determination. The ALJ recommended that the application be denied. *See* Findings of Fact and Conclusions of Law, SOAH Docket No. 502-08-1698, at 4, 11, available by request at the State Office of Administrative Hearings or in the TCEQ's Central Records. The TCEQ commissioners voted to adopt the ALJ's proposal for decision and deny the application. Ware filed suit in district court appealing the TCEQ's denial of his application and asking the court to reverse the TCEQ's decision or remand the case to the agency for further proceedings. *See Ware v. Texas Commission on Environmental Quality*, Cause No. D-1-GN-10-002342 in Travis County, Texas. The district court ruled in favor of the TCEQ. Ware appealed that decision, and the third court of appeals issued an opinion affirming the trial court's and the TCEQ's order. *See Ware v. Texas Commission on Environmental Quality*, No. 03-14-00416-CV, 2017 WL 875307 (Tex. App.—Austin Mar. 3, 2017, no pet.) (mem. op.).

Water availability determinations for return flows and new appropriations, including how drought conditions and sedimentation should be addressed in determining water availability, were issues in the Brazos River Authority's Application for Permit No. 5851, TCEQ Docket No. 2005-1490-WR; SOAH Docket No. 582-10-4184. The TCEQ commissioners determined that return flows of others may be approved as a new appropriation. Special conditions that reduce the appropriative rights in the return flows of others, however, must be included in the permits once those flows become unavailable. The flows may become unavailable either by the other dischargers' direct reuse or acquisition of a bed and banks authorization under Texas Water Code section 11.042(b) or (c). *See* An Order Granting in Part the Amended Application by the Brazos River Authority for Water Use Permit No. 5851 and Approving Its Water Management Plan; TCEQ Docket No. 2005-1490-WR; SOAH Docket No. 582-10-4184, at 23 (Findings of Fact Nos. 167, 168), http://www14.tceq.texas.gov/epic/CIO/index.cfm?fuseaction=search.download&agy_dkt_num_txt=2005-1490-WR&agenda_dt=08/24/2016 [hereinafter Brazos River Authority Order]. Such a determination requires that the model used to determine availability for these types of applications include the return flows that are requested by the applicant.

For new appropriations other than for return flows, one issue was whether the WRAP model correctly accounts for the priority date for refilling storage in existing reservoirs. Refilling storage in an existing reservoir at a senior priority date that was emptied by junior priority diversions would impact existing water rights. The protestants argued that the WRAP model incorrectly allows storage to be refilled at a senior date resulting in overstated water availability. The ALJs concluded that the water availability analysis was correct and did not allow for unauthorized junior refill of storage as alleged by the protestants. *See* Proposal for Decision on Remand, TCEQ Docket No. 2005-1490-WR; SOAH Docket No. 582-10-4184, at 76–84, available upon request to the State Office of Administrative Hearings or in the TCEQ's Central Records. A second issue was how drought conditions should be considered. During the proceedings in this case, the Brazos River Basin experienced severe drought conditions that had the potential to affect the water availability determination. The ALJs recommended that the permit be issued with a provision requiring the Brazos River Authority to conduct a drought study, and, if the results of the study identify a new drought of record that reduces the amount of water available for appropriation, the amounts of the appropriation shall be reduced. *See* Brazos River Authority Order, at 29 (Findings of Fact No. 184j). The Brazos River Authority performed the drought study and determined that the appropriation was not affected. *See* Brazos River Authority, Drought Study Report (rev. Aug. 2017), www.brazos.org/Portals/0/Documents/WMP-2018/DroughtStudyFinal.pdf.

The third issue was how sedimentation in existing reservoirs should be considered in water availability determinations. As discussed above, water availability determinations consider all water rights at their fully authorized amounts, including storage. The ALJs concluded that the amount of water available for appropriation should be reduced to account for sedimentation. However, the TCEQ commissioners addressed the sedimentation issue differently. The commissioners decided that water availability determinations should be based on the permitted capacity of the reservoir when considering a new appropriation from the same reservoir. Instead of reducing the amount of the appropriation, the commissioners implemented reductions due to sedimentation via special conditions in Permit 5851. *See* An Interim Order concerning the Administrative Law Judges' Proposal for Decision on Remand and proposed Order for the Application by the Brazos River Authority for Water Use Permit No. 5851, TCEQ Docket No. 2005-1490-WR; SOAH Docket No. 582-10-4184, at 2 (no. 4); *see also* Brazos River Authority Order, at 11–12 (Findings of Fact Nos. 63, 73–74).

Finally, determination of compliance with freshwater inflow standards using the TCEQ's WAMs was an issue during the hearing on Guadalupe Blanco River Authority's Application for Permit No. 12378, TCEQ Docket No. 2014-1658-WR; SOAH Docket No. 582-15-2477. The ALJ affirmed the TCEQ's use of the WAMs to determine compliance with freshwater inflows standards. *See* An Order Approving the Application of Guadalupe-Blanco River Authority for New Water Use Permit No.

12378; TCEQ Docket No. 2014-1658-WR; SOAH Docket No. 582-15-2477, at 9 (Findings of Fact Nos. 78–81), https://www14.tceq.texas.gov/epic/CIO/index.cfm?fuseaction=search.download&agy_dkt_num_txt=2014-1658-WR&agenda_dt=02/04/2015. In November 2020, the National Wildlife Federation filed suit in Travis County district court asking the court to reverse the TCEQ's decision or remand the case to the agency for further proceedings. *See National Wildlife Federation v. Texas Commission on Environmental Quality*, Cause No. D-1-GN-20-007096.

§ 12.9 Other Uses of the WAMs

As discussed above, the TCEQ uses WRAP and the TCEQ WAM data sets in permitting decisions. However, the model and data sets have also been used to evaluate environmental flow standards developed in response to the requirements of Senate Bill 3 of the 80th legislative session (2007). *See* Act of May 28, 2007, 80th Leg., R.S., ch. 1430 [hereinafter Senate Bill 3]. See Chapter 11 of this book regarding environmental flows. Use of the TCEQ WAM for instream environmental analyses can be limited by the fact that the TCEQ WAM is a monthly accounting model, whereas flows for aquatic habitat protection are measured on a daily or instantaneous basis. The Texas Environmental Flows Science Advisory Committee reviewed various methods for evaluating daily environmental flows standards and their impact on future water supply projects and noted that the monthly WAM "is recognized as the superior method with regard to effectively representing both water availability, consistent with the way in which TCEQ would evaluate a permit application, and e-flow requirements in the same analysis." *See* Texas Environmental Flows Science Advisory Committee, *Consideration of Methods for Evaluating Interrelationships between Recommended SB-3 Environmental Flow Regimes and Proposed Water Supply Projects* 40, Report # SAC-2010-04 (Nov. 12, 2010), www.tceq.texas.gov/assets/public/permitting/watersupply/water_rights/eflows/20101112wam_applications.pdf.

Additionally, the TWDB uses modified versions of the TCEQ WAMs in regional water planning. See Chapter 20 of this book regarding state water planning. The need for flexibility was recognized during the developmental phase of the WAMs. *See WAM Technical Issues 2015*, Issue #3 Conservation Storage Protection. For example, in TCEQ permitting decisions, a strict application of prior appropriation is required. For planning purposes, water management strategies that equitably distribute available water within a planning region may modify the prior appropriation doctrine such that an upstream junior reservoir could impound water appropriated to a downstream senior user. A planning model might also include return flows in the full authorization data set to assess the full impacts of all planning strategies. The differing assumptions used in permitting and planning have the potential to generate conflicts in the future; however, this issue has yet to arise in the courts.

§ 12.10 Conclusion

The TCEQ uses the water availability models to evaluate applications for the appropriation of state water, amendments to existing water rights, term permits, and reuse authorizations. Depending on the application, the analysis helps determine whether unappropriated water is available and whether the proposed authorization will impair existing water rights. The models are recognized as being the most reliable method for doing so. Other potential uses of the models include evaluations conducted as part of the Senate Bill 3 (2007) process and support for the state's regional water planning process. As explained in this chapter, although the models are based on scientific principles, the underlying assumptions and application of the models on a case-by-case basis are influenced by legal requirements, both common law and statutory.

CHAPTER 13

Water Rights Enforcement

Clayton Smith[1]

I. Introduction

§ 13.1 Water Rights Enforcement

If water rights are to be protected, water rights statutes, rules, and permits must be enforced. The Texas Commission on Environmental Quality (TCEQ) is the state agency charged with overseeing and enforcing water rights. *See* Tex. Water Code § 5.013(a)(1). Water rights permits and laws can be enforced both on the administrative level and in the courts, and violations can be both civil and criminal. Water rights violations include taking water from a river without a permit as well as violations of permits, TCEQ rules, and state statutes. Chapter 11 of the Texas Water Code sets up a system for water rights enforcement by the watermaster in areas where a watermaster has been appointed. In other parts of the state (generally referred to as "non-watermaster areas"), TCEQ regional offices investigate water rights violations. Persons can also file civil suits alleging water rights violations to obtain common-law remedies. *See* Tex. Water Code §§ 11.0841, 11.086.

II. Texas Water Code Violations

§ 13.2 Introduction

Several provisions of the Texas Water Code pertain to enforcement of water rights laws and permits. Statutory violations include unlawful use of water, obstruction of waterways and diversion of surface water flow, waste of water, and dam safety and levee construction violations.

§ 13.3 Unlawful Use of State Water

Several types of unlawful use of state water are prohibited by the Texas Water Code. Subchapter C of chapter 11 of the Code begins with the statement that "[n]o person may wilfully take, divert, or appropriate any state water for any purpose without first complying with all applicable requirements" of chapter 11. Tex. Water Code § 11.081. "State water" is defined as follows:

> The water of the ordinary flow, underflow, and tides of every flowing river, natural stream, and lake, and of every bay or arm of the Gulf of Mexico, and the storm water, floodwater, and rainwater of every river, natural stream, canyon, ravine, depression, and watershed in the state is the property of the state.

---

1. Clayton Smith is an attorney for the Texas Commission on Environmental Quality. He represents the Executive Director on litigation matters. Mr. Smith earned a JD from the SMU Dedman School of Law.

Tex. Water Code § 11.021(a). Although this definition is broad, it must be read in connection with case law that distinguishes between surface water runoff and water in a watercourse. *See Dietrich v. Goodman*, 123 S.W.3d 413, 418 (Tex. App.—Houston [14th Dist.] 2003, no pet.). In general, state water is water in a watercourse or bay of the state. Also, section 11.021(b) provides that state water includes water imported from any source outside the state for use in the state and transported through the bed and banks of a navigable stream in the state or by using any facilities owned or operated by the state. Tex. Water Code § 11.021(b). See Chapter 14 of this book for a discussion of interstate compacts and treaties.

Section 11.081 makes it unlawful to "take, divert, or appropriate" state water without authorization. "Appropriate" is not specifically defined in the Code, but section 11.002(6) defines "appropriator" as a person who has made beneficial use of any water in a lawful manner under any act of the legislature before the enactment of the Irrigation Act of 1913 (also known as the Burges-Glasscock Act, Acts 1913, 33d Leg., R.S., ch. 171 (H.B. 37), eff. June 30, 1913) (which required a person claiming water to file a record of his appropriation) and who has filed a record of appropriation under the Irrigation Act of 1913 or a person who has made beneficial use within the limitations of a permit lawfully issued by the TCEQ or one of its predecessors. *See* Tex. Water Code § 11.002(6).

It is unlawful for a person to willfully open, close, change, or interfere with any headgate or water box without lawful authority or to willfully use water or conduct water through the person's ditch or upon his land unless he is entitled to do so. *See* Tex. Water Code § 11.083. No person may sell or offer to sell a permanent water right unless he has obtained a water right from the TCEQ or a predecessor agency. *See* Tex. Water Code § 11.084. Additionally, activities that constitute destruction of waterworks are prohibited. Specifically, no one may willfully cut, dig, break down, destroy, or injure or open a gate, bank, embankment, or side of any ditch, canal, reservoir, flume, tunnel or feeder, pump or machinery, building, structure, or other work that is the property of another or that another owns an interest in, lawfully possesses, or uses and that is used for milling, mining, manufacturing, the development of power, domestic purposes, agricultural uses, or stock raising, with the intent to maliciously injure, gain personal advantage, or take or steal the water. *See* Tex. Water Code § 11.088.

Other prohibited acts include owning, leasing, or operating a ditch, canal, or reservoir, or cultivating land that abuts a reservoir, ditch, flume, canal, wasteway, or lateral, and permitting Johnson grass or Russian thistle to go to seed on the waterway within ten feet of the high-water line if the waterway crosses or lies on the owned or controlled land. *See* Tex. Water Code § 11.089(a). This prohibition does not apply in Tom Green, Sterling, Irion, Schleicher, McCullough, Brewster, Menard, Maverick, Kinney, Val Verde, and San Saba counties. Tex. Water Code § 11.089(b). Also, no one may deposit the carcass of any dead animal, tin cans, discarded buckets or pails, garbage, ashes, bailing or barbed wire, earth, offal, refuse of any character, or any other article that might pollute the water or obstruct the flow of a canal or similar structure into any canal, lateral, reservoir, or lake used for a lawful purpose listed in chapter 11. Tex. Water Code § 11.090.

§ 13.4 Obstruction of Waterways, Diversion of Surface Water Flow, and Interference with Water Deliveries

In addition to the prohibited unlawful use of state water, the Texas Water Code establishes that obstructing a navigable stream, impounding or diverting surface water runoff, and interfering with deliveries of water are violations of chapter 11. No person may obstruct the navigation of any stream that is navigable in fact by cutting and felling trees or by building on or across the stream any dike, milldam, bridge, or other obstruction. Tex. Water Code § 11.096. A stream is "navigable in fact" if, "in its natural and ordinary state, it can be used for travel or commerce." Black's Law Dictionary 1191 (10th ed. 2014). The TCEQ will investigate a reported natural obstruction on a navigable stream caused by the accumulation of limbs, logs, leaves, other tree parts, or other debris, on its own motion or on written request from a commissioners court. *See* Tex. Water Code § 11.097(a). The TCEQ will initiate action to remove the obstruction if it determines that the obstruction is creating a hazard or is having other detrimental effects on the stream. Tex. Water Code § 11.097(b).

Likewise, diverting or impounding the natural flow of surface waters, or allowing such diversion or impounding to continue, in a manner that damages the property of another by the overflow of the diverted or impounded water is prohibited. Tex. Water Code § 11.086(a). A person whose property is injured by an overflow of water caused by an unlawful diversion or impounding has "remedies at law and in equity and may recover damages occasioned by the overflow." Tex. Water Code § 11.086(b). See Chapter 39 of this book for further discussion.

The construction and maintenance of levees for flood control or the construction of canals for water conveyances for authorized purposes are not prohibited or affected by section 11.086, but canals, lateral canals, or ditches may not be constructed if they obstruct a river, creek, bayou, gully, slough, ditch, or other well-defined natural drainage. *See* Tex. Water Code § 11.086(c). If gullies or sloughs have cut away or intersected the banks of a river so that floodwaters from the river overflow the land nearby, the owner of the flooded land may fill the mouths of the gullies or sloughs up to the height of the banks of the river without liability to other property owners. Tex. Water Code § 11.086(d).

Water released from a dam or reservoir on an international stream, when that water is designated for use or storage downstream by a specified user legally entitled to receive it, may not be stored, diverted, appropriated, or used by anyone else, and no one else may interfere with its passage downstream. Tex. Water Code § 11.087(a). The TCEQ has implemented this statute in 30 Texas Administrative Code chapter 303 (rules concerning the watermaster operations in the Middle and Lower Rio Grande). *See* 30 Tex. Admin. Code §§ 303.34(a)(1), 303.35. The temporary diversion of water in an international stream may be authorized by the watermaster for use by water rights holders for water that spills from dams and reservoirs and would otherwise flow into the Gulf of Mexico without being used. *See* Tex. Water Code § 11.0871(a). Under commission rule, persons may obtain an excess flow permit for irrigation use of the Texas share of water in the Rio Grande below the International Boundary and Water Commission gauging station near Brownsville, Texas, that is not being beneficially used. *See* 30 Tex. Admin. Code § 303.61. See also Chapter 14 of this book.

Willful interference with the delivery of conserved or stored water under Water Code section 11.042, the bed and banks statute, is also prohibited. *See* Tex. Water Code § 11.091.

§ 13.5 Waste of Water

The wasteful use of water also violates Texas Water Code chapter 11. A person who owns or has a possessory right to land contiguous to a canal or irrigation system and who acquires the right by contract to use the water from it commits waste if he allows wasteful use of the water or allows the water to be applied to anything but beneficial use. Tex. Water Code § 11.092. The TCEQ is required to declare this wasteful use to be a public nuisance and act to abate the nuisance by directing the water supplier to close the water gates of the person wasting the water and keep them closed until the commission has determined that the wasteful use has been corrected. Tex. Water Code § 11.093(b). No person may operate or attempt to operate any waterworks or irrigation system, or use water from such a system, if it has been declared a public nuisance. Tex. Water Code § 11.094. A person who permits an unreasonable loss of water through faulty design or negligent operation of any waterworks that use water for a purpose listed in chapter 11 commits waste, and the commission may declare the waterworks causing the waste to be a public nuisance and take necessary action to abate the nuisance. Tex. Water Code § 11.093(a). Additionally, any person injured by the waste may sue in district court to have the operation of the waterworks abated as a public nuisance. Tex. Water Code § 11.093(a).

§ 13.6 Water Use Reports

All water rights holders who impound, divert, or otherwise use state water must file a water use report by March 1 of every year. *See* Tex. Water Code § 11.031(a). Water rights holders must also maintain monthly water use records and produce them to the TCEQ on request; however, the TCEQ may request such monthly water use records only during a drought or other emergency shortage of water, or in response to a complaint. *See* Tex. Water Code § 11.031(d)–(e). The penalty for not filing the annual report or not providing the TCEQ with monthly data on request ranges from $100 per day if the amount authorized in the water right is 5,000 acre-feet or less per year to $500 per day if the amount authorized in the water right is more than 5,000 acre-feet. *See* Tex. Water Code § 11.031(b). The reporting requirements found in section 11.031(a) may be waived by the commission in watermaster areas, which have their own reporting requirements in the TCEQ rules. *See* Tex. Water Code § 11.031(c); *see also* 30 Tex. Admin. Code § 295.202(a) (TCEQ rules on water use reports).

§ 13.7 Dams and Levees

In addition to the violations involving the use of state water and the obstruction of waterways, the Texas Water Code addresses dam safety and levee construction enforcement. *See* Tex. Water Code §§ 12.052 (dam safety), 16.236 (levee construction). Section 12.052(a) requires the TCEQ to make and enforce rules for dam safety. The TCEQ has enacted these rules in 30 Texas Administrative Code chapter 299. Dam owners who do not comply with the rules and orders of the TCEQ can be penalized. *See* Tex. Water Code § 12.052(c). For a full discussion of dam safety regulations, see Chapter 39 of this book.

Section 16.236 of the Code requires the TCEQ to regulate levee construction in areas that are not in the National Floodplain Insurance Program. The statute provides:

> No person may construct, attempt to construct, cause to be constructed, maintain, or cause to be maintained any levee or other such improvement on, along, or near any stream of this state that is subject to floods, freshets, or overflows so as to control, regulate, or otherwise change the floodwater of the stream without first obtaining approval of the plans by the commission.

Tex. Water Code § 16.236(a). However, under section 16.236(h), subsection (a) does not apply to several types of structures, including a dam or levee within the corporate limits of a city or town (*see* Tex. Water Code § 16.236(h)(3)), and "a levee or other improvement within the boundaries of any political subdivision which has qualified for the National Flood Insurance Program as authorized by the National Flood Insurance Act of 1968." Tex. Water Code § 16.236(h)(4). The TCEQ's regulatory requirements for levee construction are stated in 30 Texas Administrative Code chapter 301. See Chapter 39 of this book for further discussion of floodplain management, including the National Flood Insurance Program.

III. TCEQ Penalties and Other Remedies

§ 13.8 Introduction

The TCEQ has enforcement authority to assess administrative penalties, order corrective measures, and institute civil suits to enforce against violations of the Texas Water Code, TCEQ rules, and water rights authorizations. Civil and criminal penalties may also be obtained in court for certain water rights violations.

§ 13.9 Administrative Penalties

Chapter 11 of the Texas Water Code allows the commission to assess administrative penalties for violations. *See* Tex. Water Code § 11.0842. It also allows the executive director and staff, including a watermaster or a watermaster's deputy, to issue field citations. *See* Tex. Water Code § 11.0843. See sections 13.13–13.13:2 below for a discussion of the watermaster program. Except for penalties assessed under section 11.031 for not filing a water use report (discussed at section 13.6 above), administrative penalties may be assessed against a person who violates chapter 11; a rule or order adopted under chapter 11 or Water Code section 16.236 (concerning approval for levees); or a permit, certified filing, or certificate of adjudication issued under chapter 11. *See* Tex. Water Code § 11.0842(a). Penalties may be assessed in an amount up to $5,000 per day for each violation of chapter 11, a rule adopted under chapter 11, or a permit, certified filing, or certificate of adjudication issued under chapter 11. *See* Tex. Water Code § 11.0842(b). Penalties may be assessed in an amount up to $1,000 per day for each violation of a rule or order adopted under Water Code section 16.236. *See* Tex. Water Code § 11.0842(b).

The commission is required to consider several factors in determining the amount of the penalty: the nature, circumstances, extent, duration, and gravity of the prohibited acts, with special emphasis on a violation of a water right or a hazard or potential hazard to the health, safety, or welfare of the public; the impact of the violation on instream uses, water quality, fish and wildlife habitat, or freshwater inflows to bays and estuaries; the alleged violator's compliance history, degree of culpability, and demonstrated good faith, including action to rectify the violation and compensate affected persons; the economic benefit gained through the violation; the amount necessary to deter future violations; and any other matters that justice may require. *See* Tex. Water Code § 11.0842(c). The alleged violator has a right to a hearing and a right to judicial review under the substantial evidence rule. *See* Tex. Water Code § 11.0842(f), (h), (n). The procedures for filing enforcement actions, providing notice, requesting a hearing, and resolving enforcement actions are set out in section 11.0842(d)–(q). *See* Tex. Water Code § 11.0842(d)–(q).

Field citations may be issued by executive director staff, including watermasters and their deputies, for violations of chapter 11 or a rule, order, or water right issued under chapter 11. *See* Tex. Water Code § 11.0843. These citations allow the alleged violator to either pay the administrative penalty and take remedial action without admitting to or denying the violation or request a hearing on the violations. *See* Tex. Water Code § 11.0843(a); 30 Tex. Admin. Code § 303.35(b). Under 30 Texas Administrative Code section 303.35, the Rio Grande watermaster may issue field citations for the following violations of chapter 303: diversion without approval from the watermaster, failure to provide a measuring device, not passing water that the water right holder is not entitled to hold, and late pump operation reports. *See* 30 Tex. Admin. Code § 303.35(d). The South Texas, Concho River, and Brazos watermasters, under 30 Texas Administrative Code section 304.34, may issue a field citation for the same actions except that, instead of late pump reports, citations can be issued for late reporting of diversion, transport, release, or impoundment. *See* 30 Tex. Admin. Code § 304.34(d).

Water Code chapter 7 contains general provisions for enforcement by the TCEQ. Because chapter 11 contains its own enforcement provisions specific to water rights violations, these more specific provisions govern over the chapter 7 provisions; however, some provisions of chapter 7 that do not conflict with chapter 11 still apply. For example, the commission may initiate an enforcement action based on information it receives from a private individual if that information is of sufficient value and credibility to warrant initiation of enforcement. *See* Tex. Water Code § 7.0025(a). Also, the commission is not required to make findings of fact or conclusions of law in enforcement cases, other than an uncontested finding that the commission has jurisdiction, if there is an agreed order compromising or settling an alleged violation of a statute or rule under the commission's jurisdiction. *See* Tex. Water Code § 7.070. The commission can state that the order is not an admission of a violation of a statute or rule within the commission's jurisdiction. *See* Tex. Water Code § 7.070(1).

In enforcing dam safety laws, the TCEQ is required to make and enforce rules and orders and perform all other acts necessary to provide for the safe construction, operation, maintenance, repair, removal, and emergency management of dams located in the state. Tex. Water Code § 12.052(a). Under section 12.052(d), if the commission determines that the condition of a dam is creating or will cause extensive or severe property damage or economic loss to others or is posing an immediate and serious threat to human life or health, the commission may issue an emergency order directing the owner to repair, modify, maintain, dewater, or remove the dam. *See* Tex. Water Code § 12.052(d). This emergency order may be issued without notice to the dam owner, but if the order is issued without notice, there must be a hearing before the commission as soon as practicable to affirm, modify, or set aside the order. *See* Tex. Water Code § 12.052(e). When the executive director finds that a dam poses a level of danger to the public that is unacceptable under commission rules, he may go directly to the attorney general for injunctive relief or seek an emergency order from the commission to direct the owner to take appropriate action. *See* 30 Tex. Admin. Code §§ 299.71(a), 299.72. The penalty for refusing to take appropriate action is up to $5,000 per day. *See* Tex. Water Code § 12.052(c); 30 Tex. Admin. Code § 299.71(b).

In enforcing levee safety laws, the TCEQ must make and enforce rules and orders and perform all other acts necessary to provide for the safe construction, maintenance, repair, and removal of levees located in the state. Tex. Water Code § 16.236(b). The penalty for violations of a rule or order adopted under section 16.236 may be up to $1,000 per day. *See* Tex. Water Code §§ 11.0842(b), 16.236(c). Under section 16.236(d), if the commission determines that the condition of a levee is creating or will cause extensive or severe property damage or economic loss to others or is posing an immediate and serious threat to human life or health, the commission may issue an emergency order directing the owner to repair, modify, maintain, dewater, or remove the levee. *See* Tex. Water Code § 16.236(d). The emergency order may be issued without notice to the levee owner, but if the order is issued without notice, there must be a hearing before the commission as soon as practical to affirm, modify, or set aside the order. *See* Tex. Water Code § 16.236(e). When the executive director finds that a levee poses an unacceptable hazard to lives or property, he may go directly to the attorney general for injunctive relief or seek an order from the commission to direct the owner to take appropriate action. *See* 30 Tex. Admin. Code § 301.62.

§ 13.10 Remedies in Court

In addition to its administrative enforcement powers, the TCEQ has civil penalty enforcement remedies for water rights violations under Texas Water Code section 11.082. *See* Tex. Water Code § 11.082. The executive director may also initiate a suit in district court for injunctive relief to restrain a violation or threat of a violation under the TCEQ's jurisdiction. *See* Tex. Water Code § 7.032.

With regard to dam safety, injunctive relief powers supplement the administrative and civil enforcement powers in Water Code section 12.052. If the commission orders the owner of a dam to reconstruct, repair, or remove a dam to comply with TCEQ statutes and rules, and the owner fails to comply within thirty days of the order, the owner is liable for a penalty of not more than $5,000 per day. *See* Tex. Water Code § 12.052(c). Suit to enforce this provision must be brought in a Travis County district court. *See* Tex. Water Code § 12.052(c).

Under subchapter E of chapter 7, the following water rights violations of chapter 11 are criminal offenses:

- section 11.081 (taking, diverting, or appropriating state water without complying with chapter 11);
- section 11.083 (unlawful taking by interfering with a headgate or waterbox or conducting water the person is not entitled to through his ditch);

- section 11.084 (selling a permanent water right without a permit);
- section 11.087 (diverting water on an international stream);
- section 11.088 (destroying waterworks);
- section 11.089 (permitting Johnson grass or Russian thistle to go to seed in certain waterways);
- section 11.090 (depositing certain pollutants in a water body);
- section 11.091 (interfering with delivery of water under contract);
- section 11.092 (wasting water);
- section 11.093 (permitting works to be a public nuisance due to waste);
- section 11.094 (using works declared to be a public nuisance);
- section 11.096 (obstructing a navigable stream);
- section 11.203 (failing to keep accurate records for artesian wells); and
- section 11.205 (wasting water from an artesian well).

See Tex. Water Code § 7.142.

Thus, the TCEQ has broad power to ensure compliance with water rights authorizations and TCEQ rules and state law concerning water rights, including administrative and civil remedies and seeking criminal convictions.

IV. TCEQ Enforcement Procedures

§ 13.11 Introduction

The TCEQ has general jurisdiction over water rights and the enforcement of water rights. *See* Tex. Water Code § 5.013(a)(1). The TCEQ enforces water rights in both watermaster areas and non-watermaster areas. Watermaster areas also have their own rules for enforcement. In general, a watermaster is a TCEQ employee designated by the executive director to enforce water rights in a water division or a river basin or segment of a river basin. *See* Tex. Water Code §§ 11.326, 11.453.

§ 13.12 Enforcement in Non-Watermaster Areas

Because there are only four watermaster areas, most TCEQ regional offices enforce water rights and water rights statutes and rules. As section 11.0842(a) provides, the commission can assess a penalty for a violation of chapter 11, a rule or order adopted under chapter 11, or a water right, whether the violation occurs in a watermaster or non-watermaster area. The commission may also suspend or adjust water rights in non-watermaster areas. *See, e.g.*, Tex. Water Code § 11.147.

§ 13.12:1 Enforcement Initiated by a Regional Office

The TCEQ regional offices have water investigators who investigate water rights violations and respond to water rights complaints. Common complaints and violations include taking water without a permit or other water right and violating a provision of a water right. Many complaints concern whether impoundments are exempt under Tex. Water Code § 11.142(a) because they are an average of two hundred acre-feet or less and only for domestic and livestock use. Because it may be difficult to tell how water is used and because water meters and gauges are not required for most water rights outside of watermaster areas, it may be difficult for an investigator to determine whether a violation has occurred. *See* 30 Tex. Admin. Code chs. 295, 297, 303, 304. Therefore, the investigator may need to personally observe the violation occur or have a witness who has seen the violation occur and is willing to testify in a hearing.

Title 30 Texas Administrative Code chapter 70 and Texas Water Code section 11.0842 provide the requirements for an administrative enforcement action. TCEQ staff use the Enforcement Initiation Criteria guidance document to determine when violations require the initiation of a formal enforcement action, which can be initiated by a complaint. *See* Texas Commission on Environmental Quality, *Enforcement Initiation Criteria* (Rev. No. 17, eff. Sept. 1, 2020), www.tceq.texas.gov/assets/public/compliance/enforcement/eic/eic-rev17-082020.pdf [hereinafter EIC]. In general, most water rights violations are category B violations. Alleged violators of category B violations are issued a notice of violation and given an opportunity to come into compliance with the relevant rules and statutes. *See* EIC, at 27–31, 40. If the alleged violator does not correct the violation by the compliance due date, a formal enforcement action may be initiated. *See* EIC, at 28–29. Category A water rights violations, which require automatic initiation of formal enforcement when discovered, include: reported or documented use or impoundment of state water in excess of authorized amounts during times of extreme or exceptional drought conditions; breaking, tampering with, or mutilating any seal or other device used to enforce orders of the commission, executive director, a court, or a watermaster; and impounding, diverting, or using state water without a permit. *See* EIC, at 24.

Formal enforcement is initiated through the issuance of a notice of enforcement. Once a notice of enforcement is issued, due to either a category A violation or a category B violation that was not timely corrected, the violation is sent to the commission's central office in Austin. *See* EIC, at 14, 27. Under section 11.0842(d), if the executive director concludes that a violation has occurred, the executive director issues an Executive Director's Preliminary Report and Petition (EDPRP) recommending an administrative penalty and the amount of the penalty. The executive director uses the factors in section 11.0842(c) to determine the recommended amount of the penalty.

The executive director must give notice of the violation to the alleged violator within ten days of issuance of the EDPRP. The EDPRP is considered issued when it is filed with the TCEQ's chief clerk. *See* 30 Tex. Admin. Code § 70.104(a). The notice must summarize the charges, state the amount of penalty, and tell the alleged violator of the right to a hearing on the occurrence of the violation, the amount of the penalty, or both. *See* Tex. Water Code § 11.0842(e). Not later than twenty days after receiving the notice, the person charged may consent to the penalty or request a hearing. If the person does not timely respond to the notice, the commission may either assess the penalty or order a hearing on the EDPRP. *See* Tex. Water Code § 11.0842(f), (g). Under 30 Texas Administrative Code section 70.106, the executive director may request a default order. Hearings must be conducted under the Administrative Procedure Act, Texas Government Code chapter 2001, and Water Code section 11.0842(h) and may be referred to the State Office of Administrative Hearings. *See* 30 Tex. Admin. Code § 70.108.

After the commission issues an order assessing an administrative penalty, it must give notice of its decision and the person's right to judicial review of the order. *See* Tex. Water Code § 11.0842(i). Within thirty days of the commission's order, the person must pay the penalty in full or file a petition for judicial review. *See* Tex. Water Code § 11.0842(j). The person may stay enforcement of the penalty by paying the amount of the penalty to the court for placement in an escrow account or giving the court a supersedeas bond. *See* Tex. Water Code § 11.0842(k). Judicial review of the commission's order is under the substantial evidence rule and must be heard in a Travis County district court. *See* Tex. Water Code § 11.0842(n).

§ 13.12:2 Suspension and Adjustment Orders

The TCEQ may also suspend or adjust water rights in non-watermaster areas under Texas Water Code section 11.053, which was added by the 82nd Legislature in 2011. Section 11.053 provides that the executive director may temporarily suspend a water right and temporarily adjust the diversions of water by a water right holder during periods of drought or other emergency shortage of water, in accordance with the priority of water rights established by section 11.027. Tex. Water Code § 11.053(a). Section 11.053 includes several factors that the executive director must ensure are met when issuing these orders and provides that the commission must adopt rules to implement the section, including rules that define "drought" or "other emergency shortage of water," and the conditions for and terms of an order. Further, the commission must adopt rules concerning notice of an opportunity for hearing on and the appeal to the commission of one of these orders.

The executive director must ensure that an order—

1. maximizes beneficial use of water;
2. minimizes the impact on water rights holders;
3. prevents waste of water;
4. takes into consideration the efforts of the affected water rights holders to develop and implement water conservation and drought contingency plans;
5. "to the greatest extent practicable, conforms to the order of preferences established by Section 11.024 [of the Texas Water Code]"; and
6. does not require the release of lawfully stored water.

See Tex. Water Code § 11.053(b).

The commission adopted rules in 30 Texas Administrative Code chapter 36 in 2012 and has issued several curtailment and adjustment orders under those rules, mostly in the Brazos River Basin. In general, those orders did not completely curtail water rights for municipalities and power generators. The Texas Farm Bureau sued the TCEQ in 2012 after the TCEQ issued an order curtailing water rights in the Brazos River Basin. The plaintiffs argued that the TCEQ rules were invalid and exceeded its authority under section 11.053 of the Water Code and contended that the TCEQ improperly gave itself the authority to modify the prior appropriation doctrine, a fundamental part of each surface water right in Texas, when it did not suspend the junior water rights held by municipalities and power generators.

The district court issued an order on June 6, 2013, striking the chapter 36 rules and holding that the commission had exceeded its statutory authority by exempting municipal and power generation water rights from curtailment, and that the exemption of these water rights was not authorized by the TCEQ's police powers to protect public health and welfare. The TCEQ appealed, and the Corpus Christi–Edinburg court of appeals sitting in Austin heard argument from the parties on April 24, 2014. The court of appeals affirmed the district court on April 2, 2015, and the TCEQ's petition for review was denied by the Texas Supreme Court. *See Texas Commission on Environmental Quality v. Texas Farm Bureau*, 460 S.W.3d 264 (Tex. App.—Corpus Christi–Edinburg 2015, pet. denied). Water Code section 11.053 is still in effect; however, the commission would be required to follow the *Farm Bureau* decision when issuing future curtailment and adjustment orders.

§ 13.13 Watermaster Areas and Enforcement

As discussed above, the enforcement powers and procedures of the TCEQ differ in watermaster and non-watermaster areas. The state has four active watermaster areas and three active watermasters. The watermaster areas are the Rio Grande area, the South Texas area, the Concho River area, and the Brazos River area, downstream of and including Possum Kingdom Lake. The watermaster for the South Texas area is also the watermaster for the Concho River area. A petition for a watermaster for the Brazos River was filed by more than twenty-five water rights holders on January 10, 2013. That proceeding is discussed at section 13.13:1 below.

§ 13.13:1 Creation of a Watermaster

The TCEQ's 2011 Sunset Bill, H.B. 2694, amended section 11.326(g) of the Texas Water Code by adding subsection (g). *See* Act of May 28, 2011, 82d Leg., R.S., ch. 1021, § 5.05, eff. Sept. 1, 2011. Section 11.326 addresses the appointment of a watermaster in a "water division" by the executive director of the commission, as discussed below. Section 11.326(g) requires that for water basins for which a watermaster is not appointed, the executive director shall evaluate the water basin at least once every five years to determine whether a watermaster should be appointed and report the findings and make recommendations to the commission. *See* Tex. Water Code § 11.326(g). Between 2012 and 2016, the executive director conducted the first five-year cycle of evaluating the need for a watermaster in basins with no watermaster, and the second five-year cycle began in 2017. In each of these evaluations, the commission did not decide that a watermaster should be designated.

A watermaster may be appointed by the executive director for an area if that area has been designated as a water division. The commission shall divide the state into water divisions for the purpose of administering adjudicated water rights and as the necessity arises. Tex. Water Code § 11.325. The executive director may appoint one watermaster for each water division. Tex. Water Code § 11.326(a). The Rio Grande and South Texas watermasters were appointed by this method. The South Texas Watermaster was also appointed by statute as the watermaster for the Concho River Watermaster Program. *See* Tex. Water Code §§ 11.551–.561.

Another way to create a watermaster, under certain circumstances, is for a district court to appoint a watermaster when a suit has been filed in which the state is a party, the purpose of the suit is to determine the rights of the parties to divert or use water of a surface stream, and rights are asserted to use water in, or divert water to, not more than four counties. *See* Tex. Water Code § 11.401. Although accomplished before section 11.401 was enacted, a district court appointed the first Rio Grande watermaster. *See Hidalgo County Water Control & Improvement District No. 1 v. Boysen*, 354 S.W.2d 420 (Tex. App.—San Antonio 1962, writ ref'd).

Finally, a watermaster may be appointed by the TCEQ through a water rights holder petition process. *See* Tex. Water Code § 11.451. In this procedure, a petition of twenty-five or more water rights holders of a river basin or segment of a river basin must be submitted to the commission. The commission initially created the Concho River watermaster program through this method. *See* TCEQ Order Appointing a Watermaster for the Concho River Segment, TCEQ Docket No. 2000-0344-WR (Aug. 17, 2004). The legislature later created the program by statute and appointed the South Texas watermaster to be the Concho River watermaster. *See* Tex. Water Code §§ 11.551–.561. For a further discussion of that petition and program, as well as the watermaster programs in general, *see* Comment, *Texas Watermasters: A Legal History and Analysis of Surface Water Rights Enforcement*, 7 Tex. Tech Admin. L.J. 143 (2006).

A petition for a watermaster for the Brazos River Basin under Texas Water Code chapter 11, subchapter I, was filed by more than twenty-five water rights holders on January 10, 2013. After a contested case hearing, the commission created the watermaster area in the Brazos River Basin from Lake Possum Kingdom to the Gulf of Mexico. *See* TCEQ Order Granting the Petition for the

Appointment of a Watermaster in the Brazos River Basin Filed by the Brazos River Coalition, TCEQ Docket No. 2013-0174-WR (Apr. 21, 2014). A watermaster for the Brazos River Basin was hired and this area began operating as a watermaster area on June 1, 2015.

§ 13.13:2 Enforcement in Watermaster Areas

Watermasters have the same authority as regional investigators, but they also have broader authority for water rights enforcement under the Texas Water Code and require more from water rights holders in the watermaster area. Watermaster and staff are devoted exclusively to enforcing water rights.

Three separate statutes relate to the authority of a watermaster. For watermasters appointed by the executive director, the duties are set out in section 11.327. Under this statute, the watermaster shall—

1. divide the water of the streams or other sources of supply in the watermaster's division in accordance with adjudicated water rights;

2. regulate or cause to be regulated the controlling works of reservoirs and diversion works in times of water shortage, as necessary to prevent waste or unlawful diversion, or to protect the existing rights in the division;

3. regulate the distribution of water from any system of works that serves users whose rights have been separately determined; and

4. perform activities that relate to other programs of the commission only in situations of imminent threat to public health and safety or the environment.

See Tex. Water Code § 11.327.

Water Code provisions relating solely to the Rio Grande watermaster are contained in section 11.3271. *See* Tex. Water Code § 11.3271. Under section 11.3271(e), the Rio Grande watermaster's duties include activities that relate to situations of imminent threat to public health and safety or the environment. As required, the commission has adopted rules defining situations of imminent threat under this section and addressing the watermaster's duties in response to terrorism. *See* 30 Tex. Admin. Code § 303.18. The remainder of section 11.3271 provides procedures for the watermaster to authorize the storage of groundwater in a reservoir to release and transport down the bed and banks of the Rio Grande for later diversion and use. *See* Tex. Water Code § 11.3271(f)–(k).

For watermasters appointed by the commission under subchapter I of chapter 11, section 11.327 applies to the duties and authority of the watermaster in the same manner as that section applies to the duties and authority of a watermaster appointed for a water division under chapter 11, subchapter G. *See* Tex. Water Code § 11.454.

Under the Concho River watermaster program, Water Code chapter 11, subchapter K, the watermaster has the same duties and authority as the watermaster has under the South Texas Watermaster Program, which are the authority and duties in section 11.327. *See* Tex. Water Code § 11.555.

The water rights holders in a watermaster area pay the expenses and compensation for the watermaster program. *See* Tex. Water Code § 11.329(a). A watermaster advisory committee is appointed for each watermaster area to provide recommendations to the executive director on activities of benefit to the water rights holders in the administration and distribution of water, to review and comment to the executive director on the annual budget for watermaster operations, and to perform other duties as may be required by the executive director or as requested by water rights holders. *See* Tex. Water Code § 11.3261. Chapter 11 also specifically requires headgates or gates on outlets for the diversion or storage of water in a watermaster area and allows the watermaster to require measuring devices on water right diversion or storage at a place that the watermaster can assess. *See* Tex. Water Code §§ 11.330, 11.331.

All four watermaster programs have rules setting out the actions that the watermasters may take. Title 30 Texas Administrative Code chapter 303 governs the Rio Grande watermaster program, and chapter 304 governs the South Texas, Concho River, and Brazos River programs. Specific authority under those rules that differs from the authority of the commission's regional offices includes—

1. requiring meters for all water rights (*see* 30 Tex. Admin. Code §§ 303.11(e), 304.13(a));

2. requiring that water rights holders pay fees for the watermaster program (*see* 30 Tex. Admin. Code §§ 303.71–.73, 304.61–.63);

3. requiring that a declaration of intent be approved by the watermaster prior to the diversion, transport, or release of water (*see* 30 Tex. Admin. Code §§ 303.11, 304.15); and

4. requiring records of diversion, transport, and release of water (*see* 30 Tex. Admin. Code §§ 303.11(f), (h), 304.16).

The South Texas, Concho River, and Brazos River watermasters must allocate water based on seniority "in such a way as to maximize the beneficial utilization of state water, to minimize the potential of impairment to senior water rights by the diversions of junior water rights holders, and to prevent waste or use in excess of quantities to which the holders of water rights are lawfully entitled." 30 Tex. Admin. Code § 304.21(a). The watermaster can protect senior water rights when flows are low by denying diversions by junior water rights holders and requiring reservoir owners to pass through inflows for senior water rights and domestic and livestock users. *See* 30 Tex. Admin. Code § 304.21(c).

The Rio Grande watermaster has the same allocation rules in the Upper Rio Grande portion of the Rio Grande program (above Lake Amistad) as exist in chapter 304. *See* 30 Tex. Admin. Code § 303.23. Below Lake Amistad, however, the watermaster must operate on a different priority system, one established by the court in *State v. Hidalgo County Water Control & Improvement District No. 18*, 443 S.W.2d 728 (Tex. App.—Corpus Christi–Edinburg 1969, writ ref'd n.r.e.). The majority of water rights below Lake Amistad and Lake Falcon receive their water from these two lakes, and the priority of the water rights in this area is based on type of use. These allocation rules are set out in 30 Texas Administrative Code sections 303.21–.23. See discussion of the Rio Grande in Chapter 14 of this book.

§ 13.13:3 Litigation Concerning Agency Water Rights Enforcement

There is no case law discussing the TCEQ's or predecessor agencies' enforcement of water rights laws. There have been several administrative enforcement actions concerning water rights at the agency, however. For a discussion of some of those cases, *see* David Klein & Robin Smith, *Exploring the Scope of Landowner Water Rights for Domestic and Livestock Purposes*, 7 Tex. Tech Admin. L.J. 119, 138–40 (2006).

V. Private Enforcement

§ 13.14 Civil Remedies

Although the TCEQ has significant authority to enforce water rights, as discussed above, private corporations, individuals, and political subdivisions with a justiciable interest may pursue civil remedies for such violations as well. Such suits may seek any available common-law remedy to enforce a right, to seek redress or compensation for violations of a right, or otherwise to redress an injury. The prevailing party in a suit for injunctive relief to redress an unauthorized diversion, impoundment, or use of surface water in violation of chapter 11 or a rule adopted under chapter 11 may be awarded court costs and reasonable attorney's and expert fees. *See* Tex. Water Code § 11.0841(b). However, to recover litigation costs under section 11.0841, the prevailing party must be a water right holder. *See Pauli v. Hayes*, No. 04-17-00026-CV, 2018 WL 3440767, at *3 (Tex. App.—San Antonio July 18, 2018, no pet.) (mem. op.).

Section 11.086 of the Texas Water Code, which prohibits a person from diverting or impounding the natural flow of surface waters in the state, authorizes a private cause of action. *See* Tex. Water Code § 11.086. Under section 11.086(b), a person whose property is damaged may sue in law and equity for damages caused by the overflow. Courts have interpreted section 11.086 to apply to surface water runoff rather than state water or water in a watercourse. *See, e.g., Hopkins v. State*, No. 03-03-00499-CV, 2006 WL 1126224, at *12 (Tex. App.—Austin Apr. 27, 2006, pet. denied) (mem. op.); *Dietrich v. Goodman*, 123 S.W.3d 413, 418 (Tex. App.—Houston [14th Dist.] 2003, no pet.). Generally, the commission would not be involved in these cases, absent water quality concerns, because the agency's jurisdiction is over "state water." *See* Tex. Water Code §§ 5.013(a)(1), 11.002(5), 11.023(a). Also, the commission does not have the authority to provide remedies at law or equity and may not award damages for injuries. *Texas Department of Human Resources v. ARA Living Centers of Texas, Inc.*, 833 S.W.2d 689, 694 (Tex. App.—Austin 1992, writ denied) (state agencies have only the authority expressly granted to them by the legislature or implied to perform their express duties). See Chapter 39 of this book for a more detailed discussion of section 11.086.

VI. Conclusion

§ 13.15 Conclusion

Water rights authorizations and related statutes and regulations can be enforced by the TCEQ both on the administrative level and in the courts. Enforcement may include injunctions, penalties, and criminal convictions. Private citizens also have the right to seek redress for certain water rights–related activities or violations by filing a civil action in district court. Thus the Texas Water Code provides many avenues by which Texas's water resources may be protected and its system of water allocation ensured.

CHAPTER 14

Multijurisdictional Water Rights

Priscilla M. Hubenak[1] and Kellie E. Billings-Ray[2]

I. Introduction

§ 14.1 Introduction to Multijurisdictional Water Rights

Texas shares the waters of five rivers with other states and with Mexico; therefore, these streams are subject to multijurisdictional water rights. These rivers are the Rio Grande (bordered by Texas, Colorado, and New Mexico, as well as Mexico), the Pecos (bordered by Texas and New Mexico), the Canadian (bordered by Texas, New Mexico, and Oklahoma), the Red (bordered by Texas, Arkansas, Louisiana, and Oklahoma), and the Sabine (bordered by Texas and Louisiana). The waters in each of these rivers are subject to interstate compacts between Texas and these other states. In the case of the Rio Grande, two treaties provide for the division of water with Mexico. Each river compact is administered by a commission that is composed of members from each state and includes a federal government representative who is appointed by the President of the United States.

This chapter explores interstate river compacts, with special emphasis on the compacts to which Texas is a party, the international treaties that apportion water in the Rio Grande, and the unique characteristics of water rights in the Lower and Middle Rio Grande of Texas.

---

1. Priscilla M. Hubenak is Chief of the Environmental Protection Division of the Office of the Attorney General of Texas, where she has been an assistant attorney general and practiced since 1988. She is board certified in Administrative Law and represents the state concerning public lands, regulatory matters, and oil and gas issues. She has been the legal advisor to the Texas compact commissioners for the Rio Grande and Canadian River Compacts. Previously, she was a Texas Railroad Commission hearings examiner and in private practice.

2. Kellie E. Billings-Ray is a Deputy Chief in the Environmental Protection Division of the Office of the Attorney General of Texas, where she has been an assistant attorney general since 2008. She represents the state in a variety of trial and appellate matters that address environmental and natural resource regulatory issues including environmental enforcement, public utility regulation, oil and gas, public land, and water. Previously, she was an attorney advisor at the Public Utility Commission of Texas.

The authors would also like to acknowledge the following people for providing input and comments on this chapter: Jane Atwood (Austin); Tom Bohl (Austin); Douglas C. Caroom, Bickerstaff, Heath, Delgado & Acosta (Austin); Glenn Jarvis, Law Offices of Glenn Jarvis (McAllen); H. Carl Myers, Deputy Chief, Office of the Attorney General of Texas (Austin); the late Jerome C. Muys (Washington, D.C.); Stuart L. Somach, Somach Simmons & Dunn (Sacramento); and Mary E. Smith, General Counsel for the Texas Commission on Environmental Quality (Austin).

This chapter is based on the observations and opinions of the authors and does not necessarily reflect the opinions of the Office of the Attorney General, the State of Texas, the Texas Commission on Environmental Quality, or any other agency represented by the Office of the Attorney General.

II. Laws That Affect Apportionment of Interstate Streams

§ 14.2 Introduction

Interstate compacts act to apportion the waters of the major Texas streams that Texas shares with its neighboring states. An understanding of the legal framework of apportionment and interstate compacts is essential in enforcing each state's rights, to making any needed amendments, and in determining additional apportionments of surface water or groundwater that may be necessary in the future.

The authority of the federal government to apportion waters of an interstate stream comes from the government's sovereign authority to control navigation and interstate commerce under the U.S. Constitution. A state can regulate the waters of streams within its borders, but this authority is subject to the power of Congress to control commerce and navigation under the Constitution. *Leovy v. United States*, 177 U.S. 621, 632 (1900); *United States v. Rio Grande Dam & Irrigation Co.*, 174 U.S. 690, 703 (1899); *see also* U.S. Const. art. I, § 8, cl. 3 (the Commerce Clause). Congress's authority over navigable waters extends not only to the currently navigable portions of a stream but also to non-navigable and formerly navigable portions that still contribute to the navigation of other reaches of the stream. *State of Oklahoma ex rel. Phillips v. Guy F. Atkinson Co.*, 313 U.S. 508, 522–23 (1941). Congress, acting within its power to control navigation, may appropriate water, change the course of streams, build dams on portions of streams that are navigable, or even build dams on portions that are not navigable but contribute to navigation in other parts of the stream. *Guy F. Atkinson Co.*, 313 U.S. at 522–23.

Under federal law, there are three means by which the waters of interstate streams may be apportioned: (1) through an equitable apportionment lawsuit in the U.S. Supreme Court, (2) through an act of Congress, and (3) through an interstate compact. The following sections discuss each method in more detail.

§ 14.3 Equitable Apportionment by the Supreme Court

The "doctrine of equitable apportionment" is a principle of federal common law. *Colorado v. New Mexico*, 459 U.S. 176, 182–83 (1982). The U.S. Supreme Court can, under its equity jurisdiction, apportion water between two or more states under the doctrine of equitable apportionment. *Florida v. Georgia*, 138 S. Ct. 2502, 2509 (2018); *Nebraska v. Wyoming*, 325 U.S. 589, 618 (1945); *Kansas v. Colorado*, 206 U.S. 46, 98 (1907). The Court has recognized that under the doctrine, states possess "an equal right to make a reasonable use of the waters of" a river. *United States v. Willow River Power Co.*, 324 U.S. 499, 505 (1945). When confronted with competing claims of interstate water, the Court's effort should be to ensure an equitable apportionment without "quibbling over formulas." *New Jersey v. New York*, 283 U.S. 336, 343 (1931). Further, a state must show by "'clear and convincing evidence,' that it has suffered a 'threatened invasion of rights' that is 'of serious magnitude.'" *Florida v. Georgia*, 138 S. Ct. at 2506 (quoting *Washington v. Oregon*, 297 U.S. 517, 522 (1936)).

The complaining state's burden is "much greater" than the ordinary burden of a private party in a suit, and as a precondition it must be clear that the state making the complaint has more than a mere technical right but also has a right with a corresponding benefit. *Florida v. Georgia*, 138 S. Ct. at 2506; *Kansas v. Colorado*, 206 U.S. 46, 102 (1906). The Court will then consider "all relevant factors" to arrive at a "just and equitable apportionment." *Florida v. Georgia*, 138 S. Ct. at 2506; *South Carolina v. North Carolina*, 558 U.S. 256 (2009).

§ 14.3:1 Jurisdiction over Equitable Apportionment Cases

Title 28 United States Code section 1251(a) provides: "The Supreme Court shall have original and exclusive jurisdiction of all controversies between two or more States." The Court has interpreted its jurisdiction to extend to controversies between two states in a properly framed suit to apportion the water of an interstate stream between states through which it flows. *Texas v. New Mexico*, 462 U.S. 554, 567 (1983). The Court exercises its original jurisdiction judiciously and retains substantial discretion in determining whether an original action should begin there. *South Carolina v. North Carolina*, 558 U.S. 256, 267 (2010).

Lower courts have rejected motions to dismiss based on arguments that the U.S. Supreme Court has exclusive jurisdiction over interstate disputes by concluding that no real controversy existed between two or more states. These cases give insight into the types of cases that might not qualify as "properly framed" suits to apportion water of interstate streams. For example, South Dakota sought to enjoin the U.S. Army Corps of Engineers from releasing water from a dam on the Missouri River that would then flow out of South Dakota into Nebraska in *South Dakota v. Ubbelohde*, 330 F.3d 1014, 1025–26 (8th Cir. 2003), *cert. denied*, 541 U.S. 987 (2004). Because the action was really directed at the Corps of Engineers, the court of appeals held that intervention by the State of Nebraska would not strip the federal district court of jurisdiction despite the fact that the lawsuit was filed by the State of South Dakota. *Ubbelohde*, 330 F.3d at 1025–26.

Likewise, a lawsuit involving the states of Georgia, Alabama, Florida, and others was held not to be a state-versus-state controversy that would render the case within the exclusive jurisdiction of the U.S. Supreme Court. *Alabama v. U.S. Army Corps of Engineers*, 424 F.3d 1117, 1130 (11th Cir. 2005), *cert. denied*, 547 U.S. 1192 (2006). The State of Georgia and other Georgia plaintiffs had sought to compel the Corps of Engineers to increase the amount of water allocated for use in Georgia out of Lake Lanier on a stream system shared by the three states.

§ 14.3:2 Discretionary Nature of the Supreme Court's Original Jurisdiction

The fact that the U.S. Supreme Court has jurisdiction over an equitable apportionment case does not mean that the Court must—or that it will—exercise its jurisdiction over a case. The rules of the U.S. Supreme Court require a petitioner in an original action before the Court to file a motion for leave to file a complaint before proceeding, and the party against whom the petitioner seeks to file an action is allotted time to respond. Sup. Ct. R. 17. At this initial stage, the Court can dismiss an action on jurisdictional grounds. *See* Vincent L. McKusick, *Discretionary Gatekeeping: The Supreme Court's Management of Its Original Jurisdiction Docket Since 1961*, 45 Me. L. Rev. 185 (1993). This article suggests that the Court has used three additional criteria to determine whether an original action before the U.S. Supreme Court is warranted: "(i) the parties to the suit; (ii) the subject matter of the suit and its 'seriousness and dignity,' . . . that is, its importance; and (iii) the existence or not of an alternative forum for the cause of action or for at least the controlling issue." McKusick, at 197.

The U.S. Supreme Court has said it views Congress's grant of exclusive original jurisdiction under 28 United States Code section 1251(a) as providing the Court with "substantial discretion to make case-by-case judgments as to the practical necessity of an original forum in [the Supreme] Court for particular disputes" within its original jurisdiction. *Texas v. New Mexico*, 462 U.S. 554, 570 (1983). The Court exercises that discretion "with an eye to promoting the most effective functioning of this Court within the overall federal system." 462 U.S. at 570. The Court has also said that, before it intervenes in a case, the case should be "of serious magnitude, clearly and fully proved, and the principle to be applied should be one which the court is prepared deliberately to maintain against all considerations on the other side." *State ex rel. Dyer v. Sims*, 341 U.S. 22, 27 (1951) (quoting *Missouri v. Illinois*, 200 U.S. 496, 521 (1906)); *see also New York v. New Jersey*, 256 U.S. 296, 309 (1921).

§ 14.3:3 Equitable Apportionment: Criteria and Issues

Once the U.S. Supreme Court has granted leave to file a petition, the Court typically appoints a special master to address any grounds for dismissal and conduct any trial on the merits. Generally, a special master has the authority to regulate proceedings and conduct evidentiary hearings. Fed. R. Civ. P. 53(c). The recommendations of the special master will be presented in one or more special master's reports that are ultimately considered by the Court in a de novo review. Fed. R. Civ. P. 53(f)(3). The Court has emphasized that "extensive" and "specific" factual findings from a special master are essential to ensure that all of the factors that create equities have been weighed and to allow the Court to make "the delicate adjustment of interests" required by the law in equitable apportionment. *Florida v. Georgia*, 138 S. Ct. at 2515. In *Florida v. Georgia*, the Court remanded for the special master to make findings as to how much extra water would be provided to Florida as the result of a proposed cap on Georgia's water use and whether the additional water would redress the ecological and economic harm suffered by Florida. *Florida v. Georgia*, 138 S. Ct. at 2527.

"Equitable apportionment," as its name suggests, weighs a variety of factors. Some of the factors enumerated by the Court are "physical and climatic conditions, the consumptive use of water in the several sections of the river, the character and rate of return flows, the extent of established uses, the availability of storage water, the practical effect of wasteful uses on downstream areas, [and] the damage to upstream areas as compared to the benefits to downstream areas if a limitation is imposed on the former." *Colorado v. New Mexico*, 459 U.S. 176, 183 (1982) (quoting *Nebraska v. Wyoming*, 325 U.S. 589, 618 (1945)).

The doctrine of equitable apportionment applies where questions are raised beyond the interpretation of specific language of an interstate compact. *Florida v. Georgia*, 138 S. Ct. at 2505. Several questions are relevant. The Court will consider that states have an equal right to reasonable use of the waters of the stream. *Florida v. Georgia*, 138 S. Ct. at 2513 (quoting *United States v. Willow River Power Co.*, 324 U.S. 499, 505 (1945)). The Court has recognized that when confronted with competing claims to interstate water, its efforts should focus on securing an equitable apportionment—not bickering over formulas. *Florida v. Georgia*, 138 S. Ct. at 2513 (quoting *New Jersey v. New York*, 283 U.S. 336, 342-43 (1931)). Finally, in an interstate water matter where the initial threshold has been met to show real or substantial injury, the Court will attempt to achieve just and reasonable apportionment by considering all relevant factors. *Florida v. Georgia*, 138 S. Ct. at 2514 (quoting *South Carolina v. North Carolina*, 558 U.S. 256, 271 (2010)).

The seniority—that is, priority—of water rights in an interstate stream can become a guiding principle in equitable apportionment when the states involved recognize the doctrine of prior appropriation, but the laws of the contending states are not controlling. *Colorado v. New Mexico*, 459 U.S. at 183 (citing *Nebraska v. Wyoming*, 325 U.S. at 618, and *Connecticut v. Massachusetts*, 282 U.S. 660, 670–71 (1931)). The Court has also held that the source of a stream—that is, the amount that the watershed in each state contributes to the flow of the stream—"should be essentially irrelevant" to the adjudicating of competing state claims. *Colorado v. New Mexico*, 467 U.S. 310, 324 (1984).

The Court has indicated that it may weigh the amount of harm a certain apportionment scheme causes in one state against the amount of benefit it yields in another. *See Colorado v. New Mexico*, 459 U.S. at 183–88; *see also Idaho ex rel. Evans v. Oregon*, 462 U.S. 1017, 1036 (1983) (suit to apportion harvestable fish populations in the Columbia-Snake River system). In some instances, the fact that a complaining state has never made use of a stream will not bar that state from seeking or obtaining an apportionment. 459 U.S. at 182 n.9. Although evidence supporting the protection of current economies created by existing water use is viewed as compelling by the Court, it has also recognized that it would consider whether the state where existing uses are occurring can offset the impact of apportionment by greater efficiency in use. 459 U.S. at 188. In a suit by Nebraska to amend or seek further relief under a prior equitable apportionment decree, the Court held that Nebraska could present evidence that proposed new developments in Wyoming would affect wildlife and wildlife habitat. *Nebraska v. Wyoming*, 515 U.S. 1, 11–13 (1995).

Clear and convincing evidence must be offered to support equitable apportionment. A state seeking to prevent or enjoin a diversion bears the burden to prove that the diversion will cause "real or substantial injury or damage." *Colorado v. New Mexico*, 459 U.S. at 188 (citing *Connecticut v. Massachusetts*, 282 U.S. at 672); *see also Colorado v. Kansas*, 320 U.S. 383, 389–90, 400 (1943). The Court denied Colorado's request to apportion waters of the Vermejo River in part because Colorado did not prove that future diversions in Colorado could be offset by increased efficiencies in New Mexico through economically practical and feasible means. *Colorado v. New Mexico*, 467 U.S. at 319–20.

When a state petitions the U.S. Supreme Court for equitable apportionment, the Court has shown a reluctance at the initial stage to intervene too quickly and a preference for negotiated settlements under the Compact Clause of the U.S. Constitution, even after the Court granted leave to file a petition. The long-standing dispute between Kansas and Colorado over the Arkansas River may best illustrate the Supreme Court's historical position.

Before the states entered the Arkansas River Compact, Kansas and Colorado had been before the Court twice with disputes over the waters of the Arkansas River. In the first suit, the Court denied Kansas's request to enjoin diversions by Colorado of the Arkansas River because the depletions that Kansas alleged were insufficient to warrant injunctive relief. *See Kansas v. Colorado*, 206 U.S. 46 (1907). About forty years later, in a second lawsuit before the U.S. Supreme Court, Colorado sought to enjoin lower court litigation brought against Colorado water users, while Kansas sought an equitable apportionment of the Arkansas River. *See Colorado v. Kansas*, 320 U.S. 383 (1943).

The Court granted Colorado an injunction but concluded that it should not apportion the waters of the Arkansas River by equitable decree. Instead, the Court suggested that the states resolve their differences by negotiation and agreement, pursuant to the Compact Clause of the Constitution. 320 U.S. at 393. The Court noted that judicial apportionment would cause Colorado hardship and Kansas had not proven that Colorado's actions had caused "a serious detriment to the substantial interests of Kansas." 320 U.S. at 400. In 1949, Kansas and Colorado ratified and Congress approved an Arkansas River Compact. The Supreme Court recounts a history of this case in *Kansas v. Colorado*, 514 U.S. 673, 678 (1995).

Perhaps the salient point from the perspective of a state's attorney or private practitioner concerned with equitable apportionment issues is that the outcome in an equitable apportionment is never certain. Although litigation seeking equitable apportionment is part of the legal arsenal, the other apportionment options—which involve deliberation or negotiation—may present the best solution to interstate water controversies.

§ 14.4 Apportionment by Act of Congress

Congress has the authority to apportion water in interstate streams by congressional act. One example is the Boulder Canyon Project Act, now codified at 43 United States Code sections 617–617t. This apportionment is discussed in *Arizona v. California*, 373 U.S. 546 (1963) (certain dicta were disavowed on other grounds by *California v. United States*, 438 U.S. 645, 673–75 (1978)). In *Arizona v. California*, petitioners asked the Supreme Court to apportion the waters of the lower Colorado River among the states that had rivers flowing into the Colorado Basin. The Court noted that the Colorado River Compact did not make such an apportionment. The Court also noted that it had divided the waters of interstate streams before under the doctrine of equitable apportionment. *Arizona v. California*, 373 U.S. at 565–66. However, the Court refused to make the requested apportionment because Congress had already acted. Congress had made an apportionment of the waters in the main stem of the lower Colorado River among California, Arizona, and Nevada by enacting certain provisions in the Boulder Canyon Project Act. The Court held that where Congress had apportioned water by statute, the Court could not substitute its own notion of "equitable apportionment" for the apportionment chosen by Congress. 373 U.S. at 565–66. Again, in the Truckee and Carson Rivers and Lake Tahoe between California and Nevada in 1990, Congress apportioned by congressional act. Truckee-Carson-Pyramid Lake Water Rights Settlement Act of Jan. 23, 1990, Pub. L. No. 101–618, 104 Stat. 3298, 3294.

§ 14.5 Apportionment by Interstate Stream Compact

The third method of apportioning interstate streams is by interstate compact. The Texas streams apportioned and shared by other states have all been apportioned solely by this method. An interstate compact is not just a contract. It is a federal statute enacted by Congress. *Alabama v. North Carolina*, 560 U.S. 330, 351–52 (2010). The use of a carefully negotiated compact is undoubtedly the preferred method of apportioning the water of interstate streams, but compact negotiations are a complicated and often lengthy process that can be punctuated by conflicts. A comprehensive review of the many different considerations involved in interstate stream compact negotiations can be found in Jerome C. Muys et al., *Utton Transboundary Resources Center Model Interstate Water Compact*, 47 Nat. Resources J. 17–115 (Winter 2007). The amount of time that can be spent reaching agreement and the examples of potential conflicts along the way are illustrated in the U.S. Supreme Court's description of the history of the Pecos River Compact in *Texas v. New Mexico*, 462 U.S. 554, 557–59 (1983) and in Douglas Littlefield's history of the Rio Grande Compact. Douglas Robert Littlefield, Interstate Water Conflicts, Compromises, and Compacts: The Rio Grande, 1880–1938 (1987) (Ph.D. dissertation, University of California, Los Angeles) (copy available through ProQuest Communications, www.proquest.com).

§ 14.5:1 The Nature of Interstate Compacts

Certain types of agreements between states—including agreements to divide waters in an interstate stream, such as the Pecos River Compact between Texas and New Mexico—must be approved by Congress. *Texas v. New Mexico*, 462 U.S. 554, 564 (1983); *see also* U.S. Const. art. I, § 10, cl. 3 (the Compact Clause). When these agreements are approved by Congress, they take on a twofold nature: they are federal law, and they are also contracts between the states that must be construed in accordance with their terms. *Texas v. New Mexico*, 482 U.S. 124, 128 (1987) (citing *West Virginia ex rel. Dyer v. Sims*, 341 U.S. 22, 28 (1951), and *Petty v. Tennessee-Missouri Bridge Commission*, 359 U.S. 275, 285 (1959)).

A "compact" under the meaning of the Compact Clause is limited to a class of agreements that are "directed to the formation of any combination tending to the increase of political power in the states, which may encroach upon or interfere with the just supremacy of the United States." *U.S. Steel Corp. v. Multistate Tax Commission*, 434 U.S. 452, 471 (1978) (quoting *Virginia v. Tennessee*, 148 U.S. 503, 519 (1893)).

In *Virginia v. Tennessee*, the U.S. Supreme Court acknowledged that some, but not all, actions that lead to a boundary agreement require congressional approval. The Court discussed at length the actions taken by the two states, including an agreement to have surveys conducted, the actions by state legislatures acknowledging the surveyed line as the correct boundary, and the adoption by both states of the report of the survey commissioners. The Court concluded that the acts leading up to a mutual understanding, even if they could be used to bind one state against the claims of the other, did not constitute a compact. On the other hand, a mutual action acknowledging the boundaries likely would be a compact requiring congressional approval. *Virginia v. Tennessee*, 148 U.S. at 517–21.

There is some flexibility about whether certain agreements are compacts that require congressional approval. For example, in *New Hampshire v. Maine*, 426 U.S. 363 (1976), the two states reached a settlement over the meaning of certain key terms in a 1740 court decree setting certain boundaries between New Hampshire Colony and what was then the Maine portion of Massachusetts Colony. Despite the settlement, New Hampshire argued that the Court would have to make an independent determination of the meaning of the terms, or the consent decree would require congressional approval under the Compact Clause. The U.S. Supreme Court concluded that the settlement agreement was not a compact under the *Virginia v. Tennessee* test because the two states had merely resolved their differences over the meaning of a term. They had not adjusted their boundary. *New Hampshire v. Maine*, 426 U.S. at 369–70.

§ 14.5:2 What Constitutes Congressional Approval and When It Must Be Given

The Constitution does not prescribe whether the consent of Congress must be express or may be implied. However, the U.S. Supreme Court has held that it may be either. *Virginia v. Tennessee*, 148 U.S. 503, 521–22 (1893). The Court has also held that Congress's consent to an agreement between states does not need to be an express and formal statement of every proposition in the agreement. *Virginia v. West Virginia*, 78 U.S. (11 Wall) 39, 59–60 (1870).

Likewise, the U.S. Constitution does not specify when congressional consent must be given—that is, whether before or after the states enter into the agreement. *Waterfront Commission of New York Harbor v. Construction & Marine Equipment Co.*, 928 F. Supp. 1388, 1402 (D.N.J. 1996), *aff'd*, 103 F.3d 115 (3d Cir. 1996). In *Cuyler v. Adams*, 449 U.S. 433 (1981), congressional consent was given in advance. At issue in *Cuyler* was an interstate agreement relating to "detainers," notifications to a correctional institution in one state that a prisoner was wanted to face criminal charges in another state. The agreement was originally drafted in 1956 and was adopted by several state legislatures. The Court determined that Congress had given advance consent to the agreement by enacting the Crime Control Consent Act of June 6, 1934, ch. 406, 48 Stat. 909. *See Cuyler*, 449 U.S. at 441–42. On the other hand, advance consent may not always be necessary or appropriate. As the Court noted in *Virginia v. Tennessee*, 148 U.S. at 519, the Compact Clause of the U.S. Constitution is "directed to the formation of any combination tending to the increase of political power in the states, which may encroach upon or interfere with the just supremacy of the United States." Based on this rationale, the Court noted that it may not be clear whether an agreement between states requires congressional approval under the Compact Clause until after the terms of the agreement are known. Seeking congressional approval, therefore, may not be appropriate until after the agreement is negotiated. 148 U.S. at 521–23.

The U.S. Constitution gives Congress substantial flexibility in approving compacts. This flexibility is helpful where fundamental questions about the need for or the timing of approval are not addressed at the beginning of negotiations. Interstate water agreements involve many complex issues. Fundamental questions of state and federal authorization should be considered and addressed as early as possible.

§ 14.5:3 Parties Bound by Interstate Stream Compacts

Once ratified by the signatory states and approved by Congress, a compact binds various private and governmental entities at all levels of government. Because a compact is federal law, it preempts conflicting state law dealing with the same subject. *State of Nebraska ex rel. Nelson v. Central Interstate Low-Level Radioactive Waste Commission*, 902 F. Supp. 1046, 1049 (D. Neb. 1995); *see also* U.S. Const. art. VI, para. 2 (the Supremacy Clause). The contractual aspects of a compact also make it binding on signatory states. In *Green v. Biddle*, 21 U.S. (8 Wheat) 1 (1823), laws enacted by Kentucky were challenged as violating the terms of a 1789 compact with Virginia. The U.S. Supreme Court held that a state is prohibited from enacting a law that is inconsistent with an interstate compact on the grounds that such a law would violate article I, section 10, clause 1, of the U.S. Constitution, prohibiting any state from impairing the obligations of contracts, even a state's own contracts.

Likewise, a compact that apportions the waters of an interstate stream is binding on the citizens of each signatory state and all claimants to water under the laws of those states. This is true even if a signatory state had granted an affected water right before the state entered into the compact and this right had vested under state law. *Hinderlider v. La Plata River & Cherry Creek Ditch Co.*, 304 U.S. 92, 106–08 (1938). In *Hinderlider*, holders of vested Colorado water rights sued the Colorado state engineer for curtailing their water use in the La Plata River. The state engineer argued that he was acting pursuant to the terms of an interstate compact with New Mexico. Although the compact was entered into after the Colorado water rights were granted, the Supreme Court reasoned that the water rights available to Colorado to grant to its citizens could never exceed Colorado's equitable share of the La Plata River, nor could people claiming water rights under Colorado law claim more than Colorado's equitable share of the river. The states in their sovereign capacity were the entities that adjusted these equities by compact. *Hinderlider*, 304 U.S. at 104–109; *see also Nebraska v. Wyoming*, 325 U.S. 589, 627 (1945).

Whether Congress is bound by compacts is a somewhat different question than whether states are bound by them. Some courts have held that Congress itself cannot unilaterally reserve the right to amend or repeal an interstate compact. *See Riverside Irrigation District v. Andrews*, 568 F. Supp. 583, 589 (D. Colo. 1983), *aff'd*, 758 F.2d 508 (10th Cir. 1985); *Tobin v. United States*, 306 F.2d 270, 273 (D.C. Cir.), *cert. denied*, 371 U.S. 902 (1962). However, approval of a compact does not prevent Congress from exercising its constitutional authority to control commerce and navigation. *Pennsylvania v. Wheeling & Belmont Bridge Co.*, 59 U.S. (18 How.) 421 (1855).

In *Riverside Irrigation District*, a district engineer for the U.S. Army Corps of Engineers (the Corps) decided the petitioners did not qualify under a nationwide permit to discharge sand and gravel in connection with the petitioners' construction of a dam on the South Platte River in Colorado. The engineer's successor later required the petitioners to seek an individual permit from the Corps for the activity. The district engineer based his decision on the Corps' authority under section 404 of the federal Clean Water Act and on consultations with the U.S. Fish and Wildlife Service under the federal Endangered Species Act regarding protection of the endangered whooping crane. The evidence indicated that the Corps' concern lay more with the impacts that the reservoir would eventually have on habitat and water quality than with the impact that dredge and fill material would have during construction. Petitioners, including the State of Colorado and various local entities involved in water management, argued that the district engineer lacked the statutory authority to make his decision based on the impacts of reservoir operation. However, the petitioners also argued that the actions of the government under the federal Clean Water Act could not be used to affect state water rights under the South Platte River Compact, approved by Act of Mar. 8, 1926, ch. 46, 44 Stat. 195. The court held that Congress does not limit its authority to enact subsequent laws of nationwide applicability, even though they conflict with the terms of a compact. *Riverside Irrigation District*, 568 F. Supp. at 589–90.

Finally, compacts place limitations on the courts. Unless a compact to which Congress has consented is somehow unconstitutional, no court may order relief inconsistent with its express terms. *Texas v. New Mexico*, 462 U.S. 554, 564 (1983). However, the Court may exercise its full authority to promote compliance and remedy violations of the compact in order to give complete effect to the law. "When federal law is at issue and 'the public interest is involved,' a federal court's 'equitable powers assume an ever broader and more flexible character than when only a private controversy is at stake.'" *Kansas v. Nebraska*, 574 U.S. 445, 456 (2015) (quoting *Porter v. Warner Holding Co.*, 328 U.S. 395, 398 (1946)).

§ 14.6 Enforcement of Interstate Stream Compacts

§ 14.6:1 Enforcement by the States in the U.S. Supreme Court

Historically, enforcement of Texas compacts has been by the signatory states in the U.S. Supreme Court. *See, e.g., Oklahoma v. New Mexico*, 484 U.S. 808 (1987); *Texas v. New Mexico*, 421 U.S. 927 (1975); *Texas v. Colorado*, 389 U.S. 1000 (1967); *Texas v. New Mexico*, 343 U.S. 932 (1952); *Texas v. New Mexico*, 296 U.S. 547 (1935). Federal law provides that the Supreme Court has "original and exclusive jurisdiction of all controversies between two or more States." 28 U.S.C. § 1251(a). However, the U.S. Constitution does not confine state-versus-state controversies to the exclusive jurisdiction of the U.S. Supreme Court. *See Ames v. Kansas*, 111 U.S. 449, 469 (1884); *see also* U.S. Const. art. III, § 2, cl. 2. Congress can create lower courts and vest them with jurisdiction that is concurrent with that of the U.S. Supreme Court. *See* U.S. Const. art. III, §§ 1, 2, cl. 2.

The Red River Compact specifically contains language stating that U.S. district courts have concurrent original jurisdiction over suits "involving the application or construction" of the compact. *See* Tex. Water Code § 46.013, art. XIII, § 13.03. Therefore, it is important to determine whether there is a federal law other than 28 United States Code section 1251(a) that addresses jurisdiction.

§ 14.6:2 Enforcement of Compact Terms in Other Actions

States are the principal enforcers of their compacts, but lawsuits involving compact issues are not always state-versus-state actions. And this third-party litigation is usually not consigned to the U.S. Supreme Court's original jurisdiction. One example is *Hinderlider v. La Plata River & Cherry Creek Ditch Co.*, 304 U.S. 92 (1938). In *Hinderlider*, a Colorado irrigation company sued the state engineer of Colorado in the Colorado state courts for having "so administered the water of the river as to deprive the plaintiff of water which it claims the right to divert." *Hinderlider*, 304 U.S. at 95. The state engineer argued that any curtailment of water deliveries to the plaintiff was made in order to comply with water delivery obligations Colorado had to New Mexico under the La Plata River Compact. *Hinderlider*, 304 U.S. at 95. The case was decided on the meaning and applicability of the compact, but it reached the U.S. Supreme Court by way of appeal from the Colorado Supreme Court.

Compact requirements were also raised as issues by nonstate parties in *League to Save Lake Tahoe v. Tahoe Regional Planning Commission*, 507 F.2d 517 (9th Cir. 1974), *cert. denied*, 420 U.S. 974 (1975), *appeal after remand*, 558 F.2d 914 (9th Cir. 1977). In *League to Save Lake Tahoe*, a local association, the Sierra Club, and two individuals sued a regional planning commission. The commission was created under an interstate compact between California and Nevada intended to control development around Lake Tahoe to protect natural resources in the area. The plaintiffs sought an injunction, among other relief, to compel the planning commission to adopt ordinances that it was required to adopt under the compact. Standing, discussed at section 14.6:3 below, was not at issue in either the *Hinderlider* or the *League to Save Lake Tahoe* cases.

In contrast to the two situations above, not every litigant who invokes a compact claim in federal court succeeds in maintaining an action on the claim. In *United States v. City of Las Cruces*, 289 F.3d 1170 (10th Cir. 2002), the U.S. Bureau of Reclamation sought to quiet title to its claim of water rights in the Rio Grande Project, serving the region around Las Cruces, New Mexico, and El Paso, Texas. The New Mexico state engineer and other New Mexico parties cited various abstention doctrines and moved for dismissal. The New Mexico parties argued that a water rights adjudication was pending in New Mexico state court that would resolve the bureau's claims. The bureau and two Texas parties argued that federal law questions arising under the Rio Grande Compact and a 1906 treaty with Mexico needed to be resolved by the federal courts and the case should proceed. The Tenth Circuit Court of Appeals rejected the bureau's federal question arguments, saying in part, "The Treaty and the

Compact only require water deliveries to the states or Mexico, not the named defendants. Because the federal quiet title action only involves the competing claims of the United States and the named defendants, the water rights given to the states or Mexico are irrelevant." *City of Las Cruces*, 289 F.3d at 1185.

§ 14.6:3 Standing and Intervention—Enforcement of Interstate Compacts by State and Local Governments

A threshold issue in compact enforcement is standing. States usually assert standing in federal court in one of three capacities: (1) a proprietary capacity, in which the state claims to suffer a direct, tangible injury; (2) a sovereign capacity, as when a state seeks relief in a boundary dispute or a water rights dispute; and (3) as *parens patriae*, to protect "quasi-sovereign" interests. *See Alfred L. Snapp & Son, Inc. v. Puerto Rico ex rel. Barez*, 458 U.S. 592, 601–03 (1982); *see also Connecticut v. Cahill*, 217 F.3d 93, 97 (2d Cir. 2000).

The question of whether a political subdivision of a state may intervene in a compact enforcement action before the U.S. Supreme Court is another issue. Although there is little authority precisely on the point, lower courts have held that municipalities or local governments cannot base standing on the *parens patriae* doctrine. *Colorado River Indian Tribes v. Town of Parker*, 776 F.2d 846, 848 (9th Cir. 1985); *In re Multidistrict Vehicle Air Pollution M.D.L. No 31*, 481 F.2d 122, 131 (9th Cir.), *cert. denied sub nom. Morgan v. Automobile Manufacturers Ass'n, Inc.*, 414 U.S. 1045 (1973). On the other hand, lack of standing to prosecute a claim under the *parens patriae* doctrine does not preclude a local government from asserting that it has standing based on some specific proprietary or individual interest that would permit intervention generally under rule 24 of the Federal Rules of Civil Procedure. *See In re Multidistrict Vehicle Air Pollution M.D.L. No 31*, 481 F.2d at 131.

However, if the political subdivision's state is already a party to the proceeding, another standing-related issue arises. Under the *parens patriae* doctrine, the state is presumed to represent its citizens—private, corporate, and governmental. A political subdivision seeking to overcome that presumption and obtain standing in an original action before the U.S. Supreme Court must show "some compelling interest in [its] own right, apart from [its] interest in a class with all other citizens and creatures of the state, which interest is not properly represented by the state." *New Jersey v. New York*, 345 U.S. 369, 373–74 (1953) (citing *Commonwealth of Kentucky v. State of Indiana*, 281 U.S. 163, 173–74 (1930)). This standard was reaffirmed by the U.S. Supreme Court in *South Carolina v. North Carolina*, 55 U.S. 256, 268–69 (2010), in which the Court allowed a nonstate party to intervene but required it to demonstrate a "compelling interest that is unlike the interests of other citizens of the States."

In *New Jersey v. New York*, New Jersey filed a suit against the State of New York relating to the use of the waters of the Delaware River. The City of New York was also joined as defendant. When the State of Pennsylvania and the City of Philadelphia sought to intervene, the U.S. Supreme Court determined that Pennsylvania could intervene but Philadelphia could not because it was represented by Pennsylvania. The Court distinguished the inclusion of New York City as a party to the litigation on the basis that New York City was "forcibly joined as a defendant to the original action since [it] was the authorized agent for the execution of the sovereign policy which threatened injury to the citizens of New Jersey." *New Jersey v. New York*, 345 U.S. at 374–75. The holding in *New Jersey v. New York* was cited and discussed again in *Nebraska v. Wyoming*, 515 U.S. 1, 21–22 (1995).

There has been at least one situation in which the commissioners of a regional agency within a state *were* deemed to be acting for its state and were thus appropriate parties in an original action. The U.S. Supreme Court allowed the State of New York to maintain an original action against the Passaic Valley Sewage Commissioners (a New Jersey governmental agency) as well as the State of New Jersey, seeking an injunction against proposed sewage discharges from New Jersey into New York Bay. The Court said, "[T]he defendant sewerage commissioners constitute such a statutory, corporate agency of the state [of New Jersey] that their action, actual or intended, must be treated as that of the state itself, and we shall so regard it." *New York v. New Jersey*, 256 U.S. 296, 302 (1921).

Despite the cases that apply stringent standards for intervention by political subdivisions in original actions, as a practical matter there have been many incidences of political subdivisions being allowed to participate as parties in interstate water litigation without objection by the other litigants. Among that number are cases where irrigation districts in Texas or New Mexico have been parties to litigation involving the Pecos River and the Rio Grande.

If compact issues are raised in cases originating in the lower courts, the rules on intervention by political subdivisions may be different. Some federal appellate courts have recognized a distinction between intervention by political subdivisions in the lower courts and intervention in a U.S. Supreme Court original action. In *Environmental Defense Fund, Inc. v. Higginson*, 631 F.2d 738 (D.C. Cir. 1979), the court of appeals held that the "compelling state interest" criterion used in *New Jersey v. New York* applied in cases that were under the Court's original jurisdiction but not in cases that originated in the federal district courts. The court of appeals attributed the U.S. Supreme Court's more stringent standard to the high court's need to limit original actions. *Higginson*, 631 F.2d at 739–40. However, the would-be intervenor would still have to demonstrate that its interests were not adequately represented by the state. 631 F.2d at 739–40.

§ 14.6:4 Express and Implied Rights of Action

Closely related to standing is the question whether a compact affords an aggrieved state any type of remedy—express or implied. Lack of an express remedy in a compact does not necessarily prevent a state from enforcing a compact in the courts. In *Texas v. New Mexico*, 462 U.S. 554, 567 (1983), the State of New Mexico noted that the Pecos River Compact provided no express remedies for violations of its provisions and argued that the lack of an express remedy precluded an original action to enforce the compact in the U.S. Supreme Court. Therefore, New Mexico argued, the only remedy available to Texas was the Pecos River Commission, where Texas had one vote, New Mexico had one vote, and there was no provision for resolving a deadlock. The U.S. Supreme Court rejected New Mexico's argument, saying, "In the absence of an explicit provision or other clear indications that a bargain to that effect was made, we shall not construe a compact to preclude a State from seeking judicial relief when the compact does not provide an equivalent method of vindicating the State's rights." 462 U.S. at 569–70.

As with standing, nonstate parties such as political subdivisions seeking to intervene in compact enforcement cases under an implied right of action may be subject to different or greater scrutiny. There is little case law on the subject, and the case law that does exist is not published. However, at least one case follows the U.S. Supreme Court's general rules regarding private rights of action under federal statutes. In *Three Forks Ranch Corp. v. City of Cheyenne, Wyoming*, 96 Fed. App'x. 567 (10th Cir. 2004), a Wyoming corporation sued the City of Cheyenne, the Wyoming state engineer, and various local water management entities for damages based on alleged violations of the Upper Colorado River Basin Compact. The Tenth Circuit Court of Appeals employed the four-pronged analysis prescribed by the U.S. Supreme Court in *Cort v. Ash*, 422 U.S. 66, 78 (1975), for determining whether a federal statute created an implied private right of action. *Cort v. Ash* has not been expressly overruled, but in more recent cases, the U.S. Supreme Court has reduced the number of factors essentially to one—namely, whether Congress clearly manifested an unambiguous intent to confer individual rights. *See Gonzaga University v. Doe*, 536 U.S. 273 (2002). There must be a demonstration of intent on the part of Congress to create both a private right and a private remedy. *Alexander v. Sandoval*, 532 U.S. 275, 286–87 (2001).

Again, as is the case with standing, there are practical considerations. Political subdivisions or private concerns that have a stake in water rights affected by multistate stream litigation may well be included as parties without objection. The fact that they are directly affected may bolster their chances of being made parties because, among other reasons, they may be best situated to gather information important to the lawsuit.

§ 14.6:5 Parol Evidence in Compact Enforcement Actions

The U.S. Supreme Court has held that the record of the negotiations in drafting a compact may be used to ascertain the meaning intended by the parties when the interpretation of a compact is at issue and the relevant language of the compact is determined to be ambiguous. *Oklahoma v. New Mexico*, 501 U.S. 221, 234–35 (1991); *Texas v. New Mexico*, 462 U.S. 554, 568 n.14 (1983); *Arizona v. California*, 292 U.S. 341, 359–60 (1934). As is the case with the interpretation of any statute or contract, the courts and special masters have a substantial amount of latitude in determining whether an ambiguity exists, but this determination may also be subject to dispute on review. One example of this is seen in *Oklahoma v. New Mexico*, in which New Mexico questioned the special master's use of extrinsic evidence to construe certain provisions of the Canadian River Compact, but the U.S. Supreme Court upheld the master's decision. *See Oklahoma*, 501 U.S. at 235 n.5.

The signatory states' course of performance under a compact can also be a significant factor, as it was in interpreting North Carolina's obligations under an interstate waste disposal compact. *Alabama v. North Carolina*, 560 U.S. 330, 343–52 (2010); *see also Oklahoma v. New Mexico*, 501 U.S. at 235 n.5, and *Texas v. New Mexico*, 462 U.S. at 565. The U.S. Supreme Court also considered whether there had been any history of cross-border water diversions under the Red River Compact when evaluating Tarrant Regional Water District's request for relief in *Tarrant Regional Water District v. Herrmann*, 133 S. Ct. 2120, 2133–35 (2013).

§ 14.6:6 Relief: Injunction

The courts can compel a state to comply with the terms of an interstate compact. *Texas v. New Mexico*, 462 U.S. 554, 567 (1983). The relief granted may be remedial to address past violations, but it also may be prospective to prevent future violations. *See Texas v. New Mexico*, 482 U.S. 124, 128 (1987). In doing so, the Court has enforcement authority necessary to prevent abuse. *See Kansas v. Nebraska*, 135 S. Ct. 1042, 1052 (2015). However, as previously noted, because a compact is federal law, courts are bound by its terms and cannot order relief that is inconsistent with a compact's express terms. *Kansas v. Nebraska*, 135 S. Ct. at 1052–53; *see also Texas v. New Mexico*, 462 U.S. at 571–75.

In the Pecos River litigation, the Supreme Court refused to reform the Pecos River Compact to break an impasse on the Pecos River Commission that led in part to the litigation. *Texas v. New Mexico*, 462 U.S. at 564–66. The Court also refused to accept a drastically different method for water accounting than had been contemplated by the framers of the Pecos River Compact, but it did accept that a new methodology for water accounting, that it viewed as consistent with the framers' intent, could be substituted for the original (and unworkable) method of determining New Mexico's water delivery obligations. *Texas v. New Mexico*, 462 U.S. at 571–75.

§ 14.6:7 Relief: Monetary Damages

The U.S. Supreme Court can award monetary damages in an original action between states. *See Texas v. New Mexico*, 482 U.S. 124, 130–31 (1987) (holding that monetary damages could be awarded to Texas for New Mexico's violation of the Pecos River Compact in lieu of specific performance); *see also Virginia v. West Virginia*, 246 U.S. 565 (1918) (mandamus action by Virginia to compel collections of taxes by West Virginia to pay a judgment). The Eleventh Amendment is not implicated when a state seeks monetary damages against another state, even if the complaining state's claim is based in part on the losses of individuals in the petitioner state. *Kansas v. Colorado*, 533 U.S. 1, 7 (1991). However, the state's claim ultimately must be based on its own interest, and the state may not sue as a nominal party on behalf of one or a small group of its citizens. 533 U.S. at 8–9. Prejudgment interest may also be awarded. 533 U.S. at 9–12.

III. The Five Interstate River Compacts in Texas

§ 14.7 Introduction

As noted in the beginning of this chapter, Texas is a party to five interstate river compacts with its neighbors. These compacts are:

1. The Rio Grande Compact, approved by Act of May 1, 1939, ch. 155, 53 Stat. 785; codified in Texas Water Code chapter 41.

2. The Pecos River Compact, approved by Act of June 9, 1949, ch. 184, 63 Stat. 159; codified in Texas Water Code chapter 42.

3. The Canadian River Compact, approved by Act of May 17, 1952, ch. 306, 66 Stat. 74; codified in Texas Water Code chapter 43.

4. The Red River Compact, approved by Act of Dec. 22, 1980, Pub. L. No. 96-564, 94 Stat. 3305; codified in Texas Water Code chapter 46.

5. The Sabine River Compact, approved by Act of Aug. 10, 1954, ch. 668, 68 Stat. 690; codified in Texas Water Code chapter 44.

There was a sixth compact that addressed the management of Caddo Lake, in northeast Texas. Caddo Lake is on a tributary of the Red River, and it is transected by the Texas-Louisiana state line between Marshall, Texas, and Shreveport, Louisiana. The Caddo Lake Compact was ratified by Texas and codified in chapter 47 of the Texas Water Code in 1979. However, the Caddo Lake Compact failed to receive approval by Congress. *See* Paul Elliott, *Texas' Interstate Water Compacts*, 17 St. Mary's L.J. 1241, 1271 n.263 (1986). Louisiana repealed its ratification of the agreement in 1982.

The following sections provide a general overview of each of the five active interstate stream compacts Texas has with its neighboring states.

IV. The Two Rio Grandes: An Overview

§ 14.8 The River and Its Course

The Rio Grande has its headwaters at the Continental Divide in the San Juan Mountains of Colorado, northeast of Durango, Colorado. *See* Leon C. Metz, *The Handbook of Texas Online*, *Rio Grande*, www.tshaonline.org/handbook/entries/rio-grande. The river flows eastward to Alamosa, Colorado, where it begins a southern descent to New Mexico northwest of Taos, New Mexico. It then flows south roughly through the center of New Mexico, arriving in Texas just west of El Paso. From El Paso, it proceeds to mark the boundary between Texas and Mexico until the river flows into the Gulf of Mexico at the far southern tip of Texas. A map of the Rio Grande appears in Figure 1.

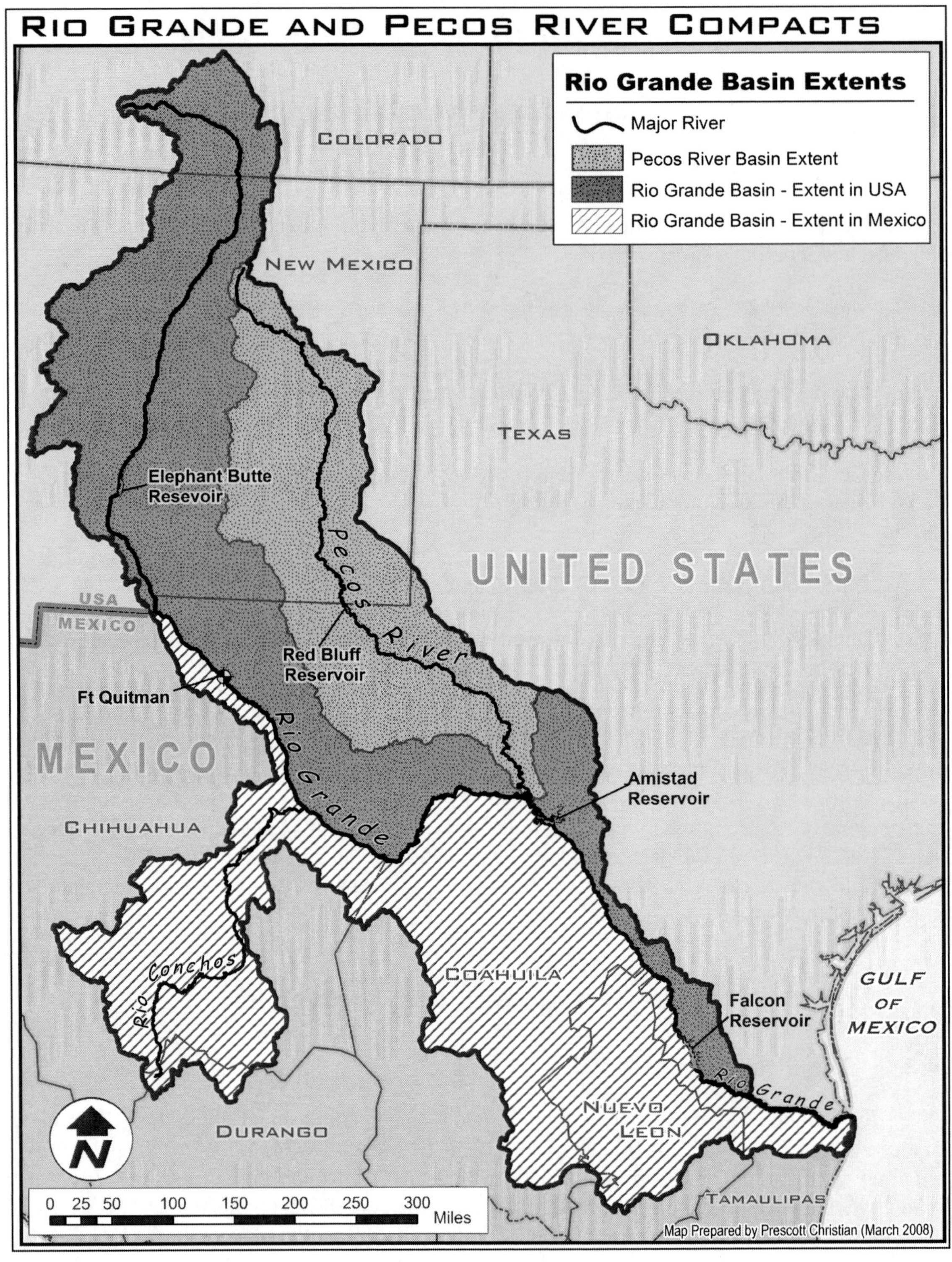

Figure 1. The Rio Grande and Pecos River Compacts. Courtesy Prescott Christian, Texas Commission on Environmental Quality.

§ 14.9 The Two Rio Grandes

A discussion of the Rio Grande Compact must begin with consideration of the broader organization of water management on the Rio Grande. Two treaties between the United States and Mexico have, legally speaking, created two "Rio Grandes" in Texas. A discussion of the two treaties is found in *State v. Hidalgo County Water Control & Improvement District No. 18*, 443 S.W.2d 728, 733–37 (Tex. App.—Corpus Christi–Edinburg 1969, writ ref'd n.r.e.).

The first "Rio Grande" encompasses the river from its source in Colorado to a point about eighty river miles below El Paso near Fort Quitman, an abandoned cavalry outpost in Hudspeth County. This Rio Grande—the Rio Grande above Fort Quitman—is governed by a 1906 treaty with Mexico commonly known as the "1906 Convention." *See* Convention for the Equitable Distribution of the Waters of the Rio Grande for Irrigation Purposes, U.S.–Mexico, May 21, 1906, 34 Stat. 2953, www.ibwc.gov/Files/1906Conv.pdf. This is the portion of the Rio Grande that is also governed by the Rio Grande Compact (discussed at section 14.11 below). The second "Rio Grande" encompasses the river from Fort Quitman to the Gulf of Mexico. This Rio Grande is governed by a treaty with Mexico, also called the "1944 Treaty" or the "1945 Treaty" because it was signed in 1944 and ratified by Congress in 1945. *See* Treaty Respecting Utilization of Waters of the Colorado and Tijuana Rivers and of the Rio Grande, U.S.–Mexico, Feb. 3, 1944, 59 Stat. 1219, www.ibwc.gov/Files/1944Treaty.pdf.

The 1945 Treaty divides the waters below Fort Quitman, including the waters of the Rio Grande stored in Falcon and Amistad reservoirs and waters in tributaries that enter the Rio Grande downstream of Fort Quitman, between the United States and Mexico. This second Rio Grande is not governed by an interstate compact, but the 1945 Treaty and the adjudication of water rights in the Lower and Middle Rio Grande of Texas have given rise to a system of water rights that is distinct from all other parts of Texas. This unique system is discussed in part VI below.

V. The Rio Grande above Fort Quitman: Its Compact and Its Treaties

§ 14.10 Overview above Fort Quitman

The portion of the Rio Grande, and all its tributaries, in Colorado, New Mexico, and Texas above Fort Quitman (about eighty miles southeast of El Paso in Hudspeth County) are subject to the Rio Grande Compact. *See* Tex. Water Code § 41.009, art. I(c). Additionally, the 1906 Convention governs use of the water above Fort Quitman by the United States and Mexico.

§ 14.11 The Rio Grande Compact

The Rio Grande Project was built by the U.S. Reclamation Service, predecessor to the U.S. Bureau of Reclamation, in accordance with the Reclamation Act of 1902. Act of June 17, 1902, ch. 1093, 32 Stat. 388 (codified at 43 U.S.C. §§ 371–390). Congress made the Reclamation Act applicable to projects in Texas and approved the Rio Grande Project in 1906. *See* Act of June 12, 1906, ch. 3288, 34 Stat. 259 (codified at 43 U.S.C. § 391). Elephant Butte Reservoir was completed around 1915, and most of the additional project works were added by the late 1930s.

In the 1920s and 1930s, use of water for irrigation in the Rio Grande above Elephant Butte increased greatly. New irrigation projects were designed and built between Elephant Butte and Albuquerque and in the mountain valleys near Alamosa, Colorado. This caused Texas (supported by interests in southern New Mexico) to file suit against the states of New Mexico and Colorado. *See Texas v. New Mexico*, 308 U.S. 510 (1939) (dismissing Texas's complaint). The Final Report of the special master explained that the controversies raised in Texas's lawsuit were resolved by the ratification of the Rio Grande Compact in 1938. The compact was approved by Congress in 1939. See Act of May 31, 1939, ch. 155, 53 Stat. 785; *see generally* Paul Elliott, *Texas' Interstate Water Compacts*, 17 St. Mary's L.J. 1241, 1241 (1986).

§ 14.11:1 Language of the Rio Grande Compact

Colorado, New Mexico, and Texas are the signatories to the Rio Grande Compact. Tex. Water Code § 41.001. The compact is administered by the Rio Grande Compact Commission, which is made up of one representative from each state. Tex. Water Code § 41.009, art. XII. The governor of Texas appoints the Texas Rio Grande Compact Commissioner, and the state engineers of Colorado and New Mexico are the representatives for their respective states. Tex. Water Code § 41.009, art. XII. By unanimous action, the three commissioners may adopt rules and regulations to govern their proceedings. Tex. Water Code § 41.009, art. XII. A chair is appointed by the president of the United States, but this person does not have a vote on any matter before the commission. Tex. Water Code § 41.009, art. XII.

The preamble of the Rio Grande Compact provides that the intent of the three states in entering into the compact is "effecting an equitable apportionment" of the waters of the river. Tex. Water Code § 41.009. The Rio Grande Compact specifically obligates the upstream states of Colorado and New Mexico to make quantifiable deliveries to their respective downstream state. Colorado delivers its water obligation to New Mexico at the Colorado-New Mexico state line. Tex. Water Code § 41.009, art. III. New Mexico delivers its water obligation into Elephant Butte Reservoir, about one hundred miles upstream of El Paso in New Mexico. Tex. Water Code § 41.009, art. IV; Resolution Adopted by Rio Grande Compact Commission at the Annual Meeting Held at El Paso, Texas, February 22–24, 1948, Changing Gaging Stations and Measurements of Deliveries by New Mexico, https://www.tceq.texas.gov/assets/public/permitting/watersupply/water_rights/1948_rg_resolution.pdf [hereinafter Resolution]. The amount of water to be delivered is calculated on a sliding scale based on the river flow past certain gauges identified in the compact. *See* Tex. Water Code § 41.009, arts. III, IV.

Although the compact purports to divide the waters of the Rio Grande from its source in Colorado to Fort Quitman, the compact does not contain an express ratio for dividing the waters between western Texas and southern New Mexico after New Mexico has met its delivery obligation at Elephant Butte Reservoir. Initially, the Bureau of Reclamation made a determination about how many irrigable acres lay in the water district in New Mexico (the Elephant Butte Irrigation District) and how many acres lay in the water district in Texas (El Paso County Water Improvement District No. 1). Water is delivered under contract to each district based on the total "irrigable acres" the bureau recognized in each district. The irrigable acres are split 57 percent to New Mexico and 43 percent to Texas. Only one formal reference to this allocation is found in writing, and that is in a 1938 bureau contract with the districts. *See* Contract between the Elephant Butte Irrigation District and the El Paso County Water Improvement District No. 1 Dated Feb. 16, 1938, Providing for a 3 percent cushion on the Irrigable Area of the Rio Grande Reclamation Project as allocated to the Districts (copy on file in the offices of the Texas Attorney General).

Under the compact, credits and debits for Colorado and New Mexico are computed annually. Tex. Water Code § 41.009, art. VI. Colorado may not accrue a debit greater than 100,000 acre-feet; New Mexico may not be in debt to Texas in excess of 200,000 acre-feet. Tex. Water Code § 41.009, art. VI. Credits and debits can be canceled by an actual spill of usable water or under conditions that would have resulted in a spill, called a "hypothetical spill." *See* Tex. Water Code § 41.009, art. I (definitions), art. VI. When less than 400,000 acre-feet of usable water are in project storage, which is a time of drought, neither Colorado nor New Mexico can store water in any reservoir built after 1929. Tex. Water Code § 41.009, art. VII.

§ 14.11:2 Operations under the Rio Grande Compact

Practically, the Rio Grande's operations under the compact generally are resolved between the states. Over the years, adoption of a resolution or a change in rules by the Compact Commission, or even a letter agreement between states, can address a specific need of one or more states on the Rio Grande. This is preferred to any attempt to change the terms of the compact, because that could be seen as submitting all issues in the compact to reconsideration, much like opening a can of worms.

For instance, the specific language of the compact provides that New Mexico's delivery obligation is to be made at San Marcial. *See* Tex. Water Code § 41.009, art. II. By resolution adopted in 1947 by the Rio Grande Compact Commission, the gauging station at San Marcial was abandoned and the station at Elephant Butte Reservoir was substituted. See Resolution, at 72. When in 2003 New Mexico needed water to meet its obligations to the silvery minnow under the Endangered Species Act, New Mexico offered through a series of letters to relinquish a portion of its accrued credits in phases so that it could store a like amount of water upstream of Elephant Butte Reservoir for later release. Texas accepted the offer of the release of credits. Rio Grande Compact Commission, Report of the Rio Grande Compact Commission 2003, at 35–39.

In March 2008, the two water districts and the Bureau of Reclamation formalized the allocation of water by executing an Operating Agreement for the Rio Grande Project. Additionally, the parties agreed to produce an operations manual to contain detailed information regarding methods, equations, and procedures used by the parties to account for water charges and operating procedures for the Rio Grande Project.

However, a little over three years later, in August 2011, New Mexico filed a lawsuit against the United States concerning the Operating Agreement. *See New Mexico v. United States*, No. 1:11-cv-00691-JB-ACT (D.N.M.). New Mexico challenged the Bureau of Reclamation's action in entering into the Operating Agreement, and sought, among numerous other claims, a declaration that the Operating Agreement was void as a matter of law and an injunction enjoining the bureau from implementing the Agreement. The two water districts intervened in the lawsuit.

In January 2013, Texas initiated an original action in the U.S. Supreme Court by filing motion for leave to file a complaint. *Texas v. New Mexico & Colorado*, No. 220141 ORG (U.S. Docketed Jan. 10, 2013). In its complaint, Texas accused New Mexico of pumping groundwater and diverting surface water in areas below the reservoir, which in turn meant that water apportioned for Texas was unlawfully redirected to New Mexico. This reduced Texas's water supplies and the apportionment of water to which Texas is entitled under the Rio Grande Compact. Texas asked the Court to declare Texas's rights to the waters of the Rio Grande pursuant to the Compact and the federal act authorizing the Rio Grande Project. Colorado and New Mexico responded, asking the Court to deny Texas's motion. A year later the Court granted Texas's motion for leave to file its complaint and shortly thereafter the United States intervened.

In November 2014, the Court appointed a special master to administer the case. The special master initially considered New Mexico's motion to dismiss Texas's complaint, and after briefing and argument, the special master issued his First Interim Report in which he recommended that (1) New Mexico's motion to dismiss be denied and (2) the complaint filed by the United States be dismissed in part. The Court heard argument in January 2018, and issued its opinion in March 2018. *See Texas v. New Mexico*, 138 S. Ct. 954 (2018). The U.S. Supreme Court held that the United States could pursue the claims it had pleaded in the case. The Court reasoned that the Rio Grande Compact is inextricably intertwined with the Rio Grande Project—including its Elephant Butte Reservoir operated by the Bureau of Reclamation—as well as the contracts that the federal government entered into with the downstream water districts. The Court noted that New Mexico itself conceded that the United States plays an integral role in the Compact's operations. The Court expressed its concern that a breach of the Compact could jeopardize the federal government's ability to satisfy its treaty obligations. Finally, the

Court recognized that the United States was seeking substantially the same relief as Texas, but Texas did not object to the United States in the lawsuit. *See Texas v. New Mexico*, 138 S. Ct. at 959–60.

Following the opinion, the Court appointed a new special master. The pace of the original action was only slightly delayed by the 2020 pandemic, and the parties have continued with discovery and summary judgment motions to limit the issues necessary to present at the upcoming trial. The special master issued an order in May 2021 addressing the states' motions for partial summary judgment and granted in part and denied in part the motions filed by Texas, New Mexico, and the United States.

§ 14.12 1906 Convention

Also affecting the Rio Grande above Fort Quitman is the United States' required delivery to Mexico. About the time the Rio Grande Project was approved by Congress, the United States also entered the 1906 Convention, cited at section 14.9 above. The 1906 Convention obligates the United States to deliver 60,000 acre-feet of water per year to Mexico at a dam between El Paso and Ciudad Juárez. The treaty requires that in cases of "extraordinary drought or serious accident to the irrigation system in the United States," the amount delivered to Mexico must be diminished in the same proportion as the water delivered to lands under irrigation in the Rio Grande Project in the United States. The rest of the water in the portion of the Rio Grande from its source in Colorado down to Fort Quitman is allocated for use in the United States.

VI. The Rio Grande below Fort Quitman: Unique in Texas Water Law

§ 14.13 The Segments of the Rio Grande below Fort Quitman

For state regulatory purposes, the Rio Grande below Fort Quitman is divided into three segments: the Upper Rio Grande (from Fort Quitman to Amistad Dam), defined at 30 Texas Administrative Code section 303.2(21); the Middle Rio Grande (from Amistad Dam to Falcon Dam), defined at 30 Texas Administrative Code section 303.2(13); and the Lower Rio Grande (from Falcon Dam to the mouth of the Rio Grande), defined at 30 Texas Administrative Code section 303.2(11).

§ 14.14 Controlling Law on the Rio Grande below Fort Quitman

The 1945 Treaty, cited at section 14.9 above, applies to the Upper, Middle, and Lower Rio Grande. The Texas Commission on Environmental Quality (TCEQ) regulates water use by Texas in these segments of the Rio Grande through its Rio Grande Watermaster, but regulation varies with the location. *See* 30 Tex. Admin. Code ch. 303. Water rights originally adjudicated in the Lower and Middle Rio Grande are based on water stored in two international reservoirs. The system used to regulate and manage these water rights was a product of those water rights adjudications in the mid-twentieth century. It is unique in Texas water law. See Chapter 13 of this book for a discussion of enforcement by the Rio Grande Watermaster.

§ 14.15 The 1945 Treaty

One of the main portions of the 1945 Treaty deals with the Rio Grande below Fort Quitman. Article 4 of the treaty apportions these waters. The flow in the main channel of the Rio Grande is divided equally between the United States and Mexico. *See* 1945 Treaty, arts. 4.A(b), (d), 4.B(b), (d). However, the water that reaches the Rio Grande from tributaries is not divided. The United States is allotted all the waters that reach the Rio Grande from significant U.S. tributaries, such as the Pecos and Devils Rivers. *See* 1945 Treaty, art. 4.B(a). Mexico is allotted all the waters that reach the Rio Grande from some of Mexico's tributaries. *See* 1945 Treaty, art. 4.A(a). However, some of the major Mexican tributaries to the Rio Grande, such as the Rio Conchos, which enters the Rio Grande near Presidio, Texas, are divided two-thirds to Mexico and one-third to the United States. *See* 1945 Treaty, arts. 4.A(c), 4.B(c). The average share of water from these Mexican tributaries that is allotted to the United States must not be less than 350,000 acre-feet per year. If it is less, Mexico is required to make up the difference over a five-year period, except in periods of "extraordinary drought." *See* 1945 Treaty, art. 4.B(c), and the final paragraph of art. 4.

Article 5 of the 1945 Treaty contemplates the construction of three or more reservoirs on the Rio Grande. Of the three sites mentioned, two have been constructed—Falcon Reservoir between Roma-Los Saenz and Laredo, and Amistad Reservoir downstream of the confluence of the Rio Grande and the Pecos River.

Article 8 of the 1945 Treaty addresses storage and provides, among other things, that the International Boundary and Water Commission (IBWC) will develop regulations for storage, conveyance, and delivery of water to the United States and Mexico. Article 8 also contains some general provisions relating to water accounting. Article 9 addresses other accounting issues and also provides that the IBWC will account for water use, storage, conveyance, water losses, and other aspects of water accounting.

The IBWC was created under a prior United States–Mexico treaty in 1889 and was called the International Boundary Commission. Its name was changed to International Boundary and Water Commission in the 1945 Treaty. IBWC has both Mexican and U.S. branches, the latter being a bureau of the U.S. Department of State. Information about IBWC is available at www.ibwc.gov/home.html.

§ 14.16 The Weighted Priorities, or Amistad-Falcon, System of Water Rights

§ 14.16:1 A Unique Enclave in Texas Water Law

In most of Texas, water rights are governed by the "prior appropriation" system. Under this system, during times of shortage, the oldest claim to water in the watercourse is senior and has priority over junior water rights whose holders could also claim a right to the water. This is true regardless of the type of use made of the water. This time-priority system is expressed as follows in the Texas Water Code: "As between appropriators, the first in time is the first in right." Tex. Water Code § 11.027. The prior appropriation system applies to water rights throughout most of Texas, including those in the tributaries of the Rio Grande and the main channel ("main stem") of the Rio Grande above Amistad Dam. See Chapter 4 of this book for further discussion of the prior appropriation system.

The one exception to the rule of prior appropriation is the "weighted priorities system," or the "Amistad-Falcon system," which was applied to water rights adjudicated in the main stem of the Rio Grande downstream of Amistad Reservoir. Then-existing water rights in the Lower Rio Grande below Falcon Reservoir were adjudicated in 1956 by the district court in Hidalgo County in a lawsuit filed by the State of Texas. *See State v. Hidalgo County Water Control & Improvement District No. 18*, 443 S.W.2d 728, 738 (Tex. App.—Corpus Christi–Edinburg 1969, writ ref'd n.r.e.). Beginning in the 1970s, existing water rights in the Middle Rio Grande (from Falcon Dam to Amistad Dam) were adjudicated under the Water Rights Adjudication Act of 1967. *See* Tex. Water Code §§ 11.301–.341. The proceeding, commonly called the "Middle Rio Grande Adjudication," was conducted before the Texas Water Rights Commission, a predecessor agency of the TCEQ. The Water Rights Commission's Final Determination applied the system of weighted priorities from *Hidalgo County* to the rights adjudicated in the main stem of the Middle Rio Grande below Amistad Dam. *See* Texas Water Rights Commission, Final Determination of Water Right Claims from the Rio Grande and Its Tributaries from

Falcon Dam Upstream to Amistad Dam (1974). The Water Rights Commission's decision to apply the priority of use system in the Middle Rio Grande Adjudication was upheld by the district court. *See In re Adjudication of the Middle Rio Grande & Contributing Texas Tributaries*, No. 322,018 (200th Dist. Ct., Travis County, Tex. Nov. 9, 1982).

In *Hidalgo County*, the appellate court recognized three categories of use, prioritized as follows:

1. Domestic, Municipal, and Industrial uses (DMI): A 60,000-acre-foot reserve was set aside for municipalities, and certain other DMI rights were recognized by the appellate court. *Hidalgo County*, 443 S.W.2d at 731–32.

2. Class A Irrigation uses: These were claimants whose rights were based on compliance with prior appropriation statutes or other legal theories. 443 S.W.2d at 748–49.

3. Class B Irrigation uses: These were claimants who had used water in good faith and whose water rights were recognized under the court's equity powers. 443 S.W.2d at 749–50.

Class A and Class B water rights also include mining and industrial uses. *See* 30 Tex. Admin. Code § 303.43.

§ 14.16:2 Water Allocations in the Lower and Middle Rio Grande

In its opinion on motion for rehearing, the *Hidalgo County* court acknowledged that the Water Rights Adjudication Act of 1967 provided for the Water Rights Commission to take over the administration of adjudicated water rights. The court therefore ordered that the Water Rights Commission assume control of adjudicated water rights in the Lower Rio Grande sixty days after the judgment in *Hidalgo County* became final. *Hidalgo County*, 443 S.W.2d at 761. The rules of the Texas Water Rights Commission and its successor agencies, including the TCEQ, have evolved from the *Hidalgo County* ruling and from its subsequent application to the Middle Rio Grande. When *Hidalgo County* was pending, a master in chancery, later called a "watermaster," administered the Lower Rio Grande for the court. Since then, as allowed by statute, the executive director of the TCEQ has appointed watermasters to administer all of the Rio Grande below Fort Quitman. *See* Tex. Water Code §§ 11.325, 11.326; see also Chapter 13 of this book.

The current operations of the Lower and Middle Rio Grande are established in the TCEQ's rules. *See* 30 Tex. Admin. Code §§ 303.21, 303.22. Falcon and Amistad reservoirs are operated as a single water storage system. Priority-of-use water right holders in the Amistad-Falcon system have accounts based on storage in the reservoirs. A reserve for all DMI rights, now consisting of 225,000 acre-feet, is maintained in the reservoirs when possible, and allocating water to the DMI reserve is the first priority under the TCEQ's allocation rules. *See* 30 Tex. Admin. Code § 303.22(a)(1).

Each month, based on figures from the IBWC for the last Saturday of the previous month, the 225,000-acre-foot reserve for DMI rights is replenished in the watermaster's accounting. *See* 30 Tex. Admin. Code § 303.22(a)(1). From the remaining water in storage, the water account balances for the Class A and Class B rights are deducted by the watermaster. Then, from the remaining water, an operating reserve of 75,000 acre-feet is deducted. If there is water remaining, it is allocated to the Class A and Class B irrigation rights. Consistent with the ruling in *Hidalgo County*, Class A rights are allocated 1.7 times as much water as Class B. *See Hidalgo County,* 443 S.W.2d at 747; *see also* 30 Tex. Admin. Code § 303.22(b).

§ 14.16:3 Water Marketing, Change of Use, and Change of Priority in the Amistad-Falcon System

The TCEQ's rules provide for the conversion of Class A and Class B rights to DMI rights. *See* 30 Tex. Admin. Code § 303.43. Section 303.43 provides that all "Class A and B priority rights in the Lower and Middle Rio Grande which have been or will be acquired for domestic, municipal, or industrial use" must be amended to authorize the change in purpose of use. One acre-foot of Class A water rights, when converted to DMI use, will become a 0.5 acre-foot of DMI rights. One acre-foot of Class B water rights, when converted to DMI use, will become a 0.4 acre-foot of DMI rights. *See* 30 Tex. Admin. Code § 303.43(1). Once converted, these irrigation or mining rights are to be allocated water from the United States' share of reservoir storage on an equal basis with any domestic, municipal, and industrial right recognized in *Hidalgo County*. *See* 30 Tex. Admin. Code § 303.43(2).

The logic of these ratios derives from the fact that within the Amistad-Falcon system balances in the water accounts for DMI are replenished on a priority basis, whereas Class A and Class B rights are not. The United States' share of water in storage is limited by treaty and by the arid climate of the Southwest, so a change in priority must be accounted for by a decrease in the amount of water that the holder of a converted water right is authorized to take.

In addition to these conversion rules, water rights in the Lower and Middle Rio Grande that have a call on water from storage in Amistad and Falcon reservoirs are subject to a number of specific procedures relating to the sale of a water right or the sale of annual water allocations under a water right ("contractual sales"). *See* 30 Tex. Admin. Code §§ 303.51–.55 (relating to contract sales), 297.81–.83, 303.41, 303.71–.72 (applying to sales of water rights). If any changes to the water rights themselves are involved (e.g., change in use, change in authorized place of diversion or use), the TCEQ's general rules on amendments apply. *See* 30 Tex. Admin. Code ch. 297. Rules at 30 Texas Administrative Code sections 303.41–.44 may apply as well.

§ 14.17 Contrasting Situation for Water Rights Originating in the Upper Rio Grande and Rio Grande Tributaries

Water rights in the Upper Rio Grande and the tributaries of the Rio Grande are subject to supervision by the watermaster. *See* 30 Tex. Admin. Code §§ 303.11, 303.13, 303.23. Like water rights holders in the Lower and Middle Rio Grande, holders of rights in the Upper Rio Grande and Rio Grande tributaries must first file declarations of intent to divert water with the watermaster (although the conditions and limitations on these Upper Rio Grande and tributary declarations are not strict). *See* 30 Tex. Admin. Code § 303.11(b). Additionally, these water rights originating upstream of Amistad and Falcon reservoirs are not part of the weighted priorities system that governs water rights based on storage in the two international reservoirs. Instead, they are based on the prior appropriation system that applies in the rest of Texas. *See* 30 Tex. Admin. Code § 303.23(a).

Historically, there has been little guidance on the relationship between water rights in the Upper Rio Grande and tributaries and water rights tied to storage in Amistad and Falcon reservoirs. Transfers of water rights between the Middle Rio Grande (between Amistad and Falcon dams) and the Lower Rio Grande (below Falcon Dam) are allowed, but transfers of water rights out of the Lower and Middle Rio Grande have been prohibited by TCEQ rule at least since 1986. *See* 30 Tex. Admin. Code § 303.42(3); *see also* 11 Tex. Reg. 1815 (proposed rule Apr. 18, 1986), 11 Tex. Reg. 2890 (notice of adoption June 20, 1986).

TCEQ rules also provide that holders of water rights that are based in the Upper Rio Grande and tributaries essentially get first use of the water flowing through those portions of the Rio Grande Basin. Thereafter the remaining water is available to holders of water rights based in the Middle and Lower Rio Grande. *See* 30 Tex. Admin. Code § 303.23(a).

Transfers of diversion points or authorized places of use into the Middle or Lower Rio Grande from outside the Middle and Lower Rio Grande were not authorized until 2001 and were limited to transfers from the Upper Rio Grande (between Fort Quitman and Amistad Dam). *See* 30 Tex. Admin. Code § 303.42(4); *see also* 26 Tex. Reg. 920, 926 (proposed rule Jan. 26, 2001), 26 Tex. Reg. 3012, 3018 (notice of adoption Apr. 20, 2001).

The TCEQ's application of these transfer rules was the subject of one reported case. *See Brownsville Irrigation District v. Texas Commission on Environmental Quality*, 264 S.W.3d 458 (Tex. App.—Austin 2008, pet. denied). In *Brownsville Irrigation District*, the Austin court of appeals discussed the rules and upheld the TCEQ's application of a "conversion factor" to compensate for the effects of the transfer. 264 S.W.3d at 464.

VII. The Pecos River and Its Compact

§ 14.18 The River and Its Course

The Pecos River is a major tributary of the Rio Grande. It rises in the mountains east of Santa Fe, New Mexico, and runs through much of eastern New Mexico. The Pecos passes through Fort Sumner, Roswell, Artesia, and Carlsbad, New Mexico, before it enters Texas, forming the boundary between Reeves and Loving counties. In Texas, the Pecos flows southeast, emptying its waters into the Rio Grande at Amistad Reservoir, between Comstock and Langtry about thirty-eight miles northwest of Del Rio, Texas. The topography of the river valley ranges from mountain pastures in the north, with an elevation of more than 13,000 feet above sea level, to grasslands, semiarid irrigated farmlands, desert with sparse vegetation, and, in the lowermost reaches of the river, deep canyons. *See* Delmar J. Hayter, *The Handbook of Texas Online*, *Pecos River*, https://tshaonline.org/handbook/online/articles/rnp02. A map of the Pecos River appears in Figure 1.

§ 14.19 The Pecos River Compact

The Pecos River Compact was born of a controversy that began early in the twentieth century. In 1914, the U.S. Reclamation Service (the precursor to the U.S. Bureau of Reclamation) issued a report on the state of irrigated agriculture in Texas that indicated agriculture in the Pecos Valley of Texas was on the rise, but that it was becoming increasingly risky because there were two dams on the Pecos upstream in New Mexico (i.e., Avalon and McMillan dams, between Carlsbad and Roswell, New Mexico) and a third dam was being contemplated. *See* G. Emlen Hall, *High and Dry: The Texas–New Mexico Struggle for the Pecos River* 38–39 (University of New Mexico Press 2003). Accounts vary; some say Texas threatened to sue New Mexico for equitable apportionment and made efforts to block federal funding for the third dam in New Mexico. Hall, at 38–39. Other accounts say Texas and New Mexico were encouraged by the successful completion of negotiations on the Colorado River Compact in 1922. Paul Elliott, *Texas' Interstate Water Compacts*, 17 St. Mary's L.J. 1241, 1253 (1986). In any event, the legislatures of both states authorized a commission to negotiate a compact for the Pecos River in 1923, and a compact was negotiated in 1924. Elliott, at 1253.

The 1924 compact provided that New Mexico could irrigate 76,000 acres of farmland between Santa Rosa, New Mexico, and the Texas state line, and it placed restrictions on the construction of additional reservoirs in New Mexico. At the same time, it authorized Texas to construct Red Bluff Reservoir near the New Mexico state line and irrigate 40,000 acres of farmland. The compact was negotiated and signed in 1924, and the Texas legislature approved it. Elliott, at 1253. However, the New Mexico legislature insisted on adding provisions that guaranteed some reservoir storage in the Upper Pecos Valley of New Mexico. This reportedly caused controversy within New Mexico between

Carlsbad-area farmers and water users in the Upper Pecos Valley. The governor of New Mexico, finding no consensus within his state, vetoed his legislature's approval of the compact. Hall, at 39–40.

The 1930s were not free of controversy, as battles in Congress ensued over the funding of a third dam in New Mexico. Attempts were made to resolve the dispute through an agreement with the Reclamation Service to which Texas and New Mexico were also parties. The agreement was ratified by Texas but not by New Mexico. New Mexico reportedly did curtail groundwater withdrawal in the Roswell area. *See Texas v. New Mexico*, 462 U.S. 554, 557 n.3 (1983). By that time, groundwater production in New Mexico near Roswell was beginning to have a significant impact on the Pecos River.

The controversies of the 1930s were followed by negotiations on the current Pecos River Compact, which began in 1945 and were completed in 1948. The compact was approved by Congress in 1949. Act of Jan. 3, 1949, ch. 184, 63 Stat. 159. See also section 14.5 above.

§ 14.19:1 Language of the Pecos River Compact

The Pecos River Compact is codified in Texas Water Code section 42.010. The compact does not expressly limit the number of acres irrigated with surface water as the 1924 compact did. Instead, it restricts depletion of flow in the Pecos beyond conditions that prevailed on the river in 1947. *See* Hall, at 40–41.

Article III, which is the heart of the Pecos River Compact, provides that New Mexico may not "deplete by man's activities the flow of the Pecos River at the New Mexico-Texas state line below an amount which will give to Texas a quantity of water equivalent to that available to Texas under the 1947 condition." The compact defines "deplete by man's activities" as any "beneficial consumptive uses of water within the Pecos River Basin," but it does not include reductions in river flow due to "encroachment of salt cedars" or "deterioration of the channel of the stream." *See* Tex. Water Code § 42.010, art. II(e).

The "1947 condition" is based on the engineering studies performed by the engineering advisory committee to the compact negotiators. The engineering advisors studied records of conditions on the Pecos River starting in 1905 and performed a set of water routing studies, showing the Pecos under six different conditions, including a simulation of water use and water supply conditions in 1947. The advisors also drafted the *Manual of Inflow-Outflow Methods of Measuring Changes in Stream-Flow Depletion*. Derived from data in the 1947 study, it was to be used in determining how much water Texas should expect to receive over a given period for any particular level of precipitation, under the consumption conditions prevailing in New Mexico in 1947. The compact negotiators approved the engineering advisory committee report on December 3, 1948. *See Texas v. New Mexico*, 462 U.S. 554, 557–59 (1983); S. Doc. No. 109, 81st Cong., 1st Sess. (1949); Pecos River Compact (codified at Tex. Water Code § 42.010, art. II(f), (g)).

The Pecos River Compact apportions water salvaged by conservation efforts and unappropriated floodwaters. *See* Tex. Water Code § 42.010, art. III(b)–(d), (f). The water salvage operations contemplated were primarily removal of phreatophytes, such as salt cedar, commonly found along the Lower Pecos in New Mexico and the Upper Pecos in Texas.

The compact creates the Pecos River Commission, which is made up of a Texas commissioner, a New Mexico commissioner, and a nonvoting federal commissioner. The commission is authorized to establish and maintain gauging stations, engage in studies of the Pecos River, collect data, and analyze data from the Pecos. The commission is also authorized to make findings on water deliveries, water salvage, and water not consumed beneficially. Tex. Water Code § 42.010, art. V(d). Notably, the commission may also "make findings on any change in depletion by man's activities." Tex. Water Code § 42.010, art. V(d)(5).

§ 14.19:2 Operations under the Pecos River Compact

The controversy between Texas and New Mexico did not end with the ratification and approval of the compact in 1948–49. It was almost immediately apparent that the engineering studies on which the compact apportionment was based did not reflect the reality on the Pecos River. Stateline flows were regularly below the levels predicted in the engineering studies, with no explanation. In 1957, the Pecos River Commission authorized a "Review of Basic Data" by its engineering advisors to try to reconcile differences. The result, reported in the early 1960s, indicated that New Mexico had fallen short in its water deliveries to Texas from 1951 to 1960 by approximately 53,000 acre-feet, far less than would have been the result had the original inflow-outflow method been used. This led to an impasse within the Pecos River Commission, which in turn resulted in Texas filing a lawsuit against New Mexico in 1974. *See Texas v. New Mexico*, 462 U.S. 554, 562–63 (1983).

The U.S. Supreme Court did several things in *Texas v. New Mexico* that affect Pecos River Compact operations to this day. Foremost among them, the Court refused to adopt a method of calculating New Mexico's water delivery obligations to Texas that it deemed wholly inconsistent with the intent of the compact framers, based on the idea that the Court was limited in its actions by the intent of the compact. However, the Court did hold that an alternative method within the contemplation of the compact framers would be within its authority to adopt. *Texas v. New Mexico*, 462 U.S. at 571–76. An alternative method, embodied in the *River Master's Manual*, mentioned below, is in use today. Second, although the Court declined to assume full control over compact management, it did determine that a special master called a "River Master" could be appointed to perform the ministerial duty of calculating New Mexico's annual delivery obligations. *See Texas v. New Mexico*, 482 U.S. 124, 134 (1987).

The Pecos River Commission remains the agency designated to administer the Pecos River Compact, but since the 1980s water accounting on the Pecos River has been conducted by a special master, the "Pecos River Master," appointed by the U.S. Supreme Court. The procedures prescribed for the river master to produce the annual accounting, including a comment period for the two states, are outlined in the Supreme Court's "Amended Decree." *Texas v. New Mexico*, 485 U.S. 388 (1988) (per curiam). On May 15 of each year, the river master submits his or her calculations for New Mexico's water delivery obligations for the previous calendar year to Texas and New Mexico in the form of a "preliminary report." The two states have until June 15 to review and reply to the calculations. The river master's "final report" is due July 1. Either state may seek review of the river master's report by the Supreme Court within thirty days of its adoption, but only on a showing that the river master's conclusions are "clearly erroneous." 485 U.S. at 393. The equations used by the river master (i.e., the replacement for the old inflow-outflow method adopted in 1948) are contained in a *River Master's Manual*, available from the TCEQ. A procedure is established in the amended decree for amending the manual. *See* 485 U.S. at 392.

§ 14.19:3 Litigation under the Pecos River Compact

In September and October 2014, the remnants of Tropical Storm Odile resulted in widespread heavy rainfall in the Pecos River Basin in New Mexico and Texas. To control the heavy rainfall and resulting flood, the Bureau of Reclamation impounded water in Brantley Reservoir in New Mexico through October 2015. After a few months New Mexico released the water, but in the interim, some of the water had evaporated. The river master's final determinations for Water Years (WY) 2014 and 2015 did not apportion evaporative losses from the floodwater in Brantley Reservoir. After efforts to negotiate a mutually acceptable accounting for WYs 2014 and 2015 failed, in 2018 New Mexico filed a motion with the river master to modify his final determinations to apportion all evaporative losses from floodwater to Texas in WYs 2014 and 2015. The river master granted New Mexico's motion in part, apportioning most of the losses to Texas.

In December 2018, Texas filed its Motion for Review of the River Master's Final Determination in the U.S. Supreme Court (Notion for Review). In its motion, Texas argued that New Mexico failed to timely challenge the final determinations and that the amended decree did not authorize the river master to extend the deadline for challenges to the determinations. *See* Motion for Review, at 14–26, *Texas v. New Mexico*, No. 65 ORG (U.S. Docketed Dec. 17, 2018). Texas also argued that the river master's modification violated the terms of the compact by apportioning evaporative losses to Texas under article XII, although the flood water was not used for a federal project in Texas. *See* Motion for Review, at 27–31.

In response, New Mexico urged that its motion was timely and that the Court should uphold the river master's modification for equitable reasons, arguing that the Bureau of Reclamation held the water for Texas at its request and that Texas agreed to bear evaporative losses for this storage. *See* State of New Mexico's Response to Texas's Motion for Review of the River Master's Final Determination, at 15–18, Texas v. New Mexico, No. 65 ORG (U.S. Docketed Feb. 22, 2019). In its reply, Texas disputed New Mexico's characterization of events and urged that such actions would be insufficient to override the governing provisions of the compact. *See* Reply Brief for Plaintiff, Texas v. New Mexico, No. 65 ORG (U.S. Docketed Apr. 26, 2019).

In an opinion authored by Justice Kavanaugh in December 2020, the Court issued its decision. *See Texas v. New Mexico*, 141 S. Ct. 509, 511–12 (2020). The Court considered what it determined to be a straightforward question—whether under the Pecos River Compact, New Mexico should receive delivery credit for evaporated water even though that water was not delivered to Texas. The Court determined that it should. The Court turned to the *River Master's Manual*, which provided "[w]hen water is stored in New Mexico 'at the request of Texas,' then New Mexico's delivery obligation 'will be reduced by the amount of reservoir losses attributable to its storage.'" 141 S. Ct. at 511–12. The water under consideration was stored in New Mexico at Texas's request, and so, in accordance with the manual's language, New Mexico's delivery obligation should be reduced by the amount of evaporation during that storage. The Court agreed with the river master's award of credit to New Mexico and denied Texas's motion for review. 141 S. Ct. at 511–12.

VIII. The Canadian River and Its Compact

§ 14.20 The River and Its Course

The Canadian River crosses from New Mexico west of Amarillo, flows eastward and northward through the Texas Panhandle, and into Oklahoma. The North Canadian is a northern tributary that flows from New Mexico into northern Texas, and then into Oklahoma, where it flows southeast to meet with the main stem of the river. *See* Hobart Huson, *The Handbook of Texas Online*, *Canadian River*, https://tshaonline.org/handbook/online/articles/rnc02. Palo Duro Creek and Wolf Creek are tributaries of the North Canadian in Texas. A map of the Canadian River Basin appears in Figure 2.

§ 14.21 The Canadian River Compact

After planning began for Sanford Dam to serve as a surface water reservoir on the river's main stem, the Canadian River Compact was established. The intention was to alleviate dependency on pumping water, to provide additional flood protection, and to store water for municipal and industrial uses. The communities lobbied for a compact on the river to define the rights of each state to the use of Canadian River water. The Canadian River Compact resulted. Paul Elliott, *Texas' Interstate Water Compacts*, 17 St. Mary's L.J. 1241, 1261 (1986).

Thus, the compact expressly states that one of its purposes is to "make secure and protect present developments within the States." Tex. Water Code § 43.006, art. I. Unlike compacts such as those on the Rio Grande and the Pecos, the Canadian River Compact does not expressly require a state to deliver a particular amount of water to the downstream state. Rather, the language of the compact addresses the uses a state may make of its Canadian River water. *See* Tex. Water Code § 42.006, arts. IV–VI.

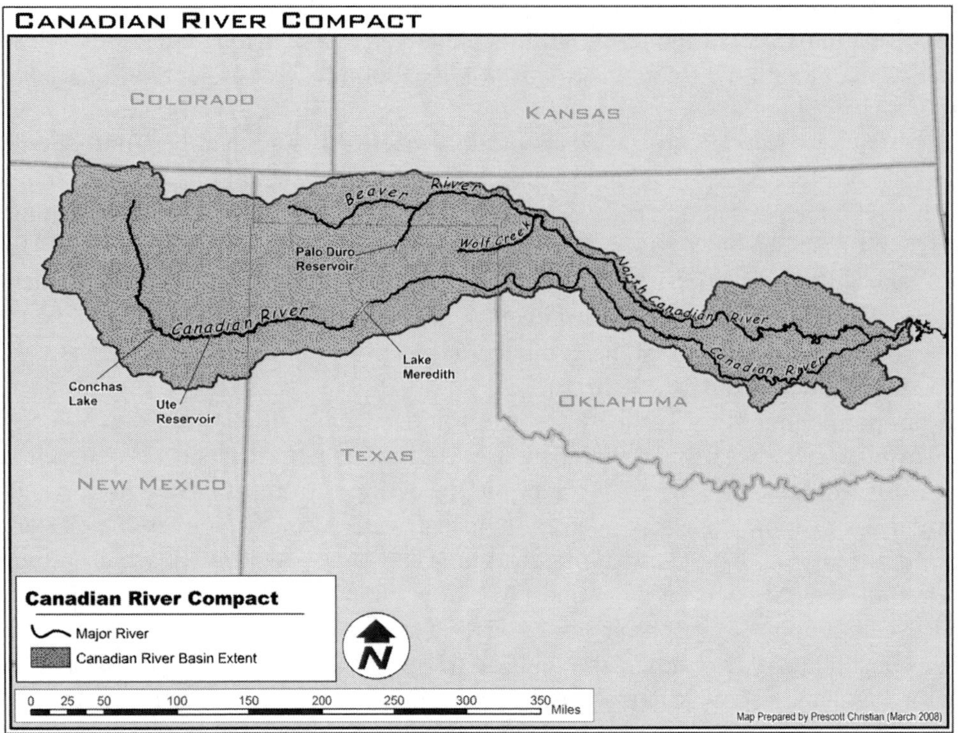

Figure 2. The Canadian River Compact, Courtesy Prescott Christian, Texas Commission on Environmental Quality.

§ 14.21:1 Language of the Canadian River Compact

The Canadian River Commission administers the Canadian River Compact. Each state designates or appoints a commissioner. The president of the United States is asked to designate a fourth commissioner, who serves as the presiding officer but has no right to vote on any deliberations before the commission. All commissioners from the states must be present for the commission to conduct business, and a unanimous vote is required for any actions taken by the commission. *See* Tex. Water Code § 43.006, art. IX(a).

The core of the Canadian River Compact is the establishment of allowed uses. Rights to water perfected by beneficial use are protected. *See* Tex. Water Code § 43.006, art. III. For Oklahoma, as the downstream state, the compact is simple—it is entitled to free and unrestricted use of all Canadian waters in the state. *See* Tex. Water Code § 43.006, art. VI. New Mexico and Texas have limitations on the amount of conservation storage. "Conservation storage" is defined as that portion available for domestic, municipal, irrigation, and industrial uses, and exempts water allocated to flood control, power production, and sediment control. Tex. Water Code § 43.006, art. II(d).

New Mexico has free and unrestricted use of all water upstream of Conchas Dam. *See* Tex. Water Code § 43.006, art. IV(a). Below Conchas Dam, New Mexico's free and unrestricted use of the Canadian River is subject to a limitation on conservation storage of no more than 200,000 acre-feet. *See* Tex. Water Code § 43.006, art. IV(b). On the North Canadian, New Mexico may store only water that is unappropriated in accordance with New Mexico and Oklahoma law. *See* Tex. Water Code § 43.006, art. IV(c).

Texas's free and unrestricted use is subject to two main limitations:

1. Texas may impound water on the North Canadian only for municipal uses, household and domestic uses, livestock watering, and the irrigation of lands for providing food and feed for those living on the land. *See* Tex. Water Code § 43.006, art. V(a).

2. On the main stem of the Canadian, Texas may impound up to 500,000 acre-feet, until Oklahoma provides more than 300,000 acre-feet of conservation storage, in which case Texas would be limited to 200,000 acre-feet plus whatever amount Oklahoma has stored.

See Tex. Water Code § 43.006, art. V(b).

The compact also sets out the remedy if Texas impounds any amount greater than specified. *See* Tex. Water Code § 43.006, art. V(c). However, the compact authorizes the commission to permit New Mexico and Texas to impound more water, provided that no state is deprived of water needed for beneficial use. *See* Tex. Water Code § 43.006, art. VII.

§ 14.21:2 Operations under the Canadian River Compact: Oklahoma and Texas vs. New Mexico—The Canadian Litigation

In the 1980s, litigation resulted after Texas and Oklahoma had a dispute with New Mexico concerning the compact's article IV(a) and (b). *See Oklahoma v. New Mexico*, 501 U.S. 221 (1991). Article IV(a) gives New Mexico free and unrestricted use of all waters originating in the Canadian River's drainage basin above Conchas Dam; article IV(b) gives the state free and unrestricted use of waters originating in the drainage basin below Conchas Dam, subject to a conservation storage limitation of 200,000 acre-feet. *See* Tex. Water Code § 43.006, art. IV(a), (b). Before the compact was negotiated and approved by the three states, Texas sought to build Sanford Dam for the purpose of serving the municipal and industrial requirements of eleven cities in the Texas Panhandle region. *Oklahoma v. New Mexico*, 501 U.S. at 224–25. New Mexico proposed that the Sanford Project could not be constructed until the compact was approved. 501 U.S. at 226. After the compact was approved, the Sanford Dam and its companion Lake Meredith were completed in 1964. Before completion, however, New Mexico built Ute Dam and Reservoir upstream of Sanford Dam, with a capacity of 109,600 acre-feet. Later, in the early 1980s, New Mexico enlarged Ute Reservoir, increasing its capacity to 272,800 acre-feet. However, a portion of this was occupied by silt and not available for storing water. 501 U.S. at 226. Initially, Texas and Oklahoma sued New Mexico over the enlargement of the Ute Reservoir, complaining that its storage capacity violated the 200,000-acre-foot limitation in article IV(b). 501 U.S. at 227. Later, the Canadian River above Conchas Dam flooded, water spilled over the Conchas Dam, and Ute Reservoir caught the majority of the spill water. Texas and Oklahoma added a complaint that the spill water was subject to the limitation. 501 U.S. at 227.

The Supreme Court found that the article IV(b) limitation applied to stored water, not the physical reservoir capacity. 501 U.S. at 230–31. However, the Court agreed with Texas and Oklahoma that waters originating in the Canadian River Basin above Conchas Dam but reaching the mainstream of the river below Conchas due to being spilled or released was subject to the limitation if it was impounded in Ute Dam or other downstream dams in New Mexico. 501 U.S. at 232. The Court considered documents showing that the building of Sanford Dam was based in part on the assumption that it would be entitled to runoff between Conchas Dam and Sanford Dam, subject to the 200,000-acre-foot limitation. 501 U.S. at 237–38. New Mexico's contention that it was entitled, without limitation, to any water originating above Conchas Dam, but flowing into Ute Reservoir, would have had a serious effect on the viability of the Sanford Dam Project. 501 U.S. at 239.

§ 14.21:3 Operations under the Canadian River Compact: Palo Duro Reservoir

More recently, the state of Oklahoma has complained at annual Canadian River Commission meetings that Texas is in violation of the compact as a result of the construction of Palo Duro Reservoir. The reservoir was constructed by the Palo Duro River Authority on Palo Duro Creek in Hansford County, Texas, about ten miles north of Spearman, Texas, and approximately twelve miles from the Texas-Oklahoma border. Members of the Palo Duro River Authority are the counties of Hansford and Moore and the city of Stinnet. The reservoir began impounding water in 1991.

The Palo Duro River Authority originally constructed the reservoir to impound water to be made available for municipal uses. As mentioned above, article V of the compact allows Texas to impound any water on the North Canadian River in Texas "for municipal uses, for household and domestic uses, livestock watering, and the irrigation of lands which are cultivated solely for the purpose of providing food and feed for the households and domestic livestock actually living or kept on the property." Tex. Water Code § 43.006, art. V(a). In addition to other contentions, Oklahoma has claimed that water is currently impounded for recreational use in violation of the compact. Texas contends that the reservoir is within the terms of the compact. In the early 1990s, the two states met to discuss the issues surrounding Palo Duro Reservoir. In 2001, Oklahoma's legislature adopted a resolution asking the Oklahoma attorney general to sue the State of Texas regarding this matter. S. Con. Res. 18, 48th Leg., 1st Reg. Sess. (Okla. 2001). No litigation has been filed to date.

IX. The Red River and Its Compact

§ 14.22 The Red River and Its Course

The Red River begins in New Mexico and flows eastward across the Texas Panhandle until it forms the boundary between the states of Texas and Oklahoma. The river becomes the state line between Texas and Arkansas at the northeastern corner of Texas. It enters into Arkansas, continues eastward, then flows southeast to enter Louisiana, where it continues in a southeasterly direction across the state. These four states are the signatory states to the Red River Compact. *See* Diana J. Kleiner, *The Handbook of Texas Online*, *Red River*, https://tshaonline.org/handbook/online/articles/rnr01. A map of the Red River Basin appears in Figure 3.

The compact defines "Red River" to be the stream below the crossing of the Texas-Oklahoma state boundary at longitude 100 degrees west. Tex. Water Code § 46.013, art. III, § 3.01(b). The "Red River Basin" is all of the drainage areas of the Red River and its tributaries east of the New Mexico-Texas border and above its junction with the Atchafalaya and Old Rivers in Louisiana. Tex. Water Code § 46.013, art. III, § 3.01(c).

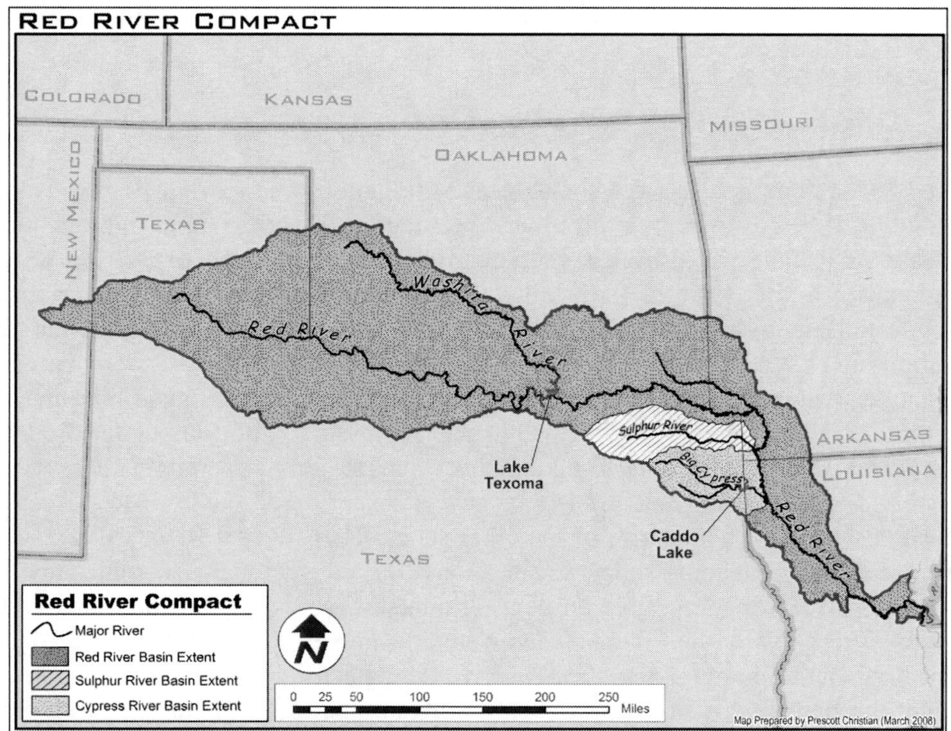

Figure 3. The Red River Compact. Courtesy Prescott Christian, Texas Commission on Environmental Quality.

§ 14.23 The Red River Compact

The Red River Compact is Texas's most recent interstate stream compact. Its creation was prompted by the drought of the 1950s, with the first negotiations occurring in 1956. Twenty years later, Texas and Oklahoma reached an agreement concerning the apportionment of water in the watershed above Denison Dam in Grayson County, and the compact was finally negotiated. Paul Elliott, *Texas' Interstate Water Compacts*, 17 St. Mary's L.J. 1241, 1267, 1273 (1986).

§ 14.23:1 Language of the Red River Compact

The Red River Compact is administered by the Red River Compact Commission, which is composed of two representatives from each state (Arkansas, Louisiana, Oklahoma, and Texas) and one representative appointed by the president of the United States. Tex. Water Code § 46.013, art. IX, § 9.01. The federal commissioner is the chair but does not have the right to vote. Tex. Water Code § 46.013, art. IX, § 9.01. The executive director of the TCEQ or a designated member of the agency serves as one of the commissioners for Texas.

Representatives from three states constitute a quorum for commission meetings. Action concerned with administration of the compact requires six concurring votes; action that affects existing water rights in a state requires eight concurring votes. Tex. Water Code § 46.013, art. IX, § 9.03.

The compact defines five reaches of the Red River, spanning from west to east, and additionally sets out subbasins in some of the reaches. Water flows in the subbasins are apportioned to the states in differing percentages. *See* Tex. Water Code § 46.013, arts. IV–VIII. If a reach or subbasin is entirely in one state, that state has free and unrestricted use of that water. *See, e.g.*, Tex. Water Code § 46.013, art.

IV, §§ 4.03(b), 8.01. There is no requirement in the compact to conduct any sort of accounting of each state's use of water on the Red River, unless an affected state deems an accounting necessary. *See* Tex. Water Code § 46.013, art. II, § 2.11.

§ 14.23:2 Litigation Relating to the Compact

The Red River Compact has been the subject of litigation. The Tarrant Regional Water District ("Tarrant Regional"), a Texas conservation and reclamation district, sought authorization from the State of Oklahoma to take water from some streams in Oklahoma and export the water to Texas. Tarrant Regional also filed suit in the United States District Court for the Western District of Oklahoma against the members of the Oklahoma Water Resources Board and Oklahoma Conservation Storage Commission ("Oklahoma"), seeking to enjoin Oklahoma officials from enforcing certain Oklahoma statutes that prohibited or restricted water export out of the state. Tarrant Regional first argued that article 5.05 of the Red River Compact, addressing a portion of the Red River Basin identified as Reach II, Subbasin 5, gave all signatory states rights to certain Subbasin 5 waters that were not used by Oklahoma, and that article 5.05 gave states or parties authorized by them the right to obtain that water within the boundaries of the other states. This, Tarrant Regional argued, meant that the Compact preempted Oklahoma's export restrictions. Tarrant Regional also argued that Oklahoma's export restrictions placed impermissible burdens on interstate commerce in water that Oklahoma was not using under article 5.05 of the Compact, and were thus unconstitutional. *See* U.S. Const. art. I, § 8, cl. 3. Tarrant Regional also argued that the Red River Compact preempted Oklahoma law. Oklahoma responded that the Red River Compact expressly provided that the signatory states had unrestricted control over water within their boundaries and that the Compact did not authorize other states to cross state boundaries to obtain water. By approving the Compact, Oklahoma argued, Congress had given its consent to the states' imposing commercial restrictions on the water so apportioned.

The district court agreed with Oklahoma's position and granted summary judgment in favor of Oklahoma. *Tarrant Regional Water District v. Herrmann*, No. CIV-07-0045-HE, 2009 WL 3922803 (W.D. Okla. Nov. 18, 2009). The Tenth Circuit Court of Appeals affirmed the district court's ruling. *Tarrant Regional Water District v. Herrmann*, 656 F.3d 1222 (10th Cir. 2011). The U.S. Supreme Court affirmed the Tenth Circuit's decision, holding that the Compact did not authorize the signatory states to cross each other's boundaries and that all waters of the Red River had been apportioned, so there was no violation of the Commerce Clause. 133 S. Ct. 2120 (2013).

The City of Hugo, Oklahoma, filed a lawsuit based on similar Commerce Clause claims in the United States District Court for the Eastern District of Oklahoma. The City of Irving, Texas, intervened in the case based on a water supply contract it had with the City of Hugo. The district court granted summary judgment for Oklahoma in this case as well. *City of Hugo v. Nichols*, No. CIV-08-303-JTM, 2010 WL 1816345 (E.D. Okla. Apr. 30, 2010). On appeal, the Tenth Circuit held that the City of Hugo lacked standing to bring its case against the State of Oklahoma. *City of Hugo v. Nichols*, 656 F.3d 1251, 1255–57 (10th Cir. 2011), *cert. denied sub nom. City of Hugo v. Buchanan*, 132 S. Ct. 1744 (2012). The court also held that the City of Irving could not sustain an action because its claims were based solely on a contract with the City of Hugo, which had no standing to sue the Oklahoma defendants. Therefore, the court determined, the City of Irving's claims were not redressable. *Nichols*, 656 F.3d at 1263–65. The court of appeals remanded the case to the district court to be dismissed for want of jurisdiction. *Nichols*, 656 F.3d at 1265.

X. The Sabine River and Its Compact

§ 14.24 The River and Its Course

Texas and Louisiana share the Sabine River. The river rises east of Dallas and flows southeasterly until the southeastern corner of Panola County, where the river forms the boundary between Texas and Louisiana. The river empties into Sabine Lake, which ultimately drains into the Gulf of Mexico. *See* Christopher Long, *The Handbook of Texas Online*, *Sabine River*, https://tshaonline.org/handbook/online/articles/rns03. The Sabine River Compact covers the "Stateline reach," which is that portion of the river from the point where its downstream waters first touch both Texas and Louisiana, defined as the "Stateline," until the river enters into Sabine Lake. *See* Tex. Water Code § 44.010, art. I(a), (d). A map of the Sabine River Basin appears in Figure 4.

§ 14.25 The Sabine River Compact

Local water users in both Texas and Louisiana had competing claims to the Sabine River. These claims included a dispute over the political boundary between the states. In 1949, a former Louisiana governor claimed that Louisiana owned the Sabine River along its length between the states. The local water users finally agreed on the need for a compact to apportion the waters. Paul Elliott, *Texas' Interstate Water Compacts*, 17 St. Mary's L.J. 1241, 1263–64 (1986).

The Sabine River Compact is administered by the Sabine River Compact Administration, made up of two members from each state, with all members appointed by their respective governor, and one ex-officio chair appointed by the president of the United States. The chair cannot vote and cannot be a resident of either state. *See* Tex. Water Code § 44.010, art. VIII(a), (b). The Louisiana members are required to be residents of the Sabine Watershed. Three members from the states constitute a quorum, and any commission action requires three votes. *See* Tex. Water Code § 44.010, art. VII(c).

All free water in the Stateline reach is divided equally between Texas and Louisiana. *See* Tex. Water Code § 44.010, art. V(a). Each state must use its apportionment of the natural stream flows as they occur, and there is a prohibition against accruing any credits or debits. *See* Tex. Water Code § 44.010, art. V(g). Each state has the right to use the main channel of the Sabine River to convey stored water, without any loss of ownership of the stored water. *See* Tex. Water Code § 44.010, art. V(e). Neither state can construct a dam in the Stateline reach without the other state's consent. *See* Tex. Water Code § 44.010, art. V(g). Additionally, domestic and stock water uses are not subject to any apportionment under the terms of the compact. *See* Tex. Water Code § 44.010, art. V(j).

In the compact, both states expressly recognize the necessity of maintaining a minimum flow at the state line for the benefit of water users below the state line. The compact sets out limitations that require a minimum flow of thirty-six cubic feet per second. Reservoirs and permits above the state line as of January 1, 1953, are not liable for the maintenance of the flow. Both states agree that after January 1, 1953, no state will authorize any additional uses that would have the effect of reducing the flow at the state line to less than thirty-six cubic feet per second. *See* Tex. Water Code § 44.010, art. V(b).

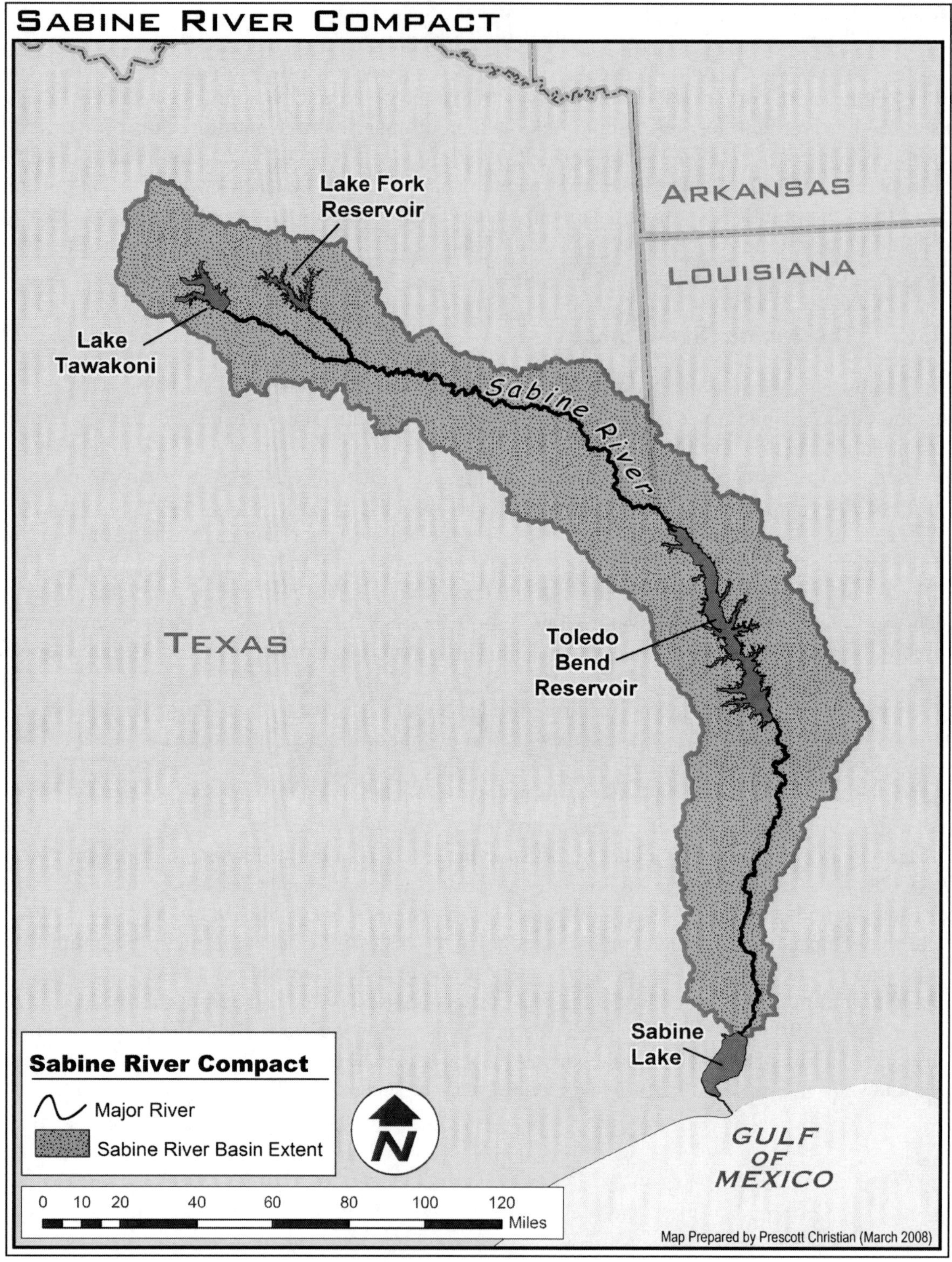

Figure 4. The Sabine River Compact. Courtesy Prescott Christian, Texas Commission on Environmental Quality.

XI. Conclusion

§ 14.26 Conclusion

The border and interstate streams of Texas reflect a variety of laws relating to the administration of water rights. Each system of laws is unique to each individual stream, depending on where the stream is located and the compacts and treaties that govern the stream. Practitioners should take care to consider the impact of these different systems on surface water, and even groundwater, transactions in interstate and international river basins.

CHAPTER 15

Surface Water Rights Transactions

Edmond R. McCarthy, Jr.,[1] Lynn Ray Sherman,[2] and Derek Seal[3]

I. Introduction

§ 15.1 Introduction

The continued development of new water supplies and the expansion, modification, and reprioritizing of existing water resources are critical to the future of Texas. The state's population is expected to grow approximately 73 percent, from 29.7 million in 2020 to 51.5 million by 2070. Texas Water Development Board, *Water for Texas 2022* 3, 6 fig. ES.2 (2022), www.twdb.texas.gov/waterplanning/swp/2022/index.asp [hereinafter 2022 State Water Plan]. During this same time period, Texas's existing water supplies are projected to decrease by approximately 18 percent, with a two percent loss in surface water supply due to sedimentation in reservoirs. 2022 State Water Plan, at 3 (Executive Summary "Quick Facts"), 7, 77. The State Water Plan predicts a 32 percent reduction in available groundwater supplies in this same time period. 2022 State Water Plan, at 7. According to the State Water Plan, these decreases in groundwater availability are due to three factors: (1) a reduced supply from the Ogallala Aquifer caused by long-term depletion, (2) mandatory reductions in pumping from the Gulf Coast Aquifer to prevent subsidence; and (3) policy decisions made through the Groundwater Management Area (GMA) so-called "joint planning process" to adopt their respective "desired future conditions." 2022 State Water Plan, at 7.

Due in part to population growth, water use will increase in all sectors. Total water needs are projected to grow by approximately 120 percent by the year 2070, from 3.1 million to 6.9 million acre-feet per year. 2022 State Water Plan, at 8. Of that total, municipal demand growth represents 46 percent, or an additional 3.1 million acre-feet per year. 2022 State Water Plan, at 8.

The reallocation of existing water supplies through wholesale water transactions and transfers of water rights by sale or lease are methods to address Texas's changing water needs. Under Texas law,

---

1. Ed McCarthy is a partner with McCarthy & McCarthy LLP. He has worked with water and water quality related issues for almost forty years. He has authored numerous articles on the subject and is a coauthor in two chapters of the Environmental Law, Texas Practice Series. He has also served on the committee responsible for the publication of the State Bar *Texas Real Estate Forms Manual*, and currently serves as the chair of that committee. His representation on water-related matters includes transactional, litigation, permitting and related administrative matters, and lobbying.

2. Lynn Sherman is recognized as a foremost authority on water rights and water transactions. He has been an award-winning author on water issues, an executive of Sustainable Water Resources, President of WaterTexas, an executive with the Lower Colorado River Authority, and a partner with the Bickerstaff law firm.

3. Derek L. Seal is a partner with McGinnis Lochridge L.L.P. He has over twenty years of regulatory and legislative experience as a former General Counsel of the Texas Commission on Environmental Quality and as a former General Counsel of the House Committee on Environmental Regulation in the Texas legislature.

supplying water pursuant to a water supply contract is distinguished from the conveyance or other transfer of either a surface water right or a groundwater right. This chapter discusses the transfer of rights in surface water by sale or lease. Surface water permitting is addressed in Chapter 10 of this book, and Chapter 18 covers transactions involving groundwater rights. Chapter 31 addresses the financing of water supply projects, and Chapter 38 discusses acquisition of water supplies by governmental entities through the exercise of eminent domain.

Surface water rights, whether evidenced by a permit or a certificate of adjudication, are treated as real property rights in Texas. Accordingly, major issues and practical considerations involved in real property transactions involving the sale or lease of permitted surface water rights are considered in this chapter. The history of Texas's prior appropriation system for surface water is discussed more fully in Chapter 4 of this book. This chapter summarizes the law of real property ownership rights of those appropriative surface water rights, describing and comparing the primary methods for conveying or acquiring surface water rights by purchase or lease. For an in-depth discussion of the history of the Texas water rights system, see Chapter 4 of this book. Due diligence considerations also are explored, followed by sections describing key issues in purchases and leases of both surface water as a commodity and the water rights themselves. Finally, this chapter discusses the Texas Water Bank and Water Trust.

II. Ownership of Surface Water Rights

§ 15.2 Introduction

The ownership of surface water is defined in terms of "state water." Although the terms "state water" and "surface water" do not refer to exactly the same water, for the most part, surface water in Texas that formed in a "watercourse" is owned by the state and considered to be state water. There are a few exemptions, such as diffused surface water or rainfall runoff, which are privately owned until such time as the water flows into a watercourse.

"State water" is defined to include all "water of the ordinary flow, underflow, and tides of every flowing river, natural stream, and lake, and every bay or arm of the Gulf of Mexico, and the storm water, floodwater, and rainwater of every river, natural stream, canyon, ravine, depression, and watershed in the state." Tex. Water Code § 11.021(a). Thus, state water does include rainfall and spring flows once they have reached a watercourse or other surface water body. Additionally, state water includes water "imported from any source outside the boundaries of the state for use in the state." Tex. Water Code § 11.021(b).

As property of the state, the use of state water is regulated by the state. *See, e.g.*, *Texas Water Rights Commission v. Wright*, 464 S.W.2d 642 (Tex. 1971). The authority to regulate this natural resource is reposed in the Texas legislature pursuant to Article XVI, § 59 of the Texas Constitution. *City of Pleasanton v. City of Corpus Christi*, 276 S.W.2d 798, 802-03 (Tex. 1954); *see* Tex. Const. Art. XVI, § 59. The legislature has delegated the authority to regulate surface water to the Texas Commission on Environmental Quality (TCEQ). Tex. Water Code §§ 5.012–.013; 11.001–.561.

In general, Texas regulates its state water under the prior appropriations doctrine, and in that context it is commonly referred to as surface water. See *Texas Commission on Environmental Quality v. Texas Farm Bureau*, 460 S.W.3d 264, 266 (Tex. App.—Corpus Christi–Edinburg 2015, pet. denied). See Chapter 4 of this book for a discussion of the development and use of the prior appropriations doctrine and Chapter 10 for discussion of permitting issues.

Because surface water is owned by the state, to sell or lease surface water the seller or lessor must hold a valid water right. *See* Tex. Water Code §§ 11.081, 11.082, 11.084, 11.121. Although there are certain exemptions from permitting, to lawfully divert, store, or use the waters of the state for any nonexempt purpose, an individual or entity must first obtain a water right from the state. *See* Tex.

Water Code § 11.121; *cf.* Tex. Water Code §§ 11.142–.143 (related to permitting exemptions). Most of the following discussion addresses the unique considerations that arise when transferring an appropriated water right, or the right to use the water, although the overall transactional concepts could be applied to water rights exempted from permitting. The sale of an appropriated water right, whether or not it is tied to the sale of land, requires a change of ownership application and, under certain circumstances, a permit amendment. The sale of land that includes exempt surface water will not trigger the need for a filing with the TCEQ unless the buyer of the land plans to change the use of the exempt water to a nonexempt use. In the latter case, a permit for the nonexempt use of the water is required. For further discussion of water rights permitting and exemptions, see Chapter 10 of this book.

Texas currently grants surface water rights by permits issued by the TCEQ. Water rights issued before or through the water rights adjudication process initiated in the 1960s are evidenced by certified filings and certificates of adjudication. *See generally* Tex. Water Code §§ 11.301–.341. These historic forms of water rights continue to exist and may be amended to implement a sale or lease of the water rights. For ease of discussion, this chapter uses the generic term "water rights permit" to apply to all variations of state-issued water rights. *See* Tex. Water Code §§ 11.022, 11.023, 11.0235(a), 11.081, 11.082, 11.084, 11.121; *see also* Tex. Water Code §§ 11.323 ("certificates of adjudication"), 11.307 ("certified filings").

A water rights permit grants a usufructuary right or a "right of use," which authorizes the permittee to divert and use the water for specified beneficial purposes. *See In re Adjudication of the Water Rights of Upper Guadalupe Segment of Guadalupe River Basin*, 642 S.W.2d 438, 444–45 (Tex. 1982); *Wright*, 464 S.W.2d at 647–48; *see generally Lakeside Irrigation Co. v. Markham Irrigation Co.*, 285 S.W. 593, 596 (Tex. 1926); *Clark v. Briscoe Irrigation Co.*, 200 S.W.2d 674, 679 (Tex. App.—Austin 1974, no writ); Frank R. Booth, *Ownership of Developed Water: A Property Right Threatened*, 17 St. Mary's L.J. 1181, 1184–85, 1187–88 (1986); R. Lambeth Townsend, *Cancellation of Water Rights in Texas: Use It or Lose It*, 17 St. Mary's L.J. 1217, 1218 (1986).

A permittee—that is, the water right holder—does not hold title to the corpus of the water; that title remains in the state. *See South Texas Water Co. v. Bieri*, 247 S.W.2d 268, 272 (Tex. App.—Galveston 1952, writ ref'd n.r.e.); Wells A. Hutchins, *Texas Law of Water Rights* 77–81 (1966). Nevertheless, a permittee owns the water right and, upon its perfection, holds it as a vested property right against everyone except the state. *See* Tex. Water Code §§ 11.025–.027; *Board of Water Engineers v. McKnight*, 229 S.W. 301 (Tex. 1921); *Clark*, 200 S.W.2d at 677; *Guelker v. Hidalgo County Water Improvement District No. 6*, 269 S.W.2d 551 (Tex. App.—San Antonio 1954, writ ref'd n.r.e.); *Harrell v. F.H. Vahlsing, Inc.*, 248 S.W.2d 762 (Tex. App.—San Antonio 1952, writ ref'd n.r.e.). The measure of a perfected right under the prior appropriation doctrine is the maximum amount beneficially used, after reasonable development, pursuant to the appropriative claim. *See In re Contests of City of Eagle Pass, to the Adjudication of Water Rights in Middle Rio Grande Basin & Contributing Texas Tributaries*, 680 S.W.2d 853 (Tex. App.—Austin 1984, writ ref'd n.r.e.).

A water right can be bought, sold, assigned, or otherwise alienated by the water rights holder. *See Pfluger v. Clack*, 897 S.W.2d 956 (Tex. App.—Eastland 1995, writ denied). As against all others, the water right holder possesses a superior property right to use the water, including the right to lawfully dispose of and reuse it. *See Bieri*, 247 S.W.2d at 272; *McKnight*, 229 S.W. 301; *Hutchins*, at 77–81; *cf.* Tex. Water Code §§ 11.025–.027. The superior right of the water right holder, however, assumes that the water will be put to beneficial, nonwasteful use. *See In re Adjudication of the Water Rights of Upper Guadalupe Segment of Guadalupe River Basin*, 642 S.W.2d at 444–45; *Wright*, 464 S.W.2d at 647–48; *see generally Clark*, 200 S.W.2d at 679; *Lakeside Irrigation Co.*, 285 S.W. at 596; Tex. Water Code §§ 11.025, 11.134(b)(3)(A); Booth, at 1184–85, 1187–88; Townsend, at 1218.

As long as the water has been legally reduced to possession by the water right holder and remains under the control of the water right holder, the water right holder has the right to use and reuse the water, and thus to sell, assign, or otherwise alienate it as a commodity. *See Guelker*, 269 S.W.2d 551;

Bieri, 247 S.W.2d 268. Once the water right holder loses physical control of the water, for example, by allowing it to escape or otherwise return to a watercourse, unless the water right holder has secured authorization to use the bed and banks of the watercourse to transport the water for subsequent reuse (*see* Tex. Water Code § 11.042), the rights of the water right holder in that water are lost and the escaped water returns to the state and becomes available for reappropriation. *See Domel v. City of Georgetown*, 6 S.W.3d 349, 353 (Tex. App.—Austin 1999, pet. denied); *Bieri*, 247 S.W.2d 268; *cf. City of San Marcos v. Texas Commission on Environmental Quality*, 128 S.W.3d 264 (Tex. App.—Austin 2004, pet. denied).

The extent and duration of the superior rights of the water right holder in the appropriated water are defined by the terms of the water right permit. As discussed in greater detail below and Chapter 10 of this book, the water right permit states the annual maximum amount authorized for diversion and identifies the priority date. *See* Tex. Water Code § 11.141. The permit also designates the location of the authorized diversion point and establishes the authorized diversion rate in gallons per minute (gpm) or cubic feet per second (cfs). The permit identifies the authorized beneficial uses of the water, which are sometimes tied to use in a specific location. The permit may include provisions known as "special conditions," such as minimum stream flow restrictions or requirements for return flow that limit or otherwise restrict the use of the water authorized for diversion under the permit. *See* 30 Tex. Admin. Code §§ 297.41–.59. Finally, the permit identifies the term or duration of the water right. Permits may be obtained in perpetuity (*see* Tex. Water Code § 11.121), on a temporary basis (*see* Tex. Water Code § 11.138), or as a "term permit" (*see* Tex. Water Code § 11.1381). In addition, permits may be "seasonal" (*see* Tex. Water Code § 11.137) or for an "emergency" (*see* Tex. Water Code § 11.139).

III. Due Diligence in Conveying or Acquiring Surface Water Rights

§ 15.3 Introduction to Due Diligence

The two major types of transactions addressed in this chapter are the purchase and lease of surface water rights. The decision whether to purchase water under a wholesale water contract or whether to purchase or lease a water right can be driven by market demands, the parties' respective needs, and the water right itself. Location, priority, quantity, quality, reliability, and authorized uses, as well as special conditions, can all affect which type of transaction will be used.

Due diligence is arguably the most important step in a potential surface water rights purchase or lease. Although every project and transaction is unique, due diligence generally covers matters related to (1) the quality, quantity, and reliability of the water right; (2) whether an amendment to the water right will be required for development and use of the water or its location of use; and (3) other issues or circumstances that affect the economic or logistical feasibility of the intended project. Completion of due diligence will facilitate the evaluation of (1) whether to purchase or lease the water rights, (2) what the terms of the agreement will be, and (3) what consideration will be paid. Likewise, due diligence is important to the water rights holder who is considering how to establish marketable surface water rights.

Some of these due diligence matters should be addressed even before determining the most appropriate location and method for acquiring surface water rights (lease, sale, supply contract, or, if available, condemnation) and for drafting and negotiating the terms of the transaction. Other matters involve investigations and analysis that are most effectively and efficiently conducted during the pendency of the transaction—for example, during an option period. The following sections provide an overview of some common due diligence considerations in a surface water rights transaction.

§ 15.4 Regulatory Due Diligence

Many of the critical aspects of the planning and investigation underlying a surface water transaction involve the assessment of the subject water right. Because a surface water right is restricted to the terms of the water right permit, an amendment to the water right is generally required to address the specific needs of the purchaser. The restrictions on the water right will affect the prospective buyer's or lessee's development and use of the water right. Surface water rights are issued and administered by the (TCEQ) pursuant to Texas Water Code sections 5.012, 5.013, and 11.121. Regulatory due diligence is essentially a matter of TCEQ regulation. *See Texas Commission on Environmental Quality v. Texas Farm Bureau*, 460 S.W.3d 264, 266 (Tex. App.—Corpus Christi–Edinburg 2015, pet. denied). *See generally* 30 Tex. Admin. Code chs. 295, 297; *see also* Tex. Admin. Code ch. 281.

In those river basins subject to the jurisdiction of the state's watermaster programs, due diligence must include a visit with the watermaster's office. *See* Tex. Water Code §§ 11.325–.3291; 30 Tex. Admin. Code chs. 303, 304.

An initial step in the due diligence process should include a visit to the Central File Room of TCEQ headquarters in Austin to review the records associated with the water right(s) covered by the transaction. Information regarding the commission's headquarters can be obtained at www.tceq.texas.gov.

§ 15.4:1 The Water Right Permit

As currently authorized, what are the parameters of the water right included in the permit, certified filing, or certificate of adjudication? The due diligence analysis should include creating a summary description of the authorized water right that contains the following:

1. The annual maximum amount authorized for diversion, including any special conditions or other operating constraints imposed.

2. The priority date established in the water right. Under the doctrine of seniority or "first in time, first in right," each water right is assigned a specific priority date. *See* Tex. Water Code §§ 11.027, 11.141. During times of shortage, this system determines the allocation of water among appropriators from the same source of supply based on the water rights holders' respective priority dates. A senior right holder is entitled to exercise its right fully before junior right holders receive any water. *See* Tex. Water Code § 11.027; 30 Tex. Admin. Code § 297.44; *but see* Tex. Water Code § 11.053 (authorizing the TCEQ's executive director to suspend water rights diversions under drought conditions but exempt "junior rights" held by municipalities and electric generators); *see generally Texas Commission on Environmental Quality v. Texas Farm Bureau*, 460 S.W.3d 264, 266–68 (Tex. App.—Corpus Christi–Edinburg 2015, pet. denied) (holding the commission exceeded its legislative authority by adopting drought rules granting exemptions inconsistent with the priority of water rights established by section 11.027).

3. The location, with a map, identifying the authorized diversion point.

4. The authorized diversion rate in gallons per minute (gpm) or cubic feet per second (cfs), including any special conditions or other operating constraints.

5. The authorized beneficial uses of the water, including any special conditions or other operating constraints.

6. The areas or locations where the respective uses are authorized, including any special conditions or other operating constraints.

7. Any minimum stream flow restriction.

8. Any return flow or surplus water requirements.

9. The term or duration of the water right.

10. Environmental flow considerations that may be triggered by amending the water right. *See* Tex. Water Code §§ 11.1471–.1491; 30 Tex. Admin. Code ch. 298.

§ 15.4:2 Change of Ownership

Upon conveyance of a water right, an application must be filed with the TCEQ requesting transfer of the right to the new owner. *See* Texas Commission on Environmental Quality, *Surface Water Rights Change of Ownership Form* (form TCEQ-10204, rev. Sept. 1, 2017), www.tceq.texas.gov/assets/public/permitting/forms/10204.pdf. This change of ownership application is required to update the commission's records and is in addition to other recording obligations triggered by the conveyance. *See* Tex. Water Code § 11.136 (requiring recording of water right in county where the appropriation is authorized to be made). The application form must be accompanied by a recording fee of $100 payable to the commission. *See* 30 Tex. Admin. Code § 295.139(d). This application is to be used only for change of ownership and cannot be used to secure any other amendment to the water right. For a more in-depth discussion of requirements related to change of ownership and amendments to water rights, see Chapter 10 of this book.

§ 15.4:3 Amending the Water Right

In order to develop and use the water right, a determination must be made about whether the parameters of the existing water right need to be changed—for example, new or additional points of diversion, increases to the rate of diversion, or additional places and/or purposes of beneficial use may be necessary for the buyer's planned implementation of the acquired water right. Due diligence should include (i) an analysis of what changes to the water right, if any, will be needed and (ii) whether such changes will require an amendment. If an amendment is needed, the question whether notice and an opportunity for hearing will be required must be addressed. *See* Tex. Water Code § 11.122; *see generally* 30 Tex. Admin. Code §§ 295.151–.161 (TCEQ rules regarding notice); *see also City of Marshall v. City of Uncertain*, 206 S.W.3d 97, 110–11 (Tex. 2006). Impacts, if any, of application of environmental flow standards triggered by any required amendment to the water right should be considered too. *See* Tex. Water Code §§ 11.1471–.1491; 30 Tex. Admin. Code ch. 298.

Water Right Amendment Application: To change the place or purpose of use, point of diversion, rate of diversion, or acreage to be irrigated or otherwise alter an existing water right, the water right must be amended. An amendment application must be filed with the TCEQ. *See* Tex. Water Code § 11.122; *see generally* 30 Tex. Admin. Code chs. 295, 297.

Any amendment to a water right must be accomplished by filing an application using form TCEQ-10214, the same form used to apply for a new water right. *See* Texas Commission on Environmental Quality, *Applications and Forms Related to Surface Water Rights: New Water Rights and Amendment Applications*, www.tceq.texas.gov/permitting/water_rights/wr-permitting/wr_applications.html.

The current forms include the Instructions for Completing the Water Rights Permitting Application (form TCEQ-10214A) (revised August 2020), Administrative Information Checklist (form TCEQ-10214B) (revised July 2017), and Technical Information Checklist (form TCEQ-10214C) (revised August 2020); *see generally* Tex. Water Code ch. 11; 30 Tex. Admin. Code chs. 281, 288, 295, 297. A water right amendment is subject generally to all of the same statutory and regulatory requirements as a new water right application, including "notice." *See* Tex. Water Code § 11.122; *see also City of Marshall*, 206 S.W.3d at 110–11.

Notice and Hearing for an Amendment: Determining whether an amendment is required is only the first step in a due diligence analysis. Equally important is determining the extent of potential public participation in the amendment process. This is critical because third-party participation in the amendment process increases the time and expense associated with obtaining an amendment.

Some amendment applications are processed and issued without the need for public notice or opportunity for a public hearing, while others require such procedural steps. *See* Tex. Water Code § 11.122(b); *City of Marshall v. City of Uncertain*, 206 S.W.3d 97 (Tex. 2006); *see generally* 30 Tex. Admin. Code §§ 295.151–.161. The *City of Marshall* case addressed the agency's interpretation of which water rights permit amendment applications require notice and hearing and which do not. The supreme court held that although section 11.122(b) significantly restricts the issues that may be reviewed in connection with a water right amendment application, the statute does not preclude the possibility of a contested case hearing being held. *City of Marshall*, 206 S.W.3d at 110–11. The court reasoned that the statute's requirement that compliance with "other applicable requirements" must be considered includes conformance with administrative requirements, beneficial use of the water right, protection of the public welfare, groundwater effects, consistency with state and applicable regional water plans, and the avoidance of waste and achievement of water conservation. *City of Marshall*, 206 S.W.3d at 108–09. Although the *City of Marshall* holding does not automatically require that a hearing be held on these issues, it does mandate that the application include sufficient information to allow the TCEQ to determine whether notice and hearing are required on the amendment's potential adverse effects. The court specifically held that these impacts "can in most instances be determined from a facial review of the permit application without an evidentiary hearing." *City of Marshall*, 206 S.W.3d at 112.

The *Marshall* court concluded that a hearing would be required for an application to amend a water right that included movement of a diversion point or a proposed change in use from a nonconsumptive to a consumptive one. *City of Marshall*, 206 S.W.3d at 111. Based on the *City of Marshall* decision, to determine which amendment applications require notice and opportunity for hearing, the TCEQ will have to determine what type of review is required by looking at the impact of an amendment application on both the public interest criteria and water rights and the environment that is beyond the full use assumption of the "four corners" doctrine. Accordingly, parties to a water rights transaction should be aware that the type and extent of necessary review, notice, and opportunity for hearing are unclear for many types of water right amendments. See Chapter 10 of this book for detailed discussion of water rights permitting issues.

Changing the Point of Diversion, Place of Use, or Point of Return Flow: To develop and use the water right, will the point or rate of diversion, place of use, or point of return flow need to be changed? If so, this will require an amendment as discussed above. Due diligence should include an analysis of whether such a change has the potential to affect other water rights and is likely to result in a reduction in the amount of water authorized to be diverted either on a seasonal or annual basis. Such changes could generate opposition to the amendment and a request for a contested case hearing.

A summary description of the water rights potentially affected by the proposed transaction and any anticipated required amendments should be created as part of the due diligence, to include the following:

1. Identify water rights immediately downstream of the existing diversion point(s) and existing return flow point(s), if any, and the proposed new diversion and/or discharge point, and locate these nearby downstream rights on a map.

2. Identify any water rights near the location where water from the existing water right is used and locate them on a map.

3. Obtain copies of the identified water rights to allow an evaluation of the potential for impacts from any required change in diversion point, location of use, or location of return flows of the water to be purchased or leased.

Reduction in the Potential Yield of the Water Right: One of the issues to be addressed when selling or buying a water right may be the need to relocate or add an additional point of diversion to facilitate the buyer's beneficial use of the water. Irrespective of whether the new diversion point is upstream or downstream of the existing diversion point, the change may result in a reduced quantity of water that can be diverted, the rate of diversion, or the timing authorized under the water right. The reduction may result from a variety of factors, including the following:

1. The movement of a diversion point upstream could result in the reduction of the potential yield of the water. This occurs when the change in diversion point leapfrogs a senior water right. It also occurs because the move upstream results in a reduction in area of the drainage basin contributing to the amount of water available for diversion. This in turn results in a smaller calculated yield of the water right, as well as a modification in the reliability of the water right.

2. If the diversion point is moved downstream, the potential yield in volume of water available for diversion pursuant to the water right may be reduced by the commission to prevent the water right holder from benefiting from the increased watershed drainage area that contributes water to the water right at the new point of diversion. Carriage losses due to evaporation and seepage between the new and old diversion points may also be required to be accounted for in the amended water right. The latter change could reduce the water right's available yield as amended. "Carriage losses" is a term used to describe the volume of water lost on a percentage basis during transport between the originally permitted diversion point and the new points of diversion, due to seepage, evaporation, evapotranspiration, and other stream losses. *See* Regulatory Guidance Document, at 8.

Other Amendment Considerations: Other amendments that may be necessary to achieve the purchaser's objectives in the transaction include authorization to reuse the water after its initial use is accomplished. Such reuse may or may not involve the treatment of the water. In any event, it may involve the reintroduction of the diverted or impounded water into the watercourse to transport it to the next point of diversion for beneficial use. The reintroduction of the water back into the river raises questions of control and abandonment of the diverted water, which triggers the potential need for a bed and banks permit pursuant to section 11.042. *See* Tex. Water Code § 11.042 (bed and banks transport authorization).

The second type of a typical amendment that may be desired is the movement of the water authorized for beneficial use to a location that is outside of the river basin from which the water is originally authorized to be diverted. Such an amendment to the water right is known as an "interbasin transfer" (IBT). The requirements for such an authorization are in addition to the standard considerations for an amendment and require compliance with the provisions of section 11.085, unless the transfer fits one of the statutorily authorized exemptions. *See* Tex. Water Code § 11.085(v). Bed and banks transport authorizations and IBTs are discussed at sections 15.4:4 and 15.4:5 below. See also Chapter 10–13 of this book.

§ 15.4:4 Bed and Banks Transport

Does the proposed water transaction contemplate the purchase of a water right associated with a large storage project (whether on-channel or off-storage) such that the purchaser's location of intended beneficial use will necessitate the transport of the water using the "bed and banks" of a state water course? If so, determine whether the originating water right authorizing the release from storage includes a right to use the downstream bed and banks of the watercourse for transport. If not, a special authorization referred to as a bed and banks permit must be obtained by the buyer. Purchases of water from storage and the requirements for permits authorizing the use of the bed and banks of state watercourses are discussed in greater detail in Chapters 10, 24, and 31 of this book.

Similarly, if the water right to be acquired involves the use of treated wastewater effluent that is to be discharged back into a state watercourse and then transported downstream to the purchaser's diversion point and place of beneficial use, a bed and banks authorization must be acquired from the TCEQ. If the treated effluent originated as state-owned surface water appropriated pursuant to a water right, it must be authorized for transport and subsequent diversion and reuse either in the existing water right or by amendment and is subject to the same regulatory criteria as a new surface water right. If the effluent sought to be reused originated as privately owned groundwater, a bed and banks authorization must still be received and granted by the commission. The criteria applied, however, are more streamlined. *See* Tex. Water Code § 11.042. See also Chapter 24 of this book.

§ 15.4:5 Interbasin Transfers

To develop and use the water right, the parties to the transaction must determine whether the water diverted is to be moved from the basin of origin to another water basin before it is applied to a beneficial use. If so, an initial step in the due diligence analysis should be to determine whether the restrictions and special requirements for IBTs will apply to the transaction and, if so, what the impacts will be to the water right. *See* Tex. Water Code § 11.085. As discussed in Chapter 10 of this book, such restrictions and requirements can be onerous. Therefore, it should be determined whether any of the IBT exceptions apply to the transaction.

IBTs are controlled by Texas Water Code section 11.085. Section 11.085(v) excepts the following transfers:

1. a proposed transfer that, in combination with any existing transfers, totals less than 3,000 acre-feet of water per year from the same water right;

2. a request for an emergency transfer of water;

3. a proposed transfer from a basin to its adjoining coastal basin;

4. a proposed transfer from the part of the geographic area of a county or municipality, or the part of the retail service area of a retail public utility as defined by Water Code section

13.002, that is within the basin of origin for use in that part of the geographic area of the county or municipality, or that contiguous part of the retail service area of the utility, not within the basin of origin; or

5. a proposed transfer that is imported from a source wholly outside the boundaries of this state, except water that is imported from a source located in the United Mexican States, for use in this state, and transported by using the bed and banks of any flowing natural stream in this state.

See Tex. Water Code § 11.085(v).

§ 15.4:6 Cancellation

Although a water right is generally treated like a vested property right, because the state retains title to the corpus of the water, to fulfill its constitutional mandate under article XVI, section 59, of the Texas Constitution to protect, preserve, and avoid the waste of our natural resources, including water, the legislature has empowered the TCEQ to cancel water rights for nonuse. *See* Tex. Water Code § 11.173. Accordingly, part of the due diligence when contracting to acquire, or simply use, a surface water right should include both a review of the annual water use reports filed with the TCEQ (*see* Tex. Water Code § 11.031) and a determination of whether the right is subject to a pending cancellation proceeding under Texas Water Code section 11.173.

Historically, the state has not had an active water right cancellation policy. Texas has not canceled many water rights, and the statutes contain multiple exemptions from cancellation for "justified nonuse." *See* Tex. Water Code § 11.173(b).

This could change, however, as Texas's population increases and our water resources become stretched even further to meet growing demands. Recommended due diligence analysis in any surface water permit transaction should include the following steps:

1. Obtain copies of the annual water use reports for the past ten years, required to be filed with the TCEQ pursuant to Water Code section 11.031.

2. Obtain copies of all documents showing water sales or other water use during the past ten years, including water contracts, leases, and so on.

3. Review TCEQ files to ensure that there have been no cancellation notices, notices of violation, or other compliance issues during the past ten years.

4. If the water right is located within the jurisdiction of one of Texas's four watermaster operations, contact the watermaster office to secure and review copies of the watermaster's records for the subject water right.

Annual water use reports are due by March 1 of each year. *See* Tex. Water Code § 11.031(a). Failure to timely file the requisite report(s) subjects a water right holder to the imposition of a fine of up to (1) $100 per day for water rights authorizing an appropriation of less than 5,000 acre-feet per year, and (2) $500 per day for appropriations in excess of 5,000 acre-feet per year. Tex. Water Code § 11.031; *see generally* Tex. Water Code ch. 11, subch. E.

A permit is also subject to cancellation or forfeiture, in whole or in part, because of the permittee's failure to construct timely all improvements required for implementation of the permit granted. *See* Tex. Water Code § 11.146 (cancellation/forfeiture for "inaction"); *see generally* 30 Tex. Admin. Code §§ 299.21–.33 (TCEQ dam construction regulations). Before the TCEQ can cancel or declare a forfeiture of a permit for failure to timely implement the terms of the permit, the commission must provide the permittee with thirty days' notice and an opportunity to be heard. *See* Tex. Water Code § 11.146(b), (c). Section 11.146 does not apply to a permit authorizing the construction of a reservoir capable of storing more than 50,000 acre-feet of water. *See* Tex. Water Code § 11.146(g). For a more detailed discussion of issues related to dams, see Chapter 10 of this book.

§ 15.4:7 Water Conservation and Drought Contingency Plans

Water conservation is considered a water development tool. Water Code chapter 16 also mandates that the TWDB conduct studies to determine, among other things, "voluntary means of encouraging aggressive water conservation" as a cost-effective water supply alternative. *See* Tex. Water Code § 16.012(b)(2); *cf.;* Tex. Water Code §§ 16.053(e)(9)(B), 16.053(h)(7)(B), 16.054(a) (state policy mandates that water conservation should occur "on an ongoing basis"). Texas's legislatively mandated state water planning process is required to provide for both the conservation of water resources and preparation for and responsive strategies to Texas's recurrent drought conditions. Tex. Water Code § 16.051.

Water conservation and drought plans are an important component of the water permitting process. Accordingly, thorough due diligence should include a determination of (1) whether the water right holder has a water conservation plan and a drought contingency plan, and (2) whether the plans were submitted to the TCEQ and TWDB. *See generally* Tex. Water Code § 11.1271; 30 Tex. Admin. Code ch. 288.

Depending on the type of use and volume of water authorized for appropriation, a holder of an existing appropriative right must develop, submit, and implement a water conservation plan. *See* Tex. Water Code § 11.1271(b); 30 Tex. Admin. Code § 288.30. This plan must also be submitted to the TWDB, and the water right holder must report annually to the TWDB on its progress in implementing the plan. *See* Tex. Water Code § 16.402; *see also* 30 Tex. Admin. Code §§ 288.1–.7, 288.30, 295.9. As a general rule, water conservation and drought management plans will need to be updated as part of any amendment to transfer ownership of the water right. See Chapter 10 of this book for further discussion of water conservation plans. See Chapter 23 of this book for a more in-depth discussion of water conservation.

All retail public water suppliers must develop drought contingency plans and periodically submit them to the TCEQ for approval. *See* Tex. Water Code § 11.1272; 30 Tex. Admin. Code ch. 288. Additionally, wholesale and retail public water suppliers and irrigation districts that hold an existing water right must develop and submit drought contingency plans. *See* Tex. Water Code § 11.1272; 30 Tex. Admin. Code §§ 288.20–.22. See Chapter 22 of this book for further discussion of drought contingency planning.

§ 15.4:8 Watermaster Programs

Another due diligence item affecting a limited number of water rights transactions in Texas is a determination of whether the water right is subject to the jurisdiction of one of the state's four watermaster programs. Watermaster programs are currently operating in the following regions: the Rio Grande Basin below Fort Quitman; South Texas, where the watermaster program includes forty-six counties in multiple basins, including the Nueces, San Antonio, and Guadalupe River Basins; the Concho River Basin; and the Brazos River Basin (below and including While the four programs differ, they each include the following requirements: (1) installation of a meter; (2) payment of a watermaster fee; (3) watermaster approval of a declaration of intent before the diversion, transport, or release of water; and (4) maintenance of records of diversion, transport, and release of water. *See* Tex. Water Code §§ 11.325–.3291; 30 Tex. Admin. Code chs. 303 (Rio Grande watermaster program), 304 (South Texas, Concho, and Brazos programs). See also Chapters 7 and 13 of this book.

If the water right is subject to the jurisdiction of a watermaster program, the following steps should be taken as part of the due diligence analysis:

1. Review and analyze the impacts of the TCEQ rules under which the applicable watermaster operates on the water right and the intended uses. *See* 30 Tex. Admin. Code chs. 303, 304.

2. Obtain documentation showing whether the water right is in compliance with any applicable water-master regulations.

3. Ensure that the water right holder is current on the payment of all applicable watermaster fees and assessments, as well as any TCEQ statewide fees.

4. Review any required records of diversion, transport, use, or release of water under the water right.

Texas Water Code section 11.326(g) mandates that the TCEQ executive director evaluate the need for appointment of a watermaster in each water basin on a five-year cycle. The results of those periodic analyses must be reported to the commissioners for evaluation and inclusion in the TCEQ biennial report to the legislature. *See* Tex. Water Code § 11.326(g)–(h).

§ 15.4:9 Environmental Issues

Environmental concerns have risen to the forefront of matters to be addressed as part of a surface water transaction.

The following factors have all contributed to this new emphasis on environmental concerns associated with surface water:

1. the continuing recurrence of drought or severe drought conditions somewhere in the state;

2. a growing population and a need to develop new water resources to meet the growth;

3. a growing need for construction of new or major repair of existing water-related infrastructure;

4. budget deficits or financial shortfalls;

5. endangered species issues; and

6. a spike in the number of reoccurring natural disasters affecting statewide water resources.

While the technical aspects of the issues and how they are addressed in the surface water permitting context are discussed elsewhere in this book, particularly as they may affect water rights permitting (see Chapters 1, 3, 10, 11, 12, and 32 of this book), they are worth summarizing here for those who will be involved in the transaction negotiations.

As discussed in Chapter 11 of this book, since the passage of Senate Bill 3 in 2007 (S.B. 3), the TCEQ must consider environmental flows in the surface water rights permitting process. *See* Tex. Water Code §§ 11.0235–.0237, 11.0841, 11.134, 11.147, 11.1471, 11.148, 11.1491. Pursuant to S.B. 3, the TCEQ adopted "appropriate environmental flow standards" for each of the state's major river basins and their respective receiving bay and estuary systems. *See* Tex. Water Code §§ 11.02362, 11.1471(a); 30 Tex. Admin. Code ch. 298. The rules establish criteria that are intended to be "adequate to support a sound ecological environment, to the maximum extent reasonable considering other public interests and other relevant factors." Tex. Water Code § 11.1471(a)(1); *see* 30 Tex. Admin. Code ch. 298.

The TCEQ's rules on environmental flow standards for surface water establish a "set aside to satisfy the environmental flow standards to the maximum extent reasonable when considering human water needs" out of the calculated volume of "unappropriated water," if any, available in the affected river basin. Tex. Water Code § 11.1471(a)(2); *see* 30 Tex. Admin. Code ch. 298 (environmental flow rules). These environmental flow standards must be considered by the commission when granting any new water right appropriation or amendment to an existing water right that would increase the volume of water appropriated. *See* Tex. Water Code §§ 11.1471(a)(3), 11.02362(b); Act of May 28, 2007, 80th Leg., R.S., ch. 1430, § 1.27; *see generally* 30 Tex. Admin. Code §§ 298.5–.25; TCEQ Interoffice Memorandum to the Commissioners (Oct. 15, 2010). See Chapter 11 of this book for further discussion of the environmental flow process.

Another uncertainty to be considered when performing due diligence for a surface water transaction is the potential effect of a suit under the Endangered Species Act (ESA). In March 2010, The Aransas Project (TAP) filed suit in federal district court in Corpus Christi, Texas, against the then three current TCEQ commissioners and the TCEQ South Texas Watermaster. *See Aransas Project v. Shaw*, No. C-10-75 (S.D. Tex. Mar. 3, 2010). In its complaint, TAP sought injunctions affecting the use of existing water rights and the development of any new water rights in the Guadalupe and San Antonio River basins. TAP alleged that diversions of water from the basins were reducing freshwater inflows into the Gulf of Mexico and its estuary systems, thereby increasing salinity levels and illegally impairing the habitat of the endangered whooping cranes. *See Aransas Project v. Shaw*, 930 F. Supp. 2d 716 (S.D. Tex. 2012). Finding that a "take" had occurred under section 9 of the ESA, the trial court concluded that the case was "well-suited for an [Incidental Take Permit] and corresponding [Habitat Conservation Plan]" and ordered the following relief:

1. the TCEQ, its chairman, and its executive director are enjoined from approving or granting new water permits affecting the Guadalupe or San Antonio Rivers until the state provides reasonable assurances to the court that such permits will not take whooping cranes in violation of the ESA; and

2. within thirty days of the date of entry of the order, the TCEQ, its chairman, and its executive director shall seek an Incidental Take Permit that will lead to development of a Habitat Conservation Plan.

See Aransas Project, 930 F. Supp. 2d at 788–89.

On appeal, the Fifth Circuit concluded that as a matter of law the evidence did not support findings of either foreseeability or causation between the deaths of the cranes and the actions of the TCEQ. *Aransas Project v. Shaw*, 756 F.3d 801, 823 (5th Cir. 2014) (per curiam). Based on a lack of causation and, therefore, liability on the part of the TCEQ, the Fifth Circuit also concluded that the injunctive relief ordered by the district court was an erroneous abuse of discretion. *Aransas Project*, 756 F.3d at 823–24. TAP's petition for writ of certiorari to the U.S. Supreme Court was denied in *Aransas Project v. Shaw*, 135 S. Ct. 2859 (2015).

While unsuccessful, the TAP litigation sent a warning that Texas must consider the environment in developing a balance between achieving its water supply needs and the ripple effects of those activities, including any resulting impacts to the environment. Accordingly, environmental flows and endangered species are issues that parties engaging in surface water transactions should incorporate into their due diligence "checklist."

§ 15.4:10 Dam Safety Issues

If an impoundment or reservoir is a part of the water right involved in the transaction, additional factors that should be considered include the following:

1. dam safety and the condition of the existing impoundment or reservoir and the dam that creates the impoundment;

2. purposes, if any, of the dam and impoundment or reservoir other than storage, including recreational uses and, in particular, flood control functions;

3. the flood control functions of the dam, if any;

4. when the dam was last inspected and the concerns, if any, raised by the inspection report;

5. whether the Federal Emergency Management Agency Flood Insurance Rate Map delineating the hundred-year flood plain has changed since the dam was constructed;

6. the historical experience of the dam operations during flood events, including whether development occurred either upstream or downstream of the dam, possibly within the hundred-year flood plain, that might create liability associated with the ownership or operation of the dam;

7. the last time the dam was evaluated with respect to its ability to withstand an occurrence of the Probable Maximum Flood and the results of that analysis;

8. whether the permittee owns or operates the dam or whether the dam is owned or operated by a third party, for example, the United States Army Corps of Engineers;

9. if the dam is owned or operated by a third party and its use, or the use of water stored in the impoundment or reservoir, is governed by a state or federal contract, and whether the contracts indicate any impacts on the planned or intended future use of the facility or the associated water;

10. the annual operating costs of the dam or impoundment or reservoir and the effect on the planned or intended future use of the facility or the associated water; and

11. whether the dam is "exempt" from permitting.

See Tex. Water Code §§ 11.142–.143; 30 Tex. Admin. Code ch. 299 (TCEQ Dam and Reservoir Regulations); *see generally*, House Natural Resources Committee, *Interim Report to the 86th Texas Legislature* 13–44 (Dec. 2018), https://house.texas.gov/_media/pdf/committees/reports/85interim/Natural-Resources-Committee-Interim-Report-2018.pdf [hereinafter 2018 Interim Report].

§ 15.5 Title Matters

Under a contract for the sale or lease of surface water rights, the buyer or lessee should have the right to conduct a title examination and to terminate the contract if there are significant uncured title problems. The acquiring party should conduct the same type of due diligence review on the title to the surface water rights that a purchaser or lessee would conduct in a traditional real property transaction.

Confirmation that the seller or lessor named in the contract owns record title to the surface water rights and the necessary property rights to access and use the diversion point is merely the first step.

The buyer or lessee should determine whether there are restrictions, leases, easements, liens, or other adverse title matters that could affect the unencumbered use of the surface water rights. As surface water rights are often tied to the land they are associated with, a lien or other encumbrance burdening the tract of land may well encumber the water right either expressly or through the application of a "Mother Hubbard" clause in the lien instrument that would affect the entirety of the property, including any associated water right.

§ 15.5:1 Marketable Water Right

Does the seller or lessor have marketable title to the surface water? That is, the water right recognized by the TCEQ? Related issues include verification that the seller has the legal right to access and use the diversion point, point of return flows, if relevant, and the necessary easements or infrastructure to transport the water from the point of diversion to the place of beneficial use.

The following steps should be taken to ensure marketable title:

1. Review all documents that relate to or otherwise constitute the water right. Specifically, identify documents that constitute the current water right. This could be a certificate of adjudication, a certified filing, or a water right permit and any amendments. Available documents that constitute the chain of title should be separately identified. This could include water deeds or other conveyance documents from the seller's or lessor's predecessors in title.

2. Secure copies of the title, deed, or other legal right needed for access to the diversion point, point of return flow, or transportation of the water from the watercourse to the place of use and have them in place and part of the transaction. Review all supporting documentation.

3. Secure copies of all memoranda in the TCEQ's files related to the issuance of the original water right and all subsequent changes in ownership.

4. If available, obtain a title commitment from a title company that issues title insurance for water rights. The title insurer will issue a title commitment that describes the surface water rights and land, if applicable, identifies the record owner of the rights and land, and lists easements, restrictions, liens, and other matters of record that affect title to the rights and, if applicable, the land. Also secure a copy of a current survey if available. Review of these documents will help identify any potential infirmities to the seller's or lessor's fee simple title to the water rights that have not been identified previously.

5. The water right holder should identify any known contracts, leases, or similar obligations that the permittee is obligated to honor that may affect the water right, directly or indirectly, because they relate to use of the water right or the surface acreage associated with the right or could impair access or use. The length of the remaining term of any such contract or lease and a summary of the obligations under the contracts should be provided. The contracts should be made available for review.

§ 15.5:2 Water Right Previously Leased or Subordinated

Is the water right issued on the basis of a contract with a third party who has leased or subordinated superior rights in order for the water right to be issued? If the answer is yes, is that contract or subordination agreement still in effect and, if so, is it being conveyed or assigned along with the water right?

IV. Structuring the Sale of a Surface Water Right

§ 15.6 Structuring the Sale of a Surface Water Right

The foregoing "primer" on the basics of surface water rights and due diligence issues leads into the structure of the deal. An important element of any water transaction is patience. Surface water right transactions do not occur overnight. Negotiations and closing can be protracted, particularly due to the potential for third-party interference not common in traditional real estate transactions. This third-party interference can come from the TCEQ or other water rights holders. Additionally, once the terms of a deal have been negotiated, the period for exercising due diligence or "closing" may need to be extended because of developments surrounding needed changes to the water right. See the discussion at section 15.4:3 above regarding water right permit amendments. Some practitioners describe water deals as moving in "geologic time."

Like any real property transaction, the parties must assess their respective goals and objectives, and then develop a structure for a deal. Several basics should be addressed in any water deal. First, who will be responsible for the transactional costs, including preparing and processing applications at the TCEQ? Second, consider what warranties, if any, will be given regarding the quantity and quality of water covered by the water right, particularly if the type and location of use or the diversion point of the water right will be changed and the requirements of implementing Senate Bill 3, as codified in Texas Water Code sections 11.0235 through 11.0237, will likely impact the ultimate volume of water available for beneficial use. *See* Tex. Water Code §§ 11.0235–.0237; *see generally* 30 Tex. Admin. Code ch. 298 (TCEQ's basin-by-basin environmental flows rules).

How much time will the parties allow for the deal to close, knowing that TCEQ processing could take at least nine months, and possibly years? *See* 2018 Interim Report, at 100 & n.211 ("Uncontested water transaction[s] are taking up to 300 days to process and contested cases are taking 900 days.").

The discussion that follows is a nonexhaustive list of the deal points that can or should be addressed in a water rights transaction and serves as a starting point. While the transactional vehicles discussed below may not all be elements found in conventional real estate transactions, they are often part of the purchase or lease of a surface water right.

§ 15.6:1 Option Contract vs. Firm Deal

Many uncertainties surround a water deal until the necessary approvals and amendments have been received from controlling regulatory entities such as the TCEQ. Thus, water deals usually require an "exit clause" for the acquiring party or possibly both parties. There are a variety of means to accomplish this, including negotiating the deal to include the granting of an "option period" during which due diligence is completed and the parties pursue the necessary regulatory approvals and amendments. Details of the option, due-diligence timetables, and termination "trigger points" should be negotiated as part of the option. The expectations of each party during the term of an option period should be addressed with specificity, including the responsibilities of the parties during the option period, who will bear the risks of any costs associated with the option period, and who has the right to use the water right during the option period.

Keep in mind that unless the purchaser's use of the water during the option period is consistent with the current terms of the water right, TCEQ approval will be required for any such use.

The option period should be of a reasonable but limited duration and should have designated benchmarks. At each benchmark, the parties may decide whether to continue or terminate the deal.

Because of the time necessary to process even a minor amendment at the TCEQ, a minimum of nine to twelve months is a reasonable initial option term. One benchmark that might be recommended is the point at which the amendment application has been determined to be "administratively complete" and notice is published. This would allow the parties the opportunity to cancel the deal if the notice triggers protests and requests for a contested case hearing. See Chapter 10 of this book regarding administrative completeness, notice requirements, and the opportunity for a contested case hearing.

Keep in mind that the TCEQ "technical review" of the application, which occurs after the determination of administrative completeness, can be a lengthy process. The technical process includes an assessment of "water availability," environmental issues, and water conservation plans for the project.

Because of the unpredictability of processing a water right amendment (see discussion above), the option term should contemplate the possibility of an extension or extensions if the approvals of amendment applications seem to be progressing but the closing requirements will not be satisfied before the end of the option period. Because an extension of the option period could require forbearance in the use and marketing of the water right, which represents a lost opportunity, payment of some additional nonrefundable consideration by the buyer or lessee may be necessary.

Whether any such additional payment should be treated as nonrefundable or as additional earnest money to be applied to the purchase price at closing is an issue to be addressed by the parties.

§ 15.6:2 Consideration

One of the biggest questions in negotiating a water deal is the value of the water right. There are usually no comparable market sales or other traditional pricing tools for "pricing" water rights similar to the sales of other real property. *See generally* 2018 Interim Report at 87–102 (discussing the lack of "water markets" in Texas)); *see also* chapter 37 of this book. The legislature has established a definition of "fair market value" in a surface water rights transaction, which is similar to the definition in traditional real estate transactions:

> Whenever the law requires the payment of fair market value for a water right, fair market value shall be determined by the amount of money that a willing buyer would pay a willing seller, neither of which is under any compulsion to buy or sell, for the water in an arms-length transaction and shall not be limited to the amount of money that the owner of the water right has paid or is paying for the water.

Tex. Water Code § 11.0275.

As with all real property transactions, the terms and conditions negotiated in a water deal will affect the purchase price to be paid for the water right. Factors that will influence the negotiated value of the water right include:

1. Quantity of permitted water. As amended, the amount of water available to the acquiring party postclosing may be less than the water right authorizes. The purchase price may be the net per-acre-foot price based on the authorized water right, with some type of reduction if the TCEQ reduces the authorized amount. (See the discussion of change in diversion point, place of use, and point of return flow at section 15.4:3 above.)

2. Quality of the water, if it affects the acquiring party's intended purpose of use.

3. Location of authorized diversion point and its proximity to the proposed diversion point and place of use.

4. Types of use authorized by the existing water right and the need for amending the use

authorization.

5. Reliability of the yield from the water right.

6. The water right's seniority based on its priority date.

7. The existence of water rights with diversion points located between the existing point of diversion and the proposed point of diversion, if those water rights could affect the reliability of yield.

8. The term or duration of the water right.

9. To the extent the information is available and verifiable, the amount paid for other water rights sold within the same river basin.

The price paid will necessarily result from negotiations between the parties, particularly in the absence of any benchmark price or comparable sale.

§ 15.6:3 TCEQ Approvals and Amendments to the Water Right

As discussed above, in many instances the transfer of a water right requires approval from the TCEQ. At a minimum, the change of ownership requires notification of the TCEQ. Often, for the water right to be used by the acquiring party, it must first be amended. These regulatory steps not only represent additional time but also pose a risk of loss and can result in significant costs. For example, certain amendments, such as changes in diversion points, purpose of use, and place of use, may result in a reduction of the authorized diversion amount, the rate of diversion or timing, or stream flow conditions under which diversions under the water right may occur.

These reductions can be imposed for a variety of reasons, including—

1. protection of senior water rights affected by the amendment;

2. changes in the reliability of the water right; and

3. protection of instream or environmental flows.

The buyer or lessee may ask the selling party to assist or otherwise cooperate during the option period in securing the necessary TCEQ approvals and amendments to the water right. Such a request is reasonable and should be agreed to at no cost to the seller or lessor. Accordingly, the deal should provide for reimbursement of the seller's or lessor's actual out-of-pocket costs, including professional fees incurred in such an effort (e.g., engineering and legal fees). If the potential costs will be significant, the parties may agree to develop a budget and provide for an upfront deposit or escrow of the monies to cover the seller's or lessor's costs as a precondition to their participation.

The bottom line is that the overall deal should be negotiated on the basis of the original water right so that the parties allocate any risk of loss resulting from needed changes to the water right. The parties, however, may choose to renegotiate a price reduction at various points in the TCEQ permitting process, particularly if reduced quantity or reliability of the water right is anticipated.

§ 15.6:4 Condemnation Proceedings

A water right is an interest in real property subject to condemnation. *See* Tex. Prop. Code § 21.0121. Because of the length of time that could pass before closing, the possibility that a water right could be the subject of or affected by a condemnation proceeding should be addressed. This is particularly true for an irrigation water right that is attached to a specific tract of land. *See generally* 30 Tex. Admin. Code §§ 297.81–.83. Specifically, in the event of condemnation, the transaction should provide for (1) how any condemnation proceeds will be paid, (2) whether the buyer or lessee can terminate the deal if the remaining quantity of water right postcondemnation is insufficient to meet its needs, and (3) if the loss of interest in the water right can be allocated between the seller and buyer and keep the buyer whole, whether the risk should be allocated to accomplish that objective. See Chapter 38 of this book for a discussion of the condemnation of water rights.

§ 15.6:5 Assignability

The seller or lessor should be entitled to assign its interests in the underlying water right as long as the assignee agrees in writing to honor the deal with the buyer or lessee. To protect the seller's or lessor's expectations under the sale, the deal should address the buyer's or lessee's right to assign the deal. The assignability provision should include, at a minimum, the following:

1. The assignee must be a qualified entity—that is, one able to perform and comply with the sale terms, particularly the financial obligations.

2. The assignee must acknowledge in writing its obligation to fulfill all terms of the sale.

3. The buyer or lessee has continued liability for the full and faithful performance of the terms of the sale, in the event of a default by the assignee.

4. If an assignment occurs while an application is pending before the TCEQ, notice and updates will need to be filed with the TCEQ.

§ 15.6:6 Miscellaneous Boilerplate Provisions

Like any real estate transaction, the sales contract should include miscellaneous boilerplate provisions such as the following:

1. governing law (Texas law applies);

2. venue of any lawsuit (any litigation must be filed in a county or counties to be selected by the seller or lessor);

3. alternative dispute resolution (ADR) (the seller or lessor may want to require or to avoid arbitration or other forms of ADR);

4. notice and contact information;

5. force majeure clause;

6. amendments and modifications of the contract;

7. savings clause;

8. third-party beneficiaries (the seller or lessor will likely want to negate the existence of any such beneficiaries);

9. drafting interpretations;

10. counterparts or duplicate originals;

11. events of default and remedies; and

12. condemnation events.

V. Structuring the Lease of a Surface Water Right

§ 15.7 Structuring the Lease of a Surface Water Right

The same basic principles applicable to the purchase of a water right, as discussed in part IV above, generally apply to the lease of a water right. Structuring a water right lease involves additional considerations, however, which are discussed below.

If a water rights holder plans to market the surface water as potentially available pursuant to its permit, there are several steps that the rights holder may wish to take in advance of any leasing of the water right in order to expedite implementation of the lease or water supply contract. This includes amending the water right to accomplish the following:

1. Authorize multiple purposes of use believed to be marketable in the region.

2. Authorize such use in multiple places and/or counties.

3. Rather than limit diversion to a single diversion point, determine whether "diversion reaches" are a possibility. This could require securing access easements from other landowners.

4. Develop water conservation plans for different types of authorized beneficial uses; for example, municipal, industrial, mining, and other purposes.

5. Determine whether any off-channel storage, including aquifer storage and recovery, is feasible.

Having these amendments to the water right could enhance both the marketability of the right and its pricing. It could also reduce the delay frequently experienced between the time a deal is closed and the time the project is implemented.

§ 15.7:1 Valuation

Because of the lack of an established market for water rights, the true value of the right is unknown. In general, however, the price per acre-foot for the sale of the water right will be higher than the per-acre-foot lease price. Over the life of the lease, however, the total return or cost could be greater than the per-acre-foot price received in a sale. At the end of the lease, the water right owner will still have the water right, and the market value of the right will likely have appreciated over the life of the lease.

§ 15.7:2 Option Period

The transaction should provide for payment of some additional consideration in the event of an extension of the term of the option period. This is because an extension of the term of the option period discussed at section 15.6:1 above could delay the lessor's receipt of rent under a lease or require forbearance in the use or marketing of the water right (i.e., lost opportunity).

§ 15.7:3 Other Provisions Affecting the Lease Price

In addition to the all-important negotiation of the lease price, the parties should address related issues that will affect the overall value of the transaction. These may include a guaranteed annual payment, payment based on beneficial use rather than on actual use, and a price escalation clause.

Surface water leases may be structured and labeled in various ways, such as take-or-pay, minimum take, or guaranteed purchase. Each of these structures ensures that the lessor receives an annual payment.

The lessor wants to negotiate a lease for the water that ensures payment whether or not water is actually used by the lessee. As mentioned above, this is easily handled if the transaction includes a take-or-pay provision. If, however, the transaction contemplates payment only if the lessee gets the benefit of the water—that is, the ability to actually use it—then the lessor should be careful how the payment obligation is structured.

It is possible for a lessee to lease water for the purpose of trading its use or nonuse to improve the reliability of, or otherwise enhance, water available from another water right or source under the control of the lessee. For example, in response to pressures from environmental interests or demands by downstream water right holders, a lessee developing a water project could negotiate a lease that would tie up a water right but that would not actually divert the water. In this manner the nonuse of the leased water right could facilitate having higher flows in a stream segment or to bays and estuaries.

To accomplish this, the lessee might lease one or more water rights and either not use them—for example, leave the water in the watercourse—or agree to have stricter stream flow conditions on the leased water right to reduce the quantity of water diverted annually. Although the lessee in such a scenario would be using the water in the sense that it would be receiving some benefit from the leased water, the lessee would not be diverting the water. If the transaction is drafted so that the lessee's obligation to pay is based on the volume of water actually diverted, then the lessor would not get paid and, therefore, would not receive the intended benefit of the bargain. Moreover, the lessee's nonuse of the water over an extended period of time could jeopardize the underlying water right by subjecting it to cancellation.

To address this possibility, the parties can negotiate a take-or-pay clause, negotiate a higher price for the water per acre-foot with a minimum annual take requirement, or require payment for the beneficial use of the water right in any form or fashion, including trading or nonuse.

The duration or term of any lease involving a substantial amount of water will likely be for twenty-plus years. The lessor will want to provide for periodic increases of the annual rent during the term to reflect the appreciation in the value of the water right over time. This can be addressed in a variety of ways. The parties may agree to increases at a set interval, such as annually or every five years. The increases could be specified as a percentage increase or could track an index like the consumer price index. The periodic increase could be tied to some other market price indicator; for example, a large water purveyor (possibly even the lessee) has a rate or price it charges third parties, which the parties agree sets the market price. Another method would be to include a most-favored-nations clause that requires an increase if the lessee pays a higher amount to some other supplier.

§ 15.7:4 Cancellation of Water Rights

Water rights are subject to cancellation, in whole or in part, for nonbeneficial use during a ten-year period. *See* Tex. Water Code § 11.173. See the discussion at section 15.4:6 above. Although a take-or-pay clause should help to ensure that the lessor will get paid, it may not ensure that the water is beneficially used during the term of the lease. To avoid the prospect of cancellation due to nonuse, the parties may negotiate various types of clauses in the lease.

1. A clause mandating that the lessee protect the water right from cancellation and beneficially use the water right by actually diverting the leased water at least once every ten years.

2. A clause mandating that the lessee defend against any action brought by the TCEQ to cancel the water right and to give immediate notice to the lessor of receipt of any notice of cancellation proceedings being initiated by the TCEQ.

3. A clause allowing the lessor to beneficially use, or cause to be beneficially used, the water right to prevent cancellation. This clause should also provide that in the event it is exercised, (a) the lessee is still required to pay the rent on 100 percent of the water (including the quantity used by the lessor), and (b) the lessor has no obligation to either replace the water used or to rebate or refund any portion of the rent (even if the lessor does a spot sale to a third party).

§ 15.7:5 Watermaster Fees and Other Assessments

If the water right is located in a river basin subject to the jurisdiction of a watermaster, the lease should address payment of watermaster fees and other assessments. Even if the water right is not located in a watermaster area, any long-term lease should address this issue because of the possibility of watermaster operations expanding throughout the state. Based on the rationale that the lessee is benefiting from the use of the water, the lease should provide that the lessee be responsible for the payment of any assessments on the water right and the use of the water. This includes, specifically, any annual watermaster fees or water quality fees under the Texas Clean Rivers Program. It also includes any other type of assessment such as ad valorem taxes.

§ 15.7:6 Annual Reports

Any requirement to file reports regarding the use of the water right or the use of water under the water right should be expressly made the obligation of the lessee. *See* Tex. Water Code § 11.031. See the discussion at section 15.4:6 above. For the lessor's protection, however, the lease should require that the lessee provide the lessor with copies of all filed reports. The copies should be required to be delivered to the lessor by a date sufficiently before the filing deadline so that the lessor can accomplish the filing in the event the lessee defaults. As noted in section 15.4:6 above, failure to file required annual reports can result in fines of $100 to $500 per day by the TCEQ.

§ 15.7:7 Third-Party Offers and a Right of First Refusal

Much can happen during the life of a lease, particularly where the term is twenty-plus years. For example, the lessor could receive an offer to purchase the underlying water rights. The lease may be negotiated to allow such a sale and should address the following related issues as well:

1. Whether the sale of the underlying water right during the term of the lease triggers a right in the lessor to terminate the lease early, if necessary to close the sale. If so, the circumstances of such a termination should be addressed, including what notice is provided to the lessee and whether the lessee is entitled to a replacement water source or some compensation because of the termination.

2. Whether the lessee should be entitled to a right of first refusal to buy the water right for the same deal offered to the lessor. If so, the terms of the right of first refusal and the lessee's

closing obligations should be specified.

§ 15.7:8 Early Termination

The lessor's right, and in some instances the lessee's right, to terminate the lease before the expiration of its term should be addressed. This includes termination for cause and nonpayment of rent, as well as termination under other circumstances, such as a third-party offer to purchase or condemnation.

§ 15.7:9 Advance Payment of Rent

The lessee should be required to pay rent in advance. There are several reasons for requiring advance payment. First, once the water is used, it cannot be recovered for nonpayment. Not only will it most likely have been consumed, but once it is diverted it counts against the water right and cannot be double counted or added back in during the calendar year. Second, because water rights are usable on an annual calendar-year basis, once the calendar year has expired, the right to use it during that year has been lost. The unused portion of the water right cannot be banked or carried forward for use in a subsequent calendar year.

§ 15.7:10 Condemnation Proceedings

As noted at section 15.6:4 above, water rights are an interest in real property and, though not a common event, can be subject to condemnation. See Tex. Prop. Code § 21.0121. Because of the limited availability of new water rights and the length of the lease term, the possibility that a water right could be the subject of condemnation proceedings should be addressed. The lease should consider how, in the event of condemnation, the condemnation proceeds should be paid. Should they be paid to the lessor, or should some portion of the proceeds be allocated to the lessee because they are intended to reimburse the lessee for some loss other than the loss of the water rights themselves? Condemnation might also be a factor in or trigger a lessee's right to terminate the lease.

§ 15.7:11 Assignability

As noted at section 15.6:5 above, to protect the parties' expectations under the lease, the lease should address the parties' respective rights to assign the deal. At a minimum, the lease should include the following requirements for assigning the lease:

1. a qualified entity—that is, one able to perform and comply with the lease terms;

2. an entity that acknowledges in writing its obligation to fulfill all of the lease terms;

3. an entity who is reasonably approved by the nonassigning party; and

4. the continued liability of the assigning party for the full and faithful performance of the lease terms by the assignee.

§ 15.7:12 Notice to the TCEQ

If the lease is considered a wholesale water supply contract pursuant to Texas Water Code section 13.144, the obligation to provide notice to the TCEQ should be designated in the agreement. See Chapter 31 of this book regarding wholesale water contracts.

VI. Other Unique "Sources" of Surface Water Rights

§ 15.8 Introduction

Although the vast majority of water rights are privately held, there are two unique sources from which one may acquire the right to use state water by either purchase or lease: the Texas Water Bank and Texas Water Trust, and canal company water rights.

§ 15.9 Texas Water Bank and Texas Water Trust

Established by the Texas legislature in 1993, the purpose of the Texas Water Bank is to facilitate water marketing and transactions to transfer water and water rights to provide sources of adequate water supplies for use within the state. *See* Tex. Water Code § 15.702. Pursuant to the enabling legislation, the TWDB adopted rules for the operation of the Water Bank, which are codified in 31 Texas Administrative Code chapter 359.

The Water Bank was envisioned as a clearinghouse for water and water rights availability information, much like a multiple listing service for real estate. The TWDB, however, does not act as a broker or agent for either buyers or sellers. The TWDB does not actively market the water or water rights posted on its website, regardless of whether the listed water or water right is deposited in the bank. *See* Tex. Water Code § 15.703.

Water rights deposited into the Water Bank can be sold or leased. One benefit of the Water Bank legislation is the authorization to deposit a water right into the Water Bank, which, during its initial ten-year term, becomes exempt from cancellation under Texas Water Code chapter 11, subchapter E. *See* Tex. Water Code § 15.704; *see also* Tex. Water Code §§ 11.171–.177. The exemption from cancellation, however, is good only one time. *See* Tex. Water Code § 15.704(a). Water rights can be listed on the TWDB website for marketing purposes, even though not actually on deposit, without paying the deposit fee. *See* Texas Water Development Board, *Texas Water Bank & Trust*, www.twdb.texas.gov/waterplanning/waterbank/. Such listed water rights do not have the same protection from cancellation as those on deposit in the Water Bank. *See* Tex. Water Code § 15.704(b).

Two sessions after it created the Texas Water Bank, the legislature established the Texas Water Trust. *See* Act of June 1, 1997, 75th Leg., R.S., ch. 1010, § 2.16 (codified at Tex. Water Code § 15.7031). The purpose of the Water Trust is to establish "within the water bank [a place] to hold water rights dedicated to environmental needs, including instream flows, water quality, fish and wildlife habitat, and bay and estuary inflows." *See* Tex. Water Code § 15.7031(a); *cf.* Tex. Water Code § 15.703(a)(10) (authorizing the TWDB Water Bank to accept and hold "donations of water rights to meet instream, water quality, fish and wildlife habitat, or bay and estuary inflow needs"); *see generally* Edmond R. McCarthy, Jr., *Environmental Flows: Water Development Perspective*, 34 St. B. Tex. Envtl. L.J. 248, 255–56 (2004). Since the creation of the Texas Water Trust, the Texas Parks and Wildlife Department (TPWD) has worked closely with the TWDB in connection with the Trust. The TPWD, along with the TCEQ, must be consulted by the TWDB in the adoption of rules that govern the process for holding and transferring water rights into the Water Trust. *See* Tex. Water Code § 15.7031(b). Additionally, the TCEQ must review and approve the dedication of any water right placed into the Water Trust. That process must be done in consultation with the TWDB and the TPWD.

See Tex. Water Code § 15.7031(c). See Chapter 11 of this book for further discussion of the Texas Water Trust and environmental flow issues.

Effective September 1, 2021, the TPWD's role over the operation of the Texas Water Trust has been substantially increased. With the passage of House Bill 2225, Act of June 15, 2021, 87 R.S. ch. 689, § 1 2021, Tex. Gen. Laws 689, section 12.028 was added to the Texas Parks and Wildlife Code granting new and additional powers to the TPWD to encourage and facilitate the dedication of water rights into the trust through lease, donation, purchase, or other voluntary transfer for the specific purpose of addressing environmental needs in our watercourses. Additionally, H.B. 2225 amended the existing section 15.7031 of the Texas Water Code to add a new subsection (e) to describe the TPWD's means to manage any water rights placed in the Water Trust. *See* Tex. Water Code § 15.7031(e).

Unlike water placed in the Water Bank, there is no limit on the duration for which water may be placed in the Texas Water Trust. Instead, water rights may be held in the Water Trust for a term specified by contractual agreement with the holder of the water right or in perpetuity. *Compare* Tex. Water Code § 15.704(a) (water right may be deposited in the Water Bank for an initial term of up to ten years), *with* Tex. Water Code § 15.7031(d) (water right may be held in the Water Trust for a term specified by contract or in perpetuity). An additional distinction between a deposit into the Water Bank and into the Water Trust is that the fees the depositor must pay for placing the water right in the Water Bank are waived in the case of deposits into the Water Trust. *See* Tex. Water Code § 15.705 (establishing fees for deposits into the Water Bank); 31 Tex. Admin. Code § 359.14(b) ("Fees associated with deposits to or transfer from the Texas Water Trust of water rights or rights to use water are waived."). Information regarding the Texas Water Bank and the Texas Water Trust can be found on the TWDB's website or by contacting the TWDB's Water Bank manager. The TWDB maintains two separate registries for "sellers" and "buyers" in the Water Bank. The Seller's Registry and the Buyer's Registry can also be viewed on the TWDB website. Application forms for making deposits into the Water Bank, as well as a statement of responsibilities of Water Bank participants, and a fee schedule are also available on the TWDB website. *See* Texas Water Development Board, *Texas Water Bank & Trust*, www.twdb.texas.gov/waterplanning/waterbank/bank/index.asp.

§ 15.10 Canal Company Water Rights

In the more common practice of an individual irrigation water right holder, the water right is tied directly to the land owned solely by the water right holder for irrigation of a specified acreage described by metes and bounds within the water right. The water right owned by a canal company, however, authorizes the water right holder with control over or possession of the water with authority to contract with or supply the water to third parties located within the service area of the water right holder. *See* Tex. Water Code § 11.036; *see generally Willis v. Neches Canal Co.*, 16 S.W.2d 266 (Tex. Comm'n App. 1929, judgm't adopted); *Town of Griffing Park v. City of Port Arthur*, 628 S.W.2d 101 (Tex. App.—Beaumont 1981, writ ref'd n.r.e.) (water right holder, not its customers, is the "appropriator" of the water); *Garwood Irrigation Co. v. Lower Colorado River Authority*, 387 S.W.2d 746, 751 (Tex. App.—Austin 1965, writ ref'd n.r.e.) ("The irrigators have no rights except through Garwood [Irrigation Company], and are not appropriators, but are customers of appropriators," citing *Willis*, 16 S.W.2d 266). See also Chapter 4 of this book for a history of canal companies and water rights. This commercial aspect of the irrigation rights causes the water right, and the canal company accordingly, to be subject to the provisions of Texas Water Code sections 11.036–.041.

Section 11.040 provides that a permanent water right is an easement that passes with the title to the land to which it is appurtenant. *See* Tex. Water Code § 11.040. The owner of a permanent water right is entitled to use the water according to the terms of his contract. In the absence of a contract, the owner of the permanent water right "is entitled to use water at a just, reasonable, and nondiscriminatory price." Tex. Water Code § 11.040(c); *see also* Tex. Water Code §§ 11.038–.039. The term "permanent water right" is not defined expressly in the statute. Based on case law, however, such a right is one that expressly entitles the holder to contract for water service from a canal company. Moreover, it is one that expressly has been conveyed or granted or reserved from a conveyance that becomes a vested property right that is treated as a covenant running with the land. It is distinguished as such from the implied right that is statutorily created. *See generally City of Wichita Falls v. Bruner*, 165 S.W.2d 480 (Tex. App. 1942, writ ref'd w.o.m.); *Edinburg Irrigation Co. v. Ledbetter*, 286 S.W. 185 (Tex. Comm'n App. 1926); *Chapman v. American Rio Grande Land & Irrigation Co.*, 271 S.W. 392 (Tex. App.—San Antonio 1925, writ ref'd); *Combs v. United Irrigation Co.*, 110 S.W.2d 1157 (Tex. App.—San Antonio 1937, writ dism'd); *Edinburg Irrigation Co. v. Paschen*, 235 S.W. 1088 (Tex. Comm'n App. 1922, judgm't adopted); Tex. Water Code § 11.040; Wells A. Hutchins, *Texas Law of Water Rights* 280 (1966).

Water Code section 11.038 creates what has come to be known as a statutory right to purchase water service from an irrigation company (or district). *See* Tex. Water Code § 11.038. This right extends to landowners who hold possessory interest in real property adjacent to a canal or similar facility. A statutory water right creates a right for a landowner who does not have a permanent right, and has not been able to reach an agreement with an irrigation company, to purchase water. Generally, cases out of which this right evolved describe the right as one based on easement. *See Edinburg Irrigation Co.*, 286 S.W. 185; *American Rio Grande Land & Irrigation Co. v. Mercedes Plantation Co.*, 208 S.W. 904 (Tex. Comm'n App. 1919, judgm't adopted). This right, however, appears to be limited by the fact that the landowner has to be willing to pay the reasonable and nondiscriminatory rates charged by the irrigation company as well as abide by the rules and regulations of the irrigation company. The statute also expressly provides that the party that owns or controls the water right must furnish the water "if the person has any water not contracted to others." *See* Tex. Water Code § 11.038(b). See Chapter 31 of this book for further discussion of wholesale water suppliers.

VII. Conclusion

§ 15.11 Conclusion

While water is recognized as a limited resource, and a hot commodity in Texas, water markets are not yet well developed in Texas. Depending on the type of project—for example, long-term municipal water supply versus year-to-year irrigation—factors that can affect the transaction and project development and implementation include (1) a lack of infrastructure—for example, treatment, transmission and delivery, or storage facilities; (2) regulatory requirements; and (3) opposition at the local level based on the project's interference with local water uses and needs. As a result, water deals take time and creativity to develop.

The history of water in Texas and the evolution of Texas's water law have both been driven by Texas's continuing cyclical state of drought. *See In re Adjudication of the Water Rights of Upper Guadalupe Segment of Guadalupe River Basin*, 642 S.W.2d 438, 441 (Tex. 1982); *see generally* Dylan O. Drummond et al., *The Rule of Capture in Texas—Still So Misunderstood after All These Years*, 37 Tex. Tech L. Rev. 1, 42 (2004). As both the terms "history" and "evolution" suggest, time and patience are needed when one engages in a water deal.

The good news for the owners of existing surface water rights is that, coupled with continually narrowing options for the development of new sources of supply, there has been an increased interest in water development to meet future demands following the passage of Senate Bill 1 in 1997, Act of June 1, 1997, 75th Leg., R.S., ch. 1010.

The value of existing, particularly "senior," water rights will continue to rise.

CHAPTER 16

Chapter 36 Groundwater Conservation Districts and Subsidence Districts

Trey Nesloney[1] and Deborah Trejo[2]

I. Introduction

§ 16.1 Constitutional Authority

Groundwater conservation districts and subsidence districts are created pursuant to article XVI, section 59, of the Texas Constitution. "There may be created within the State of Texas, or the State may be divided into, such number of conservation and reclamation districts as may be determined to be essential to the accomplishment" of preserving, conserving, and developing the natural resources of the State. Tex. Const. art. XVI, § 59(b). Both types of districts have powers to regulate the use of groundwater and to prevent the waste of groundwater or the degradation of water quality, but the types of powers granted to each type of district and the primary purposes they serve differ in certain ways.

II. Chapter 36 Groundwater Conservation Districts

§ 16.2 Introduction

A groundwater conservation district (GCD) is a local regulatory agency created "to provide for the conservation, preservation, protection, recharging, and prevention of waste of groundwater, and of groundwater reservoirs or their subdivisions, and to control subsidence caused by withdrawal of water from those groundwater reservoirs or their subdivisions." Tex. Water Code § 36.0015(b). These

1. Trey Nesloney is an attorney at Eichelbaum Wardell Hansen Powell & Munoz, P.C. He has been practicing water and environmental law for over fifteen years. During that time, he has aided clients in obtaining groundwater production permits, protested and appealed groundwater conservation district rules and orders, and challenged desired future conditions adopted by groundwater conservation districts. He received his JD from the University of Texas in 2006. Before practicing law, Mr. Nesloney worked as a civil engineer in Dallas, Texas. He is a Certified Engineer-in-Training in Texas. Mr. Nesloney graduated cum laude from Texas A&M University with a BS in civil engineering. He is a member of the American Bar Association, State Bar Association, Texas Water Conservation Association, and American Society of Civil Engineers.

2. Deborah Trejo is a partner in Kemp Smith L.L.P.'s Public and Environmental Law Department. Her practice focuses on representing private clients and governmental entities in litigation, appeals, elections, rulemaking, permitting, enforcement, transfer, legislative drafting, and open government matters, primarily in the water, environmental, and administrative areas. Ms. Trejo is a frequent speaker and presenter on water and environmental matters. Prior to joining Kemp Smith, Ms. Trejo worked in the Tulane Environmental Law Clinic and as an Assistant District Attorney for Cameron County, Texas.

districts "are the state's preferred method of groundwater management in order to protect property rights, balance the conservation and development of groundwater to meet the needs of this state, and use the best available science in the conservation and development of groundwater through rules developed, adopted, and promulgated by a district in accordance with the provisions" of chapter 36 of the Texas Water Code. Tex. Water Code § 36.0015(b). As discussed in detail at section 16.3:1 below, the Texas Commission on Environmental Quality (TCEQ) is the only administrative agency with jurisdiction to create GCDs and has significant oversight authority. *See* Tex. Water Code §§ 36.011(b), 36.301–.310.

A common mistake regarding GCDs is to assume that Water Code chapter 36 encompasses all the details as to the powers, duties, funding, administration, and authority of each specific district. In fact, one must also have a full understanding of the district's groundwater management plan, the district's rules, and the special laws or TCEQ orders creating the district to make this determination. This chapter does not attempt to survey these numerous and varied plans, rules, and legislation, but instead focuses on the general law applicable to GCDs.

§ 16.3 Creation, Addition of Territory, and Consolidation

The territory encompassed within a GCD is established when it is created. There are several methods by which a GCD can be created, as discussed below. Once a district is created, its boundaries can be changed by adding territory, which is referred to as annexation. Finally, two or more GCDs may combine, consolidating their authority and duties into a single district. These processes are discussed below.

§ 16.3:1 Creation

In Texas, a GCD can be created by special act of the legislature, upon petition to the TCEQ by landowners, or by the TCEQ through the priority groundwater management area (PGMA) process. Most GCDs have been created through the legislature. Once created, almost every GCD must be confirmed in a referendum election. *But see* Tex. Spec. Dist. Code §§ 8811.003 (confirmation election of the Corpus Christi Aquifer Storage and Recovery Conservation District not required), 8820.004 (confirmation election of the Northern Trinity Groundwater Conservation District not required).

Legislative Action: "The conservation and development of all of the natural resources of this State . . . and the preservation and conservation of all such natural resources of the State are each and all hereby declared public rights and duties; and the Legislature shall pass all such laws as may be appropriate thereto." Tex. Const. art. XVI, § 59(a). "There may be created within the State of Texas, or the State may be divided into, such number of conservation and reclamation districts as may be determined to be essential to the accomplishment" of these purposes. Tex. Const. art. XVI, § 59(b). Pursuant to this constitutional authority, the legislature may form new GCDs through special legislation.

A local senator or representative will introduce special legislation that creates a new GCD. Although the specifics of the legislation may vary in each case, typical district-creation legislation authorizes district powers and duties, appoints temporary directors, and establishes procedures for subsequent directors' elections and voter approval, which is known as confirming the GCD.

Each individual piece of special legislation that creates a new GCD may also differ in certain ways. The legislature can draft special laws that vary the powers, authorities, management, or financing mechanisms outlined in the general law. For example, district-creation legislation may give the GCD additional authority or responsibilities above those provided in chapter 36 of the Texas Water Code, such as water control and improvement. Alternatively, the legislation may also limit the powers available to a GCD, such as the power of eminent domain. To fully understand the scope of a GCD's power and structure (or any type of special district for that matter), one must read and understand not only chapter 36 but also the special laws that created the GCD, including any subsequent amendments. *See, e.g.*, Tex. Spec. Dist. Code §§ 8812.101 (prohibiting the Victoria County Groundwater Conservation District from exercising the power of eminent domain), 8819.103 (forbidding the Panola County Groundwater Conservation District from purchasing, selling, transporting, or distributing surface water or groundwater for any purpose). See Chapter 8 of this book for a discussion of other types of special law water districts.

Landowner Petition: A GCD can also be created through landowner petition. *See generally* Tex. Water Code § 36.013; *see also* 30 Tex. Admin. Code § 293.18 (creating TCEQ's implementing regulation). The petition requesting creation must be filed with the TCEQ for review and certification under section 36.015 of the Water Code. Tex. Water Code § 36.013(a). The petition must be signed by a majority of the landowners within the proposed district, or if there are more than fifty landowners in the proposed district, at least fifty of those landowners. Tex. Water Code § 36.013(b). The petition must include (1) the name of the proposed district; (2) the area and boundaries of the proposed district, including a map generally outlining the boundaries; (3) the purpose or purposes of the district; (4) a descriptive statement of any projects proposed to be undertaken by the district; (5) the names of at least five individuals qualified to serve as temporary directors; and (6) financial information, including the projected maintenance tax or production fee rate and a proposed budget of revenues and expenses for the district. Tex. Water Code § 36.013(c).

The TCEQ reviews the petition for statutory compliance, gives notice of the application, and conducts a public meeting in a central location within the area of the proposed district on the application not later than the sixtieth day after the date the commission issues notice. Tex. Water Code § 36.014(a). The notice must contain the date, time, and location of the public meeting and must be published in one or more newspapers of general circulation in the area of the proposed district. Tex. Water Code § 36.014(a).

Not later than ninety days after the date the TCEQ holds the public meeting on the petition, the TCEQ must certify the petition as administratively complete if the signatures and petition contents meet the statutory requirements. *See* Tex. Water Code § 36.015(a). The TCEQ may not certify a petition if the commission finds that the proposed district cannot be adequately funded to carry out its purposes based on the financial information provided in the petition or that the boundaries of the proposed district do not provide for the effective management of the groundwater resources. Tex. Water Code § 36.015(b). The TCEQ, after the amendments, must "give preference to boundary lines that are coterminous with those of a groundwater management area but may also consider boundaries along existing political subdivision boundaries if such boundaries would facilitate district creation and confirmation." Tex. Water Code § 36.015(b). If the TCEQ certifies the petition as administratively complete, the TCEQ must issue an order, notify the petitioners, and appoint the temporary directors named in the petition. Tex. Water Code § 36.015(e). If the TCEQ does not certify the petition, it must provide the reasons to the petitioners in writing. Tex. Water Code § 36.015(d).

If a GCD is created by landowner petition, not later than the 120th day after the date all temporary directors have been appointed and have qualified, the temporary directors must meet and order an election. Tex. Water Code § 36.017(a). The election is held to elect permanent directors and to confirm the creation of the district. Tex. Water Code § 36.017(a). If a majority of the votes cast in the election favor the creation of a district, the temporary board declares the district created. Tex. Water Code § 36.017(f). If the majority of the votes cast are against the creation of the district, the district has no further authority, except that the organization of the district is maintained until all the debts are paid. *See* Tex. Water Code § 36.017(h). A district, the major portion of which is located in one county, may not be organized to include land in another county unless the election held in the other county to confirm the creation of the district is approved by a majority of the voters of the other county voting in an election called for that purpose. Tex. Water Code § 36.019(a).

The Gonzales County Underground Water Conservation District was created by landowner petition to the Texas Water Commission (TCEQ predecessor agency) in 1993. *See* Gonzales County Underground Water Conservation District, *Creation of the District*, www.gcuwcd.org/creation. The Blanco-Pedernales Groundwater Conservation District was also created through landowner petition. *See* Texas Commission on Environmental Quality & Texas Water Development Board, *Priority Groundwater Management Areas and Groundwater Conservation Districts, Report to the 77th Legislature* 53 (Jan. 2001), www.tceq.texas.gov/assets/public/comm_exec/pubs/sfr/053_01.pdf [hereinafter 2001 PGMA-GCD Report]. It was confirmed through an election in 2001. *See* Texas Commission on Environmental Quality & Texas Water Development Board, *Priority Groundwater Management Areas and Groundwater Conservation Districts, Report to the 78th Texas Legislature* 41 (Jan. 2003), www.tceq.texas.gov/assets/public/comm_exec/pubs/sfr/053_03.pdf [hereinafter 2003 PGMA-GCD Report]. Additionally, a landowner petition was used in 1995 to create the Comal County Groundwater Conservation District covering the northern portion of the county, but its confirmation failed. *See* 2001 PGMA-GCD Report, at 62. Both creations were processed under an earlier version of the GCD-creation procedure. The current procedure was enacted in 2001. *See* Act of June 15, 2001, 77th Leg., R.S., ch. 966, §§ 2.34–.36, 36.013–.015.

In 2002, the landowner petition process under the current version of the law was used to create the Lake Country Groundwater Conservation District in Wood County. *See* 2003 PGMA-GCD Report, at 41. The electorate rejected confirmation of the district in February 2003. *See* Texas Commission on Environmental Quality & Texas Water Development Board, *Priority Groundwater Management Areas and Groundwater Conservation Districts, Report to the 79th Texas Legislature* 27 (Jan. 2005), www.tceq.texas.gov//assets//public//comm_exec//pubs//sfr//053_04.pdf [hereinafter 2005 PGMA-GCD Report].

TCEQ Action: The TCEQ can create a GCD, on its own motion, as part of the PGMA process. A PGMA is an "area designated and delineated by the commission as an area that is experiencing or is expected to experience critical groundwater problems." Tex. Water Code § 35.002(12). The procedure for designating a PGMA is detailed in chapter 35 of the Texas Water Code. *See generally* Tex. Water Code § 35.008; *see also* 30 Tex. Admin. Code ch. 294, subch. E (TCEQ's implementing regulations). The process requires the executive director of the TCEQ and the executive administrator of the TWDB to "meet periodically to identify, based on information gathered by the commission and the Texas Water Development Board, those areas of the state that are experiencing or that are expected to experience, within the immediately following 50-year period, critical groundwater problems." Tex. Water Code § 35.007(a). If the executive director of the TCEQ concludes that an area of the state should be considered for designation as a PGMA, the executive director shall prepare a report to the TCEQ. Tex. Water Code § 35.007(b). The TCEQ then must call an evidentiary hearing to consider the designation of a PGMA and to determine whether creating a GCD over all or part of the PGMA is "feasible and practicable." Tex. Water Code § 35.008(b)(2).

At the conclusion of the hearing, the TCEQ issues an order stating the findings and conclusions, including whether a PGMA should be designated and whether a GCD should be created. *See* Tex. Water Code § 35.008(f). If GCD creation has been recommended, the TCEQ then allows time for local landowners to take action to create a GCD in response to the order. *See* Tex. Water Code § 35.012(a). If local landowners do not take action to create a GCD, the TCEQ shall create a GCD "within two years, but no sooner than 120 days, from the date on which the commission issues an order." Tex. Water Code § 35.012(b); *see also* 30 Tex. Admin. Code §§ 293.19, 294.43. The TCEQ then appoints temporary directors and orders "that an election be called by the temporary directors to authorize the district to assess taxes and to elect permanent directors." Tex. Water Code § 36.0151(a). Unlike most

GCDs created through special legislation and all GCDs created by landowner petition, no confirmation election is required when a GCD is created by the TCEQ on its own motion, although all taxing authority must be approved by the voters.

Over the last three decades, the state has completed studies on eighteen separate areas to determine whether they were appropriate for designation as either a "critical area," the predecessor to a PGMA, or as a PGMA. Seven of the study areas were determined to have or were expected to have critical groundwater problems and were designated as PGMAs, two of which have been merged into the Hill Country Priority Groundwater Management Area. The study areas that have been designated as PGMAs are (1) parts of Reagan, Upton, and Midland counties; (2) all of Swisher and parts of Briscoe and Hale counties; (3) part of Dallam County; (4) part of El Paso County; (5) all of Bandera, Blanco, Gillespie, Kendall, and Kerr and parts of Bexar, Comal, Hays, and Travis counties (the Hill Country area); (6) all of Bosque, Coryell, Hill, McClennan, and Somervell counties (Central Texas–Trinity Aquifer); and (7) all of Collin, Cooke, Dallas, Denton, Ellis, Fannin, Grayson, Hood, Johnson, Montague, Parker, Tarrant, and Wise counties (North Central Texas–Trinity and Woodbine Aquifers). The TCEQ has determined that ten of the PGMA study areas do not meet the criteria for designation, and no further evaluation of those areas is planned. *See* Texas Commission on Environmental Quality & Texas Water Development Board, *Priority Groundwater Management Areas and Groundwater Conservation Districts, Report to the 82nd Texas Legislature* 1 (Jan. 2011), www.tceq.texas.gov/assets/public/comm_exec/pubs/sfr/053_07.pdf [hereinafter 2011 PGMA-GCD Report].

Locally initiated district creation or additions of territory to existing district activities have occurred in six of the seven PGMAs. The single exception is the El Paso County PGMA. Successful district creation has also not occurred in western Briscoe County in the Briscoe, Hale, Swisher County PGMA; southeast Midland County and northeast Upton County in the Reagan, Upton, Midland County PGMA; and Dallas County in the North Central Texas–Trinity and Woodbine Aquifers PGMA. *See* Texas Commission on Environmental Quality & Texas Water Development Board, *Priority Groundwater Management Areas and Groundwater Conservation Districts, Report to the 86th Texas Legislature* 21 fig. 2, 18–22 (Jan. 2019), www.tceq.texas.gov/assets/public/comm_exec/pubs/sfr/053-17.pdf [hereinafter 2019 PGMA-GCD Report]. The map at Plate 4 in this book shows the seven designated PGMAs, the areas within these designations that are currently included within a GCD, and the areas determined to not meet requirements for designation as PGMAs. *See* 2019 PGMA-GCD Report, at 21 fig. 2.

Currently, the western portion of Briscoe County is the only portion of the Briscoe, Swisher, and Hale County PGMA that has not been included within a GCD. In 2013, the TCEQ executive director issued a report recommending that it be added to High Plains Underground Water Conservation District No. 1 (HPUWCD). After a contested case hearing, on December 12, 2014, the TCEQ issued an order making this recommendation. *See* Texas Commission on Environmental Quality & Texas Water Development Board, *Priority Groundwater Management Areas and Groundwater Conservation Districts, Report to the 85th Texas Legislature* 21 (Jan. 2017), www.tceq.texas.gov/assets/public/comm_exec/pubs/sfr/053-10.pdf [hereinafter 2017 PGMA-GCD Report]. However, on March 13, 2015, the HPUWCD board of directors voted not to add the Briscoe PGMA territory to the district. *See* Texas Commission on Environmental Quality & Texas Water Development Board, *Priority Groundwater Management Areas and Groundwater Conservation Districts, Report to the 87th Texas Legislature* 25 (Jan. 2021), www.tceq.texas.gov/assets/public/comm_exec/pubs/sfr/053-20.pdf [hereinafter 2021 PGMA-GCD Report].

Similarly, portions in Upton and Midland counties in the Reagan, Upton, and Midland County PGMA have not joined or established a GCD. In December 2016, the TCEQ executive director issued a report evaluating five options for groundwater management in this area and recommended that adding northeastern Upton County and southeastern Midland County to the Glasscock GCD was the most feasible, practicable, and economic means to achieve groundwater management in this area. *See* 2019 PGMA-GCD Report, at 19. The TCEQ has continued to evaluate groundwater availability and use data for the Upton and Midland County portions in the PGMA, but no further action has been taken to advance the recommendation in the TCEQ executive director's report. *See* 2021 PGMA-GCD Report, at 11.

As of July 1, 2021, all thirteen counties in the North Central Texas–Trinity and Woodbine Aquifers PGMA are in a GCD except Dallas County. *See* 2021 PGMA-GCD Report, at 11. Before September 1, 2021, the TCEQ could not create a GCD for a PGMA in a county "in which the annual amount of surface water used is more than 50 times the annual amount of groundwater produced" and "that has a population greater than 2.3 million." Tex. Water Code § 36.0151(f). Therefore, the legislature restricted the TCEQ from creating a GCD in Dallas County before September 1, 2021. *See* 2021 PGMA-GCD Report, at 11–12.

Both western Comal County and western Travis County in the Hill Country PGMA are now within the jurisdiction of a GCD. During the 84th legislative session, the legislature created the Comal Trinity Groundwater Conservation District, which now has jurisdiction over the PGMA territory in Northwest Comal County. *See* Act of May 26, 2015, 84th Leg., R.S., ch. 656 (H.B. 2407) (codified at Tex. Spec. Dist. Code ch. 8875). The directors have been appointed by the commissioners' court. The district is not subject to a confirmation election. *See* 2017 PGMA-GCD Report, at 1–2. Additionally, during the 85th legislative session, the legislature passed House Bill 4345, creating the Southwestern Travis County Groundwater Conservation District covering western Travis County in the Hill Country PGMA. *See* Act of May 28, 2017, 85th Leg., R.S., ch. 644, § 2.02 (H.B. 4345) (codified at Tex. Spec. Dist. Code ch. 8871). The district was created subject to a confirmation election, which was held on November 5, 2019. *See* 2021 PGMA-GCD Report, at 11. The election resulted in confirmation of the Southwestern Travis County Groundwater Conservation District, and new directors were elected for the GCD. *See* 2021 PGMA-GCD Report, at 11. All areas of the Hill Country PGMA are now located within the jurisdiction of a GCD.

§ 16.3:2 Addition of Territory

There are three methods of adding territory to an existing GCD, other than through special legislation. Adjacent landowners may petition the district to add their property into the district. Those owning property that is not contiguous with a district may petition to have their property annexed into the district. Finally, the TCEQ may add territory to an existing GCD through the PGMA process.

Adjacent Landowner Petition: First, the owner or owners of land contiguous to a district may file a notarized petition with the GCD's board of directors requesting that the land be included in the district. *See generally* Tex. Water Code §§ 36.321–.324. If multiple landowners are involved, all the landowners must sign the petition. The board may annex the land in the petition if it is considered to be to the advantage of the petitioner(s) and to the existing district. *See* Tex. Water Code § 36.323(a). For example, this process has been used to add territory to the Irion County Water Conservation District, the Kenedy County Groundwater Conservation District, the Coastal Bend Groundwater Conservation District, and the Brush County Groundwater Conservation District. *See* 2003 PGMA-GCD Report, at 43 (reporting that the Irion County Water Conservation District was petitioned by three adjacent landowners and the board added the land to the district in 2001); Texas Commission on Environmental Quality & Texas Water Development Board, *Priority Groundwater Management Areas and Groundwater Conservation Districts, Report to the 80th Texas Legislature* 31 (Jan. 2007), www.tceq.texas.gov/assets/public/comm_exec/pubs/sfr/053_05.pdf [hereinafter 2007 PGMA-GCD Report] (stating that territory was added to the Kenedy County Groundwater Conservation District and the Coastal Bend Groundwater Conservation District by adjacent landowner petition in 2006); 2011 PGMA-GCD Report, at 37 (reporting addition of contiguous territory by landowner petition to the Brush Country GCD in 2010).

Annexation of Territory: Second, landowners of a defined area of territory, whether or not that area is contiguous to the existing district, may file a petition with the district's board of directors requesting inclusion in that district. *See generally* Tex. Water Code §§ 36.325–.331. If the territory is not contiguous to the district, it must be within the same groundwater management area, priority groundwater management area, or a groundwater subdivision designated by the TCEQ or its predecessors. *See* Tex. Water Code § 36.331. See also Chapter 21 of this book regarding PGMAs and GMAs. The petition must be signed by a majority of the landowners in the territory, at least fifty landowners if the number of landowners is greater than fifty, or the county commissioners court of the county in which the area is located if the area is identified as a priority groundwater management area or includes the entire county. *See* Tex. Water Code § 36.325(b). At least one hearing must be held in the existing district, and one hearing must be held in the territory to be added. *See* Tex. Water Code § 36.326. If the district's board finds after the hearing on the petition that the addition of the land would benefit the district and the territory to be added, the board may add the territory to the district by resolution. *See* Tex. Water Code § 36.327. "The board does not have to include all the territory described in the petition if it finds that a modification or change is necessary or desirable." Tex. Water Code § 36.327. Annexation of the territory is not final until ratified by a majority vote of the voters in the territory to be added. *See* Tex. Water Code § 36.328(a). This process has been used by various GCDs to add territory. *See* 2003 PGMA-GCD Report, at 43 (adding territory including all of Runnels County and portions of Tom Green and Concho counties to the Lipan-Kickapoo Water Conservation District in 2001); 2005 PGMA-GCD Report, at 27 (annexing the southeastern two-thirds of Mason County to Hickory Underground Water Conservation District No. 1); 2007 PGMA-GCD Report, at 31 (annexing Hardin and Tyler counties to the Southeast GCD in 2005). There cannot be two valid annexations of the same property to two different GCDs; however, in a case of two competing claims for the same territory, it is unknown under the current statutory provisions whether the first GCD to initiate annexation or the first to finalize annexation would acquire jurisdiction of the territory. *See* Tex. Att'y Gen. Op. No. GA-0795 (2010), https://www2.texasattorneygeneral.gov/opinions/opinions/50abbott/op/2010/pdf/ga0795.pdf (discussing jurisdiction for territory in eastern Caldwell County annexed by Gonzales County Underground Water Conservation District by landowner petition, but also annexed by individual landowner petition to the Plum Creek Conservation District before ratification election was completed for the Gonzales County Underground Water Conservation District annexation); *but see* Act of May 25, 2011, 82d Leg., R.S., ch. 658 (Senate Bill 1225 resolving this situation by allowing the landowners to select which GCD they want to have jurisdiction over their property). If territory is annexed to one GCD and then subsequently included in special legislation creating a different GCD, the special law prevails over the prior general law annexation for the purposes of statutory law. *See* Tex. Att'y Gen. Op. No. GA-0792 (2010), https://www2.texasattorneygeneral.gov/opinions/opinions/50abbott/op/2010/pdf/ga0792.pdf; *but see* Act of May 24, 2011, 82d Leg., R.S., ch. 735 (House Bill 1060 resolving this issue by deannexing approximately 410 acres of territory in Bastrop County from the Barton Springs–Edwards Aquifer Conservation District).

PGMA Process: Third, the TCEQ can add territory to an existing district through the PGMA process. *See generally* Tex. Water Code § 35.013. In this process, the TCEQ issues an order recommending that a PGMA or a portion of a PGMA be added to one or more existing GCDs. *See* Tex. Water Code § 35.008(g)(2). If the TCEQ issues an order making this recommendation, it must submit a copy of the order to the board of the GCD to which it is recommending the PGMA be added. *See* Tex. Water Code § 35.013(b). "Not later than the 120th day after the date of receiving the copy," the board of directors of the existing GCD shall vote on the addition of the PGMA to the GCD. Tex. Water Code § 35.013(b). If the board of the GCD votes to accept the addition, and the GCD has not approved an ad valorem tax by the date of the TCEQ's order, the district's board shall enter an order adding the territory to the GCD. Tex. Water Code § 35.013(b–1). If an ad valorem tax has already been approved by the date of the TCEQ's order, and the GCD board votes to accept the addition, an election must be held in the added PGMA within 270 days of the board's vote to determine if the added area will assume a proportional share of the debts or taxes of the GCD. Tex. Water Code § 35.013(c)(3). If a majority of the voters in the added area vote in favor of the proposition, the district's board declares that the PGMA assumes a proportional share of the debts or taxes of the GCD; if the voters in the added area vote against the proposition, the district's board must adopt rules to implement statutory production fees in the added area according to section 35.013(g–1) of the Water Code. Tex. Water Code § 35.013(f). If either the board of the GCD votes against the addition or if the proposition is defeated in the election by the voters within the added area, the TCEQ then has one year to create one or more GCDs covering the PGMA or recommend that the area be added to another existing GCD. Tex. Water Code § 35.013(h).

On December 12, 2014, the TCEQ considered an administrative law judge's proposal for decision and approved an order recommending that the Briscoe, Hale, and Swisher County PGMA territory located in the western portion of Briscoe County be added to the HPUWCD No. 1. 2017 PGMA-GCD Report, at 21. However, as mentioned at section 16.3:1 above, on March 13, 2015, the HPUWCD board of directors voted not to add the Briscoe PGMA territory to the district. The TCEQ maintains that adding the western portion of Briscoe County within the PGMA to the HPUWCD is the only feasible and practicable solution for the protection and management of groundwater resources and recommends statutory action be taken to add the western portion of Briscoe County within the PGMA to the HPUWCD. Texas Commission on Environmental Quality, *Priority Groundwater Management Areas*, www.tceq.texas.gov/groundwater/groundwater-planning-assessment/pgma.html.

In December 2016, the TCEQ executive director issued a report recommending the addition of northeastern Upton County and southeastern Midland County to the Glasscock GCD; the executive director determined that this was the most feasible, practicable, and economic means to achieve groundwater management in the Reagan, Upton, and Midland PGMA. *See* 2017 PGMA-GCD Report, at 21. As of July 1, 2021, no further TCEQ action has been taken to advance this recommendation. See 2021 PGMA-GCD Report, at 11.

§ 16.3:3 Consolidation

Two or more GCDs may consolidate into one district. To initiate a consolidation, the board of a district adopts a resolution proposing a consolidation and delivers a copy of the resolution to the board of each district with which consolidation is proposed. Tex. Water Code § 36.351(a). Adjacent districts may consolidate portions of either district if one district relinquishes land within that district to the jurisdiction of the other district. Tex. Water Code § 36.351(b). A consolidation occurs only if the board of each involved district adopts a resolution containing the terms and conditions of the consolidation. Tex. Water Code § 36.351(c). After a hearing, the board may, by resolution, approve the terms and conditions for consolidation and enter an order consolidating the district. Tex. Water Code § 36.353(b).

An election to ratify the consolidation is required in each district that initiates consolidation. Tex. Water Code § 36.354(a). A district may be consolidated only if a majority of the electors in each district that is required to conduct an election vote in favor of consolidation. Tex. Water Code § 36.354(d). Failure of any one district to ratify the consolidation does not prevent the consolidation of other districts. Tex. Water Code § 36.354(d).

In 2004, the Dallam County Underground Water Conservation District No. 1 was consolidated into the North Plains Groundwater Conservation District. *See* 2007 PGMA-GCD Report, at 31. In 2014, the Anderson County Underground Water Conservation District consolidated with the Neches and Trinity Valleys Groundwater Conservation District. *See* Texas Commission on Environmental Quality & Texas Water Development Board, *Priority Groundwater Management Areas and Groundwater Conservation Districts, Report to the 84th Texas Legislature* 12 (Jan. 2015), www.tceq.texas.gov/assets/public/comm_exec/pubs/sfr/053-09.pdf.

§ 16.4 Administration

Texas Water Code chapter 36 establishes the basic parameters of GCD administration. Most such provisions are found in subchapter C, which addresses the board of directors, what constitutes a quorum for purposes of conducting district business, district officers, management practices and personnel, elections, meetings, records, contracts, lawsuits, and employee benefits, as well as other administrative issues. The following sections discuss directors, officers, general manager, meetings, records, and bylaws.

§ 16.4:1 Directors

Texas Water Code chapter 36 distinguishes between temporary and permanent directors. The distinctions include how the directors are determined and their powers and duties once in office. Other general law controls certain aspects of serving as a district director, particularly on the subject of removal from office, dual officeholding, and conflicts of interest.

Temporary Directors: Once a GCD is created, temporary directors are appointed to manage the affairs of the district. (See also section 16.9:4 below, which explains that temporary directors can be appointed under Water Code section 36.303.) Their responsibilities include finding funds, conducting the confirmation election, and assisting in the election or appointment of permanent directors. Temporary directors serve until the permanent directors are elected and have qualified for office or until the voters do not approve the creation of the district in the confirmation election. *See* Tex. Water Code § 36.016(c).

If a GCD is created through action by the legislature, the special legislation usually addresses the appointment and names the temporary directors. If the GCD is created through a landowner petition, the petition must include the names of at least five individuals qualified to serve as temporary directors. *See* Tex. Water Code § 36.013(c)(5); *see also* 30 Tex. Admin. Code § 293.13. The TCEQ appoints these temporary directors when it issues an order creating the district. *See* Tex. Water Code § 36.016(a). If the TCEQ creates a GCD in a PGMA under section 36.0151, the county commissioners court of the county that contains the area of the district must appoint five temporary directors under the procedures in section 36.0161. *See* Tex. Water Code § 36.016(b).

Permanent Directors: Special legislation creating a GCD generally describes when and how the permanent directors are to be selected, through either election or appointment. *See, e.g.*, Tex. Spec. Dist. Code §§ 8819.052 (stating that permanent directors of the Panola County Groundwater Conservation District must be elected), 8830.051 (stating that the commissioners court of each county within the Upper Trinity Groundwater Conservation District must appoint two permanent directors who serve staggered four-year terms and may serve multiple consecutive terms). If a GCD is created under section 36.015 or as the result of the PGMA process, not later than the 120th day after the date all temporary directors have been appointed and have qualified, the temporary directors must meet and order an election to elect permanent directors. *See* Tex. Water Code §§ 36.017(a), 36.0171(a). The temporary directors must publish notice of the election in a newspaper with a general circulation within the boundaries of the proposed district before the thirtieth day preceding the date of the election. *See* Tex. Water Code §§ 36.017(c), 36.0171(c). The board of directors must consist of not fewer than five but not more than eleven directors elected for four-year terms. *See* Tex. Water Code § 36.051(a). Unless a district has a population of less than 50,000, a member of a governing body of another political subdivision is ineligible for appointment or election as a director. *See* Tex. Water Code § 36.051(b); *but see* Tex. Att'y Gen. Op. No. JC-0455A (2002) (stating that section 36.051(b) did not repeal the common-law doctrine of incompatibility with regard to districts of fewer than 50,000 population).

Powers and Duties: The board of directors governs and is responsible for the management of all the affairs of the district. *See* Tex. Water Code §§ 36.051(a), 36.057(a). A majority of the membership of the board constitutes a quorum for any meeting, and a concurrence of a majority of the entire membership of the board is sufficient for transacting any business of the district. Tex. Water Code § 36.053. The board may adopt bylaws to govern the affairs of the district to perform its purposes. Tex. Water Code § 36.057(f). See the discussion at section 16.4:4 below.

Removal and Vacancies: Directors are officers who are subject to removal in accordance with article V, section 24, of the Texas Constitution and chapter 87 of the Texas Local Government Code. *See generally* Tex. Const. art. V, § 24; Tex. Loc. Gov't Code §§ 87.001–.041. An officer may be removed for incompetency, official misconduct, or intoxication. Tex. Loc. Gov't Code § 87.013(a). "Incompetency" is defined as gross ignorance of official duties, gross carelessness in the discharge of those duties, or unfitness or inability to promptly and properly discharge official duties because of a serious physical or mental defect that did not exist at the time of the officer's election. Tex. Loc. Gov't Code § 87.011(2). "Official misconduct" means intentional, unlawful behavior relating to official duties by an officer entrusted with the administration of justice or the execution of the law. The term includes an intentional or corrupt failure, refusal, or neglect of an officer to perform a duty imposed on the officer by law. Tex. Loc. Gov't Code § 87.011(3).

Directors of a GCD are subject to the provisions of chapter 171 of the Local Government Code relating to the regulation of conflicts of officers of local governments. Tex. Water Code § 36.058; *see, e.g.*, Tex. Att'y Gen. Op. No. GA-0796 (2010), https://www2.texasattorneygeneral.gov/opinions/opinions/50abbott/op/2010/pdf/ga0796.pdf (discussing whether conflict of interest provisions in Local Government Code chapter 171 required two GCD directors to disclose their interests and abstain from voting on a district rule). They and the general manager are also subject to Local Government Code chapter 176, which requires the disclosure of certain business and other relationships between the officers of a local governmental entity, including a conservation district, and those who do, or seek to do, business with the local governmental entity. Each member of a district's board of directors and the general manager has disclosure obligations under chapter 176. Additionally, any person or entity (excluding another governmental entity) that contracts or seeks to contract for the *sale or purchase* of property, goods, or services with a district will qualify as a "vendor" that must comply with the applicable disclosure requirements of chapter 176. *See generally* Tex. Loc. Gov't Code §§ 176.001–.012.

A director is disqualified and vacates the office of director if the director is appointed or elected as a member of the governing body of another political subdivision, unless the GCD has a population of fewer than 50,000. Tex. Water Code § 36.051(b); *see also* Tex. Water Code § 36.051(d) (providing additional dual officeholding exceptions for GCDs with a population of fewer than 50,000).

Unless provided otherwise in its enabling legislation, the board of directors fills vacancies in the office of director by appointment. If the vacant office is not scheduled for election for longer than two years at the time of the appointment, the board must order an election for the unexpired term to be held as part of the next regularly scheduled director's election. The appointed director's term shall end on qualification of the director elected at that election. Tex. Water Code § 36.051(c).

§ 16.4:2 Officers

After a district has been created and the directors have been qualified, the board must meet; elect a president, vice president, secretary, and any other officers or assistant officers the board may deem necessary; and begin to discharge its duties. Tex. Water Code § 36.054(a). After each director's election, the board must elect officers. Tex. Water Code § 36.054(b). The board may appoint another director, the general manager, or any employee as assistant or deputy secretary to assist the secretary, and that person is entitled to certify as to the authenticity of any record of the district, including all proceedings relating to bonds, contracts, or indebtedness of the district. Tex. Water Code § 36.054(d). Within thirty days after any election or appointment of a director, a district must notify the executive director of the TCEQ of the name and mailing address of the director chosen and the date that director's term of office expires. *See* Tex. Water Code § 36.054(e); *see also* Texas Commission on Environmental Quality, District Registration Form (TCEQ-0179 Rev. 09/2013), www.tceq.texas.gov/assets/public/permitting/forms/0179.pdf.

§ 16.4:3 General Manager

Except in a district that is composed of the territory of more than one county, a director may be employed as general manager of the district. Tex. Water Code § 36.056(c). The compensation of a general manager who also serves as a director must be established by the other directors. Tex. Water Code § 36.056(c). The board may employ or contract with a person to be the general manager, and the board of directors may also delegate to the general manager full authority to manage and operate the affairs of the district subject only to the orders of the board. Tex. Water Code § 36.056(a). The board may, by resolution, authorize its general manager or another employee to execute documents on behalf of the district. Tex. Water Code § 36.057(f).

§ 16.4:4 Meetings, Records, and Bylaws

As with other aspects of GCD administration, Texas Water Code chapter 36 addresses meetings, records, and bylaws. With regard to meetings and records, however, the broader requirements of the Texas Open Meetings Act (TOMA) and the Public Information Act expand on the sparse chapter 36 requirements.

Meetings and Records: The board must designate one or more places inside or outside the district for conducting the meetings of the board. Tex. Water Code § 36.062(b). Notice of the meetings must be given pursuant to, and meetings are subject to, the TOMA, Texas Government Code chapter 551. *See* Tex. Water Code § 36.063; Tex. Gov't Code §§ 551.001–.146. The meetings must be held at least quarterly. *See* Tex. Water Code § 36.064. The board must designate and the district must maintain one or more regular offices for conducting the business of the district and maintaining the records of the district. *See* Tex. Water Code § 36.062(a). The board must keep a complete account of all its meetings and proceedings and shall preserve its minutes, contracts, records, notices, accounts, receipts, and other records in a safe place. Tex. Water Code § 36.065(a). The records are subject to the Texas Public Information Act, Texas Government Code chapter 552. *See* Tex. Gov't Code §§ 552.001–.353. Additionally, GCDs are subject to the requirements of the Local Government Records Act and must develop policies and procedures for the administration of an active and continuing records management program. *See* Tex. Loc. Gov't Code §§ 201.001–.009.

Bylaws: The board may adopt bylaws to govern the affairs of the district to perform its purposes. Tex. Water Code § 36.057(f). Bylaws differ from rules because they address the internal procedure of the board, not the GCD's interaction with the public, which is the general subject of rules. For a more in-depth discussion of GCD rules and rulemaking powers, see section 16.7:1 below. Some of the procedures or issues commonly addressed in a GCD's bylaws include the office hours of the district, board member terms, the code of ethics or code of conduct for the directors and employees of the district, indemnification of directors and employees, and the financial procedures of the GCD.

§ 16.5 Finances

As with any governmental entity, the finances of the district are strictly regulated. Texas Water Code chapter 36 includes three subchapters dedicated to this topic. Subchapter E addresses district finances in general. Subchapter F covers bonds and notes. Subchapter G establishes requirements related to district revenues and taxing authority.

§ 16.5:1 Financial Procedure

Chapter 36 provides specific requirements for district expenditures, establishing a fiscal year, annual audit and budgets, investments, and certain funding.

Expenditures: A GCD may disburse money only by check, draft, order, or other instrument. Tex. Water Code § 36.151(a). Any disbursements, other than federal reserve wire transfers or electronic fund transfers, must be signed by at least two directors; however, the board of directors by resolution may allow a certain employee, or a combination of employees and directors, to sign disbursements on behalf of the board. Tex. Water Code § 36.151(b). In 2017, the Texas legislature added provisions to section 36.151 allowing GCDs to use electronic banking. *See* Act of May 24, 2017, 85th Leg., R.S., ch. 585, § 1 (S.B. 865) (amending Tex. Water Code § 36.151).

Fiscal Year: The GCD must be operated on the basis of a fiscal year established by the board of directors. Tex. Water Code § 36.152(a).

Annual Audit: The GCD must have an annual audit made of the financial condition of the district, performed according to the generally accepted government auditing standards adopted by the American Institute of Certified Public Accountants. Tex. Water Code § 36.153(a). The only exception to this requirement is if the district had not more than $500 in receipts from any source during the calendar year; not more than $500 in disbursements of funds during the calendar year; no bonds or other liabilities with terms of more than one year outstanding during the calendar year; and no cash or investments amounting to more than $5,000 at any time during the calendar year. Tex. Water Code § 36.153(c). The annual audit and other district records must be open to inspection during regular business hours at the principal office of the district. Tex. Water Code § 36.153(b).

Annual Budget: The board of directors of a GCD shall prepare and approve an annual budget. Tex. Water Code § 36.154(a). The annual budget contains a complete financial statement for the GCD and includes (1) a statement of the outstanding obligations of the district, (2) the amount of cash on hand to the credit of each fund of the district, (3) the amount of money received by the district from all sources during the previous year, (4) the amount of money available to the district from all sources during the ensuing year, (5) the amount of the balances expected at the end of the year in which the budget is being prepared, (6) the estimated amount of revenues and balances available to cover the proposed budget, and (7) the estimated tax rate or fee revenues that will be required. Tex. Water Code § 36.154(b).

Voter Approval of Indebtedness: Article XVI, section 59(c), of the Texas Constitution, under which a GCD is created, reads in part as follows: "The Legislature shall not authorize the issuance of any bonds or provide for any indebtedness against any reclamation district unless such proposition shall first be submitted to the qualified voters of such district and the proposition adopted." Tex. Const. art. XVI, § 59(c). Therefore, if a GCD issues an obligation to pay for "indebtedness," the proposition must be approved by the voters in the district. The test for what is or is not a "debt" or "indebtedness" under

Texas law is a factual determination by the court. *See, e.g., Cameron County Water Improvement District No. 8 v. Western Metal Manufacturing Co. of Texas*, 125 S.W.2d 650, 653 (Tex. App.—El Paso 1939, writ dism'd judgm't cor.) (finding no "indebtedness" due to intent for the obligation to be paid out of current revenues for the year and burden on revenues for future years); *Hidalgo County Water Improvement District No. 2 v. Feick*, 111 S.W.2d 742, 746 (Tex. App.—Beaumont 1937, writ dism'd) (using multiple factual determinations to decide whether a contract created a "debt" within the meaning of article XVI, section 59, of the Texas Constitution); *Toole v. First National Bank*, 168 S.W. 423, 428 (Tex. App.—Galveston 1914, writ ref'd) (holding that a "debt" was created if insufficient funds were available in current revenues to cover the contract).

Account Management: The board of directors of a GCD must name one or more banks to serve as a depository for the district's funds. Tex. Water Code § 36.155(a). The district's funds, other than those transmitted to a bank for payment of bonds issued by the district, must be deposited as received with the depository bank and remain on deposit. This does not limit the power of the board of directors to place a portion of the GCD's funds on time deposit or to purchase certificates of deposit. Tex. Water Code § 36.155(b). "To the extent that funds in the depository are not insured by the Federal Deposit Insurance Corporation, they shall be secured in the manner provided by law for the security of funds by the Public Funds Collateral Act, chapter 2257, Government Code." Tex. Water Code § 36.155(c).

Funds of the GCD must be invested in accordance with the provisions of the Public Funds Investment Act, Texas Government Code chapter 2256. Tex. Water Code § 36.156(a). The board of directors, by resolution, may provide that an authorized representative of the district may invest and reinvest the district's funds and provide for money to be withdrawn from the appropriate accounts of the district for investments on such terms as the board considers advisable. Tex. Water Code § 36.156(b).

§ 16.5:2 Revenues

GCDs are financed primarily through the imposition of maintenance taxes, often referred to as ad valorem taxes, or through production and administration fees. Texas Water Code chapter 36, subchapter G, grants a GCD the power to levy taxes and set fees. However, this power is not absolute. Often the legislation that created the GCD will limit the tax rate or fees, and the Water Code also contains restrictions and conditions that apply to all districts unless overridden by special legislation.

Taxes: The board of directors of a GCD may annually levy taxes to pay the bonds issued by the district that are payable in whole or in part by taxes. Tex. Water Code § 36.201(a). The board may annually levy taxes to pay the maintenance and operating expenses of the district at a rate not to exceed 50 cents on each $100 of assessed valuation. Tex. Water Code § 36.201(b). However, a GCD may not levy a tax to pay for its maintenance and operating expenses until the tax is approved by a majority of the electors voting at an election in the district held for that purpose. Tex. Water Code § 36.201(c).

The board of directors must take into account the income of the district from other sources when setting the tax rate. Tex. Water Code § 36.203. The Texas Tax Code governs the appraisal, assessment, and collection of district taxes. Tex. Water Code § 36.204(a).

Fees: A GCD has the power to set fees for administrative acts of the district, such as filing applications, although fees cannot unreasonably exceed the costs to the district of performing the administrative function for which the fee is charged. Tex. Water Code § 36.205(a). A district shall set and collect fees for all services provided outside the boundaries of the district; however, the fees may not unreasonably exceed the cost to the district of providing the services outside the district. Tex. Water Code § 36.205(b).

A district may assess production fees based on the amount of water authorized by permit to be withdrawn from a well or the amount actually withdrawn. A district may assess the fees in lieu of, or in conjunction with, any taxes otherwise levied by the district. A district may use revenues generated by the fees for any lawful purpose. Production fees shall not exceed $1 per acre-foot payable annually for water used for agricultural use or $10 per acre-foot payable annually for water used for any other purpose. Tex. Water Code § 36.205(c). The rate of fees set for agricultural uses shall be no more than 20 percent of the rate applied to municipal uses. Tex. Water Code § 36.206(b). District fees may not be used to purchase groundwater rights unless the purchased rights are acquired for conservation purposes and are permanently held in trust, not to be produced. Tex. Water Code § 36.205(c). A GCD may assess an export fee under section 36.122 of the Water Code for transfers of groundwater out of the district. *See* Tex. Water Code § 36.205(g).

Grants: Although most districts are funded primarily by taxes and fees, some districts also accept outside funding for their operations in the form of grants or loans. A GCD may make or accept any grant, gratuity, advance, or loan that the board of directors deems appropriate and has approved. *See* Tex. Water Code § 36.158.

Funds: The Texas Water Development Board (TWDB) may allocate funds from the water assistance fund to a GCD to conduct initial data collection, develop and implement a groundwater management plan, and participate in regional water plans. Tex. Water Code § 36.159. The TWDB may provide funds to a GCD if the TWDB determines that such funding will allow the district to comply or continue to comply with the provisions of chapter 36 of the Water Code. *See* Tex. Water Code § 36.161(a). In addition, the TWDB, the TCEQ, the Parks and Wildlife Department, the Texas Agricultural Extension Service, and institutions of higher education may allocate funds to carry out the objectives of chapters 35 and 36 of the Water Code. Tex. Water Code § 36.160. See also Chapter 37 of this book, discussing financing water projects.

The TWDB uses the groundwater district loan assistance fund to provide loans to pay for the creation and initial operations of newly confirmed districts and legislatively created districts that do not require a confirmation election. Tex. Water Code § 36.372(a); *see also* Tex. Water Code ch. 36, subch. L. The TWDB establishes the rules for the use and administration of the groundwater district loan assistance fund. Tex. Water Code § 36.372(b); *see also* 31 Tex. Admin. Code ch. 363, subch. H (using TWDB rules to implement Water Code chapter 36, subchapter L).

§ 16.5:3 Bonds and Notes

A GCD may issue and sell bonds and notes in the name of the district for any lawful purpose of the district; however, a district may not issue bonds unless the TCEQ determines that the project to be financed by the bonds is feasible and issues an order approving the issuance of the bonds. Tex. Water Code § 36.171(a); *see also* Tex. Water Code ch. 36, subch. F. The TCEQ shall consider the written feasibility application submitted by the district, the engineer's report that must be submitted with the district's application, and any other evidence allowed by TCEQ rules to determine feasibility. *See* Tex. Water Code § 36.171(b)–(f); *see also* 30 Tex. Admin. Code ch. 293, subch. E (stating TCEQ rules on the issuance of bonds by districts).

A GCD may provide for the payment of principal and interest on the bonds and notes in several ways. The bonds may be paid by the levy and collection of ad valorem taxes or by fees. Tex. Water Code § 36.172(1), (2). Payment can also be made by pledging all or any part of the designated revenues from the ownership or operation of the district's works, improvements, and facilities and from the sale, transportation, and distribution of water. Tex. Water Code § 36.172(3).

Bonds or notes secured in whole or in part by taxes may not be issued by the district until authorized by a majority vote of the qualified voters of the district at an election held for that purpose. Tex. Water Code § 36.180(a).

Bonds and notes issued by a district must be submitted to the attorney general for examination. Tex. Water Code § 36.181(a). The attorney general shall approve them if the attorney general finds that the bonds or notes have been authorized in accordance with the law. Tex. Water Code § 36.181(b).

§ 16.6 Groundwater Management Powers and Duties

The numerous powers and duties of a GCD are prescribed in detail by the statutory provisions in chapter 36, subchapter D, of the Texas Water Code. *See generally* Tex. Water Code §§ 36.101–.124. However, the power of a GCD is limited by the terms of the applicable statutes authorizing its creation, and it can exercise no authority that the Texas legislature has not clearly granted. *See South Plains Lamesa Railroad, Ltd. v. High Plains Underground Water Conservation District No. 1*, 52 S.W.3d 770, 779–80 (Tex. App.—Amarillo 2001, no pet.). As previously noted, the true scope of a GCD's power and structure can be determined only by examining both the general laws, found primarily in chapter 36 of the Water Code, and the special laws or orders that created the GCD. The powers listed below could be modified or eliminated depending on special legislation or order authorizing the GCD.

Chapter 36 of the Water Code invests GCDs with unique powers designed to perform their duty to conserve, preserve, and protect groundwater; to recharge groundwater resources and prevent waste; and to control subsidence. *See* Tex. Water Code § 36.0015. These powers fall generally into three categories: planning; data collection and dissemination; and well regulation, including limiting production. Districts have additional powers to enable them to accomplish these goals. These additional powers are discussed at section 16.6:4 below.

§ 16.6:1 Planning

A GCD is required to adopt and update periodically a plan describing how it will meet its statutory duties, particularly as those duties relate to management of the groundwater resources under district jurisdiction. On a regional basis, a GCD must also participate in joint planning activities with other districts in its designated groundwater management area. These duties are discussed below.

Management Plan: A management plan outlines the goals of a GCD and the steps needed to reach those goals. *See* Tex. Water Code § 36.1071(a), (e). See also Chapter 21 of this book. A district's management plan must be developed in coordination with the TCEQ and the TWDB, which provide technical assistance to the GCD. *See* Tex. Water Code § 36.1071(c), (d); *see also* 31 Tex. Admin. Code §§ 356.50–.57 (TWDB, groundwater management plan approval). The goals of a management plan are to (1) provide for the most efficient use of groundwater; (2) control and prevent waste of groundwater; (3) control and prevent subsidence; (4) address conjunctive surface water issues; (5) address natural resources issues; (6) address drought conditions; (7) address conservation, recharge enhancement, rainwater harvesting, precipitation enhancement, and brush control; and (8) address the desired future conditions adopted by the GCD under section 36.108 of the Texas Water Code. Tex. Water Code § 36.1071(a). In the groundwater management plan, the GCD must include estimates of the modeled available groundwater in the district based on the desired future conditions, the amount of usable groundwater available, the amount being used, the amount of recharge, and the projected water supply and demand. *See* Tex. Water Code § 36.1071(e)(3). In developing its management plan, the district must use the groundwater availability modeling information provided by the TWDB together with any available site-specific information that was provided by the district and reviewed by the TWDB. Tex. Water Code § 36.1071(h). The GCD must adopt rules necessary to implement the management plan. Tex. Water Code § 36.1071(f). The district must adopt amendments to the management plan as necessary, after notice and a hearing. Tex. Water Code § 36.1071(g). The statute does not specify the nature of the notice and hearing; it is assumed TOMA procedures are adequate.

A GCD must file its management plan with the executive administrator of the TWDB for review and approval within three years of forming the district or, if the district required confirmation, not later than three years after the election confirming the district's creation. *See* Tex. Water Code § 36.1072(a–1). The executive administrator must approve a management plan if it is administratively complete. Tex. Water Code § 36.1072(b). A management plan takes effect on approval by the executive administrator of the TWDB, which must be done within sixty days or, if appealed, on approval by the TWDB. *See* Tex. Water Code § 36.1072(b), (d).

If the executive administrator does not approve the management plan, the executive administrator must provide to the district, in writing, the reasons for the action. Tex. Water Code § 36.1072(f). Within 180 days after the GCD receives notice that its groundwater management plan was not approved, the district must submit a revised plan for review and approval. The executive administrator's decision may be appealed to the TWDB. If the TWDB decides not to approve the groundwater management plan on appeal, the district may request that the conflict be mediated. If mediation does not resolve the conflict, the district can appeal the decision of the TWDB to a district court in Travis County. Tex. Water Code § 36.1072(f).

The GCD may review the management plan annually and must review and readopt the management plan with or without revisions at least once every five years. Tex. Water Code § 36.1072(e). Readopted plans must be provided to the TWDB within sixty days. Tex. Water Code § 36.1072(e). Any amendments to the management plan must be submitted to the executive administrator of the TWDB within sixty days of their adoption by the GCD board. Tex. Water Code § 36.1073.

District implementation of the management plan is subject to review by the State Auditor's Office, which determines whether the district is "operational," defined as being actively engaged in achieving the objectives of the district's management plan based on an analysis of the district's activities. *See* Tex. Water Code § 36.302(c). If a GCD fails to submit a management plan or an amendment to a management plan, or if the district is found to be not operational by the State Auditor's Office, section 36.303 of the Water Code gives the TCEQ the power to issue an order to (1) require the GCD to take certain actions or to refrain from taking certain actions; (2) dissolve the board and call an election for the purpose of electing a new board; (3) request the attorney general to bring suit for the appointment of a receiver to collect the assets and carry on the business of the GCD; or (4) dissolve the district. *See* Tex. Water Code §§ 36.301, 36.303(a); *see also* 30 Tex. Admin. Code §§ 293.22–.23 (TCEQ's implementing regulations). See also the discussion at section 16.9:4 below regarding the dissolution of a GCD.

All GCDs located within the same management area must file their management plans with the other districts in the management area and with the regional water planning groups for consideration in the regional water planning process. *See* Tex. Water Code § 36.108(b). A person with a legally defined interest in groundwater in the district or the regional water planning group may file a petition with the TWDB stating that a conflict requiring resolution may exist between the district's approved groundwater management plan and the state water plan. Tex. Water Code § 36.1072(g). If the conflict cannot be resolved with the technical assistance of the TWDB within forty-five days, the district and the person or regional water planning group may mediate the conflict. If mediation fails, the TWDB must resolve the conflict within sixty days. If the TWDB determines that the district's groundwater management plan must be revised, the district must give notice of and hold a hearing and shall revise its plan based on the information provided by the TWDB. The district must then resubmit the revised groundwater management plan to the TWDB for approval. The district may appeal the decision of the

TWDB to a district court in Travis County. Tex. Water Code § 36.1072(g). See also Chapter 20 of this book discussing regional and state water planning.

Joint Planning: GCDs are required to do joint planning within groundwater management areas. A groundwater management area is "an area designated and delineated by the [TWDB] under Chapter 35 as an area suitable for management of groundwater resources." Tex. Water Code § 36.001(13). See also Chapter 21 of this book for further discussion of groundwater management areas. The primary goal of joint planning is to define the desired future conditions of the groundwater resources within the groundwater management area. *See* Robert E. Mace et al., *A Streetcar Named Desired Future Conditions: The New Groundwater Availability for Texas (Revised)* 3, *in The Changing Face of Water Rights in Texas* (State Bar of Texas 2008).

"Not later than May 1, 2021, and every five years thereafter," GCDs within the same groundwater management area shall consider groundwater availability models and other data or information for the management area and shall propose for adoption desired future conditions for the relevant aquifers within the management area. Act of May 19, 2017, 85th Leg., R.S., ch. 471, § 2 (H.B. 2215) (amending Tex. Water Code § 36.108(d)). Before voting on the desired future conditions, the GCDs must consider (1) aquifer uses or conditions within the management area, including conditions that differ substantially from one geographic area to another; (2) the water supply needs and water management strategies included in the state water plan; (3) hydrological conditions, including for each aquifer in the management area the total estimated recoverable storage as provided by the executive administrator, and the average annual recharge, inflows, and discharge; (4) other environmental impacts, including impacts on spring flow and other interactions between groundwater and surface water; (5) the impact on subsidence; (6) socioeconomic impacts reasonably expected to occur; (7) the impact on the interests and rights in private property, including ownership and the rights of management area landowners and their lessees and assigns in groundwater as recognized under section 36.002 of the Water Code; (8) the feasibility of achieving the desired future condition; and (9) any other information relevant to the specific desired future conditions. Tex. Water Code § 36.108(d). The districts then submit these desired future conditions to the executive administrator of the TWDB. Tex. Water Code § 36.108(o). Chapter 21 of this book describes the history of groundwater management planning and the current status of the law controlling groundwater management area joint planning.

Chapter 36 of the Water Code offers two processes that allow a challenge to issues associated with desired future conditions. A petition can be filed with the TCEQ requesting an inquiry into a specific GCD's actions associated with desired future conditions. There is also a separate and independent petition procedure available whereby an appeal can be made to the TWDB to challenge the desired future conditions themselves. These processes are described in further detail in Chapter 21 of this book.

§ 16.6:2 Data Collection and Dissemination

A GCD has the power to make surveys of groundwater reservoirs or subdivisions and facilities to determine the quantity of water available for production and use and to determine the improvements, development, and recharging needed by a reservoir or its subdivision. Tex. Water Code § 36.106. A GCD may carry out research projects and collect information regarding the use of groundwater, water conservation, the practicability of recharging a groundwater reservoir, or any other research projects deemed necessary by the board of directors. *See* Tex. Water Code §§ 36.107, 36.109. On request of a district, the executive director of the TCEQ and the executive administrator of the TWDB must provide information they acquire concerning the groundwater resources within the district's jurisdiction. Tex. Water Code § 36.120.

A GCD must provide requested information to the TCEQ and the TWDB concerning the groundwater resources within its jurisdiction and its plans and activities in conserving and protecting groundwater resources. Tex. Water Code § 36.120.

§ 16.6:3 Well Regulation, Including Production Limits

One of the most contentious powers granted to a GCD is also, to some extent, a required duty of the district: well regulation, including production limits. Well regulation covers permitting, spacing, and construction, among other powers.

Well Permitting, Permit Appeals, and Permit Renewal: A GCD must require a permit for the drilling, equipping, operating, or completing of wells or for substantially altering the size of wells or well pumps. A GCD may require that a change in the withdrawal or use of groundwater during the term of a permit issued by the district may not be made unless the district has first approved a permit amendment authorizing the change. Tex. Water Code § 36.113(a). However, a district's permitting authority is limited until its groundwater management plan is approved by the TWDB.

> Prior to the development of the management plan and its approval under Section 36.1072, the district may not adopt rules other than rules pertaining to the registration and interim permitting of new and existing wells. . . . [T]he district may accept applications for permits under Section 36.113, provided the district does not act on any such application until the district's management plan is approved as provided in Section 36.1072.

Tex. Water Code § 36.1071(f).

An application for a permit or a permit amendment must be sworn to and be in writing. Tex. Water Code § 36.113(b). A GCD may require that only the following be included in the permit or permit amendment application, as applicable under the rules of the district: (1) the name and address of the applicant and the owner of the land on which the well will be located; (2) documentation establishing authority to construct and operate a well if the applicant is not the owner of the property; (3) a statement of the nature and purpose of the proposed use and the amount of water to be used for each purpose; (4) a water conservation plan or a declaration that the applicant will comply with the GCD's management plan; (5) the location of each well, and the estimated rate at which water will be withdrawn; (6) a water well closure plan or a declaration that the applicant will comply with well plugging guidelines and report closure to the TCEQ; and (7) a drought contingency plan. *See* Tex. Water Code § 36.113(c)(1)–(7). A GCD may also require other information "included in a rule of the district in effect on the date the application is submitted that specifies what information must be included in an application for a determination of administrative completeness" and that is "reasonably related to an issue that a district by law is authorized to consider." Act of May 25, 2017, 85th Leg., R.S., ch. 1119, § 1 (S.B. 1009) (amending Tex. Water Code § 36.113(c)).

The district, by rule, must determine which activities regulated by the district require a permit or permit amendment. Tex. Water Code § 36.114(a). Under chapter 36, no one may drill, alter, or operate a well without first obtaining a permit from the GCD. *See* Tex. Water Code § 36.115. A GCD must exempt wells that are to be used solely for domestic needs, or for providing water for livestock or poultry, if the well is located or to be located on a tract of land larger than ten acres and drilled, completed, or equipped so that it is incapable of producing more than 25,000 gallons of groundwater a day. *See* Tex. Water Code § 36.117(b)(1). Other mandatory exemptions are related to oil and gas or mining operations, as discussed below. A GCD may exempt other wells from obtaining an operating permit. The district, by rule, must determine whether a hearing is required for those activities that do require a permit or permit amendment. *See* Tex. Water Code § 36.114(b).

For all applications for which a hearing is not required, the board shall act on the application at a meeting unless the board by rule has delegated to the general manager the authority to act on the application. Tex. Water Code § 36.114(c). The GCD must promptly consider and act on each administratively complete application. Tex. Water Code § 36.114(d). If, within sixty days after the date an administratively complete application is submitted, the application has not been acted on or set for a hearing on a specific date, the applicant may petition the district court of the county where the land is located for a writ of mandamus to compel the district to act on the application or set a date for a hearing on the application, as appropriate. Tex. Water Code § 36.114(e). For applications requiring a hearing, the initial hearing shall be held within thirty-five days after the setting of the date, and the district shall act on the application within sixty days after the date the final hearing on the application is concluded. Tex. Water Code § 36.114(f). The district may by rule set a time when an application will expire if the information requested in the application is not provided to the district. Tex. Water Code § 36.114(g). An application is administratively complete if it contains the information set forth under sections 36.113 and 36.1131. Tex. Water Code § 36.114(h). "A district shall not require that additional information be included in an application for a determination of administrative completeness." Act of May 23, 2017, 85th Leg., R.S., ch. 1119, § 2 (S.B. 1009) (amending Tex. Water Code § 36.114(h)). In 2017, the Texas legislature enacted S.B. 1009, which amended sections 36.113(c) and 36.114(h) of the Water Code to limit a GCD's administrative completeness determination to only information that GCD is authorized to request from an applicant under chapter 36 or the GCD's rules that were in effect on the date the application was submitted.

The hearing process on a permit or a permit amendment is detailed. Chapter 36, subchapter M, of the Water Code deals specifically with the processes and procedures associated with public and contested case hearings on permits and permit amendments. *See generally* Tex. Water Code §§ 36.401–.419. Although generally subchapter M applies to contested permit applications, some provisions apply to uncontested applications as well.

When an application is received by the district, the GCD board or general manager may schedule a public hearing on a permit or permit amendment application; the public hearing may be held in conjunction with a regularly scheduled board meeting, and more than one application may be considered at the same public hearing. *See* Tex. Water Code § 36.403. Under subchapter M, the GCD must provide notice at least ten days before the date of the public hearing. *See* Tex. Water Code § 36.404(c). The GCD may require each person who participates in the public hearing on a permit or a permit amendment application to submit a hearing registration form. *See* Tex. Water Code § 36.405.

For an uncontested application, a GCD board may take action on the application at a properly noticed public meeting held after the original public hearing on the application. *See* Tex. Water Code § 36.4051(a). At the public meeting on the uncontested application, the board may issue a written order to grant the application, grant the application with special conditions, or deny the application. *See* Tex. Water Code § 36.4051(a).

For a contested application where a request for a contested case hearing is filed, the GCD board must schedule a preliminary hearing to hear the request. *See* Tex. Water Code § 36.4051(b). The preliminary hearing may be conducted by (1) a quorum of the GCD board, (2) an individual to whom the board has delegated in writing the responsibility to preside as a hearings examiner over the hearing or matters related to the hearing, or (3) SOAH. *See* Tex. Water Code § 36.4051(b). Following the preliminary hearing, the board must determine whether any person requesting a contested case hearing associated with the application has standing to make the request and whether a justiciable issue related to the application has been raised. If the board determines that no person has standing or no justiciable issue was raised, the board may issue a written order to grant the application, grant the application with special conditions, or deny the application. *See* Tex. Water Code § 36.4051(c). The applicant can demand a contested case hearing within twenty days after the GCD board issues a written order granting the application if the order includes special conditions that were not part of the application as finally submitted or grants a maximum amount of groundwater production that is less than the amount requested in the application. *See* Tex. Water Code § 36.4051(d).

If a contested case hearing is held because of a valid request being submitted or a demand by the applicant, it must be conducted by (1) a quorum of the GCD board, (2) an individual to whom the board has delegated in writing the responsibility to preside as a hearings examiner over the hearing or matters related to the hearing, or (3) SOAH. *See* Tex. Water Code § 36.406(a). Unless the hearing is conducted by SOAH, a presiding officer directs the permit hearing; the presiding officer can be the board president, a delegated hearings examiner, or a selected director. *See* Tex. Water Code § 36.406(b), (c). The presiding officer of the contested case hearing on the permit convenes the hearing, designates the parties, establishes the order for presentation of evidence, administers oaths, examines persons presenting testimony, ensures the presentation of evidence without prejudice, prescribes reasonable time limits for testimony, and exercises procedural rules under section 36.415. *See* Tex. Water Code § 36.406(d). The presiding officer may also determine how to apportion the costs related to the services of the presiding officer and the preparation of the official hearing record among the parties. *See* Tex. Water Code § 36.406(d)(10). The presiding officer can also allow testimony to be submitted in writing, allow supplemental testimony, and refer the parties to an alternative dispute resolution procedure on any matter in the hearing. *See* Tex. Water Code § 36.406(f)–(h).

Unless the hearing was conducted by a quorum of the board, the presiding officer must submit a proposal for decision of the hearing to the board within thirty days of the completion of the evidentiary hearing. Tex. Water Code § 36.410(a). The applicant and each designated party shall be provided a copy of the proposal for decision, and a party may submit to the board written exceptions to the proposal for decision. *See* Tex. Water Code § 36.410(c), (d). The board shall consider the proposal for decision at a final hearing, and the parties may present oral argument to summarize the evidence, present legal argument, or argue an exception to the proposal for decision, but no additional evidence may be presented. *See* Tex. Water Code § 36.410(f). The board must act on the permit or permit amendment application within sixty days of the date when the final hearing on the application is concluded. *See* Tex. Water Code §§ 36.411, 36.114(f).

If SOAH conducted the contested case hearing, special conditions apply with regard to the latitude a board has in its final decision on the application. The board has the authority to make a final decision on consideration of the proposal for decision issued by the SOAH administrative law judge. Tex. Water Code § 36.4165. However, the board may change a finding of fact or conclusion of law made by the administrative law judge, or may vacate or modify an order issued by the administrative law judge, only if the board determines (1) that the administrative law judge did not properly apply or interpret applicable law, district rules, written policies, or prior administrative decisions; (2) that a prior administrative decision on which the administrative law judge relied is incorrect or should be changed; or (3) that a technical error in a finding of fact should be changed. *See* Tex. Water Code § 36.4165(b).

In making a decision on a permit or permit amendment, the district must consider whether (1) the application conforms to the requirements prescribed by chapter 36 of the Texas Water Code and is accompanied by the prescribed fees, (2) the proposed use of water unreasonably affects existing groundwater and surface water resources or existing permit holders, (3) the proposed use of water is dedicated to any beneficial use, (4) the proposed use of water is consistent with the district's approved management plan, (5) the applicant has agreed to avoid waste and achieve water conservation, and (6) the applicant has agreed that reasonable diligence will be used to protect groundwater quality and has agreed to follow well-plugging guidelines at the time of well closure. Tex. Water Code § 36.113(d)(1)–(4), (d)(6), (d)(7). The district may impose more restrictive permit conditions on new permit applications and permit amendment applications to increase use by historic users if the limitations (1) apply to all subsequent new permit applications and permit amendment applications to increase use by historic users, regardless of the type or location of use; (2) bear a reasonable relationship to the existing district groundwater management plan; and (3) are reasonably necessary to protect existing use. Tex.

Water Code § 36.113(e). The Texas Supreme Court has reviewed a challenge to the transfer permit rules of one GCD, regarding whether a GCD under the Water Code may allow the conversion of a historic use to a new use without complying with the limitations applicable to all other new uses; the court held that it may not. *See Guitar Holding Co. v. Hudspeth County Underground Water Conservation District No. 1*, 263 S.W.3d 910 (Tex. 2008).

Permits and permit amendments may be issued subject to the rules promulgated by the district and subject to terms and provisions with reference to the drilling, equipping, completion, alteration, or operation of, or production of groundwater from, wells or pumps that may be necessary to prevent waste and achieve water conservation; minimize as far as practicable the drawdown of the water table or the reduction of artesian pressure; lessen interference between wells; or control and prevent subsidence. Tex. Water Code § 36.113(f). In issuing a permit for an existing or historic use, a district may not discriminate between land that is irrigated for production and land or wells on land that was irrigated for production and enrolled or participating in a federal conservation program. Tex. Water Code § 36.113(g). "A district, to the extent possible, shall issue permits up to the point that the total volume of exempt and permitted groundwater production will achieve an applicable desired future condition under Section 36.108" of the Water Code. Tex. Water Code § 36.1132(a). In issuing permits, a GCD shall manage total groundwater production on a long-term basis to achieve an applicable desired future condition and consider (1) the modeled available groundwater determined by the executive administrator of the TWDB, (2) the executive administrator's estimate of the current and projected amount of groundwater produced under exemptions granted by GCD rules and section 36.117 of the Water Code, (3) the amount of groundwater authorized under permits previously issued by the GCD, (4) a reasonable estimate of the amount of groundwater that is actually produced under permits issued by the GCD, and (5) yearly precipitation and production patterns. Tex. Water Code § 36.1132(b).

After the board makes a decision regarding an application, the applicant in a contested or uncontested hearing or a party to a contested hearing may administratively appeal the decision by requesting written findings and conclusions not later than twenty days after the board's decision. Tex. Water Code § 36.412(a). The GCD must provide certified copies of written findings and conclusions to the requestor and the other designated parties within thirty-five days of the request. Tex. Water Code § 36.412(b). A party to the contested hearing may request a rehearing within twenty days after the date the board issues the written findings and conclusions. Tex. Water Code § 36.412(b). If the board grants the request, the rehearing must be held within forty-five days of the date the request was granted. Tex. Water Code § 36.412(d). If the board performs no action on the request before the ninety-first day after it was submitted, the request is denied by operation of law. Tex. Water Code § 36.412(e).

Subchapter M provides for a suit in a district court regarding a GCD's permit decision once the decision on the permit or permit amendment is final. *See* Tex. Water Code § 36.413(b). An applicant or party must exhaust its administrative remedies under subchapter M before filing suit in a district court under subchapter H. *See* Tex. Water Code § 36.413(b), (c) (allowing a suit against the district under section 36.251 regarding a permit decision but requiring the decision to be final and a request for a rehearing to be timely filed); *see also* Tex. Water Code § 36.251(c) (stating that a subchapter H suit "may only be filed after all administrative appeals to the district are final"). See section 16.8 below for a more detailed discussion on suits filed under subchapter H.

Once granted, most groundwater operating permits contain a set term stating how long the permit is valid, usually according to time frames specified in a GCD's adopted rules. A GCD must renew or approve an application to renew an operating permit before the date the permit expires if a timely renewal application is submitted, the application is accompanied by the required fees, and the permit holder is not requesting a change as part of the renewal that would be considered an amendment under the district rules. *See* Tex. Water Code § 36.1145(a). However, a GCD is not required to automatically renew a permit if the applicant has been delinquent in paying fees, is subject to a pending enforcement action with the district (although the existing permit remains in effect until the matter is resolved), or has not paid a civil penalty or otherwise failed to comply with an order resulting from a final adjudication of a violation of a district permit, order, or rule. *See* Tex. Water Code § 36.1145(b). If the holder of an operating permit files an amendment, in connection with a renewal or otherwise, the permit as it existed before the amendment remains in effect until the conclusion of the amendment or renewal process or the final settlement or adjudication on the matter of whether the change to the permit requires a permit amendment. *See* Tex. Water Code § 36.1146(a). If the permit amendment is denied, the permit as it existed before the amendment request shall be renewed by the GCD without penalty. *See* Tex. Water Code § 36.1146(b).

Permitting in Brackish Groundwater Production Zones: During the 86th legislative session, the legislature passed House Bill 722, creating rulemaking and permitting procedures for withdrawal of brackish groundwater from designated brackish groundwater production zones (brackish zones). *See* Act of May 27, 2019, 86th Leg., R.S., ch.1044, § 1 (H.B. 722), eff. Sept. 1, 2019 (codified at Tex. Water Code § 36.1015). Under these procedures, a GCD located over any part of a brackish zone must adopt rules to govern the issuance of permits authorizing the completion and operation of a well for the withdrawal of brackish groundwater if the GCD receives a petition from a person with a legally defined interest in groundwater in the district. A GCD that receives a petition must adopt its rules not later than the 180th day after receipt of the petition. Districts located over any part of a brackish zone may also choose to adopt rules without the existence of a petition if they are so inclined. *See* Tex. Water Code § 36.1015(c). A person may obtain a permit for the completion and operation of a well for the withdrawal of brackish groundwater for projects including (1) a municipal project designed to treat brackish groundwater to drinking water standards for the purpose of providing a public source of drinking water and (2) an electric generation project to treat brackish groundwater to water quality standards sufficient for the project needs. Tex. Water Code § 36.1015(d). A GCD may not adopt rules limiting access to the production of groundwater within a brackish zone to only these two types of projects. Tex. Water Code § 36.1015(m).

Brackish groundwater production rules adopted by GCDs must (1) provide for processing an application for a brackish zone operating permit in the same manner as an application for an operating permit for a fresh groundwater well, except as provided in Water Code section 36.1015; (2) allow withdrawals and rates of withdrawal of brackish groundwater from a brackish zone not to exceed and consistent with the withdrawal amounts identified in Water Code section 16.060(e) (during the TWDB's designation of the zone); (3) provide for a minimum permit term of thirty years; (4) require a monitoring system recommended by the TWDB to monitor water levels and water quality in the same or an adjacent aquifer, subdivision of an aquifer, or geologic stratum in which the brackish zone is located; (5) for projects located in a brackish zone in the Gulf Coast Aquifer, require reasonable monitoring by the GCD of land elevations to determine if production is causing or is likely to cause subsidence; (6) require the permit holder to provide annual reports that include the amount of brackish groundwater withdrawn, the average monthly water quality of the brackish groundwater withdrawn and in the monitoring wells, and aquifer levels in both the brackish zone and in any aquifer, subdivision of an aquifer, or geologic stratum for which the permit requires monitoring; (7) provide greater access to brackish groundwater by simplifying procedure, avoiding delay in permitting, saving expense for the permit seeker, and providing flexibility to permit applicants and the GCD; (8) be consistent with and not impair property rights described by Water Code section 36.002(a) and (b); and (9) specify all additional information that must be included in an application for a brackish zone operating permit. *See* Tex. Water Code § 36.1015(e) The rules adopted by a GCD must provide that the production authorized from a brackish zone is in addition to the amount of managed available groundwater provided during the joint planning process. *See* Tex. Water Code § 36.1015(l). See Chapter 21 of this book for a discussion of managed available groundwater and joint planning. To the extent possible, a GCD shall issue permits up to the point that the total volume of exempt and permitted groundwater production in a brackish zone equals the amount of brackish groundwater that may be produced annually to achieve the groundwater availability described by the TWDB in its designation of the brackish zone. *See* Tex. Water Code § 36.1015(l). See Chapter 25 of this book for a discussion of the brackish zone designation process.

An application for a brackish zone operating permit must include (1) the proposed well field design compared to the brackish zone; (2) the requested maximum groundwater withdrawal rate for the proposed project; (3) the number and location of monitoring wells needed to determine the effects of the proposed project on water levels and water quality in the same or adjacent aquifer, subdivision of an aquifer, or geologic stratum in which the brackish zone is located; and (4) a report that includes a simulation of the projected effects of the proposed production on water levels and water quality, a description of the model used for that simulation, and sufficient information for a technical reviewer to understand the parameters and assumptions used in the model. *See* Tex. Water Code § 36.1015(g). When an application for a brackish zone operating permit is received by a GCD, the GCD must submit the application to the TWDB, which must conduct a technical review of the application. The TWDB is then required to submit a report of its review of the application that includes findings regarding the compatibility of the proposed well field design with the brackish zone and recommendations for the monitoring system. *See* Tex. Water Code § 36.1015(h). A GCD may not schedule a hearing on the application until it receives the TWDB's report of its review of the application. *See* Tex. Water Code § 36.1015(j).

GCDs are required to provide to the TWDB the annual reports submitted by permittees that include the amount of brackish groundwater withdrawn, the average monthly water quality of the brackish groundwater withdrawn and in the monitoring wells, and aquifer levels in both the brackish zone and in any aquifer, subdivision of an aquifer, or geologic stratum for which the permit requires monitoring. *See* Tex. Water Code § 36.1015(j). If the TWDB receives a request from a GCD, the board within 120 days must investigate and issue a report on whether brackish groundwater production under the project that is the subject of the report is projected to cause significant aquifer level declines, negative effects on water quality, or subsidence during the permit term (if the project is located in a brackish zone in the Gulf Coast Aquifer). *See* Tex. Water Code § 36.1015(j). After receiving the TWDB's report, the GCD, after notice and a hearing, may amend the applicable permit to establish a production limit necessary to mitigate any negative effects identified by the report, approve a mitigation plan that alleviates any negative effect identified in the report, or both amend the permit to establish a production limit and approve a mitigation plan. *See* Tex. Water Code § 36.1015(k).

Water Wells Associated with Oil, Gas, and Mineral Operations: Chapter 36 of the Texas Water Code applies to water wells, including water wells used to supply water for activities related to the exploration or production of hydrocarbons or minerals; however, chapter 36 does not apply to "production or injection wells drilled for oil, gas, sulphur, uranium, or brine, or for core tests, or for injection of gas, saltwater, or other fluids, under permit issued by the Railroad Commission of Texas." Tex. Water Code § 36.117(l). A district may not deny an application for a permit to drill and produce water for hydrocarbon production activities if the application meets all applicable rules as promulgated by the district. Tex. Water Code § 36.117(g).

A GCD may not require any permit issued by the district for—

> drilling a water well used solely to supply water for a rig that is actively engaged in drilling or exploration operations for an oil or gas well permitted by the Railroad Commission of Texas provided that the person holding the permit is responsible for drilling and operating the water well and the water well is located on the same lease or field associated with the drilling rig.

Tex. Water Code § 36.117(b)(2). However, a GCD may require a well of this type to be permitted and to comply with all district rules if "the groundwater withdrawals that were exempted under Subsection (b)(2) are no longer used solely to supply water for a rig that is actively engaged in drilling or exploration for an oil or gas well permitted by the Railroad Commission of Texas." Tex. Water Code § 36.117(d)(2). The well must be registered with the district and equipped and maintained in compliance with the district's rules requiring the installation of casing, pipe, and fittings to prevent the escape of groundwater and to prevent pollution. *See* Tex. Water Code § 36.117(h). The driller of a well of this type must also file with the GCD the well log required by Texas Occupations Code section 1901.251, and, if available, the geophysical log. Tex. Water Code § 36.117(i). For the Railroad Commission's interpretation of these chapter 36 provisions, see Railroad Commission of Texas, *Water Use in Association with Oil and Gas Activities*, https://rrc.texas.gov/about-us/faqs/oil-gas-faqs/water-use-faqs/.

A district may not require any permit issued by the district for "drilling a water well authorized under a permit issued by the Railroad Commission of Texas under Chapter 134, Natural Resources Code, or for production from the well to the extent the withdrawals are required for mining activities regardless of any subsequent use of the water." Tex. Water Code § 36.117(b)(3). However, a GCD may require a well of this type to be permitted and to comply with all district rules if "the groundwater withdrawals that were exempted under Subsection (b)(3) are no longer necessary for mining activities . . . specified in the permit issued by the Railroad Commission of Texas under Chapter 134, Natural Resources Code." Tex. Water Code § 36.117(d)(3). The GCD may require compliance with the GCD's well spacing rules for drilling of any well except a well exempted under subsection (b)(3). Tex. Water Code § 36.117(f). Someone who holds a permit issued by the Railroad Commission under chapter 134 of the Natural Resources Code that authorizes the drilling of water must still report monthly to the GCD (1) the total amount of water withdrawn during the month, (2) the quantity of water necessary for mining activities, and (3) the quantity of water withdrawn for other purposes. Tex. Water Code § 36.117(e)(1)–(3). The well must be registered with the district and equipped and maintained in compliance with the district's rules requiring the installation of casing, pipe, and fittings to prevent the escape of groundwater and to prevent pollution. *See* Tex. Water Code § 36.117(h). The driller of a well of this type must also file with the GCD the well log required by Texas Occupations Code section 1901.251, and, if available, the geophysical log. Tex. Water Code § 36.117(i).

Regarding uranium mining, a cased exploration well used for exploration or used for rig supply purposes is subject to a GCD's rules regarding registration of wells if the well is located in the GCD and the well is used for monitoring purposes, and the cumulative amount of water produced from the wells located inside the area subject to and completed under an exploration permit issued under Texas Natural Resources Code chapter 131 exceeds forty acre-feet in one permit year. *See* Tex. Nat. Res. Code § 131.354(b); 16 Tex. Admin. Code § 11.140(d). A cased exploration well used for exploration or used for rig supply purposes is subject to a GCD's rules regarding registration, production, and reporting if the well is located in the GCD and the well is used for rig supply purposes, and the cumulative amount of water produced from the wells located inside the area subject to and completed under the exploration permit exceeds forty acre-feet in one year. Tex. Nat. Res. Code § 131.354(c). A GCD must use the number of acres described in the exploration permit in determining any district production requirements. Tex. Nat. Res. Code § 131.354(e). Each month, the holder of the exploration permit must report to the district the total amount of water produced from each cased exploration well within the area subject to the exploration permit that is being used for exploration or for rig supply purposes. *See* Tex. Nat. Res. Code § 131.354(d).

The permittee shall file a groundwater production report no later than the last day of each month, and it shall contain information for the previous month regarding the water produced, reported in gallons and acre-feet. 16 Tex. Admin. Code § 11.140(e). The monthly report shall include the monthly production data and cumulative data for the permit year. 16 Tex. Admin. Code § 11.140(e)(2). Once a well begins production, monthly reports will be required until the end of the permit year, even if production temporarily ceases during that year. 16 Tex. Admin. Code § 11.140(e)(2).

When the Railroad Commission receives an application for an exploration permit, it must provide written notice to each GCD in the area and again when it issues the permit. *See* Tex. Nat. Res. Code § 131.356(a)(1), (b)(1). After an exploration permit has been issued, the permit holder must provide the GCD in that area with pre-exploration water quality information, premining water quality information, and well logs unless they contain confidential information. *See* Tex. Nat. Res. Code § 131.357(a)(1)–(3); 16 Tex. Admin. Code §§ 11.141–.142. If a permit is issued for a cased exploration well used for exploration or used for rig supply purposes, the permit holder must provide the GCD with (1) the permit holder's name, address, and telephone number; (2) the well completion information; (3) the location of each well in the district, including a legal description and the acreage of the property where the well is located; (4) verification that each well will be used for an industrial purpose; and (5) the type and capacity of the pump used in each well. *See* Tex. Nat. Res. Code § 131.357(c).

Aquifer Storage and Recovery Wells: No authorization is needed from a GCD for a well associated with an aquifer storage and recovery (ASR) project unless the amount recovered exceeds the amount authorized. Chapter 36, subchapter N, of the Water Code does authorize GCDs to require that wells located within the district that are associated with ASR projects be registered with the district. *See* Tex. Water Code § 36.453(a)(1). ASR project operators must also submit to the GCD copies of their monthly and annual reports that are required by the TCEQ, and they must report any groundwater that is produced that exceeds the amount authorized to be recovered by the TCEQ under the ASR project. *See* Tex. Water Code § 36.453(a), (b).

A GCD cannot require a permit for the drilling, equipping, operation, or completion of ASR wells. *See* Tex. Water Code § 36.454(a). A GCD's permitting, spacing, and production rules apply only if an ASR well produces groundwater that exceeds the amount authorized to be recovered by the TCEQ under the ASR project, and even then the GCD rules apply only to the exceedance. *See* Tex. Water Code § 36.454(b), (c). See Chapter 26 of this book for further discussion of ASR.

Transport Out of the District: Production of groundwater inside a GCD to be used outside the GCD is referred to as "transport," "transfer," or "export" of groundwater; these terms are seemingly used interchangeably. *See* Tex. Water Code § 36.122. If an application for a permit or a permit amendment proposes the transfer of groundwater outside of a district's boundaries, the district "may also consider" the provisions in section 36.122 of the Water Code. Tex. Water Code § 36.122(a). Section 36.122 "clearly authorizes a groundwater district to promulgate rules requiring a landowner to obtain a permit or permit amendment for the transfer of groundwater out of the district." *Guitar Holding Co. v. Hudspeth County Underground Water Conservation District No. 1*, 209 S.W.3d 146, 160 (Tex. App.—El Paso 2006), *rev'd on other grounds*, 263 S.W.3d 910 (Tex. 2008). Except as provided in section 36.113(e), a GCD may not impose more restrictive permit conditions on transporters than the district imposes on existing in-district users; however, the district may impose an export fee or surcharge. *See* Tex. Water Code § 36.122(c)–(e). The district may not deny a permit based on the fact that the applicant seeks to transfer groundwater outside the district but may limit a permit if the limitation is warranted because of (1) the availability of water in the district and in the proposed receiving area; (2) the projected effect on aquifer conditions, depletion, subsidence, or effects on existing permit holders or other groundwater users within the district; and (3) the approved regional water plan and approved district management plan. *See* Tex. Water Code § 36.122(f), (g).

Section 36.122 of the Water Code gives GCDs the option of considering its provisions when dealing with transfers of groundwater out of the district. Because of the voluntary nature of the provision, GCDs have been known to use some subsections in section 36.122 while ignoring others. See Chapter 18 of this book for a more in-depth analysis of this issue and how it affects transfers of groundwater out of a district.

Section 36.122 of the Water Code also sets limits on permit terms and transfer fees. *See* Tex. Water Code § 36.122(h)–(*l*). A transfer permit term must be at least three years if construction of a conveyance system has not been initiated before the issuance of the permit, or at least thirty years if construction of a conveyance system has been initiated before the issuance of the permit. Tex. Water Code § 36.122(i). If transfer authorization is granted through a separate transfer permit, GCDs can adopt rules that set a transfer permit term at thirty years, as required by section 36.122(i)(2), but retain a two- or five-year term for production permits. This would essentially defeat the support for infrastructure financing, which was the original goal of facilitating thirty-year permits in section 36.122(i). This could be a pressing issue for water transfers in the future.

As discussed above, Water Code chapter 36 contains automatic renewal provisions for operating permits that require GCDs to renew or approve an application to renew an operating permit before the date the permit expires if a timely renewal application is submitted, the application is accompanied by the required fees, and the permit holder is not requesting a change as part of the renewal that would be considered an amendment under the district rules. *See* Tex. Water Code § 36.1145. The 86th Legislature passed similar provisions for automatic renewal of transport/export permits. *See* Act of May 10, 2019, 86th Leg., R.S., ch.96, § 1 (H.B. 1066), eff. Sept. 1, 2019 (adding Tex. Water Code § 36.122(j–1), (j–2), (r), (s), and amending Tex. Water Code § 36.122(k)). A GCD must extend a transport/export permit term before its expiration in the manner prescribed by the operating permit term renewal procedures in Water Code section 36.1145 (1) to a term that is not shorter than the term of an operating permit for the production of water to be transferred that is in effect at the time of the extension and (2) for each additional term for which that operating permit for production is renewed under section 36.1145 or remains in effect under section 36.1146 of the Water Code. *See* Tex. Water Code § 36.122(j–1). A transport/export permit whose term is extended continues to be subject to conditions contained in the permit as issued before the extension. Tex. Water Code § 36.122(j–2).

Spacing and Production Regulation: Chapter 36 of the Water Code specifically grants a GCD the power to regulate the spacing of wells and the production of groundwater. *See* Tex. Water Code § 36.116. A district by rule may regulate well spacing by (1) requiring all water wells to be spaced a certain distance from property lines or adjoining wells; (2) requiring wells with a certain production capacity, pump size, or other characteristic related to the construction or operation of and production from a well to be spaced a certain distance from property lines or adjoining wells; or (3) imposing spacing requirements adopted by the district board. Tex. Water Code § 36.116(a)(1). A GCD may regulate the production of groundwater by (1) setting production limits on wells, (2) limiting the amount of water produced based on acreage or tract size, (3) limiting the amount of water that may be produced from a defined number of acres assigned to an authorized well site, (4) limiting the maximum amount of water that may be produced on the basis of acre-feet per acre or gallons per minute per well site per acre, (5) implementing managed depletion, or (6) using any combinations of those methods. Tex. Water Code § 36.116(a)(2). In regulating production of groundwater, a GCD must select a method that is appropriate based on the hydrogeological conditions of the aquifer or aquifers in the district and may limit the amount of water produced based on contiguous surface acreage. Tex. Water Code § 36.116(e). A GCD may adopt different rules for each aquifer, subdivision of an aquifer, or geologic strata located in whole or in part within the boundaries of the district, or each geographic area overlying an aquifer or subdivision of an aquifer located in whole or in part within the boundaries of the district. Tex. Water Code § 36.116(d). The power of a GCD to regulate spacing and production is limited by the terms of the applicable statutes authorizing its creation, and a GCD can exercise no authority that the Texas legislature has not clearly granted. *See South Plains Lamesa Railroad, Ltd. v. High Plains Underground Water Conservation District No. 1*, 52 S.W.3d 770, 779–80 (Tex. App.—Amarillo 2001, no pet.).

In promulgating any rules limiting groundwater production, the district may preserve historic or existing use before the effective date of the rules to the maximum extent practicable consistent with the district's management plan. Tex. Water Code § 36.116(b). In regulating the production of groundwater based on tract or acreage, a GCD may consider the service needs or service area of a retail water utility. Tex. Water Code § 36.116(c).

Capping and Plugging of Wells: A GCD may require the owner or lessee of land on which an open or uncovered well is located to keep the well permanently closed or capped. Tex. Water Code § 36.118(a). If the owner or lessee refuses to cap the well, any person, firm, or corporation employed by the district may go on the land and close or cap the well. Tex. Water Code § 36.118(c). A reasonable expense incurred by the district in capping the well constitutes a lien on the land on which the well is located. Tex. Water Code § 36.118(d).

Chapter 36 of the Water Code requires that a groundwater permit holder agree to comply with closure and plugging requirements for a well. *See* Tex. Water Code §§ 36.113(c)(6), (d)(7), 36.1131(b)(7). Under the Texas Water Well Drillers Act, all abandoned or deteriorated wells must be plugged within 180 days; and within thirty days of plugging, a plugging report must be submitted to the Texas Department of Licensing and Regulation and to the GCD where the well is located. *See* Tex. Occ. Code § 1901.255(c), (d). Under section 1901.256, a GCD must enforce compliance with section 1901.255 related to wells located in the boundaries of the district. Such enforcement may include bringing an action for an injunction or to recover a civil penalty. *See* Tex. Occ. Code § 1901.256. All GCDs must enter into a memorandum of understanding with the TCEQ and the Department of Licensing and Regulation regarding abandoned wells and enforcing compliance with plugging requirements. *See* Tex. Occ. Code § 1901.257; *see also* 16 Tex. Admin. Code § 76.111.

Reporting and Recordkeeping: A GCD may require that records be kept and reports be made of the drilling, equipping, and completing of water wells and of the production and use of groundwater. Tex. Water Code § 36.111(a). To implement the recording and reporting, a GCD may adopt rules that require an owner or operator of a water well that is required to be registered with or permitted by the district to report groundwater withdrawals using reasonable and appropriate reporting methods and frequency, except for domestic and livestock wells that are exempt from permitting. Tex. Water Code § 36.111(b). A GCD must require that accurate drillers' logs be kept of water wells and that copies of those drillers' logs and electric logs be filed with the district. Tex. Water Code § 36.112. The Texas Department of Licensing and Regulation requires every well driller who drills, deepens, or alters a well to record and maintain a State of Texas Well Report and provide a copy of the report to the GCD in which the well is located. *See* 16 Tex. Admin. Code § 76.70(1).

§ 16.6:4 Additional Powers

Texas Water Code chapter 36 gives GCDs powers in addition to those described above. For example, districts have powers associated with owning and operating property, including water; the power of eminent domain; and the right to enter private property to fulfill their duties.

Owning and Operating Property: A GCD has the power to build, acquire, or obtain by any lawful means any property necessary for the district to carry out its purpose and the provisions of chapter 36 of the Water Code. Tex. Water Code § 36.103(a). A GCD may (1) acquire land to erect dams or to drain lakes, draws, and depressions; (2) construct dams; (3) drain lakes, depressions, draws, and creeks; (4) install pumps and other equipment necessary to recharge a groundwater reservoir or its subdivision; and (5) provide the necessary facilities for water conservation purposes. Tex. Water Code § 36.103(b)(1)–(5). This authority extends to purchasing, selling, transporting, and distributing surface water or groundwater. Tex. Water Code § 36.104.

Eminent Domain: A GCD can exercise the power of eminent domain to acquire by condemnation a fee simple or other interest in property located inside the district if the property interest is necessary for conservation purposes, including recharge and reuse. Tex. Water Code § 36.105(a). Eminent domain may not be used by a GCD to acquire rights to groundwater, surface water, or water rights or for the purpose of production, sale, or distribution of groundwater or surface water. Tex. Water Code § 36.105(b). The special laws creating a GCD may exclude certain powers from those afforded a district under the general laws in chapter 36, including the power of eminent domain. *See, e.g.*, Tex. Spec. Dist. Code §§ 8812.101 (prohibiting the Victoria County Groundwater Conservation District from exercising the power of eminent domain), 8835.103 (stating that the Brazos Valley Groundwater Conservation District does not have the power of eminent domain granted by Tex. Water Code § 36.105), 8820.102 (prohibiting the Northern Trinity Groundwater Conservation District from exercising the power of eminent domain).

Right to Enter Land: GCD directors, engineers, attorneys, agents, operators, and employees may go on any land to inspect, make surveys, or perform tests to determine the condition, value, and usability of the property, with reference to the proposed location of works, improvements, plants, facilities, equipment, or appliances. Tex. Water Code § 36.123(a).

> District employees and agents are entitled to enter any public or private property within the boundaries of the district or adjacent to any reservoir or other property owned by the district at any reasonable time for the purpose of inspecting and investigating conditions relating to the quality of water in the state or compliance with any rule, regulation, permit, or other order of the district.

Tex. Water Code § 36.123(b). District employees or agents must give notice of their presence and exhibit proper credentials. Tex. Water Code § 36.123(b).

§ 16.7 Implementation and Enforcement

§ 16.7:1 Rulemaking

A GCD may make and enforce "fair and impartial" rules to conserve, preserve, protect, and recharge groundwater or a groundwater reservoir or its subdivisions in order to control subsidence, prevent degradation of water quality, or prevent waste of groundwater and to carry out the powers and duties as provided by chapter 36 of the Texas Water Code. *See* Tex. Water Code §§ 36.101(a), 36.102. Since GCDs have the power to make rules to prevent "waste" of groundwater, the broad definition of waste, by itself, gives a GCD extensive authority under its rulemaking power.

The Water Code defines "waste" as any one of the following: (1) withdrawing groundwater at a rate and amount that could cause intrusion of unsuitable water into the aquifer; (2) producing groundwater for nonbeneficial uses; (3) escape of groundwater to a non-groundwater-containing reservoir or geologic strata; (4) pollution of groundwater resources by intrusion of saltwater or by other deleterious matter; (5) willfully or negligently causing, suffering, or allowing groundwater to escape into any watercourse or land other than that of the owner of the well unless authorized by permit, rule, or order; (6) unauthorized escape of groundwater irrigation tailwater onto land other than that of the owner of the well; (7) for water produced from an artesian well, willfully causing or knowingly permitting the water to run off the owner's land or to percolate through the stratum above which the water is found; or (8) drilling or operating a well or wells without a required permit or producing groundwater in violation of a district rule adopted under section 36.116(a)(2) of the Water Code. *See* Tex. Water Code §§ 36.001(8), 36.119(a).

The scope of a district's rulemaking authority is tied to the contents and passage of its groundwater management plan, and a GCD must adopt rules necessary to implement its plan. *See* Tex. Water Code § 36.1071(f). Until its groundwater management plan is passed, the district's rulemaking authority is limited.

> Prior to the development of the management plan and its approval under Section 36.1072, the district may not adopt rules other than rules pertaining to the registration and interim permitting of new and existing wells and rules governing spacing and procedure before the district's board; however, the district may not adopt any rules limiting the production of wells, except rules requiring that groundwater produced from a well be put to a nonwasteful, beneficial use.

Tex. Water Code § 36.1071(f).

Except for emergency rules, the board of directors can adopt rules only after giving proper notice of and holding a rulemaking hearing. *See* Tex. Water Code § 36.101(b). This includes rules governing procedure before the board. Notice must be given at least twenty days before the date of the rulemaking hearing and must include the time and date of the rulemaking hearing, its location, a brief explanation of the subject of the proposed rules, and the location of an Internet site where the proposed rules may be reviewed and copied. *See* Tex. Water Code § 36.101(d), (e). Proper notice of the rulemaking hearing includes posting notice at the district office, providing notice to the county clerk of each county in the district, publishing notice in one or more newspapers of general circulation in the county or counties in which the district is located, making available a copy of all proposed rules at a place accessible to the public during normal business hours, and posting the proposed rules on the district's website, if available. *See* Tex. Water Code § 36.101(d). The presiding officer conducts the rulemaking hearing, and the hearing must be recorded. *See* Tex. Water Code § 36.101(f), (h). In addition to the notice provided under section 36.101(d), a person may request that the district provide personal notice of any rulemaking hearing, which is effective for the remainder of the calendar year. Tex. Water Code § 36.101(i). A district may require each person who participates in a rulemaking hearing to submit a hearing registration form. Tex. Water Code § 36.101(g).

For a district to adopt an emergency rule, which does not require notice and a hearing, the board of directors must find that a substantial likelihood of imminent peril to the public health, safety, or welfare or a requirement of state or federal law requires adoption of the rule on less than a twenty-day notice. Tex. Water Code § 36.1011(a)(1). The board of directors must prepare a written statement of the reasons for the emergency rule. Tex. Water Code § 36.1011(a)(2). The emergency rule is not effective for longer than ninety days, unless notice and a hearing, as summarized above, take place within ninety days of its adoption, in which case it is effective for an additional ninety days. *See* Tex. Water Code § 36.1011(b), (c).

A GCD must compile its rules and make them available for use and inspection at the district's principal office. Tex. Water Code § 36.101(c).

§ 16.7:2 GCD Enforcement

To enforce its rules, the board of directors of a GCD by rule may "set reasonable civil penalties against any person for breach of any rule of the district not to exceed $10,000 per day per violation, and each day of a continuing violation constitutes a separate violation." Tex. Water Code § 36.102(b). Many GCDs use this provision to set up an enforcement section in their rules with detailed notice and penalty procedures. *See, e.g.*, Cow Creek Groundwater Conservation District, *Rules of the Cow Creek Groundwater Conservation District* 64–65 (as amended eff. Apr. 12, 2021), http://ccgcd.org/wp-content/uploads/2021/05/CCGCD_Rules_2021-04-12.pdf (explaining that Rule 7.2 allows the district to issue notices of rule violations, implement enforcement fees, and penalize violators on a penalty schedule for noncompliance with a district rule, order, or permit); Hill Country Underground Water

Conservation District, *District Rules* 41–43 (amended Aug. 14, 2018), http://box2267.temp.domains/~hcuwcdor/wp-content/uploads/2020/10/Rules_Adopted_Aug-14-2018.pdf (showing that Rule 11 allows the district to send notice to violators, investigate possible violations by entering land, and assess civil penalties for violations).

A GCD may also enforce the provisions in chapter 36 of the Texas Water Code and its rules by injunction, mandatory injunction, or other appropriate remedy in a court of competent jurisdiction. Tex. Water Code § 36.102(a). However, in 2008 the Eastland court of appeals held that this section of chapter 36 authorizing GCD enforcement did not waive a political subdivision's or municipality's immunity from suit for monetary damages because the statute did not specifically authorize a suit or assessment of penalties against a political subdivision or municipality. *See City of Aspermont v. Rolling Plains Groundwater Conservation District*, 258 S.W.3d 231, 234 (Tex. App.—Eastland 2008), *aff'd*, 353 S.W.3d 756 (Tex. 2011). Although the court determined that the City of Aspermont was immune from the Rolling Plains GCD's suit for monetary damages for failure to file monthly reports and refusal to pay export fees, the court did hold that the city was not immune from a cause of action brought by the GCD asking the court to construct the applicable legislation and declare that the city is subject to and must comply with the GCD's applicable rules and regulations. *Aspermont*, 258 S.W.3d at 236. After *Aspermont*, the Texas legislature amended section 36.102 of the Water Code to specify that a district may enforce its rules "against any person," and if the person is a governmental entity that has violated the GCD's rules, the limits on the amount of fees, costs, and penalties that a district may impose "constitute a limit of liability of the governmental entity for the violation." *See* Tex. Water Code § 36.102(e).

In addition to GCD enforcement under chapter 36, chapter 26 of the Water Code allows a GCD to bring local enforcement actions with regard to water-quality-related matters. *See* Tex. Water Code §§ 26.171–.180. If a GCD prevails in any suit to enforce its rules, the district may seek and the court shall grant recovery for attorney's fees, costs for expert witnesses, and other costs incurred by the district. Tex. Water Code § 36.102(d); *see also* Tex. Water Code § 36.066(g) ("If the district prevails in any suit other than a suit in which it voluntarily intervenes, the district may seek and the court shall grant . . . recovery for attorney's fees, costs for expert witnesses, and other costs incurred by the district before the court."); *Edwards Aquifer Authority v. Day*, 274 S.W.3d 742, 755 (Tex. App.—San Antonio 2008), *aff'd*, 369 S.W.3d 814 (Tex. 2012) (holding that award of attorney's fees is mandatory when a GCD prevails in the lawsuit). If a GCD prevails on some, but not all, of the issues in a lawsuit, the court shall award attorney's fees and costs only for those issues on which the district prevails; the GCD has the burden of segregating the attorney's fees and costs in order for the court to make an award. *See* Tex. Water Code § 36.066(h).

§ 16.7:3 Complaints and Citizen Suits

A landowner or other person who has a right to produce groundwater from land that is adjacent to the land on which a well or wells are drilled or operated without a required permit or permits or from which groundwater is produced in violation of a district rule adopted under section 36.116(a)(2) of the Texas Water Code, or who owns or otherwise has a right to produce groundwater from land that lies within one-half mile of the well or wells, may sue the owner of the well or wells for damages or to restrain or enjoin the illegal drilling. *See* Tex. Water Code § 36.119(b); *see, e.g., City of Amarillo v. Premium Standard Farms, Inc.*, No. 07-06-00467-CV, 2007 WL 2163399 (Tex. App.—Amarillo July 24, 2007, no pet.) (mem. op.) (explaining that plaintiff sought injunction for alleged overproduction but court ruled that sufficient evidence was not introduced at hearing). The suit can be filed with or without joinder of the district. Tex. Water Code § 36.119(b). Before such a suit is filed, however, a written complaint must be filed with the GCD having jurisdiction over the well or wells drilled or operated without a required permit or in violation of the district rule. Tex. Water Code § 36.119(g). The district must investigate the complaint within ninety days and determine whether the district rules have been violated. *See* Tex. Water Code § 36.119(g).

§ 16.8 Judicial Review

Someone affected by and dissatisfied with any provision or with any rule or order made by a GCD is entitled to file a suit against the district or its directors to challenge the validity of the law, rule, or order. *See* Tex. Water Code § 36.251(a). See also the discussion at section 16.6:3 above regarding administrative appeals of permit actions under Texas Water Code chapter 36, subchapter M. The suit shall be filed in a court of competent jurisdiction in any county in which the district or any part of the district is located and may be filed only after all administrative appeals to the district are final. *See* Tex. Water Code § 36.251(c). The burden of proof at trial is on the petitioner. Tex. Water Code § 36.253. Generally, the review on appeal is governed by the substantial evidence rule. Tex. Water Code § 36.253. (The review is de novo, however, when an action is challenged on the ground the GCD has acted beyond its statutory authority. *Guitar Holding Co. v. Hudspeth County Underground Water Conservation District No. 1*, 263 S.W.3d 910, 917 (Tex. 2008).) The substantial evidence rule means that a court may not substitute its judgment for the judgment of the state agency on the weight of the evidence on questions committed to agency discretion but shall reverse or remand the case for further proceedings if substantial rights of the appellant have been prejudiced because the administrative findings, inferences, conclusions, or decisions are (1) in violation of a constitutional or statutory provision, (2) in excess of the agency's statutory authority, (3) made through unlawful procedure, (4) affected by other error of law, (5) not reasonably supported by substantial evidence considering the reliable and probative evidence in the record as a whole, or (6) arbitrary or capricious or characterized by abuse of discretion or clearly unwarranted exercise of discretion. Tex. Gov't Code § 2001.174. Due to the nature of the substantial evidence review, the petitioner must attempt to develop the record as much as possible when going through the administrative appeals process before the GCD board because no additional evidence can be introduced on appeal. *See, e.g., In re Edwards Aquifer Authority*, 217 S.W.3d 581 (Tex. App.—San Antonio 2006, no pet.).

§ 16.9 Oversight of GCD Duties

The State Auditor's Office (SAO) and the TCEQ have oversight authority over certain aspects of a GCD's operations and actions. The SAO must periodically audit a GCD's operations to determine whether it is fulfilling its duties. The TCEQ has oversight authority both on its own initiative and as a result of a petition for inquiry about specific GCD action or inaction.

§ 16.9:1 Legislative Audit Review

A GCD is subject to review by the SAO under the direction of the legislative audit committee. Tex. Water Code § 36.302(a). The auditor must determine whether the district is operational, defined as being actively engaged in achieving the objectives of the district's management plan based on an analysis of the district's activities. Tex. Water Code § 36.302(c). If the auditor determines that the district is not operational, the TCEQ must take proper action as provided by Texas Water Code section 36.303. Tex. Water Code § 36.302(f). Since 1999, the SAO has filed thirteen reports with TCEQ, including audit reviews for 120 GCDs; some GCDs have been audited multiple times. *See* 2021 PGMA-GCD Report, at 23.

For example, the SAO released an audit report on February 26, 2010, on the Kinney County Groundwater Conservation District concluding that the district was not operational because it had failed to meet 80 percent of the objectives of its 2008 management plan, and finding deficiencies in the financial and operation practices of the district. *See* Tex. State Auditor's Office, *A Follow-Up Audit*

Report on the Kinney County Groundwater Conservation District, SAO Report No. 10-023 (Feb. 2010), www.sao.texas.gov/reports/main/10-023.pdf. The TCEQ considered the matter on August 11, 2010, and directed TCEQ staff to enter into a compliance agreement with the Kinney County GCD to address management plan implementation, address the recommendations of the SAO, document permitting procedures, and develop a debt reduction plan. *See* 2011 PGMA-GCD Report, at 55 (reporting on TCEQ noncompliance review of the Kinney County GCD).

§ 16.9:2 Failure to Submit Management Plan or Conduct Joint Planning

Appropriate action must be taken by the TCEQ under section 36.303 of the Texas Water Code if a GCD fails to submit or receive approval of a management plan or an amendment to a management plan. *See* Tex. Water Code § 36.301. Additionally, if the TCEQ finds that a district has failed to conduct joint planning, the TCEQ may take any action it feels necessary under section 36.303. *See* Tex. Water Code § 36.3011(h); 30 Tex. Admin. Code §§ 293.22, 293.23 (the TCEQ's implementing regulations). See Chapter 21 of this book regarding groundwater management area joint planning.

§ 16.9:3 Petition for Inquiry

Texas Water Code chapter 36 allows an "affected person" with respect to a groundwater management area to file a petition with the TCEQ requesting an inquiry for any of the following reasons: (1) a GCD fails to submit its management plan to the executive administrator; (2) a GCD fails to participate in the joint planning process; (3) a GCD fails to adopt rules; (4) a GCD fails to adopt the applicable desired future conditions adopted by the management area at a joint meeting; (5) a GCD fails to update its management plan before the second anniversary of the adoption of desired future conditions by the management area; (6) a GCD fails to update its rules to implement the applicable desired future conditions before the first anniversary of the date it updated its management plan with the adopted desired future conditions; (7) the rules adopted by a GCD are not designed to achieve the desired future conditions adopted by the management area during the joint planning process; (8) the groundwater in the management area is not adequately protected by the rules adopted by the GCD; or (9) the groundwater in the management area is not adequately protected because of the failure of a district to enforce substantial compliance with its rules. Tex. Water Code § 36.3011(b). An affected person with respect to a management area is (1) an owner of land in the management area, (2) a groundwater conservation district or subsidence district in or adjacent to the management area, (3) a regional water planning group with a water management strategy in the management area, (4) a person who holds or is applying for a permit from a district in the management area, (5) a person with a legally defined interested in groundwater in the management area, or (6) any other person defined as affected by commission rule. Tex. Water Code § 36.3011(a).

Within ninety days of the filing of the petition, the TCEQ must either dismiss the petition or select a review panel. Tex. Water Code § 36.3011(c). Not later than the 120th day after appointment, the review panel must review the petition and any evidence relevant to the petition and adopt a report to be submitted to the TCEQ. Tex. Water Code § 36.3011(e)–(g). Not later than the forty-fifth day after receiving the panel's report, the TCEQ shall take action to implement any or all of the panel's recommendations. Tex. Water Code § 36.3011(h).

On February 14, 2018, a landowner filed a petition pursuant to section 36.3011 seeking a review of the Post Oak Savannah GCD. *See* 2019 PGMA-GCD Report, at 32. The petitioner alleged that the groundwater in the management area was not adequately protected (1) by the rules adopted by the district and (2) due to the failure of the Post Oak Savannah GCD to enforce substantial compliance with its rules and abide by its district mission. *See* 2019 PGMA-GCD Report, at 32. After evaluating the petition and considering the responses and replies to the petition at its May 9, 2018, agenda meeting, the TCEQ dismissed the petition. *See* 2019 PGMA-GCD Report, at 33.

On August 5, 2019, eight GCDs within Groundwater Management Area 16 petitioned the TCEQ seeking a review of the Starr County GCD. *See* 2021 PGMA-GCD Report, at 23. The petitioners alleged that the Starr County GCD failed to (1) participate in the Groundwater Management Area 16 joint planning process under section 36.108 of the Texas Water Code, (2) adopt the desired future conditions adopted by the other Groundwater Management Area 16 GCDs, and (3) update its management plan within two years of the Groundwater Management Area 16 adoption of new desired future conditions. *See* 2021 PGMA-GCD Report, at 23.

On September 20, 2019, the executive director of the TCEQ filed a response stating the petition should be granted and recommended that the TCEQ appoint a review panel to review the petition and evidence and to produce a finalized report with a summary of evidence, list of findings, and recommended actions appropriate for the TCEQ to take pursuant to Tex. Water Code § 36.303 and 30 Tex. Admin. Code § 293.22. *See* 2021 PGMA-GCD Report, at 24. On October 23, 2019, the TCEQ granted the petition and appointed a review panel. *See* 2021 PGMA-GCD Report, at 24. The review panel consisted of five GCD managers and one nonvoting TCEQ staff recording secretary. After two public meetings, the review panel submitted its report and recommendations to the TCEQ on February 13, 2020. *See* 2021 PGMA-GCD Report, at 24. The review panel's report included a summary of the evidence, a list of findings and recommended actions, and a negotiated settlement agreement between the Starr County GCD and the other GCDs from Groundwater Management Area 16 that addressed the issues raised in the petition. *See* 2021 PGMA-GCD Report, at 24.

The TCEQ adopted an order, finalized on April 27, 2020, incorporating the review panel's recommendations, the TCEQ executive director's draft order, and the requested and unopposed changes from the Starr County GCD. *See* 2021 PGMA-GCD Report, at 24. Starr County GCD is now working to address the provisions contained in the April 27 TCEQ order and to provide milestone updates to TCEQ. *See* 2021 PGMA-GCD Report, at 26.

§ 16.9:4 Action by the TCEQ, Including Dissolution

Under section 36.303 of the Texas Water Code, the TCEQ, after notice and a hearing, can issue an order requiring the GCD to take certain actions or to refrain from taking certain actions, dissolve the board and call an election for the purpose of electing a new board, request the attorney general to bring suit for the appointment of a receiver to collect the assets and carry on the business of the GCD, or dissolve the district. Tex. Water Code § 36.303(a). If the TCEQ dissolves the district's board, it must appoint five temporary directors. Tex. Water Code § 36.016(a). In addition to those options, the TCEQ may recommend to the legislature other actions that the TCEQ deems necessary to accomplish comprehensive management in the district. *See* Tex. Water Code § 36.303(b); *see also* 30 Tex. Admin. Code §§ 293.22, 293.23 (the TCEQ's implementing regulations). If the attorney general brings a suit for the appointment of a receiver for a district under section 36.303(a)(3), a district court must appoint a receiver if an appointment is necessary to protect the assets of the district. Tex. Water Code § 36.3035(a). The receiver must execute a bond in an amount to be set by the court to ensure the proper performance of the receiver's duties. Tex. Water Code § 36.3035(b). After appointment of the receiver and execution of the bond, the receiver takes possession of the assets of the district specified by the court. Tex. Water Code § 36.3035(c). Until discharged by the court, the receiver performs the duties that the court directs to preserve the assets and carry on the business of the district and must strictly observe the final order involved. Tex. Water Code § 36.3035(d). On a showing of good cause by the district, the court may dissolve the receivership and order the assets and control of the business returned to the district. Tex. Water Code § 36.3035(e).

The TCEQ may dissolve a GCD that has been determined to be not operational and has no outstanding bonded indebtedness. Tex. Water Code § 36.304(a). A district composed of territory entirely within one county may be dissolved even if the district has outstanding indebtedness that matures after the year in which the district is dissolved, under provision for the levy and collection of taxes sufficient to pay the principal of and interest on the indebtedness when due. Tex. Water Code § 36.304(b). Appeals from any TCEQ order shall be filed and heard in the district court of any of the counties in which the land is located. Tex. Water Code § 36.309.

III. Subsidence Districts

§ 16.10 Introduction

The Texas legislature often grants special powers or responsibilities to GCDs through the legislation that creates them. However, at times the legislature has formed special districts with special purposes and powers to effectively deal with specific and challenging groundwater problems. One of these types of special districts is a subsidence district.

Subsidence districts are created with the primary purpose of controlling and preventing subsidence. Subsidence is the lowering of the elevation of the surface of land caused by groundwater withdrawals, which contributes to increased flooding. *See* Tex. Spec. Dist. Code § 8801.001(5). "To minimize as far as practicable the drawdown of the water table and the reduction of artesian pressure and to control and prevent subsidence," the subsidence district is authorized to regulate the spacing of wells and the production of groundwater from those wells. Tex. Spec. Dist. Code § 8801.119(a).

§ 16.11 Creation and Purpose

Like GCDs, subsidence districts are created to regulate groundwater pursuant to article XVI, section 59, of the Texas Constitution. The two existing subsidence districts—the Harris-Galveston Subsidence District (HGSD) and the Fort Bend Subsidence District (FBSD)—have been designated as "conservation and reclamation" districts, and are no longer subject to chapter 36 of the Texas Water Code. *See* Tex. Spec. Dist. Code §§ 8801.002, 8801.102, 8834.002, 8834.006. Like GCDs, subsidence districts have powers to regulate the use of groundwater and to prevent the waste of groundwater or the degradation of water quality. *See, e.g.*, Tex. Spec. Dist. Code §§ 8801.053, 8801.108(a), 8834.052, 8834.060, 8834.110, 8834.201, 8834.203, 8834.215. However, subsidence districts have as their primary purpose the prevention of subsidence. *See* Tex. Spec. Dist. Code §§ 8801.053, 8834.003. Subsidence districts, like GCDs, are also subject to the duties and obligations of applicable general laws and likewise receive the benefits of such laws.

The HGSD and the FBSD are completely separate districts, with their own enabling legislation and separate boards of directors. However, the two boards entered into an interlocal agreement through which the staff of the HGSD serves as the staff of the FBSD. This staff-sharing arrangement was anticipated even before the FBSD was created in 1989, so the FBSD's enabling legislation was modeled after the HGSD's legislation. For example, the two subsidence districts are very similar in terms of their rules, regulatory programs, permit requirements, fee structures (but not amounts), and hearing procedures. Because the statutes and goals are similar, and because the same staff works for both boards, the rules and procedures for the two subsidence districts are almost identical, with similar registration and permitting forms used by both.

For additional information, see the Harris-Galveston Subsidence District website, http://hgsubsidence.org/, and the Fort Bend Subsidence District website, http://fortbendsubsidence.org.

§ 16.12 Board Meetings

Subsidence districts are subject to the Texas Open Meetings Act (TOMA), Texas Government Code chapter 551. The HGSD and the FBSD are required to have at least monthly meetings of their boards, also subject to TOMA. *See* Tex. Spec. Dist. Code §§ 8801.055, 8834.056.

Under TOMA, the meetings of a subsidence district's board must generally be open to the public, notice of the meeting must be posted at a place generally accessible to the public at the subsidence district's administrative offices, and notice must be provided to the county clerk at least seventy-two hours before the meeting. *See* Tex. Gov't Code §§ 551.002, 551.043, 551.054.

§ 16.13 Rulemaking

Subsidence districts are required to act pursuant to rules adopted by their boards of directors. The HGSD's and the FBSD's organic acts require the subsidence districts to adopt rules to implement the acts and to accomplish the districts' purposes. *See* Tex. Spec. Dist. Code §§ 8801.108(a), 8834.112. The HGSD and the FBSD are specifically authorized to adopt rules "to prevent the waste of groundwater or the degradation of water quality." *See* Tex. Spec. Dist. Code §§ 8801.108(a), 8834.112(b). The FBSD organic act also requires the district to adopt rules necessary to carry out the district's purposes. Tex. Spec. Dist. Code § 8834.112.

Procedurally, subsidence districts are required to provide notice and an opportunity to be heard before adopting rules. The FBSD is required to provide a ten-day notice, and the HGSD is required to provide only the seventy-two-hour TOMA notice before conducting a rulemaking hearing. *See* Tex. Spec. Dist. Code §§ 8801.110(a), 8834.115. Public comments may be submitted orally or in writing at rulemaking hearings. *See* Tex. Spec. Dist. Code §§ 8801.109(c), 8834.114(c). For the rules of the districts, see the Fort Bend Subsidence District Rules (amended Sept. 25, 2019), at https://fbsubsidence.org/wp-content/uploads/2020/07/2019-FBSD-Rules-FINAL.pdf, and the Harris-Galveston Subsidence District Rules (amended Sept. 11, 2019), at https://hgsubsidence.org/wp-content/uploads/2019/11/Harris-Galveston-Subsidence-District-Rules-%E2%80%93-Amended-September-11-2019.pdf.

§ 16.14 District Regulatory Plans

The subsidence districts have each adopted District Regulatory Plans (DRPs) "to establish policy in the areas of groundwater regulation, permits and enforcement and to establish District Regulatory Areas and regulatory requirements for each area." *See* Harris-Galveston Subsidence District, *District Regulatory Plan 2013* 1 (amended May 8, 2013), http://hgsubsidence.org/wp-content/uploads/2013/07/HGSD-2013-Regulatory-Plan-with-Amendment.pdf [hereinafter HGSD DRP]; Fort Bend Subsidence District, *2013 Regulatory Plan* 1 (adopted Aug. 28, 2013), http://fortbendsubsidence.org/wp-content/uploads/2016/09/FBSD-Regulatory-Plan-20130828.pdf [hereinafter FBSD DRP].

The HGSD DRP has as its overall goal the reduction of groundwater withdrawals to no more than 20 percent of demand as soon as possible. HGSD DRP, at 1. The HGSD DRP divides the district into three regulatory areas and sets out a schedule for required groundwater withdrawals based on the area. HGSD DRP, at 6. The HGSD has adopted disincentive fees to permitted withdrawals in excess of 20 percent of total water demand, or in excess of 10 percent of demand in the case of Region 1. HGSD DRP, at 6. The purpose of the fee is to encourage alternative water supplies.

The FBSD DRP divides the FBSD into two regulatory areas and one subarea. FBSD DRP, at 4. One of the goals of the FBSD DRP is to control and prevent subsidence as soon as possible. FBSD DRP, at 2. Disincentive fees are charged when a permittee's withdrawals exceed 40 percent of demand in Area A. FBSD DRP, at 4. Permittees in Area A are required to submit Groundwater Reduction Plans to the District. FBSD DRP, at 6.

§ 16.15 Application Processing

Subsidence districts are statutorily mandated to require certain permits and may choose to require others as part of their management of groundwater. Subsidence districts require permits for the drilling, equipping, operating, or completing of wells or well pumps. Tex. Spec. Dist. Code §§ 8801.155, 8834.206. Additionally, subsidence districts are authorized more broadly to regulate to protect water quality. *See, e.g.*, Tex. Spec. Dist. Code §§ 8801.001(5–a)(D), 8801.108(a), 8834.001(7), 8834.112. Subsidence districts may require that other types of permits be obtained before engaging in certain activities, including aquifer recharge and storage activities and groundwater monitoring. *See, e.g.*, Tex. Spec. Dist. Code §§ 8801.053(a), 8801.101, 8801.108, 8801.114, 8801.119, 8834.052, 8834.112; *but see* Tex. Att'y Gen. Op. No. GA-0498 (2007), www.texasattorneygeneral.gov/sites/default/files/opinion-files/opinion/2006/ga0498.pdf (noting that the Edwards Aquifer Authority Act specifically authorizes only term, emergency, and regular permits and opining that bifurcated permits that limit the permittee's exercise of guaranteed statutory minimums are not authorized). The subsidence districts' organic acts provide that a permit may not be required for certain types of wells, thereby establishing categories of exempt uses, depending on the use of the groundwater and the size of the wells. *See* Tex. Spec. Dist. Code §§ 8801.152, 8834.202. Otherwise providing for the same permitting exemptions, the FBSD adds an exemption that the HGSD does not have: if a well owner owns only one well and its casing diameter is less than five inches, then it is exempt, but if the well owner has more than one well, then all the wells must be permitted. Tex. Spec. Dist. Code § 8834.202; *see also* FBSD Rules § 5.7; HGSD Rules § 5.8 (outlining exemptions and exclusions from permitting requirements). Both the FBSD and HGSD exempt from metering requirements wells with a casing diameter of less than five inches that are not connected with any other well and that are not likely to exceed one million gallons of pumping per year. FBSD Rules § 8.2; HGSD Rules § 8.2.

In deciding whether to grant or deny a permit, subsidence districts are required to consider, among other things, the availability of alternative, competitively priced surface water, the economic impact on the applicant of denial weighed against the likely effects of subsidence if the permit is granted, and "other relevant factors." *See* Tex. Spec. Dist. Code §§ 8801.158(b), 8834.209(b). Subsidence districts are required to act promptly on administratively complete applications for a permit or permit amendment or to set a hearing to consider the application and are required to hold a hearing on all permit applications. *See* Tex. Spec. Dist. Code §§ 8801.157, 8834.208, 8834.209.

Permits may impose a whole host of requirements on permittees relating to the protection of groundwater resources. *See* Tex. Spec. Dist. Code §§ 8801.158(d), 8834.209(d). Among other things, permittees may be required to submit reports, pay annual fees, comply with drought restrictions or conservation requirements, and reduce reliance on groundwater. *See* Tex. Spec. Dist. Code §§ 8801.113, 8801.151, 8801.158(d), 8801.161, 8801.162, 8834.103, 8834.209(d), 8834.212, 8834.214, 8834.215. Additional permit conditions may include the requirement that a permittee prepare and implement a groundwater conservation plan and accompanying best management practices to conserve groundwater. *See* Tex. Spec. Dist. Code §§ 8801.158(d), 8834.209(d).

A cornerstone of the regulatory programs implemented by subsidence districts with respect to permits is the permit disincentive fee the subsidence districts use to discourage overreliance on groundwater. Such fees are specifically authorized by the subsidence districts' organic acts. *See* Tex. Spec. Dist. Code §§ 8801.161(a–1), 8834.212(a)–(b). The HGSD district has adopted permit disincentive fees by rule, and the FBSD has adopted permit disincentive fees by board resolution. *See* HGSD Rules § 5.6(c); Fort Bend Subsidence District, Resolution No. 13-330, *Resolution Adopting a Disincentive Permit Fee Rate* (Mar. 27, 2013), http://fortbendsubsidence.org/wp-content/uploads/2016/09/FBSD-Disincentive-Fee-Resolution-2013.pdf.

§ 16.16 Hearings

Unlike GCDs, subsidence districts must hold hearings on all applications for permits. *See* Tex. Spec. Dist. Code §§ 8801.157, 8834.208; *see also* Tex. Water Code § 36.114(b). The HGSD is required to provide written notice to applicants of the hearing. *See* Tex. Spec. Dist. Code § 8801.157(b). The FBSD's board is required to notify interested persons, post notice, and publish notice in a newspaper at least ten days before the hearing. Tex. Spec. Dist. Code § 8834.208(b). The HGSD's and the FBSD's organic acts contain permit hearing procedures authorizing persons to appear at hearings and present testimony, evidence, exhibits, or other information individually or through their counsel. Tex. Spec. Dist. Code §§ 8801.109, 8834.114. Subsidence districts may use hearing examiners to conduct their permit hearings but are required to adopt procedures for their use by rule. Tex. Spec. Dist. Code §§ 8801.109(d), 8834.114(d), (e).

Subsidence district procedural rules relate to, among other things, registering to testify, evidentiary rules, the filing of written materials, recording, and continuances. HGSD Rules §§ 7.3–7.5; FBSD Rules §§ 7.3–7.5. Following a permit hearing, the hearings examiner is required to prepare a report. HGSD Rules § 7.6; FBSD Rules § 7.6. The report must be submitted and the board must take action within sixty days of the close of the hearing record. HGSD Rules § 7.6(c); FBSD Rules § 7.6(c). Subsidence district rules allow for a motion for rehearing to be filed within twenty days of the board's decision and require that such a motion be filed as a prerequisite to appeal. HGSD Rules § 7.8; FBSD Rules § 7.8.

An appeal of a final action by a subsidence district must be filed within forty-five days of the date the action became final. Tex. Spec. Dist. Code §§ 8801.202, 8834.251(b).

§ 16.17 Programs

Subsidence districts are granted broad authority to implement and enforce their organic acts to protect groundwater within their jurisdictions similar to the authority granted districts subject to Texas Water Code chapter 36. *See* Tex. Spec. Dist. Code §§ 8801.003, 8801.053, 8801.108, 8834.002, 8834.003, 8834.052, 8834.110, 8834.112, 8834.201, 8834.203, 8834.216.

Subsidence districts' organic acts and rules are silent on the transfer of groundwater outside the district, and thus such applications would presumably be processed under substantially the same criteria as other applications. Because the districts consider the availability of alternative water supplies and permit applications must demonstrate that "there is no other adequate and available substitute or supplemental source of surface water at prices competitive with those charged by suppliers of surface water within the District" (HGSD Rules § 5.2(d); FBSD Rules § 5.2(d)), and because the districts have adopted disincentive permit fees (HGSD Rules § 5.6(c)), exportation of groundwater is not expected to be an issue for these subsidence districts.

Entities within the jurisdiction of a subsidence district, particularly those that use or intend to use groundwater, such as developers, water utilities, and other industrial, agricultural, and municipal users, or whose activities have the potential to affect groundwater, should consult the subsidence district's regulations.

§ 16.18 Enforcement

Subsidence districts are authorized to administer and enforce their organic acts and carry out their purposes of regulating groundwater to prevent subsidence through rulemaking, and indeed they are required to make and enforce rules. *See* Tex. Spec. Dist. Code §§ 8801.003, 8801.053, 8801.108, 8834.003(b), 8834.052, 8834.112, 8834.201, 8834.252.

Subsidence districts may file suit to seek injunctive relief and civil penalties or may request that the attorney general do so on their behalf. *See* Tex. Spec. Dist. Code §§ 8801.204, 8834.252.

Subsidence districts may obtain civil penalties for violating district rules of between $50 and $5,000 per day per violation, with each day of a continuing violation constituting a new violation. *See* Tex. Spec. Dist. Code §§ 8801.204(a)(2), 8834.252(a).

IV. Conclusion

§ 16.19 Conclusion

Groundwater conservation districts are created for and have been charged with protecting, conserving, and managing groundwater use in Texas. A subsidence district's purpose is to prevent subsidence, and a district accomplishes this goal by using its power to protect, conserve, and manage groundwater. The size, duties, and levels of responsibilities of these different types of districts can vary greatly. To fully understand the scope and power of the district's authority, one must investigate and understand the general and special laws associated with that specific district as well as the district rules, regulatory plans, orders and forms, and other relevant areas of law affecting local governments.

CHAPTER 17

Edwards Aquifer Authority

Marc Friberg[1]

I. Scope

§ 17.1 Introduction

This chapter discusses the regulation and management of the portion of the San Antonio segment of the Balcones Fault Zone Edwards Aquifer (Aquifer) located within the boundaries of the Edwards Aquifer Authority (EAA) pursuant to the Edwards Aquifer Authority Act (EAA Act). *See* Act of May 30, 1993, 73d Leg., R.S., ch. 626, as amended. The text of the EAA Act is uncodified, but an unofficial compilation is available at www.edwardsaquifer.org/eaa/legislation-rules/the-eaa-act-a-success-story. This chapter does not discuss the regulation of the other two segments of the Aquifer: the Northern segment in Travis, Williamson, and Bell counties, and the Barton Springs segment in Hays and Travis counties.

II. The Edwards Aquifer

§ 17.2 The Aquifer Generally

The Aquifer extends from the groundwater divide east of Brackettville in Kinney County, east to San Antonio, and then northeast to the groundwater divide near Kyle in Hays County. This segment is 180 miles long and ranges from 5 to 40 miles wide, with the Recharge and Artesian Zones of the Aquifer encompassing approximately 3,320 square miles (2.12 million acres). Approximately 1.89 million acres (89 percent) of the Recharge and Artesian Zones of the Aquifer are located within the boundaries of the EAA. The EAA's boundaries encompass approximately 5,169 square miles (3.3 million acres). Approximately 57 percent of the land within the EAA's boundaries overlies the Aquifer (not including the Saline Zone of the Aquifer). If the Saline Zone of the Aquifer is included, approximately 87 percent of the land within the EAA overlies the Aquifer. Edwards Aquifer Authority, *Hydrologic Data Report for 2014* (Report No. 15-01, Nov. 2015), www.edwardsaquifer.org/science-maps/research-scientific-reports/hydrologic-data-reports [hereinafter 2014 EAA Hydrologic Data Report]. See Figure 1.

---

1. Marc Friberg is the Executive Director, External & Regulatory Affairs, for the Edwards Aquifer Authority. Marc would like to recognize Darcy Alan Frownfelter's contributions to this chapter in earlier editions of this book and his continued support in managing, protecting, and enhancing the Edwards Aquifer.

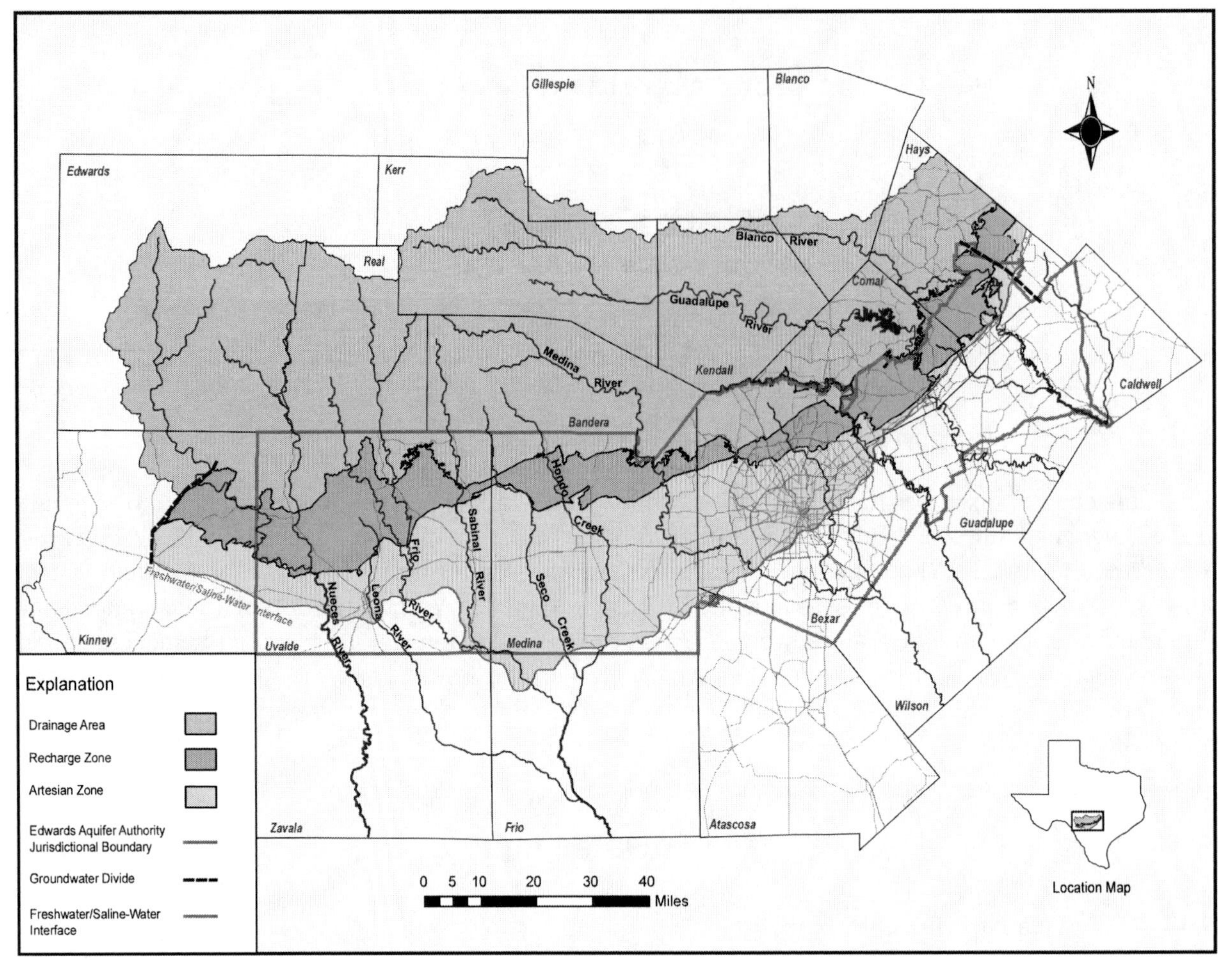

Figure 1. San Antonio segment of the Balcones Fault Zone Edwards Aquifer and other physiographic features in the region. Edwards Aquifer Authority, *Hydrologic Data Report for 2014* (Report No. 15-01, Nov. 2015), www.edwardsaquifer.org/science-maps/research-scientific-reports/hydrologic-data-reports.

The Aquifer is a karstified carbonate aquifer characterized by the presence of sinkholes, sinking or losing streams, caves, springs, and a well-integrated subsurface flow system. The Aquifer possesses triple porosity/permeability characteristics with groundwater flow occurring in the rock matrix; within fractures, faults, and bedding plane partings; and within conduits (less than one centimeter in diameter). The combined primary and secondary/tertiary porosity of the limestone creates extremely high aquifer permeability and the capability to produce large quantities of high-quality water. *See* 2014 EAA Hydrologic Data Report, at 3, 5. Because Edwards Limestone is extremely permeable, groundwater velocity in some portions of the Aquifer has been measured at more than 10,000 feet per day.

Most wells do not fully penetrate the Aquifer, yet some wells yield thousands of gallons per minute with little or no drawdown. Thus, groundwater withdrawal is generally limited by the size of the pump and not the physical properties of the Aquifer. *See* Robert W. Maclay, U.S. Geological Survey, *Geology and Hydrology of the Edwards Aquifer in the San Antonio Area, Texas*, Water-Resources Investigations Report 95-4186 (1995), https://doi.org/10.3133/wri954186.

The Artesian Zone of the Aquifer is the most productive and utilized portion of the Aquifer system. Its great economic importance to Texas is well recognized. The legislature found that the Aquifer "is the primary source of water for the residents of the region, and is vital to the general economy and welfare of the state." EAA Act § 1.06(a); *see also Shields v. Norton*, 289 F.3d 832, 834 (5th Cir. 2002), *cert. denied*, 537 U.S. 1071 (2002); *Sierra Club v. Glickman*, 156 F.3d 606, 610 (5th Cir. 1998); *Sierra Club v. City of San Antonio*, 112 F.3d 789, 791 (5th Cir. 1997), *cert. denied*, 522 U.S. 1089 (1998). Historically, the Aquifer was the sole source of water supply for the 2.1 million people living in the Aquifer region. *See* Edwards Aquifer Authority, *Groundwater Management Plan 2010–2015* 19 tbl. 6 (Oct. 2010), www.twdb.texas.gov/groundwater/docs/GCD/eaa/eaa_mgmt_plan2010.pdf.

Economic and social interests, terrestrial and aquatic life, and other water users depend on the Aquifer for water supply. EAA Act §§ 1.01, 1.06(a). Usage is broad and includes irrigation, livestock, municipal, industrial, and domestic supply. For these reasons, the Texas legislature determined that the Aquifer is "a unique and complex hydrological system." EAA Act § 1.01.

§ 17.3 Groundwater Pools

The Aquifer is divided into two "pools": the San Antonio Pool and the Uvalde Pool. *See* EAA Act §§ 1.14(f), 1.19. A pool is a region within the Aquifer where a unique set of hydrogeologic conditions exist relative to other areas of the Aquifer. These unique conditions include isolated water levels, spring-flow responses to changes in storage, and unique water quality conditions dependent on Aquifer stresses.

San Antonio Pool: The San Antonio Pool is the largest pool of the Aquifer. It is defined as all portions of the Aquifer other than under Uvalde County. Edwards Aquifer Authority Rules § 702.1(167) [hereinafter EAA Rules]. The text of the EAA rules is available at www.edwardsaquifer.org/eaa/legislation-rules/eaa-rules. The following counties within the boundaries of the EAA are included within the San Antonio Pool: Atascosa (partial), Bexar (all), Caldwell (partial), Comal (partial), Hays (partial), Guadalupe (partial), and Medina (all). The San Antonio Pool is the easternmost portion of the Aquifer and is most directly hydrogeologically connected to Comal Springs and San Marcos Springs.

Because spring flows are highly correlated with Aquifer water levels in the San Antonio Pool, the EAA uses three key reference points in its management of withdrawals from this pool: (1) Aquifer levels as measured at index well J-17 (State Well No. AY-68-37-203) in Bexar County; (2) spring discharges at Comal Springs in New Braunfels; and (3) spring discharges at San Marcos Springs in San Marcos. *See* EAA Act §§ 1.03(23), 1.26(b), at tbl. 1.

Uvalde Pool: The Uvalde Pool is defined as that portion of the Aquifer underlying Uvalde County. *See* EAA Rules § 702.1(200). The Uvalde Pool is the westernmost portion of the Aquifer and, geologically, is considered the portion of the Aquifer west of the Knippa Gap, a geologic structure that appears to influence groundwater movement from west to east. Because water levels in the Uvalde County index well do not correlate well with discharge at Comal and San Marcos springs, withdrawals from the Uvalde Pool are managed solely on index water well levels as measured at index well J-27 (State Well No. YP-69-50-302) in Uvalde County. *See* EAA Act § 1.26(b), at tbl. 2.

Other Pools: Although the EAA may designate other pools within the Aquifer (*see* EAA Act § 1.14(g)), to date the EAA has not found a technical basis to support such a designation.

§ 17.4 Contributing Zone

The Aquifer system includes the Contributing Zone, which is the dissected surface of the Edwards Plateau—also referred to as the Texas Hill Country. The Contributing Zone lies upgradient of the Recharge Zone of the Aquifer and encompasses approximately 5,486 square miles (3.51 million acres). Approximately 435,431 acres (12 percent) of the Contributing Zone fall within the EAA's boundaries. Although associated with the Aquifer, the Contributing Zone is not a part of the Aquifer itself but part of the Aquifer system. *See* Edwards Aquifer Authority, *Comprehensive Water Management Plan* 42 (2004), www.edwardsaquifer.org/science_docs/comprehensive-water-management-plan-edwards-aquifer-authority/ [hereinafter 2004 CWMP]. The essential role of this zone is to collect and concentrate diffuse surface water for transport via watercourses to the Recharge Zone. *See* EAA Rules § 702.1(50). Rain falls on the Contributing Zone; runoff enters watercourses arising there; the watercourses then traverse the Recharge Zone; and the surface water then enters the Aquifer as recharge. *See* 2014 EAA Hydrologic Data Report, at 5.

The EAA exercises no water quantity jurisdiction within the Contributing Zone, but because activities occurring within this area can cause point or nonpoint source pollution to surface waters that provide recharge to the Aquifer, the EAA has been given extraterritorial authority over water quality within portions of this area. *See* EAA Act § 1.08(c) (creating a five-mile water quality buffer zone extending from the EAA's boundaries).

§ 17.5 Recharge Zone

The Recharge Zone is the area where the Edwards and Associated Limestones outcrop at the surface. The Recharge Zone is characterized by the presence of sinking streams, caves, and sinkholes and other preferential flow paths associated with the karstic nature of the Aquifer. *See* EAA Rules § 702.1(157); 2014 EAA Hydrologic Data Report, at 5. The Recharge Zone lies upgradient of the Artesian Zone of the Aquifer and encompasses approximately 1,221 square miles (781,333 acres). Approximately 668,374 acres (86 percent) of the Recharge Zone are within the EAA's boundaries. The Recharge Zone varies in width from one-half to 44 miles and extends for approximately 180 miles.

The Recharge Zone provides the primary mechanism for recharge to the Aquifer. *See* EAA Rules § 702.1(157). First, surface streams in the eight basins that arise in the Contributing Zone flow south or east and traverse the Recharge Zone, where water then enters the Aquifer. *See* 2014 EAA Hydrologic Data Report, at 5, 22, 23 tbl. 7. During low flow conditions, most surface water is captured by the Aquifer as the surface water crosses the Recharge Zone and enters fractures, faults, and joints that transport the water into the Aquifer as recharge. Second, rain that falls directly on the Recharge Zone can also recharge the Aquifer. *See* 2014 EAA Hydrologic Data Report, at 5, 22. A third form of recharge has been shown to occur through interformational flow from adjacent aquifers. *See* 2014 EAA Hydrologic Data Report, at 22. For example, the Trinity Aquifer, which is located beneath the Contributing Zone and upgradient of the Artesian Zone of the Aquifer, is understood to directly recharge the Aquifer.

Pathways in the Recharge Zone allow for extremely rapid recharge during heavy rains. Monitoring wells located in the Recharge Zone have risen as much as 150 feet in response to heavy rains. Recharge into the Aquifer can vary widely based on the amount of precipitation received over the Contributing and Recharge zones.

Groundwater within the Recharge Zone occurs under unconfined (water table) conditions. The unsaturated zone in the Recharge Zone of the Aquifer is variable depending on water levels in the Artesian Zone and can range from 150 to 300 feet. *See* Edwards Aquifer Authority, *Edwards Aquifer Authority Synoptic Water Level Program 1999–2004 Report* 14 (Report No. 06-02, Sept. 2006), www.edwardsaquifer.org/science-maps/research-scientific-reports/science-document-library [hereinafter 2006 SWLPR]. Because of the variability of Aquifer water levels and the thickness of the Edwards and Associated Limestones in the Recharge Zone, generally only small volumes of groundwater from the Aquifer can be withdrawn from wells located on the Recharge Zone. The flow path for groundwater in the Recharge Zone is principally toward the Artesian Zone (from north to south or from northwest to southeast). *See* 2006 SWLPR, at 114.

The Recharge Zone is of particular concern to the EAA for an additional reason. Because of the preferential pathways at the surface, the Recharge Zone can be a point of entry for point or nonpoint source pollution. Spills, releases, or discharges occurring at the surface may contaminate the surface water that recharges the Aquifer or may directly enter the Aquifer through sinkholes, caves, faults, fissures, or fractures after passing through the unsaturated zone.

§ 17.6 Artesian Zone

The Artesian Zone is the down dip portion of the Aquifer and is confined between the overlying Del Rio Clay and the underlying less permeable units in the Upper Glen Rose Limestone (the upper unit of the Trinity Aquifer). *See* 2014 EAA Hydrologic Data Report, at 5. The Artesian Zone lies downgradient of the Recharge Zone and encompasses approximately 2,099 square miles (1.34 million acres). Approximately 1.22 million acres (91 percent) of the Artesian Zone are within the EAA's boundaries.

The Artesian Zone is characterized by very high porosity and permeability, a feature of many karst aquifers, and transmits large volumes of water with water levels reacting relatively quickly to discharge and recharge events. *See* 2014 EAA Hydrologic Data Report, at 5. Freshwater saturated thickness in the Artesian Zone ranges from 200 to 600 feet, with an average of 560 feet. *See* Texas Water Development Board, *Water for Texas 2007* 195 (2007), www.twdb.texas.gov/waterplanning/swp/2007/index.asp. Residence time in the Aquifer ranges from a few hours or days to many years, depending on the depth of circulation, location of recharge, distance of flow paths, and other Aquifer parameters. Groundwater in the Artesian Zone moves through the Aquifer generally from west to east and then northeast. The great majority of groundwater withdrawn from the Aquifer is produced from the Artesian Zone. Discharges from the Artesian Zone can occur in two ways—through wells and through spring discharges, principally at Leona Springs (Uvalde), San Pedro Springs and San Antonio Springs (San Antonio), Hueco Springs (Comal County), Comal Springs (New Braunfels), and San Marcos Springs (San Marcos).

Because the Artesian Zone is the most prolific zone for the production of groundwater from the Aquifer, this zone is where the major portion of the EAA's withdrawal management and regulatory functions are implemented. By contrast, because of the relatively low permeability of the overlying units above the Artesian Zone, water quality issues related to spills over this zone are of less concern to the EAA. Nevertheless, poorly constructed water wells can result in contaminated water entering the Aquifer in the Artesian Zone and thus receive considerable attention from the EAA through its abandoned wells program.

§ 17.7 Saline Zone

The southern and eastern boundaries of the Artesian Zone are generally defined as the interface between the Saline Zone and the freshwater Artesian Zone. *See* 2004 CWMP, at 61. This zone is separated from the Artesian Zone by an interface commonly referred to as the "bad water line." This line demarcates the portion of the Aquifer in which natural water quality exceeds a total dissolved solids (TDS) concentration of 1,000 milligrams per liter (mg/L). Because of its relatively poor quality, very little groundwater is produced from the Saline Zone. The primary issue associated with the bad water line is its stability during periods of long and intense withdrawals from the Aquifer—for example, during protracted droughts. It is important to the region that the freshwater Artesian Zone not become contaminated due to intrusion from the Saline Zone. Moreover, the bad water line is near Comal and San Marcos springs, posing a potential threat to those resources. The EAA has studied issues relating to the bad water line for some time. To date, no evidence indicates that movement of the Saline Zone has had an impact on any production wells in spite of the presence of large well fields adjacent to the bad water line.

§ 17.8 Water Quality of the Aquifer

The quality of the groundwater in the Aquifer is generally very high. Protecting this water quality poses challenges because of the character of the Aquifer's karstic nature. Tracer testing studies indicate groundwater velocities in the Aquifer can be very rapid in the Recharge Zone. High groundwater velocity is a common characteristic of karst systems, as is rapid recharge of the system during large rainfall events. Generally, when high volumes of recharge occur as a result of large rainfall events, that recharge receives little to no filtration before entering the Aquifer. As a result, karst aquifers can be vulnerable to various contaminants that may be entrained in surface runoff entering the Recharge Zone. Groundwater monitoring and remediation of contamination also pose challenges because of the difficulty in intercepting the preferential flow paths formed by conduit flow conditions.

§ 17.9 Hydrologic Connection of the Aquifer to Surface Water Systems

The Aquifer exists in a larger context and is a principal part of the groundwater/surface water continuum associated with the Guadalupe River Basin. This continuum consists of the surface water courses that arise in the Contributing Zone and cross the Recharge Zone and recharge the Aquifer; the Comal and San Marcos springs that sit on the eastern edge of the Artesian Zone of the Aquifer; the spring-flow discharges from these springs that provide the headwaters of the Comal and San Marcos rivers (both of which are tributaries to the Guadalupe River); and the San Antonio Bay into which the Guadalupe River discharges.

The volume of spring flow from Comal and San Marcos springs is influenced by the water level of the Aquifer, which in turn is influenced by the ratio of recharge over time to natural discharge through springs and artificial discharge through wells. *See Sierra Club v. Babbitt*, 995 F.2d 571, 573 (5th Cir. 1993). Without regulation, during drought conditions, withdrawals from the Aquifer could increase and thereby reduce flows from the springs. *See Shields v. Babbitt*, 229 F. Supp. 2d 638, 645 (W.D. Tex. 2000), *judgment vacated and remanded with instructions*, *Shields v. Norton*, 289 F.3d 832 (5th Cir. 2002), *cert. denied sub nom. Schuehle v. Norton*, 537 U.S. 1071 (2002). This is significant because during droughts the springs affect the quality of the habitat of the federally listed endangered and threatened species that are associated with the Aquifer and live in the Comal and San Marcos springs and rivers ecosystems. For a description of the species and these ecosystems, see sections 1.4, 3.4.2, and 3.4.3 of the Edwards Aquifer Habitat Conservation Plan (Nov. 2012) [hereinafter EAHCP]. The text of the EAHCP is available at www.edwardsaquifer.org/habitat-conservation-plan/documents-publications/. See also Chapter 32 of this book discussing the ESA. Moreover, reduced spring flows can affect the amount of flow in certain reaches in the Guadalupe River.

In recognition of these facts, the Texas legislature found that groundwater in the Aquifer "has a hydrologic interrelationship to the Guadalupe, San Antonio, San Marcos, Comal, Frio, and Nueces river basins." EAA Act § 1.06(a). Additionally, it found that "the Edwards Aquifer is a unique and complex hydrological system, with diverse economic and social interests dependent on the aquifer for water supply" and that in order to "sustain these diverse interests and that natural resource, a special regional management district is required for the effective control of the resource to protect terrestrial and aquatic life, domestic and municipal water supplies, the operation of existing industries, and the economic development of the state." EAA Act § 1.01. For these reasons, protecting and maintaining minimum spring-flow levels from Comal and San Marcos springs is of principal interest to the EAA in the management of the Aquifer.

III. Edwards Aquifer Authority

§ 17.10 Brief History

The Aquifer first came under management in 1959 through the creation of the Edwards Underground Water District (EUWD). *See* Act of Apr. 29, 1959, 56th Leg., R.S., ch. 99, as amended.

During the tenure of the EUWD, the common-law rule of capture remained intact for the Aquifer. See Chapter 5 of this book for a discussion of the rule of capture. Therefore, existing and future new users of the Aquifer were free to withdraw from the Aquifer as much groundwater as they could beneficially use without regard to liability to third parties. *See Houston & T.C. Ry. Co. v. East*, 81 S.W. 279 (Tex. 1904). This prospect was of great concern to downstream water rights holders in the Guadalupe River Basin and environmental spring-flow interests because of the interconnectivity of these water bodies, as discussed in part II of this chapter. No remedy existed under then prevailing case law to prevent continued reliance on the Aquifer and the reduction of spring flows at Comal and San Marcos springs. *See Pecos County Water Control & Improvement District No. 1 v. Williams*, 271 S.W.2d 503 (Tex. App.—El Paso 1954, writ ref'd n.r.e.) (stating that surface water users downstream of spring discharges have no cause of action against upgradient pumpers for diminishing spring flows due to groundwater withdrawals); *City of San Antonio v. Texas Water Commission*, 392 S.W.2d 200, 210 (Tex. App.—Austin 1965), *aff'd*, 407 S.W.2d 752 (Tex. 1966) (finding that the dependability of the natural flows of the Guadalupe River had been destroyed due to increased pumping in the San Antonio region causing decreased spring flows).

To bring the Aquifer under some form of management, downstream surface water users claimed that the Aquifer was not, in fact, percolating water, but instead was an "underground river" and, thus, was "state water" subject to management by the state under the prior appropriation doctrine. See Chapter 1 of this book comparing state water and groundwater. This claim first took form in 1989, when the Guadalupe-Blanco River Authority filed *In Re the Adjudication of Rights to Water in the Edwards Aquifer* (also known as *Guadalupe-Blanco River Authority v. Royal Crest Homes*), No. 89-0381 (22nd Dist. Ct., Hays County, Tex., filed June 15, 1989). After remaining on the docket for many years without any action, this case was finally dismissed on July 13, 2016. Taking a cue from this lawsuit, in 1992 the state issued emergency rules declaring the Aquifer to be an "underground river" subject to state regulation. *See* 17 Tex. Reg. 6601 (Sept. 25, 1992). However, these rules were promptly voided by a state trial court because the court found that the Aquifer was percolating underground water. *See McFadin v. Texas Water Commission*, No. 92-05214 (331st Dist. Ct., Travis County, Tex., 1992, appeal dism'd by agreement).

Downstream surface water users and the environmental community also tried to force the regulation of the Aquifer using the Endangered Species Act (ESA) as a legal tool. A series of ESA lawsuits were filed, with some seeking to bring the Aquifer under federal control so that withdrawals would be regulated for the benefit of threatened and endangered species dependent on discharges from Comal and San Marcos springs. *See, e.g., Sierra Club v. Lujan*, No. MO-91-CA-069, 1993 WL 151353 (W.D. Tex. Feb. 1, 1993), *appeal dism'd sub nom. Sierra Club v. Babbitt*, 995 F.2d 571 (5th Cir. 1993). The *Babbitt* case was successful in requiring the U.S. Fish & Wildlife Service (USFWS) to prepare a recovery plan and designate minimum spring flows for Comal and San Marcos springs to ensure the protection of endangered species.

The state of Texas responded in 1993 to the decision in *Sierra Club v. Lujan*. The EAA Act was enacted, which for the first time authorized the management of the Aquifer by regulating the common-law rule of capture and creating a statutory-based permit system. In so doing, it fundamentally changed the manner in which a groundwater right in the Aquifer is established—from one based on ownership of land (the rule of capture) to one based on beneficial use during a prescribed historical period. The Act created the EAA with comprehensive management powers to administer this new system.

Since creating the EAA, the state has successfully invoked the *Burford* abstention doctrine to avoid interference from federal courts in the management of the Aquifer. *See Sierra Club v. City of San Antonio*, 112 F.3d 789 (5th Cir. 1997), *cert. denied*, 522 U.S. 1089 (1998); *see also Day v. Edwards Aquifer Authority*, No. Civ. A. SA-03-CA0429-FB, 2004 WL 1118721 (W.D. Tex. Mar. 26, 2004). The legislature also made the EAA the lead agency for ensuring compliance with the ESA to protect the threatened and endangered species associated with the Aquifer at Comal and San Marcos springs. In this role, the EAA has become the intermediary between the users of the Aquifer and the USFWS. Umbrella protection for Aquifer users would be afforded by the EAA's responsibility for Aquifer management. That is, users are shielded from potential ESA liability for the taking of threatened and endangered species based on their use of the Aquifer. The basic constitutionality of this approach has been approved by the Texas Supreme Court in *Barshop v. Medina County Underground Water Conservation District*, 925 S.W.2d 618 (Tex. 1996).

§ 17.11 Legal Nature of the EAA

The EAA was created as a "conservation and reclamation district" pursuant to article XVI, section 59, of the Texas Constitution. *See* EAA Act §§ 1.02, 1.06(b), 1.08(a). The EAA is not a "state agency," because it has jurisdiction over only a portion of the state of Texas, and the members of its governing body are elected in local elections or appointed by locally elected officials. *See Guaranty Petroleum Corp. v. Armstrong*, 609 S.W.2d 529, 531 (Tex. 1980). As a conservation and reclamation district, the EAA is an instrumentality established by the Texas legislature at the local level to provide for the conservation, development, and preservation of the natural resources in its boundaries. *See* Tex. Const. art. XVI, § 59(b). It is a political subdivision of the state and stands on the same footing as counties and other political subdivisions. *See* Tex. Const. art. XVI, § 59(b); *Bennett v. Brown County Water Improvement District No. 1*, 272 S.W.2d 498, 500 (Tex. 1954), *accord Willacy County Water Control & Improvement District No. 1 v. Abendroth*, 177 S.W.2d 936, 937 (Tex. 1944). As a conservation and reclamation district, the EAA is a governmental agency and body politic and corporate. *See* Tex. Const. art. XVI, § 59(b); EAA Act § 1.02(a). The EAA performs governmental functions and exercises the state's police power essentially as agents of the state to protect the health, safety, comfort, and welfare of the public, specifically by regulating and managing the Aquifer for the overall welfare of the public. *See Banker v. Jefferson County Water Control & Improvement District No. 1*, 277 S.W.2d 130, 133–34 (Tex. App.—Beaumont 1955, writ ref'd n.r.e.).

§ 17.12 Administration of the EAA

The EAA is governed by a seventeen-member board of directors. *See* EAA Act § 1.09(a). Fifteen of the directors are elected from single-member districts, and two are appointed. *See* EAA Act § 1.09(a). One of the appointed directors is selected by the South Central Texas Water Advisory Committee. *See* EAA Act § 1.091(b). The other appointed director is named, on an alternating basis, by the county commissioners courts of Medina and Uvalde counties. *See* EAA Act § 1.091(c). On August 28, 2019, the Fifth Circuit Court of Appeals affirmed a district court decision finding that the EAA is a special-purpose district and that its regionally balanced electoral scheme fell within the exception to one-person, one-vote requirements and was constitutional. *See League of United Latin Citizens (LULAC) v. Edwards Aquifer Authority*, 937 F.3d 457 (5th Cir. 2019), *cert. denied*, 140 S. Ct. 2717 (2020). Elected directors serve staggered four-year terms, with elections occurring in even-numbered years. *See* EAA Act § 1.09(a), (b). Appointed directors also serve four-year terms. *See* EAA Act § 1.091(d).

The board governs itself through its bylaws. *See* Tex. Water Code § 36.057(f); Edwards Aquifer Authority Bylaws (2016), www.edwardsaquifer.org/wp-content/uploads/2019/04/eaa_bylaws_2016.pdf [hereinafter EAA Bylaws]. Its meetings are conducted under the Texas Open Meetings Act.

See Tex. Water Code §§ 36.063(a), 36.064(b); Tex. Gov't Code ch. 551; EAA Bylaws art. 14.05(a). The procedural rules governing board meetings are Robert's Rules of Order, as modified by the board. *See* EAA Bylaws art. 6.09(b); Edwards Aquifer Authority Parliamentary Rules of Conduct (1998). To be valid, actions of the board must be adopted by the affirmative vote of a majority of the fifteen voting members when a quorum of those directors is present. *See* EAA Act § 1.09(f). The presence of eight elected directors constitutes a quorum of the board. *See* EAA Act § 1.09(f). With the exception of voting on matters before the board, appointed directors are authorized to fully participate in board meetings in the same manner as elected directors. *See* EAA Act § 1.091(e). Directors receive no compensation for their service on the board but may be reimbursed for expenses. *See* EAA Act §§ 1.09(g), 1.091(f).

The board of the EAA may hire a chief administrator to manage the EAA who has the title of general manager. *See* EAA Act § 1.11(d)(5); Tex. Water Code § 36.056(a). The EAA may also hire employees as necessary to enable it to carry out its powers and duties. *See* EAA Act § 1.11(d)(5); Tex. Water Code § 36.056(a). The board has delegated the staff-hiring function to its general manager. *See* EAA Act § 1.11(d)(6). The general manager and staff implement the EAA Act and board policy as directed by the board. EAA staff is generally organized according to the various administration, regulatory, and research programs of the EAA.

§ 17.13 Law Applicable to the EAA

In addition to the EAA Act, the EAA may look to general law to support its authority to manage and regulate the Aquifer and conduct its affairs. Section 1.08(a) of the EAA Act as amended, effective September 1, 2019, authorizes the EAA to look to chapters 49 and 51 of the Texas Water Code and other applicable "general laws" for supplemental authority. Prior to the amendment, parts of Water Code chapter 36 applied to the EAA. *See* Act of May 27, 2019, 86th Leg., R.S., ch. 1135, §§ 1–15 (H.B. 2729), eff. Sept. 1, 2019 (amending EAA Act §§ 1.03, 1.07, 1.08, 1.09, 1.11, 1.26, 1.29, 1.37, 1.38, 3.01; adding EAA §§ 1.21, 1.211, 1.361, 1.46; repealing EAA Act § 1.25(b); amending Tex. Water Code § 36.205(e); and repealing Tex. Water Code §§ 36.101(*l*), 36.1011(e), 36.125, 36.419). The EAA Act also refers to chapter 50 of the Water Code, formerly relating to general law districts. Chapter 50 has also been repealed and recodified in chapter 49, relating to provisions applicable to all districts. *See* Act of May 25, 1995, 74th Leg., R.S., ch. 715, §§ 2, 39. The Texas Attorney General has concluded that chapter 49 applies to the EAA. *See* Tex. Att'y Gen. Op. No. JC-0006, at 2 (1999). However, in the event of a conflict, the Act prevails. *See* EAA Act § 1.08(a). It is beyond the scope of this chapter to discuss the legal authority of the EAA derived from chapters 49 and 51 and other applicable general laws.

§ 17.14 EAA Jurisdiction

The EAA was created, among other purposes, to protect the Aquifer and is empowered by the Act to prevent the waste or pollution of its groundwater. The EAA is also required to regulate withdrawals from the Aquifer and to limit such withdrawals to protect the water quality of the Aquifer, the surface springs dependent on the Aquifer, aquatic and wildlife habitat, and threatened and endangered species. *See* EAA Act § 1.14(a). The EAA is given broad powers to "manage, conserve, preserve, and protect the aquifer . . . and prevent the waste or pollution of water in, the aquifer." EAA Act § 1.08(a).

§ 17.14:1 Groundwater Quantity

For water quantity management of the Aquifer, the jurisdictional boundaries of the EAA encompass all of Bexar, Medina, and Uvalde counties and the parts of Atascosa, Caldwell, Comal,

Guadalupe, and Hays counties within the boundaries of the EAA. *See* EAA Act §§ 1.02(a), 1.04. However, the EAA may act extraterritorially to prevent the use of Aquifer water outside the boundaries of the EAA. *See* EAA Act § 1.34(a) (requiring water withdrawn from the Aquifer to be used within the EAA's boundaries).

The EAA has jurisdiction over groundwater residing *in situ* in the Aquifer underlying its boundaries. *See* EAA Act § 1.08(b). The EAA has no jurisdiction over groundwater in any other aquifer. The EAA has jurisdiction to manage withdrawals from the Aquifer and to manage points of withdrawal from which Aquifer groundwater is produced. *See* EAA Act § 1.15(a). These functions are accomplished primarily through its permit program. Persons may not generally make withdrawals from the Aquifer unless they first obtain a groundwater withdrawal permit from the EAA. *See* EAA Act § 1.15(b). Likewise, wells or other works designed for the withdrawal of groundwater from the Aquifer may not be constructed without a well construction permit having first been issued by the EAA. *See* EAA Act § 1.15(b).

Additionally, the EAA continues to retain jurisdiction over the use of groundwater after it has been withdrawn from the Aquifer. *See* EAA Act § 1.08(b) (noting that the EAA's powers extend to water *withdrawn* from the Aquifer). This jurisdiction is exercised for various purposes, including regulation to prevent waste (*see, e.g.*, EAA Act § 1.35(c)) and to further conservation (*see, e.g.*, EAA Act § 1.23). To ensure that water is used in appropriate amounts during drought conditions, the EAA may regulate the use of water by end users through its critical period program. *See, e.g.*, EAA Act § 1.26. Finally, to protect federally listed endangered and threatened species during times of drought, the EAA may administer a recovery implementation program under the ESA. The program protects spring flow through specific measures affecting withdrawals from the Aquifer. *See* EAA Act §§ 1.14(h), 1.26A.

§ 17.14:2 Groundwater Quality

For water quality management of the Aquifer, the EAA's jurisdiction includes its general jurisdictional boundaries and an extraterritorial jurisdiction of five miles beyond its boundaries, except in Bandera County. *See* EAA Act § 1.08(c). The purpose of the five-mile water quality buffer zone is to give the EAA an opportunity to prevent pollution of surface water that may enter the EAA's boundaries and ultimately recharge the Aquifer. *See* EAA Act § 1.08(c). Therefore, the EAA's water quality jurisdiction extends to the entirety of Bexar, Medina, and Uvalde counties and the parts of Atascosa, Bastrop, Caldwell, Comal, Edwards, Frio, Gonzales, Guadalupe, Hays, Kendall, Kinney, Maverick, Real, Travis, Wilson, and Zavala counties within the five-mile buffer zone. As a practical matter, though, this authority is currently applied only in the portion of the Contributing Zone that is five miles upgradient of the Recharge Zone (rather than from the EAA's boundaries). *See, e.g.*, EAA Rules § 713.401 (applicability of the regulated substances registration, storage, and planning rules). Because of this, the EAA currently asserts its extraterritorial water quality authority only in portions of Kinney, Real, Comal, and Hays counties outside the EAA's boundaries, all of which are upgradient of the Recharge Zone.

Within the EAA's boundaries, the Leona Gravels, Austin Chalk, and Buda aquifers overlie the Aquifer. At some locations, the Trinity Aquifer is adjacent to or underlies the Aquifer. *See* 2004 CWMP, at 50. Although the EAA does not regulate withdrawals from these other aquifers, it does retain jurisdiction to ensure that when a person wants to drill through the Aquifer in order to enter an underlying aquifer, it does so in a manner that protects the water quality of the Aquifer. In such an event, the person drilling the well would need to seek a well construction permit from both the EAA and, potentially, another GCD with jurisdiction over the relevant aquifer. *See* EAA Rules § 713.203(a)(4).

The EAA Act prohibits the pollution, or contribution to the pollution, of the Aquifer. *See* EAA Act § 1.35(d). The Texas Supreme Court in *Bragg v. Edwards Aquifer Authority* commented that "[t]he Legislature created the [EAA] for the express purpose of . . . managing the water in the aquifer . . . . It provided the Authority with 'all of the powers, rights, and privileges necessary to manage, conserve, preserve, and protect the aquifer and to . . . prevent the waste or pollution of water in, the aquifer.'" *Bragg*, 71 S.W.3d 729, 736 (Tex. 2002) (quoting EAA Act § 1.08(a)).

The Act defines "pollution" as "the alteration of the physical, thermal, chemical, or biological quality of any water in the state, or [its] contamination . . . that renders the water harmful, detrimental, or injurious to humans . . . or public health, safety or welfare or that impairs the usefulness of the public enjoyment of the water for any . . . purpose." EAA Act § 1.03(17). The phrase "any water in the state" is broad enough to include both groundwater in the Aquifer and surface water recharging the Aquifer.

Closely related to the authority to prevent pollution is the EAA's responsibility to prevent "waste" of groundwater in the Aquifer. *See, e.g.*, EAA Act §§ 1.03(17) (defining "pollution"), 1.03(21) (defining "waste"), 1.08(a) (authorizing the EAA to "prevent the waste or pollution of water in, the aquifer"), 1.35(c), (d) (prohibiting the waste and pollution of the Aquifer). "Waste" is defined, in relevant part, to include (1) "withdrawal of underground water from the aquifer at a rate and in an amount that causes or threatens to cause intrusion into the reservoir of water unsuitable for agricultural, gardening, domestic, or stock raising purposes"; and (2) "pollution or harmful alteration of underground water in the aquifer by salt water or other deleterious matter admitted from another stratum or from the surface of the ground." EAA Act § 1.03(21)(A), (D).

§ 17.14:3 Protection of Endangered and Threatened Species

Eight federally listed threatened or endangered species are associated with the Aquifer and located proximate to Comal and San Marcos springs. The eight species are (1) Texas Blind Salamander (*Eurycea rathbuni*) (endangered—listed in 1967); (2) Fountain Darter (*Etheostoma fonticola*) (endangered—listed in 1970); (3) Texas Wild Rice (*Zizania texana*) (endangered—listed in 1978); (4) San Marcos Salamander (*Eurycea nana*) (threatened—listed in 1980); (5) San Marcos Gambusia (*Gambusia georgei*) (endangered—listed in 1980); (6) Peck's Cave Amphipod (*Stygobromus pecki*) (endangered—listed in 1998); (7) Comal Springs Dryopid Beetle (*Stygoparnus comalensis*) (endangered—listed in 1998); and (8) Comal Springs Riffle Beetle (*Heterelmis comalensis*) (endangered—listed in 1998). The welfare of these species and their habitat is dependent on the spring flows from these springs. Withdrawals from the Aquifer, as well as the Aquifer's management, can affect the timing and volume of flows from these springs.

Under section 1.14(h) of the EAA Act, the EAA is to develop, implement, and enforce a program to ensure that the continuous minimum spring flows of Comal and San Marcos springs are maintained to protect the endangered and threatened species to the extent required by federal law. Under section 1.26A, the EAA must develop a "recovery implementation program" (RIP) for the federally listed threatened or endangered species that are associated with the Aquifer. *See* EAA Act § 1.26A(a)(1). The RIP was required to be developed through a consensus-based process with input from many governmental and nongovernmental parties. In February 2013, after six years of work, the EAA's RIP process successfully culminated when the USFWS issued an Incidental Take Permit (ITP) for implementation of the EAHCP. The ITP was issued under section 10(a)(1)(B) of the ESA. In essence, the ITP provides an exception to the EAA, and its fellow permit holders, from potential "take" liability under ESA section 9(a)(1)(B) for activities in managing and regulating the use of the Aquifer for water supply. See Chapter 32 of this book for a discussion of the ESA.

§ 17.14:4 Surface Water

After groundwater from the Aquifer is discharged through a spring, the EAA loses jurisdiction over the water. Groundwater from the Aquifer, upon arising to the surface through a spring, is no longer located "within" the Aquifer. *See* EAA Act § 1.08(b). In addition, upon discharge from the springs into a watercourse, the water becomes state surface water and is regulated by the Texas Commission on Environmental Quality (TCEQ). *See Edwards Aquifer Authority v. Day*, 369 S.W.3d 814, 822–23 (Tex. 2012). State surface water is owned by the state and held in trust for the public. *See City of Marshall v. City of Uncertain*, 206 S.W.3d 97, 101 (Tex. 2006). The EAA has no power to regulate the appropriation of surface water. *See* EAA Act § 1.08(b); *Edwards Aquifer Authority v. Day*, 274 S.W.3d 742, 752 (Tex. App.—San Antonio 2008), *aff'd*, 369 S.W.3d 814 (Tex. 2012). Therefore, the EAA has no continuing jurisdiction over discharges from springs hydrologically connected to the Aquifer. *See* EAA Act § 1.08(b).

§ 17.15 Rulemaking

The EAA generally implements its powers and duties under the EAA Act through rulemaking. *See* EAA Act § 1.11(a). The duty to adopt implementation rules applies to the administration of its substantive programs and procedural rules governing practice before the EAA. *See* EAA Act § 1.11(a). Procedural rules include rules governing matters subject to contested case hearings, consistent with subchapters C, D, and F of the Texas Administrative Procedure Act (APA), Tex. Gov't Code ch. 2001. *See* EAA Act § 1.15(f). The EAA's procedural rules governing the practice before the agency are found at chapter 707 of the EAA's rules. The EAA's rulemaking procedural rules implementing section 1.115 of the EAA Act are at chapter 703.

In conducting its rulemaking, the EAA is not required to comply with the Texas Private Real Property Rights Preservation Act, chapter 2007 of the Texas Government Code. Thus, the EAA is not required to prepare "takings impact assessments" to support its rulemaking. *See Bragg v. Edwards Aquifer Authority*, 71 S.W.3d 729, 736–37 (Tex. 2002).

The EAA must follow certain procedures when engaging in rulemaking. The rulemaking procedures apply only to "rules" of the EAA. They do not apply to the adoption of EAA bylaws or internal procedures of the board of the EAA and staff. *See* EAA Act § 1.115(f).

Before September 1, 2001, the EAA was required to comply with the rulemaking requirements of the APA. *See* EAA Act § 1.11(h), *repealed by* Act of May 28, 2001, 77th Leg., R.S., ch. 966, § 6.03. In 2001, this duty was repealed and replaced by a scaled-down set of requirements in section 1.115 of the EAA Act.

In the normal course of action, the EAA adopts its final rules through "regular" rulemaking procedures. However, it may, under appropriate circumstances, invoke more abbreviated emergency rulemaking procedures under two circumstances: (1) if circumstances may result in "imminent harm to human health, safety, or welfare," or (2) if compliance with ordinary rulemaking procedures prevents "an effective response to emergency aquifer or springflow conditions." *See* EAA Act § 1.115(e). Under these circumstances, the board needs to give only a five-day public notice of the proposed action to adopt emergency rules. *See* EAA Act § 1.115(e). Emergency rules are effective for 120 days and may be renewed for another 60 days. *See* EAA Act § 1.115(e). The EAA's rules implementing emergency rules are found at section 703.15. *See* EAA Rules § 703.15.

§ 17.16 Revenues

Revenues to support the EAA's operations and the implementation of the EAA Act are largely provided by user fees referred to as "aquifer management fees" (AMFs). The EAA is also authorized to assess a variety of fees to fund its operations. These fees include permit application fees not exceeding $25, registration fees not exceeding $10, and miscellaneous administrative fees to recover its costs of performing certain administrative acts. *See* EAA Act § 1.29(f), (g); EAA Rules §§ 709.41–.45. The EAA is prohibited from assessing ad valorem property taxes to fund its operations. *See* EAA Act § 1.28(a). EAA rules to implement its fee authority are in chapter 709. *See* EAA Rules §§ 709.15–.45.

The EAA may assess AMFs to finance its administrative expenses and programs. *See* EAA Act § 1.29(b). The EAA assesses two types of AMFs: aquifer management fees to provide revenue for its administrative expenses and "program" aquifer management fees to provide revenues to fund its EAHCP. *See* EAA Rules § 709.18(a). AMFs are not considered taxes imposed merely for the purposes of raising revenue for the EAA, but rather are assessed for the purpose of regulating the Aquifer. For this reason, the EAA is not required to conduct an election prior to assessing the AMFs against water users. *See* Tex. Att'y Gen. Op. No. LO-97-012 (1997). AMFs for agricultural use may not exceed $2 per AF and must be assessed on the amount of groundwater actually withdrawn in a calendar year. *See* EAA Act § 1.29(e). Agricultural use includes irrigation and certain industrial uses including cultivation; floriculture, viticulture, silviculture, and horticulture; nursery growers; animal breeding; wildlife management; equine animals; and cover crops. *See* EAA Act § 1.03(26), (27).

Nonagricultural users (i.e., municipal and industrial users not qualifying for agricultural treatment) are assessed AMFs based on the face value of their initial regular permits (IRPs), irrespective of the amount of groundwater actually withdrawn. *See* EAA Act § 1.29(e). The EAA may not increase AMFs on nonagricultural users by more than 8 percent per year. *See* EAA Act § 1.29(b).

§ 17.17 Other General Authority

The EAA may issue revenue bonds for land, facilities, and equipment. *See* EAA Act § 1.28(b). Any revenue bonds issued by the EAA are subject to review and approval by the Texas attorney general. *See* EAA Act § 1.28(c). Bond proceeds of the EAA may be organized into those funds and accounts and invested as the EAA deems appropriate. *See* EAA Act § 1.28(d).

The EAA may receive financial assistance through gifts, grants, awards, and loans to carry out its programs. *See* EAA Act §§ 1.11(d)(4), 1.24(b). When acquiring groundwater withdrawal permits from the Aquifer, the EAA is specifically authorized to look to the TWDB for funding assistance. *See* EAA Act § 1.22(c).

The EAA may enter into contracts. *See* EAA Act §§ 1.11(d)(2), 1.27(d). The EAA may sue and be sued. *See* EAA Act § 1.11(d)(3).

The EAA may own real and personal property. *See* EAA Act § 1.11(d)(7). This includes the right to acquire surface water and groundwater rights. *See* EAA Act § 1.22(b). Groundwater rights may be acquired from any aquifer (including the Aquifer). Surface water rights may be from any watercourse whether inside or outside of the EAA's boundaries. In administering its financial assistance programs, the EAA may also acquire all or part of a groundwater withdrawal permit to be transferred to the EAA. *See* EAA Act § 1.24(c). The amount that the EAA may require to be transferred is equal to the amount of the permit that is conserved or made available because of the construction of a water management project. *See* EAA Act § 1.24(c).

The EAA has the power of eminent domain but may not exercise this power to acquire groundwater rights. *See* EAA Act § 1.11(g).

§ 17.18 Oversight of the EAA

The South Central Texas Water Advisory Committee (SCTWAC) is a twenty-member body whose members are appointed from various cities and counties within the boundaries of the EAA and in the Guadalupe, San Antonio, and Nueces River Basins. *See* EAA Act § 1.10(a). The SCTWAC is charged with advising the EAA on downstream water rights and issues. *See* EAA Act § 1.10(a). Other duties of the SCTWAC include assisting the EAA in the development of its demand management plans. *See* EAA Act § 1.10(i)(1).

The EAA is required to send to SCTWAC members all communications of the EAA that are delivered to the EAA's board. *See* EAA Act § 1.10(e). Although SCTWAC members may participate in EAA board meetings on matters within their scope, they may not vote on matters pending before the board. *See* EAA Act § 1.10(e). Funding for SCTWAC activities is provided by the EAA from AMFs assessed on holders of EAA groundwater withdrawal permits. *See* EAA Act § 1.29(i).

Every even-numbered year, the SCTWAC must file a report with the TCEQ and the EAA assessing the "effect on downstream water rights of the management of the aquifer," and the EAA is required to consider the report in its management of the Aquifer. EAA Act § 1.10(h).

The SCTWAC may ask the board to reconsider an action taken by the board that the SCTWAC deems to be "prejudicial to downstream water interests" in the Guadalupe River Basin. EAA Act § 1.10(f). Upon such request, the board has three options: (1) it may vote to reconsider the matter, rescind the prior action, and take other action; (2) it may vote to reconsider and, after further review, let the prior action stand; or (3) it may vote not to reconsider the matter and let its prior action stand.

If the SCTWAC is not satisfied with the action taken by the board on its request for reconsideration, the SCTWAC may request the TCEQ to review the action. *See* EAA Act § 1.10(f). Although the TCEQ must conduct the requested review, it retains discretion about whether to make a recommendation to the board. *See* EAA Act § 1.10(f). Any TCEQ recommendation to the board is purely advisory. It is solely within the discretion of the board to determine the import of the TCEQ's recommendation. However, if the board determines that the board's "action is contrary to an action of the [TCEQ] affecting downstream interests," then the board must reverse itself. *See* EAA Act § 1.10(f).

The Edwards Aquifer Legislative Oversight Committee also oversees the EAA and consists of six members of the Texas legislature—three members of the senate appointed by the lieutenant governor and another three members appointed by the speaker of the house of representatives. *See* EAA Act § 3.01(a). Among other things, the committee oversees and reviews the activities of the EAA in implementing the Act, compliance with the ESA, and the control of water pollution in the Aquifer region. *See* EAA Act § 3.01(c)(1), (c)(3), (c)(4). From time to time the committee holds a hearing to perform its oversight functions. Every even-numbered year, the EAA is required to prepare and deliver a report to the committee regarding EAA operations. The report must contain a summary of issues that may impact the implementation of the EAA Act. *See* EAA Act § 3.01(d).

Although the TCEQ has no direct authority over the regulation of the Aquifer, the legislature nonetheless gave it specific oversight authority over the EAA to ensure that it was properly performing its duties under the EAA Act, in addition to the SCTWAC process discussed above. In the event the EAA does not perform its nondiscretionary duties under the Act, the TCEQ may bring a mandamus action against the EAA. The TCEQ may also bring such an action when, in its judgment, the EAA is not enforcing the Act against those in violation of its terms. *See* EAA Act § 1.39.

IV. Administration of Groundwater Rights

§ 17.19 Groundwater Rights in the Aquifer

The Act currently provides for two types of groundwater rights in the Aquifer: groundwater withdrawal permits and wells that are deemed exempt from the permitting requirement. Exempt wells are certain small production wells used for domestic, livestock, and other beneficial uses. Persons desiring to withdraw groundwater from the Aquifer must establish one of these rights to have the legal authority to make a withdrawal from the Aquifer. *See* EAA Act § 1.15(b).

§ 17.19:1 Groundwater Withdrawal Permits

The EAA has the authority to manage all withdrawals from the Aquifer and withdrawal points. *See* EAA Act § 1.15(a). The EAA must ensure that groundwater withdrawn from the Aquifer is put to a beneficial use. *See* EAA Act §§ 1.03(21)(B), 1.35(c). The EAA must manage the Aquifer to maximize the beneficial use of groundwater available for withdrawal from the Aquifer. *See* EAA Act § 1.14(a)(4). The EAA has authority to take action to prevent the waste of groundwater withdrawn from the Aquifer. *See* EAA Act § 1.35(c). The EAA possesses all powers, rights, and privileges necessary to prevent the waste of the Aquifer. *See* EAA Act § 1.08(a). The EAA primarily exerts these authorities through the administration of a groundwater withdrawal permit program, which is the linchpin of the EAA's Aquifer management.

The Texas legislature charged the EAA with ensuring compliance with permitting and regulating permits. *See* EAA Act § 1.11(b). The rules of the EAA implementing the administration and regulation of permitted wells are found at subchapter E of chapter 711. *See* EAA Rules §§ 711.90–.112. Except for exempt use wells discussed below, landowners may no longer withdraw groundwater from the Aquifer unless they first obtain a permit from the EAA. *See* EAA Act § 1.15(b). The Act recognizes three purposes of use eligible for a permitting: industrial, irrigation, and municipal uses. *See* EAA Act § 1.03(11), (12), (14).

The EAA is limited in the amount of permits it may issue. The EAA Act imposes an Aquifer-wide "cap" on the amount of permitted withdrawals. Although not used in the Act, the Texas Supreme Court coined this term in *Barshop v. Medina County Underground Water Conservation District*, 925 S.W.2d 618, 624 (Tex. 1996). The cap was the legislature's expression of the amount of groundwater that was appropriate for withdrawal from the Aquifer while providing safeguards for spring flows at Comal and San Marcos springs. The legislature originally established a pair of sequential caps while also giving the EAA the option of raising those caps if studies and consultations so justified. *See* EAA Act § 1.14(d) (repealed). The first of those two caps, 450,000 AF per year, began on June 28, 1996, and would have changed to the second, 400,000 AF per year cap, on January 1, 2008, and continued indefinitely thereafter. However, on June 15, 2007, the legislature repealed those caps and replaced them with the current 572,000 AF per year cap. In addition, this new "cap" became a "minimum" in that the EAA is now required to issue permits in the sum of no less than 572,000 AF per year cap. *See* Act of May 28, 2007, 80th Leg., R.S., ch. 1351, §§ 2.02, 2.09; Act of May 28, 2007, 80th Leg., R.S., ch. 1430, §§ 12.02, 12.09 (repealing section 1.14(b) and amending section 1.14(c) of the Act). Unlike the prior law, the EAA has no authority to raise the new cap.

EAA-issued groundwater withdrawal permits are to contain the essential elements of a groundwater right in the Aquifer, including the applicable limitations and conditions. *See, e.g.*, EAA Act § 1.16(h). Through the permit, the owner has notice of the parameters of the right and the terms and conditions under which the right may be exercised. The basic conditions for permits are found at subchapter F of chapter 711 of the EAA rules. *See* EAA Rules §§ 711.130–.134. Among the important permit elements are ownership, total annual groundwater withdrawal amount, place of use, purpose of use, point of withdrawal, and interruption conditions. *See, e.g.*, EAA Act § 1.15(d); EAA Rules § 711.112.

The Act authorizes the EAA to issue four types of groundwater withdrawal permits: (1) initial regular permits (*see* EAA Act §§ 1.15(c), 1.16); (2) additional regular permits (*see* EAA Act §§ 1.15(c), 1.18); (3) term permits (*see* EAA Act §§ 1.15(c), 1.19); and (4) emergency permits (*see* EAA Act §§ 1.15(c), 1.20). By contract, the EAA also authorizes withdrawals from the aquifer for recharge recovery. *See* EAA Act § 1.44.

Initial Regular Permits: Initial regular permits (IRPs) are the basic permits issued by the EAA. The permit term for IRPs is perpetual. *See* EAA Act § 1.16(g). An IRP's most basic feature is issuance based on historical use and priority to a proportionate share of the 572,000 AF per year cap. Because of legislative action in 2007, the EAA issued final IRPs in the fall of 2008.

A basic requirement for eligibility is that the well owner must have filed an IRP application on or before December 30, 1996. *See* EAA Rules § 711.98(a). Because future new users of the Aquifer are not able to meet this requirement, new permanent appropriations from the Aquifer are precluded. *See generally GG Ranch, Ltd. v. Edwards Aquifer Authority*, No. SA-14-CV-00848, 2015 WL 4698851 (W.D. Tex. June 2, 2015), *aff'd*, 639 F. App'x 269 (5th Cir. 2016) (per curiam). Thus, new users of the Aquifer must enter the Edwards water market to obtain groundwater rights from other existing IRP holders.

Additional Regular Permits: The EAA may issue additional regular permits (ARPs) if, after all IRPs have been issued, groundwater remains available for permitting. *See* EAA Act § 1.18(a). However, because after final action on all IRP applications was completed no water remained available for permitting under the 572,000 AF per year cap, the EAA has been foreclosed from issuing such ARPs.

Term Permits: The EAA may issue term permits if certain Aquifer level and spring-flow levels exist. *See* EAA Act § 1.19. Term permits are intended for those periods when Aquifer levels and spring-flow level are very high. Under these conditions, the Aquifer is considered to be "full" and there is essentially a temporary additional supply from the Aquifer. Because Aquifer levels and spring-flow levels are high, it is assumed that such additional withdrawals would not be detrimental to spring flows at Comal and San Marcos springs. Term permits may be issued for a period not to exceed ten years. *See* EAA Act § 1.19(a). Withdrawals under term permits do not apply against the 572,000 AF per year cap. *See* EAA Rules § 711.166(a).

Term permit withdrawals must be consistent with the EAA's critical period management plan (CPMP). Holders of term permits may exercise their rights to withdraw from the San Antonio Pool of the Aquifer only when (1) the Aquifer as measured at index well J-17 is greater than 675 mean sea level (msl), (2) spring flows at Comal Springs are greater than 350 cubic feet per second (cfs), and (3) spring flows at San Marcos Springs are greater than 200 cfs. *See* EAA Act § 1.19(b). Withdrawals may be made from the Uvalde Pool when the Aquifer as measured at index well J-27 is greater than 865 msl. *See* EAA Act § 1.19(c). When the Aquifer is equal to or below these levels for either pool, holders of term permits must cease all withdrawals from that pool until the Aquifer and spring flows recover. *See* EAA Act § 1.19(b), (c).

Emergency Permits: The EAA may issue emergency permits to prevent the loss of life or to prevent severe, imminent threats to the public health or safety. *See* EAA Act § 1.20(a). Emergency permits may not have a term exceeding thirty days. *See* EAA Act § 1.20(b). If necessary, emergency permits may be renewed. *See* EAA Act § 1.20(c). Withdrawals under emergency permits do not apply against the 572,000 AF per year cap. *See* EAA Act § 1.20(d); EAA Rules § 711.168.

Recharge Recovery Contracts: Recharge recovery contracts are intended to authorize withdrawals from the Aquifer of groundwater in storage from an artificial recharge project. *See* EAA Act § 1.44. A contract is required to authorize the recovery of the water placed in storage under recharge projects. *See* EAA Act §§ 1.15(b), 1.44. The EAA's rules implementing its aquifer recharge, storage, and recovery contracting authority are found at subchapter J of chapter 711. *See* EAA Rules §§ 711.240–.245. Because additional water is being recharged into the Aquifer over and above what would occur under normal conditions, withdrawals under recharge recovery permits do not apply against the 572,000 AF per year cap. *See, e.g.*, EAA Act § 1.44(d).

§ 17.19:2 Permit Administration

The EAA has adopted extensive rules addressing various aspects of administering permits. These include rules regarding permit transfers; placing permits in a groundwater trust; permit amendments, corrections, and conversions; forbearance of IRP rights; and permit consolidation, abandonment, or cancellation.

Permit Transfers: One purpose of the EAA Act is to create a water market in Aquifer groundwater rights. The EAA has adopted permit transfer rules designed to foster and create certainty in this market. A permit transfer is a change in ownership, point of withdrawal, purpose of use, place of use, or maximum rate of withdrawal. *See* EAA Rules § 711.324. The EAA generally has the power to regulate transfers to ensure compliance with the Act. *See, e.g., Herrmann v. Lindsey*, 136 S.W.3d 286, 288–89 (Tex. App.—San Antonio 2004, no pet.) (discussing with approval the administrative actions of the EAA to regulate transfers of irrigation permit applications). Transfer applications are not subject to contested case hearings. *See* EAA Rules § 707.601. The EAA's rules implementing its transfer program are found at subchapter L of chapter 711. *See* EAA Rules §§ 711.324–.330. During the 86th legislative session in 2019, the legislature validated all prior transfers of Edwards permits effective September 1, 2019. *See* Act of May 24, 2019, 86th Leg., R.S., ch. 904, §§ 2, 3 (H.B. 3656), eff. Sept. 1, 2019.

Ownership of groundwater withdrawal permits and IRP applications is generally transferable. *See Barshop v. Medina County Underground Water Conservation District*, 925 S.W.2d 618, 630 (Tex. 1996) (permits); *Herrmann*, 136 S.W.3d at 288 n.1 (IRP applications). With the exception of irrigation IRPs, ownership of a permit is freely transferable separately from the ownership of a place of use. *See* EAA Rules § 711.324(b). Absent an express reservation, the ownership of transfers of the place of use is presumed to transfer ownership of an IRP. *See* EAA Rules § 711.324(c). Additionally, except for irrigation IRPs, the place of use and purpose of use for an IRP are freely transferable. *See* EAA Rules § 711.324(a)(3)–(4), (d), (e).

Special Rules Applicable to Irrigation IRPs: An irrigation IRP consists of two parts: (1) a 50 percent portion that is freely transferable as to place of use and purpose of use and (2) a 50 percent portion that is permanently appurtenant to the original acres of land irrigated during the historical period that provided the basis for the original issuance of the IRP. *See* EAA Act § 1.34(c). The EAA refers to these two parts respectively as unrestricted irrigation groundwater (UIG) and base irrigation groundwater (BIG). *See* EAA Rules § 702.1(25), (197). UIG is freely transferable as to place and purpose of use. *See* EAA Rules § 711.324(a)(3)–(4), (e). For BIG, the place or purpose of use may not be transferred. *See Herrmann*, 136 S.W.3d at 288 n.1; *see also* EAA Rules § 711.324(d). Reservations of BIG in the event of a sale of the surface estate to a third party are unenforceable, and BIG is transferred with the land as a matter of law. *See Herrmann*, 136 S.W.3d at 288 n.1; *Edwards Aquifer Authority v. Horton*, No. 04-09-00375-CV, 2010 WL 374551 (Tex. App.—San Antonio Feb. 3, 2010, pet. denied) (mem. op., not designated for publication); *see also* EAA Rules § 711.324(d). On the other hand, UIG may be reserved in the grantor. *See* EAA Rules § 711.324(e). Temporary transfers of BIG not to exceed ten years are authorized; however, the BIG remains appurtenant to the original historical irrigated lands. *See* EAA Rules § 711.330(d).

Special Rules Applicable to Cibolo Creek Transfers: A "Cibolo Creek transfer" is a transfer of a point of withdrawal from west of Cibolo Creek (i.e., Bexar, Medina, Atascosa, and Uvalde counties) to east of Cibolo Creek (i.e., Comal, Guadalupe, Hays, and Caldwell counties). *See* EAA Rules § 711.329(a). Amending an IRP to transfer a point of withdrawal from west to east of Cibolo Creek is prohibited. *See* EAA Rules § 711.336(12). Similarly, transferring an IRP for this purpose is also prohibited, except for three very limited exceptions. *See* EAA Rules §§ 711.328(12)(B), 711.329(a).

First, if the transfer is a sale, and the sale was approved by the EAA on or before July 11, 2006, or the sale occurred after this date and it is to remedy certain smaller pending compliance matters for unauthorized withdrawals at an unpermitted well installed on or before January 9, 2007, a Cibolo Creek transfer is authorized. *See* EAA Rules § 711.329(a)(3). In such a situation, further amendments to move the point of withdrawal are prohibited unless the original well is plugged. *See* EAA Rules § 711.329(b). Cibolo Creek transfers to remedy compliance issues for post-January 9, 2007, wells are prohibited. Note that under this rule, post-July 11, 2006, sales involving Cibolo Creek transfers are generally prohibited. *See* EAA Rules § 711.329(a)(3)(A).

Second, Cibolo Creek transfer leases after the effective date of the rules (i.e., December 18, 2009) are authorized only if (1) the well to which the transfer is made was installed before January 9, 2007; (2) the lease terms call for the lease to expire on or before December 31, 2014; (3) a certain transfer-to-the-groundwater-trust ratio is satisfied; (4) no subsequent transfers or amendments of the point of withdrawal are made; and (5) upon expiration of the lease the point of withdrawal reverts back to west of Cibolo Creek. *See* EAA Rules § 711.329(a)(1).

Third, Cibolo Creek transfer leases that were approved by the EAA before December 18, 2009, remain in effect and are allowed to expire according to their terms, after which time the point of withdrawal reverts back to west of Cibolo Creek. *See* EAA Rules § 711.329(a)(2).

Finally, none of the Cibolo Creek transfer rules limit the transfers or amendments of originally issued IRPs, whether located west or east of Cibolo Creek, as long as a transfer of the point of withdrawal from west to east of Cibolo Creek is not implicated. *See* EAA Rules § 711.329.

Further Limits on Transfers: Permit transfers are further limited by the prohibition on transporting groundwater withdrawn from the Aquifer from a point of withdrawal located in Uvalde County or Medina County to a place of use east of those counties. *See* EAA Act § 1.28(b). Additionally, groundwater withdrawn from the Aquifer may not be transferred to a place of use outside the boundaries of the EAA. *See* EAA Act § 1.34(a).

Groundwater Trust: The EAA operates a groundwater trust. *See* EAA Act § 1.22(a). The EAA's rules implementing its trust program are at subchapter N of chapter 711. *See* EAA Rules §§ 711.502–.540. The purpose of the trust includes the acquisition of IRPs for the possible subsequent sale or other transfer to third parties in need of water. *See* EAA Act § 1.22(a)(1), (a)(3). The EAA may also acquire IRPs to manage overall demand on the Aquifer. EAA Act § 1.22(a)(2). In such a case, IRPs would not be transferred out of the trust for use. Instead, they would reside in the trust for as long as the EAA deemed appropriate.

Permit Amendments: Once a permit is issued, the permit holder may request changes to the point of withdrawal, purpose of use, place of use, or maximum rate of withdrawal. *See* EAA Rules §§ 711.332–.336.

Permit Corrections: Once a permit is issued, the general manager may make nonsubstantive changes to it. *See* EAA Rules § 711.350. This procedure is intended to allow either the EAA or an applicant to correct a permit to update basic information, to correct clerical or typographical errors, and to more accurately state physical information.

Permit Conversions: If water conservation equipment is installed on the historically irrigated lands of an irrigation IRP, the holder of the IRP may convert a portion of BIG to UIG. *See* EAA Act § 1.34; EAA Rules §§ 711.338–.342. The amount that may be converted is limited to the amount of water actually conserved by the installed conservation equipment. *See* EAA Act § 1.34(b). BIG may also be converted if the historically irrigated acres are developed or if the historically irrigated acres are impacted by surrounding development in a manner that makes them no longer practicable to farm. The amount that may be converted is limited to an amount that is in the same proportion as the proportion of developed land or land that is no longer practicable to farm. *See* EAA Rules § 711.342; *see also Persyn Family LP v. Edwards Aquifer Authority*, No. 2007-CI-18500 (407th Dist. Ct., Bexar County, Tex., judgment issued Mar. 13, 2008); Act of May 24, 2019, 86th Leg., R.S., ch. 904, §§ 1, 2, eff. Sept. 1, 2019 (H.B. 3656) (amending EAA Act § 1.34 to expressly authorize the EAA to approve the conversion of BIG in the event that the historically irrigated lands to which the BIG is appurtenant are developed, and approving prior conversions). After conversion, the portion of converted BIG becomes freely transferable as to place and purpose of use.

Forbearance of IRP Rights: IRP holders may forgo the right to make withdrawals from the Aquifer and seek a special surface water permit from the TCEQ. *See* EAA Act § 1.30(b), (c)(1). Under this conjunctive management principle, the TCEQ may issue special permits to divert water from the Guadalupe River downstream of Comal and San Marcos springs in exchange for limiting the right to make IRP withdrawals from the Aquifer. *See* EAA Act § 1.30(a), (b). The Act defines "diversion" as "the removal of state water from a watercourse or impoundment." EAA Act § 1.03(8). Special permits issued under section 1.30 of the Act may not impair senior water rights, vested riparian rights, or surface water permits issued by the TCEQ pursuant to applications that were filed before May 31, 1993. *See* EAA Act § 1.30(c), (d). As an aid to the implementation of this section, when water is discovered by the TCEQ to be available in the Guadalupe-Blanco River Basin, notice must be given to the EAA that such water is available for appropriation. *See* EAA Act § 3.02. The TCEQ has not yet issued rules to implement section 1.30.

Permit Consolidation: Persons owning two or more groundwater withdrawal permits of the same type may consolidate the permits. *See* EAA Rules §§ 711.344–.348. For consolidation, the permits must have a common point of withdrawal. If not, then all the points of withdrawal must be operated and managed by the same permit holder, be located within the same pool, and be located either east or west of Cibolo Creek.

Loss of Permit: IRPs remain in effect until the permit is abandoned or canceled. *See* EAA Act § 1.16(g). IRPs are not subject to retirement. *See* Act of May 28, 2007, 80th Leg., R.S., ch. 1351, §§ 2.03, 2.05, 2.07, 2.09; Act of May 28, 2007, 80th Leg., R.S., ch. 1430, §§ 12.03, 12.05, 12.07, 12.09 (amending sections 1.16(g) and 1.22(a)(3) and (a)(4) to delete references to *retire*; amending section 1.29(h) to prohibit the use of EAA revenues for retirement purposes; and repealing sections 1.21 and 1.29(a), (c), and (d) relating to retirement of IRPs). The EAA's rules implementing abandonment procedures are found in subchapter L of chapter 711. *See* EAA Rules § 711.352. Under these rules, permits are subject only to voluntary abandonment. At any time, the board may enter an agreed order for declaration of abandonment evidencing the present intent of the owner of an IRP to discontinue permanently the withdrawal and beneficial use of all or part of the groundwater under the IRP. The EAA has not adopted any cancellations rules.

§ 17.19:3 Exempt Wells

Owners of certain small production wells are exempt from certain aspects of the EAA's regulation. There are four types of exempt wells: (1) domestic use wells, (2) livestock use wells, (3) limited production wells, and (4) municipal use wells at certain federal facilities. *See* EAA Act § 1.33(a), (d); EAA Rules § 711.20(a)(4). Domestic use is drinking, washing, or culinary purposes and irrigation of family gardens or orchards. *See* EAA Act § 1.03(9)(A), (B). Livestock use is the watering of animals. *See* EAA Act § 1.03(9)(C). Limited production wells include any beneficial use that is authorized by the Act. *See* EAA § 1.33(d); EAA Rules § 711.61(a)(2). Federal facilities wells are those located on a federal facility and for which the EAA has not approved a transfer of the ownership of the well to another person before September 1, 2003. *See* EAA Rules § 711.20(a)(4). The exempt well rules of the EAA are found at subchapters C (Exempt Wells) and D (Limited Production Wells) of chapter 711. *See* EAA Rules §§ 711.20–.50, 711.60–.72.

Owners of exempt wells are not required to obtain groundwater withdrawal permits. *See* EAA Act § 1.15(b). The Act does not impose any limits on the number of exempt wells that may be drilled into the Aquifer or on the total aggregate volume of groundwater that may be withdrawn from all exempt wells. Managing exempt wells differently from wells requiring a permit does not violate equal protection. *See Bragg v. Edwards Aquifer Authority*, 342 F. App'x 43 (5th Cir. 2009).

Although exempt from permitting, exempt wells must be registered. *See* EAA Act § 1.33(b). For this reason, owners of exempt wells were not required to file IRP applications with the EAA. *See* EAA Act § 1.16(c). Additionally, exempt domestic or livestock wells are not required to be metered. *See* EAA Act § 1.33(a). However, exempt limited production wells may under certain circumstances be required to be metered. *See* EAA Act § 1.33(d). Finally, owners of exempt wells are not required to pay aquifer management fees for withdrawals from the wells. *See* EAA Rules §§ 709.17, 711.22(b)(4), 711.64(b)(1).

For the owner of a domestic or livestock well to qualify for exempt well status, the well must (1) produce no more than 25,000 gallons per day (gpd), (2) be used solely for domestic or livestock use, and (3) not serve a subdivision requiring platting. *See* EAA Act § 1.33(a), (c). For the owner of a limited production well to qualify for exempt well status, the well must (1) have been drilled on or before June 1, 2013, (2) have been used for a beneficial use, and (3) either not be capable of producing more than 1,250 gpd or be metered and produce no more than 1.4 AF per calendar year. *See* EAA Act § 1.33(d).

An exempt well for domestic or livestock use must be constructed such that it is incapable of producing more than 25,000 gpd. *See* EAA Rules § 711.20(1). In contrast, if it is capable of producing more than 1,250 gpd, a limited production well must be metered. *See* EAA Rules § 711.61(a)(3). Domestic or livestock wells may not be used to serve a subdivision requiring platting. *See* EAA Act § 1.33(c). The EAA has defined the serving of a subdivision requiring platting to mean "provides, or is constructed and equipped to be capable of providing, piped water for any use to more than three service connections located within a subdivision requiring platting." EAA Rules § 711.38(2). All subdivisions of land are considered to require platting unless they fall within an exception contained in Texas Local Government Code chapter 212 or 232. *See* EAA Rules § 711.34.

Exempt well status is not permanent. Changes to a well or its use or operation could impact whether or not the well continues to qualify for exempt well status. The owner of an exempt well has a duty to advise the EAA of changed circumstances that may affect the status of the well. *See* EAA Rules §§ 711.44(b), 711.70(c).

Owners of exempt wells are required to register with the EAA to assert and attain recognition of the wells' exempt status. *See* EAA Act § 1.33(b). Wells that are thought by their owners to be exempt but that have not been registered are not exempt until the EAA has recognized the status. *See* EAA Rules §§ 711.16, 711.21, 711.62. Withdrawals from unregistered wells are prohibited. *See* EAA Rules § 711.226. Well owners were first required to register their wells by May 7, 2001. *See* EAA Rules §§ 707.307 (repealed), 711.26 (repealed). This date was later amended to December 31, 2005. *See* EAA Rules § 711.16(a).

§ 17.20 Metering of Permitted Wells

The EAA must implement a metering program and ensure compliance. *See* EAA Act § 1.11(b). EAA rules implementing its meter program are at subchapter M of chapter 711. *See* EAA Rules

§§ 711.400–.422. Permitted wells are required to have meters installed. *See* EAA Act § 1.31(a). An alternative measuring method may also be used. *See* EAA Act § 1.31(a). In either case, the new installation or method must be approved by the EAA. *See* EAA Act § 1.31(a). For irrigation wells in existence on September 1, 1993, the EAA bears the costs of meter installation and maintenance. *See* EAA Act § 1.31(b). Meter costs for all other permitted wells are borne by the well owner.

§ 17.21 Reporting

Each year, permit holders are required to report to the EAA their annual groundwater use for the preceding calendar year. *See* EAA Act § 1.32. The EAA's rules implementing its reporting requirements are at section 711.414. The EAA must ensure compliance with its reporting program. *See* EAA Act § 1.11(b). Owners of domestic or livestock exempt wells are not required to file groundwater use reports. *See* EAA Rules § 711.22(b)(3). The owners of limited production wells are generally required to file annual groundwater use reports. *See* EAA Rules § 711.69.

§ 17.22 Interruption of Withdrawals

Groundwater withdrawal permits state the maximum amount a permit holder may withdraw on an annual basis. These amounts are not absolutely firm in the sense that they can be fully withdrawn in any year under any conditions. Under the EAA Act, there is no guarantee that permit holders will be able to fully exercise their authorized annual groundwater withdrawal amount in any particular calendar year. A principal feature of the EAA Act is that withdrawals may be interrupted to accomplish the Aquifer management strategies of the EAA, such as providing sufficient spring flows from Comal and San Marcos springs for the benefit of the federally listed threatened and endangered species. An interruption is a temporary curtailment of the right to withdraw groundwater from the Aquifer. *See* EAA Rules § 702.1(98).

The Act authorizes permitted withdrawals to be interrupted under the following conditions: (1) the general interruption levels for the San Antonio Pool or the Uvalde Pool are triggered (*see* EAA Act § 1.14(f)); (2) environmental flows are needed to satisfy federal law requirements to protect threatened and endangered species associated with the Aquifer (*see* EAA Act § 1.14(h)); (3) the Aquifer management objectives in section 1.14(a) of the EAA Act require additional spring flows (*see* EAA Act § 1.14(h)); and (4) the EAA's CPMP is triggered (*see* EAA Act §§ 1.14(h)(1), 1.26). In their practical application, all interruption scenarios work hand in hand to accomplish the same objective of ensuring adequate spring flows from Comal and San Marcos springs for the benefit of the federally listed threatened and endangered species associated with the Aquifer.

§ 17.22:1 Section 1.14(f) Interruptions

The EAA must interrupt the right to withdraw from the San Antonio Pool when the Aquifer at index well J-17 is below 660 msl. *See* EAA Act § 1.14(f). For the Uvalde Pool, the interruption level is measured at index well J-27 and is triggered when the Aquifer is below 845 msl. *See* EAA Act § 1.14(f). Although the Act appears to give discretion to the EAA to interrupt withdrawals when the Aquifer is above these levels, the attorney general has determined that the EAA may not interrupt IRPs when the Aquifer is equal to or above these levels. *See* Tex. Att'y Gen. Op. No. GA-0498 (2007). The EAA implements section 1.14(f) interruptions through incorporation into the CPMP under section 1.26 of the EAA Act, as described at section 17.22:4 below.

§ 17.22:2 Section 1.14(h) Interruptions

To accomplish the species protection purposes of the EAA Act, the EAA must implement and enforce water management practices to ensure that, not later than December 31, 2012, the continuous minimum spring flows of Comal and San Marcos springs are maintained to protect federally listed endangered and threatened species to the extent required by federal law. *See* EAA Act § 1.14(h). To meet this requirement, the EAA shall require (1) phased adjustments (i.e., interruptions) of the amount of water that may be used or withdrawn from the Aquifer or (2) implementation of alternative management practices. The EAA implements section 1.14(h) interruptions through incorporation into the CPMP under section 1.26 of the EAA Act, as described at section 17.22:4 below, and certain other conservation measures found in the EAHCP, as discussed below.

In February 2013, the USFWS issued an incidental take permit to the EAA, among others, under section 10(a) of the ESA. *See* U.S. Fish and Wildlife Service, Incidental Take Permit No. TE-63663A-1 (amended Jan. 2015), www.edwardsaquifer.org/habitat-conservation-plan/documents-publications/. In so doing, the USFWS also approved the EAHCP.

The approved EAHCP includes "minimization and mitigation measures" (known as "Conservation Measures"). These measures are designed to ensure that any incidental take resulting from the EAA's management of the Aquifer (as well as the activities of the other permittees) will be "minimized and mitigated to the maximum extent practicable and will not appreciably reduce the likelihood of the survival and recovery of the threatened and endangered species associated with the Aquifer in the Comal and San Marcos Springs and Rivers ecosystems." *See* EAHCP § 1.1.1.

The EAHCP contains four specific Conservation Measures that are designed as spring-flow protection measures: (1) the Voluntary Irrigation Suspension Program Option (VISPO); (2) Regional Water Conservation Program (RWCP); (3) Critical Period Management—Stage V (CPM Stage V); and (4) use of the San Antonio Water System's Twin Oaks Aquifer Storage and Recovery Project for spring-flow protection (SAWS ASR). *See* EAHCP §§ 5.1.2–.4, 5.5.1, respectively. The VISPO is a program that pays irrigators to forbear pumping from the Aquifer during certain drought conditions. The RWCP is a program that pays participating Aquifer users to implement certain conservation programs in exchange for leaving a portion of the conserved water in the Aquifer unpumped. The CPM Stage V is an additional stage added to the EAA's existing critical period management program, discussed below. The SAWS ASR is a program in which the EAA acquires Edwards groundwater rights for use in providing storage to SAWS in exchange for SAWS's agreeing to forbear pumping from the Aquifer during certain drought conditions and to instead recover water from the SAWS ASR. Once a specific amount of groundwater is stored, the acquired groundwater rights are no longer available to SAWS for storage. Instead, the rights are held by the EAA for conservation purposes and are forborne from use under certain conditions. See Chapter 32 of this book for additional discussion of the EAHCP.

§ 17.22:3 Section 1.14(a) Interruptions

The EAA may interrupt withdrawals if certain Aquifer management objectives require additional spring flows. These management objectives include, among others, protecting threatened and endangered species (*see* EAA Act § 1.14(a)(6), (a)(7)). The EAA implements section 1.14(a) interruptions through incorporation into the CPMP under section 1.26 of the EAA Act, as described at section 17.22:4 below, and certain other conservation measures found in the EAHCP, as discussed above.

§ 17.22:4 Section 1.26 Critical Period Interruptions

The EAA is required to prepare and implement a CPMP. *See* EAA Act § 1.26. Although the Act does not define "critical period," it is generally understood to be a drought condition in which Aquifer levels or spring flows at Comal or San Marcos springs decline to certain prescribed levels. The EAA's current CPMP rules are located at subchapter E of chapter 715. *See* EAA Rules §§ 715.200–.221. Notably, the CPMP must allow irrigators to finish out a crop when critical period conditions are triggered after the crop was planted. *See* EAA Act § 1.26(a)(5), (g).

§ 17.23 Prohibition on Wells Drilled after June 1, 1993

As another method of managing withdrawals, owners of wells drilled after June 1, 1993, are prohibited from making withdrawals of groundwater from the Aquifer. *See* EAA Act § 1.14(e). Exceptions to this prohibition include replacement wells, test wells, exempt wells, and wells constituting a transferred point of withdrawal from an IRP associated with a well that was constructed before June 1, 1993. *See* EAA Act § 1.14(e). Exceptions also include wells authorized by other permits, such as emergency wells or term permit wells. *See* EAA Rules § 711.224(b). The purpose of this prohibition is to protect the preferred status of well owners qualifying for an IRP based on historical use between January 1, 1972, and May 31, 1993, and to prevent a "water rush" on the Aquifer. *See Barshop v. Medina County Underground Water Conservation District*, 925 S.W.2d 618, 632 (Tex. 1996) (noting the EAA Act was passed one day before the close of the historical period to preclude new users from establishing preferred historical rights).

V. Water Management Programs

§ 17.24 Comprehensive Water Management Planning

The Act requires the EAA to develop and implement a comprehensive water management plan that addresses conservation, future water supply, and demand management. *See* EAA Act § 1.25(a). The EAA may not delegate plan development to another GCD. *See* EAA Act § 1.25(a). The EAA currently meets these requirements through a combination of its Groundwater Conservation Plan, its Edwards Aquifer Habitat Conservation Plan, and its Strategic Plan.

§ 17.25 Conservation Program

All reasonable measures must be taken to conserve water use from the Aquifer. *See* EAA Act § 1.01. The EAA must limit withdrawals from the Aquifer to achieve water conservation. *See* EAA Act § 1.14(a)(3). The Act defines "conservation" as "any measure that would sustain or enhance water supply." EAA Act § 1.03(7).

The EAA is required to develop a conservation and reuse plan, which is updated biennially. *See* EAA Act § 1.23(c). Every odd-numbered year the EAA files its conservation plan with the Texas legislature. The EAA's first plan was filed in March 2005.

Additionally, the EAA may require holders of IRPs and term permits to file and implement individual conservation and reuse plans. *See* EAA Act § 1.23(a). The EAA plan serves as a guidance document for the implementation of individual plans by permit holders. The EAA's rules implementing its conservation program are found at subchapter C of chapter 715. *See* EAA Rules §§ 715.100–.124.

The EAA may administer conservation-related financial assistance programs to water users of the Aquifer. *See* EAA Act § 1.11(d)(1). Additionally, the EAA may issue grants or loans to finance the purchase or installation of conservation equipment. *See* EAA Act § 1.24(c). The rules for the program are found at subchapter D of chapter 715. *See* EAA Rules §§ 715.136–.166.

The EAA is required to "allow for credit to be given for certified reuse of the water" withdrawn from the Aquifer. *See* EAA Act § 1.13. Among other things, the "amount of aquifer withdrawals [that will be] replaced by reuse" must be certified by the EAA. *See* EAA Act § 1.13(3).

§ 17.26 Recharge Program

The EAA has "all of the powers, rights, and privileges necessary to . . . increase the recharge of . . . the aquifer." EAA Act § 1.08(a). The Act defines "recharge" as "increasing the supply of water to the aquifer by naturally occurring channels or artificial means." EAA Act § 1.03(18).

The EAA may own, construct, operate, and maintain recharge facilities. *See* EAA Act § 1.11(f). However, projects may not have as their purpose the recirculation of water at Comal or San Marcos springs. *See* EAA Act §§ 1.11(f), 1.26A(n). Before constructing recharge facilities, the EAA must give notice to other local government units that may desire to participate in the project. *See* EAA Act § 1.11(f–1). The local government units may choose to merely comment on or participate in the project. *See* EAA Act § 1.11(f–2).

The EAA also may own, construct, operate, and maintain recharge dams for the purpose of recharging the Aquifer. *See* EAA Act § 1.45(a). The EAA currently operates and maintains four recharge dams previously constructed by the EUWD. Recharge dams may be constructed in either the Recharge Zone or the Contributing Zone of the Aquifer. *See* EAA Act § 1.45(a). However, the EAA may not construct a recharge dam for the purpose of recirculating water at Comal or San Marcos springs. Moreover, the EAA may not construct new recharge dams that would impair senior surface water rights or vested riparian rights. *See* EAA Act § 1.45(a). The TCEQ may issue a permit to appropriate state water for an EAA recharge dam in the Nueces River Basin only for unappropriated flood water in excess of "historic yield" of the flood water to the Basin. *See* EAA Act § 1.45(c). The Act provides that the TCEQ determines the historic yield, which is the lesser of the "average annual yield for the period from 1950 to 1987" or the "annual yield for 1987." EAA Act § 1.45(b).

Finally, the EAA may enter into contracts with other political subdivisions for artificial recharge of the Aquifer. *See* EAA Act § 1.44(a). These contracts are to be entered into under the Interlocal Cooperation Act to provide for the subsequent recovery of the recharged water by the contracting political subdivision or its assignee. *See* Tex. Gov't Code ch. 791. The Texas attorney general has found that the EAA has the legal authority to adopt rules regarding aquifer recharge, storage, and recovery and specifically to establish limitations based on historic recharge. *See* Tex. Att'y Gen. Op. No. GA-0708 (2009).

The EAA may not unreasonably deny requests to enter into recharge contracts. *See* EAA Act § 1.44(b). In determining whether to enter into recharge contracts, the EAA may consider the following issues: (1) identification of the source water intended for recharge; (2) identification of the recharge method (i.e., either injection wells or recharge dams); (3) if surface water is to be recharged, proof that the political subdivision is the owner of any permits issued by the TCEQ to appropriate the state water intended for recharge; (4) identification of the methodologies to quantify the amount of recharge and the amount that qualifies for recovery; (5) reports of recharge amounts; (6) protection of the water quality of the Aquifer; (7) identification of the location of the recharge points; (8) identification of points of withdrawal for the recharge recovery wells; and (9) protection of the rights of other holders of IRPs issued by the EAA. *See generally* EAA Act § 1.44(a)–(c), (e). Withdrawals of groundwater under these interlocal recharge contracts do not apply against the 572,000 AF per year cap. *See* EAA Act § 1.44(d).

Groundwater withdrawn from the Aquifer may be used as source water for an IRP holder's ASR project. Aquifer water would be withdrawn and injected into another aquifer for storage until needed at a later time. Effective September 1, 2019, section 1.44 of the EAA Act was amended to authorize the

EAA to allow other surface water–derived sources for injection into the Aquifer for ASR purposes under very limited circumstances. *See* Act of May 26, 2019, 86th Leg., R.S., ch. 585, § 1 (S.B. 520), eff. Sept. 1, 2019.

The EAA is to ensure that groundwater from the Aquifer is not wasted. The definition of waste includes the escape of groundwater from the Aquifer to any other reservoir that does not contain groundwater. *See* EAA Act § 1.03(21)(C). To prevent waste, the EAA may require that IRP holders intending to withdraw groundwater from the Aquifer for an ASR project in another aquifer ensure that the Aquifer water is recoverable and would not be lost.

§ 17.27 Research and Data Collection

The EAA is authorized to study and conduct research on the Aquifer. *See* EAA Act § 1.27. The EAA may conduct research on enhancement or augmentation of spring flows, Aquifer yield enhancement, recharge enhancement, water quality monitoring, Aquifer resource management (including conservation, water use, reuse, and drought management measures), and alternative water supplies, among other issues. *See* EAA Act § 1.27(a), (b). The EAA may also implement demonstration projects for the purpose of spring-flow augmentation, recharge enhancement, and yield enhancement. *See* EAA Act § 1.27(c). Research and data collection provide the foundation for the EAA programs and plans because the EAA seeks to use the best available science to provide the technical basis for its management strategies. The EAA funds and performs extensive research and data collection on an annual basis to improve the understanding of the Aquifer. This includes annual reports on both groundwater recharge and discharge, available at www.edwardsaquifer.org/science-maps/research-scientific-reports/hydrologic-data-reports/.

VI. Water Quality Programs

§ 17.28 Well Construction, Operation, and Maintenance

Poorly constructed wells can act as preferential pathways into the Aquifer. For this reason, the EAA's well construction program emphasizes water quality. This program is intended to ensure that wells are constructed and maintained to prevent the introduction of contaminants into the Aquifer. The details of this program are found at subchapter C of chapter 713 of the EAA's rules. *See* EAA Rules §§ 713.200–.247. These rules apply only within the boundaries of the EAA. *See* EAA Rules § 713.2001.

Well owners or drillers may not begin construction of a well or other works designed for the withdrawal of groundwater from the Aquifer without first obtaining a well construction permit. *See* EAA Act § 1.15(b). The Act defines "well" as follows: "a bored, drilled, or driven shaft or an artificial opening in the ground made by digging, jetting, or some other method where the depth of the shaft or opening is greater than its largest surface dimension, but does not include a surface pit, surface excavation, or natural depression." EAA Act § 1.03(22). The EAA requires that the owners of new wells file with the EAA the water well drillers' logs that relate to the well. *See* EAA Act § 1.11(d)(11).

§ 17.29 Closed Wells

Wells that are abandoned or closed improperly can provide unwanted conduits into the Aquifer. The EAA has an active program to identify abandoned wells and require their closure. The requirements for well closure and plugging are contained within subchapter D of chapter 713 of the EAA's rules. *See* EAA Rules §§ 713.300–.322. These rules apply only within the boundaries of the EAA. *See* EAA Rules § 713.302. To close a well, the well owner or driller must first obtain a well-plugging permit from the EAA. *See* EAA Rules § 713.306(b). A well-capping permit must first be obtained from the EAA to cap a well. *See* EAA Rules § 713.304(b).

§ 17.30 Storage Tanks

The EAA's water quality rules related to aboveground storage tanks (ASTs) and underground storage tanks (USTs) are at subchapter G of chapter 713 of the EAA's rules. *See* EAA Rules §§ 713.601–.616. These rules apply within the boundaries of the EAA and its five-mile water quality buffer zone. *See* EAA Act § 1.08(c); EAA Rules § 713.603. The installation of new ASTs on the Recharge Zone is generally authorized as long as secondary containment is provided. In addition, all existing ASTs must have been upgraded to secondary containment by December 31, 2018. The EAA generally prohibits the installation of new USTs on the Recharge Zone of the Aquifer. Existing USTs must be removed from service within thirty years of installation or be upgraded to tertiary containment. Certain exceptions are recognized for smaller or special-purpose tanks. *See* EAA Rules § 713.613.

The general prohibition of new USTs and the costs associated with upgrading existing USTs to tertiary containment led to the development of a cap-and-trade program within EAA regulations to help facilitate compliance. Essentially, all legally recognized USTs located on the Recharge Zone have been provided an associated, recognized capacity. That capacity can be bought and sold to accommodate proper removal, containment upgrades, or new installation of USTs within the EAA's regulatory jurisdiction. *See* EAA Rules § 713.612.

§ 17.31 Fire Control

The EAA is required to adopt rules for the control of fires in the Recharge Zone. In the development of these rules, the EAA is to first consult with fire departments and fire marshals whose jurisdictions overlap the Recharge Zone of the Aquifer. *See* EAA Act § 1.081. The EAA's rule on the control of fires on the Recharge Zone is found in subchapter F of chapter 713. *See* EAA Rules § 713.503.

§ 17.32 Spill Reporting

Persons spilling regulated materials on the Recharge or Contributing zones of the Aquifer must notify the EAA within seventy-two hours of the incident. *See* EAA Rules §§ 713.401(a), 713.403(b). The EAA's spilling report rules are at subchapter E of chapter 713 of the EAA's rules. *See* EAA Rules §§ 713.400–.409. The purpose of this regulation is to aid in the prevention of pollution of the Aquifer and hydrologically connected surface streams in order to protect existing and potential uses of groundwater. *See* EAA Rules § 713.400. The materials regulated under subchapter E of chapter 713 are materials discharged or released in violation of a permit issued by the TCEQ under Texas Water Code section 26.121, and discharges or spills of oil, petroleum products, used oil, hazardous substances, industrial solid waste, or other substances. *See* EAA Rules § 713.400.

The duty to notify applies only to discharges or spills in a quantity equal to or greater than the "reportable quantity" identified for the material. *See* EAA Rules §§ 713.403(a), 713.405. The responsible person must take action to abate and contain the spill or discharge to prevent the pollution of the Aquifer. *See* EAA Rules § 713.409(a). The general manager of the EAA may make other recommendations to state and local officials and third parties on how to respond to the discharge or spill. *See* EAA Rule § 713.407. Subchapter E of chapter 713 does not apply to air releases, solid waste management units, fertilizers and pesticides, discharges authorized by permit, certain continuous and stable discharges reported to the U.S. Environmental Protection Agency, motor vehicles, rolling stock, or airplanes or to sources regulated by the Railroad Commission of Texas. *See* EAA Rules § 713.401(b).

§ 17.33 Facilities Registration

Persons owning certain facilities in the Recharge Zone or Contributing Zone of the Aquifer within five miles upgradient of the Recharge Zone must register the facility with the EAA. *See* EAA Rules §§ 713.501(a), 713.503. The EAA's regulated substances, registration, storage, and planning rules are at subchapter F of chapter 713 of the EAA's rules. *See* EAA Rules §§ 713.500–.505. The purpose of this regulation is to aid in the prevention of pollution of the Aquifer and hydrologically connected surface streams in order to protect existing and potential uses of groundwater. *See* EAA Rules § 713.500.

The facilities regulated under these rules are facilities storing for resale or nonresidential use more than 1,000 gallons of "regulated substances" in containers of less than 500 gallons. *See* EAA Rules § 713.503. A regulated substance includes any hazardous substance or petroleum or petroleum product. *See* EAA Rules § 702.1(85), (137), (138), (163). Certain standards for the storage of regulated materials are provided by the rules. *See* EAA Rules § 713.505. Subchapter F of chapter 713 does not apply to underground or aboveground storage tanks regulated under subchapter G of chapter 713 of the EAA's rules or to containers greater than 500 gallons in size. *See* EAA Rules §§ 713.501(b), 713.503, 713.603.

§ 17.34 Research and Data Collection

The EAA has an active Aquifer groundwater quality monitoring program. The EAA coordinates its program with the U.S. Geological Survey and the TWDB. Sampling points for the program include springs, wells, and surface watercourses throughout the region. The results of this program are published annually and can be found at www.edwardsaquifer.org/science-maps/research-scientific-reports/hydrologic-data-reports/.

VII. Enforcement

§ 17.35 In General

The EAA is authorized to enforce the Act. *See* EAA Act § 1.40(a). Persons may not violate the Act or an EAA rule. *See* EAA Act § 1.35(e). Permittees may not violate the terms or conditions of their permits. EAA Act § 1.35(b). The EAA is to ensure compliance with the terms and conditions of its permits and the permit program. *See* EAA Act § 1.11(b). The board may issue orders to enforce the Act, its rules, the terms and conditions of permits, or its orders. *See* EAA Act §§ 1.11(c), 1.36(a). The EAA's enforcement rules are found at chapter 717. *See* EAA Rules §§ 717.100–.118.

§ 17.36 Well Enforcement

The EAA may close abandoned, wasteful, and dangerous wells. *See* EAA Act § 1.11(d)(8). The EAA may enforce Texas Occupations Code chapters 1901 and 1902, and their implementation rules at 16 Texas Administrative Code chapter 76, relating to water well drillers and water well pump installers. *See* EAA Act § 1.11(d)(10). The EAA Act actually refers to Texas Water Code chapter 32 and its implementation rules. However, chapter 32 of the Water Code was repealed by Act of May 22, 2001, 77th Leg., R.S., ch. 778, § 5; Act of May 22, 2001, 77th Leg., R.S., ch. 1421, § 13(b). Chapter 32 of the Water Code was largely recodified in Occupations Code chapter 1901.

§ 17.37 Remedies

The EAA may seek civil penalties in state district court for violation of the Act or the EAA's rules, permits, or orders. *See* EAA Act § 1.40(a). Civil penalties may range from $100 to $10,000 per violation per day. *See* EAA Act § 1.40(b). The EAA retains any civil penalties it collects. *See* EAA Act § 1.40(c). The EAA may seek injunctive relief in state district court to enforce the Act. EAA Act § 1.38. When seeking civil penalties or injunctive relief, the EAA may also recover attorney's fees. *See* EAA Act §§ 1.38, 1.40(b). If the EAA prevails in its enforcement action, the district court shall award the EAA its attorney's fees. *See* Tex. Water Code § 36.102(d). The EAA retains attorney's fees it collects. *See* EAA Act § 1.40(c).

The EAA, by rule, may provide for the suspension of a permit for violations of EAA rules, orders, or permits or the failure to pay required fees. *See* EAA Act § 1.36(b). The EAA may assess administrative penalties for violations of the Act, EAA rules, or orders. *See* EAA Act § 1.37(a). The penalty amounts may not be less than $100 or more than $1,000 for each violation and for each day of a continuing violation. *See* EAA Act § 1.37(a). In determining the appropriate penalty amount, the EAA is to consider the compliance history of the respondent, the amount required to deter future violations, any corrective efforts taken by the respondent, the enforcement costs of the EAA, and other matters that justice may require. *See* EAA Act § 1.37(b).

§ 17.38 Enforcement by the TCEQ

The TCEQ has the same authority as the EAA to seek and recover civil penalties for violation of the Act or the EAA's rules, permits, or orders. *See* EAA Act § 1.40(a). Civil penalties collected by the TCEQ are paid into the general revenue fund of the state of Texas. *See* EAA Act § 1.40(d). When seeking civil penalties, the TCEQ may also recover attorney's fees. *See* EAA Act § 1.40(b). Attorney's fees collected by the TCEQ are paid into the general revenue fund of the state of Texas. *See* EAA Act § 1.40(d). If the EAA is not performing its duties under the Act, the TCEQ may bring a mandamus action against the EAA to perform those duties and to recover attorney's fees. *See* EAA Act § 1.39. The TCEQ may also bring such an action when the EAA is not enforcing the Act against those who may be violating its terms.

CHAPTER 18

Groundwater Transactions

Susan M. Maxwell[1] *and Denise V. Cheney*[2]

I. Introduction

§ 18.1 Introduction

Transactions and water marketing involving the purchase or lease of groundwater rights, severed from the land, are becoming increasingly common throughout Texas. This trend involves both public- and private-sector entities and encompasses a broad spectrum of the financial and geographic scope of projects, including some that involve tens of thousands of acres across multiple counties. The current state water plan recognizes that Texas's population growth will continue to require development of new water supplies and more efficient use of existing supplies for growing demand for municipal and other uses. Although groundwater has historically accounted for the majority of water use in Texas, existing groundwater supplies are projected to decrease between 2020 and 2070 by approximately 32 percent. Texas Water Development Board, *Water for Texas 2022* A-6 (2022), www.twdb.texas.gov/waterplanning/swp/2022/index.asp. Because of the limited availability of unappropriated surface water in most parts of the state and groundwater shortages in some areas, groundwater resources have been the primary focus of emerging water-marketing efforts and also have been identified by municipalities and other utilities as a critical potential alternative source of supply, either alone or in conjunctive use projects with surface water.

In the context of this increased emphasis on developing new groundwater supplies and making existing supplies available for different uses (or for use in different places), transactions involving groundwater rights will continue to evolve in different forms. Some transactions involve acquisition of rights to production of previously undeveloped groundwater resources; others involve transfer of existing, quantified permitted rights. Most transactions relate to real property located within a local groundwater conservation district (GCD) and therefore subject to the district's rules and permitting requirements; however, even those that are not subject to a district's jurisdiction are affected by larger-

---

1. Susan M. Maxwell is a partner at Bickerstaff Heath Delgado Acosta L.L.P., where she practices primarily in water law, including representation of cities, water districts, river authorities, and other local governmental entities and private parties in litigation, permitting, and other administrative proceedings, and transactional work involving surface water and groundwater rights. A graduate of the University of Texas School of Law and the LBJ School of Public Affairs, Ms. Maxwell is a former judicial law clerk to the late Honorable Barefoot Sanders, Senior District Judge, U.S. District Court for the Northern District of Texas. She recently served as chair of the State Bar of Texas Environmental and Natural Resources Law Section.

2. Denise V. Cheney is a partner at Bickerstaff Heath Delgado Acosta L.L.P., where she specializes in representing governmental entities and private parties in real estate and construction law matters, including acquisition, construction, development, leasing, land use planning, and the leasing and purchase of groundwater rights. Ms. Cheney is board certified in Residential Real Estate Law and Commercial Real Estate Law by the Texas Board of Legal Specialization. She has served as vice-chair of the State Bar of Texas Real Estate Forms Committee and chair of the Real Estate, Probate and Trust Law Section's Water Law Committee. She is a frequent speaker on real estate law, construction law, and government law topics.

scale planning for groundwater resources. Because of the variability both of local regulatory regimes and of groundwater resources in different areas of Texas, as well as other financial, project, and planning issues of the parties, there are many important considerations in developing, evaluating, and documenting a potential groundwater transaction, whether a purchase or a lease.

This chapter addresses the major issues and practical considerations involved in real property transactions for groundwater rights severed from the land. First, in the context of Texas law on ownership of groundwater, which is discussed more fully in Chapter 5 of this book, this chapter describes and compares the primary methods for conveying or acquiring groundwater rights and sets out the framework within which the parties define the nature and scope of the rights thus purchased or leased, including issues involving the reserved and ongoing rights of the owner of the surface estate. Second, this chapter outlines an array of due diligence matters typically implicated in groundwater transactions, whether purchase or lease, discussing the significance of those issues for the parties. Finally, it addresses financing and other issues to be considered in the unique context of groundwater transactions, including the valuation and marketability of groundwater rights.

The chapter is not designed to be a stand-alone resource for drafting the real estate documents needed for a particular transaction and does not attempt to discuss term by term the types of provisions that may be appropriate for a particular lease, contract of sale, deed, and so on. However, the State Bar of Texas's *Texas Real Estate Forms Manual* has a chapter on water rights conveyancing documents, which contains additional practice-oriented guidance and basic forms for groundwater sales. *See* State Bar of Texas, 2 *Texas Real Estate Forms Manual* ch. 16 (2021 ed.) [hereinafter Forms Manual]. These sample forms are discussed in part III below.

II. Ownership of Groundwater Rights

§ 18.2 Common Law of Absolute Ownership

As fully discussed in Chapter 5 of this book, the Texas Supreme Court long ago applied the English common-law rule of capture to groundwater and held that the owner of land could pump unlimited quantities of water from under his land, regardless of whether his action drained water from under his neighbor's land. *See Houston & T.C. Ry. Co. v. East*, 81 S.W. 279 (Tex. 1904). There are few significant limitations at common law on the landowner's right to capture and use groundwater. A landowner cannot capture and use groundwater maliciously, for the purpose of injuring a neighbor, or in a manner that constitutes wanton and willful waste. *See City of Corpus Christi v. City of Pleasanton*, 276 S.W.2d 798 (1955). A landowner may be liable for damages if he negligently pumps groundwater in a manner that causes subsidence of neighboring land. *Friendswood Development Co. v. Smith-Southwest Industries, Inc.*, 576 S.W.2d 21, 30 (Tex. 1978).

The rule of capture in Texas also includes some general principles that facilitate groundwater transactions and marketing. Under the common law, a landowner can use groundwater at a location other than his land and sell groundwater that he captures below the surface of his land for off-site use by a third party. *See Texas Co. v. Burkett*, 296 S.W. 273 (1927). The use of groundwater at a distant location, even though the majority may be lost in transit, is also permissible. *See City of Corpus Christi*, 276 S.W.2d at 802–03. As discussed below, however, there may be practical limitations on a landowner's ability to alienate and transport groundwater based on regulation by a local GCD.

§ 18.3 Reexamining the Nature of the Ownership Interest

In recent years, a question has arisen about whether a landowner has a property right in groundwater in place under his land or whether the landowner's property interest in the groundwater actually "vests" only when the landowner has "captured" the groundwater and put it to a beneficial use. The issue has arisen in the context of whether a landowner can challenge the regulations of a GCD on the grounds that they constitute a "taking" of the landowner's groundwater rights. The Edwards Aquifer Authority (EAA) has argued that the rights of property owners to pump water in the future could not be "taken" by the Edwards Aquifer Authority Act because such rights are not yet vested and therefore are not constitutionally protected. *See Barshop v. Medina County Underground Water Conservation District*, 925 S.W.2d 618 (Tex. 1996). In *Barshop*, the supreme court found it unnecessary to address the issue, expressly declining "to definitively resolve the clash between property rights in water and regulation of water." *Barshop*, 925 S.W.2d at 626.

This issue of "ownership in place" has now been squarely addressed by the Texas Supreme Court in another case in which landowners have brought "takings" claims based on the permitting decisions of the EAA. *See Edwards Aquifer Authority v. Day*, 369 S.W.3d 814 (Tex. 2012). Affirming the judgment of the court of appeals, the court held that "land ownership includes an interest in groundwater in place that cannot be taken for public use without adequate compensation." *Day*, 369 S.W.3d at 817. The court's analysis included an extensive review of the major rule of capture cases and legislative treatment of groundwater rights and regulation, and the court concluded that the oil and gas case law precedent of recognizing both the rule of capture and ownership in place is also appropriate for groundwater. *Day*, 369 S.W.3d at 823, 828–32. The court affirmed the authority of the EAA and other GCDs to regulate groundwater production but recognized that such regulation can, at least theoretically, result in a compensable takings claim under the Texas Constitution. The takings claims were remanded for further proceedings. *Day*, 369 S.W.3d at 843.

The issue of a landowner's vested right in the groundwater under his land also arose in the context of a property conveyance by a private party to a municipality. *See City of Del Rio v. Clayton Sam Colt Hamilton Trust*, 269 S.W.3d 613 (Tex. App.—San Antonio 2008, pet. denied). The question before the court was whether the landowner legally could—and properly did—reserve to itself the corresponding groundwater rights when conveying the surface estate. The Trust had conveyed to the City a fifteen-acre tract from a ranch that it owned, from which tract the Trust had not previously produced groundwater. Although the deed contained a provision to reserve to the Trust "all water rights associated with said tract," the conveyancing documents did not include express easement rights for the Trust that would allow it to produce groundwater from the tract conveyed to the City. After the City drilled a high-capacity well on the tract to develop a supplemental municipal water supply, the Trust filed suit asserting its ownership of the groundwater beneath the City's fifteen-acre tract.

The district court entered a declaratory judgment in favor of the Trust regarding the validity and enforceability of the Trust's reservation of water rights and the Trust's ownership of the groundwater rights beneath the fifteen-acre tract. The court of appeals affirmed on the basis that "under the absolute ownership theory, the Trust was entitled to sever the groundwater from the surface estate by reservation." *City of Del Rio*, 269 S.W.3d at 617. The court rejected the City's argument that the failure of the Trust to reserve surface use rights on the fifteen-acre tract in order to drill and produce the reserved groundwater constituted a violation of the prohibition against perpetuities, because the Trust could access the groundwater beneath the fifteen-acre tract from its adjacent lands. *City of Del Rio*, 269 S.W.3d at 618–19. (The court might have reached a different decision, however, had the Trust not been able to access the reserved groundwater from its other land.) The Texas Supreme Court denied the City's petition for review. The *City of Del Rio* case well illustrates the need for careful analysis and precise document drafting regarding the parties' intended future use of both the surface rights and the water rights involved in a particular groundwater transaction.

The decisions in the *City of Del Rio* and *Day* cases have far-reaching implications for present and prospective groundwater transactions and groundwater marketing projects in Texas. As the takings claims in *Day* and *Edwards Aquifer Authority v. Bragg*, 421 S.W.3d 118 (Tex. App.—San Antonio 2013, pet. denied), have proceeded through the lower courts, and as other such cases may follow, GCDs and various stakeholders in groundwater permits and projects will continue to test the parameters of the districts' exercise of their regulatory authority.

Even before the *Day* decision, the 82nd Legislature had also addressed the issue of groundwater ownership and the rights to produce groundwater, amending chapter 36 of the Texas Water Code expressly to recognize "that a landowner owns the groundwater below the surface of the landowner's land as real property," and that "[n]othing in [the Water Code] shall be construed as granting the authority to deprive or divest a landowner [including lessees, heirs, or assigns] of the groundwater ownership and rights" described in the statute. Tex. Water Code § 36.002(a), (c). The statute, further amended in 2015, expressly extends that scope of rights to include "any other right recognized under common law," and also incorporates the common-law exceptions and defenses under the rule of capture reflected in Texas case law, but specifies that the landowner is not entitled to capture a specific amount of groundwater below the surface of his land. *See* Tex. Water Code § 36.002(b), (b–1). The statute still recognizes the authority of a GCD to impose well spacing or tract size requirements and to limit groundwater production as provided under chapter 36, discussed at section 18.10 below. *See* Tex. Water Code § 36.002(d).

§ 18.4 Examining New Issues

With the issue of ownership rights in groundwater having been firmly resolved in *Day*, Texas courts continue to examine new issues involving the extent and exercise of those rights. As discussed at section 18.3 above, the *City of Del Rio* case illustrates the importance of ensuring that the groundwater rights owner has adequate surface rights to access and develop his groundwater. A more recent Texas Supreme Court case, *Coyote Lake Ranch, LLC v. City of Lubbock*, 498 S.W.3d 53 (Tex. 2016), addressed the issue of whether a groundwater rights owner with surface use rights in the nature of a blanket easement can be restricted in his use of the surface estate through application of the accommodation doctrine.

The City of Lubbock acquired groundwater rights under a 1953 deed that gave the City a blanket easement to develop, produce, and transport its groundwater. When the City began to develop a well field on the property, the landowner sued for an injunction, alleging that the accommodation doctrine applied to groundwater development. The doctrine is one that has been imposed by courts in connection with oil and gas development, as "a sound and workable basis for resolving conflicts between ownership interests." *Coyote Lake Ranch*, 498 S.W.3d at 63. To assert the doctrine, the surface owner must prove that the use of the surface by the mineral estate is not reasonably necessary because there are alternate reasonable ways of producing the minerals that would allow the surface owner to continue his existing use. *Coyote Lake Ranch*, 498 S.W.3d at 60–62. The trial court granted the injunction, but the court of appeals reversed and remanded the case. The supreme court held, as a matter of first impression, that the accommodation doctrine does apply "to resolve conflicts between a severed groundwater estate and the surface estate that are not governed by the express terms of the parties' agreement." *Coyote Lake Ranch*, 498 S.W.3d at 64. The court affirmed the appellate court's judgment reversing the temporary injunction as overbroad and precluding the City's lawful exercise of its rights, and remanded for further proceedings. *Coyote Lake Ranch*, 498 S.W.3d at 65. Based on this decision, parties to groundwater rights acquisitions and other transactions must carefully consider and expressly provide for the full extent of easement rights necessary and beneficial to their development of the groundwater resources they have purchased or leased.

The other major emerging area since the *Day* decision involves defining the circumstances in which a GCD's regulatory decision making, including denial or limitation of groundwater permitting rights, amounts to an unconstitutional taking. Most notably, an appellate court in a closely watched case affirmed the lower court's decision that the EAA had taken the property of local pecan farmers by severely limiting their permitted groundwater rights, and quantifying the value of the denied water rights. *See Edwards Aquifer Authority v. Bragg*, 421 S.W.3d 118 (Tex. App.—San Antonio 2013, pet. denied) (applying the U.S. Supreme Court's *Penn Central* factors). With a substantial jury award for damages on remand to the district court, the outcome of the *Bragg* case, and perhaps others to come, will further inform practitioners' and property owners' strategies in groundwater transactions.

III. Methods for Conveying or Acquiring Groundwater Rights

§ 18.5 Nature and Description of Groundwater Rights

Groundwater belongs to the owner of the surface estate in land and is part of the real property. *Texas Co. v. Burkett*, 296 S.W. 273 (1927); *see* Tex. Water Code § 36.002(a). Groundwater rights may be owned or leased in place as part of the land or may be severed from the land. Severed groundwater rights, being a real property interest, may be acquired in fee simple or through a lease. Groundwater rights that are severed from the land may allow production on-site from the tract of land from which they are severed or may allow production only off-site, from different land. As another alternative, the owner of the groundwater rights may grant a license to another person for use of the groundwater.

Many factors must be considered in determining the best method of acquisition for a given transaction, including (1) the time period in which production will be commenced, (2) the duration of the intended use, (3) acquisition costs, (4) the willingness of landowners to sell or lease groundwater rights, and (5) the terms that can be negotiated for a lease or sale. For example, if the groundwater rights are being acquired for future production, with no intention to commence production in the near future, a production lease that requires production within a specified time period may be used. Such a production lease may not be practical, however, unless it contains a pooling clause that allows production from pooled groundwater to continue the lease in effect or some other provision that enables the lessee to keep the lease in effect despite the lack of production. Depending on market conditions, if immediate and long-term production is contemplated, it may be more cost-effective to purchase the groundwater rights or to purchase the land in fee than to lease the groundwater rights.

One of the most important factors in determining the method of acquisition is the willingness of the landowner to lease or sell groundwater rights. In areas where the leasing of groundwater rights is common, for example, a landowner may be unwilling to enter into any arrangement other than a lease. In areas with little or no history of separate groundwater rights transactions, some landowners may be unwilling to lease or sell the groundwater rights and will consider only a sale of the land. Conversely, persons acquiring groundwater rights may prefer to purchase the land to avoid any issues or uncertainty relating to reserved groundwater and retained use of the surface.

§ 18.5:1 Groundwater Rights for On-Site Production

In a transaction in which groundwater will be produced on-site, the ability to use the groundwater requires the right to use the surface of the land for access, testing, exploration, drilling, development, and transportation of the groundwater, as well as the right to capture, use, and produce the groundwater itself. The Texas Supreme Court relied significantly on analogous principles from oil and gas law in its *Day* decision regarding the landowner's ownership interest in groundwater in place. However, whereas the law governing oil and gas rights has been determined through many years of usage and case law, the particulars of usage and law governing groundwater rights are largely unwritten and relatively untested. It is well established in oil and gas law, for example, that an oil and gas lessee has surface use rights that are implied by law and dominant over the rights of the surface owner. *See Phillips Petroleum Co. v. Cargill*, 340 S.W.2d 877 (Tex. App.—Amarillo 1960, no writ). As the *City of Del Rio* and *Coyote Lake Ranch* cases illustrate, the case law has been less developed regarding the implied surface use rights of the owner of groundwater rights. Consequently, it is essential that the documents evidencing or conveying the groundwater rights, whether contract, lease, or deed, expressly (1) define "groundwater," (2) identify the land subject to the rights with a sufficient legal description, and (3) describe the grantee's rights in both the groundwater and the surface estates. If any groundwater rights are to be retained by the landowner, the contract or conveyance should also specifically describe the rights being reserved, including any limitations on use.

The groundwater rights sales contract form in the Forms Manual applies to a sale by a landowner that severs the groundwater rights from the land and applies to a sale of groundwater rights to be produced on-site, providing examples of provisions that can be used to address these three issues. The contract form uses the following terms:

> Real Property: The Real Property described in Exhibit A [*include if applicable:* together with the fixtures and personal property described in Exhibit A]. [*Exhibit A will set out the legal description for the land.*]
>
> Groundwater: All of the underground water, percolating water, artesian water, and any other water from any and all depths and reservoirs, formations, depths and horizons beneath the surface of the Real Property, excluding underflow or flow in a defined subterranean channel.
>
> Groundwater Rights: (1) The legal title to Groundwater [*include if applicable:* subject to the Reserved Groundwater] and the right to test, explore for, drill for, develop, withdraw, capture, or otherwise beneficially use the Groundwater; (2) the right to use the surface of the Real Property for access to and to explore for, develop, treat, produce, and transport the Groundwater; and (3) all permits, licenses, or other governmental authorizations relating to any of the foregoing. If a separate Easement Agreement is required by this contract, the Groundwater Rights include the easement rights.

2 Forms Manual ch. 16, form 16-1.

If the seller reserves any portion of the groundwater rights, the description of the groundwater rights would contain an exception for the reserved groundwater. The contract form uses the following description for the reserved groundwater:

> Reserved Groundwater: Seller reserves the right to use the Groundwater in connection with its surface estate in the Real Property for the following purposes only: [*state purposes for which the reserved groundwater may be used and any limit on the quantity of reserved groundwater that seller may use including any limit on the number of wells that seller may drill or maintain.*]

2 Forms Manual, ch. 16, form 16-1.

The rights reserved to the seller, including any limitation on those rights, should be described with specificity. If the buyer plans to use the groundwater for commercial use, for example, the buyer will want to prohibit the seller from using the reserved groundwater for commercial use or production. Such a limitation may be in the form of restricting the use of the groundwater to domestic and livestock use by the seller and seller's family members for household purposes. The buyer may also want to prohibit any lease of the reserved groundwater rights or use of the reserved groundwater in oil and gas or mineral production. If the mineral estate has been severed from the land, however, this restriction would not be enforceable against the owner of the mineral estate unless the mineral owner agreed in writing to be bound by these terms.

The seller's ability to use reserved groundwater may be limited in a number of other ways. One way would be to limit the amount of groundwater that the seller can produce from the real property within a specified period of time. Another way would be to limit the number, and pumping capacity, of the wells that the seller is permitted to operate on the land.

If the seller has obtained any permits relating to the groundwater from the local GCD, the sale contract should include a description of the permits and a requirement that the permits be transferred in connection with the closing. As discussed at section 18.10 below, these might include various types of GCD-issued permits for drilling, production and operation, or export and transport of groundwater outside the district.

§ 18.5:2 Groundwater Rights for Off-Site Production

If the groundwater rights to be acquired do not include the right to produce groundwater directly from the land from which the groundwater rights are derived, the description of the groundwater rights will exclude the right to use the surface of the land for exploration, testing, drilling, and production. The buyer may have to access the groundwater from adjacent real property, so that, in effect, the buyer is merely draining groundwater from the tract from which it purchased the groundwater rights, but the buyer would be able to include the amount of acreage from that tract in meeting applicable well spacing or production requirements established by the local GCD, if any. For further discussion of the practical implications of such regulatory controls, see section 18.10:1 below.

§ 18.5:3 Groundwater Rights in the Edwards Aquifer

Groundwater rights obtained within the jurisdiction of the EAA are highly regulated, and many of the owner's rights are derived through the EAA permit issued in connection with the groundwater rights. Although a detailed discussion of special issues and terms applicable only to EAA-permitted groundwater transactions is beyond the scope of this chapter, it is important to note that documents for groundwater transactions in the EAA may require provisions not generally applicable to the purchase of groundwater rights relating to other aquifers. For example, a contract form intended to be used for the purchase of groundwater rights within the EAA for off-site production would generally contain a description of groundwater rights different from the definition of the term used in the groundwater rights contract discussed above:

> Groundwater Rights: The Seller's perpetual right to withdraw up to ____ acre feet per annum of ______ Aquifer permitted irrigation/industrial/or municipal groundwater, (the "Groundwater") heretofore relating to the Real Property. The Groundwater includes all of the real and personal property rights, appurtenances, hereditaments, licenses, and contracts, if any, related to or pertaining to the Groundwater including Permit(s) #______ (and if recorded), recorded in Volume ___, Page ___ of the Official Public Records of ______ County, Texas (the "Permit"), as amended or modified, as applicable, insofar as it pertains to the Groundwater, including, but not limited to:
>
> (a) all of the (i) real and personal property rights, (ii) appurtenances, (iii) authorities, (iv) licenses, (v) consents, and (vi) contracts, if any, relating to or pertaining to the Groundwater, which shall also include (1) all common law property rights in and to the Groundwater as well as (2) those rights or interests that now or in the future may be useful or necessary to withdraw and/or beneficially use the Groundwater. (All of this subsection (a) is collectively referred to as the "Appurtenant Rights.");
>
> (b) all permit rights (including the right in and to the Permit that relates to the Groundwater) allowing for possession, withdrawal, and/or use of the Groundwater (the "Permit Rights"); and
>
> (c) any and all other rights to withdraw and beneficially use the Groundwater, Appurtenant Rights, Permit, or Permit Rights, together with all modifications, amendments, renew-

als, extensions, or successor or substitute permits relating to any of the above-described items.

Recent statutory amendments to the EAA's enabling legislation will prospectively modify some provisions regarding the severance and transfer of water rights for historically irrigated land. *See* Act of May 24, 2019, 86th Leg., R.S., ch. 904, § 1 (H.B. 3656), eff. Sept. 1, 2019. See Chapter 17 of this book for a discussion of the special statutory and regulatory requirements of the EAA regarding groundwater permits.

§ 18.5:4 Previously Severed Groundwater Rights

In a transaction in which the conveyance of the groundwater rights will constitute the severance of those rights from the land, the buyer and seller may negotiate the rights that the buyer will obtain, including any surface rights, and the consideration to be paid for the groundwater and the use of the surface estate. This description of these rights would be a major component of the sale contract.

Where the groundwater rights have already been severed from the land, and the buyer is purchasing these severed rights, the description of the groundwater rights has already been established in the deed, and in any easement, previously conveyed to the seller. Consequently, the description of the severed groundwater rights would be the description used in the deed and, if applicable, the easement.

§ 18.6 Purchase of Groundwater Rights in Fee Simple Absolute

Because the ownership of groundwater rights constitutes the ownership of a real property interest, the instrument for conveyance is a deed, which may be either a general warranty deed or a special warranty deed, as agreed on by the seller and buyer. The deed should contain the same description of groundwater rights used in the contract of sale, including a description of surface use rights, in the event the seller and buyer do not agree on more extensive rights to be conveyed in a separate easement document at closing. If the buyer will have the right to engage in on-site production, it is important that the surface use rights be broad enough to allow testing, exploration, drilling, installation and operation of needed facilities, production and other beneficial use, and transportation, because case law has not established that the owner of severed groundwater rights has surface use rights implied by law.

It is advisable that the contract require that the surface use rights be granted in a separate easement document to be signed at closing. Use of a separate easement document will allow the parties to address the easement terms in greater detail than would normally be set out in a deed and to provide default and remedies provisions not otherwise applicable to the conveyance of fee title to the groundwater rights.

§ 18.6:1 Contract for the Sale of Groundwater Rights from the Landowner

In a transaction for the sale of groundwater rights, the sales contract used is similar to a sales contract for land or other real property interest but with provisions applicable to the groundwater rights being conveyed. In addition to a description of those groundwater rights, the contract will contain customary sales contract provisions, such as (1) warranties and representations by the parties; (2) the requirement for the seller to provide copies of documents related to the groundwater rights; (3) a title review and objection period; (4) requirements for the provision of title insurance, if it is to be obtained; (5) an inspection period in which the buyer can perform due diligence activities; (6) closing requirements; (7) a closing date and location; and (8) default and remedies provisions.

In a sale that severs the groundwater rights from the land, the contract should provide a definition of groundwater, the legal description of the land from which the groundwater rights are obtained, and a description of the grantee's rights in both the groundwater and surface estates. If a permit from a GCD has been granted to the seller, the contract should describe the permit and require it to be transferred to the buyer as part of the sales transaction.

The contract should expressly address the obligation of the seller and buyer to pay ad valorem property taxes at closing and after closing. Currently, ad valorem property taxes are assessed against the land and improvements thereon and are not separately assessed against severed groundwater rights. This could change in the future. The contract should require the seller to continue paying the taxes assessed against the land and seller's improvements after closing and should provide that the buyer will pay taxes on the groundwater rights, if in the future they are separately assessed.

If the buyer or lessee is relying on third-party financing to acquire or develop the groundwater rights, the contract should expressly make the buyer's obligation to purchase or lease the groundwater rights contingent on obtaining such financing before closing.

The contract may contain a list of the documents to be executed at closing, which would typically include a general or special warranty deed, as agreed on by the parties, an easement agreement, and a transfer request for any existing groundwater permits. If there is a lien on the seller's land, the list of documents would include a full or partial release of the lien to be executed by the lienholder at closing. A partial release, if used, would release the lien only as to the groundwater rights being conveyed to the buyer. If a separate easement is to be granted, it is advisable to have the lienholder execute a subordination agreement at closing, in which the lienholder subordinates its lien to the rights granted to the buyer in the easement. If a subordination agreement is not obtained, a foreclosure by the lienholder at any time after closing could terminate the buyer's easement rights.

The buyer's rights to use the surface estate after closing should be addressed as part of the contract negotiations and fully set out in the sales contract. It is advisable to provide in the contract (1) the surface use rights, which will be granted in a separate easement document to be executed at closing and will fully address any limitations on the buyer's use of the surface estate; (2) the respective obligations of the buyer and seller for the payment of ad valorem property taxes; (3) the maintenance and repair of improvements; (4) any compensation to be paid to the surface owner for the use of the surface estate; (5) liability for damage to improvements; (6) insurance and indemnification requirements; and (7) default and remedies provisions. These rights could be in the form of a blanket easement for access, installation, and operation of wells, waterlines, pipelines, and other facilities or an easement granting use rights in specific areas of the land.

The Forms Manual contains forms illustrating the types of easement rights and limitations on use and payment terms that may be negotiated in a groundwater sales contract. The easement form set out in the Forms Manual for use in groundwater transactions is a blanket easement that grants the easement holder broad rights for access and for the installation and operation of wells, pipelines, electric transmission and communication lines and conduits, storage tanks, water treatment facilities, and other structures and facilities used in connection with groundwater production. *See* 2 Forms Manual ch. 16, form 16-3. The blanket easement agreement form also includes a sanitary control easement around well sites and the right to install and maintain pipelines for the transportation of groundwater. An easement document may grant the buyer the right to operate pipelines only for the use of groundwater produced from the seller's land, or it may grant the buyer the right to use the pipelines for the transportation of groundwater from any source. The latter provision gives the buyer greater flexibility in the design and operation of its groundwater system.

The rationale for granting a blanket easement with broad rights is that at the time the buyer and seller close on the sale, particularly for large groundwater projects, the buyer may not have conducted all of the testing and investigation necessary to determine the types of facilities to be installed on the land, the location of these facilities, and the time period for the commencement of installation. A blanket easement will provide the buyer with sufficient rights to conduct investigations, design its groundwater system, and determine the most advantageous placement of facilities in the land for the buyer's groundwater project, taking into account factors such as the location of the buyer's pipelines and other facilities on adjacent properties.

Although the blanket easement may contain a provision allowing the landowner to obtain one or more partial releases of the blanket easement, some landowners may not want to tie up their property with a blanket easement in perpetuity. The Forms Manual has an addendum form that may be used with the blanket easement to limit the time period available to the easement holder for making a determination of the types and location of facilities to be installed. This easement location addendum form requires the easement holder to identify the facilities to be installed and the location of the easement areas by field note description, within a specified period of time, and to release the blanket easement from areas not subject to the specific easement rights. *See* 2 Forms Manual ch. 16, form 16-4.

The Forms Manual also has an addendum form for use with the blanket easement that sets out restrictions on the easement holder's use of the surface estate. The landowner may, for example, want to require the easement holder to use existing driveways and roads on the real property, where possible, instead of building new ones, and to contribute to the cost of repair and maintenance of driveways and roads that it uses. Similarly, the landowner may want to establish construction standards for roads built by the easement holder and specific requirements for restoring the property after the installation of facilities and for removing debris. The surface use restrictions addendum form provides examples of these types of obligations and limitations on the use of the surface estate. *See* 2 Forms Manual ch. 16, form 16-6.

The Forms Manual has a third addendum form, a surface damage payment addendum, that may be used with the blanket easement form to set out the compensation to be paid in connection with the exercise of rights under the easement. It is possible for the buyer and seller to agree that the compensation paid for the groundwater rights at closing will constitute full payment to the landowner for all use made of the surface estate by the easement holder in the future. It is not uncommon, however, for landowners to want additional compensation after closing in connection with the use of the surface estate. The surface damage payment addendum form sets out the compensation to be paid to the landowner for the installation of roads, pipelines, and other facilities by the easement holder. *See* 2 Forms Manual ch. 16, form 16-5.

The deed, easement, and any full or partial release and subordination agreement executed in connection with the sale must be recorded in the real property records of the county or counties in which the real property is located. If a transfer of permit form is executed, it should be handled as required under the applicable rules of the local GCD. Although it has not been customary in areas subject to the jurisdiction of a GCD (other than the EAA) to record a copy of the groundwater permit in the county real property records, consideration may be given to doing so. To be recordable in the real property records, the permit must contain an acknowledgment or jurat, or otherwise meet the requirements for recordation set out in sections 12.001 and 12.0011 of the Texas Property Code.

§ 18.6:2 Contract for the Sale of Groundwater Rights in the Edwards Aquifer

Groundwater rights under the jurisdiction of the EAA are subject to special EAA regulations and are often acquired for production off-site. The buyer's rights to use the groundwater will be determined by the terms of the groundwater permit issued by the EAA. These groundwater rights arise from a particular well, located on a specific tract of land, as described in the groundwater permit. The sale contract will reference both the groundwater permit and the real property on which the well is located.

If the groundwater rights are subject to an existing groundwater lease, the sale contract must address the assignment of the lease rights at closing. The sale contract will contain terms generally applicable to the sale of real property and may set out a list of the documents to be signed at closing. Conveyance of the groundwater rights will be by general or special warranty deed and include transfer of any existing EAA-issued permits. The deed is recorded in the real property records of the county in which the original permit was recorded (which is the county where the real property from which the permit derives is located). The transfer of permit is filed with the EAA; if and when the EAA issues a new or amended permit to the buyer, that permit is recorded in the same real property records as the deed.

§ 18.6:3 Contract for the Sale of Previously Severed Groundwater Rights

In a sale of groundwater rights that have been previously severed from land, the definitions of groundwater and groundwater rights have already been established in the deed granted to the seller. Consequently, the description of the groundwater rights in the sale contract would refer to those rights described in the seller's deed and, if a separate easement document was executed, in the seller's easement. The contract would set out the other types of sale provisions described above and would require the groundwater rights to be conveyed by general or special warranty deed at closing, with a transfer of any existing groundwater permit. If the seller's groundwater rights include rights under a separate easement, the contract would require an assignment of the easement rights to be executed at closing.

§ 18.7 Other Methods of Conveyance or Acquisition of Groundwater Rights

Other than sales of groundwater rights by various means, parties involved in groundwater projects around Texas continue to develop other mechanisms tailored to the needs and issues associated with each transaction. Common alternatives to a groundwater rights sale include groundwater leases, a groundwater license, various forms of water supply contract, and, when available, condemnation through the power of eminent domain.

§ 18.7:1 Lease

Groundwater leases have been used in Texas for many years, borrowing to a significant extent from principles and terms from oil and gas leases. Two particularly common forms are the production-based lease and the lease for a term of years, the basic features of which are described below.

Production Lease: If a production-based lease is used, the lease may constitute the conveyance of a determinable fee interest in the groundwater rights to the lessee, as in the case of an oil and gas lease. The terms of a groundwater production lease are similar to those of an oil and gas production lease. The lease will specify a primary term in which exploration, drilling, and production are to be commenced and completed and will provide that once production is achieved, the lease will continue as long thereafter as production is maintained. The lease may require a minimum payment per acre of land, until production is achieved, and may contain provisions allowing the primary term to be extended or for the lease to be continued beyond the primary term despite a lack of production. Once production is obtained, the lessor is generally paid a royalty based on the sales price of the groundwater, as defined in the lease. The lease may contain other provisions such as a pooling agreement, a requirement to drill offset wells, and an escalation provision for the royalty payments.

There is no industry-standard groundwater production lease. The Texas Farm Bureau has a form of production lease called the Model Lease of Groundwater Rights (copyrighted), which illustrates the terms that should be addressed in drafting a groundwater rights production lease. For a copy of the lease form, see John E. Gangstad, *Drafting a Groundwater Production Lease*, *in The Changing Face of Water Rights in Texas* (State Bar of Texas 2004).

Lease for a Term of Years: A landowner who is reluctant to enter into a production lease with its potentially limitless duration may be willing to enter into a long-term lease of the groundwater rights. Often, the owner and prospective tenant will negotiate a contract to enter into a lease, which sets out the primary business terms of the lease and provides for a closing date. The contract may also contain an inspection period to enable the lessee to conduct due diligence activities and to terminate the contract if the groundwater rights are not suitable as well as provisions allowing the prospective lessee to make objections to title and giving the owner the right to cure such objections within a stated period of time.

A lease of groundwater rights for a term of years has the same types of terms found in a standard real property lease, including (1) a description of the leased property, (2) the term of the lease, (3) the rent payments due, (4) the requirements for a security deposit, (5) a description of the rights and obligations of the parties to install and maintain improvements, (6) insurance and indemnification requirements, and (7) default and remedy provisions. If the parties have not previously entered into a contract for the lease of the groundwater rights, as discussed above, the lease may provide the lessee with an initial period in which to conduct due diligence activities and to perform hydrologic and other tests to determine the economic feasibility of production of the groundwater, and with a right to terminate before the expiration of the initial period. It may also provide the lessee with the right to make title objections and the lessor with the right to cure objections.

The lease may give the lessee a period of time in which to determine the types and locations of the facilities that will be installed in the land. The lease may require the lessee to provide a map or survey specifying the location of areas to be used for the installation of roads and facilities and to provide a field note description of the areas in which the facilities will be installed. If rent is in the form of a royalty based on the sale of the groundwater, the lease may require production to be obtained within a specified time period and to be maintained for the duration of the lease or provide that the lessee has to pay rental at a rate that is equal to or greater than the anticipated royalty payment. The lease should address the responsibility of the lessor and lessee for the payment of ad valorem property taxes during the term of the lease. As in the case of a contract for the purchase of groundwater rights, the lease would normally require the lessor to pay ad valorem property taxes assessed against the land and the lessor's improvements and would provide that if ad valorem property taxes are assessed on the severed groundwater rights in the future, the lessee would be responsible for paying those taxes.

To keep the rental payments and other business terms of the groundwater rights lease private, generally a memorandum of the lease, and not the lease itself, will be recorded in the real property records of the county or counties in which the land is located. The lessee, however, may want its surface use rights to be set out in the real property records so that persons dealing with the land will be put on notice of the location and nature of the lessee's use rights in the land. The parties may therefore agree that the terms of the lease governing the location, installation, and maintenance of facilities be set out in a separate easement document that will have the same duration as the lease term and be recorded in the same county or counties as the memorandum of lease. The lessee's surface use rights may be subject to the same types of limitations as those discussed at section 18.6:1 above relating to contracts for the sale of groundwater rights.

A lease for a term of years is subject to the lease provisions of chapters 91 and 93 of the Texas Property Code. If the lessee has the right to use or occupy the lessor's property for the purpose of production, the lessee would be entitled to the right to notice and other protections given to tenants under the forcible entry and detainer statutes in chapter 24 of the Texas Property Code.

§ 18.7:2 License

A landowner may grant a license to use groundwater from a specific tract of property. A license may be granted, for example, to allow a neighboring property owner to obtain groundwater from a well located on the licensor's property. A license is a right to use real property rather than a real property interest. It differs from a lease in that it can be terminated at the will of the licensor, absent an agreement to the contrary. A lease, on the other hand, can be terminated only as provided in the lease document, or absent an agreement on termination in the lease, in accordance with the provisions of chapter 91 of the Texas Property Code. A licensee is not entitled to the rights and protections afforded a lessee by statute, including the tenant lien rights provided by section 91.004 of the Property Code.

In an agreement drafted for the use of groundwater or groundwater rights, care should be taken to distinguish whether the right granted is a license or a lease in order to clearly establish the rights and obligations of the parties.

§ 18.7:3 Water Supply Contract

In lieu of a purchase or lease of groundwater rights, the parties may prefer in some circumstances simply to enter into a water supply contract, by which the surface owner (or some other entity that controls groundwater production from the real property) sells groundwater supply to the buyer. Even in the case of a long-term supply need, this type of contract alternative may be particularly appealing in circumstances where the acquiring party cannot or does not wish to commit the capital investment for required infrastructure and other resources to develop and transport the groundwater supply itself. Depending on how the contract is structured (e.g., providing for a variable demand, or "take-or-pay" for a specified quantity of groundwater), a water supply contract may also provide more flexibility in cases where the groundwater supply is being acquired as a backup supply to surface water for times of drought or as a component of a conjunctive use project. In any event, the parties will still need to consider the most appropriate contract terms for a particular situation to deal with issues such as quantity supplied, pricing, and rights and obligations of the parties in the event of unanticipated deficiencies in groundwater quantity and quality. See Chapter 31 of this book for a discussion of wholesale water contracting.

§ 18.7:4 Condemnation

Finally, certain types of governmental entities have the power to acquire real property, including groundwater rights, through their powers of eminent domain and condemnation. In addition to exercises of eminent domain, at times owners of land or groundwater rights have challenged as "regulatory takings" or inverse condemnation the rules or other actions of a GCD or political subdivision affecting groundwater rights. *See, e.g., Edwards Aquifer Authority v. Day*, 369 S.W.3d 814 (Tex. 2012). The Texas Property Code imposes various requirements on the condemnation of water rights by municipalities and provides for separate valuation of groundwater rights in excess of the market value of the fee simple estate. *See* Tex. Prop. Code §§ 21.0121, 21.0421. To date, this is a relatively untested provision, but it signals to municipalities that condemnation of groundwater rights should be approached with careful consideration. See Chapter 38 of this book for a detailed discussion of governmental acquisition of groundwater rights by involuntary means.

IV. Due Diligence

§ 18.8 Overview of Due Diligence

For any potential groundwater rights purchase or lease, a number of due diligence matters must be addressed. Although the issues vary for different projects and transactions, these matters generally relate to (1) the quality and quantity of the subject groundwater resources; (2) the current and future uses of the surface of the land; (3) title to the groundwater rights and surface estate, and the existence of restrictions or encumbrances that could interfere with the intended use; (4) environmental concerns; (5) the regulatory regimes that will affect development and use of the groundwater; and (6) other issues or circumstances affecting the economic or logistical feasibility of the intended groundwater project. Some of these due diligence matters may be significant not only for evaluation of the terms (including consideration) of the transaction itself, but also with an eye toward establishing marketable groundwater rights and groundwater supplies for further development.

Some due diligence matters, such as needs assessment and basic regulatory due diligence, should be addressed even before determining the most appropriate location and method for acquiring groundwater rights (lease, sale, supply contract, or, if available, condemnation) and drafting and negotiating the terms of the transaction. Other matters involve investigations and analysis that are most effectively conducted during the pendency of the transaction—for example, during the inspection or feasibility period provided for in a contract of sale of groundwater rights. Although it is not possible to design a single due diligence blueprint appropriate for all groundwater transactions, the following sections provide an overview and discussion of the types of issues that parties should consider.

§ 18.9 Needs Assessment

To determine the preferred method of acquisition (usually lease or purchase) and appropriate terms for the transaction, the parties must first have a reasonably defined sense of the short- and long-term needs for groundwater that the transaction is intended to address. For the acquiring party, this assessment largely depends on (1) the amount of groundwater needed to be produced, (2) how quickly production must begin and how long it is expected to last, (3) the type(s) of groundwater use contemplated, and (4) the place of use of the groundwater, which in turn involves the extent to which other infrastructure will be required to develop and use the groundwater. The amount of investment and financial risk associated with a purchase of groundwater rights, as opposed to a lease, should also be considered.

For the conveying party (presumably, the surface owner), significant considerations include the extent to which its own intended uses of the (reserved) groundwater from the property and the surface itself will be affected by the groundwater development of the buyer or lessee. This is a matter not only regarding the current owner's present and contemplated future uses but also one potentially affecting the future marketability and value of the surface estate.

§ 18.10 Regulatory Due Diligence

Many of the critical aspects of the planning and investigation underlying a groundwater transaction involve assessment of the regulatory regimes that will affect the prospective buyer or lessee's development and use of groundwater resources as well as the surface owner's retained rights to the use of the surface and (often) some groundwater. These potential regulatory implications may have a greater or lesser degree of significance for the party interested in acquiring groundwater rights depending, among other things, on the nature of the acquiring party (individual, political subdivision, corporate entity, etc.), the amount of groundwater rights involved, and the intended purpose and place of use of the groundwater involved. Because groundwater rights are privately owned and not administered or regulated by a state agency, this regulatory due diligence is essentially a matter of various potential forms of local regulation.

Most important among these types of regulation are the rulemaking and permitting authority of local GCDs and subsidence districts. The vast majority of groundwater production in Texas occurs in areas under the jurisdiction of one of these districts, and there is great variety among their regulatory approaches. The legislature continues to create new GCDs in more parts of the state and has given those districts clearer authority over certain types of regulation of groundwater production and use. Thus, a party contemplating or negotiating a groundwater rights purchase or lease should be familiar with the applicable enabling legislation, rules, and management plan of the local district (or multiple districts), if any, with jurisdiction in the area of interest. Although the parties may be significantly constrained by the existing regulatory regime, working knowledge of the GCD's rules and practices can provide critical information for assessing the feasibility of a particular project, or at least the suitability of particular groundwater rights property for the project.

Moreover, a new framework for regional and statewide water planning has been implemented over the last several decades, and it affects many aspects of water rights transactions and project development. Thus, even beyond this primary layer of direct GCD regulation, the parties should also be familiar with the status and outcomes of joint planning efforts being conducted within the applicable groundwater management area and any applicable municipal or county regulations affecting water wells. Because this information may affect the proposed terms and conditions—or even the very feasibility—of the transaction, much of this regulatory due diligence should be conducted before drafting a lease or contract of sale and before approaching prospective sellers or lessors.

§ 18.10:1 Applicable Groundwater Conservation District or Subsidence District

The legislature has emphasized that underground water or groundwater conservation districts are the state's preferred method of groundwater management "in order to protect property rights, balance the conservation and development of groundwater to meet the needs of this state, and use the best available science in the conservation and development of groundwater." Tex. Water Code § 36.0015(b).

As of July 2021, there are 101 confirmed groundwater conservation districts and one pending confirmation. *See* Texas Commission on Environmental Quality, *Texas Groundwater Conservation Districts* (July 2021), www.tceq.texas.gov/groundwater/groundwater-planning-assessment/districts.html [hereinafter TCEQ Map]. See also Plate 2. There are two subsidence districts. See Chapter 16 of this book for a detailed discussion of GCDs and subsidence districts. Information compiled by the Texas Water Development Board (TWDB) reflects that increasingly more of the land and groundwater resources of Texas are under the jurisdiction of one of these districts. As of the publication date of this edition, two-thirds of Texas counties (173) are fully or partially within a confirmed GCD (excluding subsidence districts), covering nearly 70 percent of the area of the state, and approximately 72 percent of major and minor aquifers are overlain by a GCD. *See* TCEQ Map; Texas Water Development Board, *Groundwater Conservation District Facts*, www.twdb.texas.gov/groundwater/conservation_districts/facts.asp. Thus, the first task is to determine whether the land that is the subject of a potential groundwater rights transaction is located within one or more GCDs or subsidence districts. Information and maps of GCDs are available on the TWDB website at www.twdb.texas.gov. Contact information, website links, and (for most GCDs) copies of district rules and district management plans are available online at www.twdb.texas.gov/groundwater/conservation_districts/gcdinfo1.asp. The Texas Property Code has recently been amended to require a seller's disclosure notice to address whether the seller is aware (actual knowledge, without any duty of investigation) of any portion of the subject property being located within a GCD or a subsidence district. *See* Tex. Prop. Code § 5.008(b).

Most GCDs have been legislatively created. Thus, a determination of a district's powers and methods of groundwater regulation should begin with a review of its enabling legislation. Chapter 36 of the Texas Water Code provides the regulatory authority of general law GCDs and controls on issues not addressed in a district's enabling legislation. The powers and duties of the two subsidence districts are found in special legislation. *See* Tex. Spec. Dist. Code chs. 8801 (Harris-Galveston Subsidence District), 8834 (Fort Bend Subsidence District). The general law provisions for GCDs, Water Code chapter 36, subchapter A, expressly do not apply to the subsidence districts. *See* Act of May 13, 2005, 79th Leg., R.S., ch. 238, §§ 7, 26; *see also* Act of May 27, 2019, 86th Leg., R.S., ch. 1135 (H.B. 2729), eff. Sept. 1, 2019 (affirming that Water Code chapter 36 does not apply to the EAA). The amendment of Water Code section 36.002, regarding groundwater ownership and rights, expressly does not affect the regulatory authority of the EAA or the subsidence districts. *See* Tex. Water Code § 36.002(e). See Chapter 16 of this book for a discussion of GCDs and subsidence districts generally, including the nature of their regulatory powers, and Chapter 17 regarding the EAA.

Each GCD has the power to implement its statutory authority through rulemaking and permitting. *See* Tex. Water Code §§ 36.101, 36.113. If the subject land is within a GCD or a subsidence district, the prospective acquiring party should review, together with chapter 36 and the district's enabling legislation, the regulations of the district to determine any substantive or procedural requirements and limitations on the water rights owner's (or lessee's) ability to access and produce groundwater. By rule, a GCD determines each activity regulated by the district for which a permit or permit amendment is required. Tex. Water Code § 36.114(a). Districts may require permits for drilling water wells, for operating or producing water from a well, and for transporting produced groundwater out of the district. The terms "operating permit" and "production permit" are used interchangeably, and some GCDs combine the drilling authorization into one of those. A permit for transporting produced groundwater out of the district may be referred to as a transport, transfer, or export permit, and these terms are used interchangeably. Districts may also have specific requirements relating to test wells, which may affect a prospective acquiring party's due diligence activities during the inspection period provided for in a lease or contract of sale. Within a GCD, all wells are required to be permitted unless they are exempted by statute or the district's rules. *See* Tex. Water Code §§ 36.113, 36.115, 36.117. All exempt wells must be registered with the GCD. *See* Tex. Water Code § 36.117(h)(1). New statutory authority also allows GCDs to adopt rules and issue permits for production from designated "brackish groundwater production zones," following some required predicate technical review by the TWDB. *See* Tex. Water Code § 36.1015; see the discussion in Chapter 16 of this book. Thus, a party contemplating a lease or purchase of groundwater rights should enter into its due diligence and negotiations with an understanding of district rules that will affect the terms of various permits the party may need to obtain. The most common and significant types of rules with implications for groundwater transactions are discussed below, in terms of the general law provisions and some illustrative examples from various GCDs' rules.

Production Limitations: Depending on the type of groundwater development project the acquiring party is contemplating, production limitations imposed by the local GCD are likely to be a significant consideration in shaping the groundwater transaction. The nature and extent of production limitations, if any, have implications for the terms drafted for the transaction and the conveyancing documents, for the acquiring party's feasibility assessment of the transaction, and for the selling or leasing party's retained rights of surface use and reserved groundwater. The legislature recognizes various means by which a GCD may regulate groundwater production through district rules, namely by—

1. setting production limits on wells,

2. limiting the amount of water produced based on acreage or tract size,

3. limiting the amount of water that may be produced from a defined number of acres assigned to an authorized well site,

4. limiting the maximum amount of water that may be produced on the basis of acre-feet per acre or gallons per minute per well site per acre,

5. using managed depletion, or

6. using any combination of the regulatory methods listed above.

See Tex. Water Code § 36.116(a)(2). Most of the GCDs in Texas use one or more of these methods of groundwater production limitations. *See generally* Texas Alliance of Groundwater Districts, *GCD Index*, https://texasgroundwater.org/resources/gcd-index/. As a result of the cyclical joint planning process to determine "desired future conditions" and "modeled available groundwater" for each aquifer in Texas, discussed briefly at section 18.10:2 below and in Chapter 21 of this book, it is expected that GCDs will amend their production limitation rules in a variety of ways. *Cf.* Tex. Water Code § 36.108. Under the statute regarding groundwater ownership rights, GCDs will now also be required to consider in their rulemaking these ownership rights, the public interest in conservation, protection, recharge, waste prevention, and subsidence control, and the goals developed as part of the GCD's statutorily required management plan. *See* Tex. Water Code § 36.101(a).

A local GCD may limit groundwater production by setting restrictions tied to particular wells, such as the allowable size or capacity of individual wells or limits on the rate of production and maximum allowable annual production from each well. A party seeking to acquire groundwater rights will need to consider how these types of limitations may affect the overall scope and cost of its planned project as a result of the amount or types of equipment and related infrastructure required. For example, if more, smaller wells are required to achieve the targeted amount of production, it may be necessary to drill and operate more wells, alter well field design, or modify the supporting storage and transportation infrastructure (e.g., pipelines) required to develop the groundwater and deliver it to its place of use.

A local GCD may also regulate production using a variety of limitations relating to the tract size or amount of acreage of groundwater rights that the permit applicant owns or controls. This may take the form of a certain number or formula for the number of acres required to support a particular size well. Further, there may be a limited number of acre-feet or gallons of water produced annually for each acre of the permittee's groundwater rights. Such per-acre limits on production are often based on the permittee's total amount of contiguous acreage of groundwater rights and may be higher based on larger overall tract size.

Chapter 36 expressly provides that a GCD may limit the amount of water produced based on contiguous surface acreage. Tex. Water Code § 36.116(e)(2). Thus, a party leasing or purchasing groundwater rights may wish to strategize its acquisitions in light of the local GCD's rules regarding treatment of contiguous acreage for permitting purposes. This has obvious implications for larger scale groundwater development projects. For example, in the case of the Canadian River Municipal Water Authority (CRMWA), which serves eleven member cities in the Texas Panhandle, its groundwater program has involved the acquisition of approximately 436,000 acres of groundwater rights, mostly in a four-county area and contiguous acreage under the applicable rules of the Panhandle GCD (requiring a minimum 0.25-mile common boundary between contiguous tracts), and CRMWA's permitted rights and production authorization are based on this total amount of groundwater rights acreage (generally authorizing annual production of one acre-foot per acre). Rules on contiguous acreage, however, can be significant even in smaller scale projects. The amount of annual production authorized for a well may be tied to a required number of acres, with the GCD's rules defining "contiguous acreage" to guide the district in determining whether the permit applicant has sufficient acreage to support the permit sought. In regulating groundwater production based on tract size or acreage, a GCD may consider "the service needs or service area of a retail water utility." Tex. Water Code § 36.116(c) (referencing the definition at Tex. Water Code § 13.002).

GCDs may regulate production on the basis of "managed depletion," which is an approach that aims to control the amount and rate of depletion districtwide or in particularly sensitive areas over the long term. For example, the Panhandle GCD, with groundwater resources in the Ogallala Aquifer, has a depletion rule based on the district's "50/50" management standard that 50 percent of the current supplies or saturated thickness of groundwater in the district remain in place fifty years after the initial adoption of its depletion rule. *See generally* Panhandle GCD Rules (most recently amended Dec. 20, 2018); *see also, e.g.*, Lost Pines GCD Rules 9.1, 9.2 (allowing the district to set production limits and to designate "management zones" to facilitate long-term management of available groundwater). In cases with these types of regulatory regimes and geologic features, a party acquiring groundwater rights (as well as the party retaining only limited reserved groundwater rights) will want to consider the likelihood and implications of further production limitations based on the implementation of a "managed depletion" rule.

It is also important to keep in mind that a GCD may adopt different rules applicable to different portions of the groundwater resources and land within its jurisdiction. In the interest of better management of groundwater resources or based on the district's determination that aquifer conditions and uses differ substantially in different geographic areas of the district, the GCD may adopt different rules for each aquifer, aquifer subdivision, or geologic strata located in whole or in part within the district or for each geographic area overlying these aquifers and aquifer subdivisions. Tex. Water Code § 36.116(d). In regulating groundwater production, a district "shall select a method that is appropriate based on the hydrogeological conditions of the aquifer or aquifers in the district." Tex. Water Code § 36.116(e)(1). As hydrology and mapping of local groundwater resources have improved and become more accessible, more districts have relied on these data to customize their production regulations in ways that are tailored to aquifer-specific resources. *See, e.g.*, Brazos Valley GCD Rule 7.1(d) (setting a specific maximum production limitation for new wells drilled in the Simsboro Formation); *see also* Post Oak Savannah GCD Rule 5.2.1 (stating that land and water rights in land not located over the aquifer from which a well is authorized production are not included in calculating the volume of water production permitted). For these reasons, the parties to a groundwater transaction should focus their analysis on those portions of the GCD's rules applicable to the particular resources of interest within the district.

A transacting party may encounter a variety of other types of production limitation regulatory approaches. In some cases, the GCD's rules generally provide for production limitations under circumstances where it is deemed necessary to avoid drawdown affecting neighboring wells. Under these types of rules, the likelihood of limitations on production may be less foreseeable at the time of a groundwater transaction. In the unique case of subsidence districts, where the emphasis is on generally shifting reliance on groundwater resources to more surface water usage, groundwater production may be limited in terms relating to the adequacy and availability to the permittee of substitute or supplemental surface water supplies. *See, e.g.*, Harris-Galveston Subsidence District Rule 5.2(d). Finally, in the unique case of the EAA, groundwater production is regulated within the framework of a statutorily imposed districtwide cap on annual groundwater production. Under the EAA's rules, discussed in detail in Chapter 17 of this book, many additional substantive and procedural considerations affect groundwater transactions; these are beyond the scope of this chapter.

In summary, any party contemplating a groundwater transaction involving land within a GCD's or subsidence district's jurisdiction should carefully examine that district's rules on production limitations as they would apply to the particular groundwater project. These rules potentially have implications for, among other things, the strategic location of acquisitions, valuation (for both parties) of groundwater rights being purchased or leased, the costs of the groundwater project, and the future marketability of the groundwater rights. The extent to which these types of production limitations matter to a particular person or entity acquiring groundwater rights depends on many factors, including the intended amount of groundwater production, the short- versus long-term needs for the groundwater, and the purpose and place of use of the groundwater.

"Historic or Existing Use" Limitations: Within certain constraints, a GCD may also regulate groundwater production in a manner designed to preserve "historic or existing use" before the effective date of the district's rules, to the maximum extent practicable consistent with the district's management plan and as provided by Water Code section 36.113. *See* Tex. Water Code § 36.116(b). These constraints mean that a district may impose more restrictive permit conditions on new permits or permit amendments if the limitations (1) apply to all such subsequent applications (regardless of type or location of use), (2) bear a "reasonable relationship" to the GCD's existing management plan, and (3) are reasonably necessary to protect existing use. *See* Tex. Water Code § 36.113(e). The general law statute also prohibits a GCD, in issuing a permit for an existing or historic use, from discriminating between land that is irrigated for production and land (or wells thereon) that is no longer thus irrigated and is part of a federal conservation program. *See* Tex. Water Code § 36.113(h).

Increasingly, GCDs have incorporated "historic or existing use" limitations into their groundwater production rules, designed in a variety of ways depending on local concerns and groundwater resources. Because a "historic or existing use" recognition may give the permit holder some measure of protection or authorize a higher level of production than what the GCD currently authorizes for operating permits, this type of permit can affect the marketability and value of these groundwater rights. However, a GCD may limit the "historic or existing use" authorization to the amount, source, or type of use historically established as of the time frame set by the district, and thus these types of authorizations may or may not be readily transferable, as a practical matter.

Finally, as discussed in Chapter 16 of this book, the parameters of GCDs' ability to regulate under the "historic or existing use" groundwater production statute and the groundwater transfer ("export") statute, and thus to affect the marketability of groundwater rights, has been addressed by the Texas Supreme Court. The court found that "the District's transfer rules, in essence, grant franchises to some landowners to export water while denying that right to others. Because the limitations are not uniformly applied to these new applications and are not necessary to protect existing use, the District's transfer rules exceed the statutory authorization and are thus invalid." *See Guitar Holding Co. v. Hudspeth County Underground Water Conservation District No. 1*, 263 S.W.3d 910, 918 (Tex. 2008).

Well Spacing Requirements: Parties to groundwater transactions should also consider the implications of the GCD's well spacing requirements. In the same statute that addresses regulation by production limitations, the legislature also recognizes various means by which a GCD may regulate the spacing of water wells through district rules, namely by—

1. requiring all water wells to be spaced a certain distance from property lines or adjoining wells;

2. requiring wells with a certain production capacity, pump size, or other characteristic related to the construction or operation of and production from a well to be spaced a certain distance from property lines or adjoining wells; or

3. imposing spacing requirements adopted by the board.

See Tex. Water Code § 36.116(a)(1). Well spacing and production limitations can be used for purposes such as minimizing drawdown of the water table, minimizing reduction of artesian pressure, controlling subsidence, preventing interference between wells, preventing degradation of water quality, or preventing waste. Tex. Water Code § 36.116(a). A compiled survey of the regulatory approaches of GCDs, which includes information regarding most of the ninety-eight existing confirmed districts, demonstrates that most GCDs have adopted one or more types of regulations over well spacing. Texas Alliance of Groundwater Districts, *GCD Index*, https://texasgroundwater.org/resources/gcd-index/ (searchable interactive database).

The most common types of these regulations are minimum spacing (setbacks) from property lines (or from the perimeter of the permittee's total qualifying contiguous area) and minimum spacing in relation to existing wells. A GCD's well spacing requirements may apply differently (or not at all) to wells exempt from permitting and may vary depending on the specific aquifer or formation involved. A district may regulate in terms of a number of wells that can be located in a particular acre or section. These types of spacing requirements are often based on the size or pumping capacity of the new well sought to be permitted, with greater distances required for higher capacity wells. If a potential buyer or lessee would be acquiring rights to existing wells, those may be exempt from spacing requirements, but modifications to those wells—for example, to increase production capacity—would likely be subject to the permit amendment process and the district's spacing requirements. *See* Tex. Water Code § 36.113(a), (f).

As with production limitations themselves, a GCD's well spacing rules applicable to any new wells may affect the acquiring party's feasibility assessment regarding a transaction involving particular property. Well spacing requirements may affect the amount and cost of potential groundwater production from the subject acreage depending in part on the number and location of existing wells on or near that property. The prospective acquiring party should approach this assessment with some sense of its preferences and constraints affecting the number, size, and location of planned water well(s) (or well field design, for multiple wells), in order to evaluate these in terms of modifications that may be required as a result of GCD spacing requirements, as applied to property boundaries and existing wells. From the seller or lessor perspective, these rules may be a significant measure of the protection that existing wells may have from new wells drilled and produced by the buyer or lessee.

Permit Transfers or Amendments: In a case in which the buyer or lessee is acquiring groundwater rights that are already permitted in some form by the local GCD, the parties will need to be aware of the applicable requirements for transfer of ownership of those rights. In many cases, if only a change of ownership is involved, with *no* other modifications to the permit, such a transfer is merely a ministerial act to be performed by district staff. Even in this scenario, the parties to a groundwater transaction should at least be aware of the procedural requirements (e.g., form of request, processing time, and possibly required prior approval) of the GCD for approval of a transfer. However, if any other changes are intended upon acquisition by the buyer or lessee, such as the amount or rate of production, a change in well location, or purpose or place of use, this will instead be treated as a permit amendment subject to all of the GCD's substantive and procedural requirements. *See generally* Tex. Water Code §§ 36.113, 36.114, 36.1145. In any event, the parties should consider whether it is appropriate to condition closing on the transaction on the successful transfer or amendment of the existing permitted groundwater rights and how that would affect timing of the transaction and of the buyer's or lessee's groundwater project.

Export Requirements: Central to many groundwater development and marketing projects in Texas is the ability to develop groundwater resources for transportation to and use in another part of the state. Because many GCDs are single-county districts (some cover only a portion of a county), groundwater transactions increasingly involve the need to "export" or "transport" the groundwater out of the district issuing the drilling or production permits. Dozens of the existing GCDs exercise their statutory authority to promulgate rules requiring authorization to transfer groundwater out of the district. *See* Tex. Water Code § 36.122; see also the discussion in Chapter 16 of this book. In the case of a special law district such as the EAA, rules may be even more restrictive. For example, the EAA requires that groundwater withdrawn from the Edwards Aquifer must be used within the EAA's boundaries. *See* EAA Rule 711.220 (eff. Dec. 20, 2019), www.edwardsaquifer.org/eaa/legislation-rules/eaa-rules/. Even transfers of place of use within the EAA (if from a point located west of Cibolo Creek to a point east of Cibolo Creek) are regulated to satisfy other requirements protecting endangered and threatened species and spring flows. *See* EAA Rule 711.329. The parameters of chapter 36 districts' export regulation authority and the practice of this type of regulation are discussed at section 18.15 below, regarding the impact of export regulation on the marketability of groundwater rights acquired.

Permit Terms: The acquiring party to a groundwater rights transaction should consider the duration of permitted rights likely to be approved by the GCD whether regarding a transfer of existing permitted groundwater rights or the prospects for obtaining a future permit. Drilling permits, if separately required, are typically granted for relatively short periods of time, generally requiring commencement of drilling within several months of issuance.

The most typical feasibility issue regarding permit terms involves the duration of production or operating permits approved by the district. A GCD's rules may be open-ended regarding the duration of terms of such permits, subject to the permittee's compliance with other district rules, allowing for flexibility depending on the details of a particular permit application. However, more typically a district's rules make the term of a production or operating permit standard and relatively short (e.g., five years), although usually with some renewability provisions. The party acquiring groundwater rights should consider the term (and renewability) of permitted rights in evaluating a prospective purchase or lease, because this will have implications not only for the investment involved in the planned development and use of the groundwater but also for the future marketability of the groundwater rights. Recent statutory amendments should provide permit holders more protection, by allowing more routine (without hearing) operating permit renewals in most cases where amendments are not sought and, for permit amendment applications, maintaining the operating permit provisions in effect until the amendment process is resolved. *See* Tex. Water Code §§ 36.1145, 36.1146.

As discussed above and at section 18.15 below, the duration of permitted "export" or "transport" rights has been an issue affecting some groundwater projects. However, the legislature has recently amended chapter 36 to facilitate the extension of thirty-year transport permits, to be synchronized with the terms of corresponding operating permits. *See* Tex. Water Code § 36.122(j–1), (j–2). See also Chapter 16 of this book.

Fees: The acquiring party to a groundwater rights transaction should also consider how the fees, if any, imposed by the GCD will affect the planned development and use of the groundwater rights to be purchased or leased. Aside from administrative fees relating to processing permit applications or well registration, which are generally nominal (*see* Tex. Water Code § 36.205(a)), districts may assess water production fees on pumping in the district in lieu of, or in conjunction with, any taxes otherwise levied by the district. *See* Tex. Water Code § 36.205(c). These production fees may be based on the amount of water authorized by permit to be withdrawn from a well or on the amount actually withdrawn, but they cannot exceed the annual rates of $1 per acre-foot for water used for agricultural use and $10 per acre-foot for water used for any other purpose. *See* Tex. Water Code § 36.205(c). However, these provisions do not apply to the EAA, the two subsidence districts, or some legislatively created GCDs. *See* Tex. Water Code § 36.205(d), (e). As discussed above, a GCD may also impose an administrative processing fee and a fee or surcharge for exporting water out of the district. *See* Tex. Water Code § 36.122(d), (e). Additional considerations are the timing of and basis for the assessment. For example, a GCD might assess the fee on the amount of groundwater authorized to be exported, with assessment beginning at the time of permit issuance, or it might assess the fee on the amount of groundwater actually exported, with the assessment based on periodic export reports. In short, depending on the purpose of use, place of use, and amount of anticipated production, a prospective buyer or lessee of groundwater rights should factor into its feasibility assessment the aggregate additional costs of its groundwater project resulting from applicable water production and export fees.

Procedural Requirements: The parties to a groundwater sale or lease should also consider whether any procedural requirements in the local GCD's rules will affect the timing or process of the transaction. For example, depending on the rules governing transfer of existing permitted rights, this transfer may not be approved and effective until after closing on a sale or execution of a lease. From the perspective of the acquiring party, it may be desirable to condition the closing on that party's ability to secure reasonably acceptable permit rights from the district, without which the transaction is of little benefit to the buyer or lessee. Even if the GCD's procedural requirements do not themselves affect the buyer or lessee's assessment of the feasibility or desirability of the transaction, the acquiring party should factor into its planning the application of district rules governing (1) notice and hearing provisions regarding potential protests of a permit application and (2) the time frame and procedure for review and approval of test wells, other required studies or technical review, drilling permits, and production or operating permits.

Various recent amendments to chapter 36 of the Water Code further specify and standardize the procedures by which a GCD may conduct a hearing on a permit application or amendment, including in some circumstances contracting with the State Office of Administrative Hearings (SOAH) or other hearing examiner. These amendments require districts to revise or develop new procedural rules for permit hearings, in some cases affecting the applicant's costs of proceeding but also placing some new limitations on districts' handling of uncontested applications. *See generally* Tex. Water Code ch. 36, subch. M.

Other Permitting Practice Considerations: Beyond the local GCD's procedural rules and practices discussed above, part of the due diligence for a party acquiring or seeking to amend groundwater rights includes an assessment of the potential opposition to the permits that would be required for that party's desired use of the groundwater. In areas where groundwater development and transport projects are increasing in number and scope, there are examples of permit applicants encountering significant opposition and ending up in litigation. *See, e.g., Wimberley Springs Partners, Ltd. v. Wimberley Valley Watershed Ass'n*, No. 03-13-00467-CV, 2017 WL 2229876 (Tex. App.—Austin May 19, 2017, no pet.) (mem. op.). Other local landowners or interest organizations may contest the application and trigger the need for further proceedings. Even without any properly filed protest by such third parties, the permit applicant itself may seek a contested case hearing if, for example, the applicant anticipates from GCD staff or the board an unfavorable review or an incomplete version of the permits sought. *See* Tex. Water Code § 36.4051(d). Practitioners should also be aware that groundwater rights holders in an area subject to GCD jurisdiction may lose groundwater to groundwater rights holders in adjacent areas not subject to regulation by any GCD or regulated by a neighboring GCD with less stringent production or transport limitations. In short, a would-be permit applicant's strategy should consider the local GCD's recent permitting approach, including how the district's governing body responds to other local stakeholders, and might also include looking beyond the boundaries of the GCD with direct regulatory authority over the subject property.

Other Information to Obtain from the GCD: As part of its due diligence, the acquiring party in a groundwater rights transaction should consider other additional information obtained from the local GCD. Of course, the nature and the importance of such additional information will vary depending on the scope and nature of the transaction and the groundwater development project to which it relates. A private person acquiring groundwater rights for one well or a small amount of additional production will likely not have the same concerns as a buyer or lessee that is, for example, a municipality seeking to develop additional groundwater supplies as a long-term strategy or a private entity seeking to develop large quantities of groundwater for marketing.

Even prior to the documentary due diligence review discussed below, the prospective buyer or lessee may find it useful to communicate with staff from the local GCD to discuss the prospective transaction or project and to obtain additional information or guidance regarding the application or interpretation of district rules. This might particularly be the case where any unique aspects of the acquiring party's planned development and use of the groundwater present issues unresolved or unclear under the district's rules. Because the proliferation of GCDs in Texas is a relatively recent phenomenon, and because statutory requirements regarding groundwater planning, management, and regulation are evolving, the parties may be dealing with a GCD that has only recently adopted its management plan and initial rules or is presently undergoing that process. Although a detailed consultation regarding the acquiring party's plans for particular acquisitions and development may not be appropriate in every situation, in some cases it can assist the parties in developing appropriate terms for the transaction, especially the acquiring party in understanding and factoring in the regulatory regime that will affect its development and use of the rights to be purchased or leased.

In any event, the acquiring party should consider contacting the local GCD to review or inspect documentation relating to the subject property and existing wells in production on that property. This documentation may include records such as (1) well registrations for existing wells on the property that are exempt from permitting, which may affect the extent and production location of water rights reserved to the surface owner; (2) drilling logs and water use reports on existing wells, including exempt wells associated with oil and gas activities; and (3) documentation relating to existing permitted water rights on the property, including maps, hydrologic analysis (including water quality and quantity), and other data supporting the application for and approval of those permitted rights. These types of information will assist the prospective buyer or lessee in evaluating aspects of the transaction, including (1) the amount of groundwater that can reasonably and economically be produced from the property; (2) the nature and amount of other groundwater rights in production on the property, to which any prospective development project would be subject; and (3) the resulting implications for valuation of and consideration for the groundwater rights to be acquired.

§ 18.10:2 Groundwater Management Area Joint Planning

Parties to purchases or leases of groundwater rights should also be aware of the new tools for groundwater management implemented by the Texas legislature in recent years, because these processes and their results can affect the regulation of groundwater in a specific area of the state. Each GCD is required to develop a management plan that addresses various management goals, includes specific performance standards and detailed actions and procedures to carry out the plan, and estimates various aspects of the groundwater resources within the district. *See* Tex. Water Code §§ 36.1071(e), 36.1085.

Beyond the district level, in 2005 the legislature enacted a collaborative process whereby GCDs with groundwater resources in a common aquifer, defined by groundwater management areas (GMAs) designated by the TWDB, are now required to conduct joint planning and to make regionalized determinations of groundwater availability. See Chapter 21 of this book for a discussion of GMAs. All the GCDs within a GMA are required to meet at least annually for joint planning. *See* Tex. Water Code § 36.108(c). Each of these planning groups must determine how it wants to manage the groundwater resources within its GMA by the adoption of a policy statement known as the "desired future conditions" (DFCs) of the aquifers in the area. *See* Tex. Water Code § 36.108. The TWDB uses these DFCs to estimate the amount of groundwater that could be produced on an average annual basis while still maintaining the DFCs adopted by the districts. This water estimate is called the "modeled available groundwater" (MAG). *See* Tex. Water Code §§ 36.001(25), 36.1084.

This still evolving process of regionally adopted DFCs, which are updated in five-year cycles and become the basis for quantifying amounts of MAG, is significant for purposes of planning groundwater projects and transactions. The MAG numbers will be used by GCDs in their groundwater management plans and permitting. GCDs are now required, to the extent possible and based on proper applications, to issue permits up to the point that the total volume of exempt and permitted groundwater production will achieve an applicable DFC under Texas Water Code section 36.108 on a long-term basis. *See* Tex. Water Code § 36.1132. Parties to acquisitions of groundwater rights could be affected by the adopted DFCs and the MAG determination because these quantified assessments of groundwater conditions could thus be used by a GCD to limit local groundwater production, at the time of initial permitting or subsequently. See Chapter 21 of this book for a discussion of this joint planning process within GMAs. At this point, it remains difficult to predict how the process of adopting DFCs and calculating the MAG, overhauled by the 82nd Legislature in 2011 and fine-tuned in subsequent sessions, may affect groundwater permitting, and therefore transactions, for different areas around the state.

An additional area of complexity as well as project potential has been added by new statutes governing production from brackish groundwater production zones. If such a zone has been designated (by the TWDB) within a GCD, any permitting rules adopted by the GCD for brackish water production must provide that production from such a designated zone "is in addition to the amount of managed available groundwater" established through the joint planning process. Similar to the section 36.1132 requirement, the GCD shall, to the extent possible, issue permits up to the point that the total volume of brackish production authorized equals the groundwater availability described by the TWDB in its zone designation. *See* Tex. Water Code § 36.1015(*l*). See also Chapter 25 of this book.

Not all parts of Texas are located within a GCD or a subsidence district. However, this is a situation in flux. Additionally, as discussed in Chapter 5 of this book, the Texas Commission on Environmental Quality (TCEQ) has statutory authority to designate a "priority groundwater management area" (PGMA) if the area is currently experiencing, or is anticipated to experience within the next fifty years, critical groundwater problems, such as shortages, contamination of groundwater supplies, or land subsidence through the withdrawal of groundwater. *See* Tex. Water Code § 35.007. This PGMA designation then facilitates the creation of one or more new GCDs or the annexation of the area into an adjoining GCD. *See* Tex. Water Code § 35.012. By these various legislative and regulatory processes, there continues to be considerable momentum toward increased coverage of the state with these local and aquifer-based means of groundwater regulation and planning. For further discussion of how the PGMA process is affecting GCD formation and annexation, see Chapter 13 of this book.

Within this framework, parties to groundwater transactions not only should examine the general law provisions, enabling legislation, management plan, and current rules of the applicable GCDs in the area of interest but should also monitor the progress of the ongoing aquifer-wide joint planning process that will also affect the calculation and implementation of regionally based groundwater availability.

§ 18.10:3 Other Applicable Regulatory Authority

Because Texas's approach to groundwater regulation and management is grounded in local control through GCDs and subsidence districts, this discussion of regulatory due diligence focuses principally on issues relating to district planning and regulation. However, a prospective buyer or lessee of groundwater rights should also consider the potential effect on its intended development and use of the water from other sources of regulatory authority.

First, municipalities in Texas have varying levels of statutory authority to regulate the drilling of water wells within their city limits and their extraterritorial jurisdiction (ETJ). A home-rule municipality may regulate well drilling and groundwater production by ordinance, for the purpose of regulating for public health and safety purposes, to prohibit nuisances, and to prevent pollution. *See generally* Tex. Loc. Gov't Code §§ 51.072, 54.004, 217.042, 551.002; Tex. Water Code § 26.177; Tex. Att'y Gen. Op. No. JM-226 (1984). A general law municipality has more limited ability, for the purpose of establishing and enforcing a municipal setting designation, to regulate groundwater extraction, production, or use by persons other than retail public utilities and in order to prevent the use of or contact with groundwater that presents an actual or potential threat to public health. *See* Tex. Loc. Gov't Code §§ 212.003(a), 551.005. Therefore, if the subject land involved in the transaction is located within the city limits or ETJ of a municipality, the acquiring party should also be aware of any applicable regulations affecting drilling and equipping of water wells (location, size, drilling and casing specifications, etc.) and groundwater production.

Municipalities and counties may require a determination of groundwater availability in certain circumstances. Under Texas Water Code section 35.019, counties in PGMAs have the authority to protect a sustainable yield of that county's water supply via the adoption of certain water availability requirements for development in areas where platting is required. *See* Tex. Water Code § 35.019. Under the Texas Local Government Code, all municipalities and counties in Texas are authorized to require a water availability certification for plat applications for creating a new subdivision that would rely on groundwater for a water supply. *See* Tex. Loc. Gov't Code §§ 212.0101, 232.0032. Relatedly, some GCDs' rules expressly recognize the county's authority to adopt water availability requirements (in the county's subdivision rules) for areas where platting is required in order to prevent current or projected water use in the county from exceeding the county's safe sustainable supply. *See, e.g.*, Headwaters GCD Rule 5(G) (noting that additional Kerr County subdivision rules may apply for permitted wells drilled outside the Kerrville city limits).

Second, again depending on the nature and location of the subject land or the purpose of water use, other federal or state agencies may have regulatory jurisdiction that affects the viable development and use of the groundwater. For example, the U.S. Fish and Wildlife Service (or the Texas Parks and Wildlife Department) may have some authority that affects groundwater development and use if there are endangered or protected species (or their habitat) in a particular area. See Chapter 32 of this book for a discussion of the Endangered Species Act. If the area includes wetlands as defined under federal law, the U.S. Army Corps of Engineers may have some authority that affects groundwater development and use. See Chapters 34 and 35 of this book for discussions of the Corps' jurisdiction over water projects. For groundwater wells developed for public water supply, the TCEQ has jurisdiction over requirements for well construction, completion, and operation, including required sanitary control easements. These types of considerations should be factored in, at least in terms of their applicability and general implications, before a sale or lease of groundwater rights is finalized.

§ 18.11 Physical Inspection and Testing

For virtually every purchase or lease of groundwater rights, it will be necessary for the acquiring party to conduct some types of physical inspection of the subject land and groundwater resources to determine the feasibility of the contemplated project. Under some circumstances, the results of such examinations may even affect the ultimate terms of the transaction (e.g., price) or provide a basis for one or both parties to terminate the contract or lease. Some of the most common types of physical inspections are addressed below.

§ 18.11:1 Hydrology Issues

With nine major aquifers and twenty-two minor aquifers located wholly or partially in Texas, and a great variety of geologic features and other conditions among them, the hydrology of local groundwater resources is an important part of the due diligence relating to a groundwater rights transaction. In cases in which the party contemplating a new groundwater development or marketing project has such flexibility, this information may indeed guide or determine the ideal location for the project. Even where projects are more geographically defined by constraints affecting the parties, however, hydrologic analysis can help to shape the terms of the transaction, including valuation of the groundwater leased or sold, and terms regarding the amounts and types of production and reservation of groundwater from the property. For example, the extent and location of recharge are likely to affect the parties' assessment of such terms. In areas where there is more than one aquifer or specific formation, the transaction may be confined only to production from one of those formations or may have varying provisions for groundwater developed from each source of supply. In areas where there is documented consistency of average saturated thickness of groundwater throughout the area of interest, there may be little need to conduct further hydrologic testing.

Increasingly more and better information is available regarding groundwater supplies in each part of Texas. As discussed in Chapter 19 of this book, groundwater availability models have been developed for each major aquifer in Texas. As discussed in Chapter 21, the water planning and management processes developed by the legislature in recent years are aimed in part at developing improved data and mechanisms for evaluating groundwater resources in distinct areas.

Depending on the groundwater development project and the indicators from these generally available sources of information, the parties may also require additional hydrologic analysis to evaluate their particular transaction. One or both parties may wish to have more reliable data regarding the average saturated thickness of the groundwater in the particular subject property (and nearby properties), the variability of such thickness in the aquifer or formation involved, the features of the aquifer in the subject area, and the resulting effects of those features on the movement of the groundwater. Such analysis would typically involve drilling one or more test wells in the subject area and could also involve review of hydrologic and well production data maintained by the local GCD. In some instances, completion of the transaction may even be conditioned on the results of particular hydrologic analysis conducted by or on behalf of the parties.

Even beyond the needs and preferences of the parties, some GCDs' rules require certain types of hydrological analysis to be submitted in support of a permit application or amendment.

§ 18.11:2 Water Quality

In the same vein as hydrology issues regarding water quantity and features of the local groundwater resources, the acquiring party in many cases will also want to conduct some water quality testing during the inspection period. This can be accomplished in conjunction with drilling test wells to examine hydrologic features, as discussed above. Alternatively, the acquiring party may be able to review data available from the local GCD, if any, or conduct water quality testing based on samples provided from existing wells on the subject property. As with water quantity analysis, the outcome of water quality testing may affect the valuation of the groundwater being leased or sold. Depending especially on the type of use(s) intended to be made of the groundwater and the costs of remedying water quality problems (assuming that is possible), this analysis also may ultimately determine whether the transaction is feasible in relation to particular property and groundwater. For example, a political subdivision that is acquiring groundwater rights for municipal supply must consider whether, and at what expense, the groundwater can be treated to meet applicable drinking water standards. See Chapter 29 of this book for a detailed discussion of drinking water quality issues.

§ 18.11:3 Environmental Conditions

When drafting and negotiating a lease or contract of sale, the parties should contemplate what provisions are appropriate to provide for investigation and remediation of as well as disclosures by the surface owner regarding environmental conditions on the subject property. As in any other transaction conveying an interest in real property, the acquiring party will want to have some protection in the contract or lease in the event that environmental conditions affect the groundwater resources to a degree that makes the transaction unfeasible. Some present or past use of the surface estate may have involved, for example, an industrial use or underground storage of hydrocarbons or hazardous materials that may have contaminated the groundwater. In some cases, publicly available information regarding the present or past use of the property may signal the acquiring party that these protections may be needed; even if not, the acquiring party may wish to include these protections in any contract of sale or lease.

The transaction documents should give the acquiring party options to address these types of circumstances. For example, a contract of sale can expressly provide that the buyer can obtain (at the buyer's expense) a Phase I Environmental Assessment of the property during the review period. The contract may further provide negotiated terms for (1) notice to the seller of the results of the Phase I Assessment; (2) the seller's options and obligations regarding remediation on the basis of that assessment; (3) the circumstances under which a more extensive Phase II Environmental Assessment is appropriate, and at which party's option; (4) the seller's options and obligations regarding remediation on the basis of the Phase II Assessment, if any; and (5) the buyer's options if the seller cannot or will not remediate the conditions. For an explanation of these assessments, see American Society of Testing and Materials (ASTM) *International Standard Practice* E 1527-13 (Phase I Environmental Assessment) and E 1903-97 (2002) (Phase II Environmental Assessment).

If a buyer is concerned about potential contamination of the groundwater, including the past use of an adjacent tract, the buyer may desire to obtain protection from liability afforded by the Comprehensive Environmental Response, Compensation, and Liability Act of 1980 (CERCLA) to an innocent landowner, contiguous property owner, or bona fide prospective buyers through a Phase I Environmental Assessment that meets the ASTM standards for "all appropriate inquiries." *See* 42 U.S.C. § 9601(35)(B)(i); 40 CFR pt. 312. A buyer purchasing severed groundwater rights is acquiring a fee simple interest in real property that is separate from the surface estate. While there is no decision interpreting the liability of a groundwater rights owner under CERCLA, there are cases that have found the owner of a mineral estate liable as a CERCLA owner, because a mineral estate, under applicable state law, constitutes a separate fee simple estate in property. *See, e.g., City of Grass Valley v. Newmont Mining Corp.*, No. 2:04-cv-00149-GEB-DAD, 2007 WL 4287603 (E.D. Cal. Dec. 4, 2007) (distinguishing a mineral estate under California law from an easement); *see also Halliburton Energy Services, Inc. v. NL Industries*, 648 F. Supp. 2d 840, 896 (S.D. Tex. 2009) (citing *Grass Valley*). Because groundwater rights in Texas, like a mineral estate, constitute a separate fee simple estate in the real property, the groundwater rights owner is arguably subject to the same liability and the same protections under CERCLA as the owner of a mineral estate. See Grady B. Jolley, *Checklist for Environmental Due Diligence in Purchasing Groundwater Interest, in The Changing Face of Water Rights in Texas* 8.2 (State Bar of Texas 2015).

§ 18.11:4 Surface Use

As discussed earlier in this chapter, the parties should carefully consider what provisions in the contract of sale, lease, or conveyancing documents are needed to reflect the parties' intent regarding the surface owner's continued use of the surface estate, the nature and extent of reserved groundwater rights, and the buyer's or lessee's surface use rights. Unlike in an oil and gas lease, in groundwater transactions it has not been established that surface use rights are impliedly conveyed. Thus, careful consideration and drafting of such provisions are critically important.

Even before the inspection period or due diligence review for a contract of sale, the buyer or lessee should carefully consider what types of surface use (of land, water, and mineral resources) may or may not be compatible with the intended production and use of the groundwater resources. For example, in some parts of the state, significant oil and gas and other mineral development involves substantial infrastructure and operations on and under the surface of the land. Depending on the terms of the mineral leases in effect, these operations also (1) will involve some degree of access to and use of the surface; (2) often include rights to the use of groundwater from the property related to those operations, which may include unlimited amounts of water for flooding and secondary recovery operations; and (3) may include rights to inject water, air, saltwater, hydrocarbons, or other materials into the subsurface. In addition to oil and gas and mining, many other types of surface uses (e.g., particular types of industrial or agricultural operations) may not coexist readily with the acquiring party's intended production, use, and transportation of the groundwater.

Even if surface use issues do not outright frustrate the feasibility of the acquiring party's groundwater project, at a minimum the parties should address these matters with particularity in the contract, lease, deed, easement agreement, and so on, so that the intended resulting rights of both parties are protected following the transaction. As examples, the definition of "reserved groundwater" might well be limited (in terms of type, location, or quantity) to established historic use of groundwater by the surface owner. The contract of sale or lease may also require prospectively that any new mineral leases affecting the property contain provisions limiting the use of groundwater for certain purposes or may prospectively limit the number of residential units that may receive their water supply from groundwater produced from the property.

§ 18.11:5 Other Assessments

The parties may wish to include in the contract of sale or lease provisions for obtaining other assessments of the subject property that will help inform the parties regarding the specific terms of the transaction, which depend on a complete and correct description and valuation of the subject property.

Survey: The buyer will likely require provisions in the contract of sale that the seller provide copies of any existing surveys of the property and, at the buyer's option, that the seller provide a new survey of the real property, at the seller's expense, with the required survey category (e.g., boundary survey, land title survey) specified in the contract. Different types of surveys and survey certifications are available, depending on the nature of the property and the requirements of the parties. *See* Texas Society of Professional Surveyors, *Manual of Practice for Land Surveying in the State of Texas* (eff. Dec. 31, 2020) (describing the various categories and conditions for surveys in Texas, the level of accuracy required for each category of survey, matters to be depicted on the survey, and the nature of certificates). At a minimum, the survey will describe (and may quantify the acreage of) the real property that is the subject of the groundwater rights transaction in a manner that should conform to the legal description both in the contract of sale and in the title commitment or title opinion. More detailed types of surveys will further enable the acquiring party to assess the various types of easements, improvements, or other encumbrances that affect the subject property, as well as access to roadways and utilities. *See* 2 Forms Manual ch. 16, § 16.21:3 (discussing relevant considerations regarding specific survey categories that may be used in groundwater transactions).

Appraisal: For either a sale or lease, the parties may wish to have the groundwater rights separately appraised. As discussed at section 18.14 below, in many areas of the state, a number of variables influence the ability to achieve an accurate and substantive appraisal of groundwater rights. As groundwater markets in Texas become more developed, the basis for appraisal activity and evaluation of comparable transactions should improve.

§ 18.12 Infrastructure Needs

The party acquiring groundwater rights (or groundwater supply, under contract) should also consider, even in the early stages of mapping a targeted area for potential acquisitions, the amount, types, and cost of infrastructure that will be needed to develop and produce the groundwater from a particular location. For small projects, this may involve only the siting of one groundwater well. For projects of larger scale, in terms of either geographic area covered or amount of groundwater to be produced, this will usually involve a number of additional considerations. A multiple-wells project requires well field design factoring in the number and location of the acquiring party's planned wells in relation to existing wells and various other land use features on the surface. In addition to the wells themselves, the acquiring party must also evaluate the facilities that will be needed to transport, and possibly also to collect and store, the groundwater until it is delivered to its ultimate place of use. This involves not only the additional facilities themselves (e.g., pipelines, power supply) but also any easement rights needed for these facilities in addition to the easement rights negotiated with the owners of the property from which the groundwater is produced. As Texas groundwater development and marketing projects increasingly contemplate developing these water resources for use many miles away from the source, these infrastructure considerations, and acquisition of surface rights to provide for them, have become a critical aspect of the overall planning for, and negotiation of, groundwater transactions.

§ 18.13 Title Matters

A contract for the sale or lease of groundwater rights should give the buyer or lessee the right to conduct due diligence activities, including title examination. The acquiring party should have the right to terminate the contract if significant, uncured title problems affect the owner's title to the groundwater rights or land or unreasonably interfere with the buyer's or lessee's intended use of the groundwater rights.

A party purchasing or leasing groundwater rights should conduct the same type of due diligence on the groundwater rights that the buyer or lessee of land would conduct. This means confirming that the seller or lessor named in the contract owns the groundwater rights (and the land, if surface use rights are to be granted as part of the sale or lease) and determining the existence of restrictions, leases, easements, liens, or other title matters that could adversely affect the buyer's or lessee's use of the groundwater rights. For example, restrictive covenants that prohibit drilling groundwater wells have been upheld as being valid and enforceable. *See Dyegard Land Partnership v. Hoover*, 39 S.W.3d 300 (Tex. App.—Fort Worth 2001, no pet.). Oil and gas leases may provide the oil and gas lessee with the right to inject saltwater or other substances into the subsurface of the land, which could potentially interfere with the buyer's or lessee's groundwater rights. Similarly, existing pipeline or utility easements may be in locations that would interfere with the planned location of the groundwater facilities.

The contract should give the buyer or lessee the right to make objections to title based on its title examination and provide the landowner with the right to cure title objections. The buyer or lessee should have the right to terminate the contract or lease if the objections are not cured within a stated period of time. In general, title assurance is obtained through an attorney opinion of title based on an abstract of title or through a policy of title insurance on the groundwater rights.

§ 18.13:1 Attorney Opinion of Title

If an attorney opinion of title is to be obtained, the prospective buyer or lessee will contract with an attorney to obtain an abstract of title on the property and to review the abstract. The attorney will prepare a letter describing (1) the owner of the groundwater rights, (2) the ownership of the land if the buyer or lessee will have the right to produce groundwater on site, and (3) the existence of leases, easements, restrictions, oil and gas leases, and other title matters that could adversely affect the buyer's or lessee's groundwater rights or interfere with production.

One disadvantage to obtaining an attorney opinion of title is that it may take a long time to get the opinion because the abstract must first be prepared by a title company, landman, or abstractor, and then the attorney requires time in which to review the title and prepare the opinion letter. Another disadvantage is that in the event of an error in the opinion, the buyer or lessee may have to sue the attorney. In that case, recovery may be limited to the amount of malpractice insurance maintained by the attorney. In a high-dollar transaction, the amount of malpractice coverage may not be sufficient to cover the loss sustained by the buyer or lessee.

§ 18.13:2 Title Insurance

Title insurance covering groundwater rights in Texas was available in the past from a small number of title insurers. However, it does not appear that any major Texas underwriter is currently issuing coverage for groundwater rights. This leaves the buyer who wants to obtain title insurance with the sole option described at section 18.13:1 above. This is generally a much more costly process than obtaining title insurance (in a recent transaction, the cost of obtaining title insurance for the acquired groundwater rights, had it been available, would have been just over $2,000, while obtaining the attorney opinion of title cost more than $30,000). This approach also provides less financial assurance of recovery for mistakes than would a policy of title insurance that would provide defense of title and recovery for title defects not excluded from coverage up to the face amount of the policy, which is generally the purchase price of the groundwater rights. In addition, title insurance underwriters are required by Texas law to maintain significant reserves to cover potential losses.

It is possible that title insurance may once again be available to cover groundwater rights in Texas. Small insurers may issue policies on specific types of ownership rights, such as groundwater rights permitted by the EAA, but currently, buyers are generally without this option.

V. Other Issues for Consideration

§ 18.14 Valuation of Groundwater Rights

With newly emerging and yet undeveloped groundwater markets in various parts of Texas, there is no single standard method of determining the valuation of groundwater rights severed from the surface estate for purposes of defining terms for a purchase or lease. The field of groundwater rights appraisal is beginning to develop in Texas, but the types of data on which an appraiser may appropriately rely vary in different parts of the state. In areas where there have been numerous and robust groundwater sales, such as within the EAA, it is possible to obtain an appraisal of groundwater rights based on comparable sales. However, in areas where there have yet been few sale or lease transactions or where the water quantity and quality are highly variable, it may be difficult to obtain a reliable appraisal of groundwater rights without having hydrologic information specific to the subject groundwater resources. Moreover, for transactions involving groundwater resources subject to the jurisdiction of a GCD, the appraiser should consider the implications of the GCD's rules on the valuation and pricing of the groundwater (or groundwater rights) to be leased or sold.

Within this emerging framework, the parties to a transaction are certainly free to negotiate whatever valuation and pricing terms they deem appropriate to the local market and their own issues and concerns. For illustrative purposes, the following are two alternative approaches for determining a purchase price for groundwater rights. The first method is based on a stated price per acre of groundwater rights being purchased. (In the case of a fee simple determinable interest or a lease, this could similarly be a stated price per acre-foot of groundwater produced from the subject property.) This method may be used when the buyer or lessee is not obtaining any independent hydrologic information on the subject groundwater resources.

The second method is based on a stated price per "average saturated foot" of groundwater per acre of groundwater rights being purchased, with the estimated saturated thickness of the subject groundwater being determined by a hydrologist during the inspection period provided by the contract of sale. Under this method, the purchase price is directly related to the amount of groundwater in place under the land. Thus, the final purchase price cannot be calculated until the hydrologist's report is complete and could ultimately be significantly higher or lower than the parties' initial estimate. (Also, if a survey is to be obtained, the final purchase price depends on the precise amount of acreage determined under the survey.) Under this second method of valuation, if the parties intend to obtain a survey, appraisal, and hydrology report, these should be delivered during the inspection period so that the buyer is able to terminate the contract during the inspection period based on results affecting price. The parties may also wish to apply a minimum or maximum price to the formula provided for in the contract of sale, and in the case of hydrologic analysis, may include provisions to reevaluate the hydrology or further negotiate the final purchase price of the subject groundwater rights.

§ 18.15 Marketability and Transfers of Groundwater Acquired

A GCD's regulation of transfer (also known as "export" or "transport") of groundwater out of the district should be considered in terms of its potential effects on the feasibility of a groundwater development or marketing project. The following sections address the statutory and regulatory parameters within which GCDs have been exercising this authority and offer some other practical considerations that may affect groundwater transactions.

§ 18.15:1 Statutory Requirements

Texas Water Code section 36.122, adopted as part of S.B. 1 (1997) and substantially amended by S.B. 2 (2001), provides express but limited authority for a GCD to regulate the transfer of water out of the district. A district may promulgate rules requiring authorization for a permit (or permit amendment) involving the transfer of groundwater outside the GCD's boundaries. *See* Tex. Water Code § 36.122(a), (b). The district may not impose more restrictive permit conditions on transporters than it imposes on existing in-district users. Tex. Water Code § 36.122(c); *but see* Tex. Water Code § 36.113(e) (effectively qualifying this prohibition of discrimination against transporters by allowing more restrictive permit conditions on new or increased-use permit applications, as long as they apply to all new applications, regardless of type or location of use). A GCD must be "fair, impartial, and nondiscriminatory" in applying section 36.122. Tex. Water Code § 36.122(q). A district may also impose a fee or surcharge for an export fee under one of several statutory methods. *See* Tex. Water Code § 36.122(e), (p).

In reviewing a proposed groundwater transfer, the GCD must consider (1) the availability of water in the district and in the proposed receiving area during the period for which the water supply is requested; (2) the projected effect of the proposed transfer on aquifer conditions, depletion, subsidence, or effects on existing permit holders or other groundwater users within the district; and (3) the approved regional water plan and the GCD's approved management plan. Tex. Water Code § 36.122(f). Permits involving a groundwater transfer must specify the amount of water that may be transferred out of the district, which may be periodically reviewed and limited, and the period for which the water may be transferred. *See* Tex. Water Code § 36.122(h), (k). A GCD may not adopt rules expressly prohibiting groundwater export and may not deny a permit based on the fact that the applicant seeks to transfer groundwater, but a GCD may limit a permit if the above-mentioned conditions warrant. Tex. Water Code § 36.122(g), (o).

§ 18.15:2 GCD Rules and Practical Considerations

Part of the difficulty in evaluating the feasibility and marketability implications of a GCD's export or transport rules arises from the variability in districts' approaches to Texas Water Code section 36.122 and whether the statute's provisions are considered mandatory or optional. Some language in the statute indicates that a GCD "*may also consider* the provisions of [section 36.122]" in determining whether to grant a permit or amendment under section 36.113 that proposes groundwater transfer. *See* Tex. Water Code § 36.122(a) (emphasis added); *see also* Tex. Water Code § 36.122(b) (stating that a district "*may* promulgate rules" requiring a permit or amendment under section 36.113 for an out-of-district transfer) (emphasis added). On the other hand, numerous provisions in section 36.122, discussed at section 18.15:1 above, impose mandatory requirements on districts' handling of groundwater transfer proposals.

Under section 36.122(i), a transport permit term shall be at least three years if construction of a conveyance system has not been initiated before permit issuance, or at least thirty years if such construction has been initiated before permit issuance. *See* Tex. Water Code § 36.122(i); *see also* Tex. Water Code § 36.122(j) (automatically extending the minimum three-year term under subsection (i)(1) to a thirty-year term if construction has begun before the expiration of the initial term). These provisions were amended during the 2019 legislative session so that permit renewals involving an operating and a (thirty-year) transport permit will bring the terms into synch. See discussion at section 18.10:1 above regarding H.B. 1066.

In some cases, the GCD interprets section 36.122 to apply only when a GCD requires two permits: one for production and a separate one for transport. The GCD may adopt production permit rules that apply regardless of whether the water will be used inside or outside the district. Thus, the GCD may limit all production permits to a short (e.g., five-year) term. These differing interpretations in implementing section 36.122 may continue in spite of H.B. 1066. As a result, despite the legislature's efforts, some ambiguities remain with regard to the term of permits when the produced water will be transported out of the permitting district to be used elsewhere.

If there is uncertainty resulting from the GCD's transport permitting approach, even a smaller scale groundwater development project may be deemed inadvisable, particularly if it requires substantial infrastructure investment by the party acquiring groundwater rights.

Finally, the *Guitar* case, discussed more fully in Chapters 3 and 16 of this book, presents a significant illustration of the potential effects of a GCD's rules on the ability to develop groundwater resources for use outside the district, and provides some guidance from the Texas Supreme Court on the limits of a GCD's authority to issue permits for out-of-district transfers. *See Guitar Holding Co. v. Hudspeth County Underground Water Conservation District No. 1*, 263 S.W.3d 910 (Tex. 2008). In that case, the plaintiff-appellant challenged the "historic and existing use" permit rules of Hudspeth County Underground Water Conservation District No. 1. Because the district's rules authorized granting permits preferentially to landowners with historic irrigation use and allowed change of use and groundwater export for these historic use permits, effectively a limited number of landowners (historic irrigators) held the permits for nearly all of the reliable groundwater supply of the district. Under these circumstances, even a landowner with ownership or control of substantial acreage within the district, such as plaintiff-appellant Guitar Holding Co., was precluded from developing and marketing groundwater for export. The Texas Supreme Court found that "the District's transfer rules, in essence, grant franchises to some landowners to export water while denying that right to others. Because the limitations are not uniformly applied to these new applications and are not necessary to protect existing use, the District's transfer rules exceed the statutory authorization and are thus invalid." *Guitar Holding Co.*, 263 S.W.3d at 918.

§ 18.16 Obligations upon Termination (Sale)

The sale contract for groundwater rights should expressly provide that certain obligations survive termination of the contract. Payment and indemnification obligations as to events occurring before termination, for example, should be made to survive termination of the contract.

If easement rights are granted in a separate easement document, the easement document should expressly provide that certain obligations survive termination of the easement. Payment obligations, indemnification obligations for events occurring before termination, and the right or obligation to remove facilities after termination should expressly survive termination of the easement.

§ 18.17 Provisions Surviving Closing (Sale)

The sale contract for groundwater rights should expressly provide that certain obligations of the seller or buyer survive closing. Indemnification obligations as to events occurring before closing, for example, should be made to survive closing.

The responsibility for the payment of ad valorem property taxes on the land and the groundwater rights should also expressly survive closing. Currently, ad valorem property taxes are assessed against the land but are not separately assessed against severed groundwater rights. The contract should require the seller to continue paying the taxes assessed against the land after closing. The contract should also provide that if the taxes are ever separately assessed against the severed groundwater rights, the buyer will be responsible for paying these taxes.

VI. Financing Issues

§ 18.18 Liens on Groundwater Rights

If financing is to be obtained for the purchase, lease, or development of groundwater rights, the lender will require documentation to secure and perfect its lien against the groundwater rights. In general, the lender will obtain a deed of trust that creates a lien on the groundwater rights (or on the lessee's leasehold interest in the case of a lease of groundwater rights) on any easement obtained by the buyer or lessee and on any groundwater permit transferred to or obtained by the buyer or lessee. If the collateral includes wells, storage tanks, or other facilities that are or may become fixtures, or any items of personal property, the lender will also require the execution of a security agreement and financing statements. The deed of trust may be drafted to constitute a financing statement for fixtures, and upon recordation in the county real property records it will create a Uniform Commercial Code (UCC) lien on the fixtures. If the collateral includes personal property, the lender will require a UCC1 financing statement to be filed in the Office of the Secretary of State for the appropriate state, as required by the UCC.

§ 18.19 Security Interest in Personalty

It is not always clear whether some items of collateral, including groundwater permits, groundwater wells, or other facilities, are fixtures or personal property. Consequently, it is advisable for the lender to take the steps necessary to perfect its security interest in both personal property and fixtures.

§ 18.20 Control over Collateral

A lender may want to exert control over the groundwater permit by restricting the ability of the buyer or lessee to modify the permit without the consent of the lender during the term of the loan. The deed of trust and other loan documents should contain this prohibition. However, there is not currently a way in which a lender can require the GCD that issued the groundwater permit to obtain proof of the lender's consent before acting on an application to modify the permit. A lender may wish to provide written notice to the GCD of the lender's lien rights in the groundwater permit, as well as a document signed by the permittee acknowledging that modifications in the permit require prior lender approval. There is no assurance, however, that the district will require lender consent to the modification or even include the notice and documentation in the files maintained for the permit.

VII. Conclusion

§ 18.21 Conclusion

As the population of Texas rapidly shifts and grows, among the emerging trends in water development is an increasing focus on groundwater resources. Private and public entities of all sizes and in various parts of the state are exploring the potential for more widespread use of groundwater as a source of future water supply. Some of these negotiations and transactions involve locally based projects, while others contemplate developing and marketing groundwater resources for use in other parts of the state. In any event, this increase in and variety of transactional activity raises many questions for prospective parties buying, selling, or leasing groundwater rights in Texas. As illustrated in this chapter, parties have various options in structuring their transactions and developing their groundwater projects. As the law and new markets in groundwater transactions evolve, this will continue to be a critical area of Texas water resources law.

CHAPTER 19

Forecasting Underground Rain: Groundwater Availability Modeling

Robert E. Mace,[1] Cindy Ridgeway,[2] and Daryn Hardwick[3]

I. Introduction

§ 19.1 Introduction

Understanding and managing groundwater resources are paramount to the future of Texas. In 2016, groundwater provided 56 percent of all the water used in the state for agricultural, municipal, and industrial uses. *See* Texas Water Development Board, *Historical Water Use Estimates*, www.twdb.texas.gov/waterplanning/waterusesurvey/estimates. Texans need to know how their aquifers respond to pumping and drought. Recognizing the importance of this knowledge, the state has formalized its water planning to include an analysis of current and future groundwater supplies and resources. *See* Tex. Water Code § 16.053; see also Chapter 21 of this book. The state has enhanced its planning for groundwater management by requiring groundwater conservation districts to develop desired future conditions for their groundwater resources. *See* Tex. Water Code § 36.108(d); see also Chapter 16 of this book. Desired future conditions significantly influence projections in regional and state water planning; therefore, groundwater availability models play an important role. This chapter provides a background for how groundwater availability models are made, what the groundwater availability modeling program is, who is required to use groundwater availability models, and how groundwater availability modeling information can be used.

If you have ever watched the weather on television, you have undoubtedly heard the meteorologist refer to weather models—for example, "If the models are correct, thunderstorms are going to pass through here at about three o'clock tomorrow afternoon." The meteorologists' forecasts,

---

1. Robert Mace is the executive director and chief water policy officer at The Meadows Center for Water and the Environment and a professor of practice in the Department of Geography at Texas State University. He has a BS in geophysics and an MS in hydrology from the New Mexico Institute of Mining and Technology and a PhD in hydrogeology from the University of Texas at Austin. Robert worked at the Texas Water Development Board for eighteen years before joining Texas State University.

2. Cindy Ridgeway is the manager of the Groundwater Availability Modeling department at the Texas Water Development Board. She has a BS in geology with a minor in earth sciences from Tarleton State University, graduated summa cum laude, and an MS in geology from Baylor University. She has worked for over twenty years at the Texas Water Development Board.

3. Daryn Hardwick is a member of the Groundwater Availability Modeling department at the Texas Water Development Board. He has a BS in geography (physical environment) from the University of Wisconsin-Stevens Point, an MS in geography (geographic information science) from Saint Cloud State University, and a PhD in geography (geographic ecology) from the University of Oklahoma.

based on their computer models, predict how fronts may move over time, where rain might fall, and when weather changes might occur. These weather models are based on the physics of the atmosphere and how air flows relative to high- and low-pressure systems, among other influences. Numerical groundwater flow models are like weather models except that they are made by modelers trained in the science of hydrogeology instead of meteorology, they are guided by groundwater physics instead of atmospheric physics, and they forecast for periods of many years instead of days. Meteorologists predict the aboveground rain; groundwater modelers predict the underground rain—the rain that leaked into the aquifer days or many years ago.

If you have ever used the weather forecast to plan your activities for the weekend, then you have benefited from modeling. For example, if you are planning a picnic for Saturday, there is a good chance that you are religiously following the weather forecasts. Just as weather models are useful for planning, so are groundwater models. If you are planning to build a large well field, you probably want a forecast about whether the aquifer can support additional pumping. If you are a groundwater conservation district or a nearby landowner, you probably want to know how that pumping is going to affect the groundwater in the area. Without models, these predictions are difficult to make, especially with complicated aquifers and pumping scenarios.

Numerical groundwater flow modeling is a valuable tool for better understanding groundwater flow in aquifers and in managing groundwater resources. Numerical models are one of the few tools available that consider a complex array of aquifer variables and allow these variables to interact with one another. Exploring these interactions with a model can reveal how an aquifer behaves. A model can also be used to make predictions for managing groundwater resources, such as estimating how water levels and spring flows respond to increased pumping.

Regional groundwater flow models can be roughly divided into two types: scientific and management. The purpose of scientific models is to better understand how water flows in the aquifer and to test ideas about how the aquifer works. Management models are generally used to make predictions or test management scenarios. In many cases, management models build on previously completed scientific models. However, management models may increase considerably the understanding of an aquifer just as scientific models may help with managing aquifers. It is not uncommon to develop models with a dual purpose: to better understand the aquifer and to develop a tool for management.

Groundwater flow models have been developed for Texas's aquifers for more than fifty years. One of the earliest groundwater models in Texas was an electric-analog model (using resistors and capacitors!) developed in 1965 for the Gulf Coast Aquifer in the Houston area. *See* L.A. Wood & R.K. Gabrysch, *Analog-Model Study of Ground Water in the Houston District, Texas*, Texas Water Commission Bulletin 6508 (1965); Figure 1. An electric-analog model is based on the fact that the mathematical forms of the equations that govern the flow of electricity are the same as those that govern the flow of groundwater. One of the earliest *numerical* groundwater flow models in Texas was developed in 1970 for the Ogallala Aquifer near Lubbock. *See* B.J. Claborn et al., *Numerical Model of the Ogallala as a Management Tool, in Ogallala Aquifer Symposium*, Texas Tech University, International Center for Arid and Semi-Arid Land Studies, Special Report Number 39, at 89–110 (R.B. Mattox & J.D. Miller eds., 1970). A few aquifers have had several different models developed for them. For example, at least sixteen models have been developed for the Ogallala Aquifer in Texas (*see* R.E. Mace & A.R. Dutton, *Numerical Modeling of Ground-Water Flow in the Ogallala Aquifer in Texas, in Sociedad Mexicana de la Ciencia del Suelo, Memoria del Simposio Internacional de Aguas Subterráneas*, at 98–109 (J.Z. Castellanos et al. eds., 1998); A.R. Dutton & R.E. Mace, *Evolución de los Modelos Numéricos de Flujo de Agua Subterránea en el Acuífero de Ogallala en Texas*, 19 Revista Mexicana de Ciencias Geológicas 2, at 107–20 (2002)), and at least fifteen models have been developed for the Edwards Aquifer. Several models were developed for the same aquifer to accommodate different geographic regions and different purposes, and to reflect better modeling techniques, better understanding of the aquifers, and increased computer capabilities. Models tend to

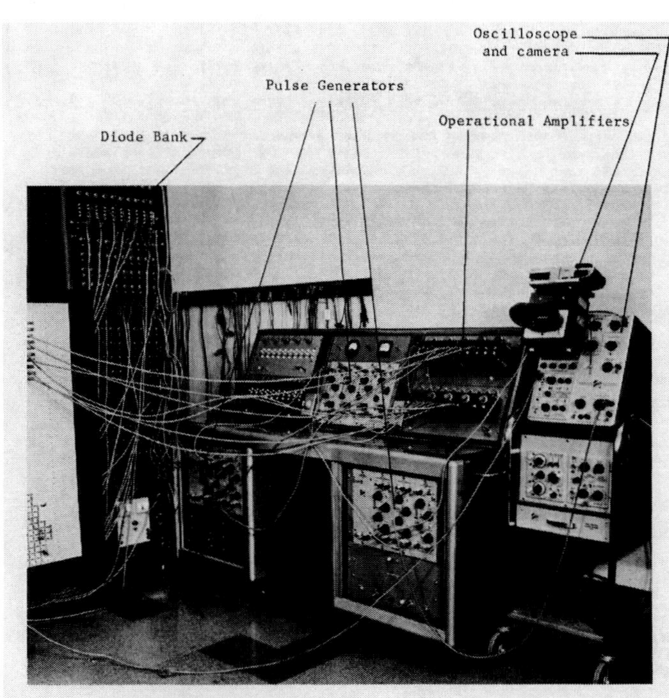

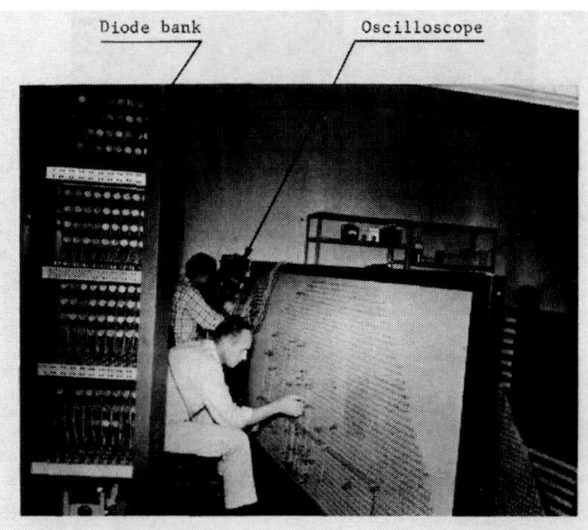

Figure 1. Photographs of an electric-analog model of the Gulf Coast Aquifer in the Houston area (from Wood and Gabrysch, 1965).

be transitory tools that improve existing models or are superseded by better models in response to additional or improved information on the aquifer or superior computing power and programs.

The Texas Water Development Board (TWDB) pioneered the development of management models for the state's aquifers with models for—

1. the San Antonio segment of the Edwards Aquifer (*see* W.B. Klemt et al., *Ground-Water Resources and Model Applications for the Edwards (Balcones Fault Zone) Aquifer in the San Antonio Region, Texas*, Texas Department of Water Resources Report 239 (1979));

2. the Ogallala Aquifer (*see* T.R. Knowles et al., *Evaluating the Ground-Water Resources of the High Plains of Texas*, Texas Department of Water Resources, Final Report LP-173 (1982); T.R. Knowles et al., *Evaluating the Ground-Water Resources of the High Plains of Texas*, Texas Department of Water Resources Report 288 (1984); T.R. Knowles, *Assessment of the Ground-Water Resources of the Texas High Plains, in Ogallala Aquifer Symposium II: Texas Tech University Water Resources Center, Proceedings*, at 217–37 (G.A. Whetstone ed., 1984)); and

3. the Gulf Coast Aquifer System (*see* W.R. Meyer & J.E. Carr, *A Digital Model for Simulation of Ground-Water Hydrology in the Houston Area, Texas*, Texas Department of Water Resources LP-103 (1979); J.E. Carr et al., *Digital Models for Simulation of Ground-Water Hydrology of the Chicot and Evangeline Aquifers along the Gulf Coast of Texas*, Texas Department of Water Resources Report 289 (1985)).

The U.S. Geological Survey has developed many of the scientific models in the state, including models for—

1. the Ogallala Aquifer (*see* R.R. Luckey, *The High Plains Regional Aquifer-Flow System Simulation of the Central and Northern High Plains*, *in Ogallala Aquifer Symposium II: Texas Tech University Water Resources Center*, *Proceedings*, at 48–66 (G.A. Whetstone ed., 1984); R.R. Luckey et al., *Digital Simulation of Ground-Water Flow in the High Plains Aquifer in Parts of Colorado, Kansas, Nebraska, New Mexico, Oklahoma, South Dakota, Texas, and Wyoming*, U.S. Geological Survey Professional Paper 1400-D (1986));

2. the Edwards Aquifer (*see* R.M. Slade et al., *Simulation of the Flow System of Barton Springs and Associated Edwards Aquifer in the Austin Area, Texas*, U.S. Geological Survey Water-Resources Investigations Report 85-4299 (1985); R.W. Maclay & L.F. Land, *Simulation of Flow in the Edwards Aquifer, San Antonio Region, Texas, and Refinements of Storage and Flow Concepts*, U.S. Geological Survey Report Water-Supply Paper 2336-A (1988));

3. the Gulf Coast Aquifer (*see* P.D. Ryder, *Hydrogeology and Predevelopment Flow in the Texas Gulf Coast Aquifer Systems*, U.S. Geological Survey Water-Resources Investigations Report 87-4248 (1988));

4. the Carrizo-Wilcox Aquifer (*see* Ryder); and

5. the Edwards-Trinity (Plateau) Aquifer (*see* E.L. Kuniansky & K.Q. Holligan, *Simulations of Flow in the Edwards-Trinity Aquifer System and Contiguous Hydraulically Connected Units, West-Central Texas*, U.S. Geological Survey Water-Resources Investigations Report 93-4039 (1994)).

More recently, the U.S. Geological Survey has used scientific models that can also be used as management tools. *See, e.g.*, L.K. Brakefield et al., *Updated Numerical Model with Uncertainty Assessment of 1950–56 Drought Conditions on Brackish-Water Movement within the Edwards Aquifer, San Antonio Region, Texas*, U.S. Geological Survey Scientific Investigations Report 2015-5081 (2015); M.C. Kasmarek, *Hydrogeology and Simulation of Groundwater Flow and Land-Surface Subsidence in the Northern Part of the Gulf Coast Aquifer System, Texas, 1891–2009*, U.S. Geological Survey Scientific Investigations Report 2012-5154 (2012); B.R. Clark et al., *Simulation of Groundwater Flow in the Edwards-Trinity and Related Aquifers in the Pecos County Region, Texas*, U.S. Geological Survey Scientific Investigations Report 2013-5228 (2013).

In 1998, the TWDB initiated work on a management model of the Hill Country part of the Trinity Aquifer and a modeling process that would become the template for the groundwater availability modeling program in Texas. *See* R.E. Mace et al., *Groundwater Availability of the Middle Trinity Aquifer, Hill Country Area, Texas—Numerical Simulations through 2050*, Texas Water Development Board Report 353 (2000). Groundwater availability models are computer-based, three-dimensional, numerical groundwater flow models to simulate groundwater flow systems at a regional scale. The models estimate current and future trends in the amount of water available for use from an aquifer. Because the groundwater availability models simulate large areas, these models allow users to see the big picture and understand groundwater flow through all or large parts of an aquifer. These models differ from the other groundwater flow models developed by the TWDB and others in that they involve substantial stakeholder involvement, are standardized, are publicly available, and are designed to be updated in the future.

Groundwater availability models are a critical part of groundwater management in Texas. The models are used by groundwater conservation districts, regional water planning groups (see Chapter 20 of this book), and others to evaluate the amount of groundwater available for use and the potential effects of pumping and drought on the state's aquifers. Groundwater availability models will be an important tool for groundwater conservation districts in evaluating desired future conditions and managing modeled available groundwater, which greatly influence projections of groundwater availability in regional and state water plans. *See* R.E. Mace et al., *A Streetcar Named Desired Future Conditions: The New Groundwater Availability for Texas*, *in The Changing Face of Water Rights in Texas* (State Bar of Texas 2006). See Chapter 21 of this book for a discussion of groundwater management area joint planning, desired future conditions, and modeled available groundwater.

II. The Birds and the Bees of Groundwater Modeling

§ 19.2 The Basics of Groundwater Modeling

Creating a regional groundwater flow model is complicated and time consuming. A tremendous amount of information is compiled, processed, and interpreted. Important decisions are made about what is important to model, what is not important to model, and what assumptions to make. Fortunately, there is a standard recipe that groundwater modelers follow when creating a model. This recipe includes (1) defining the purpose, (2) developing the conceptual model, (3) building the model architecture, and (4) calibrating the model. *See, e.g.*, M.P. Anderson et al., *Applied Groundwater Modeling—Simulation of Flow and Advective Transport* (Academic Press 2d ed. 2015). After a groundwater model is completed, it can be used to make predictions.

§ 19.3 Purpose

Defining the purpose of the model is important because it guides how large the model needs to be and what physical phenomena need to be considered. The stated purpose helps to define the focus of the model. For example, if you decide to build a house, your architect will want to know how you will use the house. Do you have six kids? Are you an empty nester? Do you frequently entertain? A house with lots of kids will generally be very different from a house with two adults who party all the time. The same is true of groundwater models. If the purpose of the model is to predict the effects of regional pumping on water levels, it will be a much larger model than if the purpose is to predict water level declines around a few wells. The purpose of the model is also tied to what you want to better understand or predict. A model developed to simulate the effects of regional pumping is very different from a model developed to predict the movement of contaminants beneath a gas station.

§ 19.4 Conceptual Model

The conceptual model is a description of the groundwater modeler's best understanding of how water moves into, through, and out of the aquifer. Instead of a computer model, it is an intellectual model—a model in the modeler's head of how the aquifer works. In developing the conceptual model, the modeler must compile, organize, and describe the information necessary for building the numerical model. The conceptual model includes information on (1) hydrostratigraphy (What are the aquifers and aquitards?); (2) framework (Where are the aquifers and aquitards located underground?); (3) water levels and regional groundwater flow (Where is the water table, what are the water pressures, and where is the water going?); (4) recharge (How much water is coming into the aquifer?); (5) rivers, streams, lakes, gulfs, and springs (How does the aquifer interact with surface water?); (6) hydraulic properties (How easily can water move through the aquifers and aquitards?); (7) water quality (How good is the water?); (8) cross-formational flow (How much water flows into and out of the aquifer from neighboring geologic formations?); and (9) discharge (How much water is being pumped? How much water flows to rivers, streams, lakes, and springs?).

To develop this conceptual model, modelers examine previous research, including earlier modeling efforts on the aquifer. In addition, the modeler often collects new information. Once this information is compiled, the modeler will evaluate the information and develop his best idea about how water enters, flows through, and exits the aquifer. The modeler usually makes assumptions about the aquifer, generally based on similar aquifers or the currently accepted scientific idea on how a hydrologic phenomenon works. When the modeler has a reasonable and defensible conceptual model, he can start to work on building the numerical model.

§ 19.5 Model Architecture

Model architecture refers to the nuts and bolts of how a model is put together. Just as an office building is assembled as a gridwork of offices or office "cells," a model is assembled as a gridwork of model cells with each cell representing a piece of the aquifer. When an office building is put up, it is built from blueprints and an architectural plan. Numerical groundwater models are built from the conceptual model, the hydrogeologic blueprint of the aquifer.

The groundwater modeler has many important decisions to make. Which aquifer layers will be modeled? How big is the model? How big should the cells be? How will the aquifer layers be modeled? How will recharge, springs, rivers, lakes, and pumping be numerically represented in the model? At what time in the past should the model start simulating the aquifer? To make the model simpler and more manageable, the modeler sometimes makes assumptions that certain aspects of the aquifer are not important enough to include in the model. As the modeler makes these decisions, the rough shell of the model begins to appear.

§ 19.6 Calibration

If the conceptual model were perfect and all the properties everywhere in the aquifer were known, the model would not need to be calibrated. This rarely, if ever, happens, especially with regional groundwater flow models, because the conceptual model is generally a simplification of the real world and all the properties everywhere in the aquifer are not known. Therefore, groundwater modelers perform a calibration. Calibration is the process by which parameters in the model are adjusted within realistic ranges (as defined during the development of the conceptual model) to get the model to reproduce measured values of historical water levels, spring flows, or other hydrologic information. The calibration process is like taking a shower. Let's say you get into the shower and the water is too hot. What do you do? You either turn down the hot water or turn up the cold water. Now let's say, after your adjustment, the shower is too cold. You keep adjusting until the temperature of the water is within an acceptable range. In other words, you calibrate the temperature of the shower by adjusting the hot and cold water until you reach the desired temperature. Calibrating a model is similar. For example, if water levels in the model are too low compared to measured values, you might increase the recharge in the model to raise the water levels to be more acceptable.

Model calibration rarely, if ever, results in a perfect fit of measured water levels, spring flows, and other hydrologic information. For example, if you have adjusted the recharge to calibrate the model, the water levels in some cells may be higher than measured values and the water levels in other cells may be lower. The differences between the measured values and the simulated values represent the error of the model. The reason calibrated models never exactly match measured values is because the groundwater model is an approximation of reality; everything about the aquifer is not known. Approximations are not perfect. Models can, however, be finely adjusted to perfectly match measured information in a process called over-calibration. Paradoxically, calibrated models that perfectly match measured information tend to be worse predictors of the future than calibrated models that do not perfectly match measured information. This is because an over-calibrated model makes assumptions and assigns model parameters, such as recharge and hydraulic properties, with no supporting information.

Making assumptions is like being up in a tree and starting to climb out on a limb. The more assumptions you make, the farther out on a limb you are. With over-calibration, you are making many assumptions not supported by the data—you are no longer climbing out on a limb, you are balancing on a twig! Good groundwater modelers calibrate only as far as their data and science-based assumptions will let them go, and no farther.

Groundwater models are usually first calibrated to steady state conditions. This is when flow into the aquifer, such as recharge from rain, is balanced with flow out of the aquifer, such as the aquifer discharging groundwater to springs or streams. Steady state or predevelopment conditions represent what the aquifer looked like before there was extensive pumping in the aquifer. After the model has been calibrated in this manner, the model is calibrated to reproduce water levels and water level changes and spring flows and spring flow changes in response to pumping and recharge since predevelopment times. Once the model is calibrated, the model is done and ready to predict the future.

§ 19.7 Predictions

After a model is calibrated, it can be used to predict how water levels and spring flows might respond to future pumping and drought. Modelers can then put projections of pumping and recharge into the model and run the model to get the answers. Modelers call this a "model run."

The accuracy of the prediction depends on how well you can project pumping and recharge into the future and how accurately the model represents the aquifer. Even if you know everything about the aquifer and have a perfectly calibrated model, the model will not give an accurate prediction if the projections of pumping and recharge are not accurate. For example, if you had a perfect model and projected 10,000 units of pumping when it turns out that people pumped only 5,000 units, the perfect model would not give the correct answer. One might say that the model was not really a good model; however, this would not be correct. The model was fine; the projection was inaccurate, resulting in an inaccurate model run.

In reality, the model prediction answered a "what if" question. What if 10,000 units of water were pumped from the aquifer? Other model runs could be easily done (for example, what if 7,000 units of water were pumped from the aquifer? What about 15,000 units?). This is the power of groundwater models: once they are developed, it is relatively easy to perform model runs with different projections of pumping and other parameters such as recharge and lake levels.

Alternatively, the projection may be perfect but the model flawed, leading to an incorrect prediction. Since no model is perfect, it is unlikely that a model will return a perfect prediction. The real question is: How accurate might the prediction be?

Some models or, for that matter, some predictions may be more accurate than others. Let's say the nurse rolls you into an operating room for brain surgery and gives you the choice of two surgeons: one who has performed a number of other surgeries, is well educated about brain surgery, but has not yet performed a brain surgery, and another who has performed a number of other surgeries, is well educated about brain surgery, and has successfully performed brain surgery a hundred times. Which surgeon would you prefer? Unless the brain damage you have suffered is clouding your judgment, you are going to go with experience.

Sometimes models used for predictive runs are like the brain surgeon who has successfully performed brain surgery a hundred times. For example, policymakers often debate about how to manage the Edwards Aquifer in the San Antonio region. Policy decisions often revolve around whether a management scheme causes Comal Springs and San Marcos Springs to go dry. The groundwater model for the Edwards Aquifer in the San Antonio region was calibrated to water levels and spring flows from 1939 to 2000, including a period during the 1950s when Comal Springs stopped flowing. Therefore, in its calibration the model has real-life "experience" in simulating when the springs go dry. This "experience" does not guarantee that the model can make accurate predictions (there are still a number of assumptions in the model and in the projections of pumping and recharge), but it does provide greater confidence that the model can predict when the springs go dry.

A little north is the Edwards Aquifer in the Austin area. Similar to the San Antonio area, policy decisions often revolve around whether a management scheme causes springs to go dry—in this case, Barton Springs. However, unlike Comal Springs, Barton Springs has not gone dry in recorded history. Therefore, the calibrated model does not have the benefit of "experiencing" the springs going dry. Like the well-educated surgeon who has not yet performed his first brain surgery, the well-calibrated model has not experienced the springs going dry. This is not to say that the model will not make an accurate or nearly accurate prediction of when the springs will go dry, but there is not as much confidence in the predictions as in the model for the San Antonio segment.

In most cases, groundwater models are like well-educated surgeons who have yet to perform their first brain surgery: the models are asked to do something they haven't experienced yet. Generally, the models have some experience, such as past water level declines and spring flow declines, which is used to calibrate them. When these models are used for predictive simulations, the groundwater modeler is assuming that the conceptual model and calibration used to develop the model also apply in the future under new conditions. A good modeler will take a close look at what the model is doing when it is asked to go where it has not been yet, such as when it simulates how the aquifer is interacting with surface water features or other aquifers. For example, if a large well field is placed in an area that has not previously experienced large water level declines, the modeler will look at the model to see how it interacts with aquifer boundaries such as streams, bordering layers, and artificial boundaries to make sure the model is still realistic. If the model is not realistic, it either cannot be used to evaluate the problem or cannot be used until it is modified to improve its performance.

§ 19.8 Limitations

All models have limitations. Just because a model makes a simulation does not mean that it should be used to make that simulation. Each model has a "comfort zone" within which it can be expected to reasonably reproduce reality. This comfort zone is often defined by the purpose of the model, the certainty of the conceptual model, the quality of the calibration, and how realistically the model behaves during predictive runs. Models cannot be used outside of their defined purpose. For example, a model developed with the purpose of simulating regional groundwater flow is unlikely to be useful for simulating contaminant transport beneath a gas station. The certainty of the conceptual model can also limit the applicability or certainty of a model. For example, uncertainty about recharge rates limits the accuracy of a model if a predictive simulation stretches the limits of the aquifer as represented in the model. The use of the model may also be limited by how well the model simulates the past. For example, if the question at hand requires accuracy down to one foot of water level change but the model has an average error of ten feet, the model is not an appropriate tool to address that question. How a model behaves during a predictive run is also important to consider when assessing limitations. For example, a model may behave realistically during calibration and for predictive simulations with modest increases in pumping; however, large increases in pumping may cause unrealistic hydrologic behavior in the model. In all cases, the judgment of an experienced modeler is needed to carefully evaluate whether the model is an appropriate tool for the task at hand.

III. The Groundwater Availability Modeling Program

§ 19.9 The GAM Program

The groundwater availability modeling program initiated by the TWDB set out to develop or obtain numerical groundwater flow models of the major and minor aquifers of the state. See Plate 6, Major Aquifers of Texas, and Plate 7, Minor Aquifers of Texas. *See* Texas Water Development Board, *Groundwater Availability Models*, www.twdb.texas.gov/groundwater/models/gam/index.asp. The legislature quickly recognized the importance of groundwater models, particularly after regional water planning came into existence in 1997. In Senate Bill 2, the 77th Legislature directed that section 16.012 of the Texas Water Code be amended to require the executive administrator of the TWDB to "obtain or develop groundwater availability models for major and minor aquifers in coordination with groundwater conservation districts and regional water planning groups." *See* Act of June 15, 2001, 77th Leg., R.S., ch. 966, § 2.15.

A unique aspect of the groundwater availability modeling program is the involvement of interested parties, or stakeholders. These parties include groundwater conservation districts, regional water planning groups, consultants, river authorities, environmental groups, state agencies, water suppliers, and other interested citizens. By including public involvement in the modeling process, the groundwater availability modeling program can address or incorporate the local constituents' ideas, data, and concerns about the aquifer. For example, groundwater conservation districts routinely provide additional information on geology, water levels, and springs to assist in modeling, in addition to operating assumptions for predictive scenarios.

Some of the larger or more complex aquifers require more than one model, while some models incorporate a combination of aquifers. As required by law, the TWDB developed or obtained the initial versions of seventeen groundwater availability models for the state's nine major aquifers before October 1, 2004. See Plate 6, Major Aquifers of Texas. These nine aquifers currently supply approximately 95 percent of the groundwater produced in the state. Since then, the TWDB has developed or adopted thirty-six additional models as well as a number of additions and enhancements to the existing models.

Some of the initial models came from external cooperators, such as El Paso Water Utilities, the Edwards Aquifer Authority, and the U.S. Geological Survey. The initial model for the northern part of the Gulf Coast Aquifer was supported jointly by the TWDB, the U.S. Geological Survey, the Harris-Galveston Coastal Subsidence District, and the Fort Bend Subsidence District.

This model was later updated in 2013 by the U.S. Geological Survey in cooperation with the Harris-Galveston Subsidence District, the Fort Bend Subsidence District, and the Lone Star Groundwater Conservation District. This model is currently being updated again by the U.S. Geological Survey in cooperation with the Harris-Galveston Subsidence District.

Updating and improving these initial models are vital components of the groundwater availability modeling program. The models are meant to be "living tools" that can be updated as new information becomes available, adapted to reflect changing aquifer conditions, or refined to better address the needs and concerns of the groups using them. To accommodate the ongoing needs of the groundwater conservation districts, planning groups, regional water suppliers, and other model users, the TWDB has adopted or developed a total of fifty-three models, of which twenty-eight are currently used. Eighteen models and seven alternative models have been retired. Alternative models were also developed to meet certain needs and therefore did not include stakeholder input.

Currently, the TWDB is working on modeling the remaining minor aquifers in Texas. Thus far, eighteen of the minor aquifers are included in existing groundwater availability models. See Plate 7, Minor Aquifers of Texas. Work has already begun on the remaining three minor aquifers not yet modeled: the Blossom, Marathon, and Cross Timbers aquifers.

All the initially completed models for the major aquifers used MODFLOW-96 (*see* A.W. Harbaugh & M.G. McDonald, *User's Documentation for MODFLOW-96, an Update to the U.S. Geological Survey Modular Finite-Difference Ground-Water Flow Model*, U.S. Geological Survey Open-File Report 96-485 (1996)), MODFLOW 2000 (*see* A.W. Harbaugh et al., MODFLOW-2000, *the U.S. Geological Survey Modular Ground-Water Model—User Guide to Modularization Concepts and the Ground-Water Flow Process*, U.S. Geological Survey Open-File Report 00-92 (2000)). Most of the models for the minor aquifers or model updates to the major aquifers use more robust variations of the MODFLOW code. All models use MODFLOW modules that are freely available (that is, no proprietary modules are used). Initially the final models (including supporting graphics) were compatible with *Processing MODFLOW for Windows (PMWIN)* version 5 or later (*see* W.H. Chiang & W. Kinzelbach, *Processing Modflow—A Simulation System for Modeling Groundwater Flow and Pollution* (1998)), a proprietary pre- and post-processor to MODFLOW. Beginning in 2006, the preferred pre- and post-processor to MODFLOW was changed to Groundwater Vistas (*see* J.O. Rumbaugh & D.B. Rumbaugh, *Guide to Using Groundwater Vistas Version 4* (Environmental Simulations, Inc. 2020)).

IV. Who Is Required to Use Groundwater Availability Models?

§ 19.10 Requirement to Use Groundwater Availability Models

Regional water planning groups are required to use modeled available groundwater values for groundwater availability. *See* Tex. Water Code § 36.1071(e)(3)(A). In addition, groundwater conservation districts are required by statute to use groundwater availability modeling information, when it is available, in developing their management plans. *See* Tex. Water Code §§ 36.1071(e)(3)(E), (h), 36.108(d); also see Chapters 16 and 21 of this book. More specifically, groundwater availability models and the data used to develop the models are useful tools for evaluating some of the parameters currently required in management plans, such as—

- the annual amount of recharge from precipitation, if any, to the groundwater resources within the district (Tex. Water Code § 36.1071(e)(3)(C));
- the annual volume of water that discharges to springs and any surface water bodies, including lakes, streams, and rivers (Tex. Water Code § 36.1071(e)(3)(D)); and
- the annual volume of flow into and out of the district within each aquifer and between aquifers in the district (Tex. Water Code § 36.1071(e)(3)(E)).

Groundwater conservation districts are also required to consider information from groundwater availability models when they develop desired future conditions for their aquifers as part of joint planning in groundwater management areas. *See* Tex. Water Code § 36.108(d); see also Chapter 21 of this book. For example, before voting on the proposed desired future conditions for a relevant aquifer within a groundwater management area, the groundwater conservation districts consider the total estimated recoverable storage, provided by the executive administrator of the TWDB, along with the other factors listed in Water Code section 36.108. The desired future conditions of an aquifer are the quantified conditions of groundwater resources at a specified time or times in the future or in perpetuity as identified by groundwater conservation districts in a groundwater management area. *See* Tex. Water Code § 36.108. The TWDB uses groundwater availability models to calculate or verify modeled available groundwater based on the desired future conditions of aquifers as identified by the groundwater conservation districts. Groundwater conservation districts are then required to include the modeled available groundwater value in their management plan and to consider it when permitting. *See* Tex. Water Code § 36.1132. Although groundwater conservation districts are required to consider groundwater availability modeling information, the choice of how to manage an aquifer still lies with groundwater conservation districts, as defined in the desired future conditions.

V. How Can Groundwater Availability Modeling Information Be Used?

§ 19.11 Use of GAM Information

There are two primary types of groundwater availability modeling information: the model itself and the information in the model. The model can be used to predict water levels and flows in response to pumping and drought. For example, if a large new well field is planned, the groundwater availability models can be used to predict possible effects of the well field on regional water levels in the aquifer. The models are not intended to be used for analysis of an individual well because of the regional scale of the models. The information inside a groundwater availability model is also very useful. For example, groundwater availability models include information on recharge, aquifer geometry (depth and thickness), and aquifer properties (transmissivity, hydraulic conductivity, storativity, and water levels). Aquifer geometry and property information is used to calculate water in storage and drawdown around individual wells. The TWDB uses the aquifer geometry, aquifer properties, and water levels when developing the volumes of estimated recoverable storage for the aquifers; *see* Tex. Water Code § 36.108(d). See also Chapter 21 of this book.

Groundwater availability models are also used to evaluate desired future conditions and estimate modeled available groundwater. For example, groundwater conservation districts might be considering a particular desired future condition, such as maintaining spring flows at 50 percent of current levels. The groundwater availability models can then be used to adjust pumping amounts until that desired future condition is reached in the model. The amount of pumping in the model that achieves this desired future condition is the estimate of the modeled available groundwater. The districts can then evaluate the modeled available groundwater number and adjust the desired future condition as appropriate. For instance, in the above example, let's say that the districts decide that the resulting modeled available groundwater number is not enough water for permitting. The districts can then revise their desired future condition (maintain spring flows at 40 percent of current levels) and use the model to reevaluate the modeled available groundwater. This iterative process is similar to defining consensus yield, a process that integrates policy and science throughout a stakeholder process. *See* R.E. Mace et al., *Estimating Groundwater Availability in Texas, in Water Allocation in Texas: The Legal Issues* (Texas Rural Water Association and Texas Water Conservation Association 2001). See also Chapter 21 of this book.

Here are two more examples of how groundwater availability modeling information can be used in evaluating desired future conditions:

1. The desired future condition of the aquifer is equal to some desired volume of water in the aquifer. For example, the desired future condition may be 50 percent of the water left in the aquifer after fifty years. Groundwater availability modeling information can be used to estimate the volume of water in an aquifer for a specified area at a specified time under specified conditions.

2. The desired future condition of the aquifer is equal to a water elevation, spring flow, or base flow level. For example, the desired future condition may be a minimum spring flow of ten cubic feet per second during a repeat of the drought of record. Groundwater availability modeling information can be used to assess the effects of pumping and drought on water levels, spring flow, and base flow. For example, the Barton Springs–Edwards Aquifer Conservation

District has used the groundwater availability model for its aquifer to assess the possible effects of increased pumping on water levels and spring flows.

Groundwater availability models are particularly suited to investigating the effects of large well fields, changes in pumping and pumping patterns, and changes in climate, such as droughts. Because they are regional models, groundwater availability models themselves cannot be used to accurately assess the impacts of individual wells. However, the collective effect of individual wells can be assessed. To predict water level declines around individual wells, groundwater availability models can be used in conjunction with analytical models. An example of an analytical model to evaluate drawdown versus time or drawdown versus distance from a pumping well is available at the TWDB website, www.twdb.texas.gov/groundwater/models/analytical/index.asp.

VI. Conclusion

§ 19.12 Conclusion

When you plan a picnic, you check the weather forecast for rain—weather predicted by models. Similarly, when you plan for your water resources, you check the aquifer forecast—water levels and spring flow changes predicted by regional groundwater flow models. Creating a regional groundwater flow model is complicated and time consuming; a tremendous amount of information must be compiled, processed, and interpreted. In developing a model, groundwater modelers (1) define the purpose (What will the model be used for?); (2) develop the conceptual model (What is our understanding of how the aquifer works?); (3) build the model architecture (How should the model be put together?); and (4) calibrate the model (How well can the model reproduce the past without making unsupported assumptions?). After a groundwater model is completed, it can be used to make predictions.

As required by statute, the TWDB initiated the groundwater availability modeling program to develop or obtain numerical groundwater flow models of the thirty major and minor aquifers of the state. Groundwater availability models are computer-based, three-dimensional, numerical groundwater flow models used to simulate groundwater flow systems on a regional scale. The models estimate current and future trends in the amount of water available for use from an aquifer. They can also be used to predict water levels and spring flows in response to different pumping and climate scenarios. In addition, they provide other important information, such as recharge values, estimates of total recoverable storage, and the location of the aquifer beneath the surface.

Groundwater conservation districts and regional water planning groups are required to use or consider groundwater availability models. Groundwater conservation districts are required by statute to use groundwater availability modeling information in developing their management plans and to consider the models when identifying the desired future conditions of their aquifers. The groundwater availability models are also tools to estimate modeled available groundwater. Regional water planning groups are required to include modeled available groundwater in their regional water plans.

The TWDB has developed or obtained groundwater availability models for all the major aquifers of the state and 86 percent of the minor aquifers. The groundwater availability models are "living tools" that are being updated as new information becomes available, adapted to reflect changing aquifer conditions, and refined to better address the needs and concerns of the groups using them. The TWDB currently is updating all the models that were developed using MODFLOW-96 and MODFLOW-2000 to more recently released and more robust modeling code.

Acknowledgments

We thank the staff of the Groundwater Availability Modeling Department and our stakeholders for many helpful conversations. We also thank Mr. John Ashworth, Ms. Mary Sahs, Ms. Merry Klonower, and Mr. Lynn Sherman for their comments on an early draft of the chapter.

References

Anderson, M.P., W.W. Woessner, and R.J. Hunt. 2015. *Applied groundwater modeling—Simulation of flow and advective transport*, 2d ed. San Diego, CA: Academic Press, 680 pp.

Brakefield, L.K., J.T. White, N.A. Houston, and J.V. Thomas. 2015. *Updated numerical model with uncertainty assessment of 1950–56 drought conditions on brackish-water movement within the Edwards aquifer, San Antonio Region, Texas*. U.S. Geological Survey Scientific Investigations Report 2015-5081, 54 pp.

Carr, J.E., W.R. Meyer, W.M. Sandeen, and I.R. McLane. 1985. *Digital models for simulation of ground-water hydrology of the Chicot and Evangeline aquifers along the Gulf Coast of Texas.* Texas Department of Water Resources Report 289, 101 pp.

Chiang, W.H., and W. Kinzelbach. 1998. *Processing MODFLOW—A simulation system for modeling groundwater flow and pollution: Software manual*, 325 pp.

Claborn, B.J., T.A. Austin, and D.M. Wells. 1970. *Numerical model of the Ogallala as a management tool, in* R.B. Mattox and W.D. Miller, eds., *Ogallala Aquifer Symposium.* Texas Tech University, International Center for Arid and Semi-Arid Land Studies, Special Report Number 39, pp. 89–110.

Clark, B.R., J.R. Bumgarner, N.A. Houston, and A.L. Foster. 2013. *Simulation of groundwater flow in the Edwards-Trinity and related aquifers in the Pecos County region, Texas*. U.S. Geological Survey Scientific Investigations Report 2013-5228, 56 pp.

Dutton, A.R., and R.E. Mace. 2002. *Evolución de los modelos numéricos de flujo de agua subterránea en el acuífero de Ogallala en Texas. Revista Mexicana de Ciencias Geológicas*, v. 19, núm. 2, pp. 107–20.

Harbaugh, A.W., E.R. Banta, M.C. Hill, and M.G. McDonald. 2000. *MODFLOW-2000, the U.S. Geological Survey modular ground-water model—User guide to modularization concepts and the ground-water flow process*. U.S. Geological Survey Open-File Report 00-92, 121 pp.

Harbaugh, A.W., and M.G. McDonald. 1996. *User's documentation for MODFLOW-96, an update to the U.S. Geological Survey modular finite-difference ground-water flow model.* U.S. Geological Survey Open-File Report 96-485, 56 pp.

Kasmarek, M.C. 2012. *Hydrogeology and simulation of groundwater flow and land-surface subsidence in the northern part of the Gulf Coast Aquifer system, Texas, 1891–2009*. U.S. Geological Survey Scientific Investigations Report 2012-5154, 55 pp.

Klemt, W.B., T.R. Knowles, G. Elder, and T. Sieh. 1979. *Ground-water resources and model applications for the Edwards (Balcones Fault Zone) Aquifer in the San Antonio region, Texas.* Texas Department of Water Resources Report 239, 88 pp.

Knowles, T. R. 1984. *Assessment of the ground-water resources of the Texas High Plains, in* G.A. Whetstone, ed., *Proceedings, Ogallala Aquifer Symposium II.* Texas Tech University Water Resources Center, pp. 217–37.

Knowles, T.R., P. Nordstrom, and W.B. Klemt. 1982. *Evaluating the ground-water resources of the High Plains of Texas.* Texas Department of Water Resources, Final Report LP-173, v. 1, 174 pp. + 46 plates.

———. 1984. *Evaluating the ground-water resources of the High Plains of Texas.* Texas Department of Water Resources Report 288, v. 1, 119 pp.

Kuniansky, E.L., and K.Q. Holligan. 1994. *Simulations of flow in the Edwards-Trinity Aquifer system and contiguous hydraulically connected units, west-central Texas.* U.S. Geological Survey Water-Resources Investigations Report 93-4039, 40 pp.

Luckey, R.R., 1984. *The High Plains regional aquifer-flow system simulation of the Central and Northern High Plains, in* G.A. Whetstone, ed., *Proceedings, Ogallala Aquifer Symposium II.* Texas Tech University Water Resources Center, pp. 48–66.

Luckey, R.R., E.D. Gutentag, F.J. Heimes, and J.B. Weeks. 1986. *Digital simulation of ground-water flow in the High Plains Aquifer in parts of Colorado, Kansas, Nebraska, New Mexico, Oklahoma, South Dakota, Texas, and Wyoming.* U.S. Geological Survey Professional Paper 1400-D, 57 pp.

Mace, R.E., A.H. Chowdhury, R. Anaya, and S.C. Way. 2000. *Groundwater availability of the middle Trinity Aquifer, Hill Country Area, Texas—Numerical simulations through 2050.* Texas Water Development Board Report 353, 117 pp.

Mace, R.E., and A.R. Dutton. 1998. *Numerical modeling of ground-water flow in the Ogallala Aquifer in Texas, in* J.Z. Castellanos, J.J. Carrillo, and C.H. Yañez, eds., *Sociedad Mexicana de la Ciencia del Suelo, Memoria del Simposio Internacional de Aguas Subterráneas.* León, Gto., México, pp. 98–109.

Mace, R.E., W.F. Mullican III, and T. (S.C.) Way. 2001. *Estimating groundwater availability in Texas, in Proceedings of the 1st Annual Texas Rural Water Association and Texas Water Conservation Association Water Law Seminar: Water Allocation in Texas: The Legal Issues.* Austin, Texas, January 25–26, 2001. Section 1, 16.

Mace, R.E., R. Petrossian, R. Bradley, and W.F. Mullican III. 2006. *A streetcar named desired future conditions: The new groundwater availability for Texas.* State Bar of Texas, 7th Annual *The Changing Face of Water Rights in Texas*, May 18–19, 2006, San Antonio, Texas, 21 pp.

Maclay, R.W., and L.F. Land. 1988. *Simulation of flow in the Edwards Aquifer, San Antonio Region, Texas, and refinements of storage and flow concepts.* U.S. Geological Survey Report Water-Supply Paper 2336-A, 48 pp.

Meyer, W.R., and J.E. Carr. 1979. *A digital model for simulation of ground-water hydrology in the Houston area, Texas.* Texas Department of Water Resources LP-103, 133 pp.

Rumbaugh, J.O., and D.B. Rumbaugh. 2020. *Guide to using Groundwater Vistas Version 8.* Environmental Simulations Inc., 517 pp.

Ryder, P.D. 1988. *Hydrogeology and predevelopment flow in the Texas Gulf Coast aquifer systems.* U.S. Geological Survey Water-Resources Investigations Report 87-4248, 109 pp.

Slade, R.M. Jr., L. Ruiz, and D. Slagle. 1985. *Simulation of the flow system of Barton Springs and associated Edwards Aquifer in the Austin area, Texas.* U.S. Geological Survey Water-Resources Investigations Report 85-4299, 19 pp.

Texas Water Development Board. 2017. *Water for Texas 2017*. Texas Water Development Board, 150 pp.

Wood, L.A., and R.K. Gabrysch. 1965. *Analog-model study of ground water in the Houston district, Texas.* Texas Water Commission Bulletin 6508, 103 pp.

Glossary

Aquifer—geologic materials that are capable of producing useful amounts of water.

Aquitard—geologic materials that are not capable of producing useful amounts of water.

Calibration—the process through which parameters in a model are adjusted within acceptable ranges to reproduce as accurately as possible observed behavior.

Confined aquifer—an aquifer that is capped by an aquitard and is fully saturated such that the water level in a well completed in the aquifer rises above the top of the aquifer.

Desired future conditions—the desired, quantified conditions of groundwater resources (such as water levels, water quality, spring flows, or volumes) within a management area at one or more specified future times as defined by participating groundwater conservation districts within a groundwater management area as part of the joint planning process. 31 Tex. Admin. Code § 356.10(6).

Hydraulic conductivity—the ease with which water can move through a unit area of geologic material. Hydraulic conductivity is equal to the transmissivity divided by the aquifer thickness.

Modeled available groundwater—the amount of water that the executive administrator determines may be produced on an average annual basis to achieve a desired future condition. 31 Tex. Admin. Code § 356.10(13).

Recharge—the water that reaches the water table of an aquifer. Tex. Water Code § 36.001(26).

Storativity—a hydrologic parameter that quantifies how much water is released or taken up by an aquifer for a change in water level.

Transmissivity—the ease with which water can move through a unit width of geologic material in an aquifer. Transmissivity is equal to the hydraulic conductivity multiplied by the aquifer thickness.

Unconfined aquifer—has a surface pressure equal to the atmosphere and has the water table as its upper boundary.

Water level—the position at which water in a well rests.

Water table—the surface to which water rises in an unconfined aquifer.

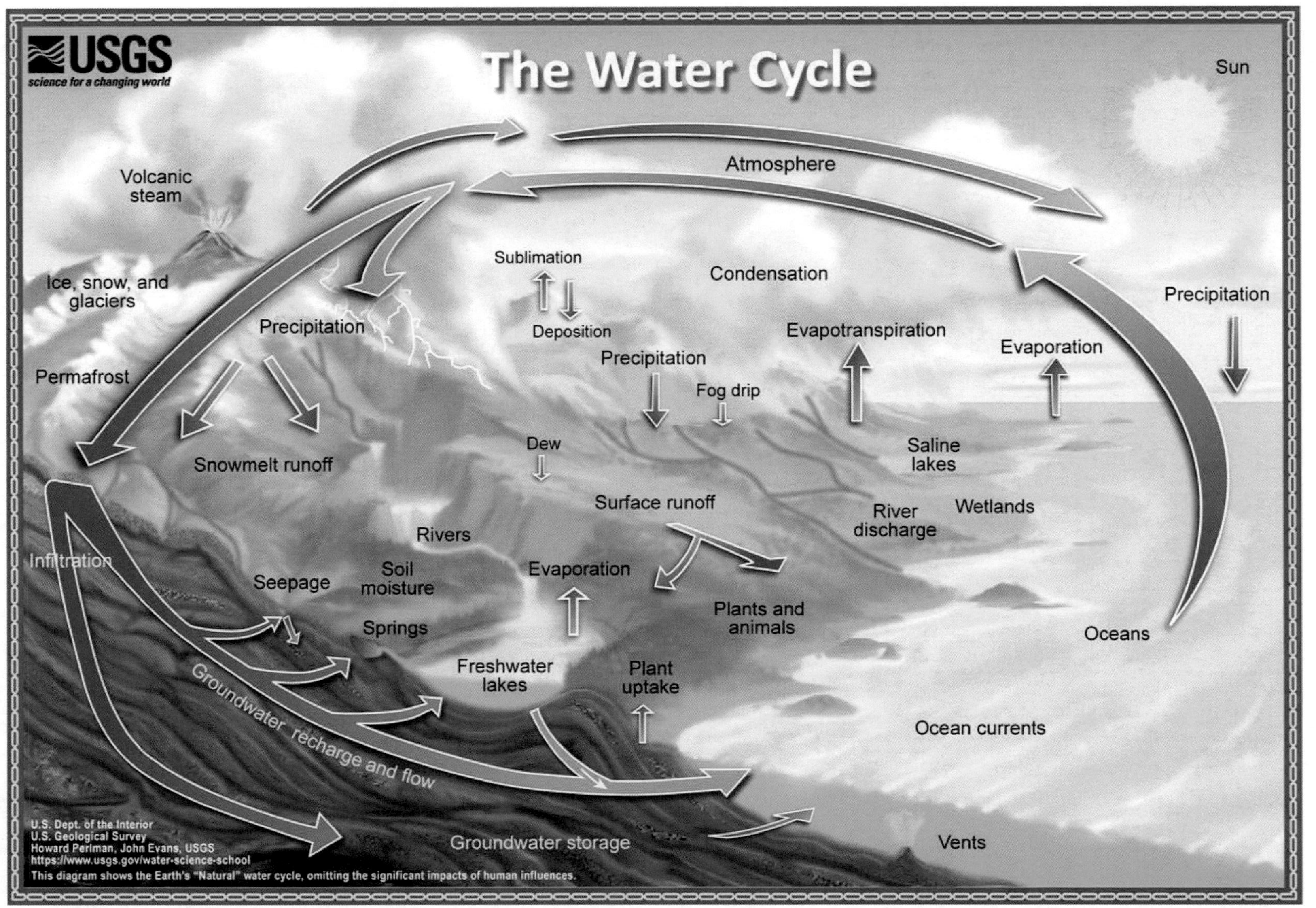

Plate 1. The Natural Water Cycle. U.S. Geological Survey, *Water Science School*, *The Natural Water Cycle*, www.usgs.gov/media/images/water-cycle-natural-water-cycle.

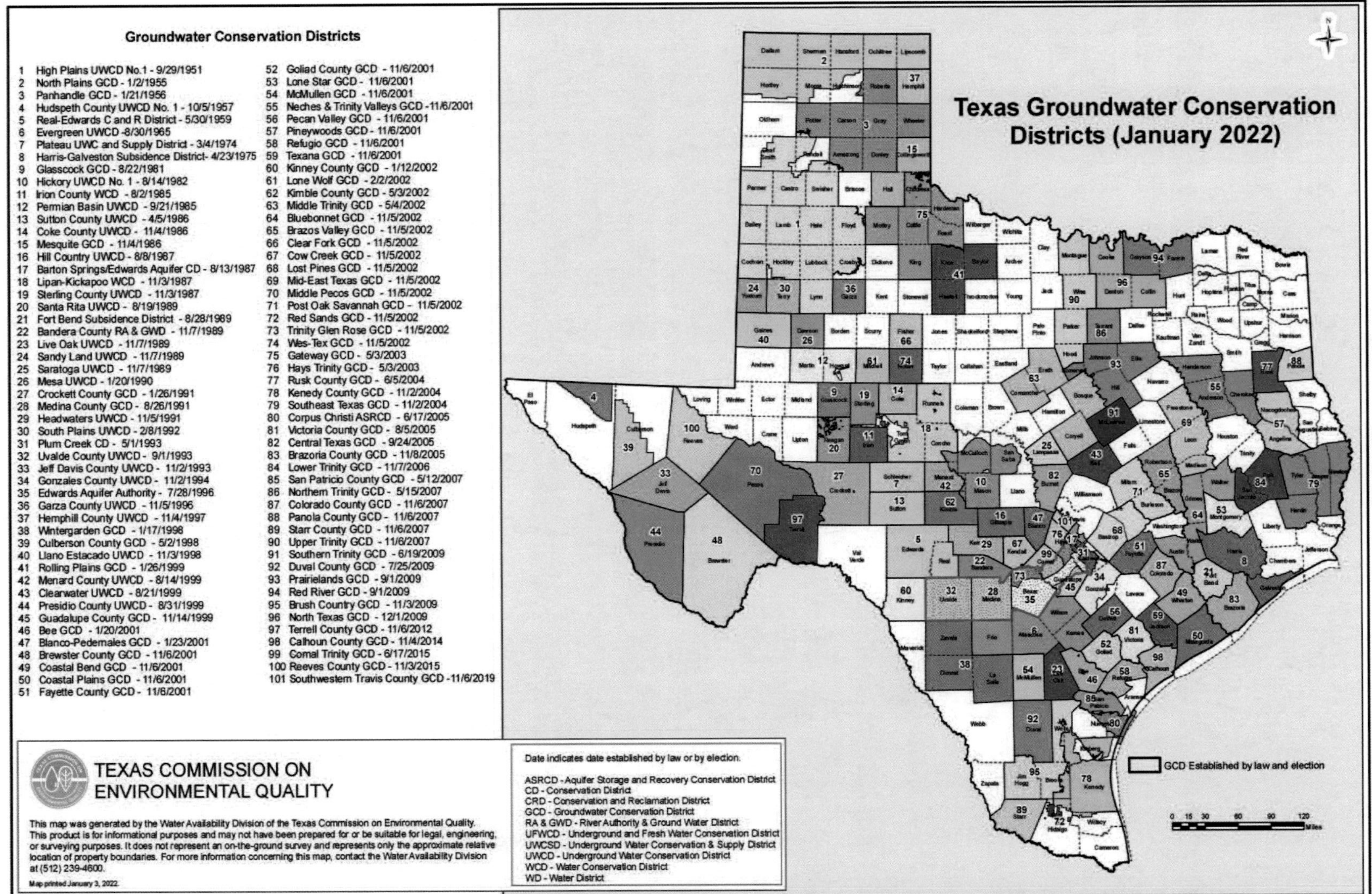

Plate 2. Texas Groundwater Conservation Districts. Texas Commission on Environmental Quality, www.tceq.texas.gov/groundwater/groundwater-planning-assessment/districts.html.

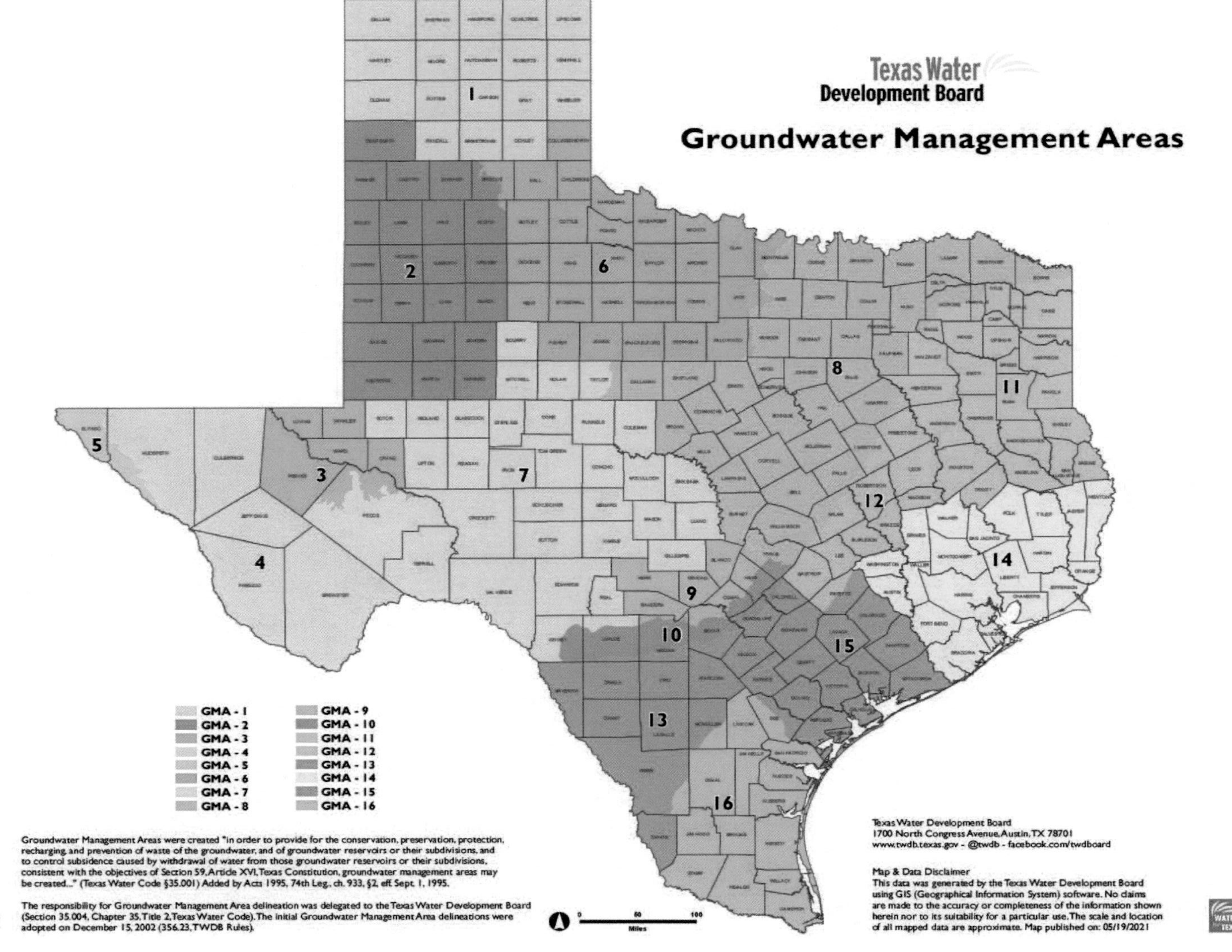

Plate 3. Groundwater Management Areas of Texas. Texas Water Development Board, https://tnris.org/maps/#twdb-groundwater-management-areas-(gma).

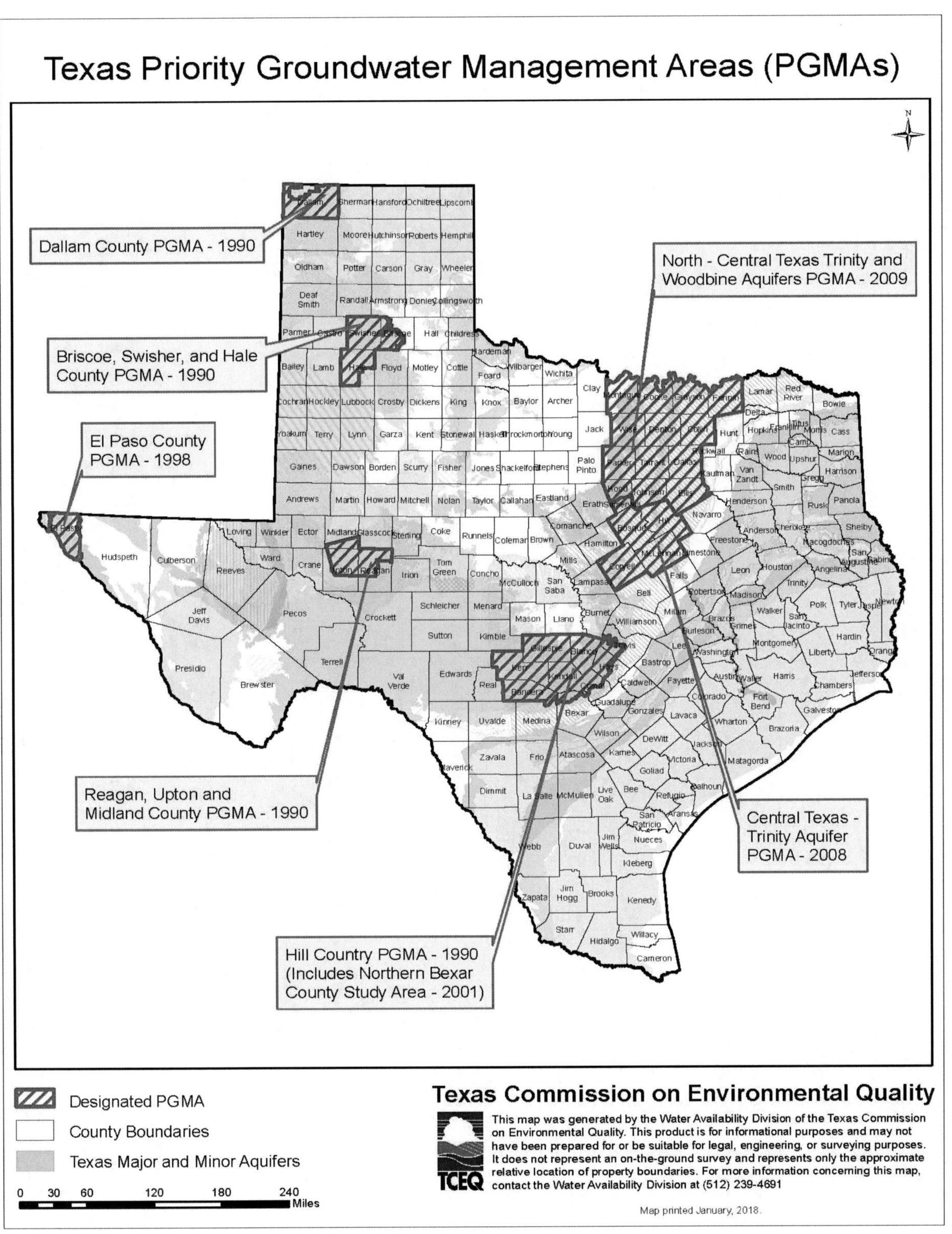

Plate 4. Texas Priority Groundwater Management Areas (PGMAs). Texas Commission on Environmental Quality, www.tceq.texas.gov/groundwater/groundwater-planning-assessment/pgma.html.

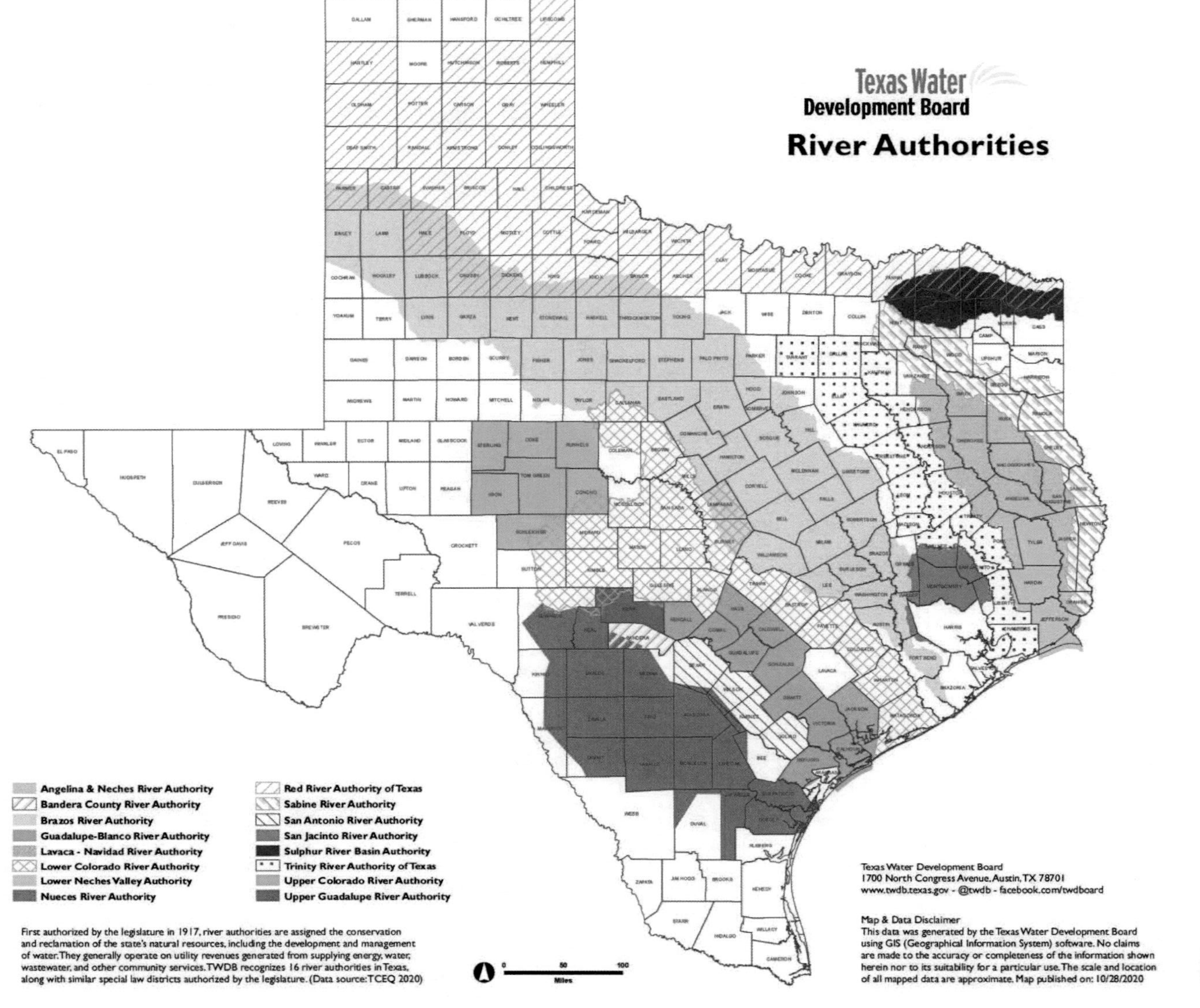

Plate 5. River Authorities of Texas. Texas Water Development Board, https://tnris.org/maps/#twdb-supplementals.

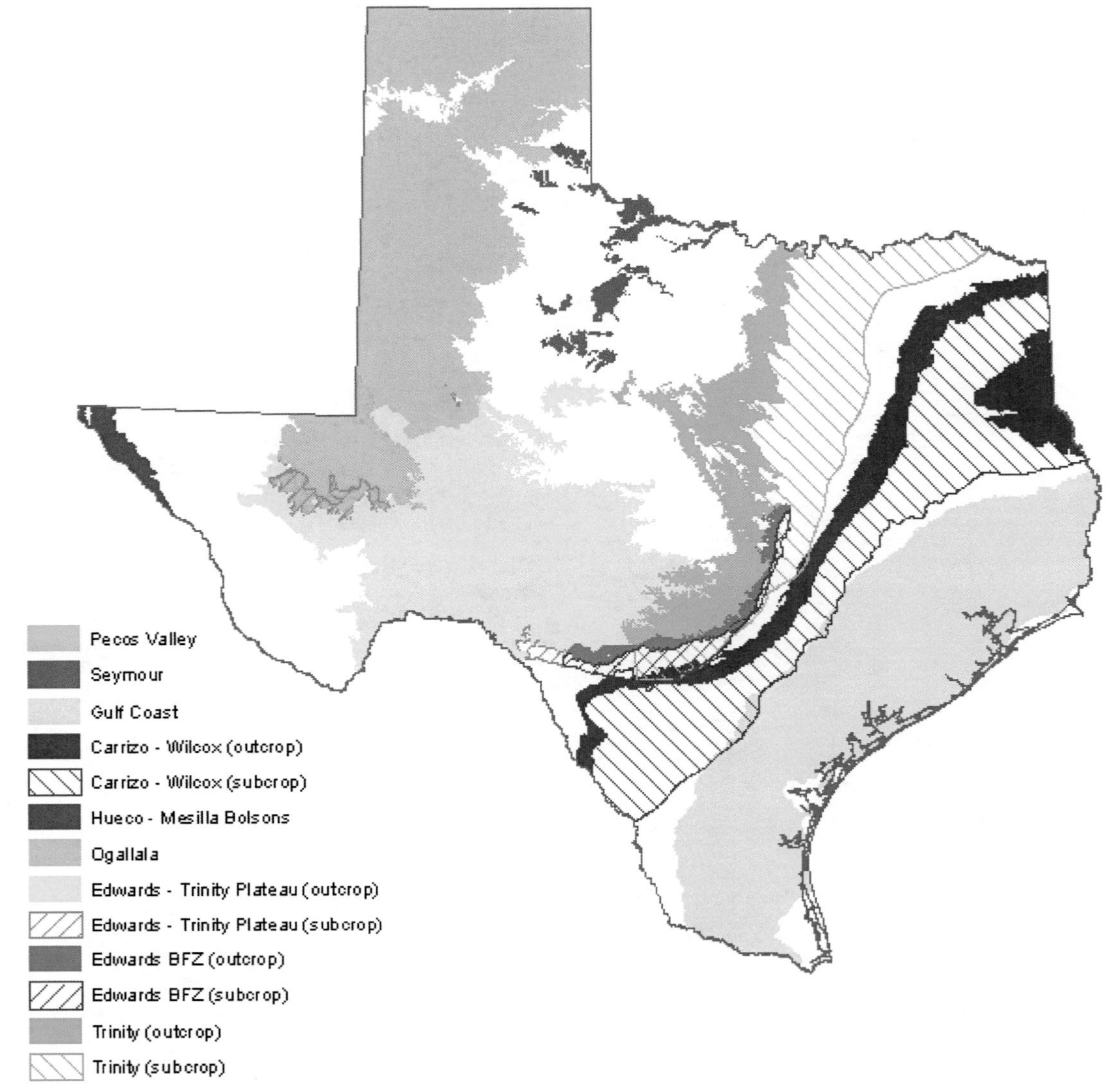

Plate 6. Major Aquifers of Texas. Texas Water Development Board, www.twdb.texas.gov/groundwater/aquifer/major.asp.

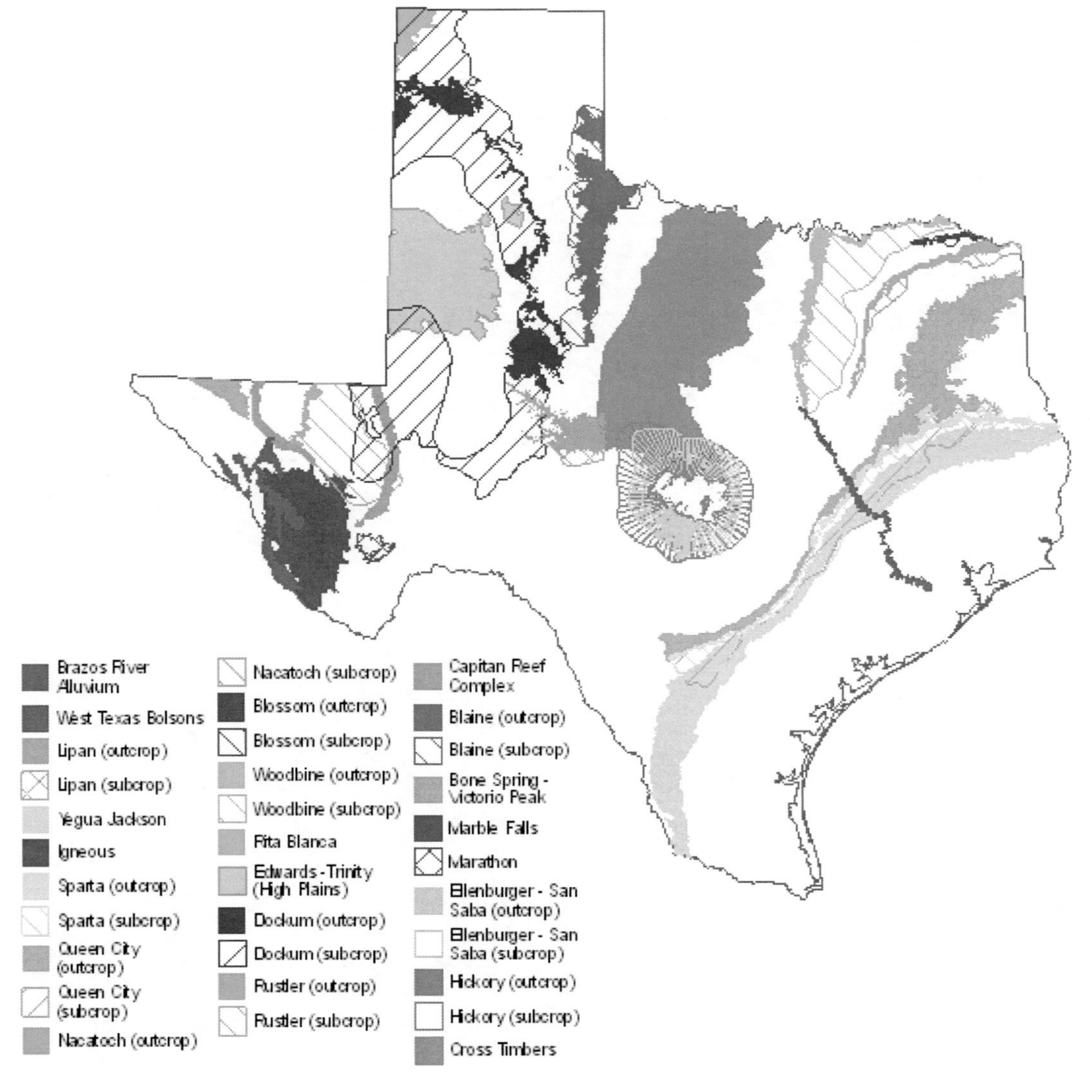

Plate 7. Minor Aquifers of Texas. Texas Water Development Board, www.twdb.texas.gov/groundwater/aquifer/minor.asp.

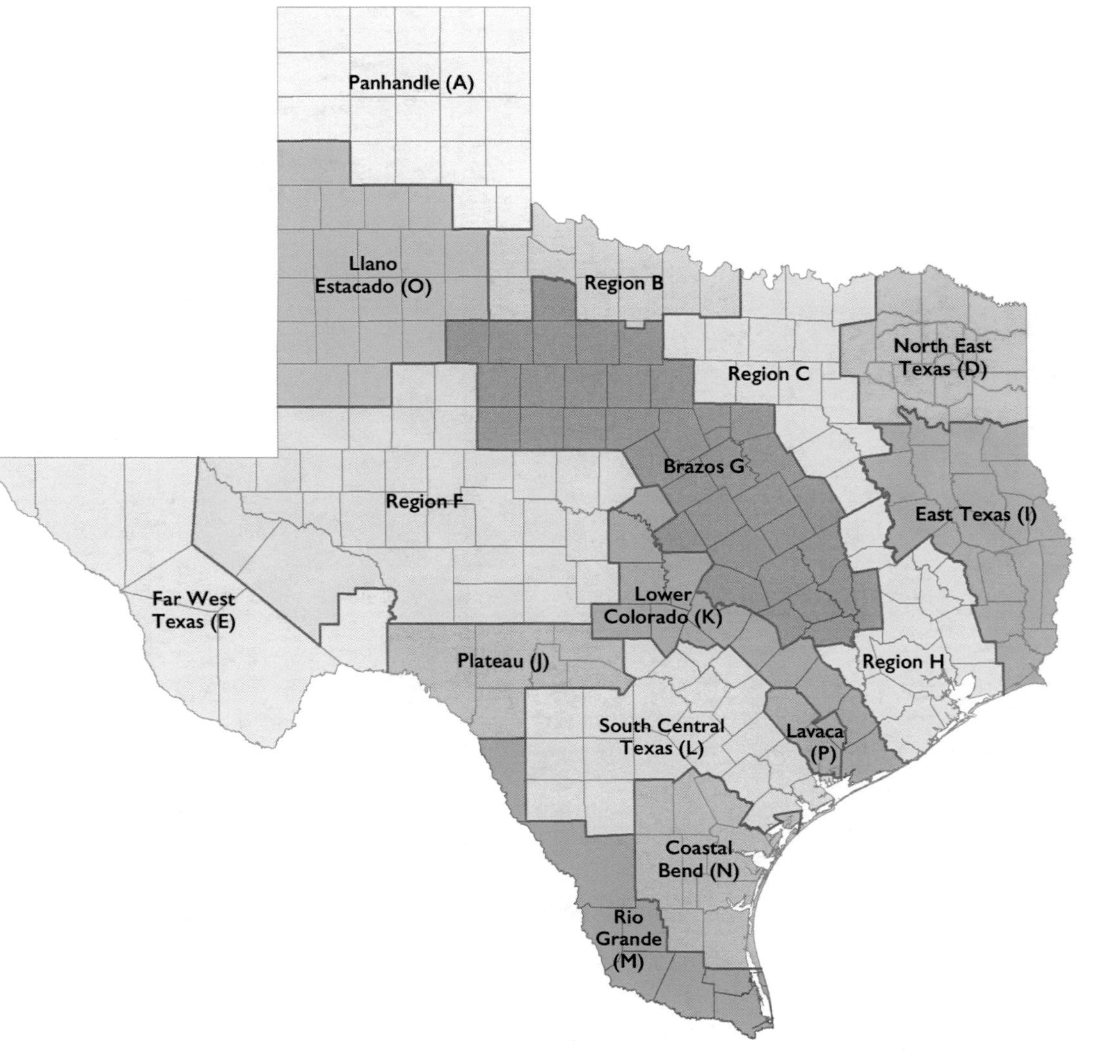

Plate 8. Regional Water Planning Areas of Texas. Texas Water Development Board, www.twdb.texas.gov/waterplanning/rwp/index.asp.

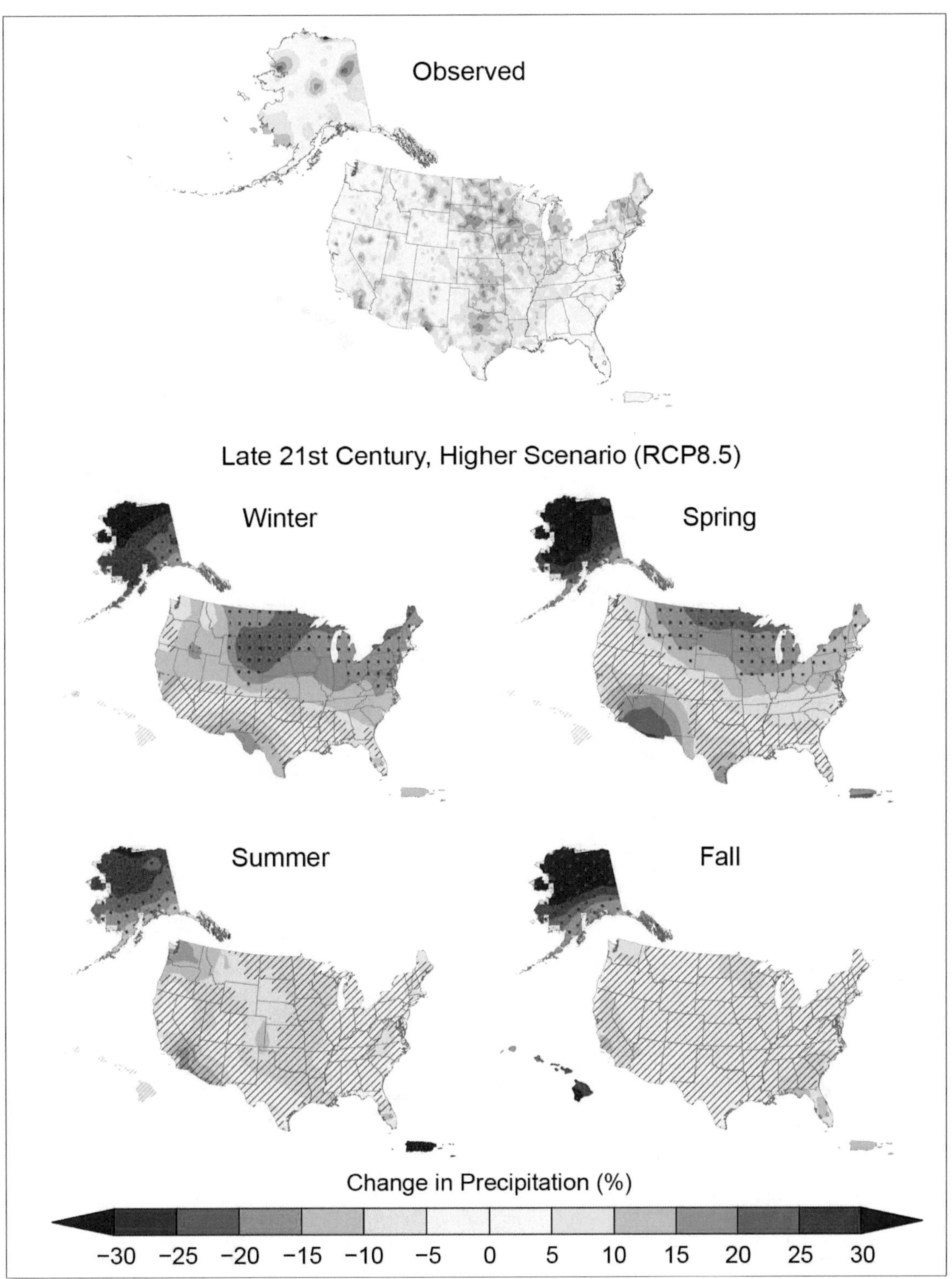

Plate 9. Observed and Projected Change in Seasonal Precipitation. Red dots show where changes are large compared to natural variations, and hashes show where changes are small compared to natural variations. U.S. Global Change Research Program, *Fourth National Climate Assessment: Impacts, Risks, and Adaption in the United States*, Vol. 2, ch. 2, *Our Changing Climate* 89 fig. 2.5 (2018), https://nca2018.globalchange.gov/downloads/NCA4_Ch02_Changing-Climate_Full.pdf.

CHAPTER 20

State Water Planning

Tony L. Smith, P.E.[1]

I. Texas Water Planning: A Historical Overview

§ 20.1 Introduction

In the early 1900s, as the vast open lands of Texas became more populated and the consequences of droughts and floods became more significant, the Texas legislature began to address the planning, management, and development of the state's water resources. The methods and tools for addressing these issues have evolved. The history of the state's water planning efforts provides an important foundation for understanding of the significance and intent of the current planning process.

§ 20.2 The Early Efforts

In July 1953, responding to a request for guidance from then U.S. Senator Lyndon B. Johnson, the U.S. Bureau of Reclamation's Area Planning Office in Austin, Texas (within the U.S. Department of the Interior), prepared a report entitled "Water Supply and the Texas Economy: An Appraisal of the Texas Water Problem." *See* Tex. S. Doc. No. 83-57 (1953). The report included planning regions and looked at water needs; it was an early version of the highly developed water planning efforts that are underway today. The latest official state water plan includes an informative discussion of Texas's water planning history. *See* Texas Water Development Board, *Water for Texas 2022* (2022), www.twdb.texas.gov/waterplanning/swp/2022/index.asp [hereinafter 2022 State Water Plan].

In the 1950s, Texas experienced one of the worst droughts in its history. In response to these severe conditions and their impacts on the availability of water supply in the state and looking for a way to avoid a repeat of the devastation that caused almost all 254 Texas counties to be classified as disaster areas, the Texas legislature reacted with a concerted effort to fund the state's water supply and conservation needs with the creation of the Texas Water Development Board (TWDB) and the Texas Water Development Fund in 1957. *See* Act of May 21, 1957, 55th Leg., R.S., ch. 425, 1957 Tex. Gen. Laws 1268 (H.B. 161); Tex. H.R.J. Res. 3, 55th Leg., R.S., 1957 Tex. Gen. Laws 1636. On November 5, 1957, Texas voters approved the constitutional amendment that added new section 49–c to article III of the Texas Constitution, and the TWDB and its funding capabilities became a reality. Also that year,

---

1. Tony L. Smith, P.E., is a professional engineer at Carollo Engineers, Inc., in Austin, Texas, where he provides consulting services related to water resources planning, surface and groundwater supply, permitting, and environmental flows. Mr. Smith has worked with water providers, users, and regulators across Texas, Oklahoma, and Arkansas along with numerous state and federal resource agency personnel, legal experts, and academia. He has served as the project manager or task lead for multiple regional water planning groups in Texas and is working in support of the development of the state of Oklahoma's Comprehensive Water Plan. Mr. Smith was selected to serve as a member of the 80th Texas Legislature's Senate Bill 3 Trinity and San Jacinto Rivers and Galveston Bay Basin and Bay Expert Science Team and serves on the board of the Texas Water Conservation Association.

the legislature passed the Texas Water Planning Act, which mandated a formal process for developing a plan to meet the state's future water needs. *See* Act of Nov. 12, 1957, 55th Leg., 1st C.S., ch. 11, 1957 Tex. Gen. Laws 23 [hereinafter S.B. 1]. These were the beginnings of the statewide water planning process that continues, with growing importance, today.

§ 20.3 Pre–1997 Senate Bill 1 Water Planning

The state began preparing water plans in 1961 and also produced plans in 1968, 1984, 1990, 1992, and 1997. *See* 2022 State Water Plan, at 157. These plans acknowledged the need to develop future water supplies to meet the increasing water needs of the state's significantly growing population, and they approached the challenge with various policy and project recommendations as the years passed. The early plans were created at a time when the primary method of supplying water was the large-scale construction of federally funded reservoirs. *See* 2022 State Water Plan, at 157. In 1977, the TWDB was designated as the state agency to coordinate with the U.S. Army Corps of Engineers and the U.S. Department of the Interior's Bureau of Reclamation in the planning of water resource development projects in Texas. *See* Tex. Water Code § 16.091. Although reservoir construction was emphasized in the first two state water plans, in the 1980s reservoir construction projects were viewed less favorably, amidst a declining federal interest in funding such projects and a growing state interest in pursuing other options. *See* 2022 State Water Plan, at 157.

In contrast to the proposed use of large-scale structures to capture and store water, the water plans of the 1980s and 1990s focused to a greater extent on water management and infrastructure development to better use existing water resources. For example, after 1984, the plans more frequently included consideration of conservation, reuse, desalination, and natural resource protection. *See* 2022 State Water Plan, at 157. The process for developing the state water plan changed over time as well. The TWDB increased participation in water planning by including stakeholders and other state agencies, such as the Texas Parks and Wildlife Department, the Texas Department of Agriculture, and the Texas Water Commission, a predecessor agency of the current Texas Commission on Environmental Quality (TCEQ). *See* 2022 State Water Plan, at 157; Tex. Water Code § 16.051(d). Then and now, the TWDB serves as the state agency with primary responsibility for water planning and for administering water financing for the state. *See* Tex. Water Code § 6.011.

§ 20.4 New Directions: S.B. 1, S.B. 2, H.B. 1763, and H.B. 4

After nearly four decades of water planning for a state that continued to experience dramatic increases in its population and economy, lawmakers realized that the state water planning process needed to be modernized and regularized. These changes and this realization led to the enactment of major water planning bills, starting in 1997: Senate Bill 1, Senate Bill 2, House Bill 1763, and House Bill 4, as discussed in the following sections.

§ 20.4:1 Senate Bill 1 (1997)

Recognizing the lack of incentive structure in previous legislation, in 1997 the legislature passed S.B. 1, one of the most extensive overhauls of the Texas Water Code in thirty years. The water planning provisions of S.B. 1 are now codified in Water Code chapter 16, subchapter C (Planning). S.B. 1 was drafted in response to the devastating drought of 1996. *See* 2022 State Water Plan, at 158. Against the backdrop of that drought and growing concerns over a rapidly increasing state population, S.B. 1 sought to (1) encourage local participation by creating a stakeholder process in the state water plan; (2) support drought contingency planning (see Chapter 22 of this book); (3) emphasize conservation and environmental protection (see Chapters 11 and 23); (4) harness and streamline the state's regulatory system; and (5) provide certain funding (see Chapter 37) and permitting incentives to achieve these goals. *See* Martin Hubert, *Senate Bill 1, the First Big and Bold Step Toward Meeting Texas's Future Water Needs*, 30 Tex. Tech L. Rev. 53, 55 (1999).

To encourage local participation, the legislature substantially modified the method for developing and adopting a state water plan. Instead of having one central agency, such as the TWDB, developing the entire plan, S.B. 1 called for the designation of regions, each composed of various interest groups, each of which would develop a localized regional water plan (RWP). Upon adoption by the respective regional water planning groups (RWPGs), these RWPs would be submitted to the TWDB for approval and incorporation into a comprehensive state water plan. In other words, the planning process evolved from a "top-down" approach to a "bottom-up" model. The 2002, 2007, 2012, and 2017 water plans were adopted using this S.B. 1 model. *See* 2022 State Water Plan, at 4.

§ 20.4:2 Senate Bill 2 (2001)

To address the funding issues lingering after the enactment of S.B. 1 in 1997, the 2001 legislature adopted Senate Bill 2, sometimes referenced as the "financial follow-up to Senate Bill 1." Act of May 27, 2001, 77th Leg., R.S., ch. 966, 2001 Tex. Gen. Laws 1880, eff. Sept. 1, 2001 [hereinafter S.B. 2].

Among other additions, S.B. 2 created two new sources of funding: the Water Infrastructure Fund (WIF) and the Rural Water Assistance Fund (RWAF), now codified at Texas Water Code chapter 15, subchapters Q and R, respectively. The WIF consisted of a general revenue fund for projects recommended by the state plan and RWPs. The RWAF was designed to assist rural political subdivisions in financing water projects that would otherwise be financially impracticable. Both funds would be administered by the TWDB. See Chapter 37 of this book for further discussion.

§ 20.4:3 House Bill 1763 (2005)

Although House Bill 1763, strictly speaking, did not address the state water plan, it sought to address the divide between surface water and groundwater planning and management. See Act of May 30, 2005, 79th Leg., R.S., ch. 970 [hereinafter H.B. 1763]. Before this legislation, the RWPGs determined water supply and demand regardless of the source as surface water or groundwater. H.B. 1763 established a formal process requiring local groundwater conservation districts (GCDs) to methodically and scientifically determine groundwater availability and the policies involved in the use of that groundwater. The new groundwater management area (GMA) joint planning process directed GCDs, on a regional basis, to articulate their groundwater resource management goals (desired future conditions or DFCs) based on groundwater availability, called "managed available groundwater" in the legislation. Subsequently, the term was changed to "modeled available groundwater." See Tex. Water Code § 36.1084; see also Tex. Water Code § 16.053. The RWPGs must use the DFCs and the managed available groundwater in developing their RWPs. See 31 Tex. Admin. Code § 357.32(d). Under the changes made during the 82nd legislative session in 2011, the planning function of the DFC adoption became more apparent, mirroring more closely the overall state water planning process. See Chapter 21 of this book for an in-depth discussion of the GMA joint planning process.

§ 20.4:4 House Bill 4 (2013)

In 2013, the state was again facing the devastating impacts of drought. Since July 2011, the governor had issued (and continuously renewed) monthly Emergency Disaster Proclamations under Texas Government Code section 418.014 certifying that exceptional drought conditions posed a threat of imminent disaster in certain listed counties. In at least seven of those gubernatorial disaster proclamations, all 254 counties in the state were listed. As a result, a substantial number of bills were filed and debated during the 83rd Legislature. Among them was House Bill 4, which significantly changed the TWDB, requiring a full-time three-member board instead of the six-member board that had served in the past. *See* Act of May 20, 2013, 83d Leg., R.S., ch. 207, §§ 1.01, 1.07, eff. Sept. 1, 2013 (codified at Tex. Water Code §§ 6.052(a), 6.061) [hereinafter H.B. 4]. Giving legislative recognition to the dire need for funding of the State Water Plan, H.B. 4 also provided sweeping changes in the funding of water projects. The water funding provisions were dependent on passage of an amendment to the Texas Constitution, which appeared on the November 5, 2013, ballot as Proposition 6 and passed, receiving 73 percent of the vote. *See* H.B. 4, § 2.27. Water funding provisions are discussed in detail in Chapter 37 of this book.

II. State Water Planning

§ 20.5 Introduction

As discussed at section 20.4:1 above, after the passage of S.B. 1 in 1997, today's state water planning process is best described as a "bottom-up" approach, using local and regional efforts to generate a comprehensive statewide plan covering the next fifty years and looking beyond the immediate future to the projected long-term needs of the state. The statutory framework for today's water planning, found in Texas Water Code chapter 16, subchapter C, is fairly detailed, with a strong emphasis on the regional planning groups, public participation, open government processes, and numerous opportunities for notice and comment. The implementing regulations for the planning process follow the statutory language establishing guidelines for regional water planning (*see* 31 Tex. Admin. Code ch. 357) and state water planning (*see* 31 Tex. Admin. Code ch. 358).

Following the bottom-up theme of today's water planning framework, the remainder of this chapter first describes the regional work that forms the basis for the state plan and then describes the TWDB's development and adoption of the state water plan.

§ 20.6 Regional Water Planning

Water planning on the regional level in the bottom-up framework began with delineation of planning areas and the appointment of representatives to form planning groups and continues with ongoing work by and coordination among those groups and the TWDB, as summarized below.

§ 20.6:1 Formation of Regional Water Planning Groups

To implement the directives of S.B. 1 and its September 1, 1998, deadline, the TWDB divided the state into sixteen regional water planning areas (RWPAs). These areas are defined predominantly by county and geographic boundaries, but the TWDB also considered other factors, such as "river basin and aquifer delineations," "water utility development patterns," "socioeconomic characteristics," and "political subdivision boundaries." The TWDB must review and update these regional planning area designations at least every five years or when necessary. *See* Tex. Water Code § 16.053(b); 31 Tex. Admin. Code § 357.11. The sixteen current planning areas, known as Regions A through P, are presented in a Regional Water Planning Areas GIS shapefile located on the TWDB website at www.twdb.texas.gov/mapping/gisdata/doc/RWPA_Shapefile.zip. While the boundaries of the planning areas have remained constant since they were delineated in 1998, the TWDB has continuing authority to alter them. *See* 31 Tex. Admin. Code § 357.11.

After designating the boundaries of the various RWPAs, the TWDB designated an "initial coordinating body" of representatives within each area to begin the planning process. *See* Tex. Water Code § 16.053(c). Once appointed, the initial coordinating body was directed to designate other persons to provide representation for the various interests in the region, including the public, counties, municipalities, industries, agricultural interests, environmental interests, small businesses, electric generating utilities, river authorities, water districts, and water utilities. *See* Tex. Water Code § 16.053(c). These groups, composed of uncompensated volunteers, became known as Regional Water Planning Groups (RWPGs). In a step toward better coordination between the legal, planning, and management aspects of surface water and groundwater, the 2011 legislature amended Texas Water Code section 16.053(c) to require GCDs in each GMA within an RWPA to appoint a representative of that district to serve on the planning group. *See* Tex. Water Code § 16.053(c); 31 Tex. Admin. Code § 357.11(d). See Chapter 21 of this book for a discussion of GMAs.

The RWPGs must maintain at least one representative of the twelve named interest groups on the RWPG. *See* 31 Tex. Admin. Code § 357.11(d). In practice, many planning groups have designated additional representatives from various water-related interests within their geographic areas, and the number of voting members in the RWPG may exceed the twelve-person minimum. Today, most RWPGs have approximately twenty-five voting members, plus alternates. More than 480 voting members participated in the development of the 2021 RWPs. *See* 2022 State Water Plan, at 19.

In addition to the voting members of the RWPG, the TWDB rules require inclusion of certain nonvoting members, who receive meeting notifications and information in the same manner as the voting members. Representatives of the TWDB, the Texas Parks and Wildlife Department, the Texas Department of Agriculture, and the State Soil and Water Conservation Board serve as ex officio members of each RWPG. *See* Tex. Water Code § 16.053(c); 31 Tex. Admin. Code § 357.11(e). Other nonvoting members include designees of adjacent RWPGs and representatives of entities with certain surface water rights or water contracts in the RWPA. *See* 31 Tex. Admin. Code § 357.11(e)(3), (e)(4).

As part of the RWPG's initial duties, each planning group was directed to adopt bylaws consistent with TWDB regulations. *See* 31 Tex. Admin. Code § 357.11(c) (providing mandates for bylaw adoption). Although the bylaws must be consistent with the regulations, in practice they differ among RWPGs. The bylaws for all sixteen of the RWPGs are available at www.twdb.texas.gov/waterplanning/rwp/regions/index.asp. RWPGs must have acceptable bylaws on file with the TWDB to obtain funding through a regional water planning grant. *See* 31 Tex. Admin. Code § 355.91(a).

§ 20.6:2 Interregional Planning Council

In 2019, the Texas legislature added a new body, the Interregional Planning Council (IPC), to the state and regional water planning process. *See* Act of May 24, 2019, 86th Leg., R.S., ch. 745, § 1, eff. June 10, 2019 (H.B. 807) (adding Tex. Water Code § 16.052). The TWDB appoints this council once during each five-year water planning cycle, and the council serves until the next state water plan is adopted. *See* Tex. Water Code § 16.052(a). Council membership consists of one member of each RWPG, who is nominated by his respective RWPG. *See* Tex. Water Code § 16.052(b). The council's primary role is to facilitate coordination and dialogue between the RWPGs in recognition of the fact that some water needs and strategies occur in aquifers, watersheds, and areas of need that cross planning area lines, and RWPGs must work together to avoid adopting or prioritizing strategies in ways that conflict with or impede broader statewide water planning needs. The council also shares best practices among the regional water planning groups. *See* Tex. Water Code § 16.052(c).

The council met several times during 2020 and submitted its required report to the TWDB on October 16, 2020. *See* Interregional Planning Council, *Report to the Texas Water Development Board* (Oct. 16, 2020) [hereinafter IPC Report 2020). The IPC Report 2020 made recommendations regarding enhancing interregional coordination, planning water resources for the state as a whole, best practices for future planning, and interregional conflicts. *See* IPC Report 2020, at 11.

The IPC concluded that certain activities would enhance interregional coordination: identifying interregional project development issues and opportunities and roles for participants in the planning process should take place at the beginning of each five-year planning cycle. Additionally, coordination between planning groups should be documented by the middle of the planning cycle. *See* IPC Report 2020, at 11 § 2.

The IPC Report 2020 believes that actions should be taken toward long-range and visionary planning so that the planning process best plans water resources for the state as a whole. *See* IPC Report 2020, at 11 § 3.

The IPC addressed best practices for future state water planning including suggestions on simplifying planning; engaging RWPG membership and the public; communicating among the TWDB, the RWPGs, and members; the TCEQ's serving as ex-officio member; reimbursing costs incurred by RWPG administrative agencies; and modifying Open Meetings Act videoconferencing requirements. The IPC Report 2020 also addresses improving the regional water planning process. *See* IPC Report 2020, at 11 § 4.

Finally, the IPC recommends coordination protocols and assistance, including funding, if an unresolved conflict exists. *See* IPC Report 2020, at 11 § 5.

§ 20.6:3 Preparation of Regional Water Plans

With bylaws in place and with designated members of the RWPGs in attendance, the regional planning groups commenced planning in 1998. Composing a regional plan is a massive endeavor that requires a substantial amount of review, research, engagement, and study as well as fulfillment of the TWDB's water plan development guidelines and the regulatory "preplanning" requirements of 31 Texas Administrative Code chapter 357. Under these rules, and generally adopted as part of their bylaws, the RWPGs must establish certain organizational ground rules, such as the definition of a quorum and terms of membership. *See* 31 Tex. Admin. Code § 357.11(c). General responsibilities and procedures for RWPGs are set forth in 31 Texas Administrative Code section 357.12.

The TWDB's water planning guidelines are at 31 Texas Administrative Code chapter 357 (Regional Water Planning Guidelines) and chapter 358 (State Water Planning Guidelines). Generally, these guidelines contain the broad goals of the regional planning process, impose deadlines for submittal of regional plans and revised regional plans, and require the plans to be consistent with chapters 357 and 358. Additionally, Senate Bill 347, effective September 1, 2017, clarified that the business of the RWPGs, including their committees and subcommittees, must comply with the Texas Open Meetings and Public Information Acts. *See* Act of May 3, 2017, 85th Leg., R.S., ch. 347, § 1 (S.B. 437), eff. Sept. 1, 2017 (adding Tex. Water Code § 16.053(h)(12)).

To assist in performing the required tasks, eligible applicants, including an RWPG, may apply to the TWDB executive administrator for a regional water planning grant. *See* 31 Tex. Admin. Code ch. 355, subch. C. These grants are available for certain activities directly related and necessary to the development or revision of RWPs. *See* 31 Tex. Admin. Code § 355.91; *but see* 31 Tex. Admin. Code § 355.92 (identifying certain activities that do not qualify for funding under this grant program). The criteria for evaluating grant applications, which include financial need, are listed in 31 Texas Administrative Code section 355.91(e).

§ 20.6:4 Contents of Regional Water Plans

After meeting the preplanning requirements, an RWPG may begin to develop its RWP. The statutory foundation for regional planning appears in Texas Water Code section 16.053. Generally, it requires each RWPG to develop an RWP using the latest state water plan and local water plans prepared under Water Code section 16.054 as guides. The RWP must provide for the "orderly development, management, and conservation of water resources and preparation for and response to drought conditions in order that sufficient water will be available at a reasonable cost to ensure public health, safety, and welfare; further economic development; and protect the agricultural and natural resources of that particular region." Tex. Water Code § 16.053(a). House Bill 30, passed during the 84th legislative session, added a new item to the list of topics to include in an RWP. Under amended Water Code section 16.053(e), RWPs must consider opportunities and benefits of developing large-scale desalination facilities for seawater or brackish groundwater. *See* Act of May 26, 2015, 84th Leg., R.S., ch. 990, § 2, eff. Sept. 1, 2015 (adding Tex. Water Code § 16.053(e)(5)(J)). See Chapter 25 of this book for a discussion of desalination. Section 16.053(e) was also amended by Senate Bill 1101, which expands the scope of an RWP to address "potential impacts on public health, safety, or welfare in this state" in conjunction with a plan's consideration of any existing water or drought planning efforts in the region. *See* Act of May 29, 2015, 84th Leg., R.S., ch. 1180, § 1, eff. Sept. 1, 2015 (amending Tex. Water Code § 16.053(e)(5)(A)). In 2019, the 86th Legislature amended section 16.053(e) to require the plans to (1) identify unnecessary or counterproductive variations in specific drought response strategies, including outdoor watering schedules, which can vary from place to place, causing confusion; (2) provide a specific assessment of the potential for aquifer storage and recovery projects to meet any significant water needs; (3) set one or more specific goals for gallons of water use per capita per day in each decade of the period covered by the plan for municipal water user groups; and (4) assess the progress of the regional water planning area in encouraging cooperation between water user groups to achieve economies of scale and otherwise incentivizing strategies. *See* Act of May 24, 2019, 86th Leg., R.S., ch. 745, § 2 (H.B. 807), eff. June 10, 2019 (adding Tex. Water Code § 16.053(e)(3)(E), (e)(10), (e)(11), (e)(12)). Extensive, detailed content requirements are contained in 31 Texas Administrative Code chapter 357. See Chapter 22 of this book for coverage of drought management planning.

One of the primary functional units for which regional water planning is performed is defined as a water user group. *See* 31 Tex. Admin. Code § 357.10(43). These users, or groups of users, include privately owned utilities that provide an average of more than 100 acre-feet per year for municipal use for all owned water systems, water systems serving institutions or facilities owned by the state or federal government, or all other retail public utilities providing more than 100 acre-feet per year for municipal use. Water user groups may also include collective reporting units, or groups of retail public utilities that have a common association and are requested for inclusion by the RWPG. Smaller water users providing municipal and domestic water use are represented in the regional planning process by aggregation at the county level and are referred to as County-Other. Nonmunicipal water uses including manufacturing, irrigation, steam-electric power generation, mining, and livestock are similarly aggregated for each category for each county or portion of a county in a region. *See* 31 Tex. Admin. Code § 357.10(43).

Much of the data collected during the regional planning process is ultimately used to determine the supply and demand for water resources. The plan must present projections of population and water demands, by decade, for the various water user groups. *See* 31 Tex. Admin. Code § 357.31. The TWDB's methodologies for projecting demands for various water users are developed and presented to RWPGs for discussion during each planning cycle. The projected population and water demand numbers are extremely important components of an RWP, as they will determine whether an RWPG identifies shortages or surpluses in its water supplies. *See* 31 Tex. Admin. Code § 357.33.

As part of its planning, an RWPG must also evaluate source water availability and adequacy during drought-of-record conditions. The TWDB rules provide specific directions on how to conduct these evaluations. *See* 31 Tex. Admin. Code § 357.32. See Chapter 22 of this book for more about the interface between state water planning and drought planning. In 2016, among other modifications to definitions of terms commonly employed in the regional water planning process, clarification was added to distinguish how the definition of the availability of water from a source differs from the supply available for use by a water user. In the present context, availability is defined as the maximum amount of raw water that could be produced by a source during a repeat of the drought of record, regardless of whether the supply is physically connected to or legally accessible by water user groups.

Existing supply is defined as the maximum amount of water that is physically and legally accessible from existing sources for immediate use by a water user group under a repeat of drought-of-record conditions. *See* 31 Tex. Admin. Code § 357.10.

After performing calculations to determine source availability and existing supply, an RWPG must compare supplies against the projected demands to identify present or future water surpluses or needs (i.e., shortage) for each water user group. *See* 31 Tex. Admin. Code § 357.33. Where water needs are identified, an RWPG must then identify potentially feasible strategies and evaluate potential water management strategies and water management strategy projects to meet those needs. *See* 31 Tex. Admin. Code § 357.34 Water management strategies represent a plan to meet a need for additional water by a discrete water user group, which can mean increasing the total water supply or maximizing an existing supply, including through reducing demands. A water management strategy may or may not require associated water management strategy projects to be implemented. A water management strategy project is defined as a water project that has a non-zero capital cost and that, when implemented, would develop, deliver, or treat additional water supply volumes or conserve water. Such a project may be associated with multiple water management strategies or address the needs for multiple water user groups. *See* 31 Tex. Admin. Code § 357.10.

House Bill 4, passed during the 83rd legislative session, added a new item to the list of deliverables to be produced as part of the regional planning process. Under amended Water Code section 15.436, RWPGs were required to prioritize the recommended water management strategy projects identified in the RWP and submit the adopted prioritization separately with its adopted RWP. This prioritization of projects was to be performed by the RWPG in accordance with uniform standards developed by a stakeholder committee established under Water Code section 15.436(c) and in place at the time of the adoption of the RWP. This prioritization was necessary for implementation of SWIFT funding, as discussed in Chapter 37 of this book. *See* H.B. 4 § 2.02 (adding Tex. Water Code § 15.436).

More recently, House Bill 1905, passed during the 87th legislative session, removed several underfunded RWPG duties deemed to be no longer informative. *See* Act of May 19, 2021, 87th Leg., R.S., ch. 68, § 15.435(g) (H.B. 1905), eff. Sept. 1, 2021 [hereinafter H.B. 1905]. As of September 1, 2021, RWPGs will no longer be required to prepare an infrastructure financing report for inclusion in the RWPs nor prioritize projects recommended in the RWPs. The infrastructure financing report detailed how local entities proposed to pay for projects in the RWP and made recommendations concerning the state's role in financing projects. It was determined that demand on the SWIFT program is currently a better indicator of the need for state funding assistance. As noted previously, RWPGs were required by statute to prioritize projects recommended in their respective RWPs, which involved significant effort. Because the TWDB ultimately only prioritizes projects that apply for funding through the SWIFT program, it was determined that the work of the RWPGs did not contribute proportionally to the final scores. Thus, with passage of H.B. 1905 the responsibility to produce this information was removed. *See* H.B. 1905 (amending Tex. Water Code §§ 15.435(g), 15.437(d), 15.438(g), 15.439(a), 15.912(b), 15.975(d), 16.131(b), and repealing §§ 15.436, 16.053(q)).

§ 20.6:5 Process for Submittal and Adoption of Regional Plans

An important feature of Texas Water Code section 16.053 is a mandatory deadline for the RWPGs to submit their adopted regional plans. Specifically, the statute requires that RWPs be submitted to the TWDB by January 5, 2001, and at least every five years thereafter. *See* Tex. Water Code § 16.053(i). Approved RWPs are incorporated into the state water plan the following year.

Before an RWPG can adopt its final RWP, however, it must prepare and submit an Initially Prepared Plan (IPP) to the TWDB executive administrator. An IPP is a draft RWP that will be presented at a public hearing and submitted to the TWDB for review and comment. *See* 30 Tex.

Admin. Code § 357.10(18). The procedures and schedules for adoption and submittal of IPPs and RWPs are set forth in 30 Texas Administrative Code section 357.50, and the TWDB executive administrator has the authority to establish the schedule for submittal of IPPs and the final RWPs. For the 2017–2021 planning cycle, the IPPs and final adopted RWPs were due in March and November 2020, respectively.

The IPP must address the requirements for the final RWP, and the RWPG must certify that its IPP is complete and was adopted by the RWPG. When the IPP is submitted to the TWDB for comment, it is also released to the public, and a process for public notice and comment begins. *See* 31 Tex. Admin. Code §§ 357.21, 357.50. During this process, the RWPG must solicit and consider comments from the TWDB executive administrator, federal or state agencies, and the general public in compliance with the time periods set forth in 31 Texas Administrative Code section 357.50(f). The RWPGs must also identify potential interregional conflicts and seek their resolution. *See* 31 Tex. Admin. Code § 357.50(d), (e). The regional water planning rules contain extensive provisions relating to notice and opportunity for comment, including a detailed list of public participation requirements. *See* 31 Tex. Admin. Code § 357.21. In December 2016, section 357.21 was amended to allow online postings of required public notices as alternatives to mailed or published notice. Once the RWPG has accepted comments for the specified periods of time, the RWPG may proceed to plan adoption as provided by its bylaws. If there are intraregional conflicts to resolve among its members, the RWPG may request the assistance of the executive administrator. *See* 31 Tex. Admin. Code § 357.61.

Continuing to work against deadlines, often with enormous amounts of information to review and consider, the RWPGs meet and address the issues raised about their IPPs during the comment period. The RWPG prepares a final RWP and votes to adopt it. At that point, the regional plan is ready to be submitted to the TWDB for approval. The submittal must include (1) technical reports and data required by 31 Texas Administrative Code chapter 357, (2) an executive summary of key findings and recommendations, (3) summaries of all comments received and the RWPG's response to those comments, and (4) the RWPG's prioritization of recommended water management strategy projects. *See also* 31 Tex. Admin. Code §§ 357.50(g)(1), 357.46.

In the 2017–2022 planning cycle, RWPGs adopted and submitted their final regional plans to the TWDB by November 5, 2020, and the RWPs for each RWPA were approved by the TWDB in January 2021.

§ 20.6:6 Process for TWDB Approval of Regional Plans

After an RWP has been adopted and submitted to the TWDB, the agency reviews it for compliance with Texas Water Code chapter 16 and 31 Texas Administrative Code chapters 357 and 358. Agency approval makes a plan eligible for incorporation into the state water plan. *See* 31 Tex. Admin. Code §§ 357.50(k), 358.4. To be approved, the RWP must be formally adopted by the RWPG that produced it. *See* 31 Tex. Admin. Code § 357.50(h). If an RWP meets the criteria mentioned above and does not present an interregional conflict, the TWDB may approve the plan. *See* 31 Tex. Admin. Code § 357.50(i). The 2021 RWPs were approved by the TWDB in January 2021. Copies of current and previous regional plans are available at www.twdb.texas.gov/waterplanning/rwp/plans/index.asp.

§ 20.6:7 Interregional Conflicts

The issue of interregional conflicts was raised in the case of *Texas Water Development Board v. Ward Timber, Ltd.*, 411 S.W.3d 554 (Tex. App.—Eastland 2013, no pet.), which involved a judicial challenge to the TWDB's approval of the 2011 Region C RWP. In late 2010, the TWDB approved the regional plans submitted by both Regions C (North Central Texas) and D (North East Texas). However, the two regions had taken different views on the proposed Marvin Nichols Reservoir in northeast Texas; Region C recommended the project as a new water supply to meet the growing water needs of North Central Texas, while Region D opposed the project due to its potential impacts on agricultural and natural resources. In approving the RWPs, the TWDB had applied the narrow definition of "interregional conflict" in its rules at that time, concluding that the regions were not arguing over a potential overallocation of the same water supply across two regions. *See* 31 Tex. Admin. Code § 357.10(16)(A). However, the enabling legislation for the rules states that the TWDB may approve an RWP only after it has determined that all interregional conflicts involving that RWPA have been resolved. *See* Tex. Water Code § 16.053(h)(7). The district court declared that the conflicting RWPs constituted an interregional conflict that the TWDB had responsibility to resolve during the process of the development and adoption of the 2012 State Water Plan, and it remanded the case back to the TWDB to resolve the conflict. *See Ward Timber*, 411 S.W.3d at 556–57.

The appeals court affirmed the district court's ruling that an interregional conflict existed between these two regions and that as a result the TWDB had improperly approved these 2011 regional plans, noting that the TWDB's narrow interpretation of interregional conflict was inconsistent with legislative intent. *See Ward Timber*, 411 S.W.3d at 574. These proceedings were followed by additional legal proceedings, hearings, and negotiations, and eventually an outcome in which both Regions C and D adopted revisions to their RWPs and submitted their revised RWPs and supporting documents to the TWDB for consideration. These proceedings also triggered a significant revision of the TWDB's water planning rules and a heightened interest in identifying and resolving potential interregional conflicts as early as possible during a planning cycle. As a result, the TWDB proposed and adopted amendments to chapter 357 of its regional water planning rules, which include special provisions relating to consistency and conflicts in RWPs and a new alternative definition of "interregional conflict" as existing when—

> in the instance of a recommended Water Management Strategy proposed to be supplied from a different Regional Water Planning Area, the Regional Water Planning Group with the location of the strategy has studied the impacts of the recommended Water Management Strategy on its economic, agricultural, and natural resources, and demonstrates to the Board that there is a potential for a substantial adverse effect on the region as a result of those impacts.

31 Tex. Admin. Code § 357.10(16)(B); *see* 31 Tex. Admin. Code ch. 357, subch. F.

During the development of the IPP, all RWPGs are encouraged to coordinate with neighboring regions to proactively identify and work cooperatively to avoid potential interregional conflicts. Formal and informal coordination occurs between the RWPGs, their technical consultants, and the TWDB. Within sixty days of the submission of IPPs to the TWDB, the RWPGs must submit in writing to the TWDB and the other affected RWPGs the identification of potential interregional conflicts. *See* 31 Tex. Admin. Code § 357.50(d). The RWPGs shall seek to resolve conflicts with other RWPGs and shall promptly and actively participate in any TWDB-sponsored efforts to resolve interregional conflicts. *See* 31 Tex. Admin. Code § 357.50(e).

§ 20.6:8 Amendment of Adopted Regional Plans

An RWPG can amend an adopted RWP in accordance with the requirements set forth in 31 Texas Administrative Code section 357.51. The proposed amendment must be submitted to the TWDB, which will consider it for approval under the standards of 31 Texas Administrative Code chapter 357. Amendments may be major or minor, and major amendments require compliance with the notice and public participation requirements contained in 31 Texas Administrative Code section 357.21, including a public hearing, before adoption.

Amendment of an adopted RWP also may be initiated by a political subdivision in the RWPA asking that an RWPG consider specific changes based on changed conditions or new information. *See*

31 Tex. Admin. Code § 357.51(a). In such an instance, the RWPG must follow the process outlined in section 357.51 to address any unresolved conflicts between a political subdivision and the planning group, and the political subdivision may petition the executive administrator to request TWDB review of the RWP. At the culmination of the petition process, if the RWPG disagrees with a change requested by the executive administrator, the matter will be presented to the TWDB for a decision. *See* 31 Tex. Admin. Code § 357.51(a).

The TWDB can also require an RWPG to amend its plan if the TWDB determines, in response to a dispute involving interregional conflicts, that an interregional conflict exists between adopted regional plans. Such amendments could be the outcome of the detailed process described in 31 Texas Administrative Code section 357.62.

An additional amendment process may occur if the TWDB determines that an adopted RWP fails to meet the requirements of Texas Water Code chapter 16 and 31 Texas Administrative Code chapters 357 and 358. *See* 31 Tex. Admin. Code § 357.63(a). If an RWPG is directed to change its RWP, the RWPG may request a reasonable amount of time to make such changes. *See* 31 Tex. Admin. Code § 357.63(b).

Beginning with the development of the 2026 RWPs, an RWPG may also amend its previously adopted plan to exclude water management strategies or projects determined to be infeasible as defined by Tex. Water Code § 16.053(h)(10). The RWPG must present its analysis of infeasible strategies contained in its currently adopted plan in conjunction with the public meeting held to determine its process for identifying potentially feasible water management strategies for its upcoming plan, and amend its adopted RWP as appropriate. *See* 31 Tex. Admin. Code § 357.12(b).

GCDs may also initiate reviews and amendments of regional (and state) water plans. The process outlined in 31 Texas Administrative Code section 357.64, the implementing rule for Water Code section 16.053(p)–(p–4), provides that a GCD may identify and propose resolutions to conflicts that exist between the GCD's approved groundwater management plan (developed under Water Code section 36.1071) and the approved state water plan. In this process, the TWDB executive administrator again plays the role of providing assistance, facilitating conflict resolution, and assisting in mediation between the GCD and the RWPG. If those efforts fail, the executive administrator makes recommendations for the TWDB's consideration, and the TWDB may ultimately require revisions to an approved RWP or to a GCD's approved management plan. *See* 31 Tex. Admin. Code § 357.64(c). See Chapter 21 of this book for further discussion.

§ 20.7 The State Water Plan

Under Texas Water Code section 16.051, the TWDB is responsible for preparing, developing, formulating, and adopting a comprehensive state water plan in successive five-year periods, which began on January 5, 2002. In this "bottom-up" process, the sixteen approved RWPs for each five-year cycle are combined by the TWDB into the comprehensive state water plan. The plan provides for the orderly development, management, and conservation of water resources and preparation for and response to drought conditions "in order that sufficient water will be available at a reasonable cost to ensure public health, safety, and welfare; further economic development; and protect the agricultural and natural resources of the entire state." Tex. Water Code § 16.051(a). Stressing the importance of the plan's critical role as a planning tool, the 2011 legislature adopted language requiring that it incorporate "an evaluation of the state's progress in meeting future water needs, including an evaluation of the extent to which water management strategies and projects implemented after the adoption of the preceding state water plan have affected that progress." Tex. Water Code § 16.051(a–1).

When adopted by the TWDB, the state water plan serves as a guide to state water policy, and the TCEQ must take the water plan into consideration in matters coming before it. *See* Tex. Water Code § 16.051(b). In coordination with the TCEQ, the Texas Department of Agriculture, and the Texas

Parks and Wildlife Department, the TWDB must adopt rules establishing guidance principles for the state water plan that reflect the public interest of the entire state. *See* Tex. Water Code § 16.051(d). These rules were adopted in 1998, as 31 Texas Administrative Code chapter 358, "State Water Planning Guidelines," and have been amended several times since the initial adoption.

To keep the guidance principles of the state water plan current, they too are reviewed and updated on a five-year schedule. *See* Tex. Water Code § 16.051(d). Development of the state plan and RWPs is guided by the principles set forth in 31 Texas Administrative Code section 358.3. These twenty-eight principles reflect a variety of important considerations in water planning, including the principle that all surface waters are held in trust by the state and are generally governed by the prior appropriation doctrine, and the principle that the use of groundwater in Texas is governed by the rule of capture doctrine, unless such use is regulated by a GCD. *See* 31 Tex. Admin. Code § 358.3(13), (15). See Chapters 4 and 10 (discussing the prior appropriation doctrine) and 16 (discussing groundwater law and regulation) of this book.

§ 20.7:1 Content of the State Water Plan

The content of the state water plan is prescribed by statute and rule. *See* Tex. Water Code § 16.051; 31 Tex. Admin. Code § 358.4. The rule lists a minimum of nine topics to be addressed in the state water plan. *See* 31 Tex. Admin. Code § 358.4(b). These topics include consideration of recommendations of river and stream segments of unique ecological value and sites of unique value for construction of reservoirs. *See* 31 Tex. Admin. Code § 358.4(b)(5). The TWDB may also include legislative recommendations to further the goals of water planning, including recommendations that would facilitate more voluntary water transfers. *See* Tex. Water Code § 16.051(e); 31 Tex. Admin. Code § 358.4(b)(6). As described at section 20.6:7 above, and dramatically illustrated in the *Ward Timber* case, interregional conflicts must be resolved before a regional plan can be approved and incorporated into the state water plan. *See* Tex. Water Code § 16.053(h)(7)(A).

In deference to concerns about meeting future water requirements, the statute, as revised by the 2011 legislature, now requires not only an evaluation of the state's progress in meeting future water needs but also an analysis of the previous plan's projects that receive the board's financial assistance. The statute also encourages the board to use implementation data from RWPGs. *See* Tex. Water Code § 16.051(a–1)(2), (a–2). See Chapter 37 of this book for a discussion of financing water projects.

§ 20.7:2 Adoption of the State Water Plan

Before adoption of a new or amended state water plan, the TWDB publishes notice in the *Texas Register* and mails notice to each RWPG at least thirty days in advance of its action. After holding a hearing, the TWDB may decide to adopt the new plan or amendment. *See* 31 Tex. Admin. Code § 358.4(a).

§ 20.7:3 Amendment of the State Water Plan

Various provisions in the TWDB rules relate to amendment of the RWPs and possible conforming amendments in the state water plan. If an RWP needs amendment after that plan has been approved and incorporated into the state plan, not only would the regional plan require amendment but the state plan would as well. Procedures for amending regional and state water plans are set forth in 31 Texas Administrative Code section 357.51. More specifically, section 357.51(h) states that following amendments of RWPs, the TWDB shall make any necessary amendments to the state water plan. Under 31 Texas Administrative Code section 358.4(a), approved RWPs shall be incorporated into the state water plan pursuant to Texas Water Code section 16.053 and 31 Texas Administrative Code chapter 357. Generally, amendments may be adopted after notice and hearing, with some exceptions for amendments associated with water supplies for clean coal projects under Water Code section 16.053(r).

§ 20.7:4 Impact of the State Water Plan on Water Projects

The inclusion of an approved RWP in the state water plan adopted by the TWDB has significant implications. First, the TWDB may provide financial assistance to political subdivisions for water supply projects only if (1) the needs to be addressed by the project will be addressed in a manner that is consistent with the state water plan; (2) there is an approved, current RWP encompassing the project's area; (3) the project is consistent with the RWP; and (4) the water audit required under Texas Water Code section 16.0121 has been completed and filed. *See* Tex. Water Code § 16.053(j). For example, water needs, as determined by a region's supply and demand analyses, may provide the impetus for new water projects. When a region determines that an increase in future supply is needed, the region will develop water management strategies or projects to achieve this goal. Later, if water management strategies or projects are proposed that are not mentioned in or that are inconsistent with the state plan and RWPs, then the TWDB may deny a request for state funding of those projects. *See* Tex. Water Code § 16.053(j).

If an RWPG does not adopt and submit its plan on time, and if financial assistance from the TWDB is in jeopardy, water suppliers within the regional planning area will have to either seek special assistance from the legislature (as did Region L in 2007—*see* Act of May 23, 2007, 80th Leg., R.S., ch. 1279, 2007 Tex. Gen. Laws 4278, eff. June 15, 2007) or pursue a waiver of the requirement. Although the TWDB may waive these prerequisites for financial assistance, the granting or denial of the waiver is left to the agency's administrative discretion. *See* Tex. Water Code § 16.053(k).

Second, when the TCEQ considers an application for use of state water (surface water), the TCEQ must consider the state water plan and any approved RWP for the area or areas in which the water is proposed to be stored, diverted, or used. *See* Tex. Water Code § 11.1501. Most important, to grant an application under Water Code section 11.121 for the appropriation of state water, the TCEQ must conclude, along with other findings, that the proposed appropriation addresses a water supply need in a manner that is consistent with the state plan and RWPs. The statute allows a waiver of this requirement if the TCEQ determines that conditions warrant a waiver. *See* Tex. Water Code § 11.134(b)(3)(E).

At times, a new project may be proposed that needs financial assistance and TCEQ water rights permits, but it is not included in the relevant regional and state water plans. To obtain the necessary financing and permits for such a project, a water supplier has two options: (1) it can attempt to obtain an amendment to include its project in the adopted, approved regional plan and the state plan, or (2) it can seek a waiver of Water Code sections 11.134(b) or 16.053(j).

§ 20.7:5 The Next Generation of State Water Plans

With the adoption and publication of the 2017 state water plan, the TWDB announced the beginning of a new generation of state water plans. Unlike prior plans, the 2017 state water plan reflected the sweeping legislative changes made in 2013 with the passage of H.B. 4 and the possibility of providing low-cost state funding for the water projects described in the state water plan. In a dramatic increase from the 2011 RWPs, the 2016 plans included 5,500 water management strategies to address water supply shortages and put greater emphasis on conservation and reuse strategies, as well as innovative technologies, to diversify water supplies in the midst of potential drought-of-record conditions. *See* 2017 State Water Plan, at 15. The 2017 state water plan included some firsts: it was the first plan to dedicate an entire chapter to drought response and the first to report on the progress toward implementing water management strategies identified in the prior plan. 2017 State Water Plan, at 16. In addition, it was the first plan to incorporate, by adoption, a data-filled interactive online state water plan, which is available on the TWDB website at https://2017.texasstatewaterplan.org/statewide. The published plan (as amended) and a link to the interactive plan may be accessed through www.twdb.texas.gov/waterplanning/swp/2017, along with the nine earlier state water plans.

RWPs were formally adopted by the TWDB in January 2021, and the 2022 State Water Plan was adopted on July 7, 2021.

III. Conclusion

§ 20.8 Conclusion

In the last twenty years, the state has made significant progress in its water planning, development, and conservation efforts. State laws enacted in recent years have taken a proactive, while somewhat prescriptive, approach to water planning that attempts to utilize a consistent approach that is sufficiently adaptive to meet the widely varying needs of a diverse state.

At the same time, the state's current consensus-driven, bottom-up approach to water planning and water projects is facing its own challenges. Meeting the demand for water in many regions of Texas is a serious challenge, even with improved planning tools. The issues faced by the RWPGs are often scientifically, logistically, and politically complex.

The tasks of the RWPGs, including the preparation and adoption of regional plans, are subject to specific deadlines and rigorous procedures. Although a five-year planning cycle may appear to provide a generous amount of time to complete the assigned tasks, in reality an RWPG may barely complete its preparation of an Initially Prepared Plan when work begins on the next planning cycle. The sophisticated planning efforts of some local water providers must be integrated into the planning process, while other providers that have not performed local planning studies simultaneously rely on the RWPG for development of their plans.

Planning groups have added members over time, and members face a constant challenge to gain the knowledge needed to address the complicated issues before them, while each year brings new twists and turns in the information they are gathering and evaluating. With rapid growth in numerous sectors, the planning process must accommodate a broad variety of conditions while producing relevant, accurate information for local- and state-level decision makers. As evidenced in recent years, locally driven plans for management of water resources may sometimes be at odds with the long-term resource development and conservation objectives of a neighboring region, of the state, or of a neighboring state. Clearly, the implementation of the state's water planning laws presents useful, interesting, and challenging work for everyone involved.

CHAPTER 21

Groundwater Management Area Joint Planning

Monique Norman[1] and William R. Hutchison[2]

I. Introduction

§ 21.1 Overview

Groundwater resource planning and management are integral to the state's overall water planning and management, as discussed in Chapter 20 of this book. Texas's dual nature of water resource law—surface water law and groundwater law—complicates these processes. Other complexities arise from the regulatory approach that has evolved for the management of groundwater resources. Groundwater conservation districts (GCDs) "are the state's preferred method of groundwater management." Tex. Water Code § 36.0015(b). These governmental entities have been created in different configurations—single county, multicounty, partial county, single aquifer, multi-aquifer, and partial aquifer. See Chapter 16 of this book for an in-depth discussion of GCDs. Groundwater planning and management must consider two hydrologic facts: (1) aquifer characteristics and uses vary greatly across the state and often across a district, and (2) the political boundary of a GCD does not necessarily coincide with groundwater flow and the effects of groundwater pumping.

In 2005, the Texas legislature addressed these hydrologic management and planning issues by creating a framework for groundwater planning that focuses on a more regional basis, while acknowledging the importance and responsibilities of local groundwater management by GCDs. This groundwater management area joint planning process requires GCDs within specified groundwater management areas (GMAs) to work together to develop policy goals for groundwater resources within those areas. The legislature created a unique model in which local, regional, state, and stakeholder interests all have important roles in groundwater planning and management to meet the future needs of Texas. This chapter explains various groundwater planning concepts, discusses the history of groundwater availability planning, and then describes the current GMA joint planning process.

---

1. Monique Milisci Norman practices water law in Austin, Texas. She primarily focuses on groundwater law, representing groundwater conservation districts across the state.

2. William R. Hutchison previously was the director of the Groundwater Resources Division of the Texas Water Development Board. He is currently an independent groundwater consultant in Jamaica Beach, Texas.

II. Available Groundwater Supplies

§ 21.2 Groundwater Availability Modeling

As discussed in Chapter 20 of this book, the limits of existing water supplies and the increasing demands of population growth necessitate cautious water planning, including determining available groundwater supplies. While the term "groundwater availability" connotes a physical inventory of developable groundwater resources, in fact it has a narrower meaning. As a result of the statutory language of the joint planning process, the term is used to define the amount of groundwater that may be used from an aquifer over a specific period of time, that is consistent with the management goals established by a governmental entity based on science and public policy considerations. *See* Robert E. Mace et al., *Estimating Groundwater Availability in Texas*, *in Water Allocation in Texas: The Legal Issues*, Texas Rural Water Association and Texas Water Conservation Association Water Law Seminar, Austin (2001) [hereinafter *Estimating Groundwater Availability*]; see also Chapter 19 of this book for an in-depth discussion of determining groundwater availability.

Currently, GCDs overlying the same aquifer determine groundwater availability for that aquifer, with the assistance of the Texas Water Development Board (TWDB). The groundwater availability estimates thus determined are one of several tools with which a GCD manages the resource and permits groundwater production. The state uses the groundwater availability estimates for planning purposes in the regional and state water plans and for the review of state loans for groundwater projects. See Chapter 20 of this book on state water planning and Chapter 37 on financing water projects. As discussed below, this system has evolved over decades.

Setting groundwater availability limits for Texas aquifers requires a balance between providing adequate water supplies for today's needs and preserving the viability of an aquifer for future generations. Groundwater availability is based on a combination of science and public policy. The science, known as hydrology or hydrogeology, aids in determining how an aquifer functions and how it reacts to different pumping scenarios. Groundwater availability determinations are also public policy statements on how the resource should be managed considering current and projected demands and other factors. Robert E. Mace, Address at the Texas Association of Groundwater Districts Meeting (Jan. 30, 2007); see also Chapter 19 of this book regarding groundwater availability modeling. Issues have been raised about not only how groundwater availability should be determined but also who should make the determination. As history reveals and as summarized below, the relationship between groundwater resource planning and management and overall state water resource planning and management has been contentious at times and continues to pose a challenge to water resource stakeholders. Views differ on whether groundwater availability should be determined by the local GCDs, the regional water planning groups (see Chapter 20), the TWDB, or the Texas Commission on Environmental Quality (TCEQ). Under current law, groundwater availability is determined by GCDs in the groundwater management area joint planning process. *See* Tex. Water Code §§ 36.108–.1086.

III. Groundwater Planning

§ 21.3 Introduction

To understand the groundwater management area joint planning process, one must be familiar with the legislatively created planning concept of GMAs and priority groundwater management areas (PGMAs). Unlike GCDs, subsidence districts, and the Edwards Aquifer Authority, these two types of areas are not political subdivisions or governmental entities. They are not legal entities—they cannot sue or be sued. Both GMAs and PGMAs are designated by the TWDB and the TCEQ, respectively, to facilitate the management of the state's groundwater resources.

§ 21.4 Groundwater Management Areas

The concept of designated areas designed to facilitate the management of the state's groundwater resources has existed since H.B. 162, 51st Legislature (1949), and has undergone many legislative changes leading up to S.B. 2 in 2001. *See* Robert E. Mace et al., *A Streetcar Named Desired Future Conditions: The New Groundwater Availability for Texas (Revised)*, at app. A ("Legislative History Concerning Groundwater Management Areas"), *in The Changing Face of Water Rights in Texas* (State Bar of Texas 2008) [hereinafter *A Streetcar Named Desired Future Conditions*]. While GMAs existed before 2001, their designation occurred piecemeal. *See* Texas Natural Resource Conservation Commission & Texas Water Development Board, *Priority Groundwater Management Areas and Groundwater Conservation Districts, Report to the 76th Legislature*, at 32 & fig. 3 (Jan. 1999). Senate Bill 2, 77th Legislature (2001), however, required the TWDB to designate GMAs for all major and minor aquifers of the state by September 1, 2003. Act of May 27, 2001, 77th Leg., R.S., ch. 966, § 2.22 (codified at Tex. Water Code § 35.004). The TWDB was given the task of designating these management areas with the objective of providing the most suitable area for the management of the groundwater resources. The TWDB was directed to establish boundaries that coincide with groundwater reservoirs or subdivisions of groundwater reservoirs, to the extent feasible. The TWDB was also authorized to consider the boundaries of political subdivisions when establishing GMA boundaries. *See* Tex. Water Code § 35.004(a). The TWDB proposed sixteen GMAs covering the entire state of Texas. Since their establishment in 2003, the boundaries between two different sets of management areas have been amended to address local concerns. See Plate 3. As discussed later in this chapter, under H.B. 1763, these GMAs serve as joint planning areas for purposes of developing desired future conditions and calculating modeled available groundwater based on large segments of the aquifers, not just political boundaries.

§ 21.5 Priority Groundwater Management Areas

As the legislature explored how best to understand and manage the state's groundwater resources, in 1985 it also introduced the concept of a "critical area process," which ultimately became the PGMA process. Based on information gathered by the TCEQ and the TWDB, the TCEQ must identify areas of the state "that are experiencing or that are expected to experience, within the immediately following 50-year period, critical groundwater problems." Tex. Water Code § 35.007(a). "The ultimate purpose of priority groundwater management areas is the creation of groundwater conservation districts, either through local initiative or by the Commission." *A Streetcar Named Desired Future Conditions*, at 1. Although adequate management of groundwater was the reason for establishing the PGMA review and designation procedure, PGMAs are not an integral part of the GMA joint planning process addressed in this chapter, but are mentioned here to avoid confusion, considering their objective and name. For additional information on PGMAs, see Chapter 16 of this book, which discusses various methods of creating GCDs, including the PGMA process.

IV. Before Joint Planning: Determining Groundwater Availability

§ 21.6 Introduction

Before the creation of GCDs, and long before the current GMA joint planning process, determining groundwater availability was merely a function of a well owner deciding whether sufficient groundwater was available at a particular well site. Under the rule of capture, no groundwater regulations existed, and groundwater availability was determined on a well-by-well basis by what was sometimes called the law of the biggest pump. *See, e.g., Houston & T.C. Ry. Co. v. East*, 81 S.W. 279 (Tex. 1904); see also Chapter 4 of this book. With the passage of the Underground Water Conservation Districts Act of 1949 and the creation of GCDs beginning in the 1950s, GCDs had the authority to manage and limit groundwater production. A GCD also had implied authority to determine groundwater availability. *See* Act of May 23, 1949, 51st Leg., R.S., ch. 306. (The High Plains Underground Water Conservation District No. 1 in Lubbock, Texas, was the first to be organized in 1951; the North Plains Groundwater Conservation District and the Panhandle Groundwater Conservation District were created in 1955.) Until 1997, the TWDB determined groundwater availability for planning purposes, but GCDs were not required to adopt their estimates. Since that time, the law has evolved as the state continues to refine all aspects of its water planning and management. See Chapters 20 and 22 of this book, which address state water planning and drought planning.

§ 21.7 Pre–Senate Bill 1: Groundwater Conservation District Management Plans and Water Availability

The next historical step toward local determination of the availability of Texas groundwater resources was the requirement that GCDs develop management plans outlining their methods for managing the groundwater resources within their boundaries. In 1989 and 1995, legislation was passed requiring GCDs to develop comprehensive management plans. *See* Act of May 29, 1989, 71st Leg., R.S., ch. 936; Act of May 29, 1995, 74th Leg., R.S., ch. 933. At that time, requirements for the contents of management plans were general: providing for “the most efficient use of the groundwater, for controlling and preventing waste of groundwater, and for controlling and preventing subsidence” and specifying “in as much detail as possible, the acts, procedures, performance, and avoidance that are or may be necessary to effect the plan, including specifications and proposed rules.” *See* Act of May 29, 1989, 71st Leg., R.S., ch. 936; Act of May 29, 1995, 74th Leg., R.S., ch. 933. GCDs were required to file a copy of their management plans and rules with the TCEQ or its predecessor agency; submittal to the TWDB was not required. *See* Act of May 29, 1989, 71st Leg., R.S., ch. 936; Act of May 29, 1995, 74th Leg., R.S., ch. 933. Additionally, joint planning was initiated as the GCDs were required to forward their management plans to other GCDs within their management area, to review the goals of each district’s management plan, and to consider how they affected groundwater planning throughout the management area and how effective the goals were in conserving and protecting groundwater. *See* Act of May 29, 1995, 74th Leg., R.S., ch. 933, § 2, sec. 36.108(b). Districts could petition the TCEQ or its predecessor agency to request an inquiry into whether neighboring districts adopted adequate rules to protect the local groundwater. *See* Act of May 29, 1995, 74th Leg., R.S., ch. 933, § 2, sec. 36.108(d).

In 1997, the passage of Senate Bill 1 (*see* Act of June 1, 1997, 75th Leg., R.S., ch. 1010 [hereinafter S.B. 1]) shifted the responsibility of determining groundwater availability for planning away from the TWDB and the GCDs to the newly created regional water planning groups. Under S.B. 1, the availability determinations in a district’s groundwater management plan had to be consistent with those of the planning groups. *See* S.B. 1, art. 1; see also Chapter 20 of this book. GCDs were required, for the first time, to include groundwater availability information in the management plans submitted to and reviewed by the TWDB. *See* Tex. Water Code §§ 16.053–.056 (as enacted by S.B. 1, § 1.01, except as provided in § 9.02(b)–(f) (1997)).

§ 21.8 Determining Groundwater Availability under Senate Bill 1

In 1997, the 75th Legislature put in place a “bottom-up” water planning process designed to ensure that the water needs of all Texans are met as Texas moves into the future. *See* S.B. 1, art. 1. Senate Bill 1 required individuals representing eleven interest groups to serve as members of regional water planning groups to prepare regional water plans for their respective areas. *See* S.B. 1, art. 1. The legislative directive in S.B. 1 was to—

> prepare a regional water plan, using an existing state water plan . . . and local water plans . . . as a guide, . . . that provides for the orderly development, management, and conservation of water resources and preparation for and response to drought conditions in order that sufficient water will be available at a reasonable cost to ensure public health, safety, and welfare; further economic development; and protect the agricultural and natural resources of that particular region.

Tex. Water Code § 16.053(a) (as enacted by S.B. 1, § 1.01 (1997)). See Chapter 20 of this book for a detailed discussion of S.B. 1 and state water planning.

Although the creation of the regional water planning groups was a step toward addressing Texas's significant water supply concerns due to population growth, it also raised local groundwater control concerns. Senate Bill 1 proclaimed that GCDs were "the state's preferred method of groundwater management." *See* Tex. Water Code § 36.0015(b) (as enacted by S.B. 1, § 4.21 (1997)). However, this local control statement was tempered by the provision that took away GCDs' authority to determine groundwater availability by delegating that responsibility primarily to the regional water planning groups. *See* Tex. Water Code § 16.053(e)(4)(B) (as enacted by S.B. 1, § 1.02 (1997) (stating that each regional water planning group must submit to the TWDB a regional water plan that includes consideration of the certified GCD management plans and other plans).

Senate Bill 1 also significantly changed the GCD management plan requirements. A GCD was required to adopt a management plan that addressed the following management goals for the district:

1. providing the most efficient use of groundwater;
2. controlling and preventing waste of groundwater;
3. controlling and preventing subsidence;
4. addressing conjunctive surface water management issues; and
5. addressing natural resource issues.

See Tex. Water Code § 36.1071(a) (as enacted by S.B. 1, § 4.28 (1997)).

Pursuant to S.B. 1, upon the required submittal to the TWDB, the board certified the plan if it was administratively complete, but the board could not make substantive determinations regarding the plan. *See* Tex. Water Code § 36.1072 (as enacted by S.B. 1, § 4.28 (1997)). Additionally, GCDs were required to submit their groundwater management plans to the regional water planning groups for their "consideration." Tex. Water Code § 16.053(e)(4)(B) (as enacted by S.B. 1, § 1.02 (1997)). After the planning groups determined the groundwater availability for the different aquifers throughout the state, they were required to submit their adopted regional water plans for approval and inclusion in the state water plan. Tex. Water Code § 16.053(i) (as enacted by S.B. 1, § 1.02 (1997)). The board approved a regional water plan only after it determined that all interregional conflicts involving that regional water planning area were resolved; the plan included water conservation practices and drought management measures; and the plan was consistent with long-term protection of the state's water resources, agricultural resources, and natural resources. *See* Tex. Water Code § 16.053(h) (as enacted by S.B. 1, § 1.02 (1997)). The board then confirmed that the GCDs' water availability calculations in their management plans would allow for the implementation of the regional water plan. *See* Tex. Water Code § 36.1071(e)(4) (as enacted by S.B. 1, § 4.28 (1997)).

§ 21.9 Conflicting Groundwater Availability Estimates under the Senate Bill 1 Process

GCDs did not always agree with the regional water plans' estimates of groundwater availability. Under such circumstances, a district could appeal the regional planning group's determinations of availability. *See* Tex. Water Code § 16.053(h)(6) (as enacted by S.B. 1, § 1.02 (1997)). After 2005, if a district filed a petition with the board stating that a conflict requiring resolution existed between the district's board-certified management plan and an approved state water plan, the board was required to provide technical assistance to and facilitate coordination between the district and the involved regional planning group to resolve the conflict. Tex. Water Code § 16.053(p). Mediation between the GCD and the planning group was required within forty-five days of the petition's being filed with the board. Tex. Water Code § 16.053(p). If the board determined that resolution of the conflict required a revision of an approved regional water plan, the board suspended the approval of the plan and provided information to the regional water planning group. Tex. Water Code § 16.053(p–1). The regional water planning group then prepared any revisions to its plan specified by the board and held at least one public hearing. Tex. Water Code § 16.053(p–1). After considering all public and board comments, the planning group prepared, revised, and adopted its plan and submitted it to the board for approval and inclusion in the state water plan. Tex. Water Code § 16.053(p–1).

If the board determined that resolution of the conflict required a revision of the GCD's approved management plan, the board provided that information to the district. Tex. Water Code § 16.053(p–2). The GCD was required to prepare any revisions to its plan based on the information provided by the board and hold a public hearing in the district. Tex. Water Code § 16.053(p–2). After considering all public and board comments, the district prepared, revised, and adopted its plan and submitted the revised plan to the board. Tex. Water Code § 16.053(p–2). If the GCD disagreed with the decision of the board, it could appeal the decision to a Travis County district court. Tex. Water Code § 16.053(p–3). The standard of review on appeal would be trial de novo. Tex. Water Code § 16.053(p–3).

V. Groundwater Management Area Joint Planning

§ 21.10 Introduction

As early as 2002, the state water plan recommended that "[t]he Legislature should consider requiring groundwater conservation districts to include in their groundwater management plans a management goal quantifying the desired future condition of the aquifer. The future condition could be described using water quantity and water quality parameters." *See* Texas Water Development Board, *Water for Texas—2002* 5 (2002), www.twdb.texas.gov/waterplanning/swp/2002/index.asp. During the 79th legislative session in 2005, the responsibility for determining groundwater availability was delegated back to GCDs through the passage of House Bill 1763. *See* Act of May 30, 2005, 79th Leg., R.S., ch. 970 [hereinafter H.B. 1763]. Under this procedure, a GCD was required to work with the other districts within its GMA to develop and manage groundwater availability. *See* Tex. Water Code § 36.1072.

The regional planning groups are required to use the groundwater availability estimates adopted by the GCDs during joint planning. *See* Tex. Water Code § 16.053(e)(3)(A); 31 Tex. Admin. Code § 357.32(d). Procedures were also put in place to allow the regional water planning groups, the affected GCDs, and other affected persons to appeal the GCDs' findings. *See* Tex. Water Code § 16.053(p)–(p–4). While the responsibility for determining groundwater availability remains with GCDs, the GMA joint planning process has evolved over time, as discussed below.

Two key phrases are at the heart of GMA joint planning: "desired future condition" and "modeled available groundwater" (previously "managed available groundwater"). *Compare* H.B.

1763, §§ 2, 8 (former versions of Texas Water Code sections 36.001(25), 36.108(o)), *with* Tex. Water Code §§ 36.001(25), 36.1084 (current versions). Under joint planning, GCDs wholly or partially within each GMA (member districts) adopt desired future conditions of the aquifers located in the GMA; the TWDB calculates available groundwater; and appeals of desired future conditions can be initiated. The deadline for *adoption* of the desired future conditions during the first cycle of joint planning was September 1, 2010. After that deadline, activities associated with the first cycle of joint planning continued: calculation of the managed available groundwater (later, modeled available groundwater), and appeals of the desired future conditions. These first-cycle activities are all controlled by the law established by H.B. 1763. As of September 1, 2011, all joint planning activities, other than those of the first cycle, are controlled by law established by Senate Bill 660. *See* Act of May 29, 2011, 82d Leg., R.S., ch. 1233, §§ 23–26, eff. Sept. 1, 2011 [hereinafter S.B. 660]. The joint planning process must be repeated, and desired future conditions adopted, every five years. Tex. Water Code § 36.108(d). In 2013, the 83rd Legislature amended section 36.108 by adding subsection (d–5), which postponed the deadline for the second round of proposals for adoption of desired future conditions until May 1, 2016. *See* Act of May 20, 2013, 83d Leg., R.S., ch. 785, § 1 (S.B. 1282), eff. Sept. 1, 2013. In 2017, the 85th Legislature amended the deadline for the third round of proposed desired future conditions to May 1, 2021, and of adopted final desired future conditions to January 5, 2022, and every five years thereafter. *See* Act of May 19, 2017, 85th Leg., R.S., ch. 471, §§ 2, 3 (H.B. 2215), eff. June 9, 2017 (amending Tex. Water Code § 36.108(d)).

For the first cycle of joint planning, member districts relied on the TWDB definition of desired future condition because it was not defined by statute. *See* 31 Tex. Admin. Code § 356.2(8), *repealed* 37 Tex. Reg. 10,238 (2012). The term is now defined as "a quantitative description, adopted in accordance with [Texas Water Code] Section 36.108, of the desired condition of the groundwater resources in a management area at one or more specified future times." Tex. Water Code § 36.001(30).

The districts in each GMA must submit their adopted desired future conditions to the TWDB. For the first cycle of desired future conditions, the TWDB calculated the managed available groundwater in the management area based on the desired future conditions adopted by the districts. The TWDB later reissued these initial estimates as modeled available groundwater estimates.

For future joint planning cycles, the term *managed available groundwater* has been replaced by the term *modeled available groundwater*. *See* Tex. Water Code § 36.1084. "'Modeled available groundwater' means the amount of water that the executive administrator [of the TWDB] determines may be produced on an annual average basis to achieve a desired future condition established under [Texas Water Code] Section 36.108." Tex. Water Code § 36.001(25). In short, the districts in a GMA adopt desired future conditions for the aquifers in the management area. The TWDB calculates water availability to achieve the desired future conditions. Under this system, policy and science play roles in the determination of groundwater availability, which is then expressed as a modeled available groundwater number. Desired future conditions are policies informed by science and collaboration between the GCDs within a GMA. The science that supports a desired future condition is contained in hydrogeologic data and groundwater availability models that are used in developing desired future conditions. Various aspects of this joint planning can be challenged through statutory appeal processes.

§ 21.11 Adoption of a Desired Future Condition

The first round of desired future conditions, which were adopted by September 1, 2010, considered the uses or conditions of an aquifer within the management area that differed substantially from one geographic area to another. *See* H.B. 1763, § 8 (former version of Texas Water Code section 36.108(d)). Once the TWDB amended 31 Texas Administrative Code chapter 356 to list issues to be considered by the TWDB when considering, during an appeal, whether a desired future condition is reasonable, member districts added these regulatory considerations when developing the desired future conditions. *See* 31 Tex. Admin. Code §§ 356.40–.42.

For subsequent changes made to a desired future condition, districts must consider nine factors:

(1) aquifer uses or conditions within the management area, including conditions that differ substantially from one geographic area to another;

(2) the water supply needs and water management strategies included in the state water plan;

(3) hydrological conditions, including for each aquifer in the management area the total estimated recoverable storage as provided by the executive administrator, and the average annual recharge, inflows, and discharge;

(4) other environmental impacts, including impacts on spring flow and other interactions between groundwater and surface water;

(5) the impact on subsidence;

(6) socioeconomic impacts reasonably expected to occur;

(7) the impact on the interests and rights in private property, including ownership and the rights of management area landowners and their lessees and assigns in groundwater as recognized under [Texas Water Code] Section 36.002;

(8) the feasibility of achieving the desired future condition; and

(9) any other information relevant to the specific desired future conditions.

Tex. Water Code § 36.108(d).

After considering and documenting the above-listed factors, GCDs may establish different desired future conditions for each aquifer, aquifer subdivision, or geologic strata located in their management area or for each geographic area overlying an aquifer within the management area. *See* Tex. Water Code § 36.108(d–1). If different desired future conditions are adopted for different geographic areas overlying an aquifer or subdivision of an aquifer, the desired future conditions must be compatible. *See* 31 Tex. Admin. Code § 356.2(8), *repealed* 37 Tex. Reg. 10,238 (2012). Desired future conditions adopted after 2015 must provide a balance between the highest practicable level of groundwater production and the conservation, preservation, protection, recharging, and prevention of waste of groundwater and control of subsidence in the management area. *See* Tex. Water Code § 36.108(d–2).

The process of establishing a desired future condition typically involves the districts meeting over an extended period of time while consulting with hydrologists, the board, stakeholders, and the public. The member districts are required to comply with the Open Meetings Act and the Public Information Act when holding GMA joint planning meetings. *See* Tex. Water Code § 36.108(e). Such meetings must also comply with the expanded requirements of section 36.108(e), (e–1), (e–2), and (e–3). The district representatives may elect one district to be responsible for providing the notice of a joint meeting. Notice must be provided at least ten days before the meeting. The notice must be submitted for posting by the secretary of state and county clerk of each county located wholly or partly in a district that is located wholly or partly in the management area. The notice must also be posted at the district office of each member district, and must include the date, time, and location of the meeting; a summary of any action proposed to be taken; the names of member districts; and contact information so the public can obtain additional information. Tex. Water Code § 36.108(e), (e–2). The failure or refusal of one or more districts to post notice for a joint meeting does not invalidate an action taken at the joint meeting. Tex. Water Code § 36.108(e–3).

While there was minimal statutory guidance regarding the procedure for establishing a desired future condition during the first cycle of joint planning, the process has been formalized for the later rounds of joint planning. *Compare* H.B. 1763, § 8 (former version of Texas Water Code section 36.108), *with* Tex. Water Code §§ 36.108–.1086 (current version). Under current law, member districts meet until they have adopted a "proposed" desired future condition. This proposal must be approved during a joint planning meeting, by a two-thirds vote of the representatives of all the member districts. *See* Tex. Water Code § 36.108(d–2). Once the proposed desired future condition is approved, it is distributed to the member districts, and a public comment period of not less than ninety days begins. During the public comment period, after posting notice as required by section 36.063, each district must hold a public hearing on the proposed desired future condition relevant to that district. During the public comment period, a copy of the proposed desired future condition and supporting materials must be available in the district office. After the close of the public comment period, the district must compile a summary of relevant comments received, any suggested revisions to the proposed desired future condition, and the basis for such revisions. These materials must be considered at the next joint planning meeting. *See* Tex. Water Code § 36.108(d–2).

A joint planning meeting to consider final adoption of the proposed desired future condition must be held after all member districts have submitted district summaries. Before voting to adopt the final desired future condition, the member districts' representatives must review the district summaries, consider any district's suggested revisions to the proposed desired future condition, and finally approve the desired future condition by resolution. The resolution adopting the desired future condition must be approved by a two-thirds vote of all the member districts' representatives. In the third round of desired future conditions, the adoption of the resolution approving the final desired future conditions must occur no later than January 5, 2022. Subsequent desired future conditions must be proposed and finally adopted by the district representatives before the end of each successive five-year period after that date. Tex. Water Code § 36.108(d–3).

Once a desired future condition is adopted, the district representatives must submit to the TWDB and to all member districts proof that notice was posted for the joint planning meeting at which the desired future condition was finally adopted, a copy of the adoption resolution, and a desired future condition explanatory report. The report must—

(1) identify each desired future condition;

(2) provide the policy and technical justifications for each desired future condition;

(3) include documentation that the factors under [Texas Water Code] Subsection [36.108](d) were considered by the districts and a discussion of how the adopted desired future conditions impact each factor;

(4) list other desired future condition options considered, if any, and the reasons why those options were not adopted; and

(5) discuss reasons why recommendations made by advisory committees and relevant public comments received by the districts were or were not incorporated into the desired future conditions.

Tex. Water Code § 36.108(d–3). After a member district receives notification from the TWDB that the desired future condition resolution and explanatory report are administratively complete, the district must adopt the applicable desired future conditions in the resolution and report. *See* Tex. Water Code § 36.108(d–4).

§ 21.12 Calculation of Water Availability

As mentioned at section 21.11 above, the adoption of desired future conditions under the first cycle of joint planning was completed by September 1, 2010. The first cycle continued, however, as managed available groundwater calculations (and later, modeled available groundwater) were issued by the TWDB and as desired future conditions were challenged. Because these first-cycle activities were controlled by pre–S.B. 660 law, the following sections discuss first-cycle joint planning water availability separately from such activities after the first cycle of joint planning.

§ 21.12:1 Managed Available Groundwater

For desired future conditions adopted before September 1, 2011, once the desired future conditions were adopted for each of the aquifers within the GMA, the desired future conditions were submitted to the TWDB as required. *See* H.B. 1763, § 8 (formerly Tex. Water Code § 36.108(o)); *see also* 31 Tex. Admin. Code ch. 356, subch. C. The board then provided each district and regional water planning group located wholly or partly in the management area with the managed available groundwater calculations in the management area, based on the desired future conditions of the groundwater resources established under section 36.108 of the Texas Water Code. *See* H.B. 1763, § 8 (formerly Tex. Water Code § 36.108(o)).

During the first cycle, several GMAs submitted desired future conditions early during the period and the TWDB issued managed available groundwater for those desired future conditions. The TWDB reported managed available groundwater as equivalent to the total pumping that would achieve the desired future condition and did not explicitly consider the uses that were exempt from permitting. Water Code section 36.117(b) sets mandatory exemptions from permitting; section 36.117(a) allows GCDs to exempt other uses from requiring a permit; and in some cases, the enabling legislation of a district either expands exempt uses or narrows their scope. For example, the Hays Trinity Groundwater Conservation District enabling legislation expanded exempt use as codified at section 8843.104 of the Special District Local Laws Code. See also Chapter 16 of this book for a discussion of exempt uses.

Based on this early experience interpreting the requirements of a rather broadly written section 36.108, questions arose about whether exempt use pumping should be considered when the TWDB calculated the managed available groundwater. These questions centered on former Water Code section 36.001(25), which defined "managed available groundwater" to mean "the amount of water that may be permitted by a district for beneficial use in accordance with the desired future condition of the aquifer." *See* H.B. 1763, § 2. The TWDB staff did not include exempt pumpage in their calculation of managed available groundwater because of the "water that may be permitted" language in the definition. Because GCDs cannot require a permit for any exempt use of groundwater, exempt use amounts were excluded from managed available groundwater numbers. *See* Memorandum from William R. Hutchison, Director, Groundwater Resources Division, & Kenneth L. Petersen, General Counsel, to Texas Water Development Board Members (June 9, 2010).

This approach was changed by the TWDB at a work session on June 17, 2010. The board directed that the practice of reporting managed available groundwater be modified to include (1) total pumping required to achieve the desired future condition; (2) estimated exempt use; and (3) the managed available groundwater, which is the total pumping minus the estimated exempt use. At the time of this change, eleven final managed available groundwater reports had been issued. Consequently, those eleven reports were reissued to conform to the revised approach.

Since that time, the managed available groundwater reports were initially released as draft reports and provided to the districts for review, particularly with respect to the exempt use estimates. Districts had the opportunity to update or revise the exempt use estimates developed by the TWDB for domestic and livestock exempt uses. In addition, districts had the opportunity to submit estimates of exempt use associated with oil and gas exploration. Before issuing a final managed available groundwater report, the TWDB staff provided to the board members a side-by-side comparison of managed available groundwater with current groundwater use, current state water plan groundwater availability numbers, recharge estimates, estimates of drainable water in place, and an estimate of the maximum sustained pumping level. An example of this comparison is contained in the memorandum from William R. Hutchison, Director, Groundwater Resources Division, to the Texas Water Development Board Members dated June 15, 2011, that covers sixteen managed available groundwater reports.

§ 21.12:2 Modeled Available Groundwater

The TWDB's calculation of water availability designed to achieve a desired future condition remains a requirement, although legislation during the 82nd Legislature made significant changes to how that is to be done and the purpose of those numbers.

"'Modeled available groundwater' means the amount of water that the [TWDB] executive administrator determines may be produced on an annual average basis to achieve a desired future condition established under [Texas Water Code] Section 36.108." Tex. Water Code § 36.001(25). The replacement of "managed available groundwater" by this term as statutorily defined, in conjunction with other changes to Texas Water Code chapter 36 made during the 82nd legislative session, represents a substantial change in how water availability is calculated and used by GCDs.

The desired future conditions submittal must include (1) the desired future conditions adopted under section 36.108, (2) proof that notice was posted for the joint planning meeting, and (3) the desired future conditions explanatory report. *See* Tex. Water Code § 36.1084(a). The TWDB executive administrator must provide to each district and regional planning group located wholly or partly in the management area "modeled available groundwater" based on the adopted desired future conditions. *See* Tex. Water Code § 36.1084(b).

The change in requirement to report modeled available groundwater, which is the pumping that will achieve the desired future condition, rather than the managed available groundwater, which accounts for the uses exempt from permitting, is significant. Before current law (during the first cycle of joint planning), there was confusion about whether the managed available groundwater was considered to be a cap on allowable permitted well production or if permits could be issued in excess of the managed available groundwater because the actual pumping was the important factor in managing the desired future condition. *See* H.B. 1763, § 11 (former version of Texas Water Code section 36.1132). Now, a GCD, to the extent possible, shall issue permits up to the point that the total volume of exempt and permitted groundwater production will achieve the applicable desired future condition. Thus the 82nd Legislature settled the discussion about whether to include exempt pumpage in the water availability numbers provided by the TWDB during the joint planning process. (However, the TWDB is still required to develop estimates of exempt use pursuant to the addition of Water Code section 36.1132(b), which states that the executive administrator's estimate of the current and projected amount of groundwater produced under exemptions granted by district rules and section 36.117 is to be considered when a district is issuing permits.)

This change, in conjunction with other changes in section 36.1132, requires GCDs to manage total groundwater production on a long-term basis to achieve the applicable desired future condition and to consider five specific factors in making permitting decisions: modeled available groundwater, current and projected exempt use, amount of permitted groundwater, estimated amount of groundwater actually being produced under permits, and annual precipitation and production patterns.

The interpretation during the first cycle of joint planning of many GCDs and other stakeholders that Water Code section 36.1132 imposed a cap imposed on the districts' ability to issue groundwater production permits put enormous pressure on the GCDs, the TWDB, and the joint planning process. Under the changes made during the 82nd legislative session, the planning function of the desired future condition adoption becomes more apparent, mirroring more closely the overall state water planning process.

§ 21.13 The First Cycle of Joint Planning

The statutory deadline for the submittal of adopted desired future conditions to the board was September 1, 2010. *See* Tex. Water Code § 36.108(d). The first desired future conditions were adopted in late 2007; the last, on August 30, 2010. All joint planning committees met the statutory deadline. What follows is a summary of the various desired future condition attributes and development processes based on the authors' count of seventy-four desired future conditions that were adopted to complete the initial cycle.

As previously noted, GCDs within a GMA were required to decide on how to express the desired future condition. Fifty-four of the adopted desired future conditions were expressed in terms of drawdown of groundwater levels over a fifty-year period. Thirteen of the adopted desired future conditions were expressed in terms of volume remaining after fifty years. Three were expressed in terms of spring flow. One was expressed as a minimum groundwater elevation. Two were expressed as a hybrid of drawdown and volume, and one was expressed as a hybrid of drawdown and spring flow.

In terms of the geographic extent of the adopted desired future conditions, thirty-nine of the adopted desired future conditions were expressed as county-wide averages; nineteen were expressed as averages over an entire GMA; eight were expressed as averages over a GCD; six were expressed as averages over a geographic area other than a county or GCD; one was expressed as a hybrid of counties and districts; and one was expressed as a hybrid of a GMA and a county.

The differences between desired future conditions adopted by different GMA joint planning committees vary. The following examples illustrate this point. The desired future condition adopted on September 17, 2008, for the Trinity Aquifer in GMA 8 was expressed as drawdown over a fifty-year period for each of the forty-one counties and four aquifer layers (Paluxy, Glen Rose, Hensell, and Houston), for a total of 159 separate desired future conditions. *See* Groundwater Management Area 8, *Resolution to Adopt Desired Future Conditions for Aquifer(s) in Groundwater Management Area 8* (attached to Memorandum from Cheryl Maxwell, Groundwater Management Area 8 Administrator, to J. Kevin Ward, Executive Administrator, Texas Water Development Board (June 9, 2008)), www.twdb.texas.gov/groundwater/docs/DFC/GMA8_DFC_Adopted_2008-0519.pdf.

In contrast, the desired future condition for the Carrizo-Wilcox, Queen City, and Sparta aquifers in GMA 13 was expressed as an overall GMA-wide average. *See* Groundwater Management Area 13, *Resolution for the Adoption of the Desired Future Conditions of the Aquifers in Groundwater Management Area 13* (attached to Memorandum from Mike Mahoney, Groundwater Management Area 13 Administrator, to J. Kevin Ward, Executive Administrator, Texas Water Development Board (Apr. 13, 2010)), www.twdb.texas.gov/groundwater/docs/DFC/GMA13_DFC_Adopted_2010-0409.pdf. In the GMA 13 example, the districts adopted one specific scenario of a specific groundwater availability model run, and the associated county-aquifer drawdowns are tied to that desired future condition statement in order to guide the development of total pumping estimates (i.e., the pumping that will achieve the desired future condition) and managed available groundwater estimates. *See* Shirley C. Wade & Marius Jigmond, Texas Water Development Board, *GAM Run 09-034* (June 29, 2010), www.twdb.texas.gov/groundwater/docs/GAMruns/GR09-34.pdf.

In comparison, the districts in GMA 11 expressed the desired future condition of the Carrizo-Wilcox, Queen City, Sparta, and Yegua-Jackson aquifers as a GMA-wide average, which was tied to a specific groundwater availability model run. *See* Groundwater Management Area 11, *Desired Future Conditions Resolutions No. 1* (attached to Memorandum from Monique Norman, Attorney, to J. Kevin Ward, Executive Administrator, Texas Water Development Board (May 4, 2010)), www.twdb.texas.gov/groundwater/docs/DFC/GMA11_DFC_Adopted_2010-0413.pdf. In contrast to

GMA 13, however, the districts in GMA 11 included a table that summarized the individual aquifer-county drawdowns in their desired future condition resolution.

The process of developing the initial seventy-four desired future conditions varied from management area to management area and sometimes even within a management area, depending on a variety of factors, including level of current use, planned future use, availability of groundwater availability models, and the confidence in the available data and models. In many cases, several model runs were completed and the results discussed before adopting a desired future condition. Some critics of the process asserted that the districts were "reverse-engineering" the desired future conditions by specifying pumping (e.g., the managed available groundwater) and then adopting the resulting drawdown results as the desired future condition. However, it must be remembered that among the input parameters for a predictive groundwater model run is pumping, and among the outputs of a predictive groundwater model run is drawdown. Thus, an iterative approach of running several predictive scenarios with models and then evaluating the results is a necessary (and time-consuming) step in the process of developing desired future conditions.

One aspect to the reverse-engineering critique of the process has been that science should be used in the development of desired future conditions. The context of this critique refers to a fairly narrow definition of the term *science* and fails to recognize that the adoption of a desired future condition is primarily a policy decision. The call to use science in the development of desired future conditions seems to equate the term *science* with the terms *facts* and *truth*. Although the Latin origin of the word means knowledge, the term *science* also refers to the application of the scientific method. The scientific method can be viewed as a means to quantify cause-and-effect relationships and to make useful predictions. *See, e.g.*, James H. Zumberge & Clemens S. Nelson, *Elements of Physical Geology* (John Wiley & Sons 1976); David Deming, *Introduction to Hydrogeology* (McGraw-Hill 2002). In the case of groundwater management, the scientific method can be used to understand the relationship between groundwater pumping and drawdown, or groundwater pumping and spring flow. A groundwater model is a tool that can be used to run "experiments" to better understand the cause-and-effect relationships within a groundwater system as they relate to groundwater management.

An example illustrating this iterative method within the process of developing desired future conditions can be found in the documents associated with the desired future condition of the Edwards-Trinity (Plateau) and Pecos Valley aquifers in GMA 7. The desired future condition resolution summarized eleven scenarios of groundwater pumping. *See* Groundwater Management Area 7, *Designation of Desired Future Conditions for the Edwards-Trinity (Plateau) Aquifer in Groundwater Management Area 7* (July 29, 2010), www.twdb.texas.gov/groundwater/docs/DFC/GMA7_DFC_Adopted_2010-0729.pdf, referencing a Groundwater Availability Model Run report (*see* William R. Hutchinson, *Draft GAM Run 09-035 (version 2)* (Aug. 7, 2010), www.twdb.texas.gov/groundwater/docs/GAMruns/GR09-35draft_v2.pdf).

The districts in GMA 7 initiated the process with a county-by-county estimate of future pumping, and this represented Scenario 1. Scenario 2 represented a 10 percent increase in pumping in each county of GMA 7 as compared to Scenario 1. Scenarios 3, 4, and 5 represented 20, 30, and 40 percent pumping increases in each county of GMA 7, respectively. The results of Scenarios 1 to 5 were summarized, distributed to the district representatives, and discussed at the July 29, 2010, meeting of GMA 7. The discussion focused on the districts' "vision" of groundwater conditions that qualitatively described the need to minimize drawdown in the eastern portion of GMA 7 in order to maintain spring flow and river baseflow and allow for drawdown in the western portion of GMA 7 where irrigated agriculture used large amounts of groundwater. The primary issue that needed to be resolved was the compatibility of these two qualitative goals. Recall that the purpose of joint planning was to regionalize groundwater management decisions among neighboring districts within a GMA. GMA 7 included twenty GCDs (the most in any GMA), and the dynamics of discussing the impacts of various pumping scenarios was unique given the large number of stakeholders.

At the meeting, and after the general relationship between pumping and drawdown was presented and discussed, the district representatives provided updates to pumping on a county-by-county basis. Those updated pumping amounts were put into the model and runs were completed at the meeting, and the results summarized and discussed. Scenarios 6 to 10 were run during the meeting in this iterative fashion based on this input from the district representatives. As a result of these model runs, the districts adopted Scenario 10 as meeting their qualitative vision of future drawdown conditions as their desired future condition.

§ 21.14 Role of Regional Water Planning Groups

The legislative changes in 2005 altered the regional water planning groups' role in determining groundwater availability. Before House Bill 1763, the planning groups had only to consider GCDs' availability estimates; they had no obligation to use those numbers. *See* Tex. Water Code § 36.1071(b) (as enacted by S.B. 1, § 4.28 (1997)). The regional water planning groups are now required to use, not just consider, the districts' modeled available groundwater calculations that were adopted through the joint planning process. Tex. Water Code § 36.1071(b). The one exception to this is Region D, in North East Texas. Region D, as of September 1, 2015, will determine the supply of groundwater for regional planning purposes. Before Region D's groundwater supply numbers can be used in its regional water plan, the TWDB is first required to review and approve that Region D's proposed groundwater supply is physically compatible, using the board's groundwater availability models, with the desired future conditions adopted under Texas Water Code section 36.108 for the relevant aquifers in the GMA that are regulated by GCDs. *See* Act of May 29, 2015, 84th Leg., R.S., ch. 1180, § 1 (amending Tex. Water Code § 16.053(e)(2–a) to affect Region D, the only regional planning group that does not have a GCD within its boundaries).

However, the regional water planning groups are not left without a voice in the groundwater availability determination process. They may petition a GCD to the State Office of Administrative Hearings (SOAH) to appeal the reasonableness of the district's desired future condition of an aquifer and file with the TCEQ petitions for inquiry regarding other related joint planning issues. *See* Tex. Water Code § 36.1083. See the discussion at section 21.17 below.

In 2011, the legislature also required, with the passage of S.B. 660, the regional water planning groups to add GMA designees to the regional planning groups. That bill amended section 16.053(c) of the Water Code to require that "the groundwater conservation districts located in each management area, as defined by Section 36.001, located in the regional water planning area shall appoint one representative of a groundwater conservation district located in the management area and in the regional water planning area to serve on the regional water planning group." S.B. 660, § 9; *see also* S.B. 660, § 20. See discussion in Chapter 20 of this book. This leaves Region D as the only regional planning group that does not have a GMA representative because it does not have a GCD located within its boundaries.

§ 21.15 Role of Unprotected Areas

Unprotected areas and *white areas* are terms used to describe areas in the state that are not included within the boundaries of a GCD. In these areas, the rule of capture still applies to groundwater production, without governmental regulations or protections. *See Sipriano v. Great Spring Waters of America, Inc.*, 1 S.W.3d 75 (Tex. 1999); *Houston & T.C. Ry. Co. v. East*, 81 S.W. 279 (Tex. 1904). This remains true even after 2011 and 2012, when both the Texas legislature and the Texas Supreme Court declared that groundwater rights are real property rights. *See* Tex. Water Code § 36.002; *Edwards Aquifer Authority v. Day*, 369 S.W.3d 814 (Tex. 2012). The common-law tort preclusion of the rule of capture remains intact, and landowners cannot sue their neighbors, whether within a GCD or not, for pumping the groundwater from their land (unless done so wastefully or maliciously). The groundwater rights laws allow a groundwater rights owner or lessee to seek action against a district for a constitutional regulatory taking. For this reason, among others, groundwater rights are more protected within a GCD.

GMAs contain varying amounts of unprotected areas. For example, in 2021, GMA 12 is almost entirely covered by GCDs, whereas GMA 5 does not have a single district. *See* S.B. 1, art. 1. In GMA joint planning, the existing districts are responsible for determining the desired future conditions for the entire area, including the unprotected areas. *See* Tex. Water Code §§ 36.108–.1086. However, there is currently no enforcement of the desired future conditions and related water availability (managed available groundwater or modeled available groundwater) in the unprotected areas. The responsibility of the GMA joint planning members to determine groundwater availability for the unprotected areas is used as a planning method and possibly as an incentive for GCDs to be formed in the unprotected areas of the state that have groundwater resources. Groundwater availability for the unprotected areas will be included in the regional water plans. If a groundwater project is not listed in the regional water plan, it will not be eligible for state funding. *See Estimating Groundwater Availability*. Additionally, if a new GCD is created in an unprotected area, the desired future conditions adopted through the joint planning process must be used, at least until the next time the desired future conditions are considered by the joint planning members.

VI. Challenging Adoption of Desired Future Conditions and Other Decisions Related to the Joint Planning Process

§ 21.16 Introduction

Inevitably, the adoption of desired future conditions will result in some conflict. GCDs' availability determinations will become increasingly more difficult as districts weigh the differing interests of existing and future users, in-district and out-of-district users, and the effects of increased pumping on the aquifers and existing wells, to name a few competing interests. As urban populations increase, conflict will likely intensify between the interests of urban and rural water needs and between the use and conservation of groundwater resources. On the administrative level, these conflicts will be addressed by the three agencies with oversight over actions related to the joint planning process. Appeals of a desired future condition go to SOAH, with input from the TWDB; petitions for an inquiry into district actions or inactions related to the joint planning process are heard by the TCEQ.

§ 21.17 Appeal of a Desired Future Condition

In the first round of adoptions of desired future conditions, a person with a legally defined interest in the groundwater could petition the TWDB that a desired future condition was unreasonable. The board would then make a reasonableness decision on the petition after it conducted a public hearing. In 2015, the Texas legislature changed the desired future condition appeal process by passing H.B. 200, which removed the TWDB from the reasonableness determination decision process and allows affected persons to directly challenge an individual GCD's adopted desired future condition through an administrative hearing process conducted by SOAH. *See* Tex. Water Code § 36.1083(b) (as amended by Act of May 31, 2015, 84th Leg., R.S., ch. 993, § 4). However, the TWDB is still required to contribute its hydrological expertise and recommendations to SOAH. The new appeals process applies to desired future conditions adopted on or after September 1, 2015.

An affected person may file a petition with a GCD within the GMA that approved the desired future condition. The act of filing a petition with a district appealing the reasonableness of a desired future condition automatically triggers the GCD to contract with SOAH to conduct the hearing. The petition is required to provide evidence that the district did not establish a reasonable desired future condition of the groundwater resources in the management area. The petition must be filed no later than the 120th day after the date on which a GCD adopts a desired future condition under section 36.108(d–4). *See* Tex. Water Code § 36.1083(b).

Although "affected person" is defined in section 36.1083(a)(1) as having "the meaning assigned by Section 36.1082," section 36.1082 was repealed by the 84th Legislature with the passage of H.B. 2767. *See* Act of May 20, 2015, 84th Leg., R.S., ch. 415, § 23. Because of the conflicting 2015 legislation between H.B. 200 and H.B. 2767, "affected person" is no longer defined in section 36.1082 of the Texas Water Code but in section 36.3011(a). *See* Tex. Water Code § 36.3011(a). The apparent intent was to define "affected person" as the former "person with a legally defined interest in groundwater" within the GMA, a GCD in or adjacent to the GMA, or a regional water planning group for a region in the GMA. *See* Tex. Water Code § 36.1083(a), (b).

The petitioned GCD must, within sixty days of receiving the petition, contract with SOAH to conduct the contested case hearing and submit a copy of the petition to SOAH. *See* Tex. Water Code § 36.1083(h). And, within ten days of receiving the petition, the district must submit a copy of the petition to the TWDB. *See* Tex. Water Code § 36.1083(e). The TWDB must then complete a study to be delivered to SOAH within 120 days of receiving the copy of the petition. *See* Tex. Water Code § 36.1083(f). The TWDB study shall be based on an administrative review determination of whether the desired future condition meets the Water Code section 36.108(d) criteria. *See* Tex. Water Code § 36.1083(e). The TWDB study must contain scientific and technical analysis of the desired future condition, including consideration of (1) aquifer hydrology; (2) the Water Code section 108(d–3) explanatory report and factors; and (3) any relevant groundwater availability models, published studies, estimates of total recoverable storage capacity, average annual amounts of recharge, inflows, and discharge of groundwater, or information provided in the petition and available to the TWDB. *See* Tex. Water Code § 36.1083(e). During the period between the filing of the petition and TWDB delivering its study to SOAH, the GCD may seek mediation assistance for the issues raised in the petition from the Center for Public Policy Dispute Resolution, the TWDB, or other alternative dispute resolution. *See* Tex. Water Code § 36.1083(j).

Before SOAH conducts the contested case hearing, it must follow notice, payment, and prehearing requirements. The administrative law judge may consolidate hearings that are requested that affect two or more districts. *See* Tex. Water Code § 36.1083(r). The notice requirements must be consistent with the GCD and SOAH rules, including a general hearing notice, and individual notice to the petitioner, persons requesting notice, nonparty GCDs and regional water planning groups in the same management area, the TWDB, and the TCEQ. *See* Tex. Water Code § 36.1083(k). At the prehearing conference, SOAH must determine preliminary matters, including whether the petition should be dismissed for failure to state a claim for which relief can be granted or whether a person seeking to participate in the hearing is an affected person who is eligible to participate. *See* Tex. Water Code § 36.1083(*l*). Initially, the petitioner is required to pay the costs associated with the SOAH contract for the hearing and to deposit a sufficient amount with the district so that the district may pay the contract amount before the hearing. *See* Tex. Water Code § 36.1083(m). However, after the conclusion of the hearing, SOAH may assess costs to one or more participatory parties, and the district shall refund any excess money to the petitioner. SOAH's decision to apportion the contract costs must take into consideration who requested the hearing, who prevailed, who is financially able to pay, how much a party participated, and any other relevant factors for a just and reasonable assessment of costs. *See* Tex. Water Code § 36.1083(m).

In conducting the hearing, SOAH is required to consider the TWDB study in response to the petition and the desired future condition explanatory report submitted to the TWDB under Water Code section 36.108(d–3). *See* Tex. Water Code § 36.1083(g)(1). The TWDB must make its relevant staff available to SOAH as expert witnesses, if requested by SOAH or a party to the hearing. Tex. Water Code § 36.1083(g)(2). The contested case hearing shall be held at the GCD's office or regular meeting location of the district's board, unless the board provides for meetings to be held in other locations, and in accordance with the Texas Administrative Procedure Act and SOAH rules. *See* Tex. Water Code §§ 36.1083(i), 36.403(c); Tex. Gov't Code ch. 2001.

When the GCD receives the SOAH administrative law judge's findings of fact and conclusions of law in a proposal for decision, including a dismissal of the petition, the district is required to issue a final order stating the district's decision on the contested case matter and the district's findings of fact and conclusions of law. Tex. Water Code § 36.1083(n). The administrative law judge must prepare separate findings of fact and conclusions of law for each GCD that is a party to the same contested case hearing. *See* Tex. Water Code § 36.1083(r). Pursuant to the Administrative Procedure Act, the district may change a finding of fact or conclusion of law issued by the administrative law judge or may vacate or modify an administrative law judge's order. *See* Tex. Water Code § 36.1083(n); Tex. Gov't Code § 2001.058(e). If the district modifies or vacates the proposal for decision, the district must issue a report detailing its reasons for disagreement and provide policy, scientific, and technical justifications for the district's decision. *See* Tex. Water Code § 36.1083(o).

If the petitioned GCD, in its final order, finds that the desired future condition is unreasonable, the districts in the same management area shall meet in a joint planning meeting to revise the petitioned district's desired future conditions. *See* Tex. Water Code § 36.1083(p). The revision meeting shall be conducted within sixty days of the district's final order and follow the desired future condition adoption procedure of Water Code section 36.108. *See* Tex. Water Code § 36.1083(p). Only the unreasonable desired future condition for the petitioned district must be amended. The petitioned district's final order deeming the condition unreasonable does not affect the desired future conditions for the other GCDs in the management area that did not participate in the contested case hearing. *See* Tex. Water Code § 36.1083(q).

Within forty-five days of the petitioned GCD's issuing a final order, the order may be appealed to a district court with jurisdiction over any part of that district's territory. *See* Tex. Water Code § 36.10835(a). The district court shall decide the appeal under the substantial evidence standard of review. *See* Tex. Water Code § 36.10835(a); Tex. Gov't Code § 2001.174. If the district court rules that the appealed desired future condition is unreasonable, the court shall strike the desired future condition and order the management area districts to reconvene within sixty days of the court order, to hold a joint planning meeting and amend the struck desired future condition under Water Code section 36.108. *See* Tex. Water Code § 36.10835(a). The court's findings do not apply to other desired future conditions that were not before the court. Tex. Water Code § 36.10835(b).

§ 21.18 Petition for a Texas Commission on Environmental Quality Inquiry

An "affected person" may file a petition with the TCEQ requesting an inquiry for numerous issues related to joint planning. *See* Tex. Water Code § 36.3011. (Citations in this section of the chapter are to the current law because only one such petition was filed under pre–S.B. 660 law.) The following have standing under the definition of "affected person":

1. an owner of land in the management area;
2. a GCD or subsidence district in or adjacent to the management area;
3. a regional water planning group with a water management strategy in the management area;
4. a person who holds or is applying for a permit from a district in the management area;
5. a person with a legally defined interest in groundwater in the management area; or
6. any other person defined as affected by TCEQ rule.

See Tex. Water Code § 36.3011(a).

An inquiry can be requested for any of the following reasons: failure of a district to submit its management plan to the TWDB; to participate in joint planning; to adopt rules; to adopt the desired future condition applicable to that district; and to update its management plan within two years of adoption of the desired future condition applicable to that district or to update its rules to implement the desired future conditions before the first anniversary of the date when it updated its management plan. A petition for an inquiry can also be filed if a district's rules are not designed to achieve the desired future condition or do not adequately protect the groundwater in the management area. Finally, such an inquiry may be sought if a district fails to enforce substantial compliance with its rules, thereby failing to adequately protect groundwater within the management area. Tex. Water Code § 36.3011(b).

Within ninety days of the petition's being filed, the commission must review the petition and either dismiss it if the commission finds inadequate evidence to support the allegations or refer the matter to a review panel. *See* Tex. Water Code § 36.3011(c).

If the commission determines referral is necessary, then it appoints a five-member review panel. The commission has the discretion to appoint a director or general manager of a district located in a different GMA to the review panel but may not appoint more than two members of a review panel from any one GCD. The proceedings of the panel must be recorded and documented by the recording secretary. *See* Tex. Water Code § 36.3011(d).

Within 120 days of the appointment, the review panel must review the petition and relevant evidence and consider and adopt a report in open meeting. The report must be submitted to the commission. The panel may hold public hearings in the GMA to take evidence, as directed by the commission, and may negotiate or resolve disputes by any lawful means. *See* Tex. Water Code § 36.3011(e).

The review panel's report must be submitted to the commission and include a summary of all evidence taken in any hearing on the petition, list findings and recommendations of actions appropriate for the commission to take and reasons the actions are appropriate, and other information deemed appropriate. *See* Tex. Water Code § 36.3011(f), (g).

Within forty-five days of receiving the panel's report, the commission or its executive director shall take action to implement the panel's recommendations including any action against a GCD that it deems necessary in accordance with Texas Water Code section 36.303. Tex. Water Code § 36.3011(h). The commission may order the GCD to take certain appropriate actions. *See* Tex. Water Code § 36.303(a)(1). In extreme circumstances, the commission may dissolve the GCD. *See* Tex. Water Code § 36.303(a)(2)–(4). The commission may also recommend to the legislature actions it deems necessary to accomplish comprehensive management in the GCD. *See* Tex. Water Code § 36.303(b).

§ 21.19 Challenges Made to the First Cycle of Joint Planning

Many of the desired future conditions adopted during the first joint planning cycle were challenged through petitions to the TWDB. One was rejected because it was submitted after the statutory deadline for submittal (GMA 8). One was withdrawn before a TWDB decision was made (GMA 11). The TWDB found in four instances that the challenged desired future conditions were reasonable, and no further appeal actions were taken (GMAs 7, 10, 12, and 13). The petitions and staff reports are available at www.twdb.texas.gov/groundwater/petitions/index.asp.

Challenges to certain desired future conditions adopted by the districts in GMAs 1 and 9 were each legally significant in their own way. The TWDB received two administratively complete petitions challenging the desired future conditions for the Ogallala Aquifer adopted by the districts in GMA 1. After considering these petitions, the board found the desired future conditions to be reasonable. *See* Minutes of the Texas Water Development Board Meeting (Feb. 17, 2010), www.twdb.texas.gov/board/agenda/Minutes.asp. The board approved the staff recommendation that the desired future conditions were reasonable. The staff's analysis concluded that (1) the GCDs engaged in joint planning; (2) the desired future conditions do not prohibit someone from pumping their groundwater; (3) county lines can be used to define geographic areas for different desired future conditions provided that aquifer uses and conditions support the areas; (4) the districts reasonably considered environmental impacts and spring flows; (5) the districts balanced the various interests, uses, and potential uses; and (6) the desired future conditions are physically possible. *See* News Release, Texas Water Development Board, *Texas Water Development Board Rules on Groundwater Management Area 1 Desired Future Conditions* (Feb. 17, 2010); *see also* Texas Water Development Board, *Report on Appeal of the Reasonableness of the Desired Future Conditions Adopted by the Groundwater Conservation Districts in Groundwater Management Area 1 for the Ogallala and Rita Blanca Aquifers* (Feb. 10, 2010), www.twdb.texas.gov/groundwater/petitions/doc/GMA1/2009_Petitions/Mesa_G&J_Ranch/TWDB_Staff_Report_GMA1_Petitions_02-10.pdf.

Following the board's decision, the petitioners Mesa Water L.P. and G&J Ranch, Inc., sued the TWDB on March 16, 2010, in Travis County district court under Texas Water Code section 6.241 seeking to set aside the board's decision and a finding that the desired future conditions were unreasonable. The plaintiffs' suit sought several declarations under the Uniform Declaratory Judgment Act and claimed, in part, that the districts in GMA 1 adopted desired future conditions contrary to Texas law because they discriminated between groundwater rights owners in the same aquifer or subdivision of an aquifer because they were based on political subdivisions. The plaintiffs sought several declarations regarding former Water Code section 36.108 and the TWDB's authority to require GCDs to revise their adopted desired future conditions in accordance with the TWDB's recommendations. The plaintiffs asserted that the appeal process resulted in a deprivation of property without due process because they were denied the right to take discovery, compel evidence, object to testimony, or cross-examine witnesses. *See* Plaintiffs' Original Petition ¶ 21, *Mesa Water L.P. & G&J Ranch, Inc. v. Texas Water Development Board*, No. D-1-GN-10-000819 (201st Dist. Ct., Travis County, Tex. Mar. 16, 2010).

The TWDB, represented by the Texas Attorney General's office, filed a plea to the jurisdiction asserting sovereign immunity to suit on the basis that the staff's recommendation that the board not find the future desired conditions unreasonable was not a final order that fixed the plaintiffs' rights or liabilities. *See* TWDB's First Amended Plea to the Jurisdiction ¶¶ 32–50, *Mesa Water L.P. & G&J Ranch, Inc. v. Texas Water Development Board*, No. D-1-GN-10-000819 (201st Dist. Ct., Travis County, Tex. Mar. 16, 2010). The TWDB also asserted that the plaintiffs' claims were not ripe; the plaintiffs lacked standing to sue; and the board's action did not result in the taking of the plaintiffs' property. *See* TWDB's First Amended Plea to the Jurisdiction, at ¶¶ 51–59. The trial court agreed and granted the plea to the jurisdiction on December 9, 2010. *See* Order Granting Plea to the Jurisdiction, *Mesa Water L.P. & G&J Ranch, Inc. v. Texas Water Development Board*, No. D-1-GN-10-000819 (201st Dist. Ct., Travis County, Tex. Mar. 16, 2010).

While pursuing the district court appeal of the TWDB's action, on October 22, 2010, Mesa Water L.P. filed with the TCEQ a request for an inquiry relating to joint groundwater management in GMA 1 under former Water Code section 36.108(f)–(k). Mesa Water claimed that the GMA 1 planning process failed to result in adequate planning and did not establish reasonable future desired conditions for the Ogallala aquifer in GMA 1. Mesa Water requested that, following the inquiry, the commission issue an order (1) requiring the districts to adopt a single desired future condition for each of the subdivisions of the Ogallala Aquifer in GMA 1 and to adopt and enforce equitably rules designed to achieve the desired future condition; (2) dissolving the boards of directors of the districts in GMA 1; or (3) dissolving the districts in GMA 1. *See* Petitioner's Request for Inquiry, TCEQ Docket No. 2010-1611-MIS (Oct. 22, 2010).

The districts in GMA 1 and the TCEQ executive director filed responses to the petition, all arguing that former section 36.108(f)–(k) does not allow for a review of the reasonableness of the desired future conditions. The executive director asserted that only the TWDB has authority to conduct such a review and that its staff had determined that GMA 1's desired future conditions were reasonable. The GCDs and the executive director asserted that Mesa Water's attack on the districts' rules was premature because the TWDB had not yet issued the managed available groundwater amounts, and the districts must have the managed available groundwater before they can amend management plans in a manner consistent with the desired future conditions. The districts also asserted that the joint planning process was adequate and that the adoption of different desired future conditions for different geographical areas over the same aquifer is authorized. *See* Executive Director's Response to Petition for Inquiry, TCEQ Docket No. 2010-1611-MIS. The commissioners dismissed Mesa Water's petition at the December 14, 2010, meeting. *See* Texas Commission on Environmental Quality, Meeting Minutes, Item 4 (Dec. 14, 2010), www.tceq.texas.gov/assets/public/comm_exec/agendas/comm/marked/2010/101214.Mrk.pdf. In 2011, T. Boone Pickens and Mesa Water sold 211,000 acres of groundwater rights, the basis of the petition, to the Canadian River Municipal Water Authority.

The TWDB also received three administratively complete petitions concerning desired future conditions established for GMA 9 during the first cycle of joint planning. The submitted desired future condition for the Edwards Group of the Edwards-Trinity (Plateau) Aquifer was the subject of a petition presented to the board on January 21, 2010. At that meeting, the board found that the adopted desired future condition of zero drawdown was not reasonable. The board further recommended that the desired future condition in Kerr County be nine feet of drawdown and that the Edwards Group of the Edwards-Trinity (Plateau) Aquifer be found not relevant in Bandera and Kendall counties. *See* Minutes of the Texas Water Development Board Special Meeting (Jan. 21, 2010), www.twdb.texas.gov/board/agenda/Minutes.asp; News Release, Texas Water Development Board, *Texas Water Development Board Rules on Groundwater Management Area 9 Desired Future Conditions* (Jan. 21, 2010). At their July 26, 2010, meeting, the GCDs in GMA 9 adopted new desired future conditions for the Edwards Group of the Edwards-Trinity (Plateau) Aquifer. In Bandera and Kendall counties, the new desired future condition is the same as the original desired future condition: zero drawdown. The districts in GMA 9 also found that the Edwards Group of the Edwards-Trinity (Plateau) Aquifer is not relevant for purposes of joint planning in Kerr County. *See* Letter from Ronald G. Fieseler, Groundwater Management Area 9 Coordinator, to J. Kevin Ward, Executive Administrator, Texas Water Development Board (Aug. 26, 2010).

§ 21.20 Challenges Made to the Second Cycle of Joint Planning

In the second cycle of adoption of desired future conditions by the GMAs, one appeal of adopted desired future conditions occurred. Two petitions filed by the cities of Conroe and Magnolia and by Quadvest, L.P., appealed the desired future conditions adopted by GMA 14 for the Lone Star Groundwater Conservation District (LSGCD). These petitions were filed with the LSGCD in December 2016.

The petition of the cities of Conroe and Magnolia claimed that the adopted desired future conditions would result in "continued, and likely even greater, more severe, and unjustified restrictions on use of the abundant groundwater that underlies Montgomery County for many years to come." *See Petition of the Cities of Conroe and Magnolia, Texas Appealing Desired Future Conditions of GMA 14 Adopted by Lone Star Groundwater Conservation District*, www.twdb.texas.gov/groundwater/petitions/doc/lsgcd/Conroe%20DFC%20Petition%20recd%2012_12_16.pdf. The petition of Quadvest asserted that the desired future conditions are based entirely on the LSGCD's "predetermined notions of how much groundwater it will 'give' the owners of groundwater in its territory" and claims that this "violation of private property rights compels the conclusion that the DFCs are unreasonable." *See Petition of Quadvest, L.P. Appealing Desired Future Conditions of GMA 14 Adopted by Lone Star Groundwater Conservation District*, www.twdb.texas.gov/groundwater/petitions/doc/lsgcd/Quadvest%20DFC%20Petition%20recd%2012_14_16.pdf [hereinafter Quadvest Petition].

In accordance with Texas Water Code section 36.1083(e) and (f), the TWDB completed a scientific and technical analysis of the desired future conditions adopted by the LSGCD. The report and names of TWDB staff that would be available as expert witnesses if requested by SOAH were submitted to the administrative law judge in April 2017. *See* Texas Water Development Board, *Scientific and Technical Analysis of Desired Future Conditions Adopted by the Lone Star Groundwater Conservation District*, www.twdb.texas.gov/groundwater/petitions/doc/lsgcd/TWDB%20Technical%20Evaluation%20Report%2004_10_17.pdf. Of note in the Quadvest petition is the suggestion that the TWDB is in an "irreconcilable conflict of interest" because the TWDB holds more than $400 million in bonds issued by the San Jacinto River Authority (SJRA). *See* Quadvest Petition, at ¶ 50. According to the petition, the TWDB's "substantial investment in SJRA bonds could be at risk if LSGCD must alter its regulations as a result of its DFCs being struck down as unreasonable." *See* Quadvest Petition, at ¶ 50.

In October 2017, the LSGCD changed its policy goals after reviewing the results of a recently completed hydrogeologic study it had been working on since 2014. The new management policy moved away from sustainability to allow measured aquifer level declines. Specifically, the LSGCD adopted "Run D" as its recommended model scenario, resulting in an additional 22,600 AF/yr of pumping in Montgomery County as compared with the model run on which the DFC had been adopted in 2016. *See* Lone Star Groundwater Conservation District, *LSGCD Strategic Planning for Groundwater Management and Development of Summary Results* (Oct. 10, 2017).

In November 2017, the LSGCD and the cities of Conroe and Magnolia approved a settlement agreement regarding the reasonableness petition. Quadvest L.P. did not dispute the settlement. In response to the settlement, a November 10, 2017, letter from the LSGCD to the GCDs in GMA 14 requested formal consideration of a new DFC based on Run D at the December 8, 2017, GMA 14 meeting. On March 9, 2018, the LSCGD sent another letter to the GCDs in GMA 14 to consider Run D as an amendment to the previously adopted DFC.

At the March 27, 2018, GMA 14 meeting, a motion to approve formal consideration of Run D as an amended DFC on an accelerated schedule was defeated (two votes for, three votes against). A vote was subsequently taken to affirm a previous vote at the December 8, 2017, GMA 14 meeting to consider Run D as part of the third round of Joint Planning (deadline of May 1, 2021 for a proposed DFC). *See Minutes of the Upper Gulf Coast Aquifer Planning Area (GMA 14) Joint Planning Group Meeting (Mar. 27, 2018)*, www.lonestargcd.org/management-planning.

§ 21.21 The Third Cycle of Joint Planning

The proposed DFCs for all GMAs were required to be adopted for the relevant aquifers no later than May 1, 2021. *See* Tex. Water Code § 36.108(d). Once the proposed DFCs were mailed to the member GCDs in a GMA, a ninety-day comment period began, in which at least one public hearing was required to be conducted in each member district on the proposed DFCs relevant to that GCD, following notice criteria prescribed by Texas Water Code section 36.063. *See* Tex. Water Code § 36.108(d–2). After comments from the public hearing are summarized by each GCD, the GMA must reconvene to review and consider all of the comments, potentially make revisions to the DFCs based on the comments, and adopt the final DFCs for each GMA no later than January 5, 2022. *See* Tex. Water Code § 36.108(d–3). The GMAs shall then submit an explanatory report to the TWDB and to each GCD within the GMA. *See* Tex. Water Code § 36.108(d–3). Once the TWDB deems the DFC resolution and explanatory report administratively complete, each district within the GMA must adopt the documents. *See* Tex. Water Code § 36.108(d–4). A DFC may be appealed by an affected person within 120 days after a GCD adopts the relevant DFCs. For the third cycle of joint planning, depending on when TWDB declares the DFCs resolution and explanatory report is administratively complete for each GMA, any appeal of DFCs will likely occur in the years 2022 and 2023.

VII. Conclusion

§ 21.22 Conclusion

Groundwater management area joint planning was mandated in 2005 by House Bill 1763, passed by the 79th Legislature. GCDs worked together in their GMAs to develop and to adopt the first set of desired future conditions by the statutory deadline of September 1, 2010. These desired future conditions were submitted to the TWDB, and the TWDB-developed managed available groundwater values were included in the 2016 regional water plans and 2017 state water plan. Currently, the third planning cycle is underway.

The most recent round of proposed desired future conditions was proposed by May 1, 2021, and must be fully adopted by January 5, 2022, and in each successive five-year period after that date. The local GCDs, the regional planning groups, the TWDB, the TCEQ, and the stakeholders all have valuable roles in groundwater management in Texas.

CHAPTER 22

Drought Planning and Response

Kim Nygren[1]

I. Introduction

§ 22.1 Drought Planning and Response

The availability of clean and plentiful water is an important concern in the United States. Many regions throughout the nation are characterized by increasing populations, increasing water demand, changing trends and patterns of water use, changing social behavior, and growing environmental awareness. How water is allocated and managed will continue to be contentious, especially during periods of drought. Droughts are a normal part of the climate for most regions.

Texas has also been plagued with the impacts associated with drought. For example, Texas's drought-related crop and livestock losses between 1998 and 2011 cost more than $14 billion, with nearly $7.6 billion of those losses attributable to 2011 alone. *See* Patrick Beach, *Drought Cost Texas Close to $8 Billion in Agricultural Losses in 2011, Study Finds*, *Austin-American Statesman*, Mar. 21, 2012. In addition, in 2011, the drought killed an estimated 5.6 million trees in urban areas and 301 million in rural areas. *See* Susan Combs, Texas Comptroller of Public Accounts, *Texas Water Report: Going Deeper for the Solution* 12, Pub. # 96-1746 (Jan. 14, 2014). As of March 25, 2015, 777 community water systems in Texas had mandatory water use restrictions in place because of drought or water shortages. *See* Texas Commission on Environmental Quality, *Map of Water Systems under Water Use Restriction*, www.tceq.texas.gov/drinkingwater/trot/location.html.

Part II of this chapter examines the concept of drought and why drought is important in the context of water rights law. Part III describes the traditional method of dealing with drought—drought response—and describes the legal powers and duties of governmental entities in dealing with dangerous drought conditions. Finally, part IV focuses on the state's move toward a more proactive approach to drought planning, discussing Texas's existing laws pertaining to preparing and planning for drought conditions and shortages of water, including the state water plan, the state drought preparedness plan, and the legal responsibilities of water rights holders and water providers to develop and implement drought contingency plans.

---

1. Kimberly Nygren is the Deputy Director for the Texas Commission on Environmental Quality in the Water Availability Division.

II. Why Is Drought Important?

§ 22.2 Introduction

Drought is a normal part of the climate in Texas. The only thing that is certain about drought conditions is that they will recur. The National Integrated Drought Information System (NIDIS), part of the National Oceanic and Atmospheric Administration (NOAA), uses the Standardized Precipitation Index (SPI) as an index to characterize meteorological drought. In Texas, the NIDIS shows abnormally dry to exceptional drought conditions occurring in Texas nearly every year since 1895. *See* National Oceanic and Atmospheric Administration, National Integrated Drought Information System, *Drought in Texas*, www.drought.gov/states/texas. Conditions with this rate of recurrence require planning to mitigate impacts. Planning for drought seeks to ensure the supply of water in an amount, rate, and quality sufficient to satisfy water needs across all sectors. When drought is severe enough, planning includes short-term response measures to water supply crises.

The following sections explore the concept of drought, the lack of a comprehensive definition of drought, and the relevance of drought in the context of water rights law.

§ 22.3 The Concept of Drought

Drought is unlike other natural disasters in many ways. Drought is the extended absence of precipitation rather than the sudden onset of an extreme weather event such as a hurricane, tornado, or earthquake. This is important to understand because planning, monitoring, and response strategies must all vary significantly from what would be employed with other types of natural disasters.

Drought often develops very slowly, although drought can develop rapidly as well in a phenomenon referred to as "flash drought." A drought usually breaks quickly, with large precipitation events that precede a wetter overall weather pattern, although drought can also dissipate slowly. Drought can be isolated to small areas but often is more widespread, covering large regions.

The impacts of drought are typically not immediate but instead accumulate over the duration of the drought, and they often extend past the drought's end. Areas not experiencing drought conditions can still be significantly impacted by their proximity to drought-affected areas, as may occur in communities located downstream from regions experiencing drought.

§ 22.4 Lack of a Comprehensive Drought Definition

A contributing factor to the difficulty of anticipating and mitigating the negative repercussions of drought is that drought is not precisely or uniformly defined. Because drought affects many economic and social sectors, scores of drought definitions have been developed by a variety of disciplines. As noted above, however, there is no universally accepted or comprehensive definition of drought. As a starting point, for example, the National Drought Policy Commission (NDPC) provides a generic definition of drought as "a persistent and abnormal moisture deficiency having adverse impacts on vegetation, animals, or people." National Drought Policy Commission, U.S. Department of Agriculture, *Preparing for the Drought in the 21st Century*, Executive Summary 3 (2000). The NDPC suggests that the definition of what drought is and what drought is not has profound implications for the environment and all segments of society, yet may be different for each.

The NOAA, on the other hand, defines drought as "a deficiency of precipitation over an extended period of time (usually a season or more), resulting in a water shortage." National Oceanic and Atmospheric Administration, National Integrated Drought Information System, *What is Drought: Drought Basics*, www.drought.gov/what-is-drought/drought-basics [hereinafter "NIDIS Drought Basics"]. NOAA asserts that the severity of drought depends on the degree of moisture deficiency, the duration of the condition, and the size of the affected area. NOAA uses five different operational definitions of drought: meteorological, agricultural, hydrological, socioeconomic, and ecological. A *meteorological* drought exists "when dry weather patterns dominate an area." NIDIS Drought Basics. Due to climatic differences, what is considered a drought in one location may not be a drought in another. An *agricultural* drought occurs "when crops become affected by drought." NIDIS Drought Basics. A *hydrological* drought exists "when low water supply becomes evident in the water system." NIDIS Drought Basics. A *socioeconomic* drought refers to "when the supply and demand of various commodities is [sic] affected by drought." NIDIS Drought Basics. Finally, an *ecological* drought occurs "when natural ecosystems are affected by drought." NIDIS Drought Basics.

Drought, as defined by the U.S. Army Corps of Engineers, "is a weather phenomenon caused by an extended period of months or years when a region experiences a deficiency in its surface or underground water supply, generally occurring when a region receives consistently below average precipitation." *See* U.S. Army Corps of Engineers, *Drought*, www.usace.army.mil/Missions/Emergency-Operations/Drought/#:~:text=Drought%20is%20a%20weather%20phenomenon,USACE%20Role%20in%20Drought.

As illustrated by these examples, a single, universally accepted definition of drought does not exist. Because "drought occurs with varying frequency in nearly all regions of the globe, in all types of economic systems, . . . the approaches taken to define [drought] should be impact and region specific. The lack of a precise and objective definition in specific situations has been an obstacle to understanding drought, which has led to indecision and/or inaction on the part of managers, policymakers, and others." Donald A. Wilhite, National Drought Mitigation Center, *Improving Drought Management in the West: The Role of Mitigation and Preparedness* 3, Report to the Western Water Policy Review Advisory Commission (June 1997), http://digitalcommons.usu.edu/elusive_docs/71 [hereinafter *Improving Drought Management*]. Therefore, it is imperative for individual water suppliers to draw on past and current conditions to develop their own definitions and concepts of drought. Specific definitions will facilitate the preparation of contingency plans for future drought conditions.

§ 22.5 The Importance of Drought in Texas Water Rights Law

The nebulous nature of drought aside, the relevance of drought in water rights law is unquestionable. The continuous availability of water is central to the water rights system in Texas. Before a permit is issued to appropriate state water, section 11.134(b)(2) of the Texas Water Code requires the Texas Commission on Environmental Quality (TCEQ) to make a determination that unappropriated water is available in the source of supply. *See* Tex. Water Code § 11.134(b)(2). In making such a determination, the TCEQ uses historic stream flow records. *See* 30 Tex. Admin. Code § 297.42(c). The drought of record, and any other drought that occurred during the period of record, is incorporated into the historic stream flow records. The resulting naturalized flows provide the baseline for water availability. In this manner, past droughts limit the amount of water available for appropriation. See Chapter 12 of this book for a more thorough discussion of how historic stream flow records are used in the TCEQ's Water Availability Modeling (WAM).

In addition to the role that drought plays in determining water availability, drought also affects other TCEQ requirements for water rights applications; namely, almost every application for a new or amended water right requires the submission of a drought contingency plan before the TCEQ will consider such an application administratively complete. *See* 30 Tex. Admin. Code § 295.9. See Chapter 10 of this book for additional discussion of drought contingency plan requirements for water rights applications. For a thorough discussion of drought contingency plans, see part IV below.

III. The State's Responses to Drought Crises

§ 22.6 Introduction

At least one serious drought plagued parts of Texas in every decade of the twentieth century. Because every decade was marred by at least one severe drought, the phenomenon of drought is hardly cyclic in nature and makes predictability a "formidable chore." Robert F. Riggio et al., *Texas Drought: Its Recent History, 1931–1985* 61 (Texas Water Commission 1987). As a subtle phenomenon characterized by too little rain for too long a period of time, fewer severe droughts manifest in "varying intensities in some parts of Texas virtually every year." Riggio et al., at 61.

The most catastrophic drought to strike Texas was the mammoth dry spell that afflicted every sector of the state in the 1950s. Riggio et al., at 1. Near the drought's end in 1957, all but ten of Texas's 254 counties were declared federal drought disaster areas. Texas Water Resources Institute, Texas A&M University, *The Drought of the 1950s*, 22 Tex. Water Resources 4 (1996). Many other droughts, some lasting only a few months and others continuing for several years, dealt harshly with Texas during the twentieth century. Riggio et al., at 61. In February 2015, the Lower Colorado River Authority (LCRA) declared the ongoing drought the "most severe drought the region has experienced since construction of the lakes began in the 1930s," putting the Highland Lakes in "a new 'critical period' marking the driest conditions on record, eclipsing the 1947–57 drought that until now was the worst on record for this region." Press Release, Lower Colorado River Authority, *Drought conditions worsen along Highland Lakes* (Feb. 18, 2015). The drought occurring 2007 through 2009 is considered by the Office of the State Climatologist to be separate from the latest drought of 2010–15. *See* John W. Nielsen-Gammon, Office of the State Climatologist, *The 2011 Texas Drought: A Briefing Packet for the Texas Legislature* (Oct. 31, 2011), https://senate.texas.gov/cmtes/82/c510/0110BI-JohnNielsen-Gammon.pdf; *Drought Disaster Proclamation by the Governor of the State of Texas* (Mar. 9, 2015), https://gov.texas.gov/news/post/drought_disaster_proclamation_by_the_governor_of_the_state_of_texas.

The General Accounting Office (GAO) first reported in 1979 that, despite this inevitable nature of drought, the traditional mind-set of government in the United States was to react to drought through emergency assistance to affected areas of the nation. Despite the obvious limitations of this method of dealing with drought, many of the statutes and regulations pertaining to drought in the state of Texas focus on event management. As is discussed in later sections of this chapter, there is currently a shift in policy toward a more proactive planning approach to drought. However, that is not to say that planning will ever completely mitigate or prevent the negative impacts of droughts. Therefore, there will always be a need for governmental entities to have the power to step in and provide assistance during the crises caused by inevitable drought situations. The following sections describe the responsibilities and authorities of the governor, the Texas Commission on Environmental Quality, and the Texas Water Development Board to respond to crisis situations caused by serious drought.

§ 22.7 The Office of the Governor

The governor's role in responding to drought situations is typically confined to providing assistance in the form of governmental aid. However, in a serious water shortage, the governor has broader authority to mobilize people and resources to address emergencies. The Texas Disaster Act of 1975 (the Disaster Act) gives the governor broad powers to declare a state of disaster and respond to such disasters. *See* Tex. Gov't Code ch. 418. The Disaster Act specifically includes drought in the definition of "disaster." *See* Tex. Gov't Code § 418.004(1). The governor, by executive order or proclamation, may declare a state of disaster if the governor finds that a disaster has occurred or that the occurrence or threat of disaster is imminent. Tex. Gov't Code § 418.014(a). Upon declaring such a disaster, the governor has broad power to intervene to provide relief in a serious water shortage emergency. The governor may even go so far as to commandeer private water resources or "reassign resources, personnel, or functions of State executive departments" in coping with a disaster. *See* Tex. Gov't Code § 418.017(c). In the drought that began October 2010, Governor Perry invoked section 418.016 of the Texas Government Code in disaster proclamations. The proclamations suspend "all rules and regulations that may inhibit or prevent prompt response to [the drought] threat" for the duration of the disaster. See Governor's Emergency Disaster Proclamation, signed July 5, 2011, and renewed multiple times as of March 9, 2015, for many counties, available on the governor's website at https://gov.texas.gov/news/proclamation/20632. The TCEQ issued at least seventeen temporary water right permits or amendments good for the duration of the disaster proclamations with certain procedural requirements waived pursuant to the governor's proclamations. However, in most drought situations, it is more likely that the governor's disaster relief will entail economic relief.

To qualify for certain federal relief for a drought disaster, the governor must first take appropriate response action under state law, including a declaration of a disaster. *See* 42 U.S.C. § 5170. For major disaster relief, such as aid from the Federal Emergency Management Agency, the president must declare a major disaster for the area. *See* 42 U.S.C. § 5191. The president will make such a declaration based only on a finding that effective response is beyond the "capabilities of the State and the affected local governments and that Federal assistance is necessary." 42 U.S.C. § 5191(a).

In most drought scenarios, there is no need for such drastic federal intervention. If federal assistance is needed, lesser measures such as low-interest Farm Service Agency loans from the U.S. Department of Agriculture (USDA) will more likely be initiated. The USDA is authorized to disperse aid with a presidential declaration of a major disaster or a designation by the secretary of agriculture or an administrator. *See* U.S. Department of Agriculture, Farm Service Agency, *Disaster Assistance Programs*, www.fsa.usda.gov/programs-and-services/disaster-assistance-program/index. In January 2006 and again in March 2009, Governor Perry declared a drought disaster for all 254 counties in Texas and requested that the USDA begin implementing its disaster relief loan program. Press Release, Office of Governor Rick Perry, Perry Declares Statewide Drought Disaster (Jan. 19, 2006), http://texaslivingwaters.org/wp-content/uploads/2013/04/tlw-news-1-19-06.pdf; Letter from Governor Rick Perry to U.S. Secretary of Agriculture Tom Vilsack (Mar. 6, 2009), http://texasagriculture.gov/Portals/0/DigArticle/1508/28675_DroughtWaiver.pdf.

To assist the governor in his efforts, the Drought Preparedness Council was created by the 76th Legislature in 1999. *See* Tex. Water Code § 16.055(b). The council creates the drought preparedness plan, now referred to as the Drought Annex, to identify drought conditions and direct and coordinate relief efforts. This topic is discussed in more detail in part IV below because it falls within the category of planning for response rather than strictly reactionary response.

The role of the office of the governor in responding to drought may be categorized as primarily economic or disaster relief. For the most part, statutes and rules that more specifically affect water rights in a time of drought are within the purview of the TCEQ.

§ 22.8 The Texas Commission on Environmental Quality

When drought occurs, the TCEQ has specific authority to grant emergency relief to water rights holders and water users. The TCEQ's authority arises out of the general authority granted under section 5.501 of the Texas Water Code, which provides that the TCEQ may issue a temporary or emergency order that is "mandatory, permissive, or prohibitory" and by such an order issue a temporary permit or temporarily suspend or amend a permit condition. *See* Tex. Water Code § 5.501(a). The TCEQ has adopted procedures for emergency and temporary orders. *See* 30 Tex. Admin Code chs. 35, 36. With respect specifically to water rights and water use, four additional provisions address emergency relief measures that the TCEQ may take.

First, in a drought emergency, the TCEQ may suspend permit conditions "relating to beneficial inflows to affected bays and estuaries and instream uses if the commission finds that an emergency exists that cannot practicably be resolved in another way." *See* Tex. Water Code §§ 5.506(a), 11.148(a); 30 Tex. Admin. Code § 35.101. Second, under Water Code section 5.506(a–1), freshwater inflow set-asides established pursuant to Water Code section 11.1471 for each river basin and bay system in the state may be made available temporarily for other beneficial uses during an emergency. *See* Tex. Water Code §§ 5.506(a–1), 11.1471. See Chapter 11 of this book for further discussion of environmental flows. Outside of the emergency relief found in Water Code section 11.148, the TCEQ may issue an emergency order under Water Code section 11.139. If the TCEQ finds that "emergency conditions exist which present an imminent threat to the public health and safety and which override the necessity to comply with established statutory procedures," the TCEQ may issue an emergency order under Water Code section 11.139 for 120 days and renew that order for an additional sixty days. Tex. Water Code § 11.139(a). Finally, Water Code section 11.053 gives the executive director the authority to temporarily suspend or adjust water rights during a period of drought or other emergency shortage of water based on the priority of the water rights. *See* Tex. Water Code § 11.053(a). See Chapter 13 of this book for further discussion of drought suspension orders. In recent dry years, several applications have been filed with the TCEQ under these provisions.

During a period of drought in 2006, the LCRA filed an application for an emergency order to suspend the instream flow requirements for its Permit No. 5715, calling on the TCEQ's authority under Water Code sections 5.506, 11.139, and 11.148. *See* Texas Commission on Environmental Quality, TCEQ Docket No. 2006-1091-WR. The LCRA estimated in July 2006 that the Lometa Reservoir had only ninety to one hundred days of usable water supply. If granted, this emergency order would have allowed the LCRA, by reducing its required instream flows, to divert more water out of the Colorado River into the Lometa Reservoir, which supplied LCRA customers in the City of Lometa. In a July 18, 2006, letter to the LCRA, the executive director of the TCEQ declined the request and, in doing so, commented that the LCRA had implemented only the first stage of its drought contingency plan. The executive director also concluded that because the LCRA had not taken steps to limit nonessential water usage, the LCRA had not shown that there was an "imminent threat to public health, safety, and welfare that overrides the necessity to comply with general procedures for changing a water right." Essentially, the executive director determined that the LCRA had failed to meet its burden under 30 Texas Administrative Code section 35.101(a)(1) and (2) by not instituting sufficient drought conservation measures and by failing to explore other feasible alternatives. The LCRA then took its request to the TCEQ commissioners.

Ultimately, the LCRA withdrew its request for the emergency order in a May 4, 2007, letter to the TCEQ. The LCRA cited an emergency interconnect agreement with the City of Lampasas and higher than average rains in the spring of 2007 as the reasons the emergency situation was abated. Although the commissioners did not have an opportunity to comment on the request for the emergency order, the executive director's response at least gives guidance to the water rights community that a request for extraordinary emergency relief must be accompanied by a demonstration that serious drought measures have been instituted and the feasibility of alternative solutions has been thoroughly explored. This interpretation of 30 Texas Administrative Code section 35.101 by the executive director seems to have been codified in section 11.053 of the Water Code, which was enacted by the 2011 legislature. *See* Tex. Water Code § 11.053(b)(4). See also the discussion of section 11.053 in Chapter 13 of this book.

During the latest drought, the LCRA repeatedly sought emergency relief under Water Code sections 5.501, 11.138, and 11.139 as well as the governor's emergency disaster proclamation. Beginning in 2011 and over the following four years, the LCRA applied for emergency orders to temporarily amend its 2010 Water Management Plan. The LCRA requested and was granted permission to curtail releases of interruptible stored water from the Highland Lakes for downstream irrigation. *See* Texas Commission on Environmental Quality, TCEQ Docket Nos. 2011-2096-WR; 2013-0225-WR; 2014-0124-WR; 2014-1044-WR. The LCRA based its request on the fact that inflows into the Highland Lakes were significantly lower than anticipated, and with persistent drought conditions releases of interruptible water could cause storage levels to fall below 600,000 acre-feet, which would have far-reaching implications for all of the LCRA's water customers.

Water Code section 11.139 allows the commission to grant an emergency order to amend an existing permit if the commission finds that emergency conditions exist that "present an imminent threat to the public health and safety and which override the necessity to comply with established statutory procedures and there are no feasible practicable alternatives to the emergency authorization." Tex. Water Code § 11.139(a). Additionally, "[i]f an imminent threat to the public health and safety exists which requires emergency action before the commission can take action . . . the executive director may grant an emergency authorization." Tex. Water Code § 11.139(f). After the executive director issues an emergency order, the TCEQ commissioners must hold a hearing to affirm, modify, or set aside the executive director's order. *See* Tex. Water Code § 11.139(f).

For each of the LCRA's requests to curtail releases of interruptible water, the executive director found an imminent threat to the public health and safety and granted the LCRA's requests to temporarily amend its 2010 Water Management Plan in accordance with Water Code section 11.139. Specifically, the executive director found that if stored water were released and water to the LCRA's firm customers were reduced before alternatives could be developed, the LCRA would have difficulty in meeting its firm customers' water needs. The TCEQ commissioners then affirmed or affirmed and modified each of the executive director's emergency orders. *See* Texas Commission on Environmental Quality, TCEQ Docket Nos. 2011-2096-WR; 2013-0225-WR; 2014-0124-WR; 2014-1044-WR. The LCRA also sought and was granted relief to temporarily suspend permit conditions related to beneficial inflows to bays and estuaries and instream uses during the spring of 2014 and 2015. Specifically, the LCRA sought to amend its water management plan to reduce the requirement to maintain a minimum streamflow of 500 cubic feet per second for six weeks between March and May of 2014 and 2015 from Bastrop to Eagle Lake for the Blue Sucker. *See* Texas Commission on Environmental Quality, TCEQ Docket Nos. 2014-0438-WR; 2015-0219-WR. The LCRA requested that its applications be processed under Water Code sections 5.506, 11.139, or 11.148 as appropriate and the governor's emergency disaster proclamation related to drought. The TCEQ granted the LCRA's request to reduce the streamflow requirements for six consecutive weeks between March and May from Bastrop to Eagle Lake in accordance with Water Code section 11.148.

In response to Dow Chemical Company's senior priority calls on November 14, 2012, and June 26, 2013, the TCEQ's executive director issued suspension orders in the Brazos River Basin in accordance with Water Code sections 11.027 and 11.053 and 30 Texas Administrative Code chapter 36. *See* Texas Commission on Environmental Quality, TCEQ Docket Nos. 2012-2421-WR; 2013-1253-WR. The executive director's orders suspended water rights in the basin below Possum Kingdom Reservoir with priority dates on or after February 14, 1942. Pursuant to 30 Texas Administrative Code section 36.5(c), the executive director elected not to suspend the use of certain water rights designated for use as municipal water supplies or for electric power generation, based on public health, safety, and welfare concerns. See Chapter 13 of this book for further discussion of drought suspension orders.

The Texas Farm Bureau and individual plaintiffs filed suit challenging the validity of the TCEQ drought rules and seeking declaratory judgment under Texas Government Code section 2001.038. The district court declared the drought rules invalid because the rules exceeded the commission's statutory authority by allowing exemption of preferred uses, contrary to the priority of water rights established by Water Code section 11.027. The district court held that exemption of junior water rights from a priority call curtailment is not authorized by the TCEQ's police power or any general authority to protect public health, safety, or welfare.

On appeal, the TCEQ argued that the district court failed to give proper deference to the agency's interpretation of the statute, the district court's interpretation was unreasonable and rendered section 11.053 meaningless, and the legislative history supported the commission's statutory interpretation.

The court of appeals looked to the statutory language of Water Code section 11.053 to determine whether the TCEQ had the authority to deviate from the "first in time, first in right" principle of section 11.027. The court found no specific language in the statute that would allow the TCEQ to depart from the time priority principle of section 11.027. Rather, the opposite is expressly stated in section 11.053(a). The court also determined that the Water Code's provisions giving the TCEQ general power to act in the public interest were limited to actions on new water permits and authorizing new appropriations. *See* Tex. Water Code §§ 11.134(b), 11.024, 12.014. The commission's authority must not exceed its express legislative mandate. Consequently, the court of appeals affirmed the judgment of the district court. *See Texas Commission on Environmental Quality v. Texas Farm Bureau*, 460 S.W.3d 264 (Tex. App.—Corpus Christi–Edinburg 2015, pet. denied). On February 19, 2016, the Texas Supreme Court declined the TCEQ's petition for review.

In light of the courts' findings that the TCEQ lacks authority to deviate from the priority doctrine during a drought to protect public health, safety, or welfare, it becomes even more crucial to encourage and develop a proactive approach to water management and drought planning. See part IV below for further discussion of the proactive approach to drought.

§ 22.9 The Texas Water Development Board

The Texas Water Development Board (TWDB) also has authority to provide water rights-related relief during times of water shortage. Under the storage acquisition fund, the TWDB is authorized to use state treasury dollars for projects "including the design, acquisition, lease, construction, reconstruction, development, or enlargement in whole or part of any existing or proposed water storage project." Tex. Water Code § 15.302(a). The water owned by the TWDB may be released "with or without charge, to relieve any emergency condition arising from drought, public calamity, or any other reason causing a severe water shortage, if the [TCEQ] first determines the existence of the emergency and requests the board to release water to alleviate the emergency condition." Tex. Water Code § 15.325(a). As the TWBD becomes involved in more water supply projects, the importance of these provisions is likely to increase.

IV. A Proactive Approach to Drought

§ 22.10 Introduction

In the late 1980s, a comprehensive study of droughts in Texas was conducted using monthly National Weather Service rainfall data at many sites from 1931 to 1980. Droughts were defined by the "quantity and duration of rainfall events." Precipitation data were normalized to account for differences in rainfall between arid west Texas and humid east Texas. Droughts covering three, six, and twelve months were identified and classified by their severity, duration, and location. The study results revealed that it was more likely that a six-month or year-long drought would occur somewhere in Texas than a near-normal or wet-weather spell for the same period. Additionally, droughts that lasted at least six months were expected once every sixteen months, while droughts lasting more than a year were likely to visit Texas once every three years. Droughts lasting six months or less occurred more frequently in west Texas, and longer droughts were found most often in north Texas. Riggio et al., at 61. Clearly, drought is a perpetual antagonist for the state. Therefore, it is crucial that drought is fully understood and anticipated if Texas is to ensure an adequate supply of water in the future.

Unfortunately, drought is not just a condition of rainfall levels; it is also greatly influenced by water demands. A relatively minor drought (in terms of low rainfall) becomes a major concern as demand and water use increase. For Texas, the population is expected to increase more than 73 percent between 2020 and 2070, from 29.7 million to 51.5 million. *See* Texas Water Development Board, *Water for Texas 2022* 3 (2022), www.twdb.texas.gov/waterplanning/swp/2022/index.asp [hereinafter 2022 State Water Plan]. In the same time span, water demands are projected to increase by approximately 9 percent, but Texas's existing water supplies are expected to decline by approximately 18 percent over those fifty years. 2022 State Water Plan, at 3. The 2022 State Water Plan estimates a potential water shortage of 3.1 million acre-feet per year in 2020 and 6.9 million acre-feet per year in 2070 in drought of record conditions. If water management strategies are not implemented, approximately one-quarter of Texas's population will have less than half the municipal water supplies needed during a drought of record in 2070. 2022 State Water Plan, at 3. It is evident from these projections that drought contingency planning in Texas is imperative.

Because widespread periods of drought conditions emphasize vulnerability, there is a need for a proactive approach to drought management that places emphasis on preparedness planning. Efforts have been made to reduce the nationwide vulnerability to drought. Unfortunately, droughts are often dealt with poorly. They are "too rarely documented, critically analyzed, and shared with other regions." *See* U.S. Army Corps of Engineers, Institute for Water Resources, *National Study of Water Management During Drought: The Report to the U.S. Congress* xi (IWR Report 94-NDS-12, Sept. 1995), www.iwr.usace.army.mil/Portals/70/docs/iwrreports/94-NDS-12.pdf. It is generally agreed that a proactive approach to drought management is a more effective mitigation tool than the reactive approach. Donald A. Wilhite, *Drought Planning: A Process for State Government*, 27 Water Resources Bull. 29 (1991) [hereinafter *Drought Planning*]; *see also* National Drought Policy Commission, U.S. Department of Agriculture, *Preparing for Drought in the 21st Century* (2000), http://govinfo.library.unt.edu/drought/finalreport/fullreport/reportdload.htm.

§ 22.11 Planning for Drought

The state has done much to create a more proactive planning approach to drought, including the development of state, regional, and local water plans; the creation of drought response and preparedness plans; and, perhaps most important, the required development of drought contingency plans by regulated communities.

§ 22.11:1 The State and Regional Water Plans

After the drought of record that occurred across Texas in the 1950s, the state began creating and implementing a state water plan. Section 16.051 of the Texas Water Code requires the TWDB to "prepare, develop, formulate, and adopt a comprehensive state water plan that incorporates the regional water plans approved under Section 16.053 [of the Texas Water Code]." Tex. Water Code § 16.051(a). The purpose of the plan is to quantify and develop the state's water resources with an eye on future population growth and to remain mindful that drought can and does inevitably occur in Texas. The goal of the plan is to meet the water needs of the state's communities, agricultural and business interests, and the environment even in times of severe drought.

The implementation of the state water plan is important to water right holders, water suppliers, and the rest of the water community because the plan defines the extent of water use in the state. The TCEQ can grant an application for state water only if the proposed appropriation "addresses a water supply need in a manner that is consistent with the state water plan and the relevant approved regional water plan for any area in which the proposed appropriation is located, unless the commission determines that conditions warrant waiver of this requirement." Tex. Water Code § 11.134(b)(3)(E). See Chapter 20 of this book for a more detailed discussion of this topic.

§ 22.11:2 The Drought Preparedness Plan

The state drought preparedness plan (now the Drought Annex) is separate from, but complementary to, the state water plan. *See* Tex. Water Code §§ 16.055, 16.0551. The purpose of the plan, when viewed in conjunction with section 16.055 of the Texas Water Code, is to quickly identify when drought conditions are occurring and to coordinate a fast, efficient response plan for dealing with all levels of drought emergencies. This plan serves as a bridge between planning and response measures. The plan does not attempt to eliminate drought emergencies but instead focuses on quickly identifying when a drought is occurring and then facilitating a fast and efficient response.

The plan is created by the Drought Preparedness Council, which is composed of representatives of many related governmental entities and other representatives of the governor's choosing and is headed by the state drought manager. The state drought manager is, by law, the coordinator of the division of emergency management of the office of the governor. *See* Tex. Water Code § 16.055(a). The goal of the council is to create a well-coordinated intergovernmental response in a drought emergency. Therefore, it is imperative that the council give clear direction and centralize control of the relief efforts.

§ 22.11:3 Drought Contingency Planning

Drought contingency planning is a proactive approach that addresses one area of disaster preparedness. Drought contingency planning is a principal tool to improve responses to drought. *See* Donald A. Wilhite et al., *Planning for Drought: Moving from Crisis to Risk Management*, 36 J. Am. Water Resources Ass'n 697 (2000).

A distinction must be made between water conservation planning and drought contingency planning. The goal of water conservation planning is to achieve lasting, year-round water use efficiency improvements for the purpose of extending existing water supplies. By contrast, a drought contingency plan is focused on a temporary supply management and demand management response to temporary and potentially recurring water supply shortages and other water supply emergencies. *See* Turner Collie & Braden Inc., *Drought Contingency Planning Survey and Evaluation Report of Findings and Recommendations: Report Prepared for the Texas Commission on Environmental Quality* 2 (1998). See Chapter 23 of this book for a discussion of conservation planning.

As stated above, the primary purpose of drought contingency planning is to ensure an uninterrupted supply of water in an amount sufficient to satisfy essential human needs. Another purpose of the drought contingency plan development process is to "improve mitigation efforts through more timely, effective, and efficient assessment and response activities." *See Drought Planning*, at 29. Experience, the expectation of future droughts, and the desire to improve future response efforts are also key factors in the decision to pursue plan development. *See Drought Planning*, at 30.

Preparedness and planning measures are "strong determinants of whether a community will reduce its future vulnerability during a disaster," while the lack of preparation may increase the vulnerability of communities to a disaster. David A. McEntire et al., *A Comparison of Disaster Paradigms: The Search for a Holistic Policy Guide*, 62 Pub. Admin. Rev. 267, 274 (2002). Drought plans are the "foundation for improved drought management in the United States." *Improving Drought Management*, at 17. During the droughts of 1986 and 1988, fewer than half of the water utilities surveyed in the U.S. had a drought contingency plan in place; however, the suppliers that had a drought contingency plan in place improved the effectiveness of water demand management measures. *See* David H. Moreau & Keith Little, *Managing Public Water Supplies During Droughts: Experiences in the United States in 1986 and 1988* iii, Water Resources Institute Report No. 250, University of North Carolina (1989).

§ 22.12 Required Drought Contingency Plans

Because drought is such a frequent event in Texas and because of population and water demand projections, drought contingency planning has become the norm for entities with water rights, entities supplying water to others, and local governments with jurisdiction over groundwater production. In the past, such planning was initiated solely as the result of policy decisions made by these entities. Now such planning is required by various statutory and regulatory schemes.

Additionally, as was illustrated by the executive director's decision in the LCRA's Lometa Reservoir request for an emergency order (discussed at section 22.8 above), the creation and enforcement of a drought contingency plan are objective standards by which the TCEQ can make a decision to provide equitable relief in a drought emergency. Essentially, the more severe the drought restrictions implemented, the more likely the entity will make its showing that relief is warranted.

§ 22.12:1 TCEQ Requirement for Drought Contingency Planning

Texas Water Code section 11.1272 requires, through the implementing rules adopted by the TCEQ, that all wholesale and retail public water suppliers and irrigation districts in Texas develop drought contingency plans. *See* Tex. Water Code § 11.1272. The heading and placement of section 11.1272 often leads to some confusion. It is located among various requirements for those applying for and holding water rights and is titled, "Additional Requirement: Drought Contingency Plans for Certain Applicants and Water Right Holders." However, the statute, and the implementing rules found in 30 Texas Administrative Code chapter 288, impose drought contingency plans on all described entities without reference to whether the entities are water right holders. The chapter 288 rules can also be somewhat confusing because they address both water conservation planning and drought contingency planning and do not consistently make a distinction between the two very different types of plans.

Be this as it may, wholesale and retail public water suppliers and irrigation water suppliers are required to submit drought contingency plans to the TCEQ, regardless of their source of water supply. *See* 30 Tex. Admin. Code ch. 288. Sections 288.20 and 288.22 mandate that the drought contingency plans for retail public water suppliers and wholesale water suppliers address public involvement, drought response triggering criteria, successive stages of response criteria, drought response management measures, enforcement, and plan adoption. *See* 30 Tex. Admin. Code §§ 288.20, 288.22; *see also* Tex. Water Code § 11.1272(b), (c). Section 288.21 requires that drought contingency plans for irrigation water suppliers address irrigation system user input, coordination with regional water planning groups, triggering criteria, allocation methods, procedures for use accounting, enforcement, and plan adoption. *See* 30 Tex. Admin. Code § 288.21.

Retail public water suppliers that provide water service to 3,300 or more connections, wholesale public water suppliers, and irrigation districts are required to submit to the TCEQ their drought contingency plans with their initial application for a water right, if any. All of these entities faced an initial deadline and are required to submit the plans to the TCEQ for review every five years thereafter. 30 Tex. Admin. Code § 288.30(5)–(7). After submitting their initial drought contingency plans to the TCEQ, retail public water suppliers with fewer than 3,300 connections are not required to submit their plans every five years but are required to make the plans available to the TCEQ if requested by the executive director. 30 Tex. Admin. Code § 288.30(5)(B).

§ 22.12:2 Groundwater Conservation and Subsidence District Drought Contingency Plans

Texas groundwater conservation districts (GCDs) and subsidence districts are not subject to Texas Water Code section 11.1272 because they are not water suppliers; they are governmental entities responsible for managing groundwater use within their boundaries. *See* Tex. Water Code §§ 36.001(1), (15), 36.0015; Tex. Spec. Dist. Code tit. 6, subtit. H ("Districts Governing Groundwater").

GCDs must adopt a management plan that outlines their goals and the steps needed to reach those goals. One of the goals of a GCD management plan is to address drought conditions. *See* Tex. Water Code § 36.1071(a), (e); 31 Tex. Admin. Code § 356.52(a)(1)(F). Generally, GCDs adopt drought contingency plans to reach this management goal. These are sometimes found in their rules, and other times are adopted as stand-alone requirements. The drought contingency plans apply to well owners within the district. In districts that include municipalities or retail water suppliers, the drought contingency plans of the GCD and those entities may be inconsistent.

In addition, under Water Code section 36.113(c), a GCD may require an applicant for a groundwater production permit to have a drought contingency plan. *See* Tex. Water Code § 36.113(c)(7). Under this provision, some districts have adopted rules requiring various groundwater users within their jurisdiction to develop drought contingency plans. Often, this creates another overlap of drought contingency plan requirements, particularly for municipalities or other retail public water suppliers located in a GCD, because these entities have drought contingency plans required by Water Code section 11.1272.

The overlap of these various drought contingency plans—a districtwide plan, a plan included in permit requirements, and a plan developed under section 11.1272—can cause confusion when plans are mandated by both the state and the groundwater conservation district, particularly when the elements required by the different regulating entities are not identical. This could result in two separate drought contingency plans being developed for the same water system to meet dueling plan requirements. Therefore, groundwater conservation districts may want to ensure that their drought contingency plan rules do not conflict with 30 Texas Administrative Code chapter 288 or to coordinate with retail water suppliers in their district.

Similar situations arise within subsidence districts. Groundwater production permits issued by subsidence districts may impose a whole host of requirements on permittees relating to the protection of groundwater resources, including compliance with drought restrictions. *See* Tex. Spec. Dist. Code §§ 8801.158(d), 8834.209(d).

§ 22.13 Watermaster Program

Sections 11.325 through 11.3291 of the Texas Water Code provide for a state watermaster program to manage water diversions. Watermasters' duties include dividing the surface water in accordance with adjudicated water rights and regulating the controlling works or reservoirs and diversion works in times of shortage as necessary to protect existing water rights. Texas Commission on Environmental Quality, *Watermasters*, www.tceq.texas.gov/permitting/water_rights/wmaster. A watermaster program marks a departure from the traditional approach to water basin management. Under the traditional approach, the TCEQ would respond to complaints and priority calls with investigation and curtailments or suspensions, as necessary. This primarily reactionary approach is still used in nonwatermaster areas across Texas.

By contrast, a watermaster provides proactive, hands-on management of river basins. A watermaster continuously monitors streamflows, reservoir levels, and water use within a basin, providing day-to-day management. Texas Commission on Environmental Quality, *Watermaster Evaluation Fact Sheet—2021*, www.tceq.texas.gov/assets/public/compliance/field_ops/wmaster/Evaluation/WM%20Fact%20Sheet%20-%202021-final.pdf. Before starting to divert water, the water user must notify the watermaster and state how much water it plans to divert. If the water is available and compliant with the user's permit, the watermaster authorizes the diversion. If the watermaster determines that a diversion will remove water that rightfully belongs to another user, the watermaster notifies the user with lower priority to reduce or cease pumping as necessary. When streamflows diminish, the watermaster allocates available water among users according to each user's priority date. If a water right holder does not comply with the water right or with TCEQ rules, the executive director may direct a wastermaster to adjust the control works, including pumps, to prevent the owner from diverting, taking, storing, or distributing water until the water right holder complies. See Chapter 13 of this book discussing enforcement.

§ 22.14 TCEQ Model Drought Planning Approach

In an effort to assist retail public water suppliers in Texas, which primarily supply water for municipal use, the TCEQ hired Turner Collie & Braden Inc. to develop a model drought contingency plan. *See* Texas Commission on Environmental Quality, *Drought Contingency Plan for a Retail Public Water Supplier* (rev. Dec. 2018), www.tceq.texas.gov/assets/public/permitting/watersupply/drought/20191.pdf. The model plan includes the quintessential components expected to be in an ideal drought contingency plan for retail suppliers of municipal water. These elements include public involvement, drought response triggering criteria, successive stages of response, drought response management measures, enforcement, and plan adoption.

The model plan was developed to serve as a tool to assist public administrators of retail public water suppliers in designing their required drought contingency plans to ensure that each component of the plan would meet the requirements of 30 Texas Administrative Code chapter 288. The water suppliers can use the model plan either to create their drought contingency plans or to develop a plan on their own. However, if a water supplier completes the model plan using the supplier's system-specific data, the plan will meet the requirements of chapter 288. *See* Tex. Water Code § 11.1272(e) (requiring the TCEQ and the TWDB to jointly develop model drought contingency programs and best management practices for different types of water suppliers for water use reductions achievable during periods of water shortages and drought).

After the model plan was developed, the water supply community was notified about the existence of the model via mail and a series of drought contingency planning workshops conducted by the TCEQ throughout Texas. The purpose of the workshops was to educate public administrators of water supply systems about the regulatory requirements of drought contingency plans and to instruct them on the use of the model plan. The workshops reached more than twelve hundred individuals representing approximately eight hundred retail public water suppliers in Texas. The workshops provided information about all elements of the plan. These elements are summarized in Table 1.

Table 1: Ideal Elements for a Municipal Drought Contingency Plan

Ideal Element	Source
Public Involvement • Public involvement in plan preparation • Notification to water users of plan initiation and termination • Program of continuing public education and information	**Campbell, Heather, and Robert Marshall.** 2000. Public involvement and planning: Looking beyond the one to the many. *International Planning Studies* 5, no. 3: 321–44. **Creighton, James L.** 1980. *Public involvement manual: Involving the public in water and power resources decisions.* U.S. Department of the Interior. **Glicken, Jessica.** 1999. Effective public involvement in public decisions. *Science Communication* 20, no. 3: 298–328. **King, Cheryl, and Camilla Stivers.** 1998. *Government is us: Public administration in an anti-government era.* Thousand Oaks, CA: Sage Publications. **McEntire, David A., Christopher Fuller, Chad W. Johnson, and Richard Weber.** 2002. A comparison of disaster paradigms: The search for a holistic policy guide. *Public Administration Review* 62, no. 3: 267–81. **Pierce, John C., and Harvey R. Doerksen.** 1976. *Water politics and public involvement.* Ann Arbor, MI: Ann Arbor Science Publishers. **Thomas, John C.** 1993. Public involvement and government effectiveness: A decision-making model for public managers. *Administration & Society* 24: 444–69. **Turner Collie & Braden Inc.** 1998. *Drought contingency planning survey and evaluation report of findings and recommendations: Report prepared for the Texas Commission on Environmental Quality.* **United States Army Corps of Engineers.** April 1, 1993. *Drought Contingency Plan*, ETL 1110-2-335. **Wilhite, Donald A.** 1991. Drought planning. *Water Resources Bulletin* 27, no. 1: 29–38.
Drought Response Triggering Criteria • Monitoring of drought indicators • Triggering criteria for the initiation of response stages • Triggering criteria for the termination of response stages	**McEntire, Fuller, Johnson & Weber** (2002) **Prasifka, David W.** 1988. *Current trends in water-supply planning.* New York: Van Nostrand Reinhold Company. **Turner Collie & Braden** (1998)
Successive Stages of Response • Reduction in available water supply • Production or distribution system limitations • Supply source contamination • System outage	**McEntire, Fuller, Johnson & Weber** (2002) **Turner Collie & Braden** (1998)

Ideal Element	Source
Drought Response Management Measures • Water supply management measures • Water demand management measures	**McEntire, Fuller, Johnson & Weber** (2002) **Prasifka** (1988) **Turner Collie & Braden** (1998)
Enforcement and Plan Adoption • Procedures for enforcement of any mandatory water use restrictions • Procedures for granting variances (exceptions) to the plan • Official adoption of the plan by the governing body	**Turner Collie & Braden** (1998) **Wilhite, Donald A.** 1997a. *Improving drought management in the West: The role of mitigation and preparedness.* Report to the Western Water Policy Review Advisory Commission, National Drought Mitigation Center.

V. Conclusion

§ 22.15 Conclusion

Every aspect of Texas water law and water regulation is designed with the next inevitable drought in mind. The laws and regulations managing water resources in the state contain both drought preparedness and drought response measures. Each method serves a unique function. Preparedness involves planning ahead to mitigate the negative effects of drought, while drought response includes measures to allow the government to intervene when planning measures have failed to prevent disaster. Each new drought will provide lessons and guidance on how to plan for the state's water needs and will renew the urgency to make more efficient use of the state's limited water resources.

CHAPTER 23

Water Conservation

Karen Guz[1]

I. Introduction

§ 23.1 The Importance of Water Conservation

The 2022 State Water Plan makes it clear that water conservation is considered critical for future Texas water security. Conservation strategies are recommended for over half of the water user groups in our state. Collectively, if the conservation strategies are implemented, conservation would make up 29% of water supply shortfalls by 2070. *See* Texas Water Development Board, *Water for Texas 2022* 2 (2022), www.twdb.texas.gov/waterplanning/swp/2022 [hereinafter 2022 State Water Plan]. The challenges outlined in the updated plan still include a fast-growing population, declining water supplies, and higher municipal water demand. Drought needs are again emphasized by estimating that the 2070 potential water shortfall of 3.1 million acre-feet per year may balloon to over 6.9 million acre feet per year under drought conditions. *See* 2022 State Water Plan, at 3. The 2022 plan builds on the conservation emphasis in the 2017 State Water Plan which included capital costs associated with municipal water conservation projects for the first time. *See* Texas Water Development Board, *Water for Texas 2017* 3 (2017), www.twdb.texas.gov/waterplanning/swp/2017 [hereinafter 2017 State Water Plan]. See Chapter 22 of this book for a further discussion of drought and drought planning.

Urban sectors of Texas are particularly motivated to plan carefully and to include conservation as a strategy, because municipal demands are expected to increase by over 87 percent between 2020 and 2070. *See* 2022 State Water Plan, at 6. The city of Forth Worth received $76 million in state loans to replace meters in a project expected to yield 9,000 acre-feet per year. 2017 State Water Plan, at 110. A similar urgency was reflected in Region L, which recommended that all user groups with water needs in 2020 reduce their 2020 demand by 5 percent during drought. 2022 State Water Plan, at 41. Given the challenge faced by municipal water providers, it is not surprising that every regional plan includes municipal conservation as a strategy. *See* 2022 State Water Plan, at 106.

Agriculture is and will remain the largest water use sector in Texas. However, agricultural use is expected to shrink. By 2070, agriculture irrigation demand should drop from 9.4 million acre-feet per year to 7.6 million acre-feet per year. Improved irrigation efficiency, reduced groundwater availability, and transfer of water rights to urban sectors will all contribute to the trend of reduced agricultural water demands. *See* 2022 State Water Plan, at 6.

---

1. Karen Guz is the Director of Conservation for the San Antonio Water System where a staff team manages diverse conservation programs that offer savings opportunities for all SAWS ratepayers. She is a licensed irrigator and serves as the Vice Chair of the Irrigator Advisory Council and is a member of the Water Conservation Advisory Council. Ms. Guz holds a Bachelor of Science from the University of Michigan and a Master's of Public Administration from the University of North Carolina in Charlotte.

Ms. Guz would like to acknowledge Scott Swanson for his assistance with this chapter. Ms. Guz would also like to acknowledge Steve Kosub for writing sections 23.16 and 23.17 of this chapter.

Many factors contribute to the move to increase water conservation across the state. One noteworthy driver of water conservation in Texas is the Endangered Species Act (ESA). In the large area of Texas underlain by the Edwards Aquifer, the ESA has been an impetus for water conservation. The Edwards Aquifer has become a highly regulated water source primarily because of the need to manage endangered species habitat in springs. See Chapter 32 of this book regarding the ESA. Because of such regulations, entities such as the San Antonio Water System have initiated extensive water conservation planning. *See* San Antonio Water System, *2017 Water Management Plan* (2017), www.saws.org/wp-content/uploads/2019/02/20171107_SAWS-2017-Water-Management-Plan.pdf. Conservation priorities in the region could expand as a result of the Edwards Aquifer Recovery Implementation Program (EARIP), which has included regional water conservation as one of the near-term strategies for species protection. *See* Edwards Aquifer Authority, *Habitat Conservation Plan*, http://eahcp.org/. See also Chapter 17 of this book.

Another conservation driver, especially in the eastern Gulf coast area of the state, is subsidence. Groundwater withdrawals have resulted in the largest area of significant subsidence in the United States. *See* Laura S. Coplin & Devin Galloway, *Houston-Galveston, Texas*, *in Land Subsidence in the United States* 35–48, U.S. Geological Survey Circular 1182 (1999), http://pubs.usgs.gov/circ/circ1182/pdf/07Houston.pdf. Subsidence solutions depend on careful regulation of groundwater withdrawals. Because conversion to surface water supplies is expensive, subsidence regulators have encouraged water users to consider conservation as one strategy to decrease their dependence on groundwater. Lone Star Groundwater Conservation District, *Groundwater Management Plan* (readopted Nov. 12, 2013), www.twdb.texas.gov/groundwater/docs/GCD/lsgcd/lsgcd_mgmt_plan2013.pdf. See also Chapter 16 of this book for discussion of subsidence districts.

This chapter discusses water conservation progress in Texas, including statewide conservation planning and reporting requirements, and the distinction between conservation, efficiency, and drought management.

II. Water Conservation: Agriculture, Energy, and the Environment

§ 23.2 Introduction

Additional conservation drivers may emerge across Texas as existing supplies are used heavily during peak demand periods. Already the need for power, agricultural products, healthy ecosystems, and protection of endangered species has added to the urgency to conserve water. With water conservation now accounting for roughly 30 percent of new water supplies by 2070, the adverse consequences to Texas residents will be severe if targets are not met. *See* 2022 State Water Plan, at 9.

§ 23.3 Agriculture

Agriculture is a significant economic driver for Texas and the largest consumer of water. In many regions, agricultural production is not possible without supplemental irrigation. *See* 2022 State Water Plan, at 114. It is good news that while agricultural water usage is declining in Texas, agricultural production has increased steadily. *See* Water Conservation Advisory Council, *Progress Made in Water Conservation in Texas, Report and Recommendations to the 85th Legislature* 3 (Dec. 1, 2016), www.savetexaswater.org/resources/doc/2016_WCAC_Lege_Report.pdf. The 2022 State Water Plan estimates that due to increased irrigation efficiency, the amount of water used for agricultural production will decline from 9.4 million acre-feet in 2020 to 7.6 million acre-feet in 2070. *See* 2022 State Water Plan, at 6.

Conservation of water and improved agricultural yields can be accomplished through changes in land management, crop selection, and irrigation scheduling. *See* Texas Water Development Board, *Agricultural Water Conservation, Irrigation Water Use Management, Best Management Practices* 8, www.twdb.texas.gov/publications/brochures/conservation/doc/AgBrochure2_irrigation.pdf [hereinafter TWDB Agricultural Irrigation BMP]. A recent analysis of the Texas High Plains suggests there could be a reduction in water demand of up to 14 percent and improved crop yields if evapotranspiration management for crops and irrigation improvements were further expanded. *See* Paul D. Colaizzi et al., *Irrigation in the Texas High Plains: A Brief History and Potential Reductions in Demand,* 58 Irrigation & Drainage 257 (2009) https://pubag.nal.usda.gov/download/31648/PDF. Technical information and funding assistance for changes in irrigation practices is available through programs administered by the TWDB, which has disbursed over $65 million in funding for agricultural conservation since 1985. See Chapter 37 of this book for a discussion of TWDB funding.

Despite progress, it is difficult to know the total impact of agricultural efficiency efforts, as water withdrawals are largely unmetered for agricultural uses and thus water usage volumes are estimates based on crop and weather data. This lack of reliable data can be addressed through continued financial assistance for installation of flow meters, well monitoring, and other technology that both assists in crop management and in tracking total consumption. TWDB Agricultural Irrigation BMP, at 6.

§ 23.4 Energy

Water delivery and treatment of wastewater consume significant amounts of power and, conversely, production of power requires vast amounts of water. It is not uncommon for a water utility to be one of the largest consumers of power, and the electric utility supplying that power is often one of the largest consumers of water. The good news is that water withdrawals for power production are declining nationwide. The U.S. Geological Survey 2010 Water Use Report found a 20 percent reduction in water withdrawals used for thermoelectric power production since 2005. *See* Molly A. Maupin et al., *Estimated Use of Water in the United States in 2010* 1, U.S. Geological Survey Circular 1405 (2014), https://pubs.usgs.gov/circ/1405/pdf/circ1405.pdf. Analyses of what is called the "water-energy nexus" have suggested that additional data should be gathered on long-term energy needs of wastewater treatment and on the withdrawal needs of power production. *See* Ashlynn S. Stillwell et al., The University of Texas at Austin, Environmental Defense Fund, *Energy-Water Nexus in Texas* (Apr. 2009), www.edf.org/sites/default/files/Energy_Water_Nexus_in_Texas_1.pdf. As the state expands industrial opportunities and gains population, the growing need for power will lead to new analyses of using conservation to address related water needs.

Most significantly, synergy savings occur in both power and water use when either resource is conserved. As growing water and energy needs are analyzed, there will be more of an emphasis on these projections and connections. Already nine states have statutes that recognize the nexus between water and energy. *See* National Conference of State Legislatures, *Overview of the Water-Energy Nexus in the United States* (updated Feb. 19, 2014). See also Chapter 41 of this book regarding the water-energy nexus.

§ 23.5 The Environment

As water consumption has grown, stakeholders have increasingly demanded that ecosystems be allocated adequate water during the water planning and management processes. Ecosystem needs for water include spring flows, environmental flows in rivers, and freshwater supply to bays and estuaries. Of primary concern is how water is allocated during dry periods and drought in order to avoid excessive stress to aquatic ecosystems. Larry McKinney, *Texas: The State of Rivers*, *Texas Parks & Wildlife* (July 2004), https://tpwmagazine.com/archive/2004/jul/ed_2. During the 2007 legislative session, the importance of maintaining healthy surface water ecosystems was codified in Senate Bill 3. *See* Act of June 16, 2007, 80th Leg., R.S., ch. 1430. Under S.B. 3, a series of scientific analyses and stakeholder recommendations have been implemented and environmental flow regulations have been adopted. See Chapter 11 of this book for a discussion of environmental flows and S.B. 3. The degree to which the environmental flows process will impact conservation efforts is unknown, but at a minimum it adds complexity to the challenge of allocating limited water resources during dry times.

III. Distinguishing between Conservation, Efficiency, and Drought Management

§ 23.6 Introduction

Conservation, efficiency, and drought management are all strategies to save water. Discussions about water may lead listeners to assume the terms are interchangeable, but using the words as if they are synonymous leads to confusion. Consider the statement, "There is a great need to conserve water during drought." Does the sentence reference the need for temporary water use regulations, the need to accelerate adoption of efficient plumbing fixtures, or the need to alter water-using behaviors? All three strategies could be implied, or only one.

§ 23.7 Distinguishing Conservation from Drought Management

The 2017 State Water Plan was the first Texas water plan with a section devoted to drought management. The plan also distinguished water conservation from drought management for the first time. Demand management was referenced as activities that reduce the need for additional water, while drought management was specifically described as "activities that temporarily restrict water usage for certain types of activities and businesses." 2017 State Water Plan, at 8. The 2022 State Water Plan continues the emphasis on drought management as a long-term strategy, with many water user groups calling out this effort. *See* 2022 State Water Plan, at 9.

Conservation and drought management are distinguished in how state agencies view required "conservation plans" and required "drought plans." The Texas Commission on Environmental Quality (TCEQ) defines conservation plans as focusing on daily, permanent changes in usage patterns. Conservation is proactive and can extend water supplies and potentially prevent the necessity of implementing a drought contingency plan. *See* Texas Commission on Environmental Quality, *Handbook for Drought Contingency Planning for Retail Public Water Suppliers* 3 (RG-424, Apr. 2005), https://www.rcac.org/wp-content/uploads/2015/08/TX_Drought_Planning_Handbook_2014.pdf. In contrast, drought management plans are defined as contingency plans intended to help communities cope with temporary shortages in water supply.

The difference between long-term efforts to extend water supplies and coping with temporary shortages influences the methods used for conservation and drought contingency planning. Drought management plans often focus on immediate reductions through regulations on usage. Long-term conservation endeavors use combinations of strategies that lead to permanent reductions in all water use sectors. In contrast, drought reductions are generally achieved through temporary regulations aimed at uses that can be temporarily reduced with no adverse consequences to health and human safety and minimal impact on economic prosperity.

The Texas Water Code and the Texas Administrative Code define conservation as practices to "increase the recycling and reuse of water so that a water supply is made available for future or alternative uses." Tex. Water Code § 11.002(8)(B); 30 Tex. Admin. Code § 288.1(4). Within conservation plans, efficiency may be one of the strategies used to save water. "At a fundamental level, water conservation involves managing existing water supplies to reduce demand and increase efficiency of use." Texas Water Development Board No. 2, *Water for Texas 2007* 259 (2007), www.twdb.texas.gov/waterplanning/swp/2007/. Conservation denotes an actual reduction of water used over time, while efficiency refers to how water is used for a particular practice. See Chapter 22 of this book regarding drought management and planning.

§ 23.8 What Is Efficiency?

The term "water efficiency" refers to practices that maximize water use per volumetric unit of water supplied. Thomas W. Chesnutt et al., *Water Efficiency Programs for Integrated Water Management* 7, AWWA Research Foundation (2007), www.waterrf.org/research/projects/water-efficiency-programs-integrated-water-management. Tremendous gains have been made in the past decade making plumbing fixtures and appliances more water efficient. Showerheads, faucets, urinals, washing machines, and dishwashers are all available in water-efficient designs. For example, older toilets use up to 5 gallons per flush, while high-efficiency toilets remove waste using no more than 1.28 gallons per flush. Some of these designs have been documented as both water efficient and effective and have received a United States Environmental Protection Agency (EPA) WaterSense label. Additional information on the WaterSense partnership program can be found on the EPA's website at www.epa.gov/watersense/about-watersense.

There is little doubt that efficiency efforts will be a critical component of meeting long-term conservation goals. Efficiency programs have been documented to save up to 39 percent on standard indoor home usage. *See* Aquacraft, Inc. & U.S Environmental Protection Agency, *Water and Energy Savings from High Efficiency Fixtures and Appliances in Single Family Homes* 3 (2005), http://aquacraft.com/wp-content/uploads/2015/09/EPA-Combined-Retrofit-Report.pdf. Retrofits and changes in management to increase water use efficiency have likewise shown impressive reductions for commercial and industrial customers in case studies. The Pacific Institute estimates that industrial and commercial water consumption in California could be reduced by up to 39 percent with widespread implementation of currently existing practices and technologies. Peter H. Gleick et al., *Waste Not, Want Not: The Potential for Urban Water Conservation in California* 2, Pacific Institute for Studies in Development, Environment, and Security (Nov. 2003), www.pacinst.org/app/uploads/2013/02/waste_not_want_not_full_report3.pdf. This illustrates that there are opportunities for tremendous efficiency in all water-use sectors.

§ 23.9 Distinguishing Efficiency from Conservation

Given how important efficiency strategies are to reducing water use, why does the distinction between water conservation and efficiency matter? The term *efficiency* implies that a reduction in consumption can be accomplished without apparent sacrifice. The term *conservation*, in contrast, may evoke a sense of doing without or giving something up. It is not surprising, then, that *efficiency* has become the more popular term. An American Rivers report includes this comparison of the two terms:

> Water efficiency is different from water conservation which, while also important, is generally more focused on changing behavior and habits like turning off the tap while brushing your teeth.
>
> Water efficiency does not mean doing less. Water efficiency isn't about asking citizens to shower once a week or plant a cactus in the front yard.

Jenny Hoffner, *Hidden Reservoir: Why Water Efficiency Is the Best Solution for the Southeast* 10, American Rivers, Inc. (Oct. 2008), www.americanrivers.org/conservation-resource/hidden-reservoir/.

The challenge of using efficiency as the only path to save water becomes apparent when discretionary uses are analyzed. Automatic irrigation systems are efficient at applying water to landscapes, but this ease of application contributes to significantly higher consumption in homes with irrigation systems. Analysis of residential water use patterns illustrates that homes having automatic irrigation systems consume significantly higher volumes of water than homes that rely on manual methods of watering landscapes. *See* William B. DeOreo et al., *Residential End Uses of Water, Version 2*, Water Research Foundation (2016), www.waterrf.org/research/projects/residential-end-uses-water-version-2. Even when using assumptions of best practices, efficient irrigation technology, and regionally appropriate plant material, calculated water budgets for home landscapes can be higher than all indoor water usage combined. *See* U.S. Environmental Protection Agency, *WaterSense, Water Budget Tool* (July 24, 2014).

The idea that efficient technology does not always prevent a resource from being overtaxed is not new. This phenomenon was first described by English economist William Stanley Jevons in 1866, who noted that steam engine efficiencies were resulting in a net increase in the total consumption of coal. The "Jevons paradox" has been applied to many environmental challenges to demonstrate that efficiency measures alone may not decrease the rate at which a resource is depleted. John M. Polimeni et al., *The Jevons Paradox and the Myth of Resource Efficiency Improvements* (Earthscan 2008). As illustrated above, practices can be highly efficient but still consume large amounts of water.

In contrast, water conservation includes "any beneficial reduction in water use or losses." Duane D. Baumann et al., *Water Conservation: The Struggle Over Definition*, 20 *Water Resources Res.*, no. 4, (Apr. 1984), at 428. By defining water conservation as including "reduction in water use or losses," it is clear that conservation programs should result in lowered water usage over time. Although this sounds similar to efficiency, the key distinction is that an efficiency program may not ultimately result in net lowered consumption. For example, newer showerheads apply water at a lower gallons-per-minute rate than older ones. Despite this, one study suggests that savings from low flow showerheads are in part diminished because those who use such showerheads take longer showers. *See* William B. DeOreo et al., *Residential End Uses of Water* 134, AWWA Research Foundation (1999), www.waterdm.com/sites/default/files/WRF%20(1999)%20Residential%20End%20Uses%20of%20 Water.pdf [hereinafter Residential End Uses 1999]. This example illustrates that while efficient technology and standards are important, they do not always guarantee a desired conservation result.

Outdoor water use is an area where both efficiency and conservation have a role in saving water. There is tremendous variability in outdoor consumption of water, even when lot sizes and landscape materials are taken into account. Residential End Uses 1999, at 193. The choice to have extensive landscaping maintained in a continually lush state is one that consumes large amounts of discretionary water regardless of how efficiently the water is applied. An efficiency approach would seek to ensure that no water is wasted in the application of water but would not suggest changes in plant material, a reduction in the irrigated area, or applying water at a rate less than optimal for plant appearance. A conservation approach, however, would suggest changing expectations to include nonirrigated areas, selection of plants needing little or no supplemental water to survive, and watering at least some plants less than what is considered to be ideal. Irrigation audits offered at homes and businesses can identify both efficiency opportunities and conservation opportunities. It is rare that people will refuse efficiency opportunities, but not everyone is willing to embrace conservation options.

Regulatory efforts to save water encompass both conservation and efficiency. Conservation regulations address how water is used on a permanent basis such as requiring that new homes install no more than half of a landscape in grass. Efficiency regulations may require a cost-effective conservation technology such as air-cooled ice makers instead of water cooled.

Once water-efficient technology becomes comparable in price to more water-intensive options, it is not difficult to get stakeholders to transition permanently to the efficient technology. Obstacles to mandated use of efficient technology can in part be overcome by providing sufficiently long transition periods to allow stakeholders to prepare for the change. An example is a 2012 San Antonio ordinance mandating that only water-efficient washing machines be installed at common-use locations by January 1, 2020. *See* San Antonio Code of Ordinances § 34-273(9). On the other hand, achieving community agreement on conservation regulations that overtly mandate a change in habit or limit a perceived freedom is generally more challenging. An example is a City of Austin ordinance that permanently limits use of spray irrigation on landscapes to no more than once per week without regard to drought conditions. *See* Austin Code of Ordinances § 6-4.

§ 23.10 Impact of Drought on Saving Water

Extended drought periods blur the lines of regulations that begin as temporary drought regulation measures but become permanent. The Texas Living Waters Project's Water Conservation Scorecard raised the profile of debates on making drought restrictions permanent by assigning a significant number of scoring points to whether a community has year-round day-of-week restrictions on landscape irrigation. Their 2020 Scorecard shows that the number of utilities that embrace limitations on outdoor watering has risen from only one third in 2017 to 40% in 2020. *See* Texas Living Waters Project, *2020 Texas Water Conservation Scorecard* 2 (June 2020), www.texaswaterconservationscorecard.org/usrfiles/files/FinalReport_6_22_20.pdf. Drought regulations may also accelerate adoption of conservation choices. During the dire drought conditions of July 2014, the Metropolitan Water District of California reported receiving a record number of rebate applications seeking to replace a total of 7.2 million square feet of turf. *See* Association of California Water Agencies, *Turf Rebate Programs See Surge of Interest*. Drought may also expand attitudes from efficiency-only to embracing a conservation outlook. Until recently the California Landscape Contractors Association took the position that as long as plants were efficiently irrigated, it was acceptable for citizens to choose landscape styles requiring significant supplemental water. During a drought-themed webinar in April 2015, the organization announced its revised view and codified the new outlook in a policy statement that embraces "transformation to the new norm" including recognizing grass as a "high-water-use plant." California Landscape Contractors Association, *CLCA Statement on Landscape Water Conservation* (Dec. 3, 2014), www.clca.org/advocacy/current-issues/water/. A more recent example of extreme drought forecasts driving landscape policy can be found in Nevada, where the legislature, in 2021, is considering the passage of a law that would allow water providers to stop providing water for commercial ornamental turfgrass in the future. This bold move appears to include incentives to make changes to a more desert-friendly landscape option. Supporters of the bill point out that removal of the grass represents the least onerous economic option to manage near-term expected reductions in water supplies. *See* Colton Lochhead, *Assembly Approves Southern Nevada Turf Removal Proposal,* Las Vegas Review-Journal (Apr. 29, 2021), www.reviewjournal.com/news/politics-and-government/2021-legislature/assembly-approves-southern-nevada-turf-removal-proposal-2342128/.

The rest of this chapter is organized around the three water-savings strategies of conservation, efficiency, and drought management, describing mechanisms and legal considerations for each.

IV. State-Level Conservation

§ 23.11 Introduction

Conservation has been embraced at the state, municipal, and local levels. As mentioned at the beginning of this chapter, the 2017 State Water Plan and 2022 State Water Plan have embraced conservation more clearly than previous plans. The state has instituted other conservation management, planning, and implementation programs, as described below.

§ 23.12 Conservation Local Networks

Some regional water providers have banded together to create voluntary, informal planning groups called Water Efficiency Networks to enhance their efforts. The Texas Living Waters Project has supported development of these networks and describes them as groups of "water providers and water conservation advocates that meet monthly with a purpose of learning about the latest conservation tools being used locally and globally." Texas Living Waters Project, *Water Efficiency Networks: Regional Cooperation and Success on Water Conservation* (Dec. 18, 2015), https://texaslivingwaters.org/water-efficiency-networks-regional-cooperation-and-success-on-water-conservation/. (The name of these groups illustrates that the distinction between efficiency and conservation, as discussed above, is not always made.) The first network formed was the Water Efficiency Network of North Texas, which includes cities around the Dallas metroplex. A second active group is the Central Texas Water Efficiency Network, which includes membership from north of Austin to San Antonio. A third has been formed, calling itself the Gulf Coast Water Efficiency Network, covering the region around Houston and the nearby coast. These groups have pooled resources for public campaigns and organized regular water conservation workshops intended to enhance the skills of conservation practitioners and to promote sharing of effective conservation practices.

§ 23.13 Water Conservation Task Force

The Texas legislature has taken many steps to ensure that water conservation strategies are successful. A Water Conservation Implementation Task Force was created by Senate Bill 1094 in the 78th Legislature to create statewide guidelines for water conservation. *See* Texas Water Development Board, *Special Report*, *Water Conservation Implementation Task Force*, *Report to the 79th Legislature* (Nov. 2004), www.twdb.texas.gov/conservation/resources/doc/WCITF_Leg_Report.pdf. The group, consisting of a wide array of water stakeholders, was convened in 2003. The Task Force also issued a "Water Conservation Best Management Practices Guide," which has been widely downloaded. *See* Texas Water Development Board, *Report 362*, *Water Conservation Implementation Task Force*, *Water Conservation Best Management Practice Guide* (Nov. 2004), www.twdb.texas.gov/publications/reports/numbered_reports/doc/R362_BMPGuide.pdf.

The Task Force special report also includes many recommendations for realizing stronger statewide gains from water conservation to meet the future water needs of Texas. Those recommendations include creating a Water Conservation Advisory Council, establishing required reporting by water providers, using water conservation success as a criterion for state water funding, supporting state conservation education programs, supporting a water conservation public education campaign, creating a standard methodology for calculation of gallons per capita per day (GPCD), and setting a goal of 140 GPCD across the state. Many of these recommendations have been implemented, while others are in progress.

§ 23.14 Water Conservation Advisory Council

The Water Conservation Advisory Council (WCAC) was created in 2007 by the 80th Legislature as a permanent group of stakeholders who "serve as a select and expert resource to state government and the public on water conservation in Texas." Texas Water Conservation Advisory Council, *Organizational Charter* (Nov. 16, 2007), www.savetexaswater.org/about/doc/Charter%20111707.pdf. The WCAC has twenty-three members from diverse water stakeholder groups. They work with TWDB staff and report on water conservation issues in even-numbered years. The mission of the group is "to establish a professional forum for the continuing development of water conservation resources, expertise, and progress evaluation of the highest quality for the benefit of Texas—its state leadership, regional and local governments, and general public." Water Conservation Advisory Council, *Progress Made in Water Conservation in Texas, Report and Recommendations to the 86th Texas Legislature* 1 (Dec. 1, 2018), www.savetexaswater.org/resources/doc/2018_WCAC_Lege_Report.pdf. The advisory council also makes recommendations to the legislature.

§ 23.15 State-Mandated Conservation Plans and Progress Reports

In addition to state water planning and the establishment of a state advisory group on conservation, there have been significant changes in state law, including required conservation planning, conservation progress reports, and water loss reports. Two state agencies are responsible for water conservation education and reporting: the TWDB and the TCEQ. Both agencies collect conservation planning and reporting information. The water loss reports, because they focus specifically on saving water through efficiency measures, are discussed at section 23.23 below. The following sections address the conservation plans and progress reports.

§ 23.15:1 Water Conservation Plans

Water conservation plans may be required of an entity by the TCEQ, the TWDB, or both. Pursuant to 30 Texas Administrative Code section 295.9, a water conservation plan is a requirement for surface water right holders and must be submitted to and approved by the TCEQ as part of the permitting and permit amendment process. 30 Tex. Admin. Code § 295.9. Additionally, 30 Texas Administrative Code section 288.30 requires certain surface water right holders to submit conservation plans to the TCEQ in addition to the plan submitted with a water right application under 30 Texas Administrative Code section 295.9. *See* 30 Tex. Admin. Code § 288.30. These include municipal, industrial, and other nonirrigation water rights holders with rights to 1,000 acre-feet per year or more. 30 Tex. Admin. Code § 288.30(1). These categories of water rights holders must submit an updated water conservation plan meeting the requirements of chapter 288, subchapter A, every five years to coincide with the regional water plan. 30 Tex. Admin. Code § 288.30(1). Water rights holders for irrigation in the amount of 10,000 acre-feet or more per year must do the same. *See* 30 Tex. Admin. Code § 288.30(3). Only a fraction of the water suppliers and water users, however, hold water rights.

Retail public water suppliers, regardless of the source of their water supply, must submit conservation plans under several different regulatory programs. Every five years, a retail public water supplier providing water service to 3,300 or more connections must submit to the TWDB a water conservation plan consistent with chapter 288, subchapter A. New retail public water suppliers in this category must submit a plan within 180 days of beginning operations. *See* 30 Tex. Admin. Code § 288.30(10)(A).

Many entities applying to the TWDB for financial assistance under the programs covered by 31 Texas Administrative Code chapter 363 must submit a water conservation plan with their application. *See* 31 Tex. Admin. Code § 363.15(a). Exceptions include (1) if the board determines an emergency exists; (2) the amount of financial assistance to be provided is $500,000 or less; (3) the board finds that a water conservation program "is not reasonably necessary"; or (4) the financing is required for flood control purposes under Texas Water Code chapter 17, subchapter G. *See* 31 Tex. Admin. Code § 363.15(c).

The content of conservation plans required by the TCEQ and the TWDB is similar. In general, plans must include five-year and ten-year targets with specific and quantified water savings, an implementation schedule, anticipated methods and measures to be used, rate information, and a description of the authority by which the water supplier will enforce the plan. For the TCEQ, the means of implementation and enforcement of the plan must be evidenced by a copy of the ordinance, resolution, or tariff indicating the official adoption of the plan by the appropriate governing body. Texas Water Development Board, *Water Conservation Plan Guidance Checklist*, TWDB Form 1968 (rev. Jan. 8, 2013), www.twdb.texas.gov/conservation/municipal/plans/doc/WCPChecklist.pdf. Plans submitted to the TCEQ and the TWDB must include a utility profile using TWDB form 1965-R or 1965-W. With regard to water conservation plans required for TWDB financing, the TWDB will accept water conservation plans determined by the TCEQ to satisfy requirements of 30 Texas Administrative Code chapter 288. *See* 31 Tex. Admin. Code § 363.15(e), (f). The reverse is true for municipal uses by public water suppliers; conservation plans that are prepared in accordance with section 363.15 and that substantially meet the requirements of section 288.2 are accepted by the TCEQ. *See* 30 Tex. Admin. Code § 288.2(b). Every entity required to submit a conservation plan to the TCEQ must also submit a copy to the TWDB. *See* 30 Tex. Admin. Code § 288.30(10)(B).

In seeking to enhance the accountability of water conservation plans, the 85th Legislature amended section 13.146 of the Water Code to require that water purveyors designate a person as the water conservation coordinator responsible for implementing the water conservation plan. Water purveyors must identify this person to the executive administrator of the TWDB. *See* Act of May 18, 2017, 85th Leg., R.S., ch. 146, § 1 (H.B. 1648), eff. Sept. 1, 2017.

§ 23.15:2 Water Conservation Progress Reports

An entity required to submit conservation plans to either the TCEQ or the TWDB must submit annual reports on the entity's conservation progress. *See* 30 Tex. Admin. Code § 288.30(10)(C). The TCEQ requires conservation implementation reports once every five years. *See* 30 Tex. Admin. Code § 288.30(1)–(4). The TWDB progress reports are required for entities covered by 30 Texas Administrative Code sections 288.30(1) and (3). The reports must include dates and descriptions of implemented conservation measures, data about whether conservation targets in the previous plan are being met, and if not, an explanation, and the actual amount of water saved. *See* 30 Tex. Admin. Code § 288.30(2), (4). The TWDB Water Conservation Plan Annual Report form specifies further required information about GPCD calculations, estimates of total water savings, and reports on specific conservation programs such as education, rebates, rate structure, and metering. Water losses are also calculated and reported, as described at section 23.23 below. *See, e.g.*, Texas Water Development Board, *Water Conservation Plan Annual Report—Retail Water Supplier*, TWDB Form 1966 (rev. Jan. 11, 2016), www.twdb.texas.gov/conservation/municipal/plans/doc/RWS_1966.pdf. Annual reports may be submitted electronically. *See* Texas Water Development Board, *Water Conservation Plan Annual Reports*, www.twdb.texas.gov/conservation/municipal/plans/ARs.asp.

Conservation reporting gained prominence as a result of House Bill 3605, which directs the TWDB to evaluate the financial assistance applications of all utilities serving more than 3,300 connections to determine compliance with the board's best management practices for conservation and to issue a report to the utility detailing the results. No later than January 1 of each odd-numbered year, the TWDB must also submit a written summary to the legislature detailing the results of the conservation program evaluations conducted. *See* Act of May 27, 2013, 83d Leg., R.S., ch. 1139, § 2, eff. Sept. 1, 2013 (adding Tex. Water Code § 17.1245).

The resolution of GPCD reporting concerns was addressed by Senate Bill 660. *See* Act of May 29, 2011, 82d Leg., R.S., ch. 1233, § 11 (adding Tex. Water Code §§ 16.403, 16.404). This legislation directed the TCEQ and the TWDB to work with the WCAC to develop GPCD metric calculation guidelines by January 1, 2013. The TWDB conservation report now distinguishes portions of GPCD by water use categories such as residential, commercial, and water loss. Guidance is provided on how to manage temporary and service populations for the GPCD calculations for cities where this is a challenge.

V. Municipal-Level Conservation

§ 23.16 Introduction[2]

Conservation is the goal not only at the state level. Municipalities and other local governments are also encouraging, and in some cases mandating, conservation. As municipal populations grow and development expands to serve the new population, conservation is becoming a more common and widespread issue at these local levels of government.

§ 23.17 Legal Authority for Municipal Water Conservation Programs

Statewide water conservation regulations have been established by legislation and TCEQ and TWDB implementing regulations, as discussed above. Adoption and implementation of conservation measures by municipalities are increasing as cities strive to manage water resources for their growing populations. The authority for such regulation derives from several sources.

Article XVI, section 59, of the Texas Constitution declares that the conservation, preservation, and development of the state's natural resources, including water, are public rights and duties, and directs the legislature to pass all such laws "as may be appropriate thereto." This amendment, adopted in 1917, is commonly known as the Conservation Amendment. However, the legislature's response to this mandate for most of the next century focused on "development" and left conservation and preservation to fend for themselves. The amendment became the constitutional basis for the creation of a wide variety of water control and improvement districts and their resulting issuance of debt for the construction of dams, levies, irrigation systems, drainage improvements, water distribution infrastructure, and wastewater collection and treatment systems. See Chapter 9 of this book for a discussion of water districts. Conservation of water was not a legislative priority.

With increasing public awareness of the limitations on our future water supplies, this mindset has slowly begun to change. In 2007, the legislature adopted Texas Local Government Code section 551.007, authorizing home-rule municipalities to adopt and enforce ordinances requiring water conservation in the municipality and by its customers in the extraterritorial jurisdiction (ETJ) of the municipality. It might be argued that this grant of authority was icing on the cake for home-rule cities, which derive the full power of local self-government from the constitution and look to the legislature only for a limitation on that authority. *City of Houston v. State ex rel. City of West University Place*, 176 S.W.2d 928, 929 (Tex. 1943). Additionally, home-rule authority over water conservation may be inferred from the language of Local Government Code section 552.017, which gives such cities the right to own, construct, operate, and regulate a water system and to take the necessary action to operate and maintain the system and to require water customers to pay charges imposed for the water furnished. At a minimum, the addition of section 551.007 facilitates enforcement of conservation measures in a city's ETJ.

Unlike a home-rule municipality, a general-law city in Texas has only the authority that it is specifically given by the legislature or that may be reasonably inferred from an existing statute. *Massengale v. City of Copperas Cove*, 520 S.W.2d 824 (Tex. App.—Austin 1975, writ ref'd n.r.e.).

---

2. Sections 23.16 and 23.17 were written by Steve Kosub. Mr. Kosub is of counsel to Sprouse Shrader Smith PLLC. His practice focuses on the development and distribution of groundwater and other water resources. His work has encompassed groundwater transactions, project negotiations, permitting activities, infrastructure agreements, intergovernmental agreements, water planning, and innovative water strategies. He received his BA in political science from Texas A&M University in 1974 and his JD from the University of Texas School of Law in 1977. Mr. Kosub is certified in administrative law by the Texas Board of Legal Specialization. He is a past chair of the Environmental and Natural Resources Law Section of the State Bar of Texas and a frequent writer and speaker on water law, regulatory takings, and development issues.

Thus attorneys for general-law cities must satisfy themselves regarding the authority of their clients to impose and enforce conservation programs. Local Government Code section 552.015 seems to offer a reasonable bridge from the Conservation Amendment to a local ordinance for at least some general-law cities. Section 552.015 provides that a Type-A general-law municipality may provide for a municipal water supply system and may establish and regulate public wells, pumps, cisterns, hydrants, and reservoirs located inside or outside the municipality for the convenience of its residents, for firefighting purposes, and for the prevention of unnecessary waste of water.

The authority of cities to enforce local or state conservation ordinances pertaining to building materials was limited by HB 2439, Act of Sept. 1, 2019, 86th Leg., R.S., ch. 1289 § 1, which prohibits stricter limits on building materials than those in model codes. Local Government Code sec. 214.217 defines national model code as a publication that is developed and periodically updated at a national level by industry stakeholders and government fire and building safety officials through a legislative or consensus process and is intended for consideration by units of government as local law. National model codes include the International Residential Code, the National Electric Code and the International Building Code. House Bill 2439, codified at Texas Government Code section 3000, prohibits state and local government entities from requiring standards for building materials that are stricter than those set by a national model code published within the last three code cycles. There are clear exemptions for fire sprinklers, historic buildings, and requirements for windstorm and hail as well as for federal standards. The term "building materials" was left undefined creating a great deal of uncertainty regarding which aspects of conservation standards currently in place may be voided. Senate Bill 1090, Act of Sept. 1, 2021, 87th Leg., R.S., ch. 475, § 1, exempts from the restrictions of HB 2439 plumbing-related ordinances adopted as part of water conservation efforts.

The question of a city's authority to make and enforce regulations for water conservation is most visible when considering the increasingly more common restrictions on landscape irrigation, as discussed at section 23.21 below.

§ 23.18 Water Conservation–Oriented Rates

Water conservation–oriented rates (WCORS) are used by many water providers to provide an incentive to customers for changing their water usage patterns. The term *WCORS* applies to many different strategies being used across the United States. An example is the use of seasonal rates, which increase the price of water during peak summer months to discourage the higher usage patterns that may drive utility expenses higher. Another example of WCORS is the use of differential indoor and outdoor rates, which address the same challenge by charging less for indoor water and more for outdoor water. A variety of WCORS measures target the highest users of water, such as excess usage rates, inclining block rates, and sliding scale rates. Young-Doo Wang et al., *Water Conservation-Oriented Rates: Strategies to Extend Supply, Promote Equity and Meet Minimum Flow Levels* 9 (American Water Works Association 2005). Regardless of the structure, the theme is to set the price of water higher as consumption increases. Customers targeted by the higher prices have considered legal challenges to these rate structures by labeling them an illegal tax. Personal Communication from Dan Crowley, former Director of Financial Planning, San Antonio Water System, to Karen Guz, Director of Conservation, San Antonio Water System (June 2011). Other challenges have focused on whether the higher rates are discriminatory against a particular customer class or without merit based on cost-of-service models. *See* American Water Works Association, *Principles of Rates, Fees and Charges—Manual of Water Supply Practices* 284 (5th ed. 2000) [hereinafter AWWA Manual].

A review of rate challenges completed by the AWWA concludes that in municipal rate-setting cases it is generally true that the burden of demonstrating that a rate is unreasonable or discriminatory rests with the party challenging the rate. *See generally* Wang et al. This does not mean that municipal rates cannot be successfully challenged. To be defended against a challenge, such rates must be supported by evidence, such as engineering and financial models, showing that costs of service are higher for high-usage customers or during times of drought. An example of a successful rate defense is *Brydon v. East Bay Municipal Utility District*, 24 Cal. App. 4th 178 (Cal. Ct. App. 1994). This California case is of particular interest in Texas because the inclining block rate was put in place during a drought to discourage excess usage. A homeowner challenged the rate, claiming that it was a "special tax" requiring voter approval. On review, the court determined that the rate was in response to a community need to reduce consumption and, further, that the large amount of use was found in only 11 percent of the households served, which were using 35 percent of the water. The court concluded that "[t]o the extent that certain consumers over-utilize the resource, they contribute disproportionately to the necessity for conservation, and the requirement that the District acquire new sources for the supply of domestic water." *Brydon*, 24 Cal. App. 4th at 202. Based on this type of case, rate experts recommend that utilities and cities be prepared with a factual basis for their rates, such as a cost-of-service study, analysis of user patterns, and how conservation-oriented rates should provide benefits to ratepayers. AWWA Manual, at 285.

§ 23.19 Funding Conservation Programs

Conservation programs are funded using a variety of methods. One option is to fund such programs through a traditional budget process using general revenue funds. For many utilities, these funds may have to be approved through utility trustees or the city council. Another funding option, and one that may be more politically acceptable, is to set aside dedicated rate revenue for conservation efforts. This method has the advantage of providing steady financial support over time and allows the program to effect changes over the long term. Customers may see water conservation as a positive goal and the conservation programs as having potential direct benefits to them. The San Antonio Water System established a dedicated conservation revenue structure in 1994 and added a commercial conservation revenue structure in 1998.

Although the ability of municipally owned utilities to set fees for services or dedicate revenue to conservation has not been challenged, there is not complete confidence among water utility groups that the option is universally available to all water providers. Clarification of this authority may be necessary through legislative action to assure wholesale providers and municipal utility districts that they may elect this mechanism to fund conservation.

Funding conservation activities through use of capital funds is an option used by a small number of utilities. Notably, the Southern Nevada Water Authority uses capital funding for its "cash for grass" programs that have succeeded in permanently altering the landscapes of Las Vegas. An argument against use of capital dollars for conservation lies in accounting regulations that expect the bond holder to retain control of the asset being financed. Personal Communication from Mary Baily, Comptroller, San Antonio Water System, to Karen Guz, Director of Conservation, San Antonio Water System (Apr. 2015).

§ 23.20 Landscape and Irrigation Design; Property Owners Associations

A recent national study concluded that more than half of homeowners greatly under estimate how much of their household water usage goes to outdoor landscape irrigation. While most believe the percentage to be only 10-30%, the actual usage is 30-60% of total usage being used for landscape watering. The Alliance for Water Efficiency, *Landscape Transformation: Assessment of Water Utility Programs and Market Readiness Evaluation.* Executive Summary. Published 2019. Available at www.allianceforwaterefficiency.org/sites/www.allianceforwaterefficiency.org/files/assets/AWE_Landscape_Transformation_Executive_Summary.pdf.

In Texas, household water use that is dedicated to landscapes ranges from under 20 percent in some communities to more than 50 percent in others, with a statewide average of 31 percent. Sam Marie Hermitte & Robert E. Mace, *Texas Water Development Board, The Grass Is Always Greener . . .*

Outdoor Residential Water Use in Texas 12, Technical Note 12-01 (Nov. 2012), www.twdb.texas.gov/publications/reports/technical_notes/doc/seasonalwaterusereport-final.pdf.

Drought periods of recent years have raised the profile of complaints coming from citizens that property owners associations (POAs) have strict regulations preventing installation of less water-needy plant material. In 2013, the Texas legislature passed Senate Bill 198, which provides that a POA may prohibit or restrict a property owner from installing drought-resistant landscaping or water-conserving natural turf. *See* Act of May 20, 2013, 83d Leg., R.S., ch. 736, § 1 (amending Tex. Prop. Code § 202.007). The concern raised by POAs that their ability to manage neighborhood aesthetics and therefore property value would be impacted was balanced by allowing the POA to require landscape designs for review to ensure aesthetic compatibility with other landscaping in the subdivision. *See* Tex. Prop. Code § 202.007(d)(8). While design may be required, the limits of this were tempered with the added provision that a POA may not unreasonably deny the approval of a proposed installation of drought-resistant landscaping or unreasonably determine that the proposed installation is aesthetically incompatible. *See* Tex. Prop. Code § 202.007(d–1).

§ 23.21 Enforcement of Landscape Irrigation Regulations

Local governments also regulate the use of landscape irrigation to achieve conservation goals. This is done through a variety of local ordinances or contract rules that are aimed at reducing waste and discouraging excess use. For example, water waste is illegal in municipalities such as Austin (*see* Austin Code of Ordinances § 6-4-63), San Antonio (*see* San Antonio Code of Ordinances § 34-288), and San Angelo (*see* San Angelo Code of Ordinances § 11.05.002). In addition, some municipalities have standard irrigation schedules to discourage excess usage. *See, e.g.*, Austin Code of Ordinances § 6-4-63.

Not only do municipalities restrict the times and days of landscape irrigation, they may also restrict other aspects of landscape irrigation usage. For example, the total size of spray irrigation systems may be limited to curtail high use at larger properties. *See* San Antonio Code of Ordinances § 34-273(2).

Despite these measures, the individual owner's right to irrigate and the need for conservation are still often at odds. Even in communities with a strong conservation ethic, debates often ensue about whether the regulations are reasonable or will alienate parts of the community. Marty Toohey, *City to Tighten Spigot on Water Use, Austin American-Statesman* (Sept. 1, 2012), www.statesman.com/story/news/local/2012/09/01/city-to-tighten-spigot-on-water-use/9893422007/.

Analysis of public water system pumping data leaves little room for doubt that mandatory landscape irrigation schedules reduce water usage. In 2009, the City of Austin's municipal water utility, Austin Water, implemented mandatory landscape irrigation schedules that set limited days for landscape irrigation using either automatic systems or hose-end sprinklers. These rules resulted in a more level peak demand and reduced consumption for high-use properties. Austin Water, *Leading Us to Water: The Austin Water Environmental Leadership Report—2010* 2 (2010), www.ci.austin.tx.us/water/downloads/envleadershipreport.pdf. The San Antonio Water System has drought rules prohibiting landscape watering except during specific times and days. Pumping data for the prohibited irrigation days shows pumping decreases up to 30 million gallons per day and overall pumping is lower when restrictions are in effect. Karen Guz, San Antonio Water System, *San Antonio's Experience with Drought of Record: Education, Citations & Big Savings*, WaterSmart Innovations 2010 Conference (Oct. 2010), https://ceregportal.com/wsi/documents/sessions/2010/10-F-1028.pdf. These results have encouraged other utilities to consider setting limits on the times and number of days when landscape irrigation with automatic systems or hose-end sprinklers may be used.

Adoption of regulations on irrigation usage may be completed through municipal ordinance processes or through actions of municipal utility districts. Municipal utilities such as the San Antonio Water System have worked with their municipal governments to set rules and enforcement policies.

Likewise, San Angelo has an extensive water conservation enforcement program. The city issues municipal citations to violators on a regular basis, and San Angelo water conservation staff report that incidents of water waste from irrigation have dramatically reduced since the program was implemented. Personal Communication from Toni Fox, Water Conservation Manager, City of San Angelo, Texas, to Karen Guz, Director of Conservation, San Antonio Water System (Dec. 2010) [hereinafter Fox Personal Communication]; *see also* City of San Angelo, Water Utilities, www.cosatx.us/departments-services/water-utilities.

The real challenge in water waste enforcement is not the adoption of water waste rules but how to react to noncompliance. For utilities where city ordinances make violating water use regulations a crime, certified peace officers may be authorized to issue citations. These citations may then be adjudicated in local courts. Fox Personal Communication. The enforcement of city criminal ordinances has benefits and drawbacks. The benefits include a built-in mechanism for citizens to resolve citations by challenging them in court and clear consequences if citizens do not resolve their violations by paying the citations or appearing in court. Drawbacks include the level of paperwork that may be required, potentially long time periods between violations and court resolutions, and the inability to enforce rules on customers not within the territorial jurisdiction or extraterritorial jurisdiction of the municipality. Water utilities often provide service to customers who reside outside of these boundaries, which complicates enforcement by local criminal statutes. Personal Communication from Dana Nichols, Conservation Manager, San Antonio Water System, to Karen Guz, Director of Conservation, San Antonio Water System (Apr. 2015).

Several Texas jurisdictions have recently adopted noncriminal financial penalties for violations of water use regulations. Austin, Pflugerville, Georgetown, and Cedar Park all use administrative fines on water bills to discourage violators. According to the staff of Austin Water, these fines are allowed under state law. For example, Texas Local Government Code section 551.007 provides that a home-rule municipality "may adopt and enforce ordinances requiring water conservation in the municipality." Tex. Loc. Gov't Code § 551.007. Also, Local Government Code section 54.001 gives authority to home-rule cities to assess fines not exceeding specific amounts. *See* Tex. Loc. Gov't Code § 54.001. Austin has administrative processes for citizens wishing to dispute their fines for violating rules of use. Personal Communication from Drema Gross, Water Conservation Manager, City of Austin, to Karen Guz, Director of Conservation, San Antonio Water System (Apr. 28, 2015).

Municipal utility districts (MUDs), like other utilities, face the challenges of managing peak demand and minimizing waste. Some have passed water waste regulations for their customers through resolutions approved by their boards. Texas Water Code section 54.205 authorizes the adoption of reasonable rules and regulations. *See* Tex. Water Code § 54.205. Such rules may be adopted to prevent waste or unauthorized use provided there is a justification for the rules. Section 54.206 treats such rules adopted by MUDs as if they are penal ordinances adopted by a city. *See* Tex. Water Code § 54.206. In theory, violators may be subject to fines each day. However, there has not been a test case of water waste fines being assessed by a MUD. The details of how a MUD would prove a violation and address customer challenges to the fines have not yet been resolved. This is an area where clarification of authority and processes may evolve in the next few years.

VI. Texas Efficiency Measures

§ 23.22 Introduction

As a subset of its water conservation measures, Texas has established reporting requirements and efficiency standards for plumbing fixtures and landscape irrigation. As discussed above, efficiency measures are usually more palatable to stakeholders than true conservation measures that seek to change stakeholder habits or lifestyles. The following sections discuss water loss reports, plumbing efficiency standards, and landscape watering efficiency standards.

§ 23.23 Water Loss Reports

The issue of water loss has become high profile during recent Texas legislative sessions. As investments in new water supplies are contemplated at great cost, state leaders are understandably concerned with just how much existing water is lost. Texas was one of the first states to require water loss audits from utilities. Water Loss Audit requirements were enhanced by House Bill 857 in 2013 by the 83rd Legislature. *See* Act of May 16, 2013, 83d Leg., R.S., ch. 278, § 1, eff. Sept. 1, 2013. Since 2014, all retail public water utilities serving a population of more than 3,300 must submit water loss audits to the TWDB by May 1 of each year. 31 Tex. Admin. Code § 358.6. House Bill 3605 increased the importance of the audits by amending Texas Water Code section 16.0121 to require that any retail utility providing potable water that receives board financial assistance use a portion of that financial assistance to mitigate the utility's water loss if, based on an audit filed by the utility, the water loss exceeds the threshold established by board rule. *See* Act of May 24, 2013, 83d Leg., R.S., ch. 1139, § 1, eff. Sept. 1, 2013. The thresholds for water loss have been established by board rule for each category of retail public utility listed in Water Code section 16.0121. The thresholds are further explained in 31 Texas Administrative Code section 358.6. Thresholds differ by size of utility and are based on water loss audit metrics associated with real and apparent losses.

Water loss auditing is a relatively new activity in the realm of public water supply. An international water loss audit methodology has been developed by the AWWA. At the heart of the audit is determining what amount of water produced by a utility is not delivered to a user or is delivered with no associated revenue collection. The difference between total water produced and total billed water is *nonrevenue water*. When expected and authorized unbilled uses, like firefighting and line flushing, are subtracted from nonrevenue water, the remaining amount is called *lost water*. *See* American Water Works Association, *M36 Water Audits and Loss Control Programs* (3d ed. 2009). Water losses are then allocated to *apparent losses*, water that was used but not accurately metered and billed, and *real losses*, water that left the system before reaching a user. A term that has fallen out of favor is *unaccounted for water*. More precise terminology has been adopted because a water loss audit should account for all water produced, place a financial value on the lost water, and help utility managers assess how all losses might be reduced.

A new measure passed by the 85th Legislature amends Water Code section 16.0121 and requires that water audits must be completed by a person trained to conduct water loss auditing. The measure further directs the TWDB to provide training on water loss auditing from the board's website, in person, or by video or functionally similar and widely available media. *See* Act of May 19, 2017, 85th Leg., R.S., ch. 347, § 1 (H.B. 1573), eff. Sept. 1, 2017. Training opportunities are offered each year by TWDB staff and an online training video has been developed in cooperation with the Texas American Water Works Association that also meets requirements.

§ 23.24 Plumbing Fixture Standards

During the 81st Legislature, through House Bill 2667, Texas became the second state to implement high-efficiency plumbing standards for fixtures. Section 372.002 of the Texas Health and Safety Code was amended to require sinks or lavatory faucets to have a maximum flow not to exceed 2.2 gallons per minute at a pressure of 60 pounds per square inch (psi). *See* Act of May 21, 2009, 81st Leg., R.S., ch. 1316, § 2 (amending Tex. Health & Safety Code § 372.002). Showerhead standards were updated: maximum flow may not exceed 2.5 gallons per minute at a constant pressure of 80 psi. Tex. Health & Safety Code § 372.002(b)(4), (6). Urinals sold after January 1, 2014, must meet a standard of maximum flush flow of 0.5 gallons per flush, while the maximum flow of a toilet sold after

January 1, 2014, shall not exceed 1.28 gallons per flush. Tex. Health & Safety Code § 372.002. The TCEQ maintains a current list of plumbing fixtures that are certified by the manufacturer to meet these savings performance standards. *See* Water Conservation Advisory Council, *A Report on Progress of Water Conservation in Texas, Report to the 82nd Texas Legislature* 70 (Dec. 2010), www.twdb.texas.gov/conservation/resources/doc/WCAC_report_2010.pdf.

New water-efficient fixtures are steadily introduced in the market. The EPA WaterSense program evaluates water-efficient fixtures expected to use at least 20 percent less than standard ones. Earning a WaterSense label further requires that the fixtures pass rigorous performance testing. Indoor fixtures earning the WaterSense label include high efficiency toilets, urinals, showerheads, and prerinse spray valves. *See* U.S. Environmental Protection Agency, *WaterSense Products*, www.epa.gov/watersense/watersense-products. Because the WaterSense program maintains updated lists of fixtures meeting the efficiency criteria, the program can be easily referenced in ordinances as a standard for construction or retrofits.

Prerinse spray valves are devices used in commercial kitchen cleanup operations. The EPA WaterSense standard for prerinse spray valves is no more than 1.28 gallons per minute. *See* U.S. Environmental Protection Agency, *Pre-Rinse Spray Valves*, www.epa.gov/watersense/pre-rinse-spray-valves. The federal standard requires installation of prerinse spray valves using no more than 1.6 gallons per minute. *See* 10 C.F.R. § 431.266. Texas has not yet adopted a prerinse spray valve efficiency standard.

The year 2020 had significant impact on the passive savings that have been accumulating from federal energy and water standards. The Energy Policy Act of 1992 included federal standards limiting showerhead spray volume to 2.5 gallons per minute and water and energy efficiency standards for dishwashers. *See* Energy Policy Act, Pub. L. No. 102-486, 106 Stat. 2776 (1991). The federal rules for showerheads were revised effective January 15, 2021, with the creation of a new class of product that is not subject to the flow limits of showerheads. Body sprays and multiple head shower products are no longer considered "showerheads" and as such do not need to meet a total flow limit of 2.5 gallons per minute. There is no limit on their flow. *See* 10 C.F.R. § 430.32(p) (2020). Dishwasher efficiency was similarly impacted by the creation of a new class of dishwashers that can cycle within one hour. This new class of one-hour cycle dishwashers are not limited in the amount of water or energy they consume. *See* 10 C.F.R. § 430.32(f)(1)(iii) (2020). The impact of these rule changes will likely take several years to present itself as manufacturers take the opportunity to create and market new products. The showerhead rule is likely to impact luxury homes, where multiple head design could be more popular. The dishwasher regulation change could be quite significant, as current dishwashers have become so efficient that they often use less than half the water consumed by hand-washing.

§ 23.25 Landscape Irrigation Efficiency

Application of water by irrigation systems is a significant driver of municipal water consumption in Texas. San Antonio homes with irrigation systems use 50 percent more water than homes without them. *See* San Antonio Water System, *2014 Conservation Plan*, Narrative Section, at 7. If irrigation systems are poorly designed or poorly maintained, must of the water used is wasted. The Texas state landscape irrigation licensing program provides a mechanism to set standards for quality of irrigation systems and for their proper operation.

Texas is one of only six states to have a state landscape irrigation licensing program. Personal Communication from Brian Vinchesi, Chair of SWAT Irrigation Association, to Karen Guz, Director of Conservation, San Antonio Water System (May 13, 2011). The irrigation industry in Texas is regulated by the TCEQ through statutory authority granted through Texas Occupations Code chapter 1903 and Texas Water Code chapter 37. TCEQ regulations implementing this authority are found at 30 Texas Administrative Code chapter 30, subchapters A and D, and chapter 344. The standards for obtaining an irrigation license through the TCEQ are high, requiring training, testing, and continuing education credits. The license may be revoked or suspended, and irrigators may also be required to take additional training to correct deficiencies. Advice on the landscape irrigation license and enforcement program is provided to the TCEQ by the Irrigator Advisory Council (IAC), comprising seven irrigators and two additional public members. Members of the IAC are appointed by the TCEQ for three-year terms. *See* Tex. Occ. Code ch. 1903; 30 Tex. Admin. Code ch. 344.

There are many detailed regulations for irrigation work in Texas, including requiring the use of individual license numbers on advertisements and trucks and individual seals on all irrigation installation plans. These requirements assist in enforcement efforts to ensure that irrigation work is not completed by unlicensed individuals. Clear identification requirements also allow accountability for rigorous quality standards.

Occupations Code sections 1301.056 and 1903.002 allow licensed plumbers to perform all irrigation services without an irrigation license. *See* Tex. Occ. Code §§ 1301.056, 1903.002(b)(2). Licensed engineers, registered architects, or a registered landscape architect can perform irrigation services if the acts are incidental to the pursuit of the person's profession. *See* Tex. Occ. Code § 1903.002(b)(2). Additionally, a license is not required if—

- the work is performed by a property owner on his property;
- a maintenance employee performs incidental repairs on property owned by the employer;
- the work is performed by a railroad employee on the premises of a railroad;
- the work is performed by an employee of a political subdivision of the state on public property; and
- the work is performed by a member of a POA on property owned by the association or in common with the association if—
    - the property is less than one-half acre, and
    - the property is used for aesthetic or recreational purposes.

See Tex. Occ. Code § 1903.002(c). Although no license is required, there is no exemption from design or safety standards for these individuals. 30 Tex. Admin. Code § 344.30.

In 2007, landscape irrigation standards and licensing requirements were strengthened through legislative direction. House Bill 4 and Senate Bill 3 directed the TCEQ to adopt rules for connection of potable water to irrigation, to define water conservation requirements for irrigation, and to clarify the duties and responsibilities of licensed irrigators. *See* Act of May 28, 2007, 80th Leg., R.S., ch. 1352 (H.B. 4); Act of May 28, 2007, 80th Leg., R.S., ch. 1430 (S.B. 3). The implementing TCEQ regulations were vetted through the IAC and statewide stakeholder groups. TCEQ compliance staff and IAC members held statewide education workshops and conducted meetings with professional associations to inform professional irrigators and municipalities of changes that became effective January 1, 2009.

One of the most significant new requirements is that either a licensed irrigator or licensed technician must be on-site during installation, maintenance, alteration, repair, or service of an irrigation system. This additional regulation resulted in the creation of a new irrigation technician training program, technician exam, and continuing education program, effective January 1, 2010. Texas Commission on Environmental Quality, *Landscape Irrigation Rules and Publications*, www.tceq.texas.gov/drinkingwater/irrigation/li_program.html. Licensed irrigation technicians may install, maintain, alter, repair, and service irrigation systems as well as connect them to water supplies as long as they complete their work under the direction of a licensed irrigator. *See* 30 Tex. Admin. Code §§ 344.30, 344.36. Since 2009, licensed irrigators have responsibility for completion of the irrigation system, conducting a final walk-through, completing a maintenance checklist, placing a permanent sticker on the automatic controller, and supplying a copy of the design plan to the owner or owner's representative. *See* 30 Tex. Admin. Code § 344.35(d)(12).

Also enacted in 2007, House Bill 1656 established a licensing program for irrigation inspectors. *See* Act of May 22, 2007, 80th Leg., R.S., ch. 874, § 1 (H.B. 1656). The intent of the inspection license is to create a class of license holders qualified to work for area governments in the role of inspecting plans and irrigation installations. Thus, requirements for holding an inspector license are higher than those for other irrigation. Municipalities and water districts may use a plumbing or irrigation inspector to inspect and enforce a landscape irrigation ordinance. A water district may also employ the water district's operator or another regulatory authority with jurisdiction over landscape irrigation.

H.B. 1656 directed all municipalities with populations of more than 20,000 to adopt ordinances relating to irrigation. The municipal landscape irrigation ordinances must be at least as stringent as the TCEQ rules; require landscape irrigation installers to be licensed; require a permit before installation of an irrigation system within the territorial limits or extraterritorial jurisdiction of the municipality; and include minimum standards and specifications for design, installation, and operation of irrigation systems. *See* Texas Commission on Environmental Quality, Chapter 344—Landscape Irrigation, Rule Project No. 2007-027-344-CE, www.tceq.texas.gov/assets/public/legal/rules/hist_rules/Complete.07s/07027344/07027344_ado_clean.pdf [hereinafter Landscape Irrigation Rules]. Water districts may also adopt and enforce irrigation rules, and both municipalities and districts may collect fees to cover costs of the licensing program. These requirements do not apply to on-site sewage disposal, irrigation for agriculture operations, or irrigation connected to groundwater wells operated for domestic use. *See* Landscape Irrigation Rules, at 3.

If all the landscape irrigation standards of Texas were rigorously followed, there would be significantly less water waste, and landscape irrigation would be highly efficient. The ongoing challenge is to achieve a high degree of compliance through reasonable enforcement at the municipal or water district level. The TCEQ may take action to sanction irrigators if there is evidence that they have not followed professional license standards. Such enforcement is administratively challenging because of limited state resources. With regard to increasing the efficiency of landscape irrigation systems to achieve conservation results, Texas uses strong state irrigation regulations coupled with state encouragement of local enforcement. In 2011, House Bill 2507 made an important advancement in strengthening irrigation licensing in Texas, making it a Class C misdemeanor to install irrigation without an irrigation license. *See* Act of May 21, 2011, 82d Leg., R.S., ch. 324, § 1 (codified at Tex. Occ. Code § 1903.256). Although exceptions still apply for homeowners and plumbers, this law makes it possible to enforce regulations across the state against unlicensed individuals who are installing irrigation systems. This bill took effect September 1, 2011, and allows peace officers to file cases in any Texas court or citizens to file cases in Justice of the Peace courts against individuals who conduct irrigation installations without irrigation licenses.

Municipalities have expanded on irrigation efficiency mandates through local regulation. Regulations requiring a maintenance check or audit of large irrigation systems help ensure that systems are better maintained. The San Antonio Water System compared the summer consumption of large commercial landscapes that complied with its irrigation checkup ordinance against those that did not. Sites that failed to comply used an average of 54,500 gallons more per month in the summer than those that documented their maintenance efforts. Personal Communication from Chad Cosper, Conservation Planner, San Antonio Water System, to Karen Guz, Director of Conservation, San Antonio Water System (Apr. 2015). The city of Austin has taken its irrigation checkup requirement further by mandating that it be completed by a qualified third-party individual who holds a TCEQ irrigation inspector license and is preapproved by Austin Water. *See* Austin Water, *Commercial Facility Irrigation Assessments*, www.austintexas.gov/department/commercial-facility-assessments.

VII. Long-Term Conservation Efforts: Demand Hardening

§ 23.26 Long-Term Conservation Efforts

"If strategies are not implemented, approximately one-quarter of Texas' population in 2070 would have less than half the municipal water supplies they will require during a drought of record." 2022 State Water Plan, at 3. Drought is so central to water in Texas that the stated goal of the 2017 State Water Plan is "to ensure adequate water supplies for all Texans in times of drought." 2022 State Water Plan, at 4. Texas must prepare for meteorologic droughts with limited precipitation, agricultural droughts with poor crop performance, and hydrologic droughts resulting in low water supplies. Conditions in 2011 made it clear that all of these could occur at the same time and affect up to 99 percent of the state at once. While conservation and efficiency planning may help mitigate drought, drought contingency plans are critical to managing extended dry periods. For this reason, all water utilities in Texas are required to have drought contingency plans. Water providers serving more than 3,300 connections must submit drought contingency plans to the TCEQ every five years. *See* 30 Tex. Admin. Code § 288.30(5). See Chapter 22 of this book regarding drought and drought planning.

An emerging concern regarding drought contingency planning is whether long-term conservation efforts inhibit the ability of a water provider to achieve additional water use reductions during drought periods. This concept is referred to as *demand hardening*. The Alliance for Water Efficiency organized a collaboration of seven utilities to study the phenomena. The study report provides extensive insight regarding how drought management plans achieve savings and concludes that "little evidence suggests that ability to curtail demand during shortages lessens as per-capita demand becomes more efficient on account of conservation programs and rates." Alliance for Water Efficiency, *Draft: An Assessment of Increasing Water Use Efficiency on Demand Hardening* 43 (Feb. 16, 2015). www.allianceforwaterefficiency.org/sites/www.allianceforwaterefficiency.org/files/highlight_documents/An-Assessment-of-Increasing-Water-Use-Efficiency-on-Demand-Hardening_%28AWE_7-2015%29.pdf. While the study is encouraging in its conclusion that demand can be reduced as needed even in already conservation-oriented communities, it does not conclude that achieving reductions will be easy. Researchers emphasize the importance of understanding current customer demand patterns and opportunities for savings as well as the importance of communication with customers who will respond best if they understand the need for immediate savings results.

VIII. Conclusion: How Can We Save More Water?

§ 23.27 Conclusion

Texas scored an A minus on a water efficiency and conservation scorecard created by the Alliance for Water Efficiency and the Environmental Law Institute. The scorecard was developed because "some of the most powerful means of promoting the efficient use of water [are] state laws." *See* Alliance for Water Efficiency & Environmental Law Institute, *The Water Efficiency and Conservation State Scorecard: An Assessment of Laws* 4 (Dec. 2017), www.allianceforwaterefficiency.org/sites/www.allianceforwaterefficiency.org/files/highlight_documents/AWE-2017-State-Scorecard.pdf. Most states earned a grade of C on conservation activities and only California tied with Texas for an A minus grade. There are twelve categories for which points are awarded: state agency in charge of drinking water, required efficiency standards, water loss statutes, conservation planning, drought planning, frequency of planning, implementation requirements, state funding for conservation, technical assistance for conservation, required volumetric billing, percent of public utility connections metered, and available evapotranspiration data for state microclimates.

Texas requirements pertaining to conservation and drought planning were noted as particularly detailed in the scoring process. A missing element is a system of rating the quality of these plans and any consequences for failure to implement them. Texas is also advanced compared to most states in requiring water loss audits but could benefit from a system to ensure validity of the data in the reports. Texas encourages utilities to use conservation-oriented rate structures, but making the use of such rate structures a statutory obligation would be more impactful. A comparison to other states on these matters is helpful for future considerations in Texas.

California has conservation plan requirements and requires targets based on state standards for expected reductions over time. This is a controversial step that Texas has not yet taken. Texas conservation plan requirements are thorough and require documentation that the plans have been adopted by a water board or city council. The Texas statute also states that plans could be rejected for failure to be complete. However, there is not a clear mechanism for state experts to review, approve, or reject plans based on how effective they will be for significantly reducing water use. Similarly, the strength of conservation efforts and planning are not metrics considered when water providers apply for new water permits. Plans with low long-term conservation savings will be accepted as part of new permit applications if they are administratively complete with all required documentation in place, and no effort is made to evaluate them further. Personal Communication from Chris Loft, Resource Protection Manager, Texas Commission on Environmental Quality, to Karen Guz, Director of Conservation, San Antonio Water System (Apr. 2015).

The closest Texas has come to setting a conservation goal for municipal water providers is the total GPCD target of 140 that was suggested by the Water Conservation Implementation Task Force in 2004. No guidance was provided regarding whether this pertained only to large urban communities with significant industrial and commercial uses or also to communities with little industrial usage, which makes a significant difference. Without this, comparing GPCD data is like comparing apples and oranges. Confusion over the 140 GPCD target remains and is reflected in a study of municipal water uses completed for the East Texas Regional Water Planning Group. The study concluded that "per capita water use is below conservation targets set by the WCITF and therefore do not support the need for development of specific conservation strategies and projections of water conservation savings in Region I." *See* East Texas Regional Water Planning Group, *2007–2009 Regional Water Planning Study No. 3* 13 (Apr. 2009), www.twdb.texas.gov/publications/reports/contracted_reports/doc/0704830694_RegionI/SpecialStudyNo3.pdf.

The WCAC recently clarified that a total per capita target or benchmark is inappropriate for comparisons of conservation progress between communities because total per capita includes demands such as industrial and commercial water consumption, which are likely to vary between communities. *See* Water Conservation Advisory Council, *A Report on Progress of Water Conservation in Texas, Report to the 82nd Texas Legislature* (Dec. 2010), www.twdb.texas.gov/conservation/resources/doc/WCAC_report_2010.pdf. A better metric would be to compare residential per capita that reflects water consumption in homes and apartments. The TWDB has standardized reporting of residential GPCD and could now suggest targets and reductions. These could be based on metrics that could include market penetration of water-efficient fixtures and percentage use of discretionary water. Clear state level residential per capita targets would alleviate confusion and the idea that conservation should not be pursued below a total 140 GPCD.

Texas water loss control statutes compare well to those of other states. It is commendable that the majority of Texas utilities must complete an annual water loss audit. However, more steps are needed to continue to improve audit quality. While legislation passed during the 85th legislative session requires training for individuals who complete required audit reports, there is still no required third-party review of audit validity in Texas. Water loss auditing is a relatively new process and will be challenging as utilities struggle to gather valid data needed for the audit and to understand how to use it. Validity of total water produced data is particularly important. If total annual water production is underestimated, the water loss audit will incorrectly conclude that there is little water loss. Currently the TWDB has no authority to question water loss audit reports, even when they seem implausible. A next step in raising the level of audit reporting would be to require documentation to back the rating given to production numbers and other key inputs as part of audit completion or to require a qualified third-party review of the audit on a regular schedule. For utilities with reported losses lower than what seem likely to be accurate, a third-party analysis could either confirm efficiency or provide better audit results.

Texas was an early adopter of water efficiency requirements for toilets, urinals, and showerheads but did not obtain the highest Alliance for Water Efficiency scorecard grade for efficiency statutes. Efficient prerinse spray valves were too new to the market to mandate an efficiency standard for them in 2009 when the Texas legislature contemplated efficiency standards. Several states including Colorado have now enacted prerinse spray valve standards of no more than 1.28 gallons per minute. Texas could consider an update to its efficiency standards to add this class of fixtures and reference the EPA WaterSense standards.

The Alliance for Water Efficiency conservation scorecard did not evaluate state efforts to educate the citizenry on water issues. Texas would get a mixed score if they had. A 2014 survey of Texan attitudes toward water revealed that motivation regarding water is high but understanding of water supplies is still low. Water conservation is now the top environmental concern of citizens. *See* Texas Water Foundation, *2014 Survey Fact Sheet*. Despite this, only 28 percent of Texans could confidently identify the source of their drinking water. This is problematic because market research for the Water IQ Campaign (a TWDB campaign designed to increase public awareness about water and conservation) found that people with little understanding of their local water supply were unlikely to take actions to save water. Personal Communication from Carole Baker, Executive Director, Texas Water Foundation, to Karen Guz, Director of Conservation, San Antonio Water System (Apr. 2015). Survey results suggest that Texas could accelerate the rate of water conservation by funding a statewide education campaign aimed at enhancing citizen awareness of water.

CHAPTER 24

Water Reuse

Tom Gooch,[1] David W. Sloan, P.E., BCEE,[2] and Ashleigh K. Myers[3]

I. Introduction

§ 24.1 Introduction

As the population of the state grows and water supplies become increasingly committed, reuse is a growing source of water supply in Texas. The 2021 Texas Regional Water Plans show that existing water reuse projects are projected to supply 620,000 acre-feet per year in 2020. Texas Water Development Board, DB22 database of 2021 regional water plan data, provided to authors (2022) [hereinafter TWDB DB22]. With increasing return flows available for existing projects and the development of new projects, the sixteen regional plans project reuse supplies to more than triple by 2070 to 2.15 million acre-feet per year. TWDB DB22.

§ 24.2 What Is Reuse?

When water is withdrawn from streams and lakes in Texas, it almost always includes some treated wastewater that was discharged upstream. For this chapter, however, "water reuse" is defined as the deliberate beneficial use of treated wastewater as a water supply. This definition does not include repeated use within an industrial facility by recycling. It also does not include what might be called unplanned or de facto reuse, where water diverted for use includes some treated wastewater

---

1. Mr. Gooch is a vice-president of the consulting engineering firm Freese and Nichols, Inc. He has been involved in the firm's efforts in water supply planning, water availability modeling, water rights analysis and permitting, reservoir system operation studies, water conservation planning, and water and wastewater rate studies for over 40 years. Mr. Gooch's experience includes planning, developing, and permitting major water reuse projects in Texas.

2. Mr. Sloan is a senior water treatment technologist with the consulting engineering firm Freese and Nichols, Inc. He has been active in the planning, development, design, permitting, and startup of major water reuse projects in Texas during his more than 35 years with the firm. Mr. Sloan's experience includes managing the development of the first direct potable reuse facility in North America, the Colorado River Municipal Water District's Raw Water Production Facility in Big Spring, Texas.

3. Ashleigh Myers is an environmental and natural resource attorney with the international law firm of Pillsbury Winthrop Shaw Pittman LLP. Ms. Myers counsels clients on an array of environmental regulatory and transactional matters, including contamination investigations, remedial actions, natural resource damages, compliance counseling, project permitting and planning, diligence, and project impacts mitigation and restoration. She also works closely with clients on water quality, water utility, and water rights matters. Ashleigh routinely advises clients on issues arising under the Clean Water Act (CWA), Safe Drinking Water Act (SDWA), Comprehensive Environmental Response, Compensation, and Liability Act (CERCLA), Resource Conservation and Recovery Act (RCRA), and National Environmental Policy Act (NEPA) and has experience with environmental issues in areas of archaeological significance under the National Historic Preservation Act and in tribal relations.

discharged upstream but there has been no deliberate effort to incorporate the wastewater into the supply or to authorize its use through water rights.

§ 24.3 Types of Reuse

The legal and technical issues involved in reuse vary depending on how a reuse project is implemented. In Texas, the most important legal distinction is between direct and indirect reuse. In *direct reuse*, treated wastewater is delivered directly from a wastewater treatment system to another use, without entering a watercourse. In *indirect reuse*, treated wastewater is returned to a watercourse, usually through a stream or lake, before being diverted at some point downstream for reuse. In Texas, direct reuse can normally be accomplished without significant legal constraints, while indirect reuse is legally intensive, at least from a water rights perspective, as discussed further in part III of this chapter.

Reuse can also be divided between potable and nonpotable purposes. *Potable reuse* is reuse that provides treated drinking water. Historically, most potable reuse in Texas has been indirect. Treated wastewater is returned to a watercourse, allowing further purification by natural processes and by blending the treated wastewater with other water. Direct potable reuse is a relatively recent development, and it is still very rare in the United States. *Nonpotable reuse* is reuse of treated wastewater not treated to potable quality, for purposes such as irrigation, oil and gas development, cooling of steam-electric power plants, or other industrial uses.

Combining the two classifications, reuse can be considered as—

- Indirect Nonpotable Reuse, where treated wastewater is returned to a watercourse and rediverted for nonpotable use;
- Indirect Potable Reuse, where treated wastewater is returned to a watercourse, blended with other water supplies, and rediverted for treatment to potable standards and use as drinking water;
- Direct Nonpotable Reuse, where treated wastewater is delivered directly to nonpotable use, without being returned to a watercourse; and
- Direct Potable Reuse, where treated wastewater is delivered directly to treatment and potable use, without being returned to a watercourse.

II. History of Reuse in Texas

§ 24.4 History of Reuse

This part provides an overview of water reuse development in Texas. The case studies in part VI of this chapter provide more detailed discussions of specific reuse projects, describing significant milestones in the development of reuse in the state.

Human life depends on finding and maintaining a reliable water supply, and this can be challenging in a largely semi-arid area like Texas. Early communities developed near dependable water supplies from springs and perennial streams. As the population grew, groundwater wells and lakes were developed to increase reliable supplies. Over time, developing needed water supplies has become more and more difficult, as demands increase and the best supplies are already developed. In recent years, the reuse of treated wastewater has become important to Texas for several reasons:

- other sources of water supply are becoming more difficult to find because the most economical sources and those near centers of use have already been developed;

- treated wastewater discharges are near urban areas, which can make them more economical than other, more distant supplies;
- treated wastewater discharges are relatively less variable than other surface water sources in Texas, with discharges continuing during even the most severe droughts; and
- wastewater treatment requirements have become increasingly stringent in the last fifty years, resulting in a significant improvement in the quality of treated wastewater and making it easier and safer to reuse.

One of the challenges of documenting the history of reuse in Texas is that there are no reliable statewide data on current or historical reuse. Data must be gathered project by project from a variety of sources.

§ 24.5 Reuse for Irrigation

The earliest recorded reuse in Texas is for agricultural irrigation, beginning in the late 1800s south of San Antonio. Through the 1900s, cities in arid West Texas and the Texas Panhandle, including Amarillo, Lubbock, Odessa, and Abilene, provided treated wastewater for the irrigation of nearby farms and ranches. Texas Water Development Board, *History of Water Reuse in Texas* 15 (Feb. 2011), www.twdb.texas.gov/innovativewater/reuse/projects/reuseadvance/doc/component_a_final.pdf [hereinafter Reuse History]. Agricultural irrigation is still a significant use of treated wastewater in Texas. Agricultural irrigation can be supplied through direct or indirect nonpotable reuse.

In recent years, reuse has also become a significant supply source for urban irrigation of golf courses, athletic fields, parks, and other large grassed areas in and around cities. Urban irrigation can be supplied by pipelines routed to specific areas of heavy use or, in some cases, by urban reuse distribution systems. This type of reuse often replaces municipal treated water as a source of supply, as discussed at section 24.7 below.

§ 24.6 Reuse for Industrial and Mining Purposes

Reuse for industrial purposes in Texas began in the 1940s, with the sale of treated wastewater to a petroleum refinery by the City of Odessa. *See* Reuse History, at 15. Reuse for industrial purposes has developed steadily since then, with cooling water for electric power generation plants being the largest category of industrial reuse in the state. This type of reuse involves nonpotable water. Like urban irrigation, industrial reuse can be provided through delivery to individual users or through reuse distribution systems. See Chapter 41 of this book for a discussion of water use associated with the energy industry.

The late 1990s and early 2000s saw a great increase in hydraulic fracturing, or “fracking,” to develop oil and natural gas from shale deposits across the state. In many parts of Texas, treated wastewater has been a significant source of supply for fracking and other oil and gas development, which is classified as a mining use. See Chapter 41 for a discussion of water use associated with oil and natural gas development.

§ 24.7 Municipal Reuse

Municipal reuse includes a wide array of potable and nonpotable supply projects, including the development of nonpotable reuse projects to replace treated drinking water with treated wastewater for urban industries and urban irrigation of golf courses, athletic fields, and large landscaped and open space areas. Reuse for golf course irrigation is particularly widespread.

As mentioned above, unplanned potable reuse for municipal water supplies began when the first wastewater treatment plants were built—downstream water suppliers would divert, treat, and use water that included upstream wastewater return flows. This sort of unplanned reuse occurs all over the state and is difficult to quantify.

In recent years, many entities have planned and implemented indirect potable reuse projects to provide municipal water supplies. The emergence of planned indirect potable reuse was spurred by the increasing cost and difficulty of developing other water supply alternatives and by the improvement in the quality of treated wastewater effluent, which makes it easier to develop a potable supply from reuse. In general, other nonpotable use in urban areas depends on the development of piping systems that deliver treated water within the city. (Such systems are often called "purple pipe" systems because purple pipe is used to indicate that the water carried is nonpotable.) San Antonio, El Paso, and Austin have significant purple pipe systems, and many other cities have recently developed or are planning nonpotable reuse distribution systems.

In general, planned indirect potable reuse requires a Texas water right permit, allowing the use of a stream bed and banks to deliver treated wastewater from a wastewater treatment plant outfall to a downstream diversion point for reuse. As discussed in part III of this chapter, such water rights often require that some portion of the wastewater flows be left in the stream to protect environmental values and senior downstream water rights.

Direct potable reuse (DPR) is a recent development in Texas, with two projects implemented to date. The first was the development of DPR of City of Big Spring treated wastewater by the Colorado River Municipal Water District. The system has a capacity of 2.5 million gallons per day (MGD), was completed in 2013, and is still in operation. David W. Sloan, *A New Spring in Big Spring*, Presentation at the 89th Annual Water Environment Federation Technical Exhibition and Conference (2016) [hereinafter Sloan Presentation]. The City of Wichita Falls developed a DPR system in 2014 as a temporary measure in response to severe drought. The system had a capacity of 5 MGD, but it was decommissioned in 2015 when the drought ended. Wichita Falls has since developed an indirect potable reuse system using the same wastewater discharges. These two projects were the first DPR projects in the United States. Other Texas communities are contemplating DPR projects, including a planned project in El Paso, which is under design as of the publication date of this edition.

§ 24.8 Current Status of Reuse in Texas

There are many large reuse supplies in Texas. In addition, hundreds of smaller projects provide thousands of acre-feet per year to golf courses, power plants, industries, and irrigated agriculture across the state. The lack of statewide data on reuse makes it difficult to determine the exact amount of reuse, but reuse is clearly a significant source of supply in Texas today.

Many of the permitted indirect reuse projects in the state have not yet been developed or are not yet fully developed. Reuse will play an increasing role in water supply for Texas as these projects are developed, other indirect reuse projects are permitted and developed, and direct reuse projects continue to grow across the state. The future of reuse in Texas is discussed in part VII of this chapter.

III. The Legal and Regulatory Framework for Reuse in Texas

§ 24.9 Overview of Legal Parameters for Reuse

Reuse projects in Texas are governed by both water right and water quality regulations, depending on the type of project. Additional statutory and regulatory requirements apply to individual projects, as discussed at section 24.12 below. The law relating to reuse will continue to evolve as reuse continues to become a more widely accepted form of water supply management in the state and as more reuse applications are considered by the Texas Commission on Environmental Quality (TCEQ) and the court system. This part outlines the basic permitting structure for all types of reuse and identifies the most significant legal and regulatory obstacles in launching a reuse project in Texas.

§ 24.10 Water Right Permitting

For any type of reuse, the TCEQ requires some form of authorization prior to the implementation of the reuse project that reflects the ownership of and ability to reuse water (excluding water that is recycled internally). In essence, the TCEQ must approve water reuse if the statutory and regulatory requirements are met, but the nature of that approval and how it is memorialized depends on whether the proposed reuse will be direct or indirect. From a legal perspective, the distinction between direct and indirect reuse is, in some respects, how and when the reuse project will involve state water. Texas Water Code chapter 11 defines state water as follows:

> (a) The water of the ordinary flow, underflow, and tides of every flowing river, natural stream, and lake, and of every bay or arm of the Gulf of Mexico, and the storm water, floodwater, and rainwater of every river, natural stream, canyon, ravine, depression, and watershed in the state is the property of the state.
>
> (b) Water imported from any source outside the boundaries of the state for use in the state and which is transported through the beds and banks of any navigable stream within the state or by utilizing any facilities owned or operated by the state is the property of the state.

Tex. Water Code § 11.021; *see also* 30 Tex. Admin. Code § 297.1(52). Pursuant to chapter 11, any use of state water, if not exempt, requires authorization thereunder. *See* Tex. Water Code § 11.022. As a practical matter, whether a reuse project requires water right permitting under chapter 11 depends on whether the water will first be returned to a state watercourse. Projects involving water first returned to a watercourse are indirect reuse projects.

§ 24.11 Indirect Reuse Water Right Permitting

Indirect reuse involves the discharge of reclaimed water back into an environmental buffer, such as a stream or reservoir, before it is diverted downstream to be used again. Generally, the state gives a water right holder permission to divert and use a specified volume of surface water designated in the water right. *See* Tex. Water Code § 11.135. After the water is used, it is often treated and discharged back into a watercourse. This is common with municipal water right holders, and industrial wastewater is also often collected, treated, and returned to a watercourse. Entities also withdraw groundwater, use the water, collect and treat the wastewater resulting from that use, and discharge the remaining effluent into a watercourse. The used water that is returned to a watercourse through effluent discharges is referred to as "return flow." Although the Texas Water Code does not define "return flow," TCEQ rules define "return water or return flow" as the "portion of state water diverted from a water supply and beneficially used which is not consumed as a consequence of that use and returns to a watercourse" and specifically includes sewage effluent. *See* 30 Tex. Admin. Code § 297.1(45); *see also Halsell v. Texas Water Commission*, 380 S.W.2d 1, 6–7 (Tex. App.—Austin 1964, writ ref'd n.r.e). Notably, however, the definition does not include return flow originating from groundwater because groundwater is not state water whose use is regulated by the TCEQ. *See* 30 Tex. Admin. Code § 297.1(45). See also the discussion at section 24.11:3 below of *City of San Marcos v. Texas Commission on Environmental Quality*, 128 S.W.3d 264, 279 (Tex. App.—Austin 2004, pet. denied), regarding pre–Senate Bill 1 treatment of groundwater-based return flows, and *Edwards Aquifer Authority v. Day*, 369 S.W.3d 814 (Tex. 2012).

Permitting indirect reuse projects under Water Code chapter 11 has proven to be challenging in part because the discharge of water into a watercourse for later diversion and use implicates a host of other water right concerns. Moreover, the two key provisions in chapter 11, sections 11.042 and 11.046, were only recently reconciled. See discussion at section 24.12:4 below. Additionally, because return flows can be derived from so many different sources, a threshold issue in any indirect reuse application is ownership of the return flows and their legal characterization once such water is discharged into a watercourse.

Some of these legal questions have been addressed to some degree, while others remain and yet more have emerged. Therefore, sections 24.11 and 24.12 provide the background of the development of the legal framework for indirect reuse authorizations, the basic framework for obtaining the necessary authorizations under chapter 11, and the uncertainties that remain after recent indirect reuse permitting decisions by the TCEQ.

§ 24.11:1 Background

Since 1913, Texas water statutes have included a provision allowing an entity to use the bed and banks of a stream to convey water from a place of storage to the place of use or diversion. *See* Acts 1913, 33d Leg., R.S., ch. 171, § 51, p. 358. The TCEQ and its predecessor agencies required accounting for conveyance losses and an authorization for this conveyance. (Conveyance losses—also referred to as "carriage losses," "transport losses," or "channel losses"—are the water lost from a stream due to evaporation, seepage into underlying formations, and other causes.) The legality of using a watercourse for transporting return flows for reuse elsewhere, however, was unclear before the enactment of Senate Bill 1 in 1997. Pre-S.B. 1 case law provided that when surface-water-based return flows entered a watercourse, the water again became state water subject to appropriation by others. *See South Texas Water Co. v. Bieri*, 247 S.W.2d 268, 272–73 (Tex. App.—Galveston 1952, writ ref'd n.r.e.); *see also* Frank E. Skillern, 1 *Texas Water Law* 81 (Sterling Press 1988).

Before S.B. 1, no specific statute or jurisprudence allowed return flows for reuse to be transported in a watercourse. Nonetheless, the TCEQ's predecessor agencies required an authorization to use the bed and banks of a stream for this purpose, similar to that required to convey water from a place of storage to the place of use. This type of authorization generally involved surface water reuse, and when the agency granted a bed and banks authorization to transport groundwater-based effluent, the agency's action was challenged. See section 24.11:3 below.

Senate Bill 1 made major changes to Texas Water Code chapter 11, including section 11.042, the bed and banks authorization statute. Act of June 1, 1997, 75th Leg., R.S., ch. 1010 (codified at Tex. Water Code ch. 11). The original text of section 11.042 related only to transporting stored water to a place of diversion and use. S.B. 1 added subsection 11.042(b), authorizing the use of the bed and banks of a watercourse to discharge and subsequently divert and reuse "existing return flows derived from privately owned groundwater." *See* Tex. Water Code § 11.042(b). Also added was subsection 11.042(c), discussing the conveyance and subsequent diversion of water in a watercourse. Both subsections 11.042(b) and (c) allow the TCEQ to include authorizations with protective provisions to mitigate impacts to existing water rights and the environment. However, for groundwater-based return flows under subsection 11.042(b), protection for existing water rights is limited to special conditions necessary to protect an existing water right that was granted based on the use or availability of these return flows. See further discussion at section 24.11:3 below.

Senate Bill 1 also added subsection 11.046(c), which makes clear that diverted water can be reused under the terms of the underlying water right "prior to its release into a watercourse or stream." *See* Tex. Water Code § 11.046(c). "Once water has been diverted under a permit, certified filing, or certificate of adjudication and then returned to a watercourse or stream, however, it is considered surplus water and therefore subject to reservation for instream uses or beneficial inflows or to appropriation by others" unless the water right expressly states otherwise. *See* Tex. Water Code § 11.046(c).

These statutory changes spawned numerous issues with permitting water rights for indirect reuse that remained largely unresolved until recently. These issues were highlighted in the 2007 State Water Plan. *See* Texas Water Development Board, 1 *Water for Texas 2007* 2–25 (2007), www.twdb.texas.gov/waterplanning/swp/2007 [hereinafter 2007 State Water Plan]. The 2007 State Water Plan referred to the Texas Water Conservation Association's Reuse Committee Report, *Texas Water Rights and Wastewater Reuse*, which framed these issues as follows:

(1) Under current law, is the use of wastewater effluent after discharge to a stream a use of "state water" subject to the laws of prior appropriation or is it subject to a different regulatory scheme?

(2) Does current law allow effluent derived from different sources of water to be treated differently for purposes of evaluating a request to reuse this effluent?

(3) Does current law provide for different treatment of effluent derived from "future" and "existing" return flows, regardless of the source?

(4) Who can obtain indirect reuse rights?

(5) To what extent should protection be afforded to the environment in reuse permitting decisions?

2007 State Water Plan, at 29.

For many years, the Brazos River Authority (BRA) grappled with these unresolved indirect reuse issues before both the TCEQ and the State Office of Administrative Hearings (SOAH). In 2016, the BRA was granted a complex new water right, the System Operation (SysOps) water right permit, which became final and nonappealable in August 2018, described in more detail at section 24.34 below. *See* An Order Granting in Part the Amended Application by the Brazos River Authority for Water Use Permit No. 5851 and Approving its Water Management Plan, TCEQ Docket No. 2005-1490-WR; SOAH Docket No. 582-10-4184 (Sept. 16, 2016) [hereinafter BRA SysOps Permit Order]; Final Order, *Lake Granbury Coalition v. Texas Commission on Environmental Quality*, No. D-1-GN-16-005965 (345th Dist. Ct., Travis County, Tex. Aug. 20, 2018); *see also* TCEQ Water Use Permit No. 5851. The final permit addressed many of the questions raised in indirect reuse permitting, yet other questions remain.

§ 24.11:2 Who Has the Right to Permit?

Texas Water Code chapter 11 contains two separate provisions often discussed in the context of indirect reuse: the section 11.042 authorization to use the bed and banks of a state watercourse to convey water for downstream diversion and reuse, and subsection 11.046(c) relating to surplus water subject to appropriation. The similarities in the language of the two authorizations created uncertainties in how the TCEQ should authorize the diversion and use of return flows and who has the right to appropriate such flows. These provisions were largely reconciled with the BRA SysOps permit (see section 24.11:1 above). In short, to indirectly reuse return flows, an entity needs both the authorization to convey water down the bed and banks of the watercourse and some memorialized ownership in or right to appropriate the return flows. See discussion of the BRA SysOps permit at section 24.34 below.

Bed and Banks: Water Code section 11.042 addresses the delivery of water through a state watercourse to some downstream diversion point. In relevant part, it provides:

(a) Under rules prescribed by the commission, a person, association of persons, corporation, water control and improvement district, water improvement district, or irrigation district supplying stored or conserved water under contract as provided in this chapter may use the bank and bed of any flowing natural stream in the state to convey the water from the place of storage to the place of use or to the diversion point of the appropriator.

(a–1) With prior authorization granted under rules prescribed by the commission, a person, association of persons, corporation, water control and improvement district, water improvement district, or irrigation district supplying water imported from a source located wholly outside the boundaries of this state, except water imported from a source located in the United Mexican States, may use the bed and banks of any flowing natural stream in the state to convey water for use in this state. The authorization must:

(1) allow for the diversion of only the amount of water put into a watercourse or stream, less carriage losses; and

(2) include special conditions adequate to prevent a significant impact to the quality of water in this state.

(b) A person who wishes to discharge and then subsequently divert and reuse the person's existing return flows derived from privately owned groundwater must obtain prior authorization from the commission for the diversion and the reuse of these return flows. The authorization may allow for the diversion and reuse by the discharger of existing return flows, less carriage losses, and shall be subject to special conditions if necessary to protect an existing water right that was granted based on the use or availability of these return flows. Special conditions may also be provided to help maintain instream uses and freshwater inflows to bays and estuaries. A person wishing to divert and reuse future increases of return flows derived from privately owned groundwater must obtain authorization to reuse increases in return flows before the increase.

(c) Except as otherwise provided in Subsection (a) of this section, a person who wishes to convey and subsequently divert water in a watercourse or stream must obtain the prior approval of the commission through a bed and banks authorization. The authorization shall allow to be diverted only the amount of water put into a watercourse or stream, less carriage losses and subject to any special conditions that may address the impact of the discharge, conveyance, and diversion on existing permits, certified filings, or certificates of adjudication, instream uses, and freshwater inflows to bays and estuaries. Water discharged into a watercourse or stream under this chapter shall not cause a degradation of water quality to the extent that the stream segment's classification would be lowered. Authorizations under this section and water quality authorizations may be approved in a consolidated permit proceeding.

Tex. Water Code § 11.042(a)–(c). As explained in more detail below, related to reuse, section 11.042 controls only the conveyance and diversion of privately owned groundwater and other sources of water. Independently, section 11.042 does not provide for the appropriation of water, nor does it authorize the expansion of an existing appropriative right. In other words, acquiring a bed and banks authorization under section 11.042 does not convey to the holder of that authorization any authority to use an underlying water right's return flows after discharge into a state watercourse when the underlying water right does not expressly authorize such a use. That right is derived elsewhere. The TCEQ's authority to grant appropriations and amendments to such appropriations are unaffected by a section 11.042 authorization. *See* Tex. Water Code §§ 11.121, 11.122, 11.134, 11.135. Therefore, a bed and banks authorization may be issued only to someone who already has a right to the water sought to be conveyed down the bed and banks of the watercourse or who is requesting such a right simultaneously with requesting the bed and banks authorization.

The TCEQ confirmed through the BRA SysOps permit process that the discharger of the return flows (or someone under contract with the discharger) or the holder of the water right from which the return flows originated can obtain a bed and banks authorization under section 11.042 to convey and ultimately divert those return flows from the watercourse. *See* BRA SysOps Permit Order, Conclusion of Law No. 16. In this way, section 11.042 governs the indirect reuse of one's own discharges.

At least with respect to surface-water-based return flows, discharging return flows prior to the discharger's obtaining a bed and banks authorization under section 11.042 does not preclude that discharger from obtaining a bed and banks permit and benefitting from the rights associated with a section 11.042 authorization. *R.E. Janes Gravel Co. v. Texas Commission on Environmental Quality*, 522 S.W.3d 506 (Tex. App.—Houston [14th Dist.] 2016, pet. denied). Thus, a discharger is not required to get an authorization under section 11.042(c) prior to discharging. The TCEQ made a consistent determination for the BRA SysOps permit. *See* BRA SysOps Permit Order, Conclusion of Law No. 16. In short, section 11.042 provides protections for a discharger of return flows to later convey and subsequently divert and reuse its own return flows.

Section 11.046(c) Surplus Flows: Water Code subsection 11.046(c) authorizes surplus water to be reserved for instream uses and appropriated by others, effectively authorizing the appropriation of surplus water by others. *See* Tex. Water Code § 11.046(c). "Surplus water" is defined as water in excess of the initial or continued beneficial use of the appropriator for the purpose or purposes authorized by law. *See* Tex. Water Code § 11.002(10); 30 Tex. Admin. Code § 297.1(55). Indirect reuse is a continued beneficial use of water, thus discharges arguably cannot be surplus water if they are being beneficially reused.

Others' Groundwater-Based Return Flows: The TCEQ determined through processing the BRA SysOps permit that both surface-water-based return flows and groundwater-based return flows discharged by others may be appropriated under section 11.121 once discharged into a watercourse. *See* BRA SysOps Permit Order, Finding of Fact No. 165, Conclusion of Law No. 16. Thus, return flows, unless specifically reflected in a chapter 11 permit, are not earmarked only for the discharger; a person or entity may appropriate others' return flows. *See* Tex. Water Code §§ 11.046(c), 11.121.

The caveat to appropriating others' return flows, however, is that others' return flows—whether surplus return flows or groundwater-based return flows—may be reduced or terminated by direct reuse by the discharger and terminated upon issuance of a bed and banks authorization to the discharger. BRA SysOps Permit Order, Finding of Fact No. 168, Conclusion of Law No. 17. As mandated by TCEQ rules, any water right based on the availability of return flows or discharges must be granted with the express provision that the water available for the right is dependent on potentially interruptible return flows or discharges. *See* 30 Tex. Admin. Code § 297.42(g). One such reduction, according to the TCEQ, is a bed and banks authorization issued to the discharger of those return flows.

§ 24.11:3 Sources of Return Flows

Generally, water in a watercourse is state water and held in trust for the public. *See* Tex. Water Code § 11.021; *In re Adjudication of the Water Rights of Upper Guadalupe Segment of Guadalupe River Basin*, 642 S.W.2d 438, 444 (Tex. 1982). Appropriated water (i.e., water authorized in a water right), by definition, is limited to state water. *See* Tex. Water Code § 11.121. However, return flows are not limited to appropriated water. In fact, return flows can also be made up of privately owned groundwater. As a result, when groundwater is released into a watercourse, the legal characterization of that water as state water is implicated. Therefore, the protection of the ownership interest in that water for future diversion for reuse requires some legal mechanism to reflect ownership.

Surface-Water-Based Return Flows: Water Code section 11.042 does not contain a provision specifically addressing return flows from surface water. However, given the specific language in subsections 11.042(a), (a–1), and (b), the TCEQ has interpreted "water" in subsection 11.042(c) as applying to return flows derived from surface water. Therefore, it is widely accepted that subsection 11.042(c) authorizes the conveyance of surface-water-based return flows down the bed and banks of a watercourse.

Notwithstanding that authorization, as explained in the preceding paragraphs, the TCEQ has determined that with respect to section 11.042 generally, and subsection 11.042(c) specifically, an authorization under section 11.042(c) is not an appropriation of water. It merely provides a way to convey and divert water placed in the watercourse. The right to reuse surface-water-based return flows must come from a separately issued appropriation. *See* BRA SysOps Permit Order, Conclusion of Law No. 17 (explaining that "section 11.042(c) does not operate to reserve return flows for the discharger or water right holder"). The TCEQ rules provide that "[a] right to take and use water is limited to the extent and purposes authorized by the water right," reinforcing that the use associated with a bed and banks authorization for surface water is derived from a water right. *See* 30 Tex. Admin. Code § 297.49.

Discharging before obtaining such an authorization, however, does not deprive the discharger of the ability to later obtain a bed and banks authorization under section 11.042(c) for those return flows. Section 11.042(c) requires only a prior approval to convey and divert water downstream but does not require prior approval to discharge that water. *See R.E. Janes Gravel Co. v. Texas Commission on Environmental Quality*, 522 S.W.3d 506, 517 (Tex. App.—Houston [14th Dist.] 2016, pet. denied). Therefore, to effectuate indirect reuse of surface water, both a bed and banks authorization under subsection 11.042(c) and an underlying appropriative right under section 11.121 or 11.122 are necessary.

Groundwater-Based Return Flows: As discussed above, the *City of San Marcos* court held—pursuant to pre-S.B. 1 law—that the privately owned groundwater-based effluent that was discharged into the river became state water and was thus subject to the jurisdiction of the state and available for appropriation. *See City of San Marcos v. Texas Commission on Environmental Quality*, 128 S.W.3d 264, 278 (Tex. App.—Austin 2004, pet. denied). After S.B. 1, section 11.042(b) now clarifies that a person who wants to discharge privately owned groundwater-based return flows to a river or stream, and then subsequently divert and reuse it, may do so after obtaining authorization from the TCEQ before the diversion and the reuse of those return flows, that is, a subsection 11.042(b) bed and banks authorization. More recently, the TCEQ instructed that applications for bed and banks authorizations to divert and reuse groundwater-based return flows are evaluated exclusively under section 11.042(b) of the Water Code and not under statutes and rules applicable to state water. *See* An Interim Order concerning the Motion to Overturn filed by the City of Bryan and the City of College Station regarding the Executive Director's decisions to return Application Nos. 5912 and 5913 pursuant to 30 Texas Administrative Code Section 281.18 without prejudice to their re-submission; TCEQ Docket Nos. 2006-1832-WR, 2006-1831-WR (Dec. 20, 2006) [hereinafter Interim Order]. Moreover, in that same proceeding, the TCEQ held that "as a matter of law with regard to bed and banks authorization applications that request authorization to divert and reuse return flows derived exclusively from privately owned groundwater that, based on Water Code Section 11.042(b), such applications *do not involve state water*." *See* Interim

Order, at 2. The TCEQ made that holding in response to a petition by the cities of Bryan and College Station concerning those cities' applications for a bed and banks authorization. The TCEQ, however, did not limit its holdings to just those applications. Rather, the TCEQ ordered that the Bryan–College Station order applies "to bed and banks authorization applications that involve exclusively groundwater-based return flows." See Interim Order, at 2. This remains the case even after the Texas Supreme Court determined that groundwater that has entered a watercourse is state water. *See Edwards Aquifer Authority v. Day*, 369 S.W.3d 814, 823 (Tex. 2012).

In the *Day* case, the court determined that groundwater flowing from a groundwater well into a watercourse and lake became state water, noting that groundwater was raw water with a constant uncontrolled flow into the watercourse, and the amount of water flowing from the well to the lake or the amount pumped from the lake into the irrigation system was not measured. *See Day*, 369 S.W.3d at 823. Thus, the character of that water as privately owned groundwater was changed upon its introduction to state streams. *See Day*, 369 S.W.3d at 822. However, critical to indirect reuse, the court distinguished these facts from groundwater-based return flows deliberately transported in a watercourse pursuant to an authorization under subsection 11.042(b). The court determined that groundwater-based return flows deliberately transported in a watercourse are an exception to the rule that groundwater becomes surface water when entering a watercourse. *See Day*, 369 S.W.3d at 823. However, "this exception proves the rule. The necessary implication is that when the water owner has not obtained the required authorization for such transportation [under subsection 11.042(b)], the water in the natural watercourse becomes state water." *See Day*, 369 S.W.3d at 822–23.

Thus, subsection 11.042(b), unlike subsection 11.042(c), not only authorizes the conveyance of return flows through the watercourse but also acknowledges that groundwater-based return flows are distinct from surface water when such water is placed in a watercourse and documented by an authorization under subsection 11.042(b). In this way, subsection 11.042(b) alone "provides affirmative means by which groundwater-based return flows may maintain the character of private groundwater when flowing in a state watercourse, and it provides a legal instrument to protect the ownership and control of the groundwater against other users in the watercourse." *See* Collette Barron Bradsby, *What Now? Indirect Reuse After the TCEQ Decision in the Brazos River Authority System Operation Permit Contested Case* 4, Texas Water Law Institute (2016).

§ 24.11:4 Protection for Other Water Rights

When return flows have been discharged to a watercourse over a significant period or have been historically discharged, other water rights may have been issued based on their existence in the stream, and this water may have preserved or enhanced the stream environment. Section 11.042 builds in protections for such rights that may be implicated by increased reuse. Particularly, both subsections 11.042(b) and 11.042(c) require the TCEQ to impose special conditions, including conditions to mitigate such impacts. Under subsection 11.042(b), special conditions must be included in the bed and banks permit to protect water rights that were issued based on the use or availability of the groundwater-based return flows. *See* Tex. Water Code § 11.042(b). Subsection 11.042(c) notes special conditions to be included in the permit to address the impact of the discharge, conveyance, and diversion on other water rights or the environment. *See* Tex. Water Code § 11.042(c). Special conditions include streamflow limitations (i.e., low-flow conditions) that must be met before water can be diverted and junior priority dates on the reuse diversion. In this way, the amount of water authorized for reuse could also be limited.

§ 24.11:5 Protection for the Environment

Indirect reuse permitting could also be affected by or conditioned on TCEQ-imposed environmental protections. As described above, Texas Water Code subsections 11.042(b) and (c) authorize the TCEQ to impose special conditions in a bed and banks authorization. In addition to protections for other water right holders, the TCEQ may also impose special conditions to maintain instream uses and freshwater inflows to bays and estuaries, collectively "environmental flows." Tex. Water Code §§ 11.042(b), 11.042(c). Such conditions are largely a judgment call based on TCEQ staff review of literature and studies relevant in making this determination. If allowing diversion of return flows will have a negative impact on the environment, the TCEQ could place streamflow restrictions on the authorization to require that a certain level of streamflow must exist before the applicant may divert the return flows. *See* Tex. Water Code § 11.042(c). In many cases, the TCEQ may apply such streamflow restrictions to return flows that were historically discharged but not to future increases in discharge.

Moreover, other provisions in Water Code chapter 11 also subject certain appropriations of return flows to additional environmental flow standards. In any application for a water right, subsection 11.134(b)(3)(D) requires the TCEQ to consider applicable environmental flow standards adopted by the agency by virtue of section 11.1471. Pursuant to section 11.1471, the TCEQ adopted regulations that vary from basin to basin but, broadly, establish environmental flow standards. However, subsection 11.147(e–3) limits environmental-flow standard considerations to only new appropriations and amendments to existing permits that would increase the amount of water to be stored, taken, or diverted under such permits. *See* Tex. Water Code § 11.147(e–3); 30 Tex. Admin. Code § 298.10(a). Therefore, consideration of environmental flow standards for indirect reuse applies only to new or increased appropriations of water. *See* Tex. Water Code §§ 11.134(b)(3)(D), 11.147(e–3), 11.1471; BRA SysOps Permit Order, Conclusion of Law No. 25. For a discussion of environmental flow standards under the 2007 Senate Bill 3, see Chapter 11 of this book.

§ 24.11:6 Accounting Plans and Reuse

In recent years, the TCEQ has required accounting plans for many new water rights. Accounting plans are spreadsheets that provide detailed information, often on a daily time-step basis, about the operation of a water right. The plans are intended to document whether operations comply with the underlying permit, and they can aid in water rights management and enforcement. The TCEQ often requires accounting plans for reuse water rights.

For bed and banks water rights required for indirect reuse, water accounting is used to determine the quantity of return flow that is actually discharged and determine how much water can be diverted after allowing for conveyance losses and meeting any restrictions to protect senior rights or the environment. *See* Kathy Alexander & Tom Gooch, *There Is No Accounting for Water—Water Accounting Plans in Texas*, Texas Water Law Institute (2015). See Chapter 27 of this book for further discussion of water accounting plans.

§ 24.12 Implications and Uncertainties Resulting from Recent Indirect Reuse Permitting Decisions

While the BRA SysOps permit provided much-needed guidance in many areas from the TCEQ on indirect reuse permitting, many issues still lack resolution. Although most pending indirect reuse applications are not nearly as complex as the BRA SysOps permit, permitting indirect reuse projects may yet require some legal trailblazing.

§ 24.12:1 Priority Date of Return Flows from Privately Owned Groundwater

The prevailing trend with respect to priority date for return flows from privately owned groundwater is that a priority date, even if assigned, cannot be enforced either by others with senior priority or by the permittee.

In 2010, the cities of Bryan and College Station, for example, each received reuse permits for groundwater-based return flows upon the TCEQ's determination that groundwater-based return flows do not involve state water and thus fall outside of the priority system. The permits explicitly provide that the return flows authorized to be conveyed pursuant to the permits "do not have a priority date and are not subject to priority calls from senior water rights." *See* Water Use Permit No. 5912 (Bryan); Water Use Permit No. 5913 (College Station). Other recent water rights have similar language.

Similarly, Water Use Permit No. 3985A, which was issued to the City of Lubbock in 2013 for groundwater-based and imported surface-water-based return flows for subsequent reuse, makes clear that neither type of return flow is subject to priority in the Brazos River Basin. On appeal, the Fourteenth Court of Appeals affirmed that the imported surface-water-based return flows were not subject to priority permitting in the Brazos River Basin (although they were in the Canadian River Basin) but did not address the waived issue relating to priority for groundwater-based return flows. *See R.E. Janes Gravel Co. v. Texas Commission on Environmental Quality*, 522 S.W.3d 506, 517 (Tex. App.—Houston [14th Dist.] 2016, pet. denied). The court suggests, however, that only indirect reuse of surplus water subject to appropriation by other water right holders under subsection 11.046(c) creates a new appropriation. *See R.E. Janes Gravel Co.*, 522 S.W.3d at 517.

On the other hand, it appears from the BRA SysOps permit that an applicant may waive this protection. The BRA specifically sought appropriation of all return flows as new appropriations, which seems to have been the impetus for the TCEQ's assigning a priority date—the same date—to all return flows, regardless of their origin. Notably, the BRA requested that its own groundwater-based return flows be given a new priority date. The TCEQ reasoned as follows:

> Because BRA's application seeks to authorize the indirect reuse of BRA's own return flows as a new appropriative right (under Texas Water Code 11.121) . . . BRA's indirect reuse of its own return flows can be authorized in the SysOps Permit as a bed and banks conveyance and as a new appropriative right—with the full quantity (47,322 acre-feet) being subject to the SysOps Permit's priority date. This is consistent with state law, prior Commission practice, and the Commission's directives in the Interim Order . . . .

BRA SysOps Permit Order, at Finding of Fact No. 165.

§ 24.12:2 Interruption and Termination of Authorization to Appropriate Others' Return Flows

The BRA SysOps Permit Order specifies that "appropriative rights in the return flows of others can be later reduced or terminated once the discharger directly reuses or obtains an indirect reuse bed and banks authorization under Texas Water Code § 11.042(b) or (c)." BRA SysOps Permit Order, Conclusion of Law No. 16; *see also* BRA SysOps Permit Order, Finding of Fact No. 168. In other words, using others' return flows is subject to interruption if the discharger directly reuses the water or subject to termination if the discharger obtains a bed and banks authorization. Thus, the TCEQ confirmed that rights to others' return flows are terminated at the time the discharger is issued the bed and banks authorization for its own return flows.

§ 24.12:3 Future Return Flows

Texas Water Code subsection 11.042(b) specifically allows requests to reuse future discharges of return flows. Particularly, it allows the diversion and reuse of future increases of return flows if authorization is obtained to reuse those increases in return flows before their discharge. Unlike subsection 11.042(b), subsection 11.042(c) does not make any specific reference to future return flows. The BRA initially sought the diversion and reuse of both its own existing and future return flows and the existing and future return flows of others. However, in the 2012 referral of the BRA SysOps permit to SOAH, the TCEQ directed the administrative law judges to limit the analysis of return flow availability to current return flows based on historic actual discharges (rather than Texas Pollutant Discharge Elimination System (TPDES) permitted discharges), not future return flows. With that direction, the BRA did not pursue reuse of future return flows. Thus, whether future return flows beyond the maximum authorized discharge in the underlying TPDES wastewater discharge permit may be appropriated and what conditions are associated with the appropriation of such future return flows are issues that remain to be meaningfully addressed. In reuse permits granted since the BRA SysOps permit, the TCEQ has authorized reuse up to current or pending TPDES permitted discharges and required an additional authorization for future discharges in excess of the TPDES permitted amount.

§ 24.12:4 Timing of Discharge and Obtaining Bed and Banks Authorization

In the case of *R.E. Janes Gravel Co. v. Texas Commission on Environmental Quality*, 522 S.W.3d 506 (Tex. App.—Houston [14th Dist.] 2016, pet. denied), the City of Lubbock had applied for and received a water use permit, in part, under Texas Water Code subsection 11.042(c) for the reuse of imported surface-water-based effluent from another river basin in Texas. On appeal, Janes Gravel argued that the permit was subject to subsection 11.046(c) rather than 11.042(c) because the city had been discharging the return flows it now sought to divert and reuse without first obtaining a bed and banks authorization, and those return flows were surplus water subject to appropriation. In other words, Janes Gravel's position was that a bed and banks authorization under subsection 11.042(c) is required before or simultaneously with the discharge sought to be reused; otherwise, that water becomes surplus water.

The court of appeals determined that subsection 11.042(c) was the controlling statute because it specifically provided for the conveyance and diversion of discharged surface-water-based effluent that the city sought, whereas subsection 11.046(c) generally describes how surface water returned to a watercourse becomes surplus water subject to appropriation by others. The court raised the question of whether the discharged surface-water-based effluent could ever become surplus water. It ultimately concluded that it did not need to decide whether the discharged effluent would ever become surplus water because it could affirm the TCEQ's order based on the city's satisfaction of subsections 11.042(c) and 11.122(b). The court determined that because the diversion was permitted under subsection 11.042(c), the discharged effluent was not surplus water subject to appropriation by other water right holders and that the city's diversions under the permit would not be a new appropriation of water. *R.E. Janes Gravel Co.*, 522 S.W.3d at 517. The TCEQ determined in issuing the BRA SysOps permit that no conflict exists between sections 11.042 and 11.046(c) in reaching a similar conclusion. *See* BRA SysOps Permit Order, at Conclusion of Law No. 17.

§ 24.12:5 Applicability and Satisfaction of Other Chapter 11 Environmental Protection Provisions

Environmental flow standards apply to permits that appropriate new water. Because the BRA SysOps permit was permitted as a new appropriation, the TCEQ was able to consider and apply environmental flow standards. However, the TCEQ indicated that the permit, as approved, would satisfy additional environmental protection provisions in Texas Water Code chapter 11, such as section 11.0235 relating to maintenance of the biological soundness of state water under the public trust doctrine, section 11.150 relating to the effects on water quality, section 11.151 relating to the effects on groundwater, and section 11.152 relating to the assessment of effects on fish and wildlife habitats. *See* BRA SysOps Permit Order, Conclusions of Law Nos. 24, 27. These conclusions imply that the application of flow standards satisfies the conditions and obligations under these additional environmental protection provisions without an analysis of whether such provisions are individually satisfied.

§ 24.13 No Chapter 11 Water Right Permit Required for Direct Reuse

Direct reuse is generally characterized as the use of reclaimed water that is delivered directly from the wastewater treatment plant via pipelines, storage tanks, and other infrastructure to the place where it is used without entering the environment. *See* 30 Tex. Admin. Code § 297.1(45). Thus, when water is piped directly from a wastewater treatment plant to a place of use but not conveyed in a state watercourse, it is directly reused. For instance, direct reuse occurs when effluent is piped via a purple pipe from a wastewater treatment plant to the user, that is, flange to flange, and never routed through a reservoir or stream.

Because diverting state water from a watercourse is not implicated by a direct reuse project, a water right permit is not required. Generally, a surface water right holder, by virtue of that right, may directly reuse all the effluent, subject only to the limitations contained in the underlying water right from which the effluent was derived. *See* Tex. Water Code § 11.046(c). Consistent with a water right holder's right to fully consume the water granted to it under a water right, the Texas Water Code provides, in relevant part, "[e]xcept as specifically provided otherwise in the water right, water appropriated under the permit, certified filing, or certificate of adjudication may, prior to its release in a watercourse or stream, be beneficially used and reused by the holder of the permit . . . for the purposes and locations of use provided [therein]." Tex. Water Code § 11.046(c). Therefore, as long as the underlying water right does not have conditions that limit or impair the reuse proposed, and the nature of the reuse project does not necessitate an amendment to the place or purpose of use, direct reuse projects require only the existing water right underlying the effluent.

As stated, direct reuse does not require additional water right authorizations under Water Code chapter 11. It does, however, require the necessary TCEQ authorization pursuant to 30 Texas Administrative Code chapter 210, described in more detail below. Consequently, even though direct reuse may limit the effluent volume that would otherwise be discharged into a watercourse and affect the amount of flow within the watercourse, the impacts of that reduced flow on other water rights and the environment are generally not considered with direct reuse.

§ 24.14 Water Quality Requirements for Reuse

Water quality is critical to the successful reclamation and reuse of water for beneficial purposes. Quality requirements are a combination of regulatory standards and practical considerations, which vary depending on the specific application. The following sections outline water quality regulatory standards related to water reuse. Additional water quality considerations are addressed in part IV of this chapter.

§ 24.14:1 Direct Nonpotable Reuse

Direct nonpotable reuse requirements are contained in 30 Texas Administrative Code chapter 210, including minimum water quality requirements. Two types of water quality are described, with requirements based on the level of human exposure likely for differing uses of reclaimed water. Well-treated secondary effluent is typically satisfactory to meet Type II uses, such as irrigation in areas not accessible to the public, industrial cooling, or construction dust control. Filtration is generally needed to consistently meet Type I uses, such as irrigation on land with unrestricted access or other applications where human contact is more likely. For each type, standards are provided for *E. coli* bacteria counts and biochemical oxygen demand; Type I uses are additionally subject to a turbidity limit, which is found at 30 Texas Administrative Code chapter 210.

§ 24.14:2 Direct Potable Reuse (Drinking Water Standards)

All drinking water supply projects must meet applicable drinking water standards. Therefore, reuse projects that serve as a component of a drinking water supply are regulated under the federal Safe Drinking Water Act (SDWA), codified at 42 U.S.C. §§ 300f–300j-27, which establishes the U.S. Environmental Protection Agency's (EPA's) authority to promulgate national primary drinking water standards that include minimum human health standards. Texas has formally adopted the SDWA requirements at Texas Health and Safety Code sections 341.031–.0315, and 30 Texas Administrative Code chapter 290 provides the regulatory framework for the TCEQ to implement the SDWA provisions applicable to DPR in Texas. For a discussion of drinking water supply legal requirements and the delegation of SDWA authority to the state of Texas, see Chapter 30 of this book.

In addition to the basic quality requirements for drinking water, of particular relevance to DPR projects is section 1435 of the SDWA, which the EPA and the TCEQ have used as authorization to regulate each new source of drinking water. *See* 42 U.S.C. § 300i-4(b); Texas Water Development Board, 1 *Final Report: Direct Potable Reuse Resource Document* 8-2 (TWDB Contract No. 1248321508, Apr. 2015), www.twdb.texas.gov/publications/reports/contracted_reports/doc/1248321508_Vol1.pdf. Section 1435 authorizes the review of the methods and means by which an alternative supply of drinking water can be provided, which has been interpreted to include DPR supplies. *See* 42 U.S.C. § 300i-4(b). Consequently, relevant Texas regulations provide a mechanism whereby DPR sources may be evaluated for suitability as a drinking water supply. *See* 30 Tex. Admin. Code § 290.41(e)(1). This evaluation includes information on several parameters, including pH, total coliform, *E. coli*, turbidity, alkalinity, hardness, total organic carbon, temperature, color, taste, odor, regulated volatile organic compounds, and other potential contaminants. *See* 30 Tex. Admin. Code § 290.41(e). Before a source may be used for DPR purposes, the TCEQ must approve the project as protective of human health based on these parameters.

The chemistry of the source water is not all that is considered when approving a DPR project, however. The TCEQ must also perform a treatability review. Because DPR presents a special risk of transmitting human pathogens, the TCEQ has required higher levels of disinfection performance as a condition of granting alternate source water approval. DPR typically includes advanced treatment methods, so the conventional water treatment provisions of chapter 290, subsection D, are insufficient. Thus, DPR projects require exceptions to the limited types of treatment technology to use the "innovative treatment processes" required for a reuse project. *See* 30 Tex. Admin. Code §§ 290.39(*l*), 290.42(g). Moreover, beyond the use of innovative technology, the TCEQ has required additional disinfection treatment levels that are not specific to a prescribed technology. While such requirements have not yet been codified, the TCEQ has developed a consistent approach in what it is requiring as part of the alternate source water approval process. Projects authorized to date have been required to provide measures in addition to those required for all drinking water. These additional measures include pathogen inactivation (for viruses, *Giardia*, and *Cryptosporidia*), stringent monitoring, and extensive requirements for operation, testing, and reporting. To date, Texas has given the necessary SDWA approvals to the Colorado River Municipal Water District and the city of Wichita Falls DPR projects and preliminary approval to the city of El Paso DPR project.

§ 24.14:3 Indirect Reuse Water Quality

The quality of the source water for an indirect reuse project is governed through the TPDES, with discharge permit requirements dictated by the water quality standards in effect for the receiving water body. Although downstream water uses may influence the standards, there is no direct link between the discharge permit limits on the source water as it enters state water and the specific downstream use attached to the reuse water right.

§ 24.15 Additional Permitting and Regulatory Requirements

No federal regulatory requirements specifically address water reuse. However, the implementation of reuse projects may trigger additional permitting requirements and regulatory oversight that are not necessarily directly related to reuse itself.

For instance, a reuse project that involves a discharge of dredge or fill material or the placement of a structure into, above, or below "waters of the United States" will be regulated under Clean Water Act sections 401 and 404. These provisions may be triggered by the placement of pipelines, intake and outfall structures, or other infrastructure necessary to implement a reuse project. See Chapter 34 of this book for a discussion of these requirements. Moreover, depending on the project, the presence of threatened and endangered species that may be affected by a reuse project will at least require a consideration about whether formal consultation under section 7 of the Endangered Species Act (ESA) is needed and may also require an incidental take permit under ESA section 10. See Chapter 32 of this book for a discussion of water resources and the ESA. Less obviously, the Texas Parks and Wildlife Department requires a sand and gravel permit to disturb or remove sediments in state-owned streambeds pursuant to its authority under Texas Parks and Wildlife Code chapter 86 and 31 Texas Administrative Code chapter 69. See Chapter 7 of this book regarding these permits.

Although the above is by no means an exhaustive list of all the regulations that may be implicated with respect to the implementation of a reuse project, this brief survey demonstrates the necessity of early planning and coordination to avoid regulatory delays.

IV. Technical Issues in Reuse

§ 24.16 Indirect Reuse Water Quality and Treatment Options

Practical considerations for indirect reuse include timing and storage to ensure that the water discharged is consistent with the subsequent withdrawal, as previously discussed in the context of the bed and banks permit and water quality issues. In part III of this chapter, it is noted that regulatory requirements for indirect reuse are specified in the discharge permit. However, some cases may present additional water quality considerations beyond those required by a TPDES permit. Key water quality considerations are discussed below.

§ 24.16:1 Nutrients

Nitrogen and phosphorus are elements critical to aquatic plant growth, but their presence in the aquatic environment can also induce excessive algal growth, perhaps leading to eutrophication. In time, eutrophication can lead to a variety of water quality issues, including reduced water clarity, fluctuations in dissolved oxygen, and unsightly appearance in water bodies. For lakes and rivers serving as drinking water supplies, these conditions can result in challenging drinking water treatment, including unpleasant taste and odor, increased formation of disinfection byproducts, and even growth of toxic algae blooms. Nutrient limits have been applied to many discharge permits, and the incidence of these limits is expected to increase significantly. Because of these impacts, nutrient management is an important consideration for indirect potable reuse. This is particularly critical in cases in which natural dilution, travel time, and detention time are low. In these cases, nitrate can be an additional concern as a direct contaminant for drinking water, with a concentration limit of 10 mg/L as nitrogen.

§ 24.16:2 Salts

Return flows generally have higher dissolved salts than the source water, and in certain cases, such as those involving the discharge of evaporative cooling waters, the increase can be dramatic. Many streams in east Texas watersheds may have low enough ambient salinity and sufficient flow to accommodate additional salt loads. Basins to the west, especially beginning with the Brazos basin, have greater ambient salinity and generally lesser flows, and the cumulative impacts from multiple use cycles can be a significant impediment to reuse. In particular, systems returning flow upstream of a primary surface water source are at risk of significant increases in salinity. At the same time, attempts to remove the salinity will usually be hindered by cost and by the difficulty of disposing of desalination concentrate. See Chapter 25 of this book for a discussion of desalination.

§ 24.16:3 Emerging Constituents

Municipal wastewater contains many man-made chemicals that typically survive conventional treatment processes. While certain highly toxic compounds, including heavy metals and certain volatile organics, have been regulated both in discharges and drinking water, many other chemicals are not currently regulated. Some of these have been shown to have subtle effects on aquatic life even at very low concentrations, and much speculation has been generated about potential effects on human health. The wide scope of potential compounds of concern and the scarcity of meaningful scientific data make this topic difficult to categorize or to draw conclusions about. These emerging contaminants include pharmaceutical compounds and their derivatives, personal care products such as deodorants and cleaning agents, fire retardants, pesticides, antimicrobial agents, and many others. Some aquatic life consequences in effluent-dominated streams have been conclusively demonstrated, such as feminization of certain fish and other organisms. Human health effects have been harder to identify or disprove, despite very active academic research in this area.

§ 24.16:4 Pathogens

Effluent discharges to freshwater streams are typically monitored for *E. coli* as a target organism to demonstrate disinfection effectiveness. This has generally been deemed sufficient to maintain designated uses in surface waters. However, where return flows have only a short residence time before subsequent withdrawals are made for public supply, additional monitoring for elevated pathogen concentrations may be appropriate. *Cryptosporidium* levels may be of particular concern because of the limitations of inactivation or removal through conventional surface water treatment.

§ 24.16:5 Treatment Options

Where treated effluent is conveyed downstream for nonpotable reuse, special treatment beyond conventional methods is not typically required, except where special stream requirements, such as nutrient limits, may apply. However, as noted above, where effluent is conveyed to a public water supply intake, additional treatment may be warranted to provide prudent public health protection and to satisfy public concerns. Such treatment may take the form of additional process units at a treatment facility or may be provided through natural processes such as wetlands.

§ 24.17 Design, Operation, and Other Direct Nonpotable Reuse Technical Requirements

Section 24.14:1 above discusses the water quality requirements of the TCEQ rules at 30 Texas Administrative Code chapter 210 governing direct nonpotable reuse. In addition to water quality requirements, chapter 210 also establishes requirements for design, operation, monitoring, reporting, and management of reclaimed water systems used for direct nonpotable reuse. These include such items as pipe labeling and color-coding, separation from other piping, integrity of storage pond liners, frequency of sampling, recordkeeping, and required terms in contracts between providers and users.

A key provision of the requirements affecting water planning is the limitation that reclaimed water be provided on a demand-only basis, meaning that the provider cannot require a contracted user to take the water. *See* 30 Tex. Admin. Code § 210.7. This provision prevents the distribution of reclaimed water from being a means of disposal. Wastewater utilities, including those generating the source water for a direct nonpotable reuse project, generally must maintain sufficient capacity to convey all wastewater flows to a permitted treatment facility and treat all flows to the quality required for discharge or land application through a TPDES or Texas Land Application Permit. *See* 30 Tex. Admin. Code § 210.1.

Like indirect reuse, the issues of timing and storage can be significant limitations to direct nonpotable reuse. Most treatment facilities produce reclaimed water in a flow pattern that mimics the flow of raw wastewater into the plant, while typical landscape irrigation demands are at night, when evaporation and exposure to people are minimized. Short-term storage to manage this daily variation can generally be addressed at a reasonable cost, either by storage at the production site or at the point of use, either by constructed tanks or ornamental ponds. Seasonal storage has been more problematic. Reclaimed water use for irrigation and cooling water has become sufficiently accepted that numerous systems have enough users to exhaust the available supply of reclaimed water during high-demand summer conditions, but there is little usage in winter, when evaporation is lower and plants are dormant. High storage volumes would be required to allow the excess volume of water available in the winter to become a usable resource for summer demands.

Some water quality issues related to direct nonpotable reuse can be encountered beyond regulatory requirements. Recirculating cooling waters, as employed by many power generation facilities, will concentrate dissolved constituents in the cooling water through evaporation until a limitation is reached, either due to system scaling risk or constituent limit on the wastewater generated. Irrigation may be limited by sodium, chloride, or other salt ions. Other uses may have other specific constituent limitations that prevent reclaimed water from being suitable or that may require additional treatment to make it suitable.

§ 24.18 Direct Potable Reuse Water Quality and Treatment Options

Direct potable reuse has become of significant interest to the water industry in recent years because of several factors:

- Nonpotable reuse has reached a practical ceiling in some systems because of the timing of demands versus available supplies.
- Available treatment technology has addressed most of the identified risks associated with DPR.
- DPR avoids water right limitations associated with many potential indirect projects.
- Although DPR typically requires expensive additional treatment steps, it can often be implemented in a constant flow strategy that achieves a high utilization of the required facilities and may thus avoid significant transmission and storage costs.
- Extreme drought conditions, coupled with successful public education, have overcome public resistance in certain areas.

§ 24.18:1 Water Quality Considerations

The most obvious consideration in developing a successful DPR project is the protection of human health, and this is the focus of the TCEQ's regulatory approach to DPR discussed in part III above. Many of the same water quality issues identified above for indirect reuse are applicable to DPR, but with some variations:

- Nutrients: Because DPR is defined by the lack of discharge to a watercourse, nutrients are not an issue in the usual sense. However, nitrate as nitrogen is typically found in significant levels in conventionally treated wastewater effluent and must be reliably reduced below the primary drinking water standard of 10 mg/L.
- Salts: Chloride, sulfate, and total dissolved solids are all regulated secondary contaminants in the Texas drinking water standards, and many systems with water supply limitations are also challenged by higher salinity source waters. Without adequate management, this issue can be compounded as dissolved solids are recycled with the reclaimed water. As noted above, treatment to reduce salinity will produce a concentrated waste stream that can be extremely difficult and expensive to manage.
- Emerging Constituents: Environmental impacts from emerging constituents are largely avoided through DPR, while potential human health risks could come under greater scrutiny. To date, there is little health-based information on which to set limits for these types of parameters, but there is consensus that employing a robust sequence of treatment reduces risks from such contaminants.
- Pathogens: TCEQ requirements for DPR focus heavily on removal or inactivation of pathogens and provide a thorough approach to this risk.

§ 24.18:2 Treatment Options for DPR Projects

DPR projects developed to date in Texas have been based on a treatment sequence (following conventional wastewater treatment) of membrane filtration, reverse osmosis, and ultraviolet light disinfection. As additional projects develop, and as significant research continues in California, Florida, and elsewhere, alternative treatment approaches will continue to be proposed, tested, and likely implemented. An alternative approach featuring ozone disinfection and biologically active filtration is often suggested as a competing treatment sequence. Prevailing opinion among Texas practitioners of DPR seems to favor a flexible approach that incorporates demonstrated water quality performance over a prescribed treatment technique.

V. Other Reuse Project Considerations

§ 24.19 Public Acceptance

Reuse in Texas has usually been well accepted by the public. The primary objections to reuse projects have come from downstream water right holders and from environmental groups. Water right holders are generally concerned about the impact a reuse project may have on the amount of water remaining in the stream and thus on their water rights. Environmental groups have focused on the need to protect streamflows for the environment and, occasionally, on the potential health impacts of reuse projects. Notwithstanding these concerns, there are numerous possible reasons for the general acceptance of reuse projects in Texas by the public at large:

- the public understands the importance of a reliable water supply in Texas, leading to support of most water supply projects;
- reuse is often relatively inexpensive compared to the development of other new supplies, which may also help with public acceptance;
- most surface water supply in Texas includes treated water return flows from upstream water uses, and indirect reuse may not be seen as essentially different from existing surface water supplies; and
- reuse projects may simply not be noticed by a large portion of the public.

Despite the historical acceptance of reuse projects, public assent should not be taken for granted in developing new projects. While reuse projects have not met major opposition in Texas, the successful opposition to the proposed Applewhite Reservoir in San Antonio in the late 1980s and early 1990s included complaints related to the upstream discharges of treated wastewater and allegations that such flows would make it unsafe to develop drinking water from the reservoir. Thus, it may be important to develop an effective public relations strategy to tell the story about the project—why is it needed, why is it desirable, and how public health will be protected.

§ 24.20 Cost and Economics

The cost of new supplies from reuse varies greatly from project to project. Because reuse supplies can often be developed near major population centers, indirect reuse is often inexpensive compared to other potential new water sources. The cost of direct reuse is largely driven by the distance from the wastewater treatment plant to the customer. Major direct nonpotable (i.e., purple pipe) reuse distribution systems in urban areas generally provide relatively expensive supplies, but unit costs may decrease as use of the system increases. The value of the potable water supplies that are "saved" when direct reuse supplies are available should also be considered. Direct potable reuse is likely to be an expensive source of supply because of the extensive treatment requirements needed to comply with the more stringent drinking water standards. Generally, the economic desirability of reuse projects can be determined only case by case, comparing the costs and benefits of the specific projects to the available alternative supplies.

§ 24.21 Environmental Impacts

Like costs, the environmental impacts of reuse vary greatly from project to project. As with any water supply project, the specific facilities built for a reuse project can have undesirable environmental impacts. Moreover, reuse projects may have impacts not common in other supplies. In general, reuse projects remove discharges of treated wastewater from the environment by using the treated wastewater before discharge for direct reuse and rediverting return flows from the stream for indirect reuse. The removal of this flow from the stream can have negative impacts on the environment, especially since return flows may be a substantial part of streamflows during dry times and in some streams return flows may make up the bulk of flows depending on the season. The blending of reuse supplies in reservoirs can increase nutrient levels, potentially increasing algae and chlorophyll *a* concentrations. Treatment for DPR generally involves desalination, and disposal of the concentrate from the process can also be an environmental issue.

§ 24.22 Operational Issues

Operational issues also vary from project to project, but there are general concerns with reuse that commonly occur. In direct reuse projects, for example, the quality of the treated effluent can be an issue. Sometimes a project requires an adjustment to treatment plant operation or development of additional treatment processes. DPR, in particular, demands constant monitoring of the process and effluent quality.

The reservoir nutrient and water quality concerns referenced above as environmental impacts of indirect reuse projects can also result in operational issues. If constructed wetlands are used in indirect reuse, the operation of the wetlands can often be challenging. Operationally, indirect reuse also requires diverting return flows by a downstream pump station, and diversions from a stream can be a challenging operations and maintenance issue.

§ 24.23 Public Health and Reuse

Does potable reuse introduce an unacceptable risk to public water supplies and human health and safety? As mentioned, indirect potable reuse is not a new idea in Texas, where almost all surface water supplies include some amount of treated wastewater return flows from upstream water suppliers. Planned indirect potable reuse involves the introduction of additional treated wastewater into raw water supplies. This does not add a new type of risk, but increasing the fraction of treated wastewater return flows in raw water supplies can bring some risk. Those risks can be mitigated in several ways:

- applying more stringent wastewater treatment discharge requirements;
- blending with freshwater from other sources;
- increasing residence time of treated wastewater in streams or reservoirs and exposure to natural attenuation processes before diversion; and
- using constructed wetlands, which may provide additional environmental benefits while providing natural treatment, thereby reducing risk.

DPR has not been common in Texas or elsewhere in the world. The increasing sophistication of treatment makes it possible to implement this supply now. Public health is protected by multiple steps in treatment, with each providing increased protection. Continued and careful monitoring is another important protection for public health with DPR.

§ 24.24 Reuse and the Value of Treated Wastewater

The development of substantial wastewater reuse projects across the state has created a new perception of the value of treated wastewater as a commodity, and in most cases reuse customers pay something for the treated wastewater they use—specifically, the cost of treatment, the cost of alternative or replacement supplies, and so forth. Payment for treated wastewater can sometimes be used to offset the cost of wastewater treatment and the reuse system, reducing the cost to the discharger's wastewater customers.

VI. Reuse Case Studies

§ 24.25 Overview of Case Studies

The following case studies are intended to provide more detail about the development of reuse in Texas, including the evolution in laws and regulations related to reuse and the compromises among interested parties. These projects include Lake Livingston, Calaveras Lake, the San Antonio Water System Reuse Program, the North Texas Municipal Water District, the Tarrant Regional Water District, the Houston area, the Colorado River Municipal Water District, Wichita Falls, and the Brazos River Authority.

§ 24.26 Lake Livingston Water Right Permit—Certificates of Adjudication Nos. 08-4248 and 08-4261

In the late 1950s, the city of Houston and the Trinity River Authority applied for a water right to develop Lake Livingston and a related impoundment that eventually became the Wallisville Salt Water Barrier. Lake Livingston is located on the main stem of the Trinity River, downstream from the Dallas–Fort Worth metroplex. One of the major issues in the Lake Livingston water right case was the treatment of return flows from the metroplex. Entities in the Dallas–Fort Worth area argued that their return flows should not be included in the water appropriated to Lake Livingston but should instead be reserved for future use in the metroplex.

In the hydrologic studies performed during the permitting process, return flows were estimated by multiplying projected upstream demands by return flow factors that reflected the assumed ratio of return flows to water use. As a result, return flows were assumed to increase over time as upstream water use increased. During the hearing on the Lake Livingston water right application, the Board of Water Engineers (a predecessor agency of the TCEQ) received legal briefings on the question whether the state had the power to appropriate future return flows. *See Historical Treatment of Reuse in Texas Water Rights: Hearings on Brazos River Authority System Operation Permit* (Feb. 2015) (exhibit by Tom Gooch) [hereinafter Gooch Exhibit].

The permit was granted with the appropriation to Lake Livingston made subordinate to the metroplex's right to reuse its municipal and industrial wastewater effluent return flows, even if such flows were returned to the stream. The subordination of Lake Livingston to future upstream reuse is reflected in the following special condition in the Lake Livingston water right:

> This certificate of adjudication is specifically subordinate to the present and future use and reuse and consumptive use of any return flows from waters impounded in each of the existing and above described proposed reservoirs and the return flows from water imported into the river basin, for municipal and industrial purposes within the Trinity Basin above Lake Livingston authorized herein and notwithstanding the re-entry of such return flows into a public stream they may nevertheless be used again, diverted and routed through such treatment facilities as may be considered necessary for their purification, under authority of permits heretofore or hereafter issued by the [Board] for such purposes in the upstream watershed . . . .

Certificate of Adjudication No. 08-4248, at 5, Special Condition 5.E. The special condition goes on to allow reuse of the return flows for navigation as well as municipal and industrial purposes. The reservoirs referenced in this special condition are described in the permit as existing reservoirs, permitted but unbuilt reservoirs, reservoirs then being considered for permits, and a specific list of proposed future reservoirs.

Several conclusions can be drawn from the stated treatment of reuse in the Lake Livingston water right permit:

- Dallas–Fort Worth area water suppliers sought to protect their right to reuse return flows in the permit hearing. Even in the late 1950s, well before reuse was highly developed in Texas, the possibility of reuse and the value of return flows as a supply for reuse was recognized.
- The fact that the water right is specifically subordinate to the reuse of certain return flows clearly implies that, absent such subordination, the water right would have appropriated those return flows to the applicants.
- The fact that the upstream return flows are reserved for future reuse indicates that the Board of Water Engineers felt that it had the authority to determine the treatment of future return flows.

See Gooch Exhibit.

§ 24.27 Reuse in Calaveras Lake by San Antonio City Public Service—Certificate of Adjudication No. 19-2162

San Antonio City Public Service (SACPS), the power provider for the city of San Antonio, received a water right in 1967 allowing the construction of a reservoir on Calaveras Creek, a tributary of the San Antonio River. The water right allows the SACPS to impound "not to exceed 60,000 acre-feet per year of the unappropriated public waters of the San Antonio River, including sewage effluent released upstream from the point of diversion." The right also includes the following special conditions relating to the reuse of sewage effluent:

> A. Owner is authorized to use the bed and banks of the San Antonio River and its tributaries named herein for the conveyance of sewage effluent from the point of release in Bexar County to the point of diversion authorized herein.
>
> . . . .
>
> C. All rights acquired under this authorization may be terminated or modified by the Commission upon notice and hearing should owner's right to use sewage effluent dedicated by City of San Antonio's ordinance 35228 be terminated or substantially changed.

Certificate of Adjudication No. 19-2162, at 2, Special Conditions 5A, 5C.

The Calaveras Lake water right (Certificate of Adjudication No. 19-2162) was authorized based at least in part on the release of upstream treated wastewater dedicated to the SACPS by the city of San Antonio. This water right is also a very early grant by the state of the right to use the bed and banks of a state stream to transport treated wastewater for downstream use. The San Antonio Water System (SAWS) has committed 50,000 acre-feet per year of wastewater discharges to the SACPS for power plant cooling. *See* Steve Clouse, San Antonio Water System, Presentation on Reuse (Aug. 2, 2016) [hereinafter Clouse Presentation]. Figure 1 shows the historical reuse under this water right.

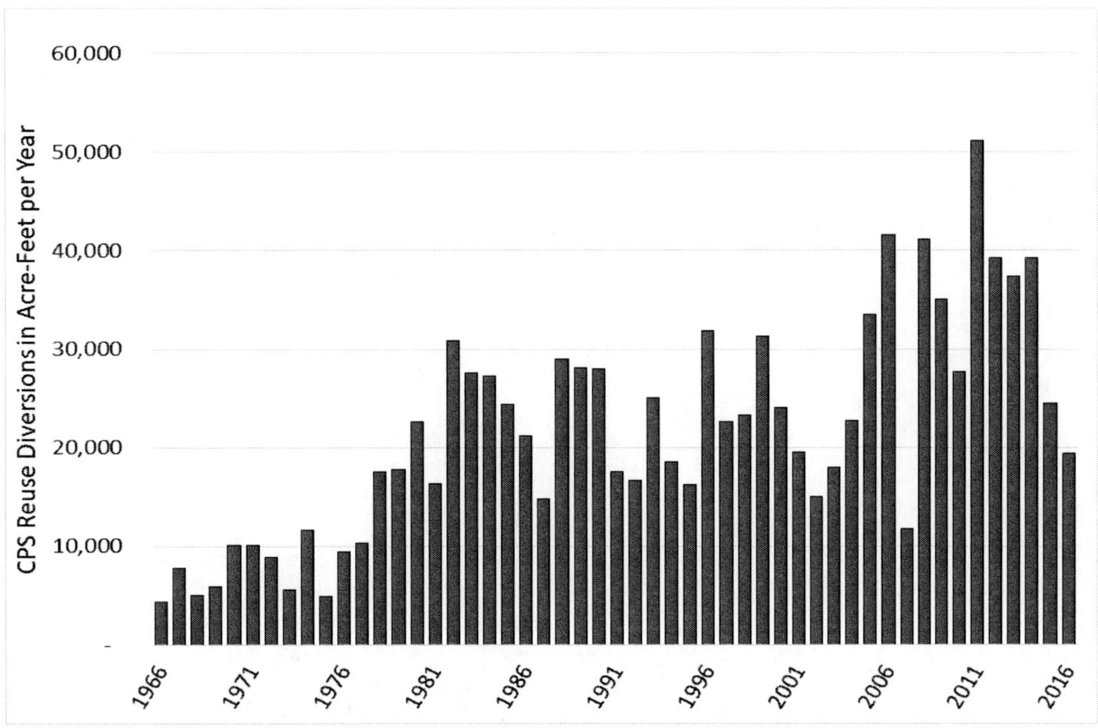

Figure 1. San Antonio City Public Service reuse diversions from the San Antonio River, 1966–2016. Data provided by Kimberly Stoker, SACPS Energy, via email to authors (Feb. 9, 2017).

§ 24.28 San Antonio Water System Reuse Program

San Antonio has the largest urban direct reuse distribution system in the United States. *See* Clouse Presentation. The idea of developing a reuse distribution system was identified in the late 1980s. Market analyses identified military installations, golf courses, large landscaped areas, industries, and the San Antonio Riverwalk (streamflow augmentation) as potential customers of a reuse system. Following the drought of 1996–98, SAWS built an urban distribution system for reuse supplies. The east branch has a capacity of 13,000 acre-feet per year and the west branch 22,000 acre-feet per year, for a total capacity of 35,000 acre-feet per year. Current users of recycled water include streamflow augmentation for the Riverwalk, federal installations (cooling towers), golf courses, and industries. *See* San Antonio Water System, *Recycling Centers*, www.saws.org/your-water/water-recycling/recycling-centers/.

The SAWS urban water reuse project includes 130 miles of pipe, installed at a cost of about $140 million. The system has about 75 customers who have contracted for 13,000 acre-feet per year of consumptive use and 5,800 acre-feet per year of nonconsumptive use. (Streamflow augmentation for urban streams, including the Riverwalk, is considered nonconsumptive because the water flows through the city to the San Antonio River downstream.) The SAWS reuse distribution system has some capacity for additional contracts, but the system is more fully committed in the summer months when irrigation and cooling demands are higher. *See* Clouse Presentation.

Figure 2 shows the use from the SAWS reuse distribution system in recent years. SAWS's current policy is to commit 50,000 acre-feet per year of treated wastewater to SACPS for downstream reuse for power plant cooling, 50,000 acre-feet per year to releases to the San Antonio River to provide environmental flows, and 25,000 acre-feet per year for consumptive use in the reuse distribution system. SAWS currently has an application pending at the TCEQ for a bed and banks authorization for SAWS's groundwater-based return flows discharged from SAWS's existing water recycling centers to the San Antonio and Guadalupe rivers for subsequent diversion and reuse. *See* SAWS Application No. 13098.

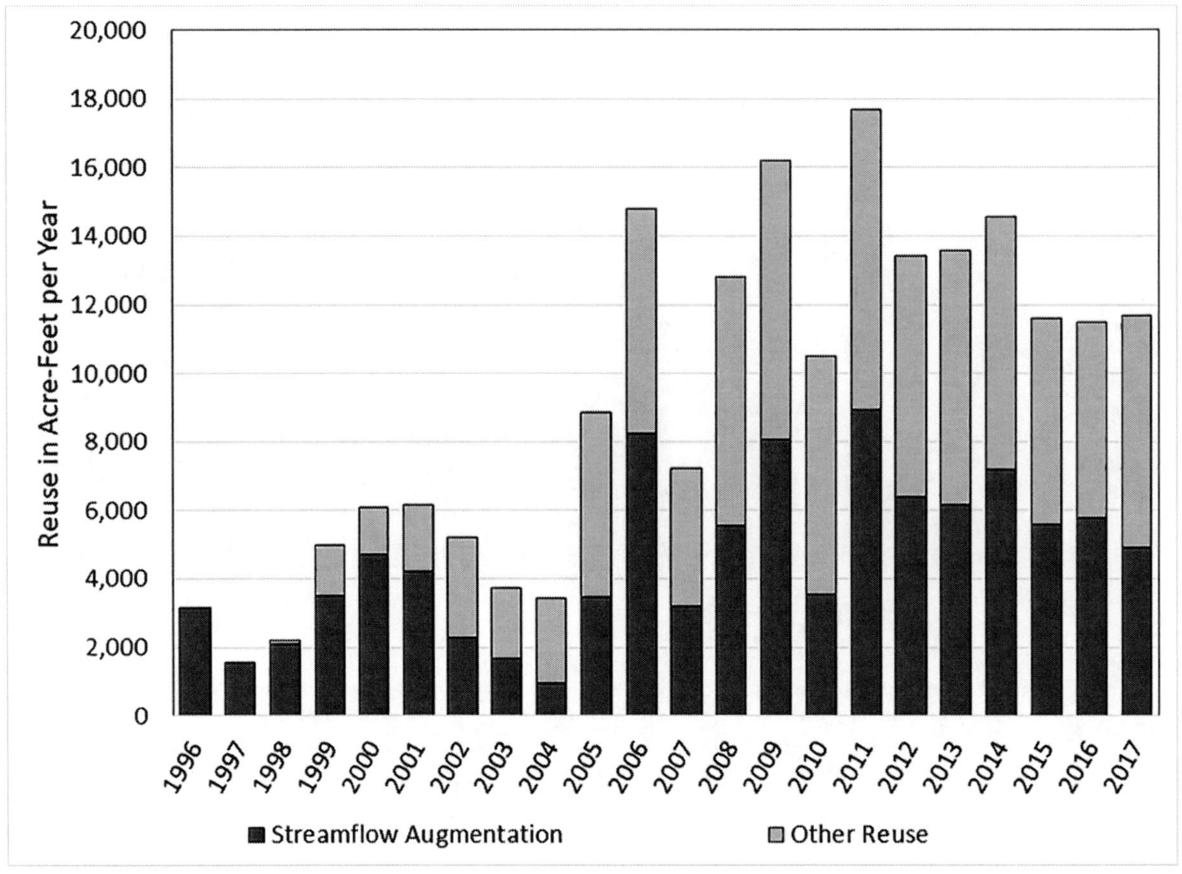

Figure 2. San Antonio Water System reuse system, 1996–2017. Data provided by Barbara Martinez, SAWS, via email to authors (Feb. 15, 2017), and taken from 2018 presentation to San Antonio City Council.

§ 24.29 North Texas Municipal Water District Reuse—Certificate of Adjudication No. 08-2410, as Amended

In 1985, the North Texas Municipal Water District (NTMWD) was planning the Wilson Creek Wastewater Treatment Plant, a regional wastewater plant that discharges into the watershed of Lake Lavon, the NTMWD's primary water supply reservoir. The original permitted capacity of the Wilson Creek Plant was 8 MGD, and in 1985 the NTMWD amended its Lake Lavon water right to allow reuse of treated wastewater discharged from the plant of up to 8,896 acre-feet per year (8 MGD). *See* Certificate of Adjudication No. 08-2410. The plant was completed in 1987, and the NTMWD started reuse from the plant that year. As the plant was expanded over the years, the district increased its reuse authorization to 26,957 acre-feet per year (24 MGD) in 1989, 35,941 acre-feet per year (36 MGD) in 2000, and 71,882 acre-feet per year (64 MGD) in 2002. The NTMWD's reuse under this authorization has varied with wastewater discharges but tended to increase with increasing discharges from the Wilson Creek Plant, reaching more than 62,000 acre-feet per year in recent years. *See* North Texas Municipal Water District, records of reuse.

In 2005, the NTMWD amended its Lake Lavon water right to authorize the East Fork Water Supply Project. The project reuses return flows discharged into the East Fork of the Trinity River watershed from NTMWD-owned and NTMWD customer-owned wastewater treatment plants other than the Wilson Creek Plant. The right authorizes reuse of actual discharges from sixteen specific wastewater plants up to a total of 157,393 acre-feet per year. Two of the plants discharge into Lake Lavon, and their flows can be diverted from the lake. The other fourteen plants discharge downstream from the lake, and the NTMWD is authorized to divert those discharges from the East Fork of the Trinity River, convey them through a 2,000-acre constructed wetland for treatment, and then collect and pump them 47 miles back to Lake Lavon for reuse. The permit includes requirements for bypasses of flow at the East Fork diversion pump station. In conjunction with this water right, the NTMWD reached an agreement with the city of Dallas that Dallas would release NTMWD return flows discharged into the Lake Ray Hubbard watershed through Lake Ray Hubbard, for subsequent diversion at the East Fork diversion pump station. The facilities needed for the project (diversion pump station, constructed wetlands, conveyance pump station to pump the water to Lake Lavon, and pipeline to Lake Lavon) were completed in 2009 at a cost of about $230 million. Personal communication from NTMWD staff.

The district also has several small direct reuse projects. Figure 3 shows historical reuse totals for the NTMWD. The level of reuse has increased dramatically in recent decades, from 5,000 acre-feet in 1987 to over 100,000 acre-feet in recent years. The district has recently constructed a pump station on the main stem of the Trinity River that will allow additional reuse by diversion of treated wastewater return flows purchased from Trinity River Authority wastewater plants upstream.

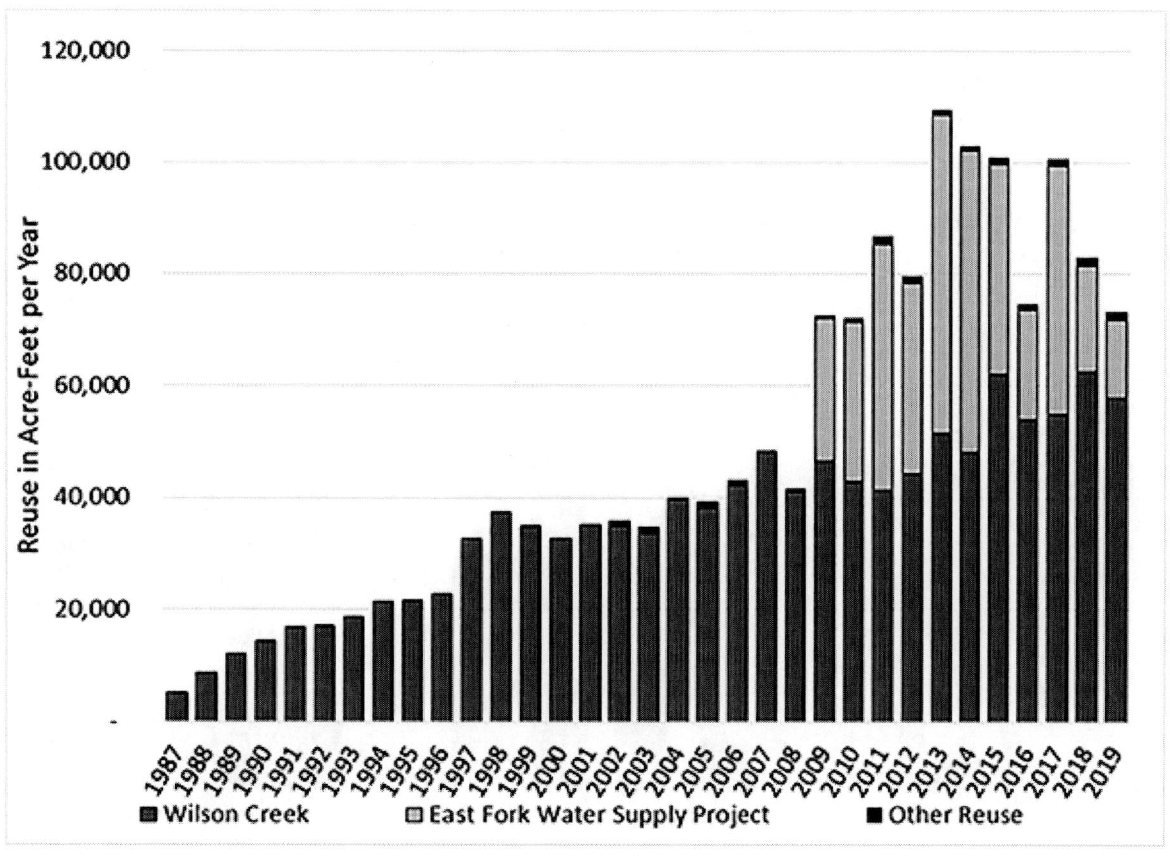

Figure 3. North Texas Municipal Water District historical reuse, 1987–2019. Data obtained from records maintained by the NTMWD.

§ 24.30 Tarrant Regional Water District Reuse—Certificate of Adjudication Nos. 08-4976 and 08-5035

In its 1990 Long Range Water Supply Plan, the Tarrant Regional Water District (TRWD) decided to pursue reuse as its next major water supply source. The plan was to develop indirect reuse by diverting treated wastewater return flows from the Trinity River through constructed wetlands into Cedar Creek Reservoir and Richland-Chambers Reservoir. In 1992, the TRWD developed a pilot scale constructed wetland to test the treatment benefits of the proposed wetlands. The district applied to amend Certificates of Adjudication Nos. 08-4976 (Cedar Creek Lake) and 08-5035 (Richland-Chambers Lake) to allow diversion of return flows from the Trinity River into constructed wetlands and then to the lakes. The original authorization, granted in 2005, was for reuse of up to 52,500 acre-feet per year through Cedar Creek Lake and up to 63,000 acre-feet per year through Richland-Chambers Lake. This was later increased to 88,059 acre-feet per year from Cedar Creek Lake and 100,465 acre-feet per year from Richland-Chambers Lake. The water right limits diversions to 70 percent of upstream district return flows (return flows originating from district supplies) and includes instream flow limits for the Trinity River. *See* Certificates of Adjudication Nos. 08-4976, 08-5035.

Construction of the facilities needed for reuse through Cedar Creek Reservoir (Trinity River pump station and wetlands) started in 2005. Reuse started in 2009, and the George W. Shannon Wetlands were fully completed in 2013. Figure 4 shows the historical reuse from the Shannon Wetlands. Reuse was temporarily discontinued in 2015 because of high lake levels and flood damage to the levees. Construction of facilities to implement reuse through the Cedar Creek Reservoir is currently in the planning stages. Tarrant Regional Water District, records of reuse; personal communication from Tarrant Regional Water District staff.

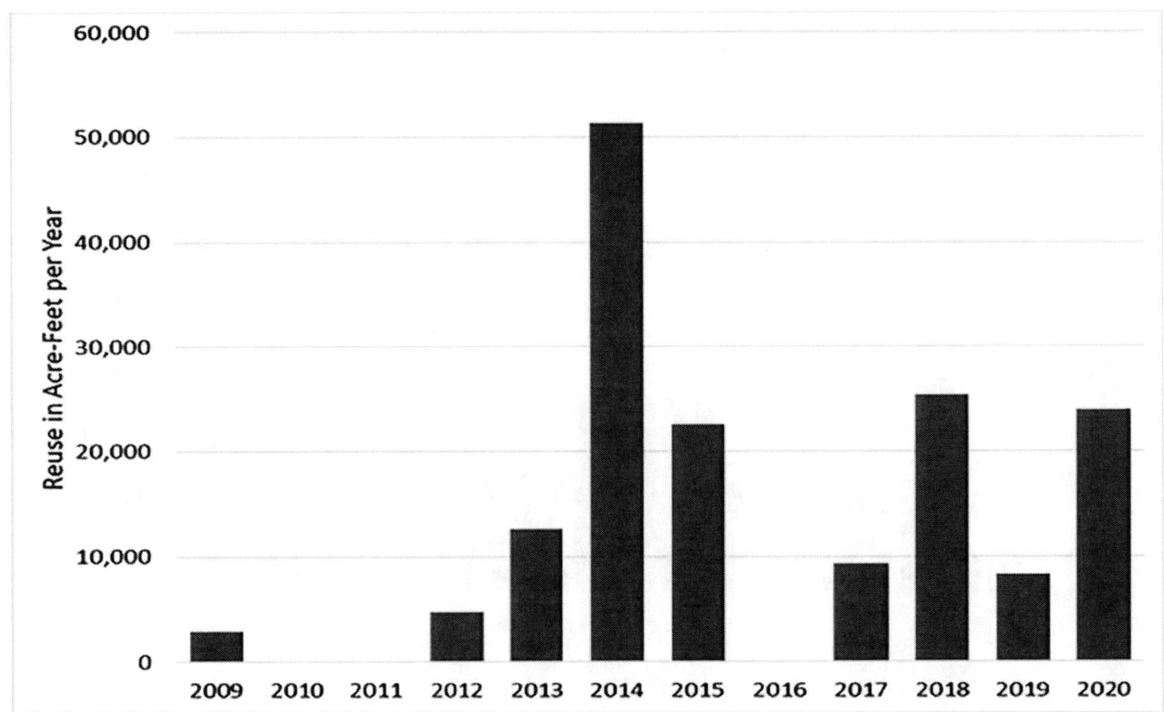

Figure 4. Tarrant Regional Water District historical reuse, 2009–2020. Data provided by Samantha Drumm, TRWD, via email to authors (Feb. 3, 2017); by Rachel Ickert, TRWD, via email to authors (Jan. 16, 2019); and by Nicole Rutigliano, TRWD, via email to authors (Feb. 3, 2021).

§ 24.31 Reuse in the Houston Area—Permit Nos. 5809 and 5827

Reuse has been increasingly developed as a source of water supply in the Houston area over the past decade, with several direct and indirect reuse projects developed by cities, utility districts, and industrial facilities. The largest existing Houston-area reuse project is the San Jacinto River Authority (SJRA) indirect reuse project (see Permit No. 10-5809, available in the TCEQ Central Records), with maximum historical reuse of slightly over 5,000 acre-feet in 2014. The SJRA is authorized to reuse up to 14,944 acre-feet per year. Other recently granted major bed and banks transfer authorizations for indirect reuse are held by the city of Conroe and SJRA (11,200 acre-feet per year under Permit Nos. 10-12788 and 10-13183) and the city of Huntsville (4,593 acre-feet per year under Permit No. 10-12754) (see TCEQ Central Records for these permits).

In 2011, the city of Houston was granted the largest reuse water right in the state, authorizing indirect reuse of up to 580,923 acre-feet per year from thirty-two wastewater treatment plants, with a 2004 priority date. The permit includes requirements for environmental flows and restricts diversions to one-half of the water actually discharged from each wastewater plant. Because of the large population in the Houston area and the resulting large wastewater discharges, reuse could become a major water supply in the area. The Region H 2021 Regional Water Plan addresses the Houston area and calls for the development of over 400,000 acre-feet of new supplies from reuse. *See* Region H Water Planning Group, *2021 Regional Water Plan* (Oct. 2020), available at www.twdb.texas.gov/waterplanning/rwp/plans/2021. The largest reuse projects recommended in the Region H plan include the following:

- development of the city of Houston indirect reuse permit (about 240,000 acre-feet per year);
- development of a San Jacinto Basin Regional Return Flows Project (about 120,000 acre-feet per year);
- development of wastewater reclamation for municipal irrigation (about 20,000 acre-feet per year); and
- development of a reuse supply for Galveston County industries (about 22,000 acre-feet per year).

§ 24.32 Colorado River Municipal Water District Big Spring Direct Potable Reuse Project

In 2013, the Colorado River Municipal Water District (CRMWD) began operating the first DPR water supply in the United States. The project was one of several water supply strategies developed in response to a long-term drought in the district's service area that had greatly reduced the supply available from its surface water supply reservoirs. In 2004, the CRMWD was seven years into a severe drought and began a feasibility study of DPR as a supplemental supply. Investigating reuse of effluent from Odessa, Midland, Big Spring, and Snyder, the CRMWD found it to be feasible and proceeded with the Big Spring project. The preliminary design for the project was completed in 2007, five qualified membrane manufacturers were invited to participate in pilot testing, and two manufacturers successfully completed pilot tests. The final design was completed in 2010, and construction was completed in 2013. *See* Sloan Presentation.

Figure 5 is a schematic illustration of the treatment process for the facility. Following the standard wastewater treatment process shown in the top portion of Figure 5, treated effluent is conveyed through membrane filtration, reverse osmosis, and ultraviolet oxidation for additional treatment before being blended with other raw water in the CRMWD's forty-two-inch raw water pipeline. The purified water from the project is limited to a maximum of 50 percent of the pipeline flow. The blended raw water then flows through standard water treatment processes at the water treatment plants for the CRMWD's customers, as shown at the bottom of Figure 5. *See* Sloan Presentation.

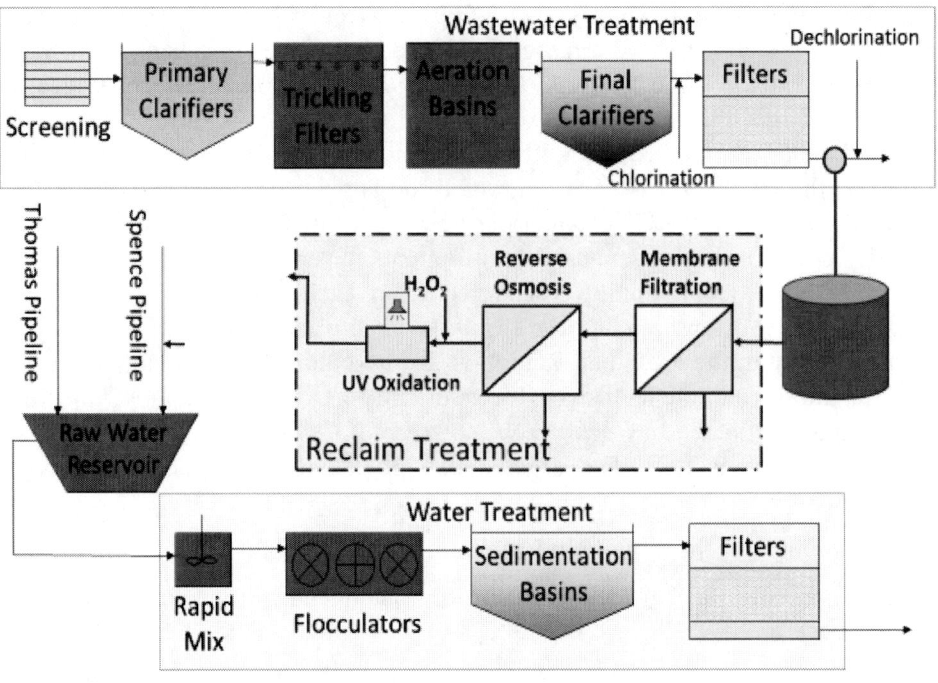

Figure 5. Schematic diagram, direct potable reuse for Big Spring Wastewater, Colorado River Municipal Water District. Image created by David Sloan.

Because the CRMWD's Big Spring DPR project was the first of its kind, the TCEQ did not have explicit rules or a process for review and approval of the project pursuant to its obligations under the SDWA. The TCEQ decided to review the project under its source water approval authority. Review and approval required the following steps:

- review of pilot study protocol and report;
- review of plans and specifications;
- inspection and monitoring of facilities as a public water source;
- notification of receiving water suppliers;
- description of the source in consumer confidence reports;
- continuous monitoring of effluent quality;
- turbidity and chlorine residual requirements;
- direct and indirect monitoring of membrane integrity;
- return of out-of-specification water to the wastewater plant;
- testing and documentation of fail-safe provisions;
- verification of finished water quality for SDWA requirements and pathogens; and

- two-day special inspection following start-up.

See Sloan Presentation. The reuse facility has a maximum capacity of 2.5 MGD. Figure 6 shows the reuse supply made available from the project since it began operation in 2013.

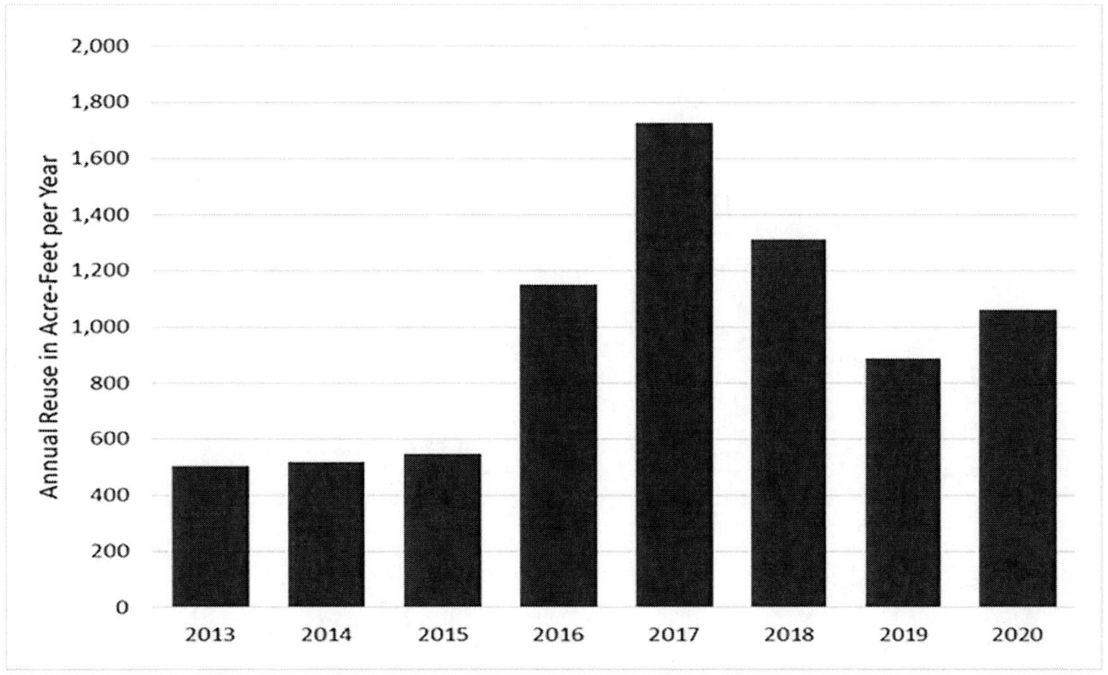

Figure 6. Colorado River Municipal Water District historical reuse, 2013–2020. Data provided by John Womack, CRMWD, via emails to authors (Feb. 14, 2017, Jan. 21, 2019, and Feb. 3, 2021).

§ 24.33 Wichita Falls Direct Potable Reuse Project

Wichita Falls experienced extreme drought conditions from 2010 through 2015. Despite dramatic water conservation efforts that reduced water use from 35 MGD to 11 MGD, the city's three water supply reservoirs fell below 25 percent content in 2014. In April 2012, the city began planning an emergency DPR project in response to the ongoing drought. The city's River Road Wastewater Treatment Plant was discharging 7.5 MGD (down from an average of 12 MGD before the drought). The plan was to pump 7.5 MGD of treated wastewater in a twelve-mile pipeline from the River Road Wastewater Plant to an existing desalination treatment plant at the Cypress Water Treatment Facility. (The desalination plant was not being operated because drought conditions had made the usual source water too salty for treatment.) Personal communication from Russell Schreiber, Director of Public Works, City of Wichita Falls.

The treated wastewater was run through a clarifier, microfiltration, and reverse osmosis filtration at the Cypress Facility. This process yielded 5 MGD of treated permeate, with 2.5 MGD of concentrate discharged to the Wichita River. The purified treated wastewater was then blended with at least an equal amount of raw water from other sources, then treated through a conventional plant at the Cypress Water Treatment Facility and sent to Wichita Falls' treated water distribution system. Figure 7 shows the DPR treatment processes at the Cypress Water Treatment Facility.

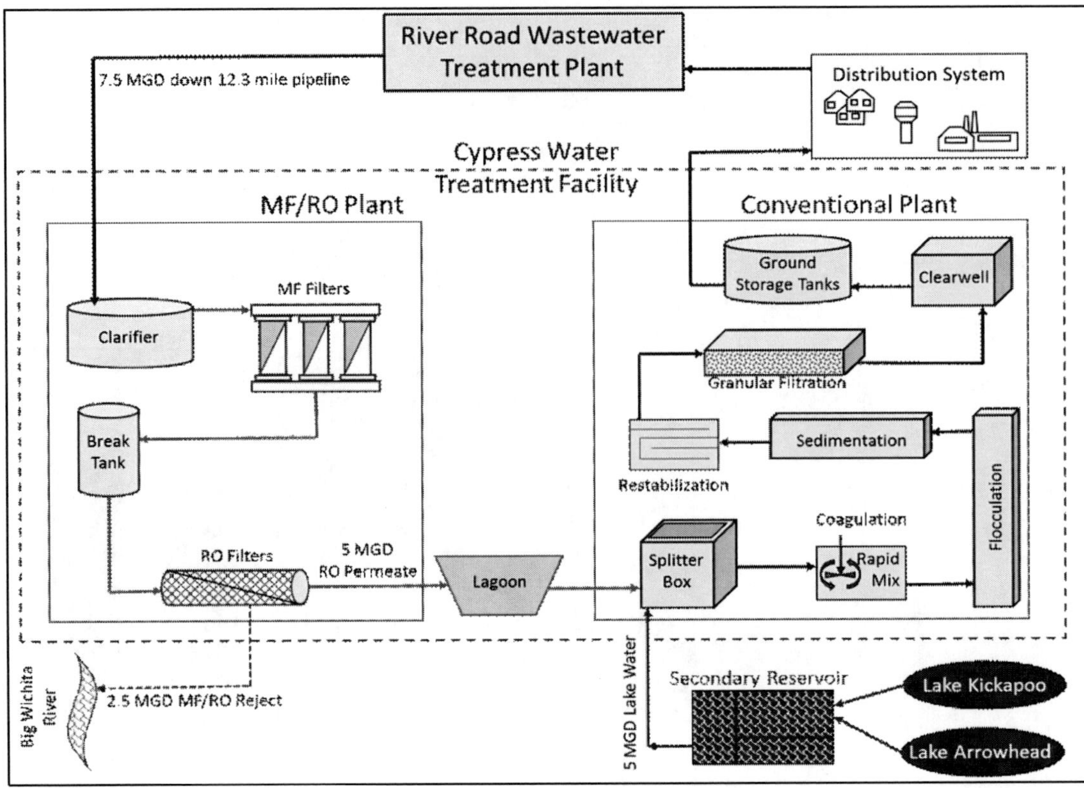

Figure 7. Schematic diagram, direct potable reuse treatment at the Cypress Water Treatment Facility, Wichita Falls. Image created by City of Wichita Falls staff.

Wichita Falls began construction of the emergency reuse project in August 2013 and received approval for the project from the TCEQ in September 2013. Full-scale verification testing began in January 2014, and DPR began July 9, 2014. The project operated for about a year, supplying 5,461 acre-feet of water for use by the city's customers. The emergency direct reuse project ended when Wichita Falls' lakes refilled, effectively ending the drought. Figure 8 shows the monthly supply from the emergency reuse project.

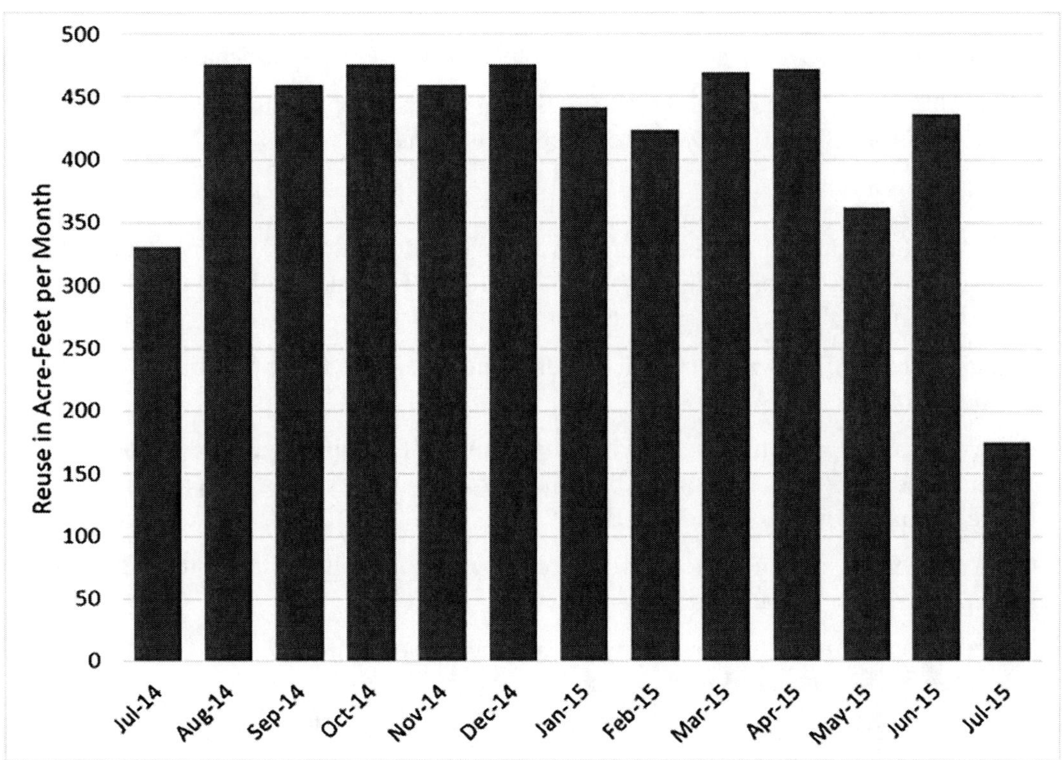

Figure 8. Wichita Falls emergency direct reuse project. Data provided by Russell Schreiber, City of Wichita Falls, via email to authors (Jan. 30, 2017).

The drought emergency was well understood by the public in Wichita Falls since outdoor water use was prohibited and stringent emergency demand reduction measures were in place. Wichita Falls sought support for the emergency reuse project from its wholesale customers, the Health Board, and the local Health Coalition. The city also maintained continuous coordination on conservation and reuse with local media and engaged with a group of doctors and scientists to understand and support the reuse project.

Once the drought ended, Wichita Falls began developing a permanent indirect reuse project through Lake Arrowhead, one of its principal water supply reservoirs. This $29 million project is expected to supply 8 to 10 MGD of water and was completed in 2018. Wichita Falls has received an indirect reuse water right for this project.

§ 24.34 The Brazos River Authority System Operation Permit—Permit No. 5851

In 2004, the Brazos River Authority (BRA) filed an application for a System Operation (SysOps) Permit allowing system operation of the Authority's reservoirs and unappropriated water in the Brazos Basin. The unappropriated water sought in the permit included return flows of treated wastewater. After two contested case hearings, the TCEQ issued the SysOps permit, TCEQ Water Use Permit No. 5851, in 2016, and a district court upheld the permit's issuance in 2018. The permit is final and nonappealable.

The treatment of return flows was one of the major issues considered in the hearings on the BRA SysOps permit and has been described as "the most complex portion of the most complex water right application ever filed with the TCEQ." Proposal for Decision on Remand, at 215, TCEQ Docket No. 2005-1490-WR; SOAH Docket No. 582-10-4184 (July 17, 2015) [hereinafter Proposal for Decision].

The decisions made on return flows in this case indicate the current TCEQ position on many of the issues involved in permitting indirect reuse.

In the BRA SysOps permit water right case, return flows were divided into two classes:

- BRA return flows, which are return flows from water supplied under BRA water rights and discharges from BRA wastewater treatment plants, and
- return flows of others.

The BRA argued that both classes of return flows should be treated as state water available for appropriation under Texas Water Code subsection 11.046(c). The final Proposal for Decision indicates that—

> if discharged return flows were treated as state water available for appropriation, the results would be as follows:
>
> - Once discharged, all return flows would be available for appropriation pursuant to Texas Water Code section 11.046(c) for beneficial use by any existing water right holder or future appropriator.
> - Once discharged, all return flows would be subject to established rules regarding the use and appropriation of state water.
> - To the extent return flows make up part of a new appropriation, return flows would be subject to environmental flow requirements.
> - The appropriation of current return flows would be permitted only to the extent they are available as unappropriated water after meeting the needs of all senior water rights.

Proposal for Decision on Remand, at 215–16.

The executive director of the TCEQ disagreed with the BRA's approach and proposed that the BRA should be able to obtain a bed and banks authorization for the BRA's own return flows but should not be able to appropriate the return flows of others. The Proposal for Decision issued provided that—

> under the ED's approach, use of return flows would be implemented as follows:
>
> - A Texas Water Code section 11.042(c) bed and banks authorization for indirect reuse could be obtained by the holder of the base water right, the owner or operator of the wastewater treatment facility, or a third party with contractual right from either of them.
> - The authorization, while not considered an appropriation, would be given the priority date of the application insofar as it applies to historically discharged return flows to protect existing rights.
> - Historically discharged return flows would be subject to environmental flow and beneficial inflow requirements.
> - Discharges in excess of historically discharged amounts would not be subject to call by senior water rights and would have no environmental flow requirements.
> - The maximum bed and banks authorization would be limited to the current TPDES permitted discharge amount. Any increase in the TCEQ permitted discharge would necessitate an amendment of the bed and banks permit to authorize use of the increased volume.

Proposal for Decision, at 216.

The TCEQ eventually adopted an approach to return flows that differed from both the BRA's and the executive director's positions. Major elements of the final permit's treatment of return flows include the following:

- Return flows, once returned to a state watercourse, are unappropriated flows available for appropriation.
- The permit is based only on historically discharged return flows, and potential future return flows are not appropriated. Many previous reuse water rights were based on TPDES-permitted wastewater discharges, which generally exceed historical discharges.
- The BRA's indirect reuse of its own return flows is treated as a bed and banks authorization and a new appropriation and is thus subject to environmental flow requirements and calls from senior water rights.
- The BRA's use of return flows of others can be interrupted by direct reuse and terminated by indirect reuse upon issuance of a bed and banks permit to the discharging entity. *See* BRA SysOps permit, at 9–12.

The BRA SysOps permit authorized the reuse of 47,332 acre-feet per year of the BRA's return flows and 50,076 acre-feet per year of the return flows of others.

VII. The Future of Reuse in Texas

§ 24.35 Decreasing Per Capita Return Flows

Municipal return flows of treated wastewater are a great resource for Texas, and in recent decades reuse projects have enabled water suppliers in the state to increase the use of that resource. At the same time, as the population of the state has been increasing, wastewater flows have not increased proportionally. For example, Figure 9 shows the total discharges from major Dallas–Fort Worth area wastewater treatment plants from 2000 through 2018, generated from data collected by the EPA, the TCEQ, and wastewater treatment plant operators. The graph shows a relatively flat pattern of discharges, varying year to year and higher in wetter years. Yet, over these eighteen years, the population of the area served by these plants increased by over 40 percent. Per capita return flows have declined markedly in recent years. The same pattern has been seen in other areas of the state. The primary cause of this change has probably been the decrease in indoor water use in the United States caused by using low-flow plumbing fixtures (toilets and showers) and low-water-use appliances. A recent Water Research Foundation report showed a decrease of 15 percent in per capita indoor water use between 1999 and 2016. Water Research Foundation, *Residential End Uses of Water, Version 2: Executive Report* 8 (Apr. 2016), www.circleofblue.org/wp-content/uploads/2016/04/WRF_REU2016.pdf [hereinafter Water Research Foundation Report]. Since indoor water use is what is primarily discharged to wastewater collection and treatment systems following use, this decrease could be tied to the decrease in per capita wastewater flow that has occurred. At the same time, increased attention to improving wastewater collection systems has decreased infiltration and inflow, further reducing wastewater discharges.

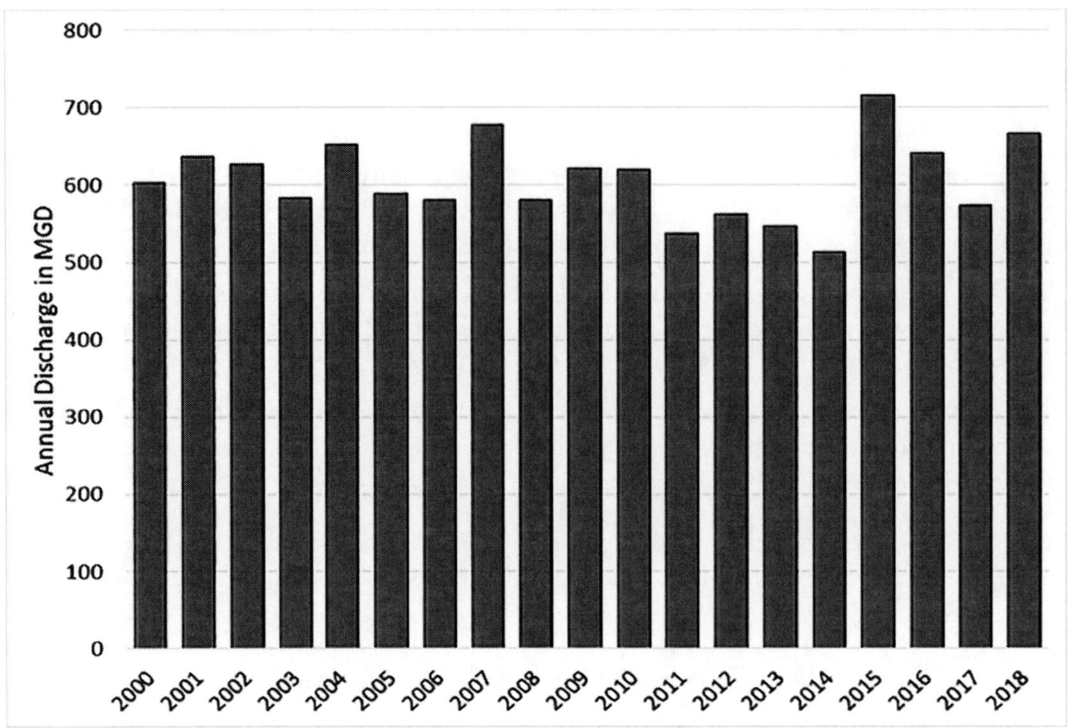

Figure 9. Historical discharge from major Dallas–Fort Worth area wastewater plants, 2000–2018. Data obtained from the TCEQ, EPA records, and discharge records of major wastewater plant operators in the Dallas–Fort Worth area and compiled by Freese and Nichols, Inc.

This trend of reducing indoor water use is likely to continue. The Water Research Foundation report showed modern houses with current low-flow plumbing and low-water-use appliances use about 35 percent less water than the average house in 2016. Water Research Foundation Report, at 10. As more homes are built with modern plumbing and appliances, per capita indoor use will continue to drop. The current emphasis on decreasing sanitary sewer overflows of untreated wastewater will require continued improvements to wastewater collection systems. Dry-year return flows should not be expected to increase substantially in the near term over much of the state.

§ 24.36 Reuse in State and Regional Water Plans

Figure 10 shows planned reuse supplies from the 2021 Regional Water Plans (TWDB DB22). Existing water reuse projects are projected to supply 620,000 acre-feet per year in 2020. With increasing return flows feeding existing projects and the development of new projects, the plans project reuse supplies to more than triple to 2.15 million acre-feet by 2070. Most of the planned reuse is in major metropolitan areas, with three quarters of the reuse planned for 2070 in four planning regions: Region C (Dallas–Fort Worth, 37 percent of state total), Region H (Houston, 31 percent), Region K (Austin, 12 percent), and Region L (San Antonio, 8 percent). TWDB DB22.

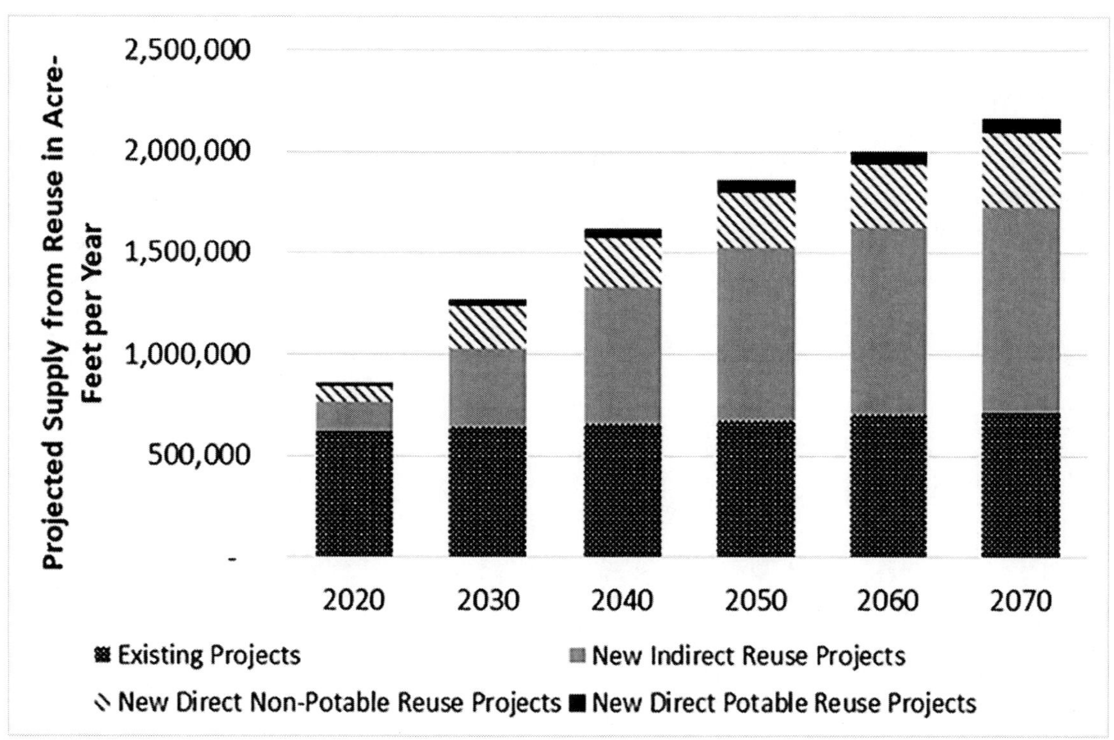

Figure 10. 2020 Regional Water Plan planned supplies from reuse. Data obtained from Texas Water Development Board DB22 database of 2021 regional water plan data, provided to authors.

Major new reuse projects in the 2021 Regional Water Plans include:

- development of indirect reuse projects from city of Houston return flows (multiple projects, Region H, 240,000 acre-feet per year by 2070);
- development of indirect reuse projects for Dallas (Main Stem Pump Station and Main Stem Balancing Reservoir, Region C, 158,000 acre-feet per year by 2070);
- development of indirect reuse supplies in the San Jacinto Basin (Region H, over 120,000 acre-feet per year by 2070);
- development of Tarrant Regional Water District (TRWD) Cedar Creek Reuse Project (Region C, 88,000 acre-feet per year by 2070);
- development of indirect reuse from Austin return flows (Region K, 78,000 acre-feet per year by 2070);
- additional reuse by North Texas Municipal Water District (Region C, 76,000 acre-feet per year by 2070);
- TRWD reuse from the TRA Central Wastewater Treatment Plant (Region C, 60,000 acre-feet per year by 2070);
- development of City Public Service of San Antonio direct reuse (Region L, 50,000 acre-feet per year by 2070); and
- development of additional direct reuse projects for San Antonio Water System (Region L, 40,000 acre-feet per year by 2070).

TWDB DB22.

§ 24.37 Beyond Planned Projects

In each round of regional water planning completed so far, new reuse projects have been recommended and the total supply from reuse has increased. It is virtually certain that new reuse projects, not included in the 2021 Regional Water Plans, will be planned and developed in the future. Reuse will be an increasing source of supply in Texas, limited only by the return flow available for reuse, environmental considerations, and the economics of project development.

CHAPTER 25

Desalination for Texas: A Water-Rich Future

Carolyn Ahrens,[1] Joseph W. Norris, P.E.,[2] and Justin Sutherland[3]

I. Introduction

§ 25.1 Chapter Overview

Making unusable, mineralized water newly "fresh" or "sweet" through desalination is vital to a water-rich future for Texas as the state's growing population increases the pressure on more traditional but limited resources. Desalinating inland brackish surface water, marine and other seawater, and produced and other brackish groundwater can yield dependable water supplies while also indirectly extending the usefulness of naturally freshwater reserves and delaying or replacing the need for supply strategies that have more significant environmental impacts. Using mineralized source water is the best option available for satisfying some water supply demands now, particularly considering that

---

1. Carolyn Ahrens is of counsel to Booth & Associates, P.C. in Austin, Texas, focusing on obtaining, defending, and securing the water rights and supplies of the firm's clients through traditional and nontraditional permitting and contracting strategies and legislation. Ms. Ahrens is a leader in numerous professional associations focused on water resources and is positioned to work effectively toward intergovernmental, regional, and statewide solutions to water supply challenges. Among other industry awards, she has twice received the prestigious Texas Water Conservation Association President's Award for "outstanding dedication, contribution and service to the water resources of the State of Texas," as well as the President's Award from the national Water Reuse Association for "dedication, passion and vision," the Arthur Sidney Bedell Award from the Water Environment Federation, and two Watermark awards for raising the public's level of understanding of Texas water issues.

2. Joseph William Norris, P.E., has over thirty-five years' experience in the planning, design, and project management, construction, and operations of municipal and industrial desalination facilities. Mr. Norris has been involved in the research and application of advanced treatment methods of potable and reclaimed water and has been instrumental in the expansion of brackish groundwater desalination in Texas. Several of his desalination projects have been awarded honors from around the world. He is a life member of American Water Works Association and a member of the Texas Water Conservation Association, National Society of Professional Engineers, and Texas Society of Professional Engineers and served as a director of the American Membrane Technology Association and founding member of the South Central Membrane Association. He currently serves as president of the Texas Desalination Association.

3. Dr. Justin Sutherland is a Chief Technologist with Carollo Engineers, Inc., and a licensed professional engineer in Texas. He has twenty-two years' experience in water quality assessments, applied drinking water research, and design work, including ion exchange, desalination, water reuse applications, and produced water treatment. Dr. Sutherland earned a BS in chemical engineering, MS in environmental engineering, and PhD in civil engineering, all from the Missouri University of Science and Technology. He currently serves on the board of directors for the South Central Membrane Association and is the incoming president of the Texas Desalination Association (TDA).

desalination treatment systems are becoming increasingly cost effective. The contribution of desalination on a broader scale to sustain Texas's population and its vibrant economy is expected to increase in the decades ahead because of state support and a friendly regulatory framework, continuing technological advances in treatment and concentrate management, and vast sources of raw supply.

In this chapter, the term "desalination" refers to strategies for applying water to a first beneficial use after reducing the water's dissolved solids content to achieve a quality suitable for its intended purpose. Although in a sense all water has been used before, limiting the working definition to "first use" clarifies that this chapter's scope does not include wastewater reuse (otherwise addressed in Chapter 24 of this book), treatment of water produced incidentally in oil and gas operations for reuse in those operations for fracking and other purposes (see Chapter 41), or satisfaction of water quality standards for discharging wastewater (as discussed in Chapter 34), even though the same or similar treatment processes may be employed in those efforts. Federal requirements related to water supply projects generally are excluded as well, reserving focus for issues directly specific to desalination strategies.

Part II introduces desalination by reference to the origin of mineralized water in Texas and through historical context, considering that Texas both benefits from and contributes to the development of desalination globally. Among more recent accomplishments, Texas can point proudly in the state to—

- the largest inland brackish desalination facility in the northern hemisphere, the Kay Bailey Hutchison Brackish Groundwater Desalination Plant in El Paso;
- San Antonio Water System's innovative project design that colocates brackish groundwater desalination and on-site research facilities with aquifer storage and recovery (ASR) and fresh groundwater production;
- a ground-breaking enterprise for monetizing concentrated minerals separated from water in the desalination process; and
- a new legislatively created consortium for accelerating the advanced treatment of produced water for beneficial use.

Case studies in this chapter highlight the story of desalination in Texas through some of these projects and others, each of which contributes to a worldwide body of knowledge regarding the technical feasibility and cost effectiveness of producing high quality water supplies through desalination.

Part III addresses the legal framework for using inland surface water, marine and other seawater, and groundwater as water resources suitable for desalination. Legislative initiatives to facilitate broader implementation of desalination are included through the 2021 Texas legislative session. Regulatory criteria implemented by the Texas Commission on Environmental Quality (TCEQ) also are addressed, as are related initiatives implemented by the Texas Parks and Wildlife Department (TPWD) and the General Land Office of Texas (GLO). Citations are provided to facilitate independent legal research into water rights for desalination.

Water quality, design, and treatment process issues are the focus of part IV of this chapter. The viability of desalination to meet current and future demands has greatly improved with familiarity and advances in technology in each of these areas. What was considered "innovative" a decade ago may be "standard" today. Technical drivers are introduced through discussion of intake, pretreatment, treatment, and posttreatment steps. Posttreatment issues are critical because applying desalination treatment techniques to separate mineral constituents from source water (also referred to as feed water) results in a stream of both high quality, usable water and of highly mineralized liquid that sometimes is referred to as "reject," "brine," "residuals," or, in this chapter, "concentrate." The recent attention to commercialization of highly treated produced water using desalination technologies as an alternative to disposal or reuse in oil and gas operations bridges the issues of disposal and beneficial use in ways that are very promising for the future water supply in Texas.

For any water supply project, considerations regarding the quantity and quality of the supply are related to issues of cost. The legal availability of source water and enhanced sustainability are commonly recognized as advantages of desalination projects, while concentrate disposal issues remain one of the most significant concerns. Costs are sometimes viewed as a drawback, but many desalination projects have proved to be less costly than alternative options. How to identify and weigh advantages and challenges and mitigate risk, when determining whether desalination is practical for satisfying particular water needs for municipal, manufacturing, and other industrial purposes, is the focus of part V.

Part VI brings together state policy and projections for desalination with an emphasis on information resources. The Texas Water Development Board's (TWDB) Biennial Report on the Future of Desalination in Texas is a significant resource, *The Future of Desalination in Texas: 2020 Biennial Report on Seawater and Brackish Groundwater Desalination, (Report to the 87th Texas Legislature, Dec. 1, 2020)*, www.twdb.texas.gov/innovativewater/desal/docs.asp [hereinafter the Biennial Report]. This report catalogs both the state's successes with desalination and the existing research, regulatory, technical, and financial impediments to further development. The Texas State Water Plan is another significant resource for desalination information, as it reflects regional decisions about desalination strategies to meet current and future water needs. Texas' statewide water planning process, including the most recent plan update in 2022, is the focus of Chapter 20. The Biennial Report, the Texas State Water Plan, and other information resources for desalination are listed at the end of the chapter.

The chapter concludes that desalination strategies have earned their place in Texas's water supply portfolio and will continue to have an important role in building resilience against periodic drought.

II. Mineralized Water in Texas and Advancing Usability

§ 25.2 Mineralized Water in Texas

Geological phenomena in Texas's distant past included shallow seas that covered some regions and evaporated, leaving behind salt deposits. Salt can still be seen covering the ground in some areas of the state, and that salt washes from the land into streams, rivers, and other bodies of surface water. Seeps and springs sometimes bring mineralized groundwater to the surface where it either evaporates or contributes to watercourse salinity, completing a natural cycle. Anthropogenic (man-made) sources of salinity include water produced during oil and gas development, upflow through improperly abandoned or deteriorated wells, injection, and agricultural chemicals.

Total Dissolved Solids by the Numbers

The U.S. Environmental Protection Agency (EPA) secondary standards suggest that drinking water not exceed total dissolved solids (TDS) of 500 milligrams per liter (mg/L). Texas's enforceable secondary drinking water standards set a limit of 1,000 mg/L, with levels in the higher range still being safe but with possible taste or hardness issues.

Water is considered brackish when it contains dissolved solids in the range of 1,000 to 10,000 mg/L. Brackish groundwater and inland surface water may be classified further as slightly saline (1,000–2,999 mg/L), moderately saline (3,000–9,999 mg/L), and saline (greater than 10,000 mg/L). For comparison, seawater usually contains 25,000 to 40,000 mg/L of TDS. Actual values for seawater and estuarine waters are site-specific, varying seasonally and with freshwater inflow levels.

Desalination concentrates may range from 4,000 mg/L to greater than 35,000 mg/L, depending on the source water quality and treatment system design. *See, e.g.*, Texas Water Development Board, *Brackish FAQs*, www.twdb.texas.gov/innovativewater/desal/faqbrackish.asp.

Watercourses approaching an interface with seawater may also be affected periodically by saltwater intrusion, particularly during drought when freshwater flows may be unavailable to push back saltier waters. For marine and other seawater desalination, however, Texas benefits from its prime location on the nation's "third coast," with seemingly limitless raw water and disposal capacity available in the Gulf of Mexico. In reality, salinity in gulf waters varies by proximity to the shore, and there are important environmental considerations related to the location of off-coast diversions for desalination and facilities for concentrate disposal.

Shallow seas of the past and the natural dissolving of minerals as water percolates through an aquifer have also affected Texas groundwater. Some groundwater reserves are highly mineralized in comparison to freshwater aquifers. Groundwater with 1,000 to 10,000 mg/L of dissolved salts is commonly referred to as "brackish." Brackish groundwater reserves may be delineated by the confining layers of a geologic formation or may be relatively unconfined and identified by a "distinct water line" that more or less separates water with higher mineral concentrations from fresher supplies by density. Along the Texas coastline, groundwater having an interface with seawater may also be affected by the seawater's higher salinity. According to the Biennial Report, Texas is estimated to have more than 2.7 billion acre-feet (AF) of brackish groundwater available in twenty-six of its major and minor aquifers. *See* the Biennial Report, at 7. For comparison, total annual usage of groundwater in Texas from all sources in 2015 was roughly seven million AF while only another 8.9 million AF of water are available each year from surface water reservoirs. *See* Texas Water Development Board, *Groundwater Conservation Districts and Groundwater Management Plan FAQs*, www.twdb.texas.gov/groundwater/faq/index.asp; Texas Water Development Board, *Texas Lakes & Reservoirs*, www.twdb.texas.gov/surfacewater/rivers/reservoirs/index.asp.

§ 25.3 The Texas Connection to Early Development of Desalination

Texas's historic drought of the 1950s demonstrated in harsh terms the human and economic necessities of freshwater and the need to increase supply reliability in the state. Major reservoir construction was an obvious water supply solution during the several decades that followed, counting on rain to fill and then refill new storage capacity. The drought of the 1950s also accelerated the development of desalination technology as a more immediate solution. The value of desalination had already been recognized at the federal level during World War II, when ships and submarines for battle were outfitted for small-scale seawater purification. Of course, the concept of freshening seawater was far from new even then, and there are much older records related to usable techniques, but larger scale desalination for drinking and industrial purposes was about to step forward on a national and international scale. *See* Arturo Buenaventura, *A Short History of Desalination*, www.theenergyofchange.com/short-history-of-desalination.

As the drought that was already ravaging Texas continued to expand across other states, Congress passed the Saline Water Conversion Act in 1952 to provide federal support for desalination research and development. *See* Saline Water Conversion Act, Pub. L. No. 82-448, 66 Stat. 328 (1952), *as amended by* Act of June 29, 1955, 69 Stat. 198; Act of June 24, 1967, 81 Stat. 78; *see also* Saline Water Conversion Act of 1971, Pub. L. No. 92-60, 85 Stat. 159 (1971) (repealing the 1952 act). The Office of Saline Water was created within the Department of Interior in 1955, and federal funding for desalination multiplied. One source recounts that the office was tasked with opening five demonstration desalination plants around the country: "Each plant would be built in a different region (those not near the coast would draw brackish water from the ground), and each would use a different technology; the most efficient and successful plant would, it was hoped, pave the way for dozens more like it." Jacob Roberts & Kenton G. Jaehnig, *Nor Any Drop to Drink*, *Distillations* (Nov. 12, 2018), www.sciencehistory.org/distillations/magazine/nor-any-drop-to-drink.

When President John F. Kennedy participated in the dedication of the nation's first demonstration desalination facility at Freeport, Texas, in 1961, his remarks described making freshwater from salt water as one of mankind's oldest dreams. Having previously delivered a special message to Congress outlining the federal programs to address the nation's drinking water crisis, his remarks promised to share the information that the United States developed with the world. He continued, "This is a work which in many ways is more important than any other scientific enterprise in which this country is now engaged." *See* John F. Kennedy Presidential Library and Museum, Archives, *Remarks upon Activating by Remote Control the Saline Water Conversion Plant at Freeport Texas, 21 June 1961*, www.jfklibrary.org/asset-viewer/archives/JFKWHA/1961/JFKWHA-040-003/JFKWHA-040-003.

Dateline June 21, 1961—Freeport, Texas

President John F. Kennedy pressed a switch installed in his office in Washington, D.C., to remotely dedicate the first practical plant for the conversion of seawater to drinking water. Vice President Lyndon Johnson attended the ceremony in person, in Freeport, Texas. As President Kennedy remarked, Vice President Johnson, being from Texas, had known throughout his life how important it was to secure freshwater.

Built by Dow Chemical Company in cooperation with the U.S. Department of the Interior, the Freeport facility was one of five government-planned pilot plants. It was constructed in less than a year and used a long-tube distillation process in a million-gallon-a-day operation. The 11,619 residents of Freeport had already begun drinking seawater on May 8, 1961. When the rains came again, the need for the Freeport facility to serve both industrial and municipal purposes subsided along with federal funding, and the plant ceased operation in 1969. Newsreel footage of President Kennedy's remarks, and of Vice President Johnson in Freeport, is available for viewing through the Texas Archive of the Moving Image at www.texasarchive.org/2014_01957. President Kennedy's remarks also were published in the *New York Times* on June 21, 1961, and are available at jfklibrary.org.

During the 1950s and 1960s, the United States government invested what today would be more than $2 billion in desalination research conducted through the Office of Saline Water. Reverse osmosis (RO) or membrane separation technology was perhaps the most notable innovation that emerged from this federal investment, usable in both seawater and brackish groundwater supply projects. Nevertheless, by the 1970s, the national imperative for desalination had dissipated, although federal efforts have continued primarily through the U.S. Bureau of Reclamation. That agency's work with

Sandia National Laboratories produced in 2003, for example, the *Desalination and Water Purification Technology Roadmap*, which continues to be a resource for scientists and engineers. *See* U.S. Department of Interior, Bureau of Reclamation & Sandia National Laboratories, *Desalination and Water Purification Technology Roadmap* (Jan. 2003), www.usbr.gov/research/dwpr/reportpdfs/report095.pdf.

Worldwide, desalination continued to gain momentum. According to the International Desalination Association, by June 2019 more than 20,000 desalination plants were contracted in 150 countries. The plants produce more than 95 million cubic meters per day, providing water for 300 million people. *See* International Desalination Association, *Dynamic Growth for Desalination and Water Reuse in 2019* (Feb. 18, 2019), https://idadesal.org/dynamic-growth-for-desalination-and-water-reuse-in-2019/.

Although seawater desalination has been slower to progress in the United States than President Kennedy likely imagined, two major seawater purification facilities are now operational, in Carlsbad, California, and Tampa Bay, Florida. Texas interests are positioning to host the next major seawater desalination plant in the nation.

Texas also took the lead in the most recent technological advance for inland desalination in the area of concentrate management innovated in conjunction with the Kay Bailey Hutchison Desalination Plant. Since the inception of desalination, the biggest issue facing inland projects has been the disposal of concentrate from the treatment process. Experts expect that while advances will continue for minimizing the disposal from desalination plants in general, the biggest advances likely will be in the recovery of minerals in that process for commercialization with little to no waste.

III. The Legal Availability of Source Water for Desalination

§ 25.4 Introduction

Key to determining the viability of any desalination project is whether source water is legally available for use. Legal availability in this sense refers to statutory and regulatory limitations that affect the quantity of water available on a reliable basis as well as how the right of use is secured procedurally. Each of three categories of source water for desalination are discussed below with regard to the legal availability of raw water for use: inland brackish surface water, marine and other seawater, and brackish groundwater.

§ 25.4:1 Desalination and Inland Surface Water Rights

Ownership and use rights relevant to surface water in Texas are defined in the broadest sense by the physical location of the water. Texas law declares state ownership of the water of the ordinary flow, underflow, and tides of every flowing river, natural stream, and lake and the storm water, floodwater, and rainwater of every river, natural stream, canyon, ravine, depression, and watershed in the state. *See* Tex. Water Code § 11.021(a). Water diffused and present on the land, not within any of the categories identified in section 11.021, belongs to the owner of the land where it occurs. Private water also may be collected in usable quantities, such as in gravel pits or ponds, as long as the water is contained without communication to a state watercourse. In such cases, the primary water legal availability question would be proving that the water is, indeed, private.

Using surface water that originates in state ownership implicates all the general state laws and regulations for appropriating and applying state water to a beneficial purpose. See Chapter 10 of this book. Those laws and regulations do not distinguish basic legal availability by reference to the mineral qualities of inland water or the necessity of using particular treatment strategies. This is not to imply that water quality is not relevant in water rights matters generally. If a proposed use of state water would have a detrimental impact on water quality, for example, there is a statutory basis for the TCEQ to deny an application to appropriate surface water altogether or to impose special conditions on use. *See* Tex. Water Code § 11.150.

Explicit but narrow legal connections between inland surface water use and desalination were created when Texas Water Code chapter 18 was adopted in 2015 and by amendment to section 11.122 in 2017. In both instances, the change in law applied after water had already been desalinated. Water Code section 18.004, and the TCEQ rules implementing chapter 18, enhanced the opportunity to use bed and banks conveyance, in flowing natural streams, lakes, reservoirs, or other impoundments, of desalinated marine seawater after treatment. The information to be included in an application for authorization to convey is similar to information required for other TCEQ bed and banks authorizations pursuant to Water Code section 11.042, and there are provisions for public notice and comment. However, unless the application to convey treated marine seawater requests authorization to convey through a reservoir or impoundment, public notice will state that no person may request a contested case hearing. *See generally* 30 Tex. Admin. Code §§ 295.305–.306, 297.210. The 2017 legislation was less direct by comparison, crafting an incentive for marine seawater desalination by changing the chapter 11 provisions for amending surface water rights in section 11.122.

Changes to section 11.122 over time have been intended to make the amendment process for surface water rights more favorable for redistributing permitted water supplies through purchase, or "water marketing." *See, e.g.*, Act of June 2, 1997, 75th Leg., R.S., ch. 1010, § 1.03 (S.B. 1). Relevant to desalination, Water Code section 11.122(b–1) was added in 2017 to give an advantage in the water rights amendment process to any surface water right holder that begins using treated seawater, thereby providing incentives for desalination projects indirectly. To better understand the connection made, consider that some of the state's oldest priority water rights and much of the state's population are centered near the Texas coast, while significant unmet future demand may be projected upstream. In one possible scenario, the development of alternative supply through desalination might free traditional surface water rights for sale to others, for different purposes of use in different areas of use. Section 11.122(b–1) states that, if enumerated criteria are met, "[a] holder of a water right that begins using desalinated seawater after acquiring the water right has a right to expedited consideration of an application for an amendment to the water right." Tex. Water Code § 11.122(b–1). Criteria include that the permit amendment relate to an amount of water that is equal to or less than the amount of desalinated seawater "used by" the applicant and that the water may not be transferred to another basin. *See* Tex. Water Code § 11.122(b–1)(2). Under the TCEQ rules implementing section 11.122(b–1), however, the agency may include special conditions in a permit, including a re-opener provision to mitigate adverse impacts on the availability of water for applications that were administratively complete prior to an application that triggered the expedited technical review. *See* 30 Tex. Admin. Code § 295.73.

Inland Surface Water Desalination

The Salt Fork of the Brazos River and other tributaries feed Lakes Possum Kingdom and Granbury, both permitted and adjudicated to the Brazos River Authority of Texas (BRA) pursuant to statutes now codified in chapter 11 of the Texas Water Code. The Brazos Regional Public Utility Agency employs desalination techniques at the Lake Granbury Surface Water and Treatment System (SWATS) to treat the water for regional needs. The plant currently has a finished water treatment capacity of 13 million gallons per day (MGD). To meet applicable drinking water standards, the current treatment train includes reverse osmosis for desalting.

The City of Granbury also diverts raw water from Lake Granbury that it purchases wholesale from the BRA. The city's newest treatment plant began operations using microfiltration/reverse osmosis technology when it went online in October 2017. The plant expanded the city's treated surface water capacity by more than 500 percent, and planning has already begun to double the treatment capability of the plant to 5 MGD. *See* Brazos River Authority, www.brazos.org/; City of Granbury, *Water Treatment Plant*, www.granbury.org/83/Water-Treatment-Plant.

§ 25.4:2 The Legal Availability of Marine and Other Seawater

Seawater (using the common meaning of the word) generally can be considered drought proof as a supply of raw water, although a lack of freshwater can affect the salinity of water near shore. The right to use water diverted from the Gulf of Mexico and affiliated waters is not determined based on whether water remains available for use by others, distinguishing the source legally from both inland surface water (where first in time is first in right, according to state law) and groundwater (where pumping has off-site effects on water levels, and local districts, in effect, apportion a common supply). This characteristic gives seawater desalination a significant relative advantage in terms of the legal availability of source water. The state does, however, claim ownership of seawater where it has jurisdiction, making usable seawater subject to the requirements of Texas Water Code chapter 11 and to regulation by the TCEQ. *See* 30 Tex. Admin. Code § 295.300(f).

Texas claims ownership to most surface water within its boundaries under Water Code section 11.021, and that provision also states that the waters of every bay or arm of the Gulf of Mexico are the property of the state. Water Code section 11.023(f) refers also to "inlets," where it provides, "[t]he water of any arm, inlet, or bay of the Gulf of Mexico may be changed from saltwater to sweet or freshwater and held or stored by dams, dikes, or other structures and may be taken or diverted for any purpose authorized by this chapter." Tex. Water Code § 11.023(f).

"Bays," "arms," and "inlets" are not defined geographically in Water Code chapter 11, and the seaward boundary of Texas jurisdiction in the Gulf of Mexico has been variously claimed over time according to statute and to judicial contests over seabed riches. Currently, the state's territorial waters extend nine nautical miles from shore, with federal programs applicable beyond that boundary. *See* Submerged Lands Act, Pub. L. No. 83-31, 67 Stat. 29 (1953) (codified at 43 U.S.C. §§ 1301–1315); *United States v. Louisiana*, 364 U.S. 502 (1960). To the extent questions regarding the state's reach for permitting desalination of seawater remained, they were mooted for all practical purposes by state legislation in 2015 and subsequent TCEQ rulemaking.

Focused in 2015 by drought and the anticipated inability of traditional firm water supplies to satisfy projected long-term water needs in the state, the Texas legislature enacted a number of bills to provide incentive for and facilitate the use of mineralized waters to serve as freshwater supplies through desalination. During the 84th legislative session House Bill 2031 was passed, adding Water Code chapter 18 to encourage the development of marine seawater desalination. *See* Act of May 29, 2015, 84th Leg., R.S., ch. 756, § 10 (H.B. 2031). Chapter 18 did not supplant chapter 11 for permitting the use of state water diverted from the Gulf of Mexico, but when there is a conflict between the two, chapter 18 controls. *See* Tex. Water Code § 18.002(b). In addition, House Bill 4097 was enacted, adding Water Code section 11.1405 to facilitate desalination of seawater for industrial purposes. *See* Act of May 23, 2015, 84th Leg., R.S., ch. 829, § 4 (H.B. 4097).

Together, House Bills 2031 and 4097 stand as a strong policy statement: the use of state water for desalination projects should be facilitated as to both time and cost but with due regard for potential environmental and other impacts. The key differences in the two bills were reconciled in the TCEQ implementing rules after extensive public comment. The rules adopted subchapters dedicated to desalination in both the agency's procedural and substantive rules sections for water rights. *See* 41 Tex. Reg. 9539 (Dec. 2, 2016) (rule adoption preamble); 30 Tex. Admin. Code ch. 295, subch. G; 30 Tex. Admin. Code ch. 297, subch. K.

To accommodate differences in the 2015 legislation, the rules distinguish between "marine seawater" and "seawater." The implementing regulations define "marine seawater" as any water that is derived from the Gulf of Mexico and "seawater" as water that is derived from a bay or arm of the Gulf of Mexico for desalination and use solely for industrial purposes. *See* 30 Tex. Admin. Code § 295.301(2), (3). In effect, any nonindustrial desalination diversion from a bay or estuary is subject to the general provisions of Water Code chapter 11.

Based on common language in both bills, section 295.300(a) of the TCEQ rules states that a person must obtain a permit to divert and use state water that consists of seawater or marine seawater if the point of diversion is less than three miles seaward of any point located on the coast *or* the seawater contains a TDS concentration of less than 20,000 mg/L. *See* 30 Tex. Admin. Code § 295.300(a). In the nature of a permitting exemption in subsection (b), a person may divert and use seawater without a permit if subsection 295.300(a) does not apply and if the requirements are met for demonstrating that the exemption applies. *See* 30 Tex. Admin. Code § 295.300(a).

When section 295.300(a) applies, permitting is expedited relative to permitting pursuant to Water Code chapter 11 generally. Expedited permitting is implemented through regulatory requirements that are intended to reduce the time and cost required to develop marine seawater desalination projects. Among other things for this purpose, the agency is expressly not required to make a finding of water availability when granting a permit for diversion and use of marine and other seawater, which reduces the burden of technical review and of processing permits by priority date. *See* 30Tex. Admin. Code § 297.203. See the discussion of water availability technical review in Chapter 10 of this book. Conservation planning and avoidance of waste still are required, as is consideration of beneficial use, the public welfare, consistency with environmental flow standards, enhanced protections against impingement and entrainment, and consistency with state and regional water supply planning. *See* 30 Tex. Admin. Code ch. 295, subch. G; ch. 297, subch. K. Unique to such applications is the requirement that evidence be provided that the water will be treated properly under agency rules applicable to the specified purpose of use. *See* 30Tex. Admin. Code § 295.302(f). TDS concentration data of the source water based on monthly sampling and analysis must also be provided in the application. *See* 30Tex. Admin. Code § 295.302(i). Although shortened review time frames are specified, notice and the opportunity for comment and contested case hearings still apply. *See* 30Tex. Admin. Code §§ 295.303–.304.

Unpredictability in the application of environmental considerations has historically been a cause of expense and delay during surface water rights permitting. Water Code chapter 18 addresses that concern by directing the TPWD and the GLO to study and identify zones in the Gulf of Mexico that are appropriate for the diversion of marine seawater, as well as for discharge of marine desalination waste, taking into account the need to protect marine organisms. To that end, an interagency work group was formed to develop the study. The work group included expertise on coastal ecosystems, marine fisheries, water resources and water quality, natural resources management, geographic information science, water quality permitting, and legal perspectives.

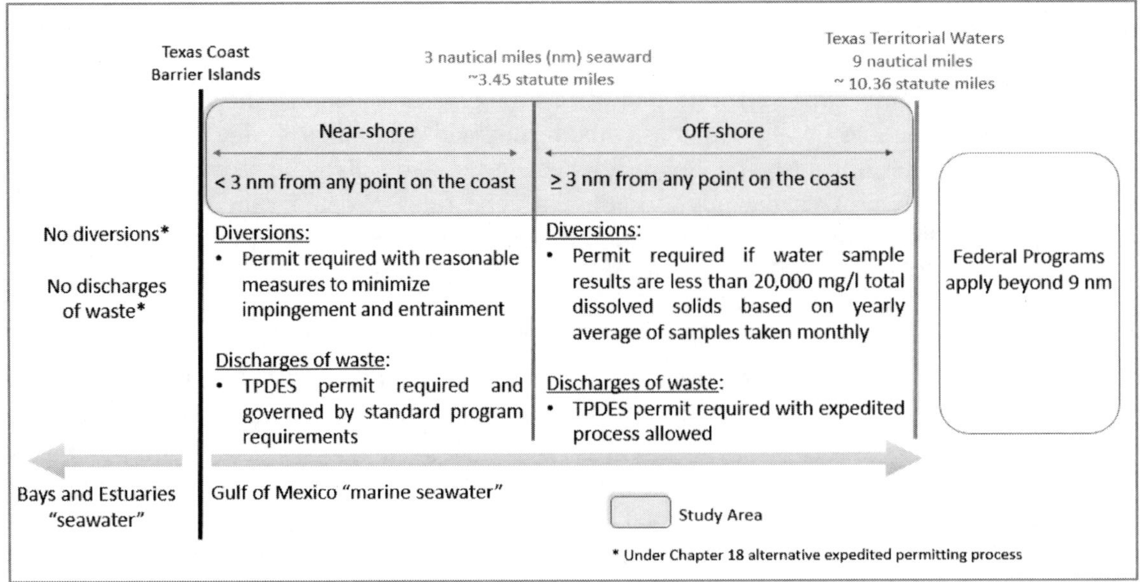

Figure 1. Illustration of the study area under Texas Water Code chapter 18. *See* Texas Parks and Wildlife Department & Texas General Land Office, *Marine Seawater Desalination Diversion and Discharge Zones Study* 5, fig.1 (2018), https://tpwd.texas.gov/publications/pwdpubs/media/hb2031dz.pdf.

The TPWD and GLO's first "Marine Seawater Desalination Diversion and Discharge Zones Study" was released in 2018. *See* Texas Parks and Wildlife Department & Texas General Land Office, *Marine Seawater Desalination Diversion and Discharge Zones Study* (Sept. 1, 2018), https://tpwd.texas.gov/publications/pwdpubs/media/hb2031dz.pdf; Figure 1. The study includes desalination zone maps for diversion and discharge areas and planning and design recommendations noting that detailed design specifications for any particular facility are beyond the scope of the report. Identifying practical limitations on their analyses and the dynamic nature of the Gulf of Mexico, the agencies also recommended that the maps be periodically updated and that the agencies monitor changes in nearshore and offshore submerged tracts to determine whether areas should be added or removed from the zones. For its part, the TCEQ was required to and did designate zones by rule, referencing the TPWD and GLO work. *See* House Bill 2031; Tex. Water Code § 18.003(j); 30 Tex. Admin. Code §§ 295.302, 297.202.

Although discussion of concentrate discharge is reserved for parts IV and V of this chapter, it is significant that the legislature addressed streamlining the regulatory process for discharge, as well as diversion, in the same 2015 desalination legislation. Specific marine seawater desalination permitting application forms available on the TCEQ's website bridge the issues of water rights and water quality permitting. *See* Texas Commission on Environmental Quality, *Instructions for Completing the Marine Seawater Desalination Permit Application* (Dec. 2016), www.tceq.texas.gov/assets/public/permitting/waterquality/forms/20775_20776_ins.pdf [hereinafter Seawater Desalination Permit Instructions].

Despite such procedural and regulatory advancements, the Biennial Report identifies the regulatory impediment for seawater desalination as being that permitting requirements are not yet "refined by practice." Biennial Report, at 11. As of the publication of this book, the first contested case for permitting discharge from a major seawater desalination project in Texas is pending before the TCEQ. *See* Application by Port of Corpus Christi Authority of Nueces County for Texas Pollutant Discharge Elimination System (TPDES) Permit No. WQ00052530001, SOAH Docket No. 582-20-1895; TCEQ Docket No. 2019-1156-IWD.

Although modern Texas desalination projects using marine or other seawater have been planned, initially permitted, and even demonstrated during the last decade, so far none have been pursued to full scale whether due to regulatory uncertainty or financial considerations. The state's desalination community has high expectations for the decade ahead.

§ 25.4:3 Authorizing the Use of Brackish Groundwater

The underground reserve of brackish water in Texas is a prolific raw water source for desalination. Brackish groundwater is, of course, groundwater. It is subject generally to all the judicial precedent, laws, and regulations related to owning and producing groundwater in Texas and to regulation by local districts, as detailed in Chapters 5 and 16 of this book. On a district-specific basis, and as allowed by Texas Water Code section 36.1086, districts in a groundwater management area may jointly conduct studies or research and implement projects to make groundwater available through desalination, among other things. *See* Tex. Water Code § 36.1086. Texas also can take advantage of brackish and saline groundwater formations for aquifer storage and recovery, as discussed in Chapter 26.

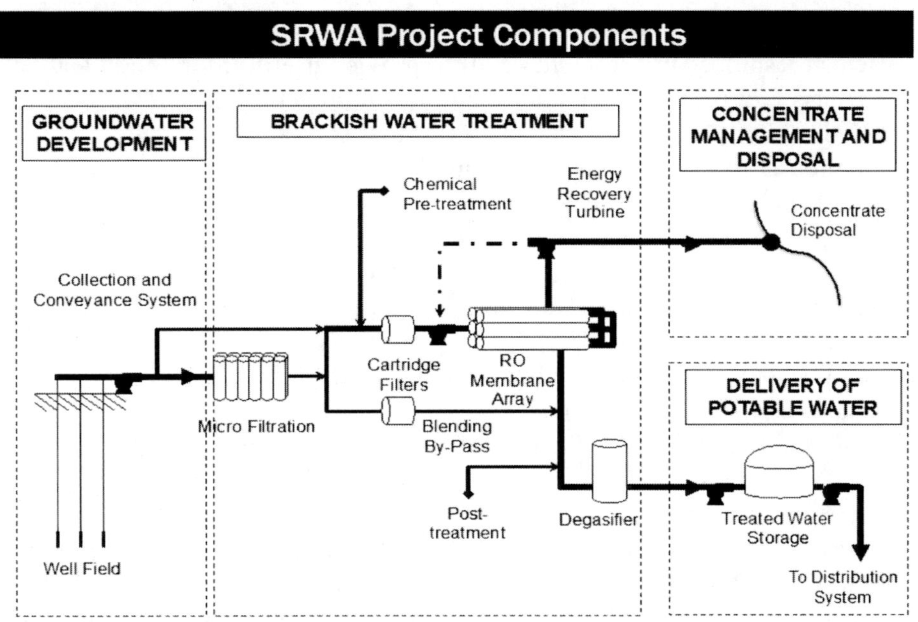

Figure 2. Southmost Regional Water Authority (SRWA) treatment process. The SRWA Plant was the first major brackish groundwater desalination plant in Texas, constructed in 2004 and expanded in 2015. The plant has a capacity of 11 MGD. The plant provides approximately 40 percent of the water demand for the Brownsville Public Utilities Board and is the regional provider for the Valley Municipal Utility District No. 1, City of Los Fresnos, Town of Indian Lake, and Port of Brownsville. Southmost Regional Water Authority, *Our Treatment Process*, http://srwadesal.com/water-treatment-plant/our-treatment-process/.

Where a local groundwater district has specific statutory authorization or rules that are specific to brackish groundwater formations within its jurisdiction, those rules will have been developed taking local characteristics into consideration and are best researched individually. A common challenge is the relative lack of historic information regarding the long-term effects of production. In general, however, such rules would likely define the brackish resource by either formation or mineral content and include provisions for monitoring potential impact on freshwater resources. Short permit terms and uncertainty about maintaining authorized production amounts would be particular impediments to financing desalination projects that require deeper and therefore more costly wells and more intensive treatment infrastructure. Development of brackish groundwater desalination also may face obstacles at the local level if development of desired future conditions (DFCs) does not distinguish between brackish and fresh groundwater resources. See Chapter 21 for an explanation of DFCs.

The dual circumstances of less historical development and competition for brackish groundwater, and the increased cost of infrastructure for development of the resource, have opened the door to special accommodations on a statewide level related to legal availability for use. As explained in 2015 by House Bill 30, the state encourages development of brackish groundwater in areas where that development would have a minimal impact on existing fresh groundwater use, while respecting private property rights and continuing the direct use of brackish groundwater as a replacement for freshwater applied to purposes other than human consumption. *See* Act of June 1, 2015, 84th Leg., R.S., ch. 990, § 1(d) (H.B. 30). The first step essential to facilitating brackish groundwater production is to advance understanding regarding the extent and characteristics of the resource on a broad scale, while brackish resources also continue to be investigated by local groundwater districts.

Although the mapping of Texas's saline water resources dates back to 1956, the TWDB began laying the modern foundation for specialized information resources with the creation in 2004 of its Brackish Groundwater Desalination Initiative. The goal of the initiative was to demonstrate the use of innovative and cost-effective desalination technologies and to offer realistic solutions to key challenges such as concentrate management and energy optimization. In 2009, the 81st Legislature funded the TWDB's Brackish Resources Aquifer Characterization System (BRACS) to map and characterize brackish resources in sufficient detail to provide useful information and data to regional water planning groups and other entities interested in using brackish groundwater as a water supply. By 2015, the drought conditions that focused the legislature on seawater desalination also drove policy forward for underground resources. H.B. 30 required the TWDB to designate brackish groundwater production zones in four aquifers by December 1, 2016, to determine the volumes of water that a brackish groundwater production zone could produce over thirty- and fifty-year periods, and to make recommendations on reasonable monitoring to observe the effect of brackish groundwater production within the zone. The TWDB was given an initial deadline of December 1, 2022, for designating brackish groundwater production zones in other parts of the state. Certain areas were excluded from zone designation altogether, including notably part of the Edwards Aquifer. *See* Act of June 1, 2015, 84th Leg., R.S., ch. 990, §§ 3, 4 (H.B. 30).

With significant opportunity for stakeholder participation, BRACS has performed as outlined in the 2020 Biennial Report. A discontinuation of appropriations in 2017 limited the TWDB's ability to comply fully with H.B. 30; however, appropriations were renewed subsequently, with support of the state's water interests. *See* Act of May 27, 2019, 86th Leg., R.S., ch. 1353, § 1, Rider 24 (H.B. 1), eff. Sept. 1, 2019. The TWDB is currently working toward a new deadline of December 1, 2032, for identifying and designating additional brackish groundwater production zones. *See* Act of May 17, 2019, 86th Leg., R.S., ch. 342, § 1 (S.B. 1041), eff. Sept. 1, 2019. As of December 2020, when the House Natural Resources Committee reported to the state's 87th legislative session, the TWDB has designated thirty-one brackish groundwater production zones with moderate to high availability, and productivity of brackish groundwater in six aquifers. A TWDB study report in August 2021 investigated whether that agency's conservative buffer of fifteen miles from all class II injection wells within a shared stratum was too limiting in the zone designation process. *See* Texas Water Development Board, *Develop Procedures and Tools to Delineate Areas Designated or Used for Class II Well Wastewater Injectate* (Aug. 2021), www.twdb.texas.gov/groundwater/bracs/projects/Injection/index.asp. To more fully support the use of brackish groundwater in the future will also require distinguishing between brackish and fresh groundwater in the TWDB's groundwater availability models (GAMs). See Chapter 19 for an explanation of GAMs.

Permitting the legal availability for brackish groundwater production was advanced during the legislature's 2017 session with House Bill 2377, which was intended to provide a stable regulatory structure within brackish groundwater production zones and to provide incentives to producers to choose developing brackish projects rather than those that rely on more scarce freshwater. *See* Tex. H.B. 2337, 85th Leg., R.S. (2017). The governor vetoed H.B. 2377, confirming in his message the importance of developing brackish water resources as a potential means of meeting the state's future water needs but encouraging a modified approach. Nevertheless, the legislation provided a platform for stakeholders through the Texas Alliance of Groundwater Districts, the Texas Desalination Association, and the Texas Water Conservation Association to continue encouraging groundwater desalination. *See* House Committee on Natural Resources, *Interim Report to the 86th Texas Legislature* (Dec. 2018), https://house.texas.gov/_media/pdf/committees/reports/85interim/Natural-Resources-Committee-Interim-Report-2018.pdf [hereinafter 2018 Interim Report]. Their efforts contributed to passage in 2019 of House Bill 722, facilitating production permitting by groundwater districts located over a designated brackish groundwater zone and providing for a minimum thirty-year permit term in specified circumstances. *See* Act of May 27, 2019, 86th Leg., R.S., ch. 1044, § 1 (H.B. 722), eff. Sept. 1, 2019. House Bill 722 also directed the TWDB to assist with technical reviews of operating permit applications submitted to groundwater conservation districts and with investigating the impacts of brackish groundwater production when requested by a district. To clarify its role and those processes the TWDB adopted a new subchapter G of its section 356 rules in 2020. *See* 31 Tex. Admin. Code §§ 356.70–356.72.

IV. Technical Strategies for Satisfying Design Rules, Water Quality Standards, and Concentrate Management Requirements

§ 25.5 Water Quality Standards for Desalination

The application of desalination technologies is typically driven by a need to reduce the total dissolved solids in a water source to meet standards that are suitable for an intended purpose. When the purpose is industrial in nature, treatment design will be sensitive to the type of industry using the supply. The most pressing needs in Texas, however, are expected to be municipal because of growing population, limitations on available freshwater resources, and recurring drought. Desalination strategies for municipal water supply must meet federal and state drinking water standards, which are the focus of Chapter 30 of this book.

Seawater desalination facilities designed to produce potable water must comply with Texas Health and Safety Code chapter 341, which supplements the federal Safe Drinking Water Act, 42 U.S.C. §§ 300f–300j-27, for regulating drinking water quality. In 2015, the Texas legislature passed House Bill 2031, which added Health and Safety Code section 341.0316, "Desalination of Marine Seawater for Drinking Water." *See* Act of May 26, 2015, 84th Leg., R.S., ch. 756, § 12 (H.B. 2031). While section 341.0316(b) states that the TCEQ must adopt rules to ensure that marine or seawater treated by a desalination facility for use as public drinking water meets the same requirements as other public drinking water sources, the agency saw no need to supplement the 30 Texas Administrative Code chapter 290 drinking water regulations. *See* Tex. Health & Safety Code § 341.0316(b); 30 Tex. Admin. Code § 297.206 (during the water rights application process, the TCEQ determines whether proposed treatment is adequate for proposed use).

§ 25.6 Design, Technologies, and Processes for Desalinating Water

Desalination technologies can be broadly classified as thermal, electrically driven, or pressure-driven separation processes. In each process, water is separated from the brackish or seawater sources to produce a low-TDS treated water (or product) stream and high-TDS concentrate stream. The product stream may be sent to post treatment processes before being served to the public. The concentrate may be disposed of or further treated by other processes to remove additional water and minimize the volume for disposal or for potential beneficial use. The selection of which technology to use depends on the site-specific source water, application (end-use), and economics.

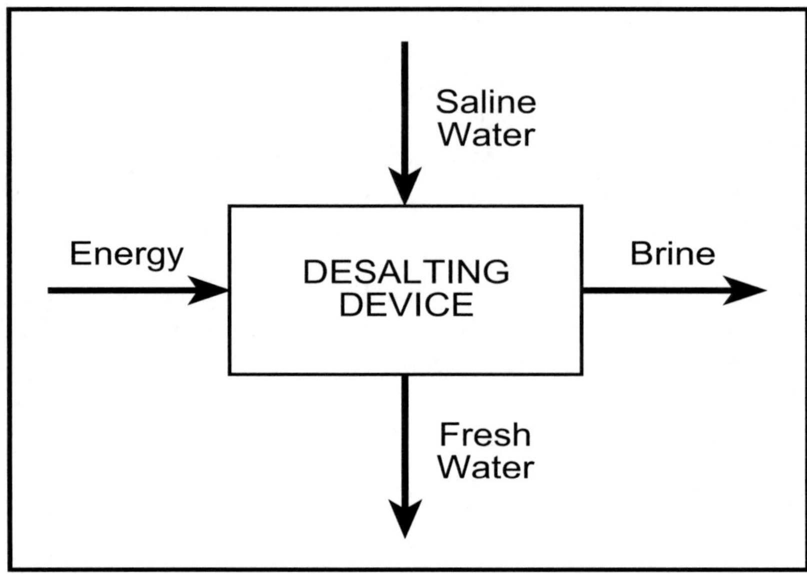

Figure 3. Summary of the desalination process. O.K. Buros, International Desalination Association, *The ABCs of Desalting* 5 (2d ed. 2000), https://faculty.ksu.edu.sa/sites/default/files/abcs_of_desalination.pdf.

The most common method of brackish water treatment today is reverse osmosis (RO): the use of a semipermeable membrane under pressure (100–400 pounds per square inch (psi)) to pass water molecules and reject the dissolved minerals, commonly referred to as salt or TDS. The other common method is the use of electrodialysis reversal (EDR): electricity is applied to electrodes to pull naturally occurring dissolved salts through an ion exchange membrane to separate the water from the salts. The EDR method is used to treat brackish water with moderate TDS concentration and water that has a high scaling potential due to elevated levels of particular contaminants such as barium (Ba) and strontium (Sr). The EDR technology is also effective on high silica (SiO2) source water.

Thermal desalination is an energy-intensive method of separating water from a source water by boiling it, separating the vapor from the concentrate, and then condensing the vapor. Some thermal-based technologies use a membrane designed for this application. *See* International Desalination Association, *IDA Desalination Yearbook 2016–2017*, Global Water Intelligence (Sept. 2016). Thermal-based technologies may be used in zero liquid discharge applications to recover the remaining water from RO brine, leaving only salt for disposal or potential beneficial use.

In 1967, the small west Texas community of Dell City became the first municipality in Texas to provide drinking water using inland desalination. Originally the facility used an electrodialysis (ED) process and, in 1975, switched to an electrodialysis reversal (EDR) process, becoming the first municipality in the U.S. to use this technology. Desalinated water from the 100,000 gallon-per-day EDR system is blended with raw groundwater to produce 220,000 gallons-per-day of drinking water. The concentrate stream is disposed of by land application. *See* Oram J. Morin, *Membrane Plants in North America* 42–54 Journal AWWA (Dec. 1994), http://awwa.onlinelibrary.wiley.com/doi/10.1002/j.1551-8833.1994.tb06285.x.

Desalination plants, regardless of the source of saline water, consist of five main processes: intake, pretreatment, water/salt separation, posttreatment, and concentrate disposal. Since RO membranes are the most common desalination process used to produce drinking water, that method will be the focus of the discussion below. Depending on the source, there are some differences in the desalination process, and, where relevant, those differences are also discussed.

Intake Process: Intake facilities are needed to obtain and transport the source water to the point of treatment. Brackish groundwater desalination systems, in their simplest form, may consist of a well or well field and transmission lines to transport the water—usually a short distance—to the desalination plant. In more complex cases, such as surface brackish water or seawater desalination, these facilities may encompass open intakes, pipelines, screens, and canal structures.

A brackish groundwater desalination project typically involves a study of the aquifer formation where source water is to be extracted to ensure that sufficient and sustainable water is available for the desalination plant. The wells are designed and constructed to eliminate the potential contamination of fresh groundwater sources as a result of the production of saline water. Often, particularly for smaller projects, the brackish groundwater wells and the desalination plant are located in relativity close proximity. This avoids the need for long transmission lines and, consequently, lowers the capital and operating costs of the facility. Intakes for brackish surface water desalination are the same as those required for fresh surface water projects and typically consist of concrete structures and screens and pipes on the side of a reservoir, river, or channel.

The ocean is a more complex and dynamic source; consequently, "[t]he design, modeling, monitoring, and permitting activities that surround them, may represent as much as 20 percent of the capital cost of the entire facility, and it is possible that intake-related issues may ultimately determine the feasibility and performance of the desalination plant itself." Tom Pankratz, *An Overview of Seawater Intake Facilities for Seawater Desalination* 1, *in The Future of Desalination in Texas, Volume II: Technical Papers, Case Studies, and Desalination Technology Resources* (Texas Water Development Board 2004), www.twdb.texas.gov/publications/reports/numbered_reports/doc/R363/Report363.asp.

A major concern in the design, construction, and operation of seawater intake facilities is the potential trapping of marine organisms in the screens of the intake structure or the suction and destruction of these organisms in the desalination process. These issues, referred to as entrainment and impingement in the desalination literature, often dictate the type of intake facility that can be used. Entrainment occurs when fish or macroinvertebrate eggs or larvae are taken into the intake and exposed to processing, which typically approaches 100 percent mortality. Impingement occurs when fish and other marine life are trapped or pinned by the force of intake flow, which can result in high mortality. *See Ecological Modeling for Resource Management* (Virginia H. Dale ed., 2002).

Subsurface ocean intakes, such as beach wells or infiltration galleries, minimize entrainment and impingement. *See* Pankratz, at 9. Open intakes are designed to minimize the velocity of the water at the intake point to limit the draw of marine organisms; also, open intakes are fitted with screens or deterring mechanisms to discourage fish from approaching the intake points. The seawater desalination facilities currently under consideration in Texas all involve open intakes.

Pretreatment: The purpose of pretreatment for a desalination facility is to remove suspended and organic matter from the source water. For RO membranes, failure in the pretreatment process may cause problems, such as excessive scaling or fouling of the membranes. In severe cases this may require a premature replacement of the membranes. For either case this adds to the production cost of a desalination facility.

In the case of brackish groundwater desalination, the source water is typically clean, with low organic contaminant and turbidity levels. For these cases, all that is required is screening of small particles (sand or silt) that may have been drawn into the water stream by the well pumps. Removal of these particles is accomplished by use of cartridge or bag filters; however, brackish groundwater may contain other contaminants or substances, such as iron, that may precipitate and foul the membranes. Additionally, arsenic and boron are naturally occurring in some groundwater sources in Texas. Most groundwater desalination facilities address arsenic issues by chemical or physical means during the pretreatment process. Common examples of such chemical means include the use of iron or manganese reduction systems, antiscalants, or pH control using acid. *See* NRS Consulting Engineers, *Guidance Manual for Brackish Groundwater Desalination in Texas* 61 (Texas Water Development Board 2008), www.twdb.texas.gov/publications/reports/contracted_reports/doc/0604830581_BrackishDesal.pdf?d=3625 [hereinafter Guidance Manual for BGD].

In the case of arsenic in the source water, RO systems can remove some chemical forms of arsenic, but chemical coagulation followed by microfiltration (MF) may be needed, depending on its source-water concentration. Higher pressure RO membranes and two-pass systems have been effective in removing boron in groundwater containing boron concentrations from 4 to 12 mg/L. Boron, although not regulated by the TCEQ or the EPA, is recognized by the World Health Organization (WHO) to cause issues in unborn fetuses and to have other potential risks. The WHO recommends removal to 2.4 mg/L. *See* Environmental Protection Agency, Regulatory Determinations Support Document for Selected Contaminants from the Second Drinking Water Contaminant Candidate List (June 2008), www.epa.gov/sites/production/files/2014-09/documents/chapter_3_boron.pdf. The pretreatment for surface brackish and ocean source plants is generally similar to that required for a conventional fresh surface water source: removal of suspended solids by flocculation and sedimentation followed by sand and anthracite media filtration or, in some cases, micro- or ultrafiltration membranes. Surface water sources are more prone to seasonal changes in the quality of water, and pretreatment designs need to account for that variability. This need is commonly addressed by performing pilot plant studies at the site of proposed large-scale facilities. The pilot plant studies provide data on the seasonal variability of the source water and inform the design of the pretreatment.

Salt Separation by Reverse Osmosis Membranes: Osmosis is a natural process that occurs when two aqueous solutions of differing concentrations of dissolved solids are separated by a permeable membrane. In these situations, water will flow from the solution of lower concentration, through the membrane, to dilute the solution of higher concentration. Thomas M. Messimer, *Water Supply Development, Aquifer Storage, and Concentrate Disposal for Membrane Water Facilities* 44 (Schlumberger Water Services, 2009). The RO process relies on pressure to reverse the osmotic tendency of water to flow in the direction of higher concentration and forces water across a semipermeable membrane while impeding the passage of salt across the membrane. *See* Guidance Manual for BGD, at 18 fig. 13.

The pressure required to desalinate water in an RO process is a function of the salinity of the source or feed water; the greater the salinity, the greater the pressure required—and, consequently, the higher the energy needs and cost to desalinate water. For brackish desalination systems, the pressure requirements are on the order of 50 to 600 psi, and for seawater desalination, 800 to 1,200 psi. *See* R.W. Beck, Inc., *Guidance Manual for Permitting Requirements in Texas for Desalination Facilities Using Reverse Osmosis Processes* 4-3 tbl. 4-1 (Texas Water Development Board 2004), www.twdb.texas.gov/publications/reports/contracted_reports/doc/2003483509.pdf?d=159032 [hereinafter Guidance Manual for PR]. For example, pressure of approximately 160 psi is required to treat the average brackish groundwater with 3,000 mg/L of TDS.

Generating the needed pressures to accomplish RO filtration requires energy. For seawater desalination, the specific energy usage is typically about 2.5 to 3.5 kilowatt-hours per cubic meter of water produced. *See* American Membrane Technology Association, *Membrane Desalination Power Put in Perspective* (Apr. 2016), www.amtaorg.com/wp-content/uploads/07_Membrane_Desalination_Power_Usage_Put_In_Perspective.pdf. Brackish water desalination uses 0.5 to 3 kilowatt-hours per cubic meter of water produced. *See* National Research Council, *Desalination: A National Perspective* 77 (National Academies Press 2008).

The RO membranes are nearly impermeable to the passage of salts; however, as salts are deposited on the feed side of the membrane, a small portion, typically less than 1 percent, will move across the membrane and comingle with the product water, which is also referred to as permeate. An RO system is capable of producing permeate with salinities below the secondary maximum contaminant level of 500 mg/L set by the EPA. *See* U.S. Environmental Protection Agency, *Secondary Drinking Water Standards: Guidance for Nuisance Chemicals*, www.epa.gov/dwstandardsregulations/secondary-drinking-water-standards-guidance-nuisance-chemicals#table ("EPA has established National Secondary Drinking Water Regulations (NSDWRs) that set non-mandatory water quality standards for 15 contaminants. EPA does not enforce these 'secondary maximum contaminant levels' (SMCLs). They are established as guidelines to assist public water systems in managing their drinking water for aesthetic considerations, such as taste, color, and odor. These contaminants are not considered to present a risk to human health at the SMCL."). Nevertheless, SMCLs adopted by the TCEQ are enforceable.

Some of the rejected salts and particles settle on the feed side of the membranes and may obstruct the passage of water. This process is referred to as scaling and fouling of the membranes and, if not handled appropriately, could lead to irreversible failure of the membranes. Chemical additives to lessen the rate of precipitation of salts, periodic cleaning, and higher cross-flow velocities on the feed side of the membrane are mechanisms for reducing fouling potential.

In July 2015, the TCEQ adopted desalination design rules in 30 Texas Administrative Code chapter 290, subchapter D, to provide expedited approval of RO and nanofiltration (NF) membranes for desalination facilities. The rules apply to the removal of primary and secondary drinking water contaminants (except microbiological contaminants) from surface water and groundwater. The RO/NF designs may use manufacturers' computer models, a site-specific pilot study, comparable data from an alternative site, or manufacturers' allowable operating parameters (only for capacities less than 300 gallons per minute). The use of manufacturers' computer models for this purpose was validated in a TWDB study, and guidance for their proper use is presented in a manual of practice. *See* Erika Mancha et al., *Part II. Performance Evaluation of Reverse Osmosis Membrane Computer Models* (Texas Water Development Board 2014), www.twdb.texas.gov/publications/reports/contracted_reports/doc/1148321310_Part%20II_Performance%20Evaluation.pdf; Don DeMichele et al., *Manual of Practice for the Use of Computer Models for the Design of Reverse Osmosis/Nanofiltration Membrane Processes* (Texas Water Development Board 2014), www.twdb.texas.gov/publications/reports/contracted_reports/doc/1148321310_Manual%20of%20Practice.pdf.

Posttreatment: The product water or permeate from an RO membrane system is typically very low in concentrations of dissolved solids. For delivery to a drinking water distribution system, this level of purity is problematic and must be addressed.

Product water from membrane desalination is typically in the range of 25 to 500 mg/L of TDS, depending on the source-water concentration. Low concentration of calcium and bicarbonate results in water that is unstable. If not treated, the water will attempt to stabilize itself by dissolving materials it comes in contact with, such as pipelines or existing sediment in old distribution systems. Adding calcium and bicarbonate and adjusting the acidity of the water is required to avoid corrosion of pipes, storage systems, and even pipes of the end customer. *See* U.S. Bureau of Reclamation, *Desalting Handbook for Planners* 36 (3d ed. 2003) [hereinafter Desalting Handbook]; Wen yi Shih et al., *Upflow Calcite Contactor Study* (Texas Water Development Board 2012), www.twdb.texas.gov/innovativewater/desal/projects/carollo/doc/2012_carollo_final_rpt.pdf.

Where brackish groundwater is the source water with TDS of around 3,000 mg/L, a portion of the filtered groundwater can be used to increase the TDS to stabilize the drinking water with little or no chemical posttreatment. *See* Guidance Manual for BGD, at 65 fig. 21.

§ 25.7 Methods of Concentrate Stream Disposal

The salts and other minerals rejected in the RO process accumulate in the unfiltered portion of the feed stream for disposal. In addition to the original dissolved solids and particulate matter, the reject stream may contain chemicals added in the process to minimize chemical or biological fouling of the membranes. The volume and salinity of a desalination concentrate stream are a function of the source water salinity and of the overall recovery rate (percentage of product water extracted from the source water). The concentrate may contain up to ten times the salinity and other individual constituents (such as arsenic or combined radium) in the waste stream as the raw water, depending on the treatment system design. For example, a 1 MGD brackish desalination system with source water salinity of 2,000 mg/L and a recovery rate of 85 percent may produce a concentrate stream of 150,000 gallons per day having a salinity of 13,000 mg/L.

The disposal of desalination concentrate is regulated to ensure safe disposal. Sometimes these by-products are disposed of in underground injection wells under waste rules pertaining to class I wells in 30 Texas Administrative Code chapter 331, subchapter D. See discussion below. The design and evaluation of alternative means of disposal typically employ modeling of the contents and impacts of discharges on ecological resources. *See* Ibrahim Alameddine & Mutasem El-Fadel, *Brine Discharge from Desalination Plants: A Modeling Approach to an Optimized Outfall Design*, 214 Desalination 241 (2006). Concentrate may also be authorized for discharge to waters in the state under a Texas Pollutant Discharge Elimination System (TPDES) permit and as outlined by the TCEQ. *See* Texas Commission on Environmental Quality, *Procedures to Implement the Texas Surface Water Quality Standards* (RG-194, June 2010), www.tceq.texas.gov/assets/public/permitting/waterquality/standards/docs/june_2010_ip.pdf. See further discussion below.

Surface Water Discharge: Surface water discharge is the most frequent disposal method for brackish plants, and it is the disposal method for nearly all seawater plants. *See* Desalting Handbook, at 170. This type of discharge includes the direct disposal of undiluted concentrate to a surface water body, including the Gulf of Mexico, and a comingling of the concentrate with other discharge streams such as power plant cooling water or treated municipal wastewater effluent. Discharging the concentrate to surface water requires a TPDES permit from the TCEQ. *See* Guidance Manual for BGD, at 51.

Texas Water Code section 18.005 provides that section 26.011 of the Water Code applies to marine seawater discharges in the same manner that the section applies to discharges governed by Water Code chapter 26. *See* Tex. Water Code § 18.005(b). The TCEQ has promulgated rules regulating marine seawater desalination discharges under Water Code chapter 18. *See* 30 Tex. Admin. Code ch. 318. The TCEQ also has developed an instruction guideline to assist in the discharge application process. *See* Seawater Desalination Permit Instructions. The Marine Seawater Desalination Diversion and Discharge Zones Study, discussed at section 25.4:2 above in connection with the legal availability of seawater for discharge, is an important resource related to seawater discharge as well. Based on available information and known concerns, the recommended diversion and discharge zones identified in that report are identical. The report also includes recommendations that should be considered during planning and design phases, since the protection of marine organisms can be accomplished by giving appropriate attention to site-specific factors that include the chemical properties of the waste being discharged and the physical design of discharge facilities. It is important to note, however, that seawater desalination does not necessarily require deep ocean discharge. Following is a brief discussion of the more common concentrate disposal options.

Evaporation Ponds: Concentrate disposal by evaporation ponds works well in some areas of Texas where land is available at a relatively low cost and evaporation rates are high. However, the lining requirements for these types of facilities are costly and limit their use to smaller-scale systems. Use of evaporation ponds requires a TCEQ permit for Land Application of Water Treatment Sludge. *See* Guidance Manual for BGD, at 51.

Underground Injection: Underground injection of concentrate is an important option for desalination systems in Texas, particularly inland projects. The concentrate is injected into a subsurface stratum, generally beneath all strata containing freshwater, via a well designed for disposal of industrial, municipal, or oil and gas waste. Additionally, the concentrate may be injected via a well initially drilled to produce oil and gas, but which no longer serves that purpose and is used for deep well injection disposal. *See* Tex. Water Code § 27.002(11); Guidance Manual for BGD, at 51.

Beneficial Use of Concentrate: Desalination concentrate may also be reused in a beneficial manner, for example, by using the brine in flooding operations for enhanced oil recovery processes by injecting via a well designed and permitted for that purpose. A typical flooding operation is not continuous, which presents a practical limitation for the use of this disposal method for municipal desalination facilities. Municipal facilities require a disposal method that will be available throughout the entire service life of the desalination facility. *See* Guidance Manual for PR, at 4-14.

Other beneficial uses of concentrate include solar ponds, irrigation, zero liquid discharge, salt separation processes, aquaculture, and creating or restoring wetlands. Fifteen years ago, many of these methods were still being developed or researched and were not feasible means for large-scale disposal or minimization of concentrate. *See* Jim Jordahl, *Beneficial and Nontraditional Uses of Concentrate* (Water Reuse Foundation 2006). Today concentrate minimization technologies, such as zero liquid discharge, salt separation processes, and aquaculture, are beginning to be implemented.

Kay Bailey Hutchison Desalination Plant and EWM
Full Recovery Desalination

The Kay Bailey Hutchison (KBH) Desalination Plant in the desert of West Texas is a joint project of the El Paso Water Utility (EPWU) and Fort Bliss capable of producing up to 27.5 million gallons of freshwater daily. Sixteen production wells and sixteen blend wells feed groundwater from the Hueco Bolson aquifer to the facility. The EPWU plans to expand the plant in coming years to as much as 42 MGD to meet future water needs.

The original plant design included pumping concentrate to a surface injection facility and disposal via deep-well injection into geological formations twenty-two miles northeast of the plant site. However, the EPWU has partnered to innovate concentrate management by chemically separating high-purity, industrial-grade mineral products from wastewater that are valued in commercial markets. *See* El Paso Water, Desalination, www.epwater.org/cms/one.aspx?portalId=6843488&pageId=7416477. The goal of such innovation is full-recovery desalination. Beneficial use with cost efficiency of what otherwise is waste would open a new era in desalination for inland communities.

In Texas, several concentrate disposal approaches are used. According to the TWDB desalination plant database, in 2011 fifteen systems discharged directly to surface water bodies and fourteen did so indirectly through sewerage systems and wastewater treatment plant discharges. Eight plants disposed of the concentrate through irrigation systems, five used land application, seven used evaporation ponds, two used underground injection, and one reused the concentrate stream for industrial purposes. *See* Saqib Shirazi & Jorge Arroyo, *Desalination Database Updates for Texas*

3.4(f) fig. 3-9 (Texas Water Development Board 2011), www.twdb.texas.gov/innovativewater/desal/doc/2011_03_desaldb_whitepaper.pdf.

§ 25.8 Overview of Treatment for Produced Water

Produced water from oil and gas operations includes both "flowback" of water injected to initiate production, as well as naturally occurring water. The volume of produced water and contaminant concentrations contained therein vary significantly, both from one wellfield to the next and during the lifecycle of operations. The ratio of water to oil produced from a well may start low (2:1) and increase over the life of the well. In some cases, the ratio might reach up to 10:1. In 2020 alone the volume of water from oil and gas production in Texas disposed by underground injection was approximately 7.6 billion barrels (321 billion gallons), according to the Railroad Commission. *See* RCC Online System, H10 Filing System, http://webapps.rrc.state.tx.us/H10/searchVolume.do?.

The contaminants found in produced water depend on site-specific geology, chemical interactions with the oil and water, and the chemical additives needed for oil production. They may include high levels of TDS (up to around 200,000 mg/L), oil and grease, dissolved and volatile organics, inorganics (including rare-earth elements), naturally occurring radionuclides, suspended solids, bacteria, and additives used for oil production.

Because of the variety of contaminants, treatment of produced water can be complex, requiring several technologies. Adding to this complexity is the potential to target specific minerals for recovery, which may require additional, specialized processes. Depending on the produced water quality and the intended end-use of the treated water, combinations of technologies to achieve this goal may include oil separators; degassifiers; coagulation, flocculation, or sedimentation; dissolved air flotation; granular media filtration; low-pressure membrane filtration; desalination; ion exchange; carbon adsorbers; aerators; advanced oxidation; biological reactors; and disinfection. Even though a variety of technologies are needed to treat produced water, desalination is the key component to the reuse of produced water. Reuse of produced water will help provide a valuable water resource for Texas while minimizing the disposal of contaminated water from oil and gas production. Potential end uses for treated produced water include oil and gas development, environmental discharge, agriculture, industry, and potable water needs. Desalination is a key component to achieve most of these end-uses and recover other valuable minerals, such as rare-earth elements. The recovery of these types of minerals during treatment of produced water is expected to significantly improve its cost effectiveness.

V. Determining the Viability of Desalination for Meeting Demand

§ 25.9 Planning Projections

When is desalination the answer or at least one of the answers for a municipal or industrial user needing a new or additional water source? When planning and designing for the desalination of water, the goal is to create a cost-effective and reliable system that satisfies the primary objectives of the end user. If a water source is available, the user should consider everything including supply, water quality requirements and goals, treatment needs, and concentrate management.

When an entity is planning its water supply needs, diversification plays an important role to safeguard against drought or other issues that may cause interruption of service to its customers. Deciding if desalination is the best strategy to provide all or some of its water supply needs, the entity has several questions to consider:

- Is a drought-proof or drought-resistant source important?

- Is there a source of brackish water or seawater in the area? What are the regulatory constraints for using that source?
- Is there enough fresh surface or groundwater to meet future demands? If so, how would using these supplies compare with desalination?
- Is diversification of the entity's water supply portfolio important?
- What are the concentrate management options?
- Are there other entities planning their water supply needs so that a regional facility could be considered?
- What are the costs of each water supply being considered?
- What are the environmental impacts?

NRS Consulting Engineers developed a decision matrix to help an entity analyze the feasibility of using desalination as a water source. *See* Guidance Manual for BGD, at 40 fig. 18.

Assuming there is a source of brackish groundwater or seawater, the most important and most asked question is, "How much does it cost?" To make cost comparisons between using desalination and other water sources, what is and is not included in the cost of each comparison must be understood. In many cases, brackish desalination is less costly than the equivalent conventional surface water treatment plant. Such a cost comparison is certainly site specific. Factors for the cost of water from a desalination plant generally include power, chemicals, labor, sinking fund, concentrate management, and debt service.

Power costs for a brackish groundwater desalination project are affected by two major categories: TDS concentration and the number, depth, and distance of brackish groundwater wells from the treatment plant. The higher the TDS content, the higher the power costs and the lower the capacity of the treatment plant. The deeper and farther the wells are from the plant, the greater are the pumping costs and construction costs for pipelines to move the water from the wells to the plant.

Chemical costs are directly related to the quality of the water treated. See discussion at section 25.6 above. In some cases brackish groundwater desalination can also be affected by the constituents in the water besides the general TDS category. Most notable are iron and arsenic, which can be naturally occurring in the groundwater in some areas. This requires a pretreatment method, such as microfiltration, ahead of the desalination treatment. This also increases the cost.

Seawater is more costly to treat than brackish groundwater because of higher TDS and pretreatment needs. When comparing desalination of 3,000 mg/L TDS (brackish water) to 30,000 mg/L TDS (seawater), the seawater desalination cost is two to three times that of the brackish water treatment because of special intake and discharge requirements, higher treatment pressures, lower recovery rates, pretreatment needs, and higher capital costs.

Even though seawater desalination is more costly than brackish desalination, it offers a great advantage to Texas because there exists an unlimited source of water, the process is comparable in cost to building a new reservoir, and two-thirds of the state's population live within 150 miles of the Gulf Coast, affecting distribution considerations.

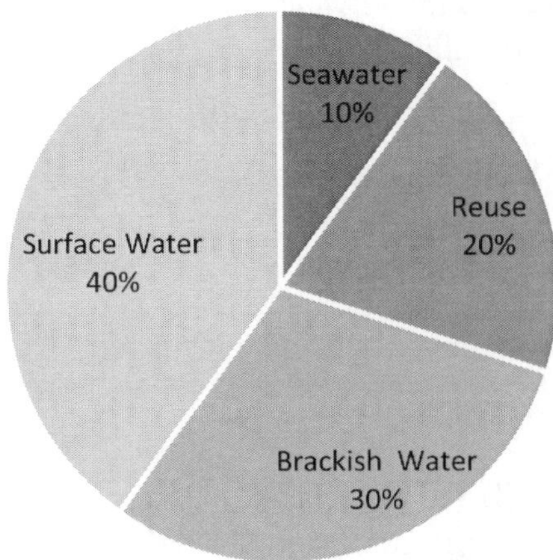

Figure 4. Water source diversification strategy. General diversification strategy of cities with major desalination facilities in Texas.

While generally the cost of desalination is one of the most important factors in the decision-making process, diversification and reliability can be equally important, especially where drought has been an issue in the past and the area has seen increased population growth without a comparable increase in supplies. Some strategies will not be equivalent in cost; a blended rate for all could be considered. Cities with major desalination facilities in Texas all have multiple water strategies, such as is shown in Figure 4.

The last major factor influencing the decision whether to add desalination to the water supply mix is how to handle the concentrate. As discussed at section 25.7 above, a seawater desalination plant generally can readily dispose of concentrate by discharging it back to the feed water source. While the TCEQ has allowed concentrate discharge into waters not impacting downstream users, there are fewer options for inland disposal. *See* Texas Commission on Environmental Quality, *Texas Surface Water Quality Standards*, www.tceq.texas.gov/waterquality/standards.

Of Texas's three largest brackish desalination plants, only the Southmost Regional Water Authority (SRWA) desalination plant discharges concentrate into a drainage ditch that ultimately discharges into the feed source, the Brownsville Ship Channel. When the discharge permit was applied for in 2003, relatively little was known about the water-quality effect of this type of discharge, and ultimately the permit authorized a discharge limitation of approximately 12,000 mg/L TDS, or four times the source water being treated. The SRWA plant was required to monitor TDS concentrations upstream and downstream during the initial permit duration. During the permit renewal process, the TCEQ determined, based on the monitoring results, that the discharge had a beneficial impact on the receiving waters; the TDS limitation was nearly tripled in the renewed permit.

The other two major facilities, KBH Desalination Plant and San Antonio Water System Desalination Plant, currently discharge their concentrate into deep wells, adding to the cost of the treatment system. As discussed at section 25.7, El Paso Water Utilities is in the process of changing that paradigm.

VI. Policy and Projections for Desalinated Water Supply in Texas

§ 25.10 Recognizing the Potential of Desalination to Meet Demand

Texas policymakers continue to recognize both the challenge of meeting a growing population's need for reliable water supply and that the resources available through desalination are vast. In 2002, forty years after the Freeport facility was dedicated, desalination for Texas regained momentum when Governor Rick Perry announced his vision for meeting future water supply needs from seawater. *See* Governor Rick Perry, Speech, *Text of Gov. Perry's Announcement in San Antonio on Securing Abundant Water Supplies for Texas' Future Needs* (Apr. 29, 2002), https://lrl.texas.gov/scanned/govdocs/Rick%20Perry/2002/remarks042902.pdf (Governor Perry's 2002 desalination directive). Subsequent legislation to support state desalination policy peaked in 2015, while drought conditions created a new urgency, with regard to developing both seawater resources and brackish groundwater resources. The key water rights provisions from House Bills 30, 2031, and 4097 passed that year are discussed at part III above. House Bill 4097 also recognized the need for a bridge to energy requirements. The bill addressed the state's ability to provide power for seawater desalination projects by directing a study by the Public Utility Commission of Texas (PUC), in cooperation with transmission and distribution utilities and the Electric Reliability Council of Texas (ERCOT). *See* Act of May 23, 2015, 84th Leg., R.S., ch. 829, §§ 1, 2 (H.B. 4097) (adding Texas Utilities Code section 39.9055 related to demand response potential of seawater desalination projects.). The PUC and ERCOT presented their study to the Texas legislature in January 2017, finding that existing transmission and distribution planning processes are sufficient to provide adequate infrastructure for seawater desalination projects. *See* Electric Reliability Council of Texas, *Study on the Demand Response Potential for Seawater Desalination Projects* (Nov. 18, 2016), www.ercot.com/files/docs/2016/11/18/Demand_Response_Potential_for_Seawater_Desalination_Projects_11_18_2016.pdf.

The suite of desalination bills in 2015 recalls the critical push that the 1950s drought gave both desalination and surface water reservoir construction in Texas. The article by Roberts and Jaehnig cited at section 25.3 above regarding the relative hiatus in federal support for desalination after the 1960s quite simply explains: "Then the rain came back." Nonetheless, that early push to build the state's water supply reservoirs laid the foundation for Texas's economic prosperity today. That single generation constructed over 65 percent of the state's present conservation storage capacity, including capacity that would be used only with the passage of time. In some cases, the TWDB's state participation mechanism was used to assume a temporary ownership interest in water projects in order to fund excess capacity for future use. *See* Texas Water Development Board, *State Participation*, www.twdb.texas.gov/financial/programs/spp/index.asp.

A similar vision may be required to advance desalination now. A critical component of all water supply development for uses that require reliable supply, of course, is to develop capacity in advance of actual demand, anticipating both population growth and the inevitability that drought will recur. Texas is faced with population growth that has taken Texas's per capita reservoir storage capacity numbers to a predrought level, which is alarming. *See* George H. Ward, Jr., *Texas Water at the Century's Turn—Perspectives, Reflections and a Comfort Bag in Water for Texas: 2000 and Beyond* (Texas A&M University 2000). The state faces what may be a greater challenge: not the higher cost of new supply but the underpricing of water from existing supplies. It is encouraging however, that when the rains came back in the past decade, with municipal water supply storage reservoirs flush with freshwater, recent Texas legislatures continued to advance desalination, through statutory authorization and appropriations, as the next great water supply strategy necessary to satisfy continued growth.

§ 25.11 TWDB Leads the State's Effort to Develop Desalination Resources

Implementing Governor Perry's 2002 desalination directive, Texas Water Code section 16.060 directs the TWDB to further the development of desalination for both seawater and brackish groundwater, through research, feasibility and facility planning studies, investigations, and surveys. The TWDB has also pursued demonstration projects and pilot and other studies, supports a Brackish Groundwater Desalination Initiative, and maintains a stand-alone desalination program under its Innovative Water Technologies Department. Agency collaboration since 2013 with the U.S. Bureau of Reclamation on research initiatives and federal funding also supports the innovative technologies effort. Technological advances in desalination, of course, will also benefit inland surface water desalination projects indirectly. *See* Texas Water Development Board, *Desalination*, www.twdb.texas.gov/innovativewater/desal/index.asp.

Desalination projects for all sources of supply implemented by political subdivisions are eligible for financing from various TWDB programs, including the Drinking Water State Revolving Fund, the State Participation Program, the Texas Water Development Fund, and the State Participation Program already mentioned. The TWDB has provided funding to support at least two seawater desalination projects and one brackish groundwater desalination project through the State Water Implementation Fund for Texas. Existing TWDB funding programs can accommodate public-private partnerships for desalination to an even greater extent since the legislature passed the Texas State Water Investment Fund Act in 2019. *See* Act of May 25, 2019, 86th Leg., R.S., ch. 752 (H.B. 1052), eff. Sept. 1, 2019 (authorizing state participation in certain desalination projects with private partners). Because public-private partnership is a promising method of implementing large-scale desalination projects, the TWDB refers public entities to the Center for Alternative Finance and Procurement at the Texas Facilities Commission for more information. *See* Center for Alternative Finance and Procurement, *About*, http://cap.texas.gov/about.html. Private entities also benefit from tax exemptions, including for equipment, services, or supplies used solely for desalination of surface water or groundwater. *See* Tex. Tax Code §§ 11.32, 151.355. See Chapter 37 of this book for a discussion of financing water supply projects.

Texas Water Code section 16.060 requires the TWDB to update the Biennial Report by December 1 of each even-numbered year and catalog the state's progress in desalination. Each report is an invaluable resource of information on desalination efforts in Texas, and includes—

1. the results of the TWDB's studies and activities related to seawater and brackish groundwater desalination during the preceding biennium;

2. identification and evaluation of research, regulatory, technical, and financial impediments to implementing seawater or brackish groundwater desalination projects;

3. evaluation of the role the state should play in furthering the development of large-scale seawater or brackish groundwater desalination projects in the state;

4. estimated appropriation from general revenue necessary to continue investigating water desalination activities in the state during the following biennium; and

5. identification and designation of local or regional brackish groundwater production zones in areas of the state with moderate to high availability and productivity of brackish groundwater that could be used to reduce the use of fresh groundwater.

See Tex. Water Code § 16.060(b). Significantly, the Biennial Report catalogs both the state's successes with desalination and the existing research, regulatory, technical, and financial impediments to further development. For the TWDB's efforts themselves, the most striking need is for continued funding by the state legislature. The continued ability of the TWDB to financially support desalination research, feasibility study, and demonstration and other projects requires continuing appropriations.

§ 25.12 Implementing Desalination at the Local Level

State support is critical to the viability of desalination in Texas, but actual development requires local and regional investment. In that regard the House Natural Resources Committee's 2018 Interim Report found that the state is lagging behind its neighbors to the east and west in terms of embracing technological advancements in desalination. *See* 2018 Interim Report, at 72.

The TWDB produces its state water plan for Texas every five years through a locally driven planning process guided by sixteen regional water groups, as discussed in more detail in Chapter 20 of this book. Three regional water planning groups included seawater desalination as a recommended water management strategy in the 2022 plan, and nine regional water planning groups, including for western, central, and southern parts of Texas, recommended groundwater desalination strategies. To be sure, the two categories of strategy are identified to provide only a small fraction of the state's overall water portfolio over the next few decades. *See* 2022 State Water Plan, at 104 fig. 7-4. However, the vital importance of desalination for meeting the needs of some individual communities and industries may grow more quickly. The City of Corpus Christi, for example, began developing plans for two potential seawater desalination plants after the drought years of 2011 and 2013 in the Nueces River Basin made the need to diversify the city's water supply apparent. *See* Municipal Water Leader, *Adding Seawater Deal to Corpus Christi's Water Portfolio: An Interview with Steve Ramos* (Feb. 4, 2019), http://municipalwaterleader.com/adding-seawater-deal-to-corpus-christis-water-portfolio/. As embodied in the 2017 amendments to Texas Water Code section 11.122 discussed at section 25.4:1 above, desalination can also play an important role in making traditional freshwater supplies available for others, including those that may not have any alternatives to their traditional supplies.

Statewide projections for the future of desalination will continue to be refined through the regional planning process in anticipation of subsequent state water plans. The state's sixteen regional water planning groups are in their fifth planning cycle. Each group will prepare a plan that meets the requirements of Water Code section 16.053, including identifying opportunities for and benefits of developing large-scale desalination facilities for marine seawater or brackish groundwater that serve local or regional brackish groundwater production zones identified and designated under Water Code section 16.060(b)(5). Their plans were to be submitted by October 14, 2020, for TWDB approval and inclusion in the 2022 state water plan. As recent feasibility studies and permitting continue to progress, the 2022 plan reflects that Texas's first modern seawater-only desalination facility will be operational in the near future to serve the state's coastal communities and industries.

Perhaps no region in the state could benefit more from additional water supply than west Texas, where even traditional brackish groundwater options are limited. The state's great oil and gas production industry is adding new focus to that region for the application of desalination technologies to make produced water useful for new purposes. To bridge the gap between potential supply and actual beneficial use, the Texas Legislature passed Senate Bill 601, Act of June 18, 2021, 87th Leg., R.S., ch. 941, § 1 (S.B. 601), establishing the Texas Produced Water Consortium at Texas Tech University. The consortium will identify the potential economic feasibility of converting produced water to potable water and will report policy recommendations and an outline for a potential pilot project. The consortium will do this based on state agency, industry, and local government stakeholder participation; research directed by consortium members; and an economic analysis of viable technologies needed to accomplish the state's goals. The inclusion of produced water as a new water supply is an innovative step for Texas, made possible by advancements in desalination technology and recognition that its application may unlock previously untapped water and mineral resources. See Senate Bill 601 adding new Subchapter E to the Texas Education Code, Chapter 109.

VII. Conclusion

§ 25.13 Conclusion

Whether to implement desalination is, in each instance, a local decision regarding the most cost-effective option to meet water supply demand under the circumstances and over a prudent planning horizon. Nevertheless, desalination of brackish, saline, and produced waters has already earned a place in Texas's overall water supply portfolio. For meeting growing demand desalination fits, not instead of, but alongside the more traditional strategies of using water efficiently through conservation practices and developing additional surface and fresh groundwater supplies for use and reuse where economically and environmentally feasible. Within the portfolio, desalination may have the advantage of being relatively drought proof in a drought-prone state, meriting a friendly regulatory environment and the kind of long-term investment in research and development that only the state itself can make.

As a matter of policy, the 2015 desalination bills may have said it best. The legislature acknowledged in House Bill 2031 that the state's projected long-term water needs far exceed the firm supplies that are currently available and that reasonably *can be made available* from freshwater sources. The legislature spoke for the people of Texas when it stated:

> With this state facing an ongoing drought, continuing population growth, and the need to remain economically competitive, every effort must be made to secure and develop plentiful and cost-effective water supplies to meet the ever-increasing demand for water. The purpose . . . is not to hinder efforts to conserve or develop other surface water supplies but rather to more fully explore and expedite the development of all this state's water resources in order to balance this state's supply and demand for water, which is one of the most precious resources of this state.

Act of May 26, 2015, 84th Leg., R.S., ch. 756, § 1 (H.B. 2031). Texans do, after all, understand the value of all their water.

Resources

American Water Works Association, *Manual of Water Supply Practices (M61)—Desalination of Seawater* (2011).

American Water Works Association, *Manual of Water Supply Practices (M69)—Inland Desalination and Concentrate Management* (2019).

International Desalination Association, https://idadesal.org/about/.

NRS Consulting Engineers, *Guidance Manual for Brackish Groundwater Desalination in Texas* (Texas Water Development Board 2008), www.twdb.texas.gov/publications/reports/contracted_reports/doc/0604830581_BrackishDesal.pdf?d=3625.

Sandia National Laboratories, *Implementation of the National Desalination and Water Purification Technology Roadmap: Structuring and Directing the Development of Water Supply Solutions* (2006), https://www.osti.gov/servlets/purl/983683/.

Texas Commission on Environmental Quality, *Instructions for Completing the Marine Seawater Desalination Permit Application* (Dec. 2016), www.tceq.texas.gov/assets/public/permitting/waterquality/forms/20775_20776_ins.pdf.

Texas Desalination Association, www.texasdesal.com/.

Texas Parks and Wildlife Department & Texas General Land Office, *Marine Seawater Desalination Diversion and Discharge Zones Study* (Sept. 1, 2018), https://tpwd.texas.gov/publications/pwdpubs/media/hb2031dz.pdf.

Texas Water Development Board, *The Future of Desalination in Texas: 2020 Biennial Report to on Seawater and Brackish Groundwater Desalination* (2020), www.twdb.texas.gov/innovativewater/desal/docs.asp.

Texas Water Development Board, *Water for Texas 2022* (2022), www.twdb.texas.gov/waterplanning/swp/2022/.

CHAPTER 26

Aquifer Storage and Recovery

Neil Deeds, PhD, PE,[1] *Joe Freeland,*[2] *and Tom Bohl*[3]

I. Introduction

§ 26.1 Introduction

Aquifer storage and recovery (ASR) has proven to be an efficient and cost-effective means of storing available water for future use in at least fifteen foreign countries and twenty-one states in the United States, including Texas, as evidenced by the large number of new projects in operation. This chapter presents background information on ASR as a water management strategy, a general discussion of ASR technologies, requirements for a successful ASR project, and selected case studies of ASR projects in the state.

---

1. Neil Deeds is a Senior Water Resources Engineer at INTERA Inc. in Austin, Texas. As a registered professional engineer, Mr. Deeds has spent twenty years at INTERA performing quantitative hydrogeologic studies for public and private clients. He is also a lecturer at the University of Texas at Austin where he teaches groundwater hydraulics in the Civil Engineering department. He received his BS in environmental engineering at the University of Oklahoma and his MS and PhD in civil engineering from the University of Texas at Austin.

2. Joe Freeland is a founding partner in the Austin law firm of Mathews & Freeland, LLP. He enjoys a diverse practice relating to utility (electric and water), environmental, and water rights. Before practicing law, he earned his BS in civil engineering, with an emphasis in hydrology, from Rice University and a JD from the University of Texas School of Law in Austin where he graduated Order of the Coif. Following law school, Joe clerked for the Honorable J. Woodfin Jones for the Texas Third Court of Appeals.

3. Tom Bohl is General Counsel to the Guadalupe-Blanco River Authority. Before joining the GBRA, he served as an Assistant Attorney General in the Natural Resources Division for twenty-two years, representing the Texas Commission on Environmental Quality, the Texas Water Development Board, the Railroad Commission of Texas, and the Texas Department of Agriculture in litigation related to water rights, water utilities, injection wells, and various administrative law matters. He also served as legal advisor to the Texas Commissioners for each of the five interstate stream compacts to which the State of Texas is a party. Before that, he served as Senior Attorney for Water Rights and Uses at the TCEQ's predecessor, the Texas Water Commission. Mr. Bohl has a JD from Baylor University School of Law and a BA in history from the University of Texas at Austin.

II. Overview of Aquifer Storage and Recovery

§ 26.2 Definition of Aquifer Storage and Recovery

The definition of ASR developed by David Pyne is "the storage of water in a suitable aquifer through a well during times when water is available, and recovery of the water from the same well during times when the water is needed." R. David G. Pyne, *Aquifer Storage Recovery: A Guide to Groundwater Recharge Through Wells* (ASR Press 2d ed. 2005) [hereinafter ASR Guide]. Texas has defined ASR from a regulatory perspective as "the injection of water into a geologic formation, group of formations, or part of a formation that is capable of underground storage of water for later retrieval and beneficial use." 30 Tex. Admin. Code § 331.2(8).

When ASR is used for water supply management purposes, the aquifer essentially acts as an underground reservoir to be filled up when water is plentiful and drawn on during times of drought or any time available water falls short of demand. The source of the stored water may be treated surface water from a lake, stream, or river; groundwater from the same or another aquifer; or treated wastewater effluent. To prevent potential contamination of the aquifer, Texas Commission on Environmental Quality (TCEQ) regulations require that the water injected must first be treated to comply with the standards in the federal Safe Drinking Water Act, 42 United States Code sections 300f–300j-27. Water from almost any source can legally be used in an ASR system, provided it meets these water quality standards. See Chapter 30 of this book for a discussion of drinking water standards. Water recovered from ASR storage that is delivered to a public water system must meet all of the applicable requirements of 30 Texas Administrative Code chapter 290.

§ 26.3 History of Aquifer Storage and Recovery in Texas

Projects that recharge aquifers to prevent saltwater intrusion, reduce subsidence, or maintain baseflow in streams have been around for decades. However, aquifer storage and recovery—the use of an aquifer as a means to store excess water during times of plenty and to draw on when water shortages occur—is a relatively new concept. The Colorado River Municipal Water District (CRMWD) operated such a project from 1963 to 1970. In the 1980s, El Paso Water Utilities (now El Paso Water) began injecting treated wastewater effluent into the underlying aquifer rather than discharging it into the Rio Grande. See discussion at section 26.16 below. Around the same time, the Upper Guadalupe River Authority (UGRA) filed a permit application with the Texas Natural Resource Conservation Commission (TNRCC), predecessor agency to the TCEQ, to store surface water in a confined aquifer for retrieval at a later date. See the discussion at section 26.17 below.

§ 26.4 Aquifer Storage and Recovery Requirements

A viable ASR project has five basic requirements: (1) a demand for water or the need for water storage, (2) access to an adequate volume and quality of source water for storage, (3) an aquifer of suitable hydraulic and geochemical characteristics, (4) surface acreage sufficient to support infrastructure and to control access to the water stored in the aquifer, and (5) the ability to deliver the required water supply at the appropriate time at a lower cost than alternative water management strategies (economic viability). Implicit in these five requirements is the need for a defined regulatory framework.

§ 26.5 The Need for Aquifer Storage and Recovery in Texas

Nationwide, the use of ASR is increasing because of its economic viability and minimal impacts to the land surface when compared to surface reservoirs, because it can be easily developed in phases or increments, and because it is well suited to supplement conjunctive-use groundwater and surface water systems. In 1969, there was one ASR well in the United States, located in New Jersey. By one estimate, there are now more than 175 functioning ASR well fields and more than 500 individual ASR wells operating in twenty-one states. R. David G. Pyne et al., Presentation at the Colorado State University Subsurface Water Storage Symposium (Nov. 15, 2016) (on file with authors).

ASR has been slow to develop in Texas, but the momentum is building. In the 2012 State Water Plan, ASR was a recommended water management strategy in only a few regions, and the proposed projects were not scheduled to come online until the fifth decade of the fifty-year planning horizon. In the 2017 State Water Plan, ASR was a recommended water management strategy in seven regional planning groups, with a total of seventeen ASR projects. Some of the projects are scheduled to come online as early as the first decade of the planning horizon, starting in 2020. *See* Texas Water Development Board, *Water for Texas 2017* 93 (2017), www.twdb.texas.gov/waterplanning/swp/2017 [hereinafter 2017 State Water Plan].

One clear advantage of ASR over surface water reservoirs in Texas is that evaporation is virtually eliminated. Surface reservoirs in central Texas have an average net loss of about twenty inches of water per year because of evaporation. West Texas reservoirs experience significantly greater loss. Lake Travis, which has a surface area of 18,600 acres when full, loses a net volume of about 31,000 acre-feet to evaporation in a normal year. In a drought year, net evaporation rates can be much higher. As discussed at section 26.14 below, ASR projects typically cost much less and are less environmentally intrusive than reservoirs. Some impediments remain to more widespread implementation of ASR, including legal and policy issues, the general lack of understanding in the water development community about how ASR projects work, and the unsuitability of some aquifers for efficient storage and recovery of large quantities of water.

III. Technologies

§ 26.6 Introduction

From a design and operational standpoint ASR projects are site specific, but the basic technologies employed are similar for all projects. These include injection (recharge) and recovery wells (discussed at section 26.7 below) and, when surface water or wastewater effluent is used as the source of supply, typically some type of water treatment system (discussed at section 26.8). Monitoring during the demonstration testing period is also needed (discussed at section 26.9). Pipeline, pumping, disinfection, and ancillary storage technologies are employed at the typical site, but they are features of most water supply strategies; therefore, they will not be discussed here. Section 26.10 below briefly summarizes surface recharge basins, which, although not considered by the TCEQ to be ASR, serve a similar purpose and are used in Texas.

§ 26.7 Recharge and Recovery Wells

The prototypical ASR well needs to be capable of both injection and extraction. The basic requirement of such a well is its ability to recharge (inject) and to recover water at the design rates without significant well losses (pressure loss between the well and the aquifer). There are many texts and standards for designing and developing groundwater wells. *See, e.g.*, Fletcher G. Driscoll, *Groundwater and Wells* (Johnson Filtration Systems, Inc., 2d ed. 1986). However, ASR well design must also take a number of additional factors into account. For example, design considerations may include well screen and well casing specifications to reduce potential corrosion and clogging when using nonpotable aquifers for storage. The ASR wellhead must be properly designed for a recharge rate that reduces the potential for cascading down the well. Such cascading can obstruct the well with air. In addition, ASR wells are typically designed so that they can be backflushed on a regular basis.

The purpose of the injection process is to create a reservoir of recoverable water in the target aquifer. To accomplish that, a volume of "buffer zone" water is created that is not recovered. Figure 1 describes the basic elements of an ASR well completed in a confined aquifer. See Chapter 1 of this book for a discussion of confined and unconfined aquifers. In this example, the injection well also serves as the recovery well. When water is injected under pressure, it displaces the native groundwater within a target storage radius forming a "bubble" and a buffer zone. This bubble structure is typically several hundred feet to as much as a thousand feet from each well. The bubble and buffer zone structure separates the native groundwater from the stored water. The stored water is available for recovery; however, the buffer zone water remains underground and is not recovered.

The buffer zone is typically formed one time during development of the ASR well. As discussed below, the buffer zone volume may need to be supplemented from time to time during operations if portions of the bubble migrate away from the well. The Target Storage Volume (TSV) is defined as the stored water volume plus the buffer zone volume.

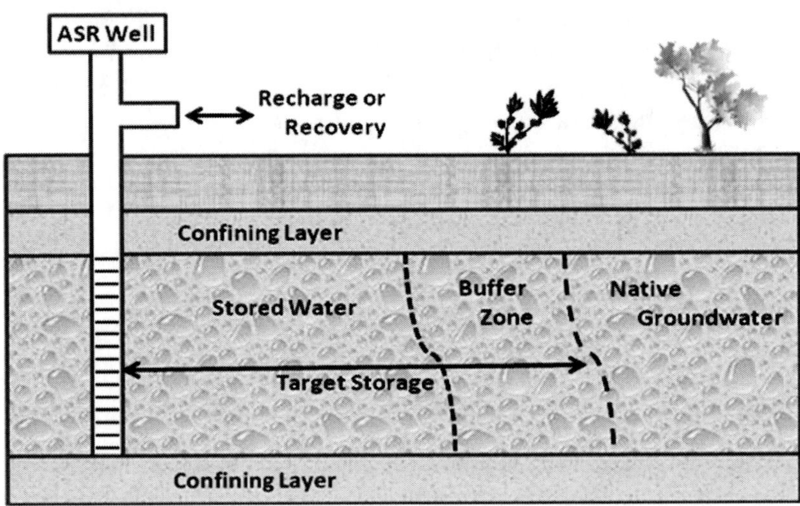

Figure 1. Physical characteristics of an aquifer storage and recovery well in a confined aquifer. Courtesy Aqua Strategies, Inc.

Recovery efficiency can be defined as the percentage of the volume of water recovered divided by the volume of water recharged during an operation cycle of injection and recovery, while meeting the target water quality criterion in the recovered water. *See* ASR Guide. Long-term recovery efficiency is improved through evaluation of storage locations during the feasibility phase and by appropriate well design and operation. With an adequate buffer zone and proper operation, close to 100 percent efficiency is typically attained. Although it is desirable to reach 100 percent efficiency, this level of efficiency is generally not required for an ASR project to be feasible, as some loss of stored water is expected in ASR projects. This is particularly true when water is stored for many years in an aquifer that experiences lateral movement, under the influence of a regional gradient in the aquifer water levels. Like water on the earth's surface, groundwater is under the influence of gravity and tends to migrate toward a lower point unless otherwise impeded.

While typically developed in confined aquifers, ASR wells can also be developed in unconfined aquifers, but the design is more complex. In addition, water chemistry issues can be exacerbated in an unconfined aquifer situation due to proximity to the oxygen-rich vadose zone. Because storage volume in an unconfined aquifer is dependent on the physical mounding of groundwater, a deep vadose zone (or region of aeration above the water table) is desirable.

Existing ASR wells in the United States vary in depth from 30 to 2,700 feet. They use aquifers whose storage thickness is anywhere between 20 and 400 feet. Although some stand-alone ASR wells exist, it is more common to see ASR well fields, where sometimes as many as thirty ASR wells operate within the same aquifer. The use of multiple wells allows for operational redundancy, improves hydraulic control, and also allows operators to inject large volumes at manageable rates and injection pressures. In properly designed wellfields, it is common for the storage bubbles to merge together, thereby improving the recovery efficiency. In other words, it is desirable (and typical) for one ASR well in a well field to be able to draw on the bubble created by injection from another well.

§ 26.8 Water Treatment

Many ASR projects use surface water as the main or sole supply source. To prevent potential degradation of the aquifer and plugging of the ASR well, and to be in compliance with TCEQ regulations, the water is treated before injection. The water treatment plant, ideally located close to the ASR wellfield, is typically a conventional treatment plant using coagulation/flocculation, filtration, pH stabilization, and disinfection processes. Membrane treatment processes can also be used before ASR recharge. In addition to treating surface water and reclaimed water before injection to meet regulations, the source water may need treatment, such as pH adjustment, to make it more compatible with the native water in the aquifer.

Typically, the stored water does not need retreatment (other than providing a disinfectant residual) when it is recovered. Sometimes, however, treatment is necessary to ensure that the recovered water is compatible with existing water in the distribution system. The San Antonio Water System's (SAWS's) Twin Oaks ASR Facility has a treatment plant for two purposes: to treat native Carrizo Aquifer water that it produces from groundwater wells on the site, and to treat water inadvertently recovered from the buffer zone around the ASR wells. To date, SAWS has needed to treat recovered buffer zone water only once since the project went into operation in 2004. See section 26.18 below for additional discussion of the SAWS ASR project.

The extent of the treatment needed before injection and upon recovery is site specific. Generally, water quality issues and treatment needs can be determined during the feasibility study and demonstration testing phases before final design and construction. In most cases, proper formation and maintenance of the buffer zone reduces or eliminates the need for supplemental treatment of the recovered water from ASR wells.

§ 26.9 Well Monitoring

The subsurface of an ASR project is difficult to characterize fully, especially during the feasibility study phase. Therefore, it is important to monitor water levels and gather water quality and geochemical data around the ASR well site during the demonstration testing period and to meter the flow rates and volumes of water injected and recovered. Wireline coring and construction of monitor wells may be needed to gather enough data to permit and design the well.

Metering provides assurances that the volume of recovered water is not greater than the volume that was injected. This helps the local groundwater conservation district understand the impacts to native groundwater and nearby well owners. In some cases groundwater modeling and accounting systems may be necessary to optimize performance and to confirm that there are no detrimental impacts on surrounding groundwater users.

Monitor wells may be needed in both the storage zone and the water table zone. The storage zone monitor wells should be logged with geophysical tools to gather additional information. For some projects a water table monitoring well is needed to confirm the adequacy of the surficial aquifer confining layer. Data from a water table monitoring well will confirm that recharging under pressure at the wellhead will not saturate the soils in the area surrounding the ASR well.

§ 26.10 Surface Recharge Basins/Vadose-Zone Wells

Though not strictly ASR under the TCEQ's definition and common practice, groundwater is often added to an unconfined formation through surface recharge basins or structures. This is typical of high-permeability alluvial deposits in arid intermontane (between mountains or mountain ranges) regions. This approach basically reproduces a natural process of recharge through surface infiltration. Because the recharging water is focused in a closed basin or impoundment, infiltration is enhanced. This works well where there is a dependable source of reasonably good quality water for recharge, where there is a lack of evapotranspiration and vadose zone redistribution, and when saturated conditions can be maintained under the impoundment (increased hydraulic conductivity of the vadose zone). See also discussion at section 26.11 below regarding new legislation to encourage aquifer recharge via injection wells.

El Paso Water successfully uses six spreading basins as part of its ASR project. Two pairs of one-acre basins were originally installed, achieving infiltration rates of about nine feet per day. Evaporation loss from the basins is estimated to be about eight feet per year. Travel time from the basin floor to the water table is about thirteen days. Infiltration basins are now the preferred method for aquifer recharge at El Paso Water because of the conducive surface geology. See section 26.16 below for additional discussion of the El Paso Water project.

A vadose-zone well is similar to a traditional well, but it is not completed through to the saturated zone. As a result, the stored water is diverted into the well and infiltrates through part of the vadose zone before accreting to the water table aquifer. Methods have been developed to estimate recharge flux from a vadose-zone well, assuming one knows the hydraulic conductivity of the vadose zone and the height of the infiltrating water. *See* Herman Bouwer, *Groundwater Hydrology* (McGraw-Hill 1978). The concepts of TSV and buffer zone may not be strictly applicable for the case of surface infiltration or vadose-zone wells.

IV. Legal and Policy Issues

§ 26.11 Introduction

In 2011, the Texas Water Development Board (TWDB) funded a study to consider, in part, why ASR was not being implemented to a greater extent in Texas and what unique features have made it more attractive in other areas of the United States and internationally. The study found that the technical challenges could be overcome if the system design appropriately addresses the physical and chemical characteristics of the storage aquifer. One of the key findings of the TWDB study is that the principal challenges for ASR in Texas are related to institutional factors and the evolving legal and regulatory framework. *See* Malcolm Pirnie, Inc. (now Arcadis-U.S.) et al., *An Assessment of Aquifer Storage and Recovery in Texas* (Texas Water Development Board, Feb. 2011), www.twdb.texas.gov/publications/reports/contracted_reports/doc/0904830940_AquiferStorage.pdf.

In 2015, the 84th legislature took two actions to address these challenges. First, the legislature appropriated $1,000,000 from general revenues to the TWDB to fund grants for demonstration projects for alternative water supplies such as ASR, and the TWDB awarded three grants for partial funding of ASR demonstration projects by the City of Victoria, New Braunfels Utilities, and the City of Corpus Christi. Second, the legislature passed House Bill 655, which significantly enhanced the ability to permit and operate ASR projects. *See* Act of May 21, 2015, 84th Leg., R.S., ch. 505 (H.B. 655).

To implement H.B. 655, the TCEQ adopted rules in 2016 revising four chapters in title 30 of the Texas Administrative Code: Chapter 39 (Public Notice), Chapter 295 (Water Rights, Procedural), Chapter 297 (Water Rights, Substantive), and Chapter 331 (Underground Injection Control).

During the 2019 legislative session, ASR was again supported through two house bills (720 and 721), and two senate bills (483 and 520). The two senate bills are discussed in section 26.11:1. House Bill 720 was enacted, which amends Texas Water Code chapter 11 to authorize appropriation of state water for aquifer recharge under section 11.023 and establishes a technical review process specifically for such applications. Aquifer recharge is a process whereby surface water is introduced into an aquifer formation by physical means, such as via injection wells, to increase the amount of groundwater in the aquifer. The TCEQ must adopt rules that will establish the frequency with which the water for recharge must be available before it may be appropriated. *See* Act of May 25, 2019, 86th Leg., R.S., ch. 742, § 1 (H.B. 720), eff. June 10, 2019.

Additionally, H.B. 720 adds Water Code chapter 27, subchapter H, prescribing procedures for TCEQ consideration of an aquifer recharge project as a Class V injection well. *See* Act of May 25, 2019, 86th Leg., R.S., ch. 742, § 3 (H.B. 720).

Further, H.B. 720 allows a water right authorizing storage that has not been constructed or that has been lost to sedimentation to be amended to convert to ASR use. The TCEQ is authorized to adopt an expedited process for acting on these applications. For unbuilt storage amendments, the rules must establish evaporation credits, taking into account the amount of water that would have evaporated if the surface reservoir had been constructed. Such an amendment does not require notice and hearing "if the requested change will not cause a negative effect on other water rights holders or the environment that is greater than the effect that the original permit would have had were the permit rights exercised to the full extent of the original permit." *See* Act of May 25, 2019, 86th Leg., R.S., ch. 742, § 2 (H.B. 720).

House Bill 721 was also enacted during the 2019 legislative session and directs the TWDB to conduct studies of ASR projects in the State Water Plan, and to conduct a statewide survey of the suitability of all major and minor aquifers in Texas for ASR. *See* Act of June 10, 2019, 86th Leg., R.S., ch 1043, § 1 (H.B. 721), eff. Sept. 1, 2019. This study was completed in September 2020, and along with a comprehensive evaluation of the aquifers, provided an online interactive tool for exploring the details behind the aquifer ratings. The final report can be found at www.twdb.texas.gov/publications/reports/contracted_reports/doc/2000012405.pdf.

As an overview, the remaining legal and policy issues relate to the authority of groundwater conservation districts (GCDs) over ASR projects, discussed at section 26.11:1 below; and the legal right to use the water to be placed in storage (source water), discussed at section 26.11:2; to use the real property in which the water will be stored and protect the water once stored (property rights), discussed at section 26.11:3; and to inject the water into the ground for storage without contaminating native groundwater (underground injection control rights), discussed at section 26.11:4.

§ 26.11:1 Authority of Groundwater Conservation Districts

Before September 1, 2015, GCDs in Texas could fully regulate the injection and recovery of water in ASR projects irrespective of the source of the water or the quantities removed. Not all GCDs had rules related to ASR projects, but more than twenty of the ninety-nine districts had some form of aquifer storage rules as of 2011.

After the passage of H.B. 655 in 2015, the role and power of GCDs in the regulation of ASR injection and recovery wells greatly diminished. While GCDs continue to have authority over groundwater produced within the district and used as source water for ASR projects, their power to regulate the injection and recovery of water in ASR projects irrespective of the source of the water has been limited as follows.

All ASR injection and recovery wells located within a GCD must be registered with that GCD. *See* Tex. Water Code § 36.453(a)(1). The ASR project operator must also send to the GCD copies of the reports filed with the TCEQ regarding injection and recovery amounts. *See* Tex. Water Code § 36.453(a)(2), (a)(3).

Beyond those requirements, GCDs have little authority over an ASR project as long as the amount of water recovered from the project does not exceed the volume of water authorized by the TCEQ to be recovered from the project. *See* Tex. Water Code § 36.454(b). Unless production exceeds authorized amounts, a GCD may not require a permit for the drilling, equipping, completion, or operation of an ASR injection well or an ASR recovery well that is authorized by the TCEQ. Additionally, ASR recovery wells are not subject to the spacing and production requirements of a GCD unless the amount of groundwater recovered from the wells exceeds the volume authorized by the TCEQ to be recovered under the project. *See* Tex. Water Code § 36.454(b).

Because ASR projects are typically designed such that recovery of water may occur months or years after being placed into storage, the time frame used to determine compliance should reflect the intended use. Producing more water in any one month or one year than the amount injected should not immediately subject an ASR project to GCD regulation. The TCEQ rules suggest this determination is based on the cumulative amount of water placed into storage over the entire life of the project and not on a shorter basis. *See* 30 Tex. Admin. Code § 331.186(a)(2).

Additionally, a GCD may assess well registration or other administrative fees but may not assess production, transportation, or export fees for groundwater recovered by an ASR recovery well unless the amount of water recovered exceeds the amount authorized to be recovered. *See* Tex. Water Code § 36.455.

House Bill 655 is generally applicable statewide, but the changes adopted by the legislature do not affect the regulation of an aquifer recharge project authorized by the Edwards Aquifer Authority or the Barton Springs–Edwards Aquifer Conservation District. Senate Bill 520 (*see* Act of June 10, 2019, 86th Leg., R.S., ch 585, § 2 (S.B. 520), eff. Sept. 1, 2019), however, enacted during the 2019 session, amended the Edwards Aquifer Authority Act (Section 1.44, Chapter 626, Acts of the 73rd Legislature, Regular Session, 1993) to allow the City of New Braunfels's municipally owned utility to recharge water of less that 1,500 milligrams per liter (mg/L) of total dissolved solids (TDS) in the brackish portion of the Edwards Aquifer, defined as the portion of the aquifer containing water with TDS greater than 5,000 mg/L. Senate Bill 483, which amends Texas Water Code § 27.0516 "Permits for Injection Wells That Transect or Terminate in Portion of Edwards Aquifer Within External Boundaries of Barton Springs-Edwards Aquifer Conservation District," allows for recharge of fresh water into a well that transects the Edwards Aquifer. *See* Act of June 9, 2019, 86th Leg., R.S., ch 583, § 2 (S.B. 483), eff. Sept. 1, 2019.

§ 26.11:2 Regulating the Use of Source Water

Source water for ASR projects comes from both surface water and groundwater. These sources are regulated separately, as discussed below.

Surface Water Source Water: In Texas, surface water can be appropriated only if it is put to beneficial use such as for drinking water or irrigation. Before 1995, whether the use of surface water for storage in an ASR project met the beneficial use requirement was not clearly established in Texas law, which effectively prevented the use of surface water for ASR. In 1995, the legislature added provisions to the Texas Water Code authorizing a two-step process for obtaining authorization for the storage and recovery of appropriated surface water in an ASR project. Under the legislation, a project developer first had to conduct a pilot project to demonstrate the feasibility of the project and obtain a temporary or term water right from the TCEQ. The legislation also made projects subject to additional regulation by GCDs, including permitting, well spacing, production limits, and water quality requirements. *See* Act of May 18, 1995, 74th Leg. R.S., ch. 309, § 2.

House Bill 655 repealed the surface water rights two-phase permitting process. Under H.B. 655, no additional water rights authorization is required to store surface water in an ASR project. *See* Tex. Water Code § 11.153. A water right holder, or a person who has contracted for use of water under a contract that does not prohibit the use of the water in an ASR project, may store surface water in an ASR project as long as the water right holder complies with the terms of its water right and has obtained authorizations for injection under Water Code chapter 27. *See* Tex. Water Code § 11.153(b). This change recognizes that storage of surface water in an ASR project is essentially no different (from a water rights perspective) from storing surface water in an off-channel reservoir. Beneficial use is determined by looking at the end use of the water, not the storage of the water before use.

House Bill 655 also clarified that new or amended water rights associated with an ASR project do not have to be based on the continuous availability of historic normal stream flow. *See* Tex. Water Code § 11.153(c). This clarification allows the TCEQ to authorize diversion amounts in new or amended water rights that exceed the amounts that would otherwise be allowed based on an analysis of the availability of unappropriated water. Specifically, this change authorizes the TCEQ to issue water rights when water is available only during wetter years with higher river flows, which allows greater efficiencies in the use of surface water. Again, this change allows the TCEQ to treat storage in ASR projects in a manner similar to the way the TCEQ treats storage in off-channel reservoirs.

Groundwater Source Water: Groundwater to be produced at one location and stored in an ASR project must be produced in accordance with Texas law. If the source water is groundwater and the well is located inside a GCD, the well must be drilled and operated in compliance with the rules of the district that apply to other groundwater production.

§ 26.11:3 Property Rights

Another impediment to the development of ASR projects in Texas is uncertainty regarding property and associated rights. Legal clarification is needed with respect to what property rights are required to inject and store water under land and what authority a project developer has to protect water once stored.

The developer of an ASR project needs to ensure that it has acquired the legal right to use the property in which the injected water will be stored and that it has sufficient property rights to protect the water in storage. One area of uncertainty in the law is the issue of who owns the subterranean pore space where the injected water will be stored—the owner of the surface estate, the groundwater estate (if severed), or the mineral estate. Because of this uncertainty, a developer should obtain authorization from the owner of (1) the surface estate covering the entire areal extent of where the injected water is expected to be stored and (2) the groundwater rights for the same property (if the groundwater rights have been severed from the surface estate). In addition to obtaining the right to store water, the developer should also obtain an agreement from the owner of the groundwater rights that the owner will not pump any of the water stored by the developer.

The migration of injected water across a property line might be a trespass. The legal remedies for a trespass include an injunction against the continuance of the trespass and damages. The Texas Supreme Court has held that some activities, such as water flooding as part of a permitted secondary recovery operation, do not constitute a trespass, even if the injected fluid crosses lease lines. *See Railroad Commission of Texas v. Manziel*, 361 S.W.2d 560 (Tex. 1962). This same immunity from tort liability, however, has not been extended to the injection of fluids under the underground injection control (UIC) program of Texas Water Code chapter 27. Compliance with a UIC permit does not insulate the operator of the injection well from tort liability, including liability for trespass. *See FPL Farming, Ltd. v. Environmental Processing Systems, L.C.*, 351 S.W.3d 306 (Tex. 2011). In 2015, the court clarified its position somewhat by holding that consent by a neighboring landowner precludes liability for trespass. *See Environmental Processing Systems, L.C. v. FPL Farming Ltd.*, 457 S.W.3d 414 (Tex. 2015). In the 2015 opinion, however, the court did not decide whether the migration of materials injected as authorized by a UIC permit would constitute trespass or would give rise to injunctive relief or damages.

Another significant concern is the risk that third parties will access and produce the water stored in the ASR project. Currently, there is no clear legal barrier preventing the owner of groundwater rights (either the owner of the surface estate or the severed groundwater estate) from lawfully producing water stored beneath his land, even if that water was injected by another. The best way to prevent the production of stored water by others is through agreements with all landowners potentially capable of accessing the stored water. If the ASR project is located within municipal boundaries, the municipality might be able to use its zoning powers to provide some protection for water stored in an ASR project.

Additional contractual protections may be needed in areas with active oil and gas exploration or production. If a mineral estate has previously been severed from the surface estate within the footprint of the ASR project, the mineral estate has the right to use as much of the surface, subsurface, and adjacent airspace of the property as reasonably necessary to enjoy the mineral estate, with "due regard" to the rights of the surface estate under the accommodation doctrine. *See Getty Oil Co. v. Jones*, 470 S.W.2d 618, 621 (Tex. 1971). In the absence of any express reservation to the surface estate owner, the mineral estate owner may use surface water or groundwater to the extent essential to the enjoyment of the grant of the mineral estate. *See Guffey v. Stroud*, 16 S.W.2d 527, 528 (Tex. 1929). Under this legal doctrine, the operator of an ASR project needs to be concerned both with oil and gas wells being drilled through its stored water and with the oil and gas operator using the water stored in the ASR project, or in the buffer zone, because such use may be reasonably necessary to enjoy the mineral estate. The ASR developer needs to thoroughly research ownership of mineral rights within the project area and obtain the agreements of the mineral owners as part of the development process.

§ 26.11:4 Underground Injection Control Authorization

The federal Safe Drinking Water Act (SDWA), Pub. L. No. 93-523, 88 Stat. 1660 (1974) (codified at 42 U.S.C. §§ 300f–300j-27), regulates injection activities that could endanger underground sources of drinking water. *See* 42 U.S.C. § 300h. Under the SDWA, states apply to the U.S. Environmental Protection Agency (EPA) for authorization for primary enforcement and permitting authority (primacy) over injection wells within the state (the "UIC program"). *See* 42 U.S.C. § 300h-1. The TCEQ program was granted primacy over classification of most injection wells, including Class V wells, which include wells that inject nonhazardous fluids underground. *See* Tex. Water Code ch. 27; 30 Tex. Admin. Code ch. 331. ASR injection wells are classified as Class V Wells under the EPA's and the TCEQ's UIC rules. *See* 40 C.F.R. §§ 144.80(e), 144.81; 30 Tex. Admin. Code § 331.131.

Before 2015, an ASR developer could obtain UIC authorization by complying with TCEQ standards at 30 Texas Administrative Code sections 331.9(b) and 331.131 or by obtaining an individual permit from the TCEQ. With the passage of H.B. 655 in 2015, the TCEQ has exclusive jurisdiction over the regulation and permitting of ASR injection wells. *See* Tex. Water Code § 27.152. The new legislation is generally applicable statewide, but the changes adopted by the legislature do not affect the regulation of an aquifer recharge project authorized by the Edwards Aquifer Authority or the Barton Springs–Edwards Aquifer Conservation District or the regulation of ASR wells by the Harris-Galveston Subsidence District, the Fort Bend Subsidence District, or the Corpus Christi ASR Conservation District. *See* Tex. Water Code § 27.157(a). Class V injection wells associated with an ASR project may now be authorized by individual permit, general permit, or by rule. *See* 30 Tex. Admin. Code § 331.7(h).

As a result of H.B. 655, the TCEQ adopted technical standards governing the approval of ASR injection wells. *See* Tex. Water Code § 27.154; H.B. 655, § 6. These technical standards detail, among other things, how the TCEQ will determine the volume of water that may be recovered by the project so that the volume recovered does not exceed the amount of water injected, less any loss into the aquifer as determined by the TCEQ. *See* Tex. Water Code § 27.154(b). If the TCEQ determines that the proposed injection of water will result in a loss of injected water or native groundwater, and the injection well is located in a GCD, the TCEQ shall impose additional restrictions on the amount of water that may be recovered to account for the loss. *See* Tex. Water Code § 27.154(b). Also under H.B. 655, the TCEQ developed construction and completion standards and metering and reporting requirements for ASR injection and recovery wells. *See* Tex. Water Code § 27.154(c). The TCEQ may not, however, adopt or enforce groundwater quality protection standards for the quality of water injected by an ASR injection well that are more stringent than applicable federal standards. Tex. Water Code § 27.154(d).

The TCEQ's standards are set out in 30 Texas Administrative Code sections 331.183 and 331.184. The standards include the requirement that all wells associated with the ASR project must be located within a continuous perimeter boundary of one parcel of land or two or more adjacent parcels of land under common ownership, lease, joint operating agreement, or contract. Tex. Water Code § 27.153(c); 30 Tex. Admin. Code § 331.183(5).

As mentioned above, the TCEQ may authorize an ASR injection well by rule, under an individual permit, or under a general permit. Tex. Water Code § 27.153(a); *see* 30 Tex. Admin. Code § 331.7(h). Injection into a Class V well, including ASR injection wells, is authorized by 30 Texas Administrative Code section 331.9(b) unless the executive director requires an individual permit. 30 Tex. Admin. Code § 331.9(c). An individual permit may be required for wells seeking variances from TCEQ standards. The TCEQ has stated that it expects that most ASR projects can be authorized by rule. *See* 41 Tex. Reg. 3514 (May 13, 2016). No public notice is required for authorizations by rule. *See* Response to Comments, 41 Tex. Reg. 3502–3503 (May 13, 2016). The executive director is required, however, to notify an affected GCD of an ASR project proposed to be authorized by rule that is located within the jurisdictional boundary of the district. 30 Tex. Admin. Code § 331.7(h).

An applicant for an ASR well, whether authorization is sought by rule, for an individual permit, or for a general permit, must provide detailed information for the "area of review," which is defined as the area determined by a radius of one-half mile from the proposed ASR injection well or a radius of one-half mile from the centroid of an ASR injection well field. Such information includes the location of all artificial penetrations into the stratum, completion and construction information for such penetrations (where available), location and description of site-specific, significant geologic features such as faults and fractures, and all other information necessary to evaluate the ASR project under 30 Texas Administrative Code section 331.186. *See* 30 Tex. Admin. Code § 331.182.

If an individual permit is required, the developer shall file a complete application within ninety days after receipt of a letter from the TCEQ informing him of the individual permit requirement. *See* 30 Tex. Admin. Code § 331.9(c). To obtain an individual permit for a Class V ASR injection well, the developer must provide notice of the application by first-class mail to any GCD in which the proposed wells will be located and by publishing notice in a newspaper of general circulation in the county in which the wells will be located. *See* Tex. Water Code § 27.153(d); 30 Tex. Admin. Code § 39.651(h).

In authorizing a permit by rule or issuing an individual permit for a Class V ASR injection well, the TCEQ shall consider—

- whether the injection of water will comply with SDWA standards;
- the extent to which the cumulative volume of water injected for storage in the aquifer can be successfully recovered from the aquifer for beneficial use, taking into account that injected water may be commingled with native groundwater;

- the effect of the ASR project on existing water wells; and
- whether the introduction of water into the receiving geologic formation will alter the physical, chemical, or biological quality of the native groundwater to a degree that would render the groundwater harmful or detrimental to people, animals, vegetation, or property or require an unreasonably higher level of treatment to render the groundwater suitable for beneficial use.

See Tex. Water Code § 27.153(b); 30 Tex. Admin. Code § 331.186.

ASR injection and recovery wells are subject to the following metering and reporting requirements, whether authorized by rule or by individual permit:

- each ASR injection and recovery well must be metered (*see* Tex. Water Code § 27.155(a));
- monthly reports must be provided to the TCEQ showing the volume of water injected and recovered (*see* Tex. Water Code § 27.155(b); 30 Tex. Admin. Code § 331.185(a));
- annual testing must be performed of the quality of the water injected and recovered (*see* Tex. Water Code § 27.156(a)); and
- annual reports of water quality testing must be provided to the TCEQ (*see* Tex. Water Code § 27.156(b); 30 Tex. Admin. Code § 331.185(b)).

In adopting its ASR rules, the TCEQ expressly recognized that it could authorize the injection of source water that had been treated to less than SDWA levels. *See* 41 Tex. Reg. 3520 (May 13, 2016). The TCEQ agreed that, on a case-by-case basis, it may consider the effects of natural processes including microbial, geochemical, and geophysical process in the subsurface to remove contaminants in the injected water. This approach will provide developers and the TCEQ with the flexibility to authorize needed water supply projects while protecting existing drinking water supplies.

If an ASR project is located in the boundaries of a GCD, the project developer must also—

- register ASR injection and recovery wells with the district (*see* Tex. Water Code § 36.453(a)(1));
- provide the district with copies of monthly volume reports and annual water quality reports (*see* Tex. Water Code § 36.453(a)(2), (a)(3)); and
- report any volume of water recovered in excess of the volume authorized to be recovered (*see* Tex. Water Code § 36.453(b)).

ASR wells do not need a separate permit from the GCD (nor do they need to comply with district spacing and production requirements) for either injection or recovery unless the amount of water recovered from the wells exceeds the volume authorized to be recovered. *See* Tex. Water Code § 36.454. See the discussion at section 26.11:1 above. Additionally, the TCEQ has taken the position that wells used for the development of ASR projects, including test wells, will be treated as ASR wells and need authorization from the agency but do not require separate authorization from a GCD.

V. Requirements for Success

§ 26.12 Introduction

As discussed at section 26.4 above, basic ASR requirements include access to an adequate volume and quality of source water for storage, an aquifer of suitable hydraulic and geochemical characteristics, and surface acreage sufficient to support infrastructure and to control access to the water stored in the aquifer. ASR wells should ideally be located near treatment plants, pumping and storage stations, high-capacity distribution pipelines, and demand centers where the wells can provide the most benefit to the water utility with the least capital cost. The greatest benefit and most successful projects are achieved by selecting a well field site located where the water is needed the most, and then dealing with the hydrogeology through appropriate design, construction, and operation. *See* ASR Guide. There are some minimum hydrogeologic requirements that cannot be overcome by design, as discussed at section 26.13 below. Section 26.14 discusses costs compared to other water management strategies.

§ 26.13 Hydrogeologic, Aquifer, and Native Water Quality Characteristics

The success of ASR is based on the concept of recovering (producing from underground storage) a high percentage of the injected water at the desired flow rate and time and at a suitable water quality. These factors are largely controlled by the hydrogeologic and other physical aspects of the aquifer and native groundwater, including water quality characteristics, which must be considered by the designer of the ASR system. While many physical constraints can be accommodated in the design process, desirable aspects for ASR include the following:

- high aquifer transmissivity and hydraulic conductivity;
- sufficient unit depth and thickness to maximize the aquifer storage potential;
- native water chemistry and aquifer matrix mineralogy that limits geochemical reactions with injected water;
- aquifer gradients that preclude rapid migration of stored water;
- acceptable density contrasts between injected and native waters;
- overlying and underlying aquitards (a bed of low permeability adjacent to an aquifer) in confined aquifers; and
- in the case of unconfined aquifers, deep water tables.

These seven characteristics are discussed below.

The aquifer must have sufficient transmissivity and hydraulic conductivity to accept injected fluids at the injection pressure design rates (including hydraulic losses). Some of this information can be gathered and analyzed during the feasibility study, but addressing these issues often involves aquifer testing to confirm transmissivity, wellbore geophysical logging to confirm porosity and the transmissivity intervals (heterogeneity in productivity), and in some cases hydrogeophysical logging to physically define the vertical distribution of transmissivity and native groundwater quality.

A second and related aquifer physical aspect is storage potential. Storage potential is a product of porosity and rock and water compressibility in confined aquifers. The best ways to characterize these properties are through physical sampling (coring), geophysical logging, and aquifer testing. Because storativity (or specific yield) cannot be determined from a single-well aquifer test, this will require aquifer testing with observation well responses (interference testing). Once these physical aquifer properties are determined, the analyst has the information needed, from a hydraulics perspective, for designing the well.

In Texas, the regional aquifers that have high transmissivity and storage potential in an unconfined setting tend to be in the western portions of the state (Ogallala, Pecos Valley Alluvium, and the West Texas Bolson aquifers). The regional aquifers that have high potential for storage in a confined aquifer include the Trinity Aquifer in parts of the state and the Tertiary Coastal Plain aquifers, which include the Carrizo-Wilcox Aquifer, the Queen City and Sparta aquifers, and the Gulf Coast Aquifer. The Yegua-Jackson Aquifer may be a candidate in some places, but it is typically a lower transmissivity aquifer than those mentioned above and has very poor water quality in the confined sections.

A third physical aspect that is desired for a successful ASR project is native water chemistry and aquifer matrix mineralogy that minimize geochemical reactions with injected water. A significant difference in water quality between the injected and native water can pose challenges unless a sufficient buffer zone is maintained. *See* R. David G. Pyne, ASR Systems LLC, *Aquifer Storage and Recovery Issues and Concepts* (St. Johns River Water Management District Special Publication SJ2005-SP12 2005), www.sjrwmd.com/documents/technical-reports/special-publications/2005-2004; ASR Guide; *see also* Bouwer; Robert G. Maliva & Thomas M. Missimer, *Aquifer Storage and Recovery: Developing Sustainable Water Supplies*, 2 IDA J. Desalination & Water Reuse 74 (International Desalination Ass'n 2010), www.researchgate.net/publication/272249602_Aquifer_Storage_and_Recovery_Developing_Sustainable_Water_Supplies; Michael L. Merritt, *A Review of Factors Affecting Recovery of Freshwater Stored in Saline Aquifers, in Artificial Recharge of Ground Water Symposium* (American Society of Civil Engineers 1988). Although about one-third of the world's ASR projects store water in brackish or saline aquifers (generally defined as aquifers having more than 1,000 mg/L of TDS), using an aquifer containing water with a high concentration of TDS has a higher potential for geochemical complications and can increase the presence of trace elements/ions in the recovered water.

Even though water injected through a Class V well for ASR storage must comply with federal SDWA standards, well clogging can still occur due to particle rearrangement, air entrainment, or biological growth. Likewise, unwanted geochemical reactions between the aquifer matrix and the source water can occur. ASR projects in other parts of the world have been abandoned or have become significantly more expensive as a result of having to treat the recovered water for fluoride, arsenic, manganese, nickel, cobalt, or other heavy metals that may increase in concentration as a result of the geochemical reactions between injected water, aquifer water, and the aquifer mineralogy. Again, maintaining an adequate buffer zone can reduce problems associated with the assimilation of these constituents.

If the injected water is treated before injection into aerobic aquifers, disinfection by-products, such as trihalomethanes and haloacetic acids in the recovered water, can also compromise an ASR project. However, most ASR storage zones are in deep, anaerobic aquifers that cause natural attenuation of these disinfection by-products.

Relatively flat natural groundwater gradients are desirable because they increase the likelihood of recovering the highest percentage of water with an acceptable water quality (recovery efficiency). If natural hydraulic gradients are steep, some injected water could be lost to migration between cycles of injection and recovery. Stored-water migration is primarily an issue for ASR programs designed for long-term water banking (for example, storage to meet demands during a repeat of the drought of record).

Minimizing density contrasts between injected and native waters is desirable for ASR. Injection of fluids into native fluids of high contrasting density increases the required buffer zone (mixing zone) volume and generally, though not in all cases, decreases recovery efficiencies. *See* Merritt; James D. Ward et al., *Integrated Assessment of Lateral Flow, Density Effects and Dispersion in Aquifer Storage and Recovery*, 370 J. Hydrology 83 (2009). A higher density difference increases the likelihood that density stratification will occur. This problem becomes worse if the aquifer permeability is high (inherently desirable) because it can lead to higher velocities, higher dispersivity, and increased likelihood of stratification. Fortunately, almost all ASR well fields are developed in aquifers where the difference in TDS concentration between the injected water and the native groundwater is less than 5,000 mg/L. With this differential or less, density stratification is typically not an issue. High TDS is not an insurmountable problem. As stated above, there are a large number of successful ASR projects worldwide that store water in brackish or saline aquifers.

In confined aquifer settings it is desirable to define a storage horizon that has good aquitards both underlying and overlying the target storage formation. This allows for improved storage volumes because of the ability to isolate higher pressures, and it also isolates the storage horizon hydraulically, preventing the potential for impacting other portions of the aquifer system over the life of the well or well field.

In unconfined aquifer settings, it is important to have a relatively deep water table. The depth to the water table basically provides a direct indication of the potential storage volume available given that the bulk of the water will be stored in what was the vadose zone. A second aspect of a deep water table is that it provides some assurance that injection will not raise the water table to near the surface. Developing a shallow water table would improve the chance of impacting surficial structures and will enhance the potential evaporative flux off the water table in arid environments.

Because of the many complex and sometimes interrelated physical factors that can impact the potential for a successful ASR design, it is critical to determine the physical characteristics of the system during a first-phase feasibility study and a second-phase demonstration test program. In addition, because site-specific conditions are so important to success, modeling studies are sometimes needed to estimate the TSV, the buffer zone requirement, recovery efficiency, potential migration, and potential geochemical reactions. Many ASR studies are documented, providing insight into successful methods for modeling and also providing information that can be used as guidance in assessing the potential performance of ASR systems. *See, e.g.*, Ward et al.; Christopher S. Lowry & Mary P. Anderson, *An Assessment of Aquifer Storage and Recovery Using Ground Water Flow Models*, 44 Ground Water 661 (2006).

§ 26.14 Costs Compared to Other Water Management Strategies

The cost of an ASR project depends on factors such as (1) source water quality, (2) physical characteristics of the storage aquifer that affect the recharge and recovery rates for each well, (3) native groundwater quality and potential geochemical reactions, (4) treatment required to meet regulatory standards, and (5) the ability to use existing infrastructure such as treatment plants, pipelines, and storage facilities.

Despite the difficulty of comparing costs, favorable project economics have been the principal driver for ASR development in the United States during the past thirty years. In many instances, there are two primary reasons why ASR is often more affordable than other water management strategies:

- ASR projects can be implemented using a phased or incremental approach rather than having to build all the facilities at one time. For example, ASR wells can be added as needed, whereas a reservoir dam has to be constructed at one time even though all the stored water may not be needed for many years.
- The costs of source water treatment are typically just the marginal or incremental expenses. For example, with the ability to store excess water in an ASR well field, a water utility can run its treatment plant(s) at the most efficient constant rate. The only additional treatment costs for the stored water are variable expenses such as chemicals, power, and residuals handling. All the fixed costs (for example, debt service, labor, and insurance) remain unchanged.

VI. Case Studies

§ 26.15 Introduction

Currently, three ASR projects are operating in Texas. The El Paso Water project is discussed at section 26.16 below. The Kerrville and San Antonio Twin Oaks projects are described at sections 26.17 and 26.18. In Corpus Christi, an Aquifer Storage and Recovery Conservation District has been created to promote the use of ASR, which is discussed at section 26.19.

§ 26.16 El Paso Water Project

In the 1980s, El Paso Water began injecting treated wastewater effluent into the underlying aquifer rather than discharging it into the Rio Grande. The Fred Hervey Water Reclamation Plant, which treats 12 million gallons per day (MGD) wastewater to potable standards, was constructed near an existing well field. Most of the treated water is used for irrigation and power plant cooling. The remaining water is either injected via wells or placed into spreading basins to infiltrate into the Hueco-Bolson Aquifer. The injected water is later recovered from production wells located approximately one-half mile down gradient of the injection sites. Estimated transit time for the water from the injection points to the recovery points is about five years. El Paso uses groundwater rights ownership between the injection and recovery wells to protect stored water from being pumped by others.

§ 26.17 City of Kerrville Aquifer Storage and Recovery Project

The city of Kerrville inherited an ASR project from the UGRA in 1998. The source water is treated surface water from periodic excess flows in the Guadalupe River, and the storage aquifer is the Lower Trinity (Hosston and Sligo Formations). The initial project had two ASR wells. The project was to be expanded, and a third ASR well (Well R-3) was to be constructed. However, there were technical problems with the third well. Those technical problems have evidently been partially resolved, and the well is in operation, but at a reduced capacity. The recovery capacity of the initial project was 2.6 MGD; Well R-3 was to have increased that capacity to 3.6 MGD, but that total recovery capacity may not have been achieved. Personal communication, R. David G. Pyne, Dec. 2016.

Near the end of the most recent drought (January 8, 2015), there were 590 million gallons (1,810 acre-feet) of water in storage and available for recovery from the ASR wells. Before the drought, the city had as much as 800 million gallons (2,450 acre-feet) in storage. Personal communication, Stuart Barron, Director of Public Works, City of Kerrville (Jan. 2015).

Before filing its permit request, the UGRA considered building an off-channel surface water reservoir to meet its future water supply needs. Despite the delays and court costs associated with its ASR permit application, the ASR project took much less time to implement and cost substantially less—by almost an order of magnitude ($3 million versus an estimated $30 million)—than the reservoir project would have, while still meeting the community's anticipated future water supply needs.

§ 26.18 San Antonio Water System Twin Oaks Project

Another successful but larger-scale ASR project can be found in southern Bexar County, just south of San Antonio. With a capacity of 60 MGD, the SAWS Twin Oaks ASR Facility is an important part of both the SAWS long-term water resources plan and the Edwards Aquifer Habitat Conservation Plan (EAHCP). The SAWS ASR system is now one of the largest in the United States, with only the Las Vegas Water District system in Nevada being larger and the Calleguas Municipal Water District system in California being comparable in size.

The source of water is the Edwards Aquifer and the storage location is the Carrizo Aquifer. The SAWS concept is to store excess Edwards Aquifer water produced when allowed under its Edwards Aquifer Authority (EAA) permits and regulations and to recover that water from storage during times of need. There are currently twenty-nine Class V wells in the Twin Oaks ASR Facility. Some thirty miles of sixty-inch steel pipe and ten miles of forty-two-inch steel pipe connect the facility to the existing SAWS distribution system. The ASR well field can produce up to 60 MGD, which was critical to meeting customer demands during the most recent drought. During 2014, SAWS recovered approximately 20,000 acre-feet of water from the Twin Oaks facility. This water allowed SAWS to meet its customer demands despite Edwards Aquifer reduction requirements of 35 percent under the

EAA's Critical Period Management Rules. As of December 21, 2016, SAWS had approximately 121,000 acre-feet of water in ASR storage. Personal communication, Steven Siebert, San Antonio Water System (Dec. 2016).

The total cost of the SAWS ASR project (both phases combined) is estimated at $255 million; a significant portion of that cost was for the thirty-mile transmission pipeline and the 30 MGD water treatment plant.

§ 26.19 Corpus Christi Aquifer Storage and Recovery Conservation District

The first special purpose district created to promote the use of ASR in Texas was the Corpus Christi Aquifer Storage and Recovery Conservation District (CCASRCD) in 2005 by Senate Bill 1831 of the 79th Legislature pursuant to article XVI, section 59, of the Texas Constitution. The CCASRCD's mission states that the district is—

> committed to managing and protecting the groundwater resources of the District, including those injected into the ground for storage and later use. The District is committed to maintaining a sustainable, adequate, reliable, cost effective and high quality source of groundwater to promote the vitality, economy and environment of the District.

City of Corpus Christi, *CC Aquifer Storage and Recovery Conservation District*, www.cctexas.com/departments/water-department/cc-aquifer-storage-recovery.

The CCASRCD has all the rights, responsibilities, and authorities of a GCD created under Texas Water Code chapter 36, although it is not a groundwater district. *See* Tex. Spec. Dist. Code § 8811.004. The district's enabling legislation also prescribes that "the district may not allow more water to be recovered from a municipal aquifer storage area in San Patricio County than the amount of water stored by the district at the municipal aquifer storage area." Tex. Spec. Dist. Code § 8811.052.

Implementing ASR is an express power of the CCASRCD. The district does not currently operate any ASR facilities; however it is currently involved in studies related to the technology. *See* Assessment of ASR in Texas, at 45–46.

VII. Conclusion

§ 26.20 Conclusion

To date, Texas has lagged behind other states in the adoption of ASR as a water management strategy. However, the physical and chemical conditions necessary for the successful development of ASR wells are present in many parts of the state, and the new regulations related to the injection and recovery of water should make ASR a more attractive water supply option for many of the water providers in their medium- to long-range water plans. Examples of operational ASR systems are described in this chapter, and it is expected that many more will be developed over the years to come. In the 2012 State Water Plan, ASR was a recommended water management strategy in only a few regions. In the 2017 State Water Plan, seven regional planning groups recommended a total of seventeen ASR projects. Texas will continue to expand its use of ASR as a water management strategy in the future. *See* Texas Water Development Board, *Water for Texas 2022* 99 (2022), www.twdb.texas.gov/waterplanning/swp/2022.

CHAPTER 27

Reservoirs

Lyn Clancy[1] and Greg Graml[2]

I. Introduction

§ 27.1 Introduction

Although most of Texas's water supplies in the earlier part of its history came from groundwater and unregulated river flows, devastating floods and the historic 1950s drought made many realize that significant reservoir construction was needed to ensure a safer and more reliable water supply for the growing Texas population. Indeed, it was during and soon after this 1950s drought that many of the state's reservoirs were constructed.

This chapter provides a general overview of the water rights permitting requirements and exemptions specific to reservoirs, including potential opportunities and considerations relevant to reservoir operations. It also identifies other permitting and legal considerations that may apply to a reservoir project in Texas. This chapter's focus is on the use of reservoirs for water supply purposes. The use of reservoirs in controlling floods, and the liability associated with flood management, as well as dam safety regulations are fully discussed in Chapter 39 of this book.

II. Nonexempt Reservoirs

§ 27.2 Water Rights Permit Application Requirements

With the exception of the circumstances described at section 27.3 below, a water rights permit must be obtained prior to impounding any state water in a reservoir or before impounding private water in a reservoir located on a state watercourse. *See* Tex. Water Code § 11.121; 30 Tex. Admin. Code § 297.11; *see also* Tex. Water Code § 11.144 (requiring approval before making alterations to a reservoir or dam). Chapter 10 of this book discusses the general requirements for water rights applications. Additional information is required in permit applications involving reservoirs. Such applications must identify the locations of dams or off-channel reservoirs (including maps) and include

---

1. Lyn Clancy is a Managing Associate General Counsel and Senior Water Policy Advisor with the Lower Colorado River Authority (LCRA). She has worked for the LCRA since 2000, focusing on water rights, water supply, and river management. Lyn worked on environmental and utility litigation as an associate at Fulbright & Jaworski prior to joining the LCRA and as a briefing attorney for the Texas Supreme Court upon graduating from the University of Texas School of Law. Lyn has master's degrees in water chemistry and water resources management from the University of Wisconsin–Madison.

2. Greg Graml is an Attorney with the Lower Colorado River Authority. He focuses on water rights and water supply contracts. Prior to attending law school, he was employed as an engineer performing water supply studies for river authorities, municipalities, and state agencies. He received his undergraduate degree in civil engineering from the University of Texas and graduated from the University of Texas School of Law.

technical design information for a dam that is proposed for construction, modification, or repair. *See* Tex. Water Code § 11.125; 30 Tex. Admin. Code §§ 295.7, 295.121, 299.3(b).

The Texas Commission on Environmental Quality (TCEQ) may also require that plans and specifications be prepared by a registered professional engineer and submitted to the TCEQ executive director for approval. *See* Tex. Water Code § 11.126(c); 30 Tex. Admin. Code § 295.41. Additional provisions specifically related to dam safety are discussed in Chapter 39 of this book.

Reservoir projects also require additional notice and specific application fees. Notice of proposed reservoir construction must be provided to county and municipal officials for each county and municipality in which the reservoir, or any part of the reservoir, will be located. *See* Tex. Water Code § 11.124(f); 30 Tex. Admin. Code § 295.42. Fees include an application filing fee and a one-time use fee. Both fees are based on the amount of water to be impounded, with the application filing fee limited to $2,000. *See* 30 Tex. Admin. Code § 295.132(a). The one-time use fee of $0.50 per acre-foot of stored water (or $1.00 per acre-foot if used for in-place recreational use) is limited to $50,000. *See* Tex. Water Code § 5.701(i), (k); 30 Tex. Admin. Code §§ 295.133, 295.134.

Finally, for water rights that have been authorized for storage, if the impoundment has not been constructed, or if storage capacity has been lost to sedimentation, specific procedures facilitate converting storage that was initially authorized for a reservoir to instead be part of an aquifer storage and recovery project. *See* Tex. Water Code § 11.158; 30 Tex. Admin. Code §§ 295.158(c)(3)(F), 297.42(g).

§ 27.3 Water Availability and Reservoir Operations

As discussed in Chapter 10 of this book, the TCEQ will grant an application only if unappropriated water is available for a sufficient amount of time such that the proposed project is viable and makes a beneficial use of water without waste. *See* Tex. Water Code § 11.134; 30 Tex. Admin. Code § 297.42(a). For a proposed on-channel reservoir project for domestic or municipal purposes, the amount of water available for appropriation is normally limited to the project's firm yield. *See* 30 Tex. Admin. Code § 297.42(h). The firm yield is generally the amount of water that the reservoir could have produced annually during a repeat of the worst hydrologic drought on record. 30 Tex. Admin. Code § 297.1(21). However, when there is a drought management plan or alternative sources of water such as groundwater or system reservoirs, annual diversions may be authorized in amounts greater than the firm yield. *See* 30 Tex. Admin. Code § 297.42(h).

Most newer reservoirs were issued permits based on hydrologic modeling such that the authorized diversion amounts are close to the firm yields from recent water availability studies similar to the diversion amount that would be authorized using the analysis required by 30 Texas Administrative Code section 297.42(h). For older reservoirs, however, the authorized diversion amount often exceeds the firm yield. See Chapter 12 of this book for a discussion of hydrologic modeling.

Once reservoirs are constructed, they often begin to accumulate sediment, which, over time, can reduce the storage volume and reliable supply from the reservoir. The Texas Water Development Board (TWDB) has an ongoing program to evaluate sedimentation in water supply reservoirs in Texas. *See* Texas Water Development Board, *Hydrographic Survey Program*, www.twdb.texas.gov/surfacewater/surveys/.

When an entity owns or controls several supplies of water, it may seek to operate them together as a system. This system operation or conjunctive use of multiple water supplies may afford a greater overall yield than the sum of the yields from the individual water supplies. If a permit for state water is to be used as part of such a system, TCEQ rules recognize that the individual permit need not meet the reliability requirements that would otherwise apply if the permit were operated on a stand-alone basis. *See* 30 Tex. Admin. Code § 297.42(d), (h). Some water rights explicitly authorize system use, with limits on the annual diversions from the system or on the diversions from a reservoir over a multiyear period. Alternatively, where water rights authorize diversions in excess of the firm yield, the reservoir owner may overdraft one reservoir and subsequently rely on alternative supplies in critical periods. In any event, a water rights permit that allows a system operation approach often contains a requirement that the permittee develop and implement an accounting plan that details how the water will be used in conjunction with other water supplies and ensures that permit conditions, environmental flow requirements, and senior water rights are respected. See discussion of the Brazos River Authority's System Operation Permit in Chapter 24 of this book.

While firm yield is the primary basis of determining water available for permitting, there are other approaches to quantifying the available supply. Under a "safe yield" approach for reservoirs, the supply is quantified as the amount of water that could be diverted on an annual basis such that in a repeat of the drought of record, the reservoir would maintain a minimum storage amount equal to one year's diversion.

In the permit evaluation process, although a proposed reservoir may be able to produce a known firm yield, the TCEQ will issue water rights consistent only with water supply needs reflected in the state water plan and an approved regional plan (unless the TCEQ determines that conditions warrant a waiver). *See* Tex. Water Code § 11.134(b); 30 Tex. Admin. Code § 297.41(a)(3)(E); see also Chapter 20 of this book. To assist in the optimum development of reservoir projects, the TCEQ may issue permits for the storage of water where demands may not warrant such a volume, and later convert them to permits for beneficial use. *See* Tex. Water Code § 11.140.

§ 27.4 Acquisition of Land to Be Used for a Reservoir

§ 27.4:1 Rights to Reservoir Location Property

To construct a reservoir, one must demonstrate that one has rights to the property on which the dam and reservoir will be located. In instances in which an applicant is not relying on condemnation powers and proposes to inundate or place facilities on the lands of another, the application must include evidence of a written agreement between the applicant and the landowner, such as a copy of a written easement, consent, license, or lease. *See* 30 Tex. Admin. Code § 295.10. An application to use an existing reservoir inundating land owned by multiple parties must be joined by all landowners, or the application must include a suitable agreement from the landowners that do not join the application. *See* 30 Tex. Admin. Code § 295.11. If the applicant seeks to appropriate water in another party's existing reservoir, a document acknowledging consent of the reservoir owner must be provided with the application. *See* 30 Tex. Admin. Code §§ 295.12, 297.22.

By statute, the holder of an authorization to construct a dam or reservoir is granted the necessary right-of-way over any public school land, university land, or asylum land, with the compensation for such lands to be determined by the TCEQ. *See* Tex. Water Code § 11.034. Further, persons may enter the land of another for purposes of examining and surveying in order to select sites for reservoirs. *See* Tex. Water Code § 11.049. If a public road, highway, or bridge is located on the site necessary for a dam, reservoir, or lake, the county commissioners court shall relocate the road, highway, or bridge, and the party constructing the dam, reservoir, or lake shall pay the expense of the relocation. Tex. Water Code § 11.044(b). For projects planned on private lands, condemnation may be used, if necessary, to obtain rights-of-way and land necessary for reservoirs and associated facilities. *See* Tex. Water Code § 11.035(a). When the party seeking to condemn private property is not a corporation, district, city, or town, the party must apply to the TCEQ for condemnation. Tex. Water Code § 11.035(c). The TCEQ must give notice to the landowner and hold a hearing, and, if the TCEQ determines that condemnation is necessary, the executive director may institute condemnation proceedings. *See* Tex. Water Code § 11.035(d), (e).

For condemnation proceedings in which the petition is filed on or after February 1, 2008, the Landowner's Bill of Rights Act is applicable. *See* Tex. Gov't Code § 402.031; Tex. Prop. Code ch. 21. The entity with eminent domain authority must provide the property owner with a copy of the Landowner's Bill of Rights no later than the seventh day before the entity makes a final offer to the property owner. Tex. Prop. Code § 21.0112(a). In addition, the entity must provide the Landowner's Bill of Rights before or at the same time as the entity first represents in any manner to the landowner that it possesses eminent domain authority. Tex. Prop. Code § 21.0112(a). This document, prepared by the attorney general, must notify the property owner of the right to (1) notice of the proposed acquisition; (2) a bona fide, good-faith effort to negotiate by the entity proposing to acquire; (3) an assessment of damages that will result from the taking; (4) a hearing; and (5) an appeal of a judgment. *See* Tex. Gov't Code § 402.031(a), (b). The Landowner's Bill of Rights is available at the Texas Attorney General's website at www.texasattorneygeneral.gov/open-government/open-reports-and-publications. See also Chapter 38 of this book regarding condemnation.

§ 27.4:2 Unique Reservoir Designations

In 1997, the Texas legislature passed Senate Bill 1, which amended the Texas Water Code to implement a state water plan addressing drought and water conservation, development, and management. *See* Tex. Water Code § 16.051. As part of state water planning, Senate Bill 1 authorized the legislature to designate river or stream segments of unique ecological value and sites of unique value for the construction of a reservoir. *See* Tex. Water Code § 16.051(f), (g). Further amendments have specified that the designation of unique ecological value prohibits a political body from financing the actual construction of a reservoir in a designated river or stream segment. *See* Tex. Water Code § 16.051(f). Designation of unique value for the construction of a reservoir prohibits a political body from obtaining a fee title or an easement that would significantly prevent the construction of a reservoir on a designated site. *See* Tex. Water Code § 16.051(g). However, if the fee title or easement is acquired for the purpose of providing retail utility service to the property in the reservoir site or allowing a property owner to improve property, such an acquisition may not be considered a significant impairment that prevents the future construction of a reservoir on a designated site. *See* Tex. Water Code § 16.051(i).

Sites can be designated to have unique value for construction of a reservoir if the development is recommended as a specific water management strategy or as a unique reservoir site in an adopted regional water plan. *See* 31 Tex. Admin. Code § 358.2(7)(a). Sites also can be designated if the location, hydrologic, geologic, topographic, water availability, water quality, environmental, cultural, and current development characteristics, or other pertinent factors, make the site uniquely suited for reservoir development to provide water supply for the current planning period, or where a reservoir might reasonably be needed to meet needs beyond the fifty-year planning period. *See* 31 Tex. Admin. Code § 358.2(7)(b). The sites are identified by the TWDB in coordination with the Texas Parks and Wildlife Department and the TCEQ or identified in an approved regional water plan. 31 Tex. Admin. Code § 358.2(7). The TWDB is to include stream segments or reservoir sites in the state plan that it will recommend to the legislature for protection. *See* Tex. Water Code § 16.051(e). The recommendations require legislative action to take effect. *See* Tex. Water Code § 16.051(f), (g).

Beginning in 2007, the state water plans have included recommendations of unique reservoir sites, with the 2007 plan including recommendations for nineteen sites, the 2012 plan including three, and the 2017 plan including three—two of which were also in the 2012 plan. The 2022 State Water Plan includes the same three recommendations as the 2017 plan. *See* Texas Water Development Board, *Water for Texas 2007* 268 (2007), www.twdb.texas.gov/waterplanning/swp/2007; *Water for Texas 2012* 236 (2012), www.twdb.texas.gov/waterplanning/swp/2012; *Water for Texas 2017* 13, 27 (2017), www.twdb.texas.gov/waterplanning/swp/2017; *Water for Texas 2022* 33 (2022), www.twdb.texas.gov/waterplanning/swp/2022 [hereinafter 2022 State Water Plan]. Prior to these plans, the legislature had designated three sites. *See* 2022 State Water Plan, at 33. Of the sites recommended in the state water plans, the legislature has only acted to designate the nineteen sites from the 2007 plan as sites of unique value for the construction of a reservoir. *See* Tex. Water Code § 16.051(g–1). For those sites, the designation terminated on September 1, 2015, unless, before that date, there was an affirmative vote by a proposed project sponsor to make expenditures necessary to construct or file permit applications as required under federal or state law. *See* Tex. Water Code § 16.051(g–1). In 2015, the legislature redesignated one of the sites designated in 2007, the Ringgold Reservoir in the Red River basin. Act of May 7, 2015, 84th Leg., R.S., ch. 48, § 1 (H.B. 1042), eff. May 21, 2015. The majority of the other sites have maintained their designations as the result of actions taken by project sponsors. Reservoirs continue to be part of the statewide long-term planning, with "new major reservoirs" composing 11 percent of Texas's recommended water management strategies by 2070 under the 2022 State Water Plan. *See* 2022 State Water Plan, at 105.

Supporters of the 2007 legislation establishing the unique reservoir designations argued that reservoir construction is a necessary part of the state's water future and that the designations would deter federal action that might otherwise impede future reservoir construction, such as a federal designation of the site as a National Wildlife Refuge, as has previously occurred as discussed below. *See* Senate Commission on Natural Resources, Bill Analysis 19, Tex. S.B. 3, 80th Leg., R.S. (2007) [hereinafter S.B. 3 Bill Analysis]. On the other hand, landowners argued that the designation would create a cloud of title on the land. S.B. 3 Bill Analysis, at 20–21. They argued unsuccessfully that landowners should be compensated for the loss of value of their land through the designation. S.B. 3 Bill Analysis, at 20–21. Additional opponents maintained that reservoirs are outdated methods of water storage and that state efforts should be focused elsewhere, such as on conservation or desalination. S.B. 3 Bill Analysis, at 20–21. The expiration of the designation in 2015, in the absence of actions by proposed project sponsors, was intended to address some of these concerns. Nonetheless, there has been significant litigation regarding reservoir sites.

§ 27.4:3 Litigation Regarding Potential Reservoir Sites

One of the nineteen sites designated in 2007 in Texas Water Code section 16.051(g–1) is the Fastrill Reservoir site, a site first identified in the 1960s. *See* Gilbert E. Kretzschmar et al., *Reservoir Site Protection Study* 73 (Texas Water Development Board July 2008), www.twdb.texas.gov/publications/reports/numbered_reports/doc/R370_ReservoirSite.pdf. This designation as a site of unique value for construction of a reservoir was particularly controversial because the site was already affected by the U.S. Fish and Wildlife Service's (FWS) designation of the Neches River National Wildlife Refuge just a year earlier, an action the TWBD and the City of Dallas challenged in federal court.

The FWS proposed a designation of the site as a refuge to protect a wintering habitat for migrating waterfowl, first in 1985 and then again in 2003. *See City of Dallas v. Hall*, 562 F.3d 712, 715 (5th Cir. 2009), *cert. denied*, 559 U.S. 935 (2010). Before designating the site as a wildlife refuge on June 11, 2006, the FWS prepared an Environmental Assessment (EA), as required under the National Environmental Policy Act (NEPA). *Hall*, 562 F.3d at 716. The EA resulted in a "Finding of No Significant Impact," which meant that the FWS was not required to perform an Environmental Impact Statement (EIS) under NEPA. *Hall*, 562 F.3d at 716.

In January 2007, the City of Dallas and the TWDB filed suit against the FWS, hoping to reverse the refuge designation. *Hall*, 562 F.3d at 716. The plaintiffs claimed that the FWS performed an ineffective EA by failing to consider alternatives, failing to consider the impact of the designation, relying on old data, and using an unacceptable decision-making process. The Fifth Circuit affirmed that the EA prepared by the FWS was sufficient, the decision-making process engaged in by the FWS was not arbitrary and capricious, and an EIS was not required under NEPA. *Hall*, 562 F.3d at 724.

Regarding alternatives, the court held that the EA sufficiently considered alternatives to the refuge designation by considering the alternatives of no refuge, a small refuge, and a large refuge. *Hall*, 562 F.3d at 718. The TWDB and the City argued the EA should have considered the alternative of both the refuge and the reservoir coexisting, but the court held that the FWS's stated inability to evaluate a dual proposal was reasonable. *Hall*, 562 F.3d at 718. The FWS had noted in the EA that plans for the reservoir were speculative in the short term and beyond the planning horizon for the refuge proposal. *Hall*, 562 F.3d at 718. Further, each of the other alternatives envisioned building the reservoir, thus destroying vegetation in that region, which was contrary to the FWS's goal of preserving the bottomlands and wetlands of the Upper Neches. *Hall*, 562 F.3d at 718.

The court also rejected the argument that the EA was ineffective for failing "to analyze the effect of establishing the refuge on the City's water supply and urban planning process, given projected population growth" as part of their impact study. *Hall*, 562 F.3d at 719. The court held that, because of "the uncertainty over whether the reservoir will be constructed and its impact on water supplies, and the long timeframe for the project, the effects of establishing the refuge on water supplies [were] not concrete enough, nor closely enough related to the federal action, to require that they be included in the EA." *Hall*, 562 F.3d at 719–20. The court concluded that the TWDB and the City could not demonstrate that this analysis was required on a site that was only a proposed water source, as opposed to an existing one. *Hall*, 562 F.3d at 719. Moreover, the City's plans were not complete, it had not yet determined the role of the reservoir in the City's long-term water plans, and it had not planned to tap the reservoir until 2060. *Hall*, 562 F.3d at 719. The court stated that a "but for causal relationship" is not enough to determine agency responsibility for impacts; the City needed and failed to show the refuge designation was the proximate cause for effects on planning, water supply, and population. *Hall*, 562 F.3d at 719–20.

The Fifth Circuit also rejected the argument that the data relied on was too old to support a reasoned decision. *Hall*, 562 F.3d at 720. Although the data was from 1988, it was not unreasonable for use in an EA, which is by definition a "rough cut, low budget" assessment. *Hall*, 562 F.3d at 720 (citing *Sabine River Authority v. U.S. Department of Interior*, 951 F.2d 699, 677 (5th Cir. 1992)). Newer data showing clearing of much of the habitat did not preclude the FWS from determining the site should be protected and could support the migrating waterfowl. *Hall*, 562 F.3d at 720. However, the court noted that had a plaintiff shown that the site could not support migrating waterfowl even if protected, such a showing might have rendered the decision arbitrary. *Hall*, 562 F.3d at 720.

The court also did not agree with the TWDB and the City that a twenty-year planning horizon was an arbitrary and capricious time frame for the FWS's evaluations of impacts of a refuge designation and, considering the FWS's engagement with the public and local officials, and efforts to find an alternative site, found the FWS's decision-making process was acceptable. *Hall*, 562 F.3d at 720–21.

The Fifth Circuit also affirmed that an EIS was not required under NEPA. *Hall*, 562 F.3d at 721. The TWDB and the City argued that the FWS's NEPA guidelines include determining the adverse effects on water supply or water quality as criteria for determining whether an EIS is needed. *Hall*, 562 F.3d at 721. The court held that these guidelines have no binding force and are meant only to assist in EIS determinations, not dictate them. *Hall*, 562 F.3d at 721. The court found the NEPA regulations issued by the Department of the Interior, which normally require an EIS when the action involves substantive conflicts over state and local land use or significant controversy over the environmental effects of the proposal, did not require an EIS. *Hall*, 562 F.3d at 722. Because the dispute was over a potential future use and not existing state or local use, the court found the controversy highly speculative with uncertain effects that could not be considered "significant." *Hall*, 562 F.3d at 722. The land had not yet been put to use, so federal action of setting a boundary for the refuge would have no significant effects on the use or character of the land, and thus no EIS was required. *Hall*, 562 F.3d at 723.

As a result of the holding, the Fastrill Reservoir, as originally conceived, will not proceed unless the federal government, through an act of Congress, abandons the Neches River National Wildlife Refuge.

In 2012, the Texas Supreme Court issued a decision related to another of the unique reservoir sites, the Marvin Nichols Reservoir Site. Hearts Bluff Game Ranch purchased land in 2003 and 2004 within the site of the proposed Marvin Nichols Reservoir and sought a permit from the U.S. Army Corps of Engineers (USACE) for a wetlands mitigation bank. *Hearts Bluff Game Ranch, Inc. v. State*, 381 S.W.3d 468 (Tex. 2012), *cert. denied*, 569 U.S. 947 (2013). The site of the proposed Marvin Nichols Reservoir has been included in state water plans for decades and was designated by the Texas legislature as a unique reservoir site in 2007. *Hearts Bluff*, 381 S.W.3d at 474–75. The USACE denied the permit application, because if Texas were to construct the reservoir the mitigation bank would not be perpetual. *Hearts Bluff*, 381 S.W.3d at 475. Hearts Bluff alleged that the designation as a unique reservoir site was the factual cause of the denial and claimed that the designation was a government action that caused a taking of its property. *Hearts Bluff*, 381 S.W.3d at 479.

In the federal claim against the USACE, the Court of Appeals for the Federal Circuit applied a two-step test for determining whether the action constituted a taking. *Hearts Bluff Game Ranch, Inc. v. United States*, 669 F.3d 1326, 1329 (Fed. Cir. 2012), *cert. denied*, 567 U.S. 917 (2012). Under the first step, the court found that there was no property interest in obtaining a mitigation permit. *Hearts Bluff*, 669 F.3d at 1331. Thus, the court did not need to address whether the interest was taken. *Hearts Bluff*, 669 F.3d at 1329.

In the state claim, the Texas court considered the *Penn Central* factors: the economic impact of the regulation, the character of the governmental action, and the extent of interference with investment-backed expectations. *Hearts Bluff*, 381 S.W.3d at 477–78. The court noted that an action could be an unconstitutional taking if it does not serve a public purpose, but in this case, water management was a legitimate governmental interest. *Hearts Bluff*, 381 S.W.3d at 478. With respect to the character of the governmental action, the court noted repeatedly that it was the USACE and not the state that had the authority to issue or deny the mitigation bank permit. *Hearts Bluff*, 381 S.W.3d at 472–74, 476, 480–89, 491. The court found that there was no direct governmental action by the state and that the state was not the proximate cause of the harm; therefore, the state's action in recommending against the issuance of the USACE mitigation bank permit was not an unconstitutional taking by the state. *Hearts Bluff*, 381 S.W.3d at 484, 491.

The proposed Marvin Nichols Reservoir was also the subject of litigation regarding interregional conflicts between regional water supply plans. The reservoir was identified as a water supply strategy in the 2011 Region C (Dallas–Fort Worth area) water plan, while Region D (northeast Texas), in which the reservoir would be located, opposed the reservoir in its plan and asserted that it gave rise to an interregional conflict because of its potential impacts on timber, agricultural, environmental, and other natural resources. *Texas Water Development Board v. Ward Timber, Ltd.*, 411 S.W.3d 554, 556 (Tex. App.—Eastland 2013, no pet.). The TWDB may approve a regional water plan only after it has determined that all interregional conflicts involving that planning area have been resolved. Tex. Water Code § 16.053(h)(7)(A). The TWDB asserted that, for purposes of the state water plan, an interregional conflict under section 16.053(h) of the Texas Water Code exists only when two regions are seeking the same source of water. *Ward Timber*, 411 S.W.3d at 556 (citing the TWDB's rules in effect at the time, 31 Tex. Admin Code § 357.10(15) (2012)). The court acknowledged the deference generally afforded to administrative agencies in interpreting statutes that they implement; however, it found that the legislature intended that concerns be addressed early in the water development process, and not simply be put off until later in the permitting phase, when bureaucratic inertia may have taken hold. *Ward Timber*, 411 S.W.3d at 572, 574. The Water Code provides that the TWDB may approve a regional water plan only if, among other things, "the plan is consistent with long-term protection of the state's water resources, agricultural resources, and natural resources." Tex. Water Code § 16.053(h)(7)(C). The court found that impacts of a project on such resources could be the subject of interregional conflicts and as such should be addressed through the process for resolving such conflicts called for under section 16.053(h)(6). *Ward Timber*, 411 S.W.3d at 573, 576.

Following the ruling, the TWDB began the process for resolving the Region C and Region D interregional conflict in 2013 with an unsuccessful attempt to negotiate a resolution through a facilitated mediation for the Region C and D regional water planning groups. *See* Order concerning the interregional conflict between the 2011 North Central Texas Regional Planning Area Regional Water Plan and the 2011 North East Texas Regional Planning Area Regional Water Plan in accordance with Tex. Water Code § 16.053, Findings 7 and 8 (Texas Water Development Board, Jan. 8, 2015) [hereinafter TWDB Order]. The matter was ultimately decided by the TWDB in January 2015, with a decision that the Marvin Nichols Reservoir Project be included in the Region C plan. *See* TWDB Order, Ordering Provision 1. The board noted the significant timber industry in Region D and also included findings that the reservoir would impact 5.2 percent of the wetlands, 2.4 percent of the bottomland hardwoods, 1.6 percent of the total timberland, and 0.76 percent of the prime farmland in Region D. *See* TWDB Order, Findings 30, 37, 47, and 48. However, the board also found that a new reservoir could stimulate the economy of the area through new recreational business and local improvements. TWDB Order, Finding 31. The board also noted the estimated annual economic value associated with Region C potential water shortages in year 2060 of more than $50 billion. TWDB Order, Finding 32. The TWDB concluded that the Region C 2011 Regional Water Plan, along with the additional analysis and quantification of impacts of the project on agricultural and natural resources of Region D provided by Region C, satisfied the statutory requirements. TWDB Order, Conclusion of Law 7.

§ 27.5 Passing Inflows and Habitat Mitigation

Reservoir permits may, where appropriate, include provisions for passing inflows and for habitat mitigation.

§ 27.5:1 Passing Inflows to Meet Downstream Uses and Environmental Needs

As with run-of-river water rights (those water rights that allow for the diversion but not the storage of stream flows), permits for reservoirs may include conditions requiring the passage of minimum stream flows to satisfy downstream domestic and livestock users, senior water rights, instream flow requirements, and estuarine requirements. *See* Tex. Water Code §§ 11.1351, 11.147; 30 Tex. Admin. Code §§ 297.44, 297.45, 297.55, 297.56, 297.59. If the passage of all reservoir inflows does not meet downstream use and flow requirements, in general, no releases from water previously stored in the reservoir are required. *See, e.g.*, 30 Tex. Admin. Code § 304.21(c)(2), (c)(3) (requiring that reservoir owners pass inflows but silent regarding stored water); Tex. Water Code § 11.053(b)(6); 30 Tex. Admin. Code § 36.5(b)(6) (prescribing that an emergency order under section 11.053 shall not require the release of water stored in a reservoir).

The owner of a dam is required to maintain a suitable outlet to ensure the passage of water the owner is not entitled to divert or impound. *See* Tex. Water Code § 11.330; *see also* Tex. Water Code § 11.087 (providing for passage of water released from a reservoir on an international stream for the use or storage downstream); 30 Tex. Admin. Code § 295.186 (providing that the TCEQ may order the installation of a low-flow outlet in an existing dam); 30 Tex. Admin. Code § 297.59(b) (requiring outlets in proposed dams).

In considering an application, the TCEQ must also assess the effects of the permit on the bays and estuaries of Texas and, for permits within two hundred river miles of the coast, shall include in the permit conditions necessary to maintain beneficial inflows to the extent practicable. *See* Tex. Water

Code § 11.147(b); 30 Tex. Admin. Code § 297.55. Furthermore, for reservoir projects within two hundred river miles of the coast on which construction began on or after September 1, 1985, and that are constructed with state financial participation, at least 5 percent of the annual firm yield is to be appropriated to the Texas Parks and Wildlife Department for releases to bays and estuaries and for instream uses. Tex. Water Code § 16.1331(a); 30 Tex. Admin. Code § 297.55(c). However, where the 5 percent value is not sufficient to meet the instream or bay and estuary needs, the commission may impose permit conditions with a greater impact on firm yield to meet those needs. *See* 30 Tex. Admin. Code § 297.55(c). The TCEQ's process for determining appropriate environmental flow conditions for water rights permits is more fully discussed in Chapter 11 of this book.

§ 27.5:2 Habitat Mitigation

In addition to the instream flow and estuarine needs, the TCEQ must review permit applications to impound or divert more than 5,000 acre-feet of state water per year for potential impacts on fish and wildlife habitats at the project site as well as upstream and downstream of the site and may require mitigation of adverse impacts. *See* Tex. Water Code § 11.152; 30 Tex. Admin. Code § 297.53(a), (c). An applicant may be required to mitigate unavoidable wetland loss to achieve "no net loss" of wetlands' functions including aquatic and wildlife habitat, water quality protection, flood control, erosion control, and groundwater recharge. *See* 30 Tex. Admin. Code § 297.53(e). Mitigation for habitat loss is generally required to be on site and in-kind whenever possible. 30 Tex. Admin. Code § 297.53(f)(2), (f)(4). Where on-site, in-kind habitat replacement is not possible, TCEQ rules require the mitigation to be in the same watershed and ecoregion. *See* 30 Tex. Admin. Code § 297.53(f)(4). Habitat mitigation plans and agreements must be in the form of binding legal contracts, permit provisions, and detailed management plans, and the mitigation habitat must be managed in perpetuity by a party approved by the TCEQ. *See* 30 Tex. Admin. Code § 297.53(f)(7).

§ 27.6 Time Limits for Construction, Forfeiture, and Cancellation

A water rights permit that allows construction, modification, or repair of a reservoir must contain a condition setting a deadline by which construction must begin, which cannot exceed two years after the date the permit is issued. *See* Tex. Water Code § 11.145(b); 30 Tex. Admin. Code § 297.51. The TCEQ may grant an extension of time upon payment of the required fees and a demonstration that reasonable diligence has been exercised toward commencement or completion of the project or there is other reasonable cause for delay or other reason why the permit should not be forfeited. *See* Tex. Water Code § 11.145(b); 30 Tex. Admin. Code § 295.72; *see also* 30 Tex. Admin. Code § 295.138 (fees for extension); 30 Tex. Admin. Code § 295.159 (notice of application to extend). Reasonable diligence does not require unusual or extraordinary effort; however, it does require the showing of a good-faith attempt to proceed with the permitting process. *See* 30 Tex. Admin. Code § 295.72(b). Reasonable causes for delay include legal proceedings or other causes that were not within the reasonable control of the permittee and that were reasonably unforeseeable at the time the water right was granted by the commission. *See* 30 Tex. Admin. Code § 295.72(b). Generally speaking, financial hardship is not, by itself, sufficient to support a request for an extension. *See* 30 Tex. Admin. Code § 295.72(b).

Generally, if construction is not begun within the time frame required by the permit and no extension is granted, a permit is subject to forfeiture. *See* Tex. Water Code § 11.146(a); 30 Tex. Admin. Code §§ 297.51, 297.74(a). However, a permit for construction of a reservoir designed for storage of more than 50,000 acre-feet of water is not subject to forfeiture for failure to timely commence or complete construction. *See* Tex. Water Code § 11.146(g); 30 Tex. Admin. Code § 297.74(d).

Water rights are generally subject to cancellation if all or part of the water authorized is not put to beneficial use during a ten-year period and the water rights holder has not used reasonable diligence or is otherwise unjustified in the nonuse. *See* Tex. Water Code §§ 11.173(a), 11.177(a); 30 Tex. Admin.

Code § 297.71. However, cancellation does not apply to water rights obtained as the result of the construction of a reservoir funded by the water right holder as part of the holder's long-term water planning. *See* Tex. Water Code § 11.173(b)(4); 30 Tex. Admin. Code § 297.71(b)(6). In the event of a cancellation of diversion rights for nonuse, the TCEQ may allow the holder of the water right to retain the impoundment for domestic, livestock, or recreation purposes. *See* Tex. Water Code § 11.183. In any event, cancellation of water rights is rare. See Chapters 10 at 10.11 and 15 at 15.4:6 of this book for additional discussion of cancellation.

III. Exempt Reservoirs

§ 27.7 Introduction

As noted at the beginning of this chapter, certain categories of reservoirs are exempt from obtaining a water rights permit. The following sections discuss exemptions for domestic and livestock ponds, wildlife management, sediment control related to surface-mining operations, spreader dams, and contouring and terracing and concludes with a discussion of the use of exempt reservoirs for nonexempt purposes.

§ 27.8 Domestic and Livestock Ponds

As discussed in Chapter 4 of this book, the use of state water for domestic and livestock purposes is generally exempt from state water rights administration—specifically, permitting. With regard to reservoirs, the Texas legislature has specifically exempted reservoirs used for these purposes (and other related but limited purposes, discussed below).

§ 27.8:1 Storage Capacity

A person may construct on his own property a dam or reservoir with up to two hundred acre-feet of normal storage and use that reservoir for domestic and livestock purposes without obtaining a permit from the TCEQ. Tex. Water Code § 11.142(a); 30 Tex. Admin. Code § 297.21(b). For purposes of this exemption, "normal storage" means the conservation storage of the reservoir—that is, the amount of water the reservoir can hold before water is released uncontrolled through a spillway or into a standpipe. 30 Tex. Admin. Code § 297.21(b). A person may temporarily store more than two hundred acre-feet of water in a reservoir that has a normal storage of more than two hundred acre-feet without triggering the permit requirement if the person can demonstrate through records maintained by the owner that the person has not stored in the reservoir more than two hundred acre-feet of state water on average in any twelve-month cycle. *See* Tex. Water Code § 11.142(a); 30 Tex. Admin. Code § 297.21(b).

§ 27.8:2 Rights to Divert and Location

Texas courts interpreted a prior version of the domestic and livestock exemption statute to allow a person not only to construct a reservoir or dam but also to divert and use the stored water for domestic and livestock purposes without obtaining a permit. In *City of Anson v. Arnett*, 250 S.W.2d 450, 452–53 (Tex. App.—Eastland 1952, writ ref'd n.r.e.), the court found that, although the statute did not specify that the water impounded could be used (i.e., diverted from the reservoir) without a permit, the legislature intended for the impounded water to be used and not simply impounded in the reservoir. This holding is reflected in the TCEQ rules. *See* 30 Tex. Admin. Code § 297.21(a).

Under TCEQ regulations, exempt domestic and livestock reservoirs may be on-channel, adjacent to the stream, or on a contiguous piece of property through which flows the stream from which the water is diverted. Tex. Water Code § 11.142(a); 30 Tex. Admin. Code § 297.21(b). Thus, a person may divert water from an adjacent watercourse to fill an exempt impoundment, and the diversion is also exempt from permitting.

The domestic and livestock exemption does not apply to a reservoir built on a navigable stream. *See* 30 Tex. Admin. Code § 297.21(c). "Navigable stream" is defined as "a stream which retains an average width of 30 feet from the mouth up." Tex. Nat. Res. Code § 21.001(3).

In *Garrison v. Bexar-Medina-Atascosa Counties Water Improvement District No. 1*, 404 S.W.2d 376, 377 (Tex. App.—Austin 1966, writ ref'd n.r.e.), the court held that a landowner's dam and impoundment of water on the west prong of the Medina River did not fall within the provisions of the predecessor to section 11.142. The court held that all titles to riverbeds vesting in individual grantees are subject to the rights reserved by the state in the beds of statutory navigable streams or watercourses under the public policy and laws of the state. *Garrison*, 404 S.W.2d at 380 (citing *State v. Bradford*, 50 S.W.2d 1065, 1076 (Tex. 1932)). The Medina River was a navigable stream; thus, its bed and banks did not constitute the landowner's "own property" on which he could construct a reservoir. *Garrison*, 404 S.W.2d at 377. A landowner who constructs a dam on a navigable stream, even if such dam enables him to divert water into his exempt off-channel reservoir, is thus not exempt from permitting requirements for the on-channel dam.

§ 27.8:3 Uses

Domestic and livestock exempt reservoirs cannot be used for a commercial operation; however, by rule, the use of land for livestock purposes is not a commercial operation and thus can fall within the exemption. *See* 30 Tex. Admin. Code § 297.21(b). Furthermore, the use of a domestic and livestock reservoir by free-ranging wild game and fur-bearing animals that may be harvested by hunters and trappers who pay a fee or other compensation to hunt or trap on the property will not result in a loss of exempt status. *See* 30 Tex. Admin. Code § 297.21(d). Additionally, the water may be used in making products from a family garden or orchard that are traded with a neighbor or used in a local bake sale or potluck dinner without risk of losing the exemption. *See* 30 Tex. Admin. Code § 297.21(d).

Finally, under certain circumstances, for lands sold by a municipality that are located within 5,000 feet of where the shoreline of a lake would be if filled to its storage capacity, to protect the availability of water for municipal purposes, the domestic and livestock exemption is not available. *See* Tex. Loc. Gov't Code § 272.001(h); 30 Tex. Admin. Code § 297.21(b).

§ 27.8:4 Comparison to Riparian and Adjudicated Rights

Important differences exist between the common-law riparian right, discussed in Chapter 4 of this book, and the exempt domestic and livestock storage right. Whereas riparian rights originated in court decisions, exempt reservoirs are a statutory creation. The earliest statutory measure authorizing the construction of storage reservoirs for domestic use is found in the 1889 Irrigation Act, further refined in the 1895 Act. Act of Mar. 26, 1889, 21st Leg., R.S., ch. 88, § 10; Act of Mar. 9, 1895, 24th Leg., R.S., ch. 21, § 10. Since that time, the Texas legislature has amended the statutory exemption numerous times, with the allowed amount of storage ranging from fifty to as much as five hundred acre-feet. See Chapter 10 of this book, which further discusses storage rights.

As a general matter, TCEQ rules nowhere indicate that an exempt domestic and livestock reservoir owner has any right, vested or otherwise, to force an upstream adjudicated right holder or riparian user to pass flows downstream so that the exempt user can fill his reservoir. *See generally* 30

Tex. Admin. Code § 304.21. By contrast, when available flow is insufficient to meet the demands for riparian domestic and livestock purposes, a watermaster or a court may order persons with exempt domestic and livestock reservoirs or certificated or permitted water rights to pass flows for the benefit of the downstream riparian domestic and livestock users. *See* 30 Tex. Admin. Code § 304.21(c)(3). Domestic and livestock reservoirs in place prior to the state's first permitting scheme established in 1913 *may* be similar in character to common-law riparian rights and have some right that is, indeed, superior to formally adjudicated water rights. Such a right could be limited to the capacity and under the terms specifically allowed under either the 1889 or 1895 statutes, depending on when the reservoir was constructed. For all other exempt reservoirs, however, one can argue that the domestic and livestock storage exemption is not a superior right. Rather, most of these users are simply exempt from the filing, reporting, and permitting requirements imposed through the water rights adjudication process.

Even if exempt domestic and livestock reservoir owners cannot call on upstream users to pass inflows, they clearly have special rights. For instance, they can generally store or use water regardless of the impacts on downstream adjudicated water right holders. *See* Tex. Water Code § 11.142(a) (containing no requirements for passing water through the exempt reservoir to honor downstream appropriative (senior) water rights). The TCEQ's watermaster rules do require an exempt domestic and livestock reservoir to pass flows to downstream riparian domestic and livestock users but are notably silent about the exempt domestic and livestock reservoir owner's obligation to pass flows to downstream appropriative rights holders or permit holders. *See* 30 Tex. Admin. Code § 304.21(c)(3); *see also* 25 Tex. Reg. 8971 (Sept. 8, 2000) (acknowledging that section 11.142 does not require reasonable use or the passage of inflows).

Unlike the riparian domestic and livestock users, the exempt domestic and livestock reservoir users are nowhere limited by statute or rule to use only the normal and ordinary flow of the river. Rather, one could argue that this exemption allows a person to store any "state water" on his property, even floodwaters. *See* Tex. Water Code § 11.021(a) (stating that "[t]he water of the ordinary flow, underflow, and tides of every flowing river, natural stream, and lake, and of every bay or arm of the Gulf of Mexico, and the storm water, floodwater, and rainwater of every river, natural stream, canyon, ravine, depression, and watershed in the state is the property of the state"). Furthermore, section 11.142 lacks any specific time limitations during which one must exercise the right, so termination of the exemption for nonuse is not an issue. *See* Tex. Water Code § 11.142(a).

§ 27.8:5 Domestic and Livestock Use from Unsponsored and Storage-Limited Projects

A person may apply to divert water for domestic and livestock purposes from reservoirs that were constructed by the federal government but for which no permit has been issued or reservoirs for which the permit allows storage only. *See* 30 Tex. Admin. Code §§ 295.182, 297.32. However, the TCEQ will deny the request if the TCEQ determines that an existing water supply is reasonably available to the property. *See* 30 Tex. Admin. Code § 297.32. Any TCEQ commissioner may issue a letter authorizing the diversion of water for such use. *See* 30 Tex. Admin. Code § 295.182(a). This letter may contain conditions for diversion, and the authorization to divert may be revoked for failure to comply with the conditions or when water becomes reasonably available from a water supply system. *See* 30 Tex. Admin. Code § 295.182(b).

Although not entirely exempt from permitting requirements, no use fees are required for permit applications under these provisions. *See* 30 Tex. Admin. Code § 295.137. Moreover, permitting of such use is not subject to the same contested case hearing requirements that generally are applicable to water rights applications. *See* 30 Tex. Admin. Code § 295.174 (the TCEQ may conduct such hearings as it deems appropriate); *see also* 30 Tex. Admin. Code § 295.153(e) (notice is as deemed appropriate by the commission).

§ 27.9 Wildlife Management

In 2001, the Texas legislature expanded the reservoir exemption to include the use of a reservoir with normal storage of up to two hundred acre-feet per year for certain wildlife and fish management purposes. *See* Tex. Water Code § 11.142(b); 30 Tex. Admin. Code § 297.21(e). The TCEQ defines "normal storage" for purposes of this exemption as "the *conservation storage* of the reservoir, i.e., the amount of water the reservoir may hold before water is released uncontrolled through a spillway or into a standpipe." 30 Tex. Admin. Code § 297.21(e) (emphasis added).

In fact, the legislature actually enacted two statutes on the subject, which provide that—

> [w]ithout obtaining a permit, a person may construct on the person's property a dam or reservoir with normal storage of not more than 200 acre-feet of water for fish and wildlife purposes if the property on which the dam or reservoir will be constructed is qualified open-space land, as defined by Section 23.51, Tax Code. This exemption does not apply to a commercial operation.

Tex. Water Code § 11.142(b) (as added by Act of May 27, 2001, 77th Leg., R.S., ch. 966, § 2.09); and that—

> [w]ithout obtaining a permit, a person may construct on the person's property in an unincorporated area a dam or reservoir with normal storage of not more than 200 acre-feet of water for commercial or noncommercial wildlife management, including fishing, but not including fish farming.

Tex. Water Code § 11.142(b) (as added by Act of May 28, 2001, 77th Leg., R.S., ch. 1427, § 1). The TCEQ promulgated rules that attempt to reconcile these differences. Thus, to claim an exemption, TCEQ rules require that—

1. the reservoir be used for either (a) wildlife management, as that term is defined in Texas Tax Code section 23.51(7), or (b) fish management purposes, excluding aquaculture or fish farming;

2. the property must qualify as open-space land, as defined by Tax Code section 23.51; and

3. the reservoir not be used for a "commercial operation," defined by rule as "use of land for industrial facilities, industrial parks, aquaculture facilities, fish farming facilities, or housing developments."

See 30 Tex. Admin. Code § 297.21(e).

As to the first requirement, Tax Code section 23.51(7) defines "wildlife management" as—

> actively using land that at the time the wildlife-management use began was appraised as qualified open-space land . . . in at least three of the following ways to propagate a sustaining breeding, migrating, or wintering population of indigenous wild animals for human use, including food, medicine, or recreation:
>
> i. habitat control;
>
> ii. erosion control;
>
> iii. predator control;
>
> iv. providing supplemental supplies of water;

v. providing supplemental supplies of food;

vi. providing shelters; and

vii. making of census counts to determine population . . . .

Tex. Tax Code § 23.51(7). For land to be "qualified open-space land," it must currently be devoted principally to agricultural use (which, for purposes of the statute, includes use for wildlife management) to the degree of intensity generally accepted in the area, and it must have been devoted principally to agricultural use or to the production of timber or forest products for five of the preceding seven years. *See* Tex. Tax Code § 23.51(1), (2).

Finally, TCEQ rules provide that the incidental use of the reservoir in a manner that does not remove the land from the definition of "qualified open-spaced land" will not require a permit. *See* 30 Tex. Admin. Code § 297.21(e) (noting that using a photograph of the reservoir in advertising does not convert an otherwise exempt reservoir into a reservoir requiring a permit).

Some have argued that the TCEQ's reconciliation of the legislation has limited the scope and availability of the exemption more than was intended by lawmakers. In one suit, a property owners association sought to claim that the exemption applied to an existing previously exempt domestic and livestock reservoir that was now located within a ranch-turned-residential subdivision where the property on which the pond is located was owned by the property owners association. *Spring Lake Owners' Ass'n v. Texas Natural Resource Conservation Commission*, Cause No. 53,727-A in Randall County, Texas (filed Nov. 7, 2003). In the settlement of this dispute, the association agreed to obtain a water rights permit without admitting that such permit was legally required. *See* Water Rights Permit No. 5845 (available at TCEQ Central Records). Since the settlement, the TCEQ has issued numerous recreational use permits for reservoirs that were previously unpermitted. *See, e.g.,* Water Rights Permit Nos. 5846, 13117 (available at TCEQ Central Records).

§ 27.10 Sediment Control: Mining

Another limited exemption applies to reservoirs constructed or maintained for sediment control as part of a surface coal mining operation under the Texas Surface Coal Mining and Reclamation Act (codified at Texas Natural Resources Code chapter 134). *See* Tex. Water Code § 11.142(d); 30 Tex. Admin. Code § 297.27(b) (also exempting use for fire and dust suppression).

§ 27.11 Spreader Dams, Contouring, and Terracing

Although not expressly exempt by the water rights statutes, certain agricultural practices that are primarily aimed at capturing diffuse surface water and controlling erosion are exempt from water rights permitting by TCEQ rules. Specifically, the rules exempt contouring, terraces, spreader dams, and other such practices designed to maximize the beneficial use of diffused surface water and overbank flooding and to implement any generally accepted conservation practices necessary to prevent or reduce erosion on one's own property. *See* 30 Tex. Admin. Code § 297.23.

§ 27.12 Use of Exempt Reservoir for Nonexempt Purposes

The owner of a reservoir that is exempt under Texas Water Code section 11.142(a) or (b) may apply for a regular, seasonal, or term permit from the TCEQ to use the stored water for purposes other than the exempt uses. *See* Tex. Water Code § 11.143(a), (b); *see also* 30 Tex. Admin. Code §§ 295.51, 295.126, 297.15. The owner may elect to obtain the permit under section 11.143 or under the other provisions of chapter 11, such as section 11.124, which are discussed in more detail in Chapter 10 of this book (addressing surface water rights permitting). *See* Tex. Water Code § 11.143(a). A permit requested under section 11.143 must comply with notice and hearing processes and the payment of fees. *See* Tex. Water Code § 11.143(d)–(h); 30 Tex. Admin. Code § 295.153(c), (d). The TCEQ may act on the application without holding a public hearing only if certain public notice requirements are satisfied and no hearing is requested. *See* Tex. Water Code § 11.143(d).

The TCEQ may approve an application under section 11.143 only if it determines that—

1. there is unappropriated water in the source of supply;
2. the applicant has met the application and notice requirements of section 11.143;
3. the water is to be used for a beneficial purpose;
4. the proposed use is not detrimental to the public welfare or to the welfare of the locality; and
5. the proposed use will not impair existing water rights.

See Tex. Water Code § 11.143(i).

IV. Selected Issues

§ 27.13 Introduction

In addition to the permitting requirements to store or divert water discussed above, additional TCEQ requirements apply when water is used at a location upstream or downstream of the reservoir. The following sections provide an overview of those requirements, also addressing littoral claims to water in a reservoir, limitations on hydropower generation, issues associated with storage of groundwater in reservoirs, and a disclosure requirement for the sale of lakefront property. See also Chapter 10 of this book regarding surface water rights permitting.

§ 27.14 Bed and Banks Transport from Reservoirs

Subject to TCEQ rules, a reservoir owner may use the bed and banks of any flowing natural stream in Texas to convey water from the reservoir to the place of use or to the diversion point downstream. *See* Tex. Water Code § 11.042(a); 30 Tex. Admin. Code § 297.91. This authorization may be obtained as part of the initial permitting of the reservoir or as a separate authorization.

TCEQ rules require the seller or purchaser of conveyed stored water to file with the TCEQ a copy of the purchase contract and a written statement of the intended transit of the water, giving the details of the proposed transport and use of the water. *See* 30 Tex. Admin. Code § 295.111(a). The statement must include, among other things, the method for measuring and accounting for the water released and subsequently diverted such that only the water being released is diverted at the point of delivery, less the amount of water lost to transportation, evaporation, seepage, channel, or other associated carriage losses from the point of release to the point of delivery. *See* 30 Tex. Admin. Code § 295.111(a). Exceptions to these requirements are made only in an emergency or if a separate TCEQ order exists. *See* 30 Tex. Admin. Code §§ 295.111(b), 297.91.

Water that is released from storage for delivery downstream is protected to its intended diversion location against the willful taking, diversion, appropriation, or interference by others. *See* Tex. Water Code § 11.091; 30 Tex. Admin. Code § 297.94. To ensure this, once a bed and banks application is granted, the TCEQ sends notice to each diverter of record on the watercourse between the origin and terminus of the transit. *See* 30 Tex. Admin. Code § 295.160.

Typically, delivery of water from a reservoir using the bed and banks of a watercourse is sought pursuant to a contract between the reservoir owner and a downstream customer. The TCEQ may require the alteration or amendment of any such contract for the transportation of water if it finds the change is necessary to protect vested rights or prevent the undue loss of water. 30 Tex. Admin. Code § 297.92. Furthermore, a reservoir owner who is releasing water for downstream customers may not allow the water to overflow the banks of any stream, nor may he interfere with those who have a lawful right to the use of that rate of flow of the stream that would prevail in the absence of the water in transit. 30 Tex. Admin. Code § 297.93. The TCEQ authorization for the transport must include a flow rate of delivery, and all interested parties must be notified of the rate. *See* 30 Tex. Admin. Code § 297.92–.93. Furthermore, the water released for downstream use must be of a quality that will not affect adversely or harmfully the quality of water in the stream or in storage below. 30 Tex. Admin. Code § 297.93.

§ 27.15 Downstream Water Sales from Reservoirs

A reservoir owner who contracts to sell water from a reservoir to a downstream user must make releases of water to the extent of the purchaser's downstream diversions within the limits of the supplier's water rights or the contract. *See* 30 Tex. Admin. Code § 297.103(a). However, a seller is not required to release water to satisfy contractual obligations when such release would aggravate existing flooding conditions; but the purchaser may divert water during such conditions pursuant to the contract. 30 Tex. Admin. Code § 297.103(a)(1). The conditions under which this could occur may be included in any contractual permit issued by the TCEQ. *See* 30 Tex. Admin. Code § 297.103(a)(2).

Generally speaking, contracts for downstream water sales should include provisions for water transportation and evapotranspiration losses from the reservoir to the downstream point of diversion. If a contract is silent on this issue, and it is a contract that must be filed with the TCEQ, the supplier must bear such losses. *See* 30 Tex. Admin. Code § 297.103(c). See Chapter 31 of this book for a discussion of wholesale water suppliers.

§ 27.16 Upstream Water Sales from Reservoirs

A supplier may also contract with a user upstream of the reservoir to allow the user to divert water upstream of a supplier's storage reservoir in a manner that would otherwise impair the supplier's water rights. In such cases, the purchaser or supplier must obtain a permit (or permit amendment) from the TCEQ to the extent of the purchaser's maximum annual diversions of water for the term of the contract. *See* 30 Tex. Admin. Code § 297.104. In considering an application for a permit based on an upstream water sale, the TCEQ may include conditions in the permit to address the impacts of the proposed sale on instream flows or water rights holders located between the proposed upstream diversion point and the supplier's reservoir.

§ 27.17 Littoral Rights and Artificial Reservoirs

As experienced by owners of large water supply reservoirs, many landowners around artificial reservoirs mistakenly believe that their land ownership entitles them to divert and use water from the reservoir. In fact, such landowners are unlikely to have any legal right to use water from the reservoir unless the landowner has a contract for water from the person or entity that holds the water rights to the reservoir. For a lakefront property owner to establish that his land is vested with rights to divert and use the water for his own domestic and livestock purposes, he must (1) be able to trace his title back to a grant from the sovereign between 1823 and 1895 or present a certificate of adjudication from the state and (2) establish that his land, as granted in the deed, borders a natural lake with a "normal flow" of water. *Cummins v. Travis County Water Control & Improvement District No. 17*, 175 S.W.3d 34, 45 (Tex. App.—Austin 2005, pet. denied). In *Cummins*, the court held that the landowners had no riparian or littoral right to place a dock over the lake (or use the water for domestic purposes) because their title failed to originate before 1895, and the waters filling Lake Travis were not "normal flow" but were instead floodwaters.

§ 27.18 Limitations on Hydroelectric Generation

In some instances, the Texas legislature has limited the use of reservoirs for hydroelectric generation. For example, the Lower Colorado River Authority's enabling statute expressly subordinates the authority's rights to impound and use waters of the Colorado River and its tributaries for the generation of hydroelectric power to the rights of certain municipalities and other political subdivisions to build dams or impound floodwaters for municipal or domestic purposes. *See* Tex. Spec. Dist. Code § 8503.005(b), (f). Furthermore, some water rights restrict water rights holders from making releases solely for hydroelectric generation purposes except under emergency or other very limited conditions.

§ 27.19 Groundwater and Reservoirs

A discussion of reservoirs is incomplete without some mention of the role groundwater may play. As discussed in Chapter 5 of this book, the use of groundwater is governed either by chapter 36 of the Texas Water Code and local groundwater conservation districts (GCDs) or by the common-law principles, such as the rule of capture and other court decisions. The storage of groundwater in reservoirs can trigger local regulation by a GCD and also, in the case of on-channel reservoirs, require state water rights permitting under section 11.042 of the Water Code. For a water right application that would rely on groundwater, notice must be provided to the GCD with jurisdiction over the groundwater. *See* Tex. Water Code §§ 11.132(d), 11.143(f). In basins where no state water is available for appropriation, the TCEQ will require a permittee who wishes to maintain an on-channel reservoir for nonconsumptive purposes (e.g., recreation or aesthetic enhancement of a housing subdivision) to pass all inflows and make up for evaporative losses with another source of supply. Often, permittees will turn to groundwater as their alternative source of supply to keep the reservoir full. *See, e.g.*, Water Use Permit No. 5928 (available at TCEQ Central Records). Whether the use of groundwater to make up for evaporative losses can be authorized under local GCD rules will be determined on a case-by-case basis in accordance with the specific rules of each district. See Chapter 16 of this book.

Areas of the state that have seen an increase in hydraulic fracturing activity have also seen an increase in the storage, albeit temporary, of groundwater in reservoirs. A typical case involves pumping groundwater into an existing on-channel reservoir for temporary storage until the stored groundwater can be diverted to use for hydraulic fracturing activities. A bed and banks permit is required. The permit provides for recordkeeping to show that no state water has been diverted. *See* Tex. Water Code §§ 11.042, 11.121; *see also* Water Use Permit No. 13481 (available at TCEQ Central Records).

§ 27.20 Disclosure Requirements for the Sale of Reservoir-Related Property

The seller of lakefront property on a reservoir impounding at least 5,000 acre-feet must disclose to a potential buyer that the lake level fluctuates as a result of the use of the water stored in the reservoir or drought or flood conditions. *See* Tex. Prop. Code § 5.019. Additionally, the seller must disclose knowledge of prior flood events, flood insurance coverage, and a location wholly or partly in a floodplain, floodway, flood pool, or reservoir. *See* Tex. Prop. Code § 5.008(b). See Chapter 39 of this book for additional discussion of flood management.

V. Federal Considerations for Reservoirs

§ 27.21 Overview

Although the focus of this book is on Texas state water rights law, this chapter identifies a few of the more significant federal regulatory requirements that may be triggered as a result of a reservoir project. The discussion makes no attempt to provide the level of detail that would be required to comply with these requirements. Rather, the intent is to provide the reader with a general understanding of these requirements. Additional discussion of many of these considerations is found in other chapters in this book, as referenced below.

In 2016, the USACE initiated rulemaking related to the use of Corps reservoirs authorized under section 6 of the 1944 Flood Control Act and the Water Supply Act of 1958. *See* 81 Fed. Reg. 91,556 (Dec. 16, 2016), Docket No. COE-2016-0016, www.regulations.gov/docket?D=COE-2016-0016. Historically, water supply uses have been accommodated at more than one hundred Corps reservoirs but in a somewhat inconsistent manner and at best under an internal guidance document that is more than fifteen years old. *See* 81 Fed. Reg. 91,556, 91,557. The Corps' stated goal in formalizing its policies includes improving consistency and facilitating access to Corps reservoirs for water supply while not "upset[ting] the balance between federal purposes and state prerogatives or assert[ing] any greater federal control over water resources." 81 Fed. Reg. 91,556, 91,558–59. Numerous entities, including many from Texas, provided comments urging that the rulemaking be withdrawn or delayed, expressing concerns including that the proposed rules would result in federal overreach and interfere with states' roles in allocating water resources. *See* Docket No. COE-2016-0016. The rulemaking was withdrawn on March 16, 2020. *See* 85 Fed. Reg. 16,307 (Mar. 23, 2020).

Section 404 permitting by the USACE applies to any project that will discharge dredge or fill material into waters regulated by the Clean Water Act and thus is often triggered by reservoir construction. Section 404 permitting is discussed generally in the context of water supply projects in Chapter 3 and in greater detail in Chapter 35 of this book.

Section 401 of the Clean Water Act requires that any project that may cause a discharge into waters of the United States and seeking a federal permit, whether for construction or operation, must first obtain state certification that the project will comply with all effluent limitations and water quality standards imposed by the state in which the discharge will occur. The Supreme Court has made clear that section 401 certification requirements apply to dams and reservoirs. *See S.D. Warren Co. v. Maine Board of Environmental Protection*, 547 U.S. 370 (2006) (section 401 triggered when seeking renewal of federal licenses for hydroelectric dams due to the potential for a discharge). Section 401 is discussed generally in the context of water supply projects in Chapter 3 and in greater detail in Chapter 34 of this book.

Any reservoir project that involves a federal permit will likely trigger the requirements of the National Environmental Policy Act (NEPA). Section 102 of NEPA requires all federal agencies to assess and quantify in a systematic, interdisciplinary manner the environmental impact of any proposed federal action (e.g., funding or issuance of a permit) that has the potential to significantly affect the quality of the human environment. NEPA is discussed in greater detail in Chapter 3 of this book.

If a reservoir project is to be "authorized, funded, or carried out" by any federal agency, under section 7 of the Endangered Species Act (ESA), the federal agency must consult with the U.S. Fish and Wildlife Service to ensure that the action is not likely to jeopardize the continued existence of any endangered or threatened species or result in the destruction or adverse modification of critical habitat. *See* 16 U.S.C. § 1536(a)(2). The ESA also requires that any project that will "take" an endangered species must obtain an incidental take permit. *See* 16 U.S.C. § 1539(a)(1)(B). "Take" is defined broadly to include "harass, harm, pursue, hunt, shoot, wound, kill, trap, capture, or collect, or to attempt to engage in any such conduct." 16 U.S.C. § 1532(19). The ESA is discussed in greater detail in Chapter 32 of this book.

§ 27.22 FERC Jurisdiction

If the dam to be constructed as part of the reservoir project will include hydroelectric facilities, one must determine whether jurisdiction under the Federal Energy Regulatory Commission (FERC) is triggered. FERC has authority under the Federal Power Act (FPA) to license and relicense certain hydroelectric facilities. *See* 16 U.S.C. §§ 791a–823g, as amended by various acts, including the Electric Consumers Protection Act of 1986, Pub. L. No. 99-495 (1986), the Energy Policy Act of 1992, Pub. L. No. 102-486 (1992), the Hydropower Regulatory Efficiency Act of 2013, Pub. L. No. 113-23 (2013), and the America's Water Infrastructure Act of 2018, Pub. L. No. 115-270 (2018). FERC may issue a license to operate a hydroelectric facility upon satisfaction of certain criteria. *See generally* 16 U.S.C. § 797 (FPA § 4). The license is valid for up to fifty years. *See* 16 U.S.C. § 799 (FPA § 6). Upon expiration of the license, one of several things can happen: the licensee can apply for relicense, another entity can apply for a license to operate the facility, FERC itself may take over operations, FERC may issue a "non-power" license, or the facility may be decommissioned. *See* 16 U.S.C. §§ 807, 808 (FPA §§ 14, 15) (decommissioning is considered in detail in FERC Docket No. RM93-23.000: Policy Statement—Project Decommissioning and Relicensing, 60 Fed. Reg. 339 (Jan. 4, 1995)).

The Hydropower Regulatory Efficiency Act of 2013 recognized that only 3 percent of the 80,000 dams in the United States generate electricity and directed FERC to investigate the feasibility of issuance of hydropower licenses at nonpowered dams and closed-loop pumped storage projects in a two-year period. Following a pilot study by FERC, the America's Water Infrastructure Act of 2018 directed FERC to establish an expedited licensing process for nonpowered dams. *See* 16 U.S.C. § 823e, 18 C.F.R. pt. 7.

Among the requirements to qualify for expedited processing for a hydroelectric facility at a nonpowered dam are that the operations not make any material changes to the storage, release, or flow operations of the dam. *See* 16 U.S.C. § 823e; 18 C.F.R. § 7.2. The application is required to include information regarding section 401 of the Clean Water Act, the Endangered Species Act, and the National Historic Preservation Act. *See* 18 C.F.R. § 7.2.

Of specific interest with regard to state water rights is FERC's authority to impose conditions related to environmental considerations, because this authority has the potential to conflict with the TCEQ's determinations on this subject.

The FPA mandates that FERC consider environmental concerns in evaluating license applications:

> In deciding whether to issue any license under [the FPA] for any project, the Commission, in addition to the power and development purposes for which licenses are issued, shall give *equal consideration* to the purposes of energy conservation, the protection, mitigation of damage to, and enhancement of, fish and wildlife (including related spawning grounds and habitat), the protection of recreational opportunities, and the preservation of other aspects of environmental quality.

16 U.S.C. § 797(e) (FPA § 4(e)) (emphasis added); *see also PUD No. 1 of Jefferson County v. Washington Department of Ecology*, 511 U.S. 700, 722 (1994); *Platte River Whooping Crane Critical Habitat Maintenance Trust (I) v. FERC*, 876 F.2d 109, 118 (D.C. Cir. 1989) ("[Section 4(e)] is important

because it is intended that FERC give these nondevelopmental values the same level of reflection as it does to power and other developmental objectives.").

The FPA mandates that FERC impose conditions to protect fish and wildlife, and such conditions may be based on recommendations from the U.S. Fish and Wildlife Service, the National Marine Fisheries Service, and state fish and wildlife agencies as conditions on the license. *See* 16 U.S.C. § 803(j) (FPA § 10(j)). To comply with section 10(j), FERC reviews recommendations from the relevant agencies during the application process. *See* Federal Energy Regulatory Commission, *Handbook For Hydroelectric Project Licensing* 3.2.6 (2004). However, FERC is not obligated to incorporate every recommendation proposed by the relevant agencies. *See American Rivers v. FERC*, 201 F.3d 1186, 1202–03 (9th Cir. 2000); *National Wildlife Federation v. FERC*, 912 F.2d 1471, 1480 (D.C. Cir. 1990). If FERC decides not to impose the recommendations but instead impose its own conditions, it must show that the agency recommendation is inconsistent with the FPA or other applicable law and that the FERC conditions adequately protect fish and wildlife. *See* 18 C.F.R. § 4.34(e). FERC must publish findings explaining its rejection of section 10(j) recommendations, and FERC must afford "*significant* deference" to the agencies' recommendations. *See American Rivers*, 201 F.3d at 1205 (citing *Kelley v. FERC*, 96 F.3d 1482, 1486 (D.C. Cir. 1996)).

Section 10(j) also provides authority for FERC to impose water quality conditions as part of the licensing process. *See, e.g., United States Department of Interior v. FERC*, 952 F.2d 538 (D.C. Cir. 1992) (upholding FERC conditions imposing minimum dissolved oxygen levels and other conditions to protect water quality and fish habitat).

FERC has broad discretion to impose conditions on licenses. 16 U.S.C. § 803(g) (FPA § 10(g)). "Congress intended by Section 10(g) 'to give the Commission wide latitude and discretion in the performance of its licensing and regulatory functions.'" *Pennsylvania Department of Environmental Resources v. FERC*, 868 F.2d 592, 597–98 (3rd Cir. 1989) (citing *Metropolitan Edison Co. v. F.P.C.*, 169 F.2d 719 (3d Cir. 1948)).

FERC also must "require the construction, maintenance, and operation by a licensee at its own expense of . . . such fishways as may be prescribed by the Secretary of the Interior or the Secretary of Commerce, as appropriate." 16 U.S.C. § 811 (FPA § 18). Items that qualify as fishways "are limited to physical structures, facilities, or devices necessary to maintain all life stages" of migrating fish. Energy Policy Act of 1992, Pub. L. No. 102-486, § 1701(b), 106 Stat. 3008. FERC has no discretion to reject fishway conditions imposed by the secretaries. *See American Rivers*, 201 F.3d 1206–11 (distinguishing the language in FPA § 10(j)—which allows the Commission to reject a recommendation of the secretaries—from the language in FPA § 18).

As with the Clean Water Act, the FPA expressly states that it does not affect state water allocation. 16 U.S.C § 821 (FPA § 27). The U.S. Supreme Court, however, has upheld conditions that impose minimum flow rates, concluding that these fall *outside* of the state water allocation jurisdiction. *See California v. FERC*, 495 U.S. 490 (1990); *First Iowa Hydro-Electric Cooperative v. Federal Power Commission*, 328 U.S. 152 (1946). In *First Iowa*, the Supreme Court held that the FPA essentially preempts state law with respect to hydroelectric facilities. Although section 27 preserves state control over appropriation, control, and diversion of water, this is a limited reservation that applies only to proprietary rights. *First Iowa*, 328 U.S. at 176. In *California*, the Court held that "California's minimum stream flow requirements neither reflect nor establish 'proprietary rights' or 'rights of the same nature as those relating to the use of water in irrigation or for municipal purpose'" and therefore the licensee had to comply only with minimum flow requirements of the federal permit and not the significantly higher minimum requirements California would impose. *California*, 495 U.S. at 498 (quoting *First Iowa*, 328 U.S. at 176).

CHAPTER 29

Drinking Water Supply Issues: Water Utilities—CCNs and Rates

Leonard H. Dougal[1]

I. Introduction

§ 29.1 Introduction

Drinking water in Texas is supplied by a variety of retail public utilities. Although these entities have a similar purpose—to provide retail water service—their structures and powers differ. This chapter begins with a description of the types of retail public utilities that provide water service. The chapter next discusses certificates of public convenience and necessity, which delineate the service territory of a retail public utility and are required for some, but not all, retail public utilities. Also included is a discussion of the rates and fees that different retail public utilities use to support water service and the level at which these rates and fees are supervised. The various methodologies for developing the rates and fees are beyond the scope of this chapter.

II. Types of Utilities

§ 29.2 Water Utility Regulation in Texas: From the PUC and Back Again

The Texas legislature enacted the Public Utility Regulatory Act (PURA) in 1975, creating the Public Utility Commission of Texas (PUC) and providing for comprehensive regulation of utilities. *See* Act of June 2, 1975, 64th Leg., R.S., ch. 721 (codified at Tex. Util. Code §§ 11.001–66.016). Enactment of PURA was based on the legislature's recognition that public utilities are by definition monopolies in the areas they serve, necessitating state regulation of their rates and service policies. Through PURA, the PUC was charged with implementing regulations for electric, gas, telephone, water, and sewer utilities. Jurisdiction over retail public utilities providing water supply and sewer services was later transferred from the PUC to the Texas Water Commission (a predecessor agency of

---

1. Leonard H. Dougal is a partner with Jackson Walker L.L.P. in Austin where his practice focuses on environmental permitting; water rights; water utility CCN matters; and the purchase, sale, and financing of utility assets. He has also been instrumental in the creation of numerous special utility districts at the Texas legislature and is a frequent speaker on water law topics.

The author gratefully acknowledges the contributions and assistance of Cassandra Quinn, formerly an associate at Jackson Walker L.L.P., in drafting and updating revisions to this chapter; of Kenneth L. Peterson, Jr., deceased, formerly General Counsel for the Texas Water Development Board, in his counsel and writing of the original chapter; of Lara Nehman Zent, Texas Rural Water Association, for her assistance and work on the original chapter; and Danica Milios, Alicia French, Mallory Beck, and Alisha Mehta in researching and updating this chapter.

the Texas Commission on Environmental Quality (TCEQ)). *See* Act of May 25, 1985, 69th Leg., R.S., ch. 795. Texas Water Code chapter 13 was enacted to "establish a comprehensive regulatory system that is adequate to the task of regulating retail public utilities to assure rates, operations, and services that are just and reasonable to the consumers and to the retail public utilities." Tex. Water Code § 13.001(c).

Effective September 1, 2014, the economic regulation of water utilities, including oversight of water and wastewater rates, regulation of certificates of public convenience and necessity (CCNs), and review of certain transactions concerning water and wastewater systems, was transferred back to the PUC. *See* Act of May 14, 2013, 83d Leg., R.S., ch. 171 (S.B. 567); Act of May 14, 2013, 83d Leg., R.S., ch. 170 (H.B. 1600). The responsibility for ensuring safe drinking water remains with the TCEQ, as well as oversight of activities of water districts, including bond approvals and reviews of impact fees and standby fees. Before this latest transfer, the TCEQ and the PUC entered into a memorandum of understanding. *See Memorandum of Understanding between the Texas Commission on Environmental Quality (TCEQ) and the Public Utility Commission of Texas (PUC)* (July 31, 2014), www.tceq.texas.gov/assets/public/agency/puc-tceq-mou-accessible.pdf. Initially, the PUC adopted the TCEQ's existing rules with minor changes. *See* 39 Tex. Reg. 5920 (Aug. 1, 2014). Since that time, however, the PUC has reviewed and revised numerous regulations, including making changes that materially alter the regulation of retail public utilities and how CCNs are granted, amended, and revoked. *See* 41 Tex. Reg. 9820 (Dec. 16, 2016); 43 Tex. Reg. 6826 (Oct. 12, 2018).

§ 29.3 Types of Retail Public Utilities

Chapter 13 of the Texas Water Code uses numerous, similar terms to describe the various types of retail water providers over which the PUC has authority. Understanding these terms is essential to analyzing the various regulations that apply. The terms "water and sewer utility," "public utility," and "utility" are used interchangeably and refer to what is commonly known as an investor-owned utility (an entity operated for profit). The terms expressly exclude municipal corporations, political subdivisions of the state, and water supply and sewer service corporations. *See* Tex. Water Code § 13.002(23). The term "water supply or sewer service corporation" refers to a nonprofit corporation operating under chapter 67 of the Water Code. Tex. Water Code § 13.002(24). The term "retail public utility" is much more expansive and includes "any person, corporation, public utility, water supply or sewer service corporation, municipality, political subdivision or agency operating, maintaining, or controlling in this state facilities for providing potable water service or sewer service, or both, for compensation" without any limitation. Tex. Water Code § 13.002(19).

The definitions have important consequences. For example, a municipality is a "retail public utility" but not a "water and sewer utility," "public utility," or "utility." As a result, whether a provision of chapter 13 applies to a municipality depends on whether the provision applies to a "utility" or a "retail public utility." However, as with all public water systems, municipalities must comply with minimum health and sanitation requirements promulgated by the TCEQ under the authority of Texas Health and Safety Code chapter 341, subchapter C. *See generally* 30 Tex. Admin. Code ch. 290. See Chapter 30 of this book for a discussion of health and sanitation requirements for water suppliers.

§ 29.3:1 Municipalities

Municipalities have broad statutory authority to provide water service inside and outside of their corporate limits and do not require a CCN to do so unless the municipality extends service into an area currently served by another retail public utility. *See* Tex. Loc. Gov't Code § 552.001 (authority to operate a utility system inside or outside municipal boundaries); Tex. Water Code § 13.242 (requiring a "utility" to obtain a CCN; since a municipality is not a "utility," no CCN is required). The services provided by municipalities are subject to limited state oversight. In general, municipalities are not subject to the PUC's regulations regarding quality of service or customer service and protection, and they are not required to file their rates with the PUC. If a municipality chooses to obtain a CCN, however, the PUC's regulations pertaining to quality of service will apply. *See* 16 Tex. Admin. Code § 24.151.

There is also limited state oversight of the rates and fees charged by a municipality. The PUC has no jurisdiction—not even appellate jurisdiction—over the rates charged by a municipally owned utility within the municipality's corporate boundaries. The PUC does have appellate jurisdiction over rates charged by a municipally owned utility outside of the municipality's corporate boundaries and those charged by an investor-owned utility operating within the municipality's boundaries. *See* Tex. Water Code § 13.043(b)(2), (b)(3). Municipalities are authorized to assess impact fees but must comply with the provisions of Texas Local Government Code chapter 395, including the development of a capital improvements plan, the development of land use assumptions, and public hearings before the adoption or amendment of impact fees. *See* Tex. Loc. Gov't Code ch. 395, subch. C. The land use assumptions and capital improvements plan must be updated at least every five years thereafter. *See* Tex. Loc. Gov't Code § 395.052. Municipalities are not authorized to assess standby fees. *See Graham v. City of Lakewood Village*, 796 S.W.2d 800, 804 (Tex. App.—Fort Worth 1990, writ denied). See Chapter 8 of this book for further discussion of impact fees and standby fees.

If a municipality that provides retail water or sewer service to customers outside its boundaries changes its rates, it must provide individual written notice within sixty days after the final decision on the rate change to each affected ratepayer that is eligible to appeal who resides outside the municipality's boundaries. The notice must include, at a minimum, the effective date of the new rates, the new rates, and the location where additional information on rates can be obtained. *See* Tex. Water Code § 13.043(i). An appeal must be initiated by filing a petition with the PUC and the municipality within ninety days after the date of the municipality's final decision and must be signed by the lesser of 10,000 or 10 percent of the affected ratepayers. *See* Tex. Water Code § 13.043(c).

If a ratepayer is a customer of a municipally owned utility and is within the corporate boundaries of the municipality, the person's initial recourse is to complain to elected council members. If dissatisfied by that response, the ratepayer has no recourse to the PUC and may seek to challenge the municipality's services or rates by a lawsuit in district court. However, the courts have determined that they play a limited oversight role. In one case where a ratepayer challenged a city's rates as discriminatory, the court concluded that determining whether differences in rates between classes of customers are to be made and, if so, the amount of the differences are legislative questions rather than judicial questions and are for the determination of the governing bodies of municipalities. *Gillam v. City of Fort Worth*, 287 S.W.2d 494, 497 (Tex. App.—Fort Worth 1956, writ ref'd n.r.e.). Even so, courts may review whether rates are discriminatory. *Black v. City of Killeen*, 78 S.W.3d 686, 699 (Tex. App.—Austin 2002, pet. denied). The presumption is in favor of the legality of the rates established by the rate-making authority, and courts may interfere only in clear cases of illegality. *Gillam*, 287 S.W.2d at 497.

Legislative Compromise in Enacting PURA: Today, the broad authority of municipalities within their corporate limits is a remnant of the larger regulatory function they historically performed. Before the enactment of PURA, municipalities played a major role in public utility regulation in Texas. *City of Sherman v. Public Utility Commission*, 643 S.W.2d 681, 683 (Tex. 1983). When statewide regulation was proposed, many municipalities were concerned that they could lose their power to franchise and regulate utilities and that municipally owned utilities could become state regulated. *City of Sherman*, 643 S.W.2d at 683 (citing Jack Hopper, *A Legislative History of the Texas Public Utility Regulatory Act of 1975*, 28 Baylor L. Rev. 777 (1976)). As a compromise, PURA retained municipal regulation of investor-owned utilities within the territorial boundaries of municipalities and exempted municipally owned utilities from most of PURA's regulatory provisions. *City of Sherman*, 643 S.W.2d at 683. In *City* *of Sherman*, the Texas Supreme Court concluded that the PUC had no jurisdiction to regulate the operations or services of municipally owned utilities. The court observed that the legislature clearly intended to exclude municipally owned utilities from PURA's jurisdictional requirements. *City of Sherman*, 643 S.W.2d at 684–88.

Municipal Regulation of Utilities Operating within Municipal Boundaries: Municipalities have exclusive original jurisdiction over the rates, operations, and services of "water and sewer utilities" operating within their corporate limits. *See* Tex. Water Code § 13.042(a). Municipalities may yield their jurisdiction to the PUC, though this is rare in the water utility context. If a municipality does not surrender its jurisdiction, local utility service within the boundaries of the municipality is exempt from PUC regulations applicable to local service. *See* Tex. Water Code § 13.082(b). For service within its boundaries, a municipality has the right to exercise the same regulatory powers under the same standards and rules as the PUC or other standards and rules that are not inconsistent with them. A municipality may adopt its own rules relating to service and responses to requests for services for utilities that operate within its corporate limits, but if it does not do so, then the PUC's rules apply. A municipality exercising its jurisdiction over water and sewer utilities must require from those utilities all the data that are necessary to make a reasonable determination of rate base, expenses, investment, and rate of return within the municipal boundaries. *See* Tex. Water Code § 13.083.

Often the governing body of a municipality will set the rates of an investor-owned utility at a level the utility believes is insufficient to recover its costs. In such a case, the utility (or any other party) may appeal the rate decision to the PUC, which will hear the appeal de novo. *See* Tex. Water Code § 13.043(a). In addition, the ratepayers of an investor-owned utility who are located inside the corporate limits of the municipality and are under the municipality's jurisdiction may appeal decisions affecting their water, drainage, or sewer rates to the PUC. *See* Tex. Water Code § 13.043(b)(2).

Municipalities also play a role in regulating general and special law districts that provide retail water utility services within their boundaries. In general, no district may provide services or facilities to serve areas outside the district that are also within the corporate limits of a municipality without securing a resolution or ordinance of the municipality granting consent for the district to serve the area within the municipality. *See* Tex. Water Code § 49.215(a). If the resolution, ordinance, or agreement requires the district to purchase water or sewer service from the municipality, the district may appeal to the PUC the rates the municipality charges. The burden of proof is on the municipality to establish that the rates are just and reasonable. If the PUC must establish just and reasonable rates, the municipality may not increase those rates without the agency's approval. *See* 16 Tex. Admin. Code § 24.45.

For a special utility district (SUD) that operates within a municipality's corporate limits or extraterritorial jurisdiction, a municipality has authority to set construction standards for water system facilities to be built by the SUD. *See* Tex. Water Code § 65.016.

§ 29.3:2 Districts and Other Political Subdivisions

Another common form of retail public utility is a political subdivision. Texas Water Code chapter 13 does not define "political subdivision"; however, throughout the Code a "political subdivision" typically includes a district or authority created under Texas Constitution article III, section 52, or article XVI, section 59. Although certain statutory schemes include nonprofit water supply and sewer service corporations (WSCs) in the broader definition of "political subdivision" along with districts (*see, e.g.*, Tex. Water Code §§ 15.001(5), 16.001(7), 17.921(3), 36.001(15)), WSCs generally are not considered political subdivisions. *See* Tex. Att'y Gen. Op. No. GA-0111 (2003).

Texas has many types of districts. The most common ones that provide retail water service to residential customers include municipal utility districts (MUDs), water control and improvement districts (WCIDs), fresh water supply districts (FWSDs), special utility districts (SUDs), and river authorities such as the Guadalupe-Blanco River Authority. See Chapter 8 of this book for a discussion of water districts.

There is limited agency oversight of the policies and rates for services provided by districts. As with municipalities, the PUC's customer service policies and rate-filing policies do not apply to districts. Again, like municipalities, districts are not required to obtain a CCN, but if they choose to do so, they may be subject to additional PUC regulation. *See* 16 Tex. Admin. Code § 24.161.

District Rates, Fees, and Charges: There is also limited agency oversight of the rates and fees charged by a district. The PUC does not have original jurisdiction over a district's rates; however, it does have appellate jurisdiction if the requisite number of customers (the lesser of 10,000 or 10 percent) formally protest the rate within ninety days after the effective date of the rate change. *See* Tex. Water Code § 13.043(b)(4), (c). For purposes of determining the affected ratepayers, customers who reside outside the district's boundaries are considered a separate class because these customers do not participate in elections of the district's governing body.

Oversight of certain water district fees was retained by the TCEQ and not transferred to the PUC. In many cases, TCEQ approval is required before a district may charge certain types of fees, including impact fees and standby fees. *See* Tex. Water Code §§ 49.212, 49.231. See Chapter 8 of this book for a discussion of impact fees and standby fees. Certain charges are expressly excepted from the need for TCEQ approval, however, including charges that might otherwise be considered an impact fee, such as a charge that (1) does not exceed three times the actual costs to the district for a tap or connection; (2) is made by a taxing district to a nontaxable entity for retail or wholesale service, which does not exceed the actual costs for the facilities to provide service; and (3) is made by a district for retail or wholesale service to land that at the time of platting was not being provided with water, wastewater, drainage, or stormwater detention or retention service by the district. Tex. Water Code § 49.212(d); 30 Tex. Admin. Code § 293.171(1). Some districts, especially those with large geographic reach, have found the TCEQ impact fee approval process to be cumbersome, especially the requirement to mail individual notice to landowners.

As an alternative to the TCEQ approval process, a district may follow the requirements of Texas Local Government Code chapter 395. See section 29.3:1 above for discussion of these requirements.

§ 29.3:3 Nonprofit Water Supply Corporations

Rural areas of the state are often served by a "water supply or sewer service corporation" ("water supply corporation" or WSC). A WSC is a nonprofit, member-owned, and member-controlled corporation organized and operating under Texas Water Code chapter 67 that provides potable water service or sewer service for compensation. *See* Tex. Water Code § 13.002(24).

Water supply corporations historically used low-cost federal financing for water utility system construction and improvements in rural areas where no other provider was willing to supply service. First authorized in 1933 by the 43rd Legislature, WSCs were often initially financed with borrowed money from a federal agency and incorporated by local community representatives. *See* Act of Oct. 25, 1933, 43d Leg., 1st C.S., ch. 76. The federal program providing the financing is typically the U.S. Department of Agriculture, Rural Development (USDA RD) (formerly the Farmers Home Administration (FmHA)). USDA regulations provide this funding to rural communities served by a city or political subdivision, such as a special utility district, or by "an organization operated on a not-for-profit basis, such as an association, cooperative, or private corporation" that has "a broadly based ownership by or membership of people of the local community." 7 C.F.R. § 1780.7(a)(2). See section 29.9:5 below.

In contrast to incorporating a municipality or creating a district, a WSC is relatively easy to create by filing a certificate of formation under the Texas Non-Profit Corporation Law and complying with Water Code chapter 67. *See* Tex. Water Code § 67.003. The requirement under chapter 13 that a WSC be "member-owned and member-controlled" satisfies USDA RD financing requirements. *See* Tex. Water Code § 13.002(11), (24). The USDA regulations for entities that qualify for assistance are contained in 7 Code of Federal Regulations part 1780.

Unlike municipalities and districts, WSCs are required to obtain a CCN before providing retail water utility service. *See* Tex. Water Code § 13.242(a). With certain exceptions, a WSC must apply for an amendment to its CCN before providing service beyond its existing CCN boundaries. *See* Tex. Water Code § 13.243. Many of the PUC's rules under 16 Texas Administrative Code chapter 24, subchapter E, governing customer service requirements do not apply to WSCs. This level of supervision in part reflects that WSCs operate on a nonprofit basis. More fundamentally, however, it reflects that WSCs must be governed by boards of directors elected by member customers. *See* Tex. Water Code § 13.002(11), (24).

Importantly, WSCs are expressly authorized to acquire land or interests in land by condemnation. *See* Tex. Water Code § 49.222.

Ratepayers of a WSC may appeal decisions of a WSC's board of directors that affect their water, drainage, or sewer rates to the PUC. *See* Tex. Water Code § 13.043(b)(1). An appeal is initiated by filing a petition for review with both the PUC and the WSC within ninety days of the effective date of the rate change. The petition must be signed by the lesser of 10,000 or 10 percent of those ratepayers whose rates have been changed and who are eligible to appeal. *See* Tex. Water Code § 13.043(c).

The PUC may also hear appeals of certain fees charged by WSCs. For instance, an applicant for service from a WSC may appeal to the PUC a decision affecting the amount to be paid to obtain service other than the regular membership or tap fees. An appeal of a fee must be filed within ninety days after the date written notice of the WSC's decision is provided to the applicant. If the PUC finds the amount charged to be "clearly unreasonable," it must establish the fee to be paid by the applicant. The agency's determination is binding on all similarly situated applicants for service. *See* Tex. Water Code § 13.043(g); 16 Tex. Admin. Code § 24.101(g).

In addition, a customer of a WSC may file an appeal with the PUC of a water conservation penalty imposed by the WSC. The PUC will uphold the penalty if (1) the penalty is clearly stated in the tariff, (2) the penalty is reasonable and does not exceed six times the minimum monthly bill in the WSC's current tariff, and (3) the WSC has deposited the penalty in a separate account dedicated to enhancing the water supply for the benefit of all of its customers. Tex. Water Code § 67.011(b); 16 Tex. Admin. Code § 24.101(j).

Although the PUC generally has only appellate jurisdiction over a WSC's rates, the agency may obtain original jurisdiction if it finds that the WSC is failing to conduct annual or special meetings in compliance with Water Code section 67.007 or is operating in a manner that does not comply with the requirements for classification as a WSC prescribed by Water Code section 13.002(11) and (24). *See* Tex. Water Code § 13.004. If the PUC obtains original jurisdiction over a WSC, then the PUC regulations pertaining to a "water and sewer utility" apply. *See* 16 Tex. Admin. Code § 24.47(a).

While under the PUC's jurisdiction, the WSC may request that the "cash needs method" for setting rates be used. The cash needs method allows a utility to recover reasonable and prudently incurred debt service, a reasonable cash reserve account, and other expenses not allowed under standard methods of establishing rates. *See* 16 Tex. Admin. Code § 24.75(c).

The PUC's original jurisdiction over a WSC ends if the WSC voluntarily converts to a special utility district, the PUC's order expires, or the WSC demonstrates that for the past twenty-four consecutive months it has conducted annual meetings as required and has operated in a manner that complies with the membership and nonprofit organization requirements for WSCs. *See* 16 Tex. Admin. Code § 24.47(b).

WSCs must file tariffs with the PUC showing all rates that are subject to the appellate jurisdiction of the commission and that are in effect for any utility service, product, or commodity offered. *See* Tex. Water Code § 13.136(c); 16 Tex. Admin. Code § 24.25(i). The tariffs must include all rules and regulations relating to or affecting the rates, utility service, product, or commodity furnished. For WSCs, the filing of a tariff is for informational purposes only.

WSCs that elect to be exempt from ad valorem taxes under Texas Tax Code section 11.30 fall within the definition of a "governmental body" under both the Public Information Act and the Open Meetings Act. As such, they must comply with the requirements of both acts. *See* Tex. Gov't Code §§ 551.001(3)(K), 552.003(1)(A)(ix).

§ 29.3:4 Counties

As political subdivisions of the state, counties that provide retail water or sewer service fall within the Texas Water Code chapter 13 definition of a "retail public utility." *See* Tex. Water Code § 13.002(19). The more limited definitions for a "water and sewer utility," "public utility," and "utility" exclude political subdivisions except for "an affected county." *See* Tex. Water Code § 13.002(23). Thus, whether a particular provision of chapter 13 is applicable to a county depends on (1) whether the provision applies to a "retail public utility" and (2) whether the county is an "affected county."

An "affected county" is defined as a county to which Texas Local Government Code chapter 232, subchapter B, applies. Tex. Water Code § 13.002(26). Subchapter B applies only to a county located (1) within fifty miles of an international border or (2) within one hundred miles of an international border that contains the majority of the area of a municipality with a population of more than 250,000. Tex. Loc. Gov't Code § 232.022(a). The Texas legislature enacted subchapter B after finding that economically distressed subdivisions commonly called *colonias* were found throughout these affected counties and that the vast majority of housing units in these colonias lacked an adequate potable water supply and concomitant wastewater or sewer services, creating serious and unacceptable health hazards. *See* Act of May 28, 1995, 74th Leg., R.S., ch. 979, § 4.

Affected counties are subject to greater regulation under chapter 13 than other counties. The PUC has appellate jurisdiction over the water, drainage, and sewer rate decisions of affected counties if the ratepayers are actually or may be adversely affected. *See* Tex. Water Code § 13.043(b)(5). Also, as with WSCs, the PUC may hear an appeal of an affected county's decision that involves the amount to be paid to obtain service other than for a tap fee. *See* Tex. Water Code § 13.043(g); 16 Tex. Admin. Code § 24.101(g).

A utility operated by an affected county must obtain a CCN before in any way rendering retail water or sewer utility service directly or indirectly to the public. *See* Tex. Water Code § 13.242(a). The PUC can revoke the CCN if it finds that the cost of providing service is so prohibitively expensive as to constitute denial of service. *See* Tex. Water Code § 13.254(a)(2).

§ 29.4 "Public Utilities"

Except for affected counties, all the entities discussed above are "retail public utilities" but not "utilities." In contrast, water and sewer utilities, also referred to simply as "utilities," are the most highly regulated category of retail water service providers. The definition of "utility" includes any person, corporation, cooperative corporation, affected county, or any combination of these persons or entities owning or operating for compensation facilities to provide potable water or sewer service to the public, but specifically excluding municipal corporations, WSCs, and political subdivisions (such as districts). By far the most common form of "utility" is a for-profit "investor-owned utility" (IOU). However, the term also includes nonprofit corporations, such as homeowners associations, that are not organized under Texas Water Code chapter 67 and that do not qualify as member-owned and member-controlled as required for water supply corporations.

§ 29.4:1 Rates and Tariffs

The rates a utility may charge are highly regulated, generally by the PUC, although, as discussed at section 29.3:1 above, municipalities may play a role in oversight as well. To cover both of these scenarios, Texas Water Code chapter 13 uses the term "regulatory authority" to refer to the PUC or a municipality, depending on the context. *See* Tex. Water Code § 13.002(18).

A utility may not charge, collect, or receive any rate for utility service or impose any rule or regulation other than as provided by chapter 13. Tex. Water Code § 13.135.

The regulatory authority may fix and regulate rates of utilities, including rules and regulations for classifying customers and services and for determining the applicability of rates. Tex. Water Code § 13.181(b). The regulatory authority must ensure that every rate made, demanded, or received by any utility or any two utilities jointly is just and reasonable. Tex. Water Code § 13.182(a). Rates may not be unreasonably preferential, prejudicial, or discriminatory. The state of Texas may recover from an IOU, for refund to customers, charges collected in excess of the charges approved by the PUC. *See Texas Natural Resource Conservation Commission v. Lakeshore Utility Co.*, 164 S.W.3d 368 (Tex. 2005).

In 2013, the Texas legislature established new utility classifications for IOUs based on connection count, and in 2019 the legislature updated the classifications. *See* Act of May 14, 2013, 83d Leg., R.S., ch. 171, § 8 (S.B. 567); Act of May 14, 2013, 83d Leg., R.S., ch. 170, § 2.08 (H.B. 1600); Act of May 25, 2019, 86th Leg., R.S., ch. 967 (S.B. 700), eff. Sept. 1, 2019. Class A utilities are IOUs with 10,000 or more connections; Class B utilities are IOUs with 2,300 or more, but fewer than 10,000 connections; Class C utilities are IOUs with 500 or more, but fewer than 2,300 connections; and Class D utilities are IOUs with fewer than 500 connections. *See* Tex. Water Code § 13.002(4–a)–(4–d). These classifications were created to end the one-size-fits-all treatment of IOUs for rate-setting purposes, with Class B, Class C, and Class D utilities being authorized to use abbreviated, less burdensome procedures for changing rates.

When the PUC fixes the rates of a utility, the agency must fix overall revenues at a level that will provide the utility a reasonable opportunity to earn a reasonable return on its invested capital and that will preserve the financial integrity of the utility. *See* 16 Tex. Admin. Code § 24.43(a). The rates must be designed to take into account conservation; utilities cannot employ rate structures that offer discounts or encourage increased usage within any customer class. To provide funds for necessary capital improvements and for debt repayments and associated costs, the PUC may permit the utility to collect additional revenues from customers. The PUC may use an alternative rate method for establishing rates to ensure that retail customers receive higher quality, more affordable, or more reliable service; to encourage regionalization; or to maintain financially stable and technically sound utilities. *See* Tex. Water Code § 13.183(c); 16 Tex. Admin. Code § 24.75(a).

Rates are based on a utility's cost of rendering service. The two components of cost of service are allowable expenses and return on rate base. *See* 16 Tex. Admin. Code § 24.41(a). Allowable expenses include only those expenses that are reasonable and necessary to provide service to the ratepayers. Payments to affiliated interests for costs of service, or any property, right, or thing, or for interest expense are not allowed as an expense for cost of service except as provided in Tex. Water Code § 13.185(e). *See* 16 Tex. Admin. Code § 24.41(b). Return on rate base is calculated by multiplying a reasonable rate of return by rate base. *See* 16 Tex. Admin. Code § 24.41(c). For a detailed analysis of water and wastewater rate design considerations, see American Water Works Association, *Principles of Water Rates, Fees, and Charges (M1)* (6th ed. 2012); and Water Environment Federation, *Financing and Charges for Wastewater Systems (MOP 27)* (2005).

Every utility must file with each regulatory authority tariffs showing all rates that are subject to the original or appellate jurisdiction of the regulatory authority and that are in effect for any utility service, product, or commodity offered. *See* Tex. Water Code § 13.136(a). The tariffs must include all rules and regulations that relate to or affect the rates, utility service, product, or commodity furnished. *See* 16 Tex. Admin. Code § 24.25. Utilities also must keep and render to the appropriate regulatory authority in the manner and form prescribed by the PUC uniform accounts of all business transacted. *See* Tex. Water Code § 13.131(a).

§ 29.4:2 Elements of a Rate Case

A utility may not make changes in its rates except by delivering a statement of intent to each ratepayer and with the regulatory authority that has original jurisdiction at least thirty-five days before the effective date of the proposed change. Tex. Water Code §§ 13.187(a–1), 13.1871(b). A utility may not file a notice of intent to increase rates more than once in a twelve-month period with limited exceptions as provided at 16 Texas Administrative Code section 24.29(b). *See* Tex. Water Code §§ 13.187(p), 13.1871(w); 16 Tex. Admin. Code § 24.29.

When the statement of intent is delivered, the utility must also file with the regulatory authority an application to change rates. Tex. Water Code §§ 13.187(c), 13.1871(d).

The PUC may conduct a public hearing on any rate change application. For Class A utilities, the PUC is required to begin a hearing within thirty days after the effective date of the change to determine the propriety of the change. Tex. Water Code § 13.187(f). For other than Class A utilities, a hearing is not required unless the regulatory authority receives a complaint within ninety days after the rate has become effective from any affected municipality or from a certain number of ratepayers. *See* Tex. Water Code § 13.1871(i). If the PUC does not receive sufficient customer complaints or if the PUC staff does not request a hearing within 120 days after the effective date of the rates, the utility's proposed tariff will be approved as long as it complies with the Texas Water Code and the PUC's rules. 16 Tex. Admin. Code § 24.35(c).

If a hearing is held and the regulatory authority finds that the rates currently being charged or those proposed to be charged are unreasonable or in violation of law, the regulatory authority will determine and order the rates to be charged by the utility. Tex. Water Code §§ 13.187(h), 13.1871(o); 16 Tex. Admin. Code § 24.35(d).

A more streamlined process that does not require a hearing is available for Class C and Class D utilities. A Class C or D utility may change its rates by filing an application with the PUC for a rate adjustment and providing notice at least thirty-five days before the effective date of the proposed change. *See* Tex. Water Code §§ 13.1871, 13.18715; 16 Tex. Admin. Code § 24.27(d)(1). Alternatively, a Class C or D utility may adjust its rates by complying with the rate change procedures for Class B utilities. *See* Tex. Water Code § 13.1872(c)(2). A Class C or D utility may not use the rate adjustment process more than once each year and not more than four times between proceedings using the Class B utility rate change process. *See* Tex. Water Code § 13.1872(f).

§ 29.4:3 Customer Service Policies and Complaint Process

In addition to regulating a utility's rates, services, and fees, the PUC regulates a utility's customer service policies. *See* 16 Tex. Admin. Code §§ 24.151–.171. The PUC's regulations address grounds for refusal to serve, use of deposits, responses to requests for service, water and sewer service connections, billing, discontinuance of service, meter requirements, readings, tests, and service interruptions. The specific policies and rules of a utility are contained in its tariff, which must be filed with, and approved by, the PUC. A utility's tariff may not be changed or amended except with approval of the PUC. *See* 16 Tex. Admin. Code § 24.25(b)(2).

Any customer or service applicant who requests the opportunity to dispute any action or determination of a utility under the utility's customer service rules must be given an opportunity for a review by the utility. *See* 16 Tex. Admin. Code § 24.155(a). Upon receipt of a complaint, the utility must promptly investigate and report its findings to the complainant. In the event the complainant is dissatisfied with the utility's report, the utility must advise the complainant of recourse through the

PUC's complaint process. If the utility receives a complaint from the PUC on behalf of a customer or service applicant, the utility must make an initial response to the PUC within fifteen days. The PUC may require the utility to provide a written response to the complainant, the commission, or both. Pending resolution of a complaint, continuation or restoration of service may be required. *See* 16 Tex. Admin. Code § 24.153(b)(3).

III. Certificates of Public Convenience and Necessity

§ 29.5 Introduction

Certain retail public utilities are required to obtain a CCN before they may provide retail water or sewer service. A CCN is a permit issued by the PUC that authorizes and obligates a retail public utility to furnish, make available, render, or extend continuous and adequate retail water or sewer utility service to a specified geographic area. *See* 16 Tex. Admin. Code § 24.225(a). Entities that are not required to obtain CCNs may choose to do so in order to protect their service areas from encroachment by other retail public utilities.

§ 29.6 Types of CCNs

CCNs are issued to water and sewer utilities for various types of service areas. The most common CCN is a "bounded area" or "geographic" CCN, which is issued for a specific enclosed geographic area described by known physical boundaries such as property lines, roads, creeks, railroad tracks, or political boundaries.

Occasionally, however, utilities have obtained a "facilities only" CCN, which is much more limited in scope and purpose. A facilities-only CCN is issued for a "point of use" service area that covers only the customer connections at the time the CCN was granted and typically corresponds to the location of a utility's distribution lines in the ground. Use of facilities only CCNs is currently restricted to small systems or small areas of larger CCNs.

A variation on the facilities only CCN includes not only the facilities but also a buffer of a specified number of feet, usually two hundred feet (a "facilities plus 200 feet CCN"). The lines typically correspond to distribution lines or facilities in the ground and normally follow along roads.

Both facilities only CCNs and facilities plus two hundred feet CCNs are in disfavor and rarely used today for new or amended CCNs. In the past, the holders of these types of CCNs had more flexibility to extend service outside their certificated areas; however, they are now explicitly excepted from doing so. *See* 16 Tex. Admin. Code § 24.229(a)(1).

§ 29.7 Dual Certification

Typically, a retail public utility with a CCN is the sole, monopoly water or sewer service provider in the territory covered by the CCN. In some instances, however, the service areas of two CCNs may overlap, allowing two utilities to serve the same territory (known as "dual certification"). The PUC's rules expressly provide that the agency may grant additional certification to any other retail public utility of all or any part of a previously certificated area if the PUC finds that the public convenience and necessity require the additional certification. *See* 16 Tex. Admin. Code § 24.251. Typically, however, the PUC does not grant dual certification unless both retail public utilities consent.

It is unclear whether Texas Water Code chapter 13 allows dual certification in the absence of the consent of both retail public utilities. The only reference to dual certification in the Water Code is found at section 13.255(a), which provides for dual certification between an annexing municipality and an annexed retail utility by agreement—which, if by agreement, is consistent with the concept that otherwise retail public utilities are "by definition monopolies." *See* Tex. Water Code §§ 13.001(b)(1), 13.255(a).

§ 29.8 Applying for a CCN

To obtain a CCN, a retail public utility must file an application with the PUC that contains the items listed in 16 Texas Administrative Code section 24.227. These items include the PUC's application form, which is available on its website; a map and description of the proposed service area; a description of any requests for service; any evidence required by the PUC to show that the applicant has received the necessary consent, franchise, permit, or license from the proper municipality or other public authority; and an explanation of the applicant's reasons for contending that the requested certificate is necessary for the service, accommodation, convenience, or safety of the public. *See* 16 Tex. Admin. Code § 24.227.

Notice of the application and the opportunity to request a hearing must be provided. *See* 16 Tex. Admin. Code § 24.235. If no hearing is requested, the PUC may, but is not required to, grant the proposed CCN without a hearing. *See* 16 Tex. Admin. Code § 24.237. If a hearing is requested, any person affected by the application may intervene at the hearing. *See* Tex. Water Code § 13.246(a). "Affected persons" include current customers of the utility, if any; landowners whose property is within the area to be certificated; and any retail public utility that would be affected by the PUC's actions, such as adjacent or competing utilities. *See* Tex. Water Code § 13.002(1).

The burden of proof at the hearing is on the entity seeking the CCN. *See* 16 Tex. Admin. Code § 24.12.

In determining whether to grant or amend a CCN, the PUC must ensure that the applicant possesses the financial, managerial, and technical capability to provide continuous and adequate service. *See* Tex. Water Code § 13.241(a); 16 Tex. Admin. Code § 24.227(a). For water utility service, the applicant must have access to an adequate supply of water and must be capable of providing drinking water that meets the requirements of Texas Health and Safety Code chapter 341, the TCEQ rules, and the Texas Water Code. *See* Tex. Water Code § 13.241(b); 16 Tex. Admin. Code § 24.227(a)(1). It is not required that the applicant itself own the facilities; it is sufficient that the applicant demonstrate that it has the capability to provide water service through contracts and interlocal agreements. *See Bexar Metropolitan Water District v. Texas Commission on Environmental Quality*, 185 S.W.3d 546 (Tex. App.—Austin 2006, pet. denied).

If granting a new CCN for an area would require constructing a physically separate water or sewer system, the applicant must demonstrate that regionalization or consolidation with another retail public utility is not economically feasible. *See* Tex. Water Code § 13.241(d). The PUC may grant or amend a CCN only after finding that the CCN or amendment is necessary for the service, accommodation, convenience, or safety of the public. *See* 16 Tex. Admin. Code § 24.227(d).

A Class A utility may apply for an amendment of a water or sewer CCN held by a MUD, other than a MUD located wholly or partly inside of the corporate limits or extraterritorial jurisdiction of a municipality with a population of two million or more, to allow the Class A utility to have the same rights and powers under the CCN as the municipal utility district. The MUD that holds the CCN must consent to the application. *See* 16 Tex. Admin. Code § 24.227(c).

If a CCN application is uncontested or if all protests are withdrawn at the end of the thirty-day notice period, the PUC may act on the application. *See* 16 Tex. Admin. Code § 24.237. An applicant or other person who wishes to overturn the PUC's decision must file a motion for rehearing within twenty-five days after receiving notice of the PUC's decision. *See* Tex. Gov't Code § 2001.146(a); 16 Tex. Admin. Code § 22.264.

If the CCN application is protested, it is sent to the State Office of Administrative Hearings (SOAH) for a preliminary hearing conducted by an administrative law judge. If the parties cannot reach an agreement at the preliminary hearing, the judge holds an evidentiary hearing. At the conclusion of the evidentiary hearing, the judge issues a proposal for decision that is submitted to the PUC commissioners for formal consideration. The PUC commissioners then approve, deny, or modify the proposal for decision. A party that is unsatisfied with the commissioners' decision may file a motion for rehearing with the agency. If the motion is granted, the application may be returned to SOAH to take additional evidence. If the motion is not granted, the decision may be appealed to district court.

§ 29.9 Decertification of CCNs

Acquiring a CCN does not protect the CCN holder from later decertification of all or part of the territory covered by the CCN. Challenges to a CCN can come from various directions: the PUC may revoke or amend a CCN under certain circumstances; owners of property can petition to have their property removed from a CCN; and cities that annex part of the territory in a CCN may take that area for themselves, with or without the consent of the incumbent utility, but must pay certain compensation to the CCN holder.

§ 29.9:1 Revocation or Amendment of CCN

The PUC can revoke or amend a CCN if it makes one of the following four findings:

1. The CCN holder is not providing continuous and adequate service to all or part of the area covered by the CCN, as required by Texas Water Code section 13.250.

2. In counties with certain economically distressed areas, the cost of providing service by the CCN holder is so prohibitively expensive as to constitute denial of service.

3. The CCN holder has agreed in writing to allow another retail public utility to provide service within its service area, except for an interim period, without amending its CCN.

4. The CCN holder has failed to file a cease and desist action within 180 days of becoming aware that another retail public utility was providing service within its service area.

See Tex. Water Code § 13.254(a).

The PUC may make findings relevant to decertification on its own motion; however, decertification is most often used by other retail public utilities seeking to obtain a CCN for territory that is already certificated to another retail public utility. If a CCN is revoked or amended, the PUC may require one or more retail public utilities with their consent to provide service to the area in question. *See* Tex. Water Code § 13.254(c). The retail public utility taking over the service area must provide compensation to the decertified retail public utility for any property that the PUC determines is rendered useless or valueless because of the decertification. *See* Tex. Water Code § 13.254(d).

§ 29.9:2 Petitions by Owners of Large Tracts—"Expedited Release"

The territory covered by a CCN may also be affected by the petitions of certain landowners. In 2005, the Texas legislature established an "expedited release" process authorizing certain landowners of tracts of fifty acres or more to petition the TCEQ, and now the PUC, to have their property removed from the existing retail water provider's CCN. *See* Tex. Water Code § 13.254(a–1). In 2011, the legislature created an alternative expedited release process that applies to tracts of twenty-five acres and greater, known as "streamlined expedited release." *See* Tex. Water Code § 13.2541(b).

Expedited Release of Tracts of Fifty Acres or More under Section 13.254(a–1): A landowner with at least fifty acres that is not in a platted subdivision and not actually receiving water or sewer service may petition the PUC for expedited release of the land from one retail public utility's CCN area so that the land may receive service from another retail public utility. *See* Tex. Water Code § 13.254(a–1); 16 Tex. Admin. Code § 24.245(f)(1). To use this process, the landowner must first make a request for service to the incumbent utility, which then has ninety days in which to respond. The incumbent utility's response allows the landowner to file a petition for expedited release if the utility (1) refuses to provide service; (2) is not capable of providing adequate service within the time frame, at the level, at the approximate cost that the alternative provider is capable of providing for a comparable level of service, or in the manner reasonably requested by the landowner; or (3) conditions the provision of service on a payment of costs not properly allocable to the petitioner's service request. The petitioner must demonstrate that the alternative retail public utility from which the petitioner will be requesting service possesses the financial, managerial, and technical capability to provide continuous and adequate service within the time frame, at the level, at the cost, and in the manner reasonably needed or requested by current and projected service demands in the area. *See* Tex. Water Code § 13.254(a–1).

In most counties, if a CCN holder has never made service available through planning, design, construction of facilities, or contractual obligations to serve the area a petitioner seeks to have released under section 13.254(a–1), the PUC is not required to find that the proposed alternative provider is capable of providing better service than the CCN holder, but only that the proposed alternative provider is capable of providing the requested service. *See* Tex. Water Code § 13.254(a–8). However, counties meeting certain population and location parameters are excluded from this requirement. *See* Tex. Water Code § 13.254(a–9)–(a–11). The initially excluded counties are Cameron, Fannin, Grayson, Guadalupe, Hidalgo, Willacy, and Wilson. *See* 16 Tex. Admin. Code § 24.245(f)(12).

After a petition for expedited release is deemed administratively complete, the PUC must grant the petition within sixty days unless it finds that the petitioner has failed to satisfy the elements required by statute. *See* Tex. Water Code § 13.254(a–3); 16 Tex. Admin. Code § 24.245(f)(10). If a petition is granted, the process then moves to valuation and compensation, if any, to the incumbent utility. *See* Tex. Water Code § 13.254(a–3). A party aggrieved by the decision of the PUC on an expedited release petition filed under section 13.254(a–1) (whether the landowner or the incumbent utility) has only a right to seek reconsideration of the action within the agency but may not appeal the decision to district court. *See* Tex. Water Code § 13.254(a–4).

A successful petition for expedited release was filed by Jona Acquisition, Inc., on May 7, 2008, seeking decertification of approximately 1,960 acres from the CCN of the Creedmoor-Maha Water Supply Corporation. *Petition from Jona Acquisition, Inc. for an Expedited Release from Water Certificate of Convenience and Necessity (CCN) No. 11029 of Creedmoor-Maha Water Supply Corporation (WSC) in Travis County, Texas*; Application No. 36051-D (TCEQ Order Issued Aug. 5, 2008). Jona had requested water service from Creedmoor sufficient to serve 10,300 living unit equivalents, but according to Jona's petition, Creedmoor did not have sufficient existing capacity to meet Jona's needs and had no binding commitments to secure new water supplies. The city of Austin was available nearby as an alternative water provider. The executive director of the TCEQ granted Jona's petition for expedited release, and the proceeding advanced to the valuation stage. The executive director's decision was subsequently upheld on appeal. *Creedmoor-Maha Water Supply Corp. v. Texas Commission on Environmental Quality*, 307 S.W.3d 505 (Tex. App.—Austin 2010, no pet.).

For a discussion of expedited release cases and practice tips, see Leonard H. Dougal & Mallory Beck, *Current Water Utility CCN Decertification Issues at the Public Utility Commission of Texas, in Advanced Real Estate Strategies* (State Bar of Texas 2014); and Leonard H. Dougal & Mallory Beck, *Water Utilities and CCNs: The Latest Issues at the Public Utility Commission of Texas, in The Changing Face of Water Rights* (State Bar of Texas 2017).

Even if the CCN holder has an outstanding federal debt, this is no bar to a landowner seeking an expedited release. *See* Tex. Water Code § 13.254(a–1); 16 Tex. Admin. Code § 24.245(f)(4). See section 29.9:5 below for a discussion of federal debt protection.

Streamlined Expedited Release by the Landowner of Tracts of Twenty-Five Acres or More: As an alternative to the original expedited release process, the owner of a tract of land that is at least twenty-five acres and that is not receiving water or sewer service may petition for streamlined expedited release (SER) of the area from a CCN and is entitled to that release if the landowner's property is located in a county that falls within certain population parameters. *See* Tex. Water Code § 13.2541(b). The eligible counties are Atascosa, Bandera, Bastrop, Bexar, Blanco, Brazoria, Burnet, Caldwell, Chambers, Collin, Comal, Dallas, Denton, Ellis, Fort Bend, Galveston, Guadalupe, Harris, Hays, Johnson, Kaufman, Kendall, Liberty, Montgomery, Parker, Rockwall, Smith, Tarrant, Travis, Waller, Williamson, Wilson, and Wise. *See* Public Utility Commission of Texas, *Streamlined Expedited Release (SER)*, www.puc.texas.gov/industry/water/Forms/SER_Counties.pdf; *see also* Public Utility Commission of Texas, *Streamlined Expedited Release Guidance*, www.puc.texas.gov/industry/water/Forms/StreamlineFAQs.pdf.

The SER process is set forth in 16 Texas Administrative Code section 24.245(h). To initiate the SER process, the landowner must submit a verified petition containing the following: (1) a statement that the petition is being submitted under Texas Water Code section 13.2541 and 16 Texas Administrative Code section 24.245(h); (2) proof that the tract is twenty-five acres or greater in size; (3) proof that at least part of the tract is in the current CCN holder's certificated service area and at least some of that part is located in a qualifying county; (4) a statement of facts demonstrating that the tract is currently not receiving water service (or sewer service, if applicable); (5) copies of deeds demonstrating that the applicant is the owner of the tract; (6) proof that a copy of the petition was mailed to the current CCN holder by certified mail on the day the petition is submitted to the PUC; and (7) the mapping information described at 16 Texas Administrative Code section 24.245(k). *See* 16 Tex. Admin. Code § 24.245(h)(3).

Elements (2) and (4) of an SER petition have been the subject of disputes. With regard to the twenty-five-acre requirement, the PUC has determined that the twenty-five-acre property may consist of separate tracts, as long as the tracts are under common ownership and are contiguous or only separated by public rights-of-way. *See* Petition of SLF IV-114 Assemblage, L.P. to Amend Aqua Texas, Inc.'s Certificate of Convenience and Necessity in Denton County by Expedited Release, PUC Docket No. 44667, Final Order (Sept. 11, 2015).

The most contentious issue regarding SER petitions is whether a property is "receiving water or sewer service." Tex. Water Code § 13.2541(b). The Austin court of appeals has examined the meaning of this phrase a number of times in recent cases. *See, e.g., Johnson County Special Utility District v. Public Utility Commission of Texas*, No. 03-17-00160-CV, 2018 WL 2170259 (Tex. App.—Austin May 11, 2018, pet. denied) (mem. op.); *Mountain Peak Special Utility District v. Public Utility Commission of Texas*, No. 03-16-00796-CV, 2017 WL 5078034 (Tex. App.—Austin Nov. 2, 2017, pet. denied) (mem. op.); *Texas General Land Office v. Crystal Clear Water Supply Corp.*, 449 S.W.3d 130 (Tex. App.—Austin 2014, pet. denied). In *Crystal Clear*, the General Land Office (GLO) sought a streamlined expedited release for five contiguous tracts, each more than twenty-five acres, that did not contain any active meters, lines, or other facilities serving those tracts. The GLO did not seek decertification of approximately 151 acres from five additional contiguous tracts that did have certain facilities. The CCN holder argued that (1) the GLO could not choose to decertify only a portion of its contiguous property, and (2) the property was, in fact, "receiving water service." *Crystal Clear*, 449 S.W.3d at 134. The court agreed with the agency's grant of decertification, noting that nothing in section 13.254(a–5) (now section 13.2541(b)) prohibited the GLO from selecting only a portion of its property for the decertification request. The court also found, based in part on the broad definition of "service" in Texas Water Code chapter 13, that the determination of whether a tract is receiving water service is—

> a fact-based inquiry requiring the Commission to consider whether the retail public utility has facilities or lines committed to providing water to the particular tract or has performed acts or supplied anything to the particular tract in furtherance of its obligation to provide water to that tract pursuant to its CCN.

Crystal Clear, 449 S.W.3d at 140. Ultimately, the court upheld the TCEQ's decision that the property was not "receiving water service" under the substantial-evidence standard. *Crystal Clear*, 449 S.W.3d at 142. Likewise, in *Mountain Peak*, the court upheld the PUC's decertification of a tract where the court concluded there was no evidence that the CCN holder's nearby water lines were "committed" to providing water to the *specific* tract that was to be decertified. *Mountain Peak*, 2017 WL 5078034, at *5.

This decision, and decisions in subsequent PUC SER petition dockets, have largely settled the position of the PUC regarding the meaning of the phrase "receiving water service." Since the *Crystal Clear* decision, the PUC has not denied an SER petition on the basis that the property is receiving service without an active water meter on the property. Further, the PUC has even allowed petitioners to amend petitions to remove established tracts of land to eliminate tracts with existing water service. *See, e.g., Petition of City of Midlothian to Amend Mountain Peak Special Utility District's Certificate of Convenience and Necessity by Expedited Release in Ellis County*, PUC Docket No. 44394, Final Order (May 1, 2015).

The PUC must grant a petition filed pursuant to this process not later than the sixtieth day after the date the landowner files the petition. *See* Tex. Water Code § 13.2541(c). The PUC considers the petition to be "filed" on the date it is declared "administratively complete." *See* 16 Tex. Admin. Code § 24.245(h)(7). The PUC may require an award of compensation by the petitioner to a decertified retail public utility. *See* Tex. Water Code § 13.2541(f).

If a response to an SER petition raises the issue of federal debt protection (discussed in section 29.9:5 below), the PUC generally ignores it. Presumably, this is because of Texas Water Code section 13.2541(d) and 16 Texas Administrative Code section 24.245(h)(8), which state that federal indebtedness does not preclude approval of a petition for release. Another related provision prohibits the CCN holder from beginning an application to borrow money from a federal loan program once a petition is filed. The prohibition lasts until the commission makes its final decision on the release. *See* Tex. Water Code § 13.2541(e); 16 Tex. Admin. Code § 24.245(h)(8). See section 29.9:5 below for a discussion of federal debt protection.

Requirements Applicable to Both Types of Expedited Release: The incumbent utility is not a party in either type of expedited release unless it files a motion to intervene and the PUC administrative law judge (ALJ) grants it. An intervenor is added to the official mailing list, has rights as a party, and can appeal an adverse decision. Absent intervention, the incumbent utility receives no notice of filings, orders, deadlines, or commission open meetings in the docket.

Neither type of expedited release case requires public notice, nor is there an opportunity for a contested case hearing.

Expedited release from a retail public utility's existing CCN is not available to landowners whose property is (1) within the boundaries of a municipality or the extraterritorial jurisdiction of a municipality with a population of more than 500,000 where the municipality or a municipally owned utility is the CCN holder or (2) in a platted subdivision that actually receives water or sewer service. However, owners of property that fall within either of these categories are eligible to contest the inclusion of their property within a new CCN. *See* Tex. Water Code § 13.254(a–2). Under either process, the PUC requires specific mapping information complying with the requirements found in 16

Texas Administrative Code section 24.233 showing the location of the property subject to the expedited release petition.

A CCN holder that has land removed from its certificated service area may not be required, after the land is removed, to provide service to the removed land for any reason, including the violation of law or PUC rules by a water or sewer system of another person. *See* Tex. Water Code § 13.254(h).

§ 29.9:3 Municipal Annexations

A municipality's annexation of land within the CCN of another retail public utility does not automatically affect the authority of the retail public utility to continue providing service to the area. *See* Tex. Water Code § 13.247. However, if a municipality incorporates or annexes territory that is currently certificated to a water supply and sewer service corporation, a special utility district, or a fresh water supply district, then the municipality has a couple of alternatives if it wants to provide retail water or sewer service to the area. One option is to enter into an agreement with the incumbent utility to determine which entity will provide service to the annexed territory—the incumbent utility, a municipally owned utility, or a retail public utility that has been granted a franchise by the municipality (a "franchised utility"). *See* Tex. Water Code § 13.255(a); 16 Tex. Admin. Code § 24.259(b)(2). The agreement may grant the exclusive right for one of these entities to serve all or part of the area ("single certification") or may permit more than one entity to serve all or part of the area ("dual certification"). The agreement also may provide for the purchase of facilities or property. The executed agreement must be filed with the PUC, which will incorporate the terms of the agreement into the respective CCNs of the parties. No notice or hearing is required.

If an agreement cannot be reached, a mechanism similar to condemnation exists that allows a municipality to purchase the right to serve the annexed territory without the incumbent utility's consent. Before providing service to the area, the municipality must file an application with the PUC seeking single certification of the area to a municipally owned utility or a franchised utility. Tex. Water Code § 13.255(b); 16 Tex. Admin. Code § 24.259(c). The application may include a request to transfer specified property of the incumbent utility to the municipality. While the application is pending, the municipality may begin serving the area without a CCN if the area is not served and if the municipality meets the requirements of 16 Texas Administrative Code section 24.229. The PUC must grant the application for single certification unless the municipality fails to demonstrate compliance with the TCEQ's minimum requirements for public drinking water systems. *See* Tex. Water Code § 13.255(c), (m). The municipality must pay adequate and just compensation, as determined by the PUC, to the incumbent utility for any property that is rendered useless or valueless or that will be transferred to the municipality. Tex. Water Code § 13.255(c). Any party that is aggrieved by the PUC's final order may file an appeal in a Travis County district court. Tex. Water Code § 13.255(e).

Municipal annexations typically occur as areas that were once rural become more urban. For a discussion of the considerations in extending water utilities to rural areas from a municipal perspective and a rural perspective, see Emily W. Rogers, *Extending Water Utilities to Rural Areas: The Municipal Perspective, in The Changing Face of Water Rights in Texas* (State Bar of Texas 2007); Kenneth L. Petersen, Jr., *Extending Water Utilities to Rural Areas: The Rural Perspective, in The Changing Face of Water Rights in Texas* (State Bar of Texas 2007).

§ 29.9:4 Compensation Following Decertification

For decertification or single certification under Texas Water Code sections 13.254, 13.2541, and 13.255, the statutes allow compensation to be paid to the retail public utility that is losing territory. *See* Tex. Water Code §§ 13.254(d), 13.2541(f), 13.255(c). As discussed below, the PUC's practice in SER decertifications before the enactment of Senate Bill 2272 by the 86th Legislature was to find that no compensation was due. The passage of S.B. 2272 opened the door to monetary compensation to the decertified CCN holder in SER decertification cases. *See* Act of May 26, 2019, 86th Leg., R.S., ch. 688 (S.B. 2272), eff. Sept. 1, 2019. The statutory language regarding the method for determining compensation is similar for both sections 13.254 and 13.255. The value of real property owned and used by the retail public utility for its facilities is determined using the standards that govern actions in eminent domain; the value of personal property is determined by analyzing, at a minimum, certain factors listed in the statutes. *See* Tex. Water Code §§ 13.254(g), 13.255(g). The factors include the amount of debt allocable to the lost service area; the value of service facilities in the area; the amount expended by the affected retail utility on planning, design, and construction preparatory to service to the area; the amount of any contractual obligations, such as take-or-pay contracts, allocable to the area; any impairment of services or increase in cost to remaining customers; the loss of future revenues from existing customers that are transferred to the acquiring retail utility; and legal and other professional fees incurred by the affected retail utility. In the case of section 13.255, additional factors relevant to maintaining the current financial integrity of the affected retail utility are included. The factors under section 13.255(g) are considered to be the minimum components of compensation; by contrast, the factors under section 13.254(g) are not thus qualified.

Under Water Code sections 13.254 and 13.2541, which include SER petitions, a retail public utility may not render retail water or sewer service in an area that has been decertified unless "just and adequate compensation" as required under 13.254(g) has been paid to the decertified retail public utility. *See* Tex. Water Code § 13.254(d). Before S.B. 2272, in proceedings involving an expedited release or SER petition, the PUC rules required that a determination of whether any property of the incumbent CCN holder was rendered useless or valueless be made at the time the PUC issued its order granting the release of land from the CCN. *See* former 16 Tex. Admin. Code § 24.245(n). Since the rule adoption in 2017, and prior to implementation of the S.B. 2272 changes, the PUC had not found any property rendered useless or valueless in an SER proceeding and, hence, had not ordered any compensation to be paid to the incumbent CCN holder. However, in some cases compensation was voluntarily determined by agreement between the incumbent CCN holder and the landowner, typically as a mechanism to minimize litigation risk. *See, e.g.*, *City of Austin's Notice of Intent to Provide Water Service to Area Decertified from Creedmoor-Maha Water Supply Corporation in Travis County*, PUC Docket No. 48118, Final Order (May 25, 2018).

However, S.B. 2272 now requires the PUC, for petitions filed on or after September 1, 2019, to use qualified appraisers to determine what amount of compensation is due to the decertified CCN holder following the grant of an SER petition. The long-standing statutory valuation factors set forth in section 13.254(g) remain the basis for the compensation, but the standard is now to ensure "just and adequate" compensation to the former CCN holder, rather than compensation for property rendered "useless or valueless" as under the former law. The compensation amount is to be determined by either (1) an agreed independent appraiser (which experience shows rarely occurs), paid for by the SER petitioner; or (2) if not agreed, three appraisers, one selected by each party and the third selected by the PUC. *See* Tex. Water Code § 13.2541(g)–(i). The PUC has held that the deadlines for filing appraisal reports are mandatory not directory and, in one case, the PUC commissioners overturned an ALJ's grant of an after-the-fact one-day extension to file. *See Petition of Colorado River Project LLC to Amend SWWC Utilities, Inc. DBA Hornsby Bend Utility's Certificate of Convenience and Necessity in Travis County by Expedited Release*, PUC Docket No. 51166, Final Order (May 13, 2021); *see also*, 16 Tex. Admin. Code § 24.245(i)(4) ("If the former CCN holder fails to . . . file an appraisal within the timeframes required by this subsection, the amount of compensation to be paid will be deemed to be zero."). In Docket No. 49818, the PUC keeps a list of experts qualified to conduct economic valuations of water utilities, pursuant to H.B. 3542 (2019), many of which will be qualified to prepare the type of appraisal reports required in decertification matters. To date, the majority of compensation cases at the PUC have settled, and hence there remains significant uncertainty as to how the commissioners will apply the section 13.2541(g) factors and how that will translate into actual monetary compensation to the decertified CCN holder.

Similarly, under Water Code section 13.255, the PUC must determine whether single certification would result in property of a retail public utility being rendered "useless or valueless" to the incumbent utility and must determine in its order the monetary amount that is adequate and just to compensate the incumbent utility for such property. If the municipality in its application for single certification requested the transfer of specified property of the retail public utility to the municipality or to a franchised utility, the PUC must also determine in its order the adequate and just compensation to be paid for such property, including an award for damages to property that remains in the ownership of the retail public utility after single certification. *See* Tex. Water Code § 13.255(c).

Finally, the PUC will not order compensation to a decertified retail public utility if service to its entire service area is transferred to another retail public utility pursuant to Water Code section 13.2551. *See* 16 Tex. Admin. Code § 24.245(*l*).

§ 29.9:5 "Federal Debt Protection"

Many rural water systems, including water supply corporations and special utility districts, as well as some small cities, are indebted to the USDA RD through loans made pursuant to title 7 United States Code section 1926 or have private loans that are federally guaranteed through the same provision. In circumstances where a utility is federally indebted to the USDA RD, the service area of these federally indebted utilities, along with most other assets of the utility, are subject to a federal lien imposed to ensure repayment of the debt. The effect of the lien is to accord federal protection to the service area from encroachment by competing utilities. *See* 7 U.S.C. § 1926(b). Similarly, the service area and assets of a utility with federally guaranteed debt are likewise protected from encroachment. *See* 7 U.S.C. § 1926(b). This federal protection (which, as discussed here, includes both federally indebted utilities as well as those with federally guaranteed debt) is sometimes at odds with Texas Water Code provisions, such as sections 13.254 and 13.2541, regarding CCN decertification actions by the PUC as discussed at sections 29.9:2 and 29.9:3 above, and section 13.255, which would otherwise permit a municipality to annex an area, pay compensation to the existing water provider, and acquire single certification of the area.

The courts have recognized that federal debt protection under section 1926(b) serves two congressional purposes: (1) to encourage rural water development by expanding the number of potential users of such systems, thereby decreasing per-user cost, and (2) to safeguard the viability and financial security of such rural water providers to ensure repayment of USDA RD loans. *Green Valley Special Utility District v. City of Schertz*, 969 F.3d 460, 475 (5th Cir. 2020) (en banc); *City of Madison, Mississippi v. Bear Creek Water Ass'n*, 816 F.2d 1057, 1060 (5th Cir. 1987). Accordingly, local governments may not encroach on services provided by a federally protected water association, be that encroachment in the form of competing franchises, new or additional permit requirements, or similar means, such as condemnation of the association's facilities or CCN. *City of Madison*, 816 F.2d at 1059. Recognizing the economic incentives at play with new subdivisions located at a city's edge, the Fifth Circuit court of appeals noted that Congress did not intend to allow expanding municipalities to "skim the cream" by expanding into the service area of a federally indebted rural utility. *City of Madison*, 816 F.2d at 1060.

In the encroachment cases, federal preemption of state law occurs, and federal courts have uniformly applied section 1926(b) to preclude the application of state law from usurping a federally protected rural utility's certificated service area or otherwise curtailing the utility's water service rights. The language of the statute is clear and unambiguous on the protection afforded the federally protected utility. Section 1926(b) states, in part:

> The service provided or made available through any such association shall not be curtailed or limited by inclusion of the area served by such association within the boundaries of any municipal corporation or other public body, or by the granting of any private franchise for similar service within such area during the term of such loan . . . .

7 U.S.C. § 1926(b); *see also North Alamo Water Supply Corp. v. City of San Juan*, 90 F.3d 910, 915 (5th Cir. 1995), *cert. denied*, 519 U.S. 1029 (1996), *overruled on other grounds*, *Green Valley*, 969 F.3d at 475. The phrase "such loan" includes loans the USDA RD makes or insures under section 1926(a)(1) or guarantees under 1926(a)(24). *See Rural Water District No. 4, Douglas County, Kansas v. City of Eudora*, 659 F.3d 969, 976 (10th Cir. 2011).

A water utility is not, however, entitled to federal protection merely because it has a federal loan or a federally guaranteed loan. Rather, section 1926(b) protects a water utility's service area from encroachment only if three elements are met: the utility must (1) be an "association" within the meaning of section 1926(b), (2) have qualifying federal or federally guaranteed debt, and (3) have "provided or made service available" in the disputed area. *Le-Ax Water District v. City of Athens*, 346 F.3d 701, 705 (6th Cir. 2003).

Litigation dealing with the applicability (or nonapplicability) of section 1926(b) protection typically centers on the third element—whether the utility has "provided or made service available" to the area the utility seeks to protect from encroachment. In this regard, the law in Texas has recently changed.

Prior Fifth Circuit precedent, established in *North Alamo*, held that a utility seeking to protect its service area under section 1926(b) met the requirement that it had "provided or made service available" to the subject property just by evidence that the utility held a CCN covering the property. *North Alamo*, 90 F.3d at 916. The rationale for the court's decision was grounded in the Texas legal obligation imposed on a CCN holder to render continuous and adequate service to every customer within its CCN area. *North Alamo*, 90 F.3d at 915–16. Thus, under *North Alamo*, a utility with federal or federally guaranteed debt could insulate its service area from encroachment (or competition) merely by showing that it held the CCN covering the property. *North Alamo*, 90 F.3d at 915–16.

The *en banc* Fifth Circuit overruled *North Alamo* in *Green Valley*. *Green Valley*, 969 F.3d at 477. In doing so, the Fifth Circuit overruled the district court's judgment, which had invalidated two PUC decertification orders removing a service area from a federally indebted special utility district and granting the area to two competing service providers. *Green Valley Special Utility District v. Walker*, 351 F. Supp. 3d 992, 1003–04 (W.D. Tex. 2018), *overruled*, 969 F.3d 460 (5th Cir. 2020).

The Fifth Circuit began its analysis in *Green Valley* by noting that the *North Alamo* test found "no support" in the text of section 1926(b)—in particular, the decision did not consider the terms "provided" and "available" in any manner. *See Green Valley*, 969 F.3d at 475–76. Adopting the "ordinary meaning" of the terms, the *Green Valley* court concluded that "provide" generally means "to make available," "furnish," or "to supply something needed or desired," and "available" means "present and ready for use; at hand; accessible" or "capable of being gotten; obtainable." *See Green Valley*, 969 F.3d at 476 (quoting *American Heritage Dictionary*). Applying these ordinary definitions, the court explained that "[i]nherent in the concept of providing service or making service available is the capability of providing service, or, at a minimum, of providing service within a reasonable time." *See Green Valley*, 969 F.3d at 476 (quoting *Sequoyah County Rural Water District No. 7 v. Town of Muldrow*, 191 F.3d 1192, 1203 (10th Cir. 1999)).

The *Green Valley* court also noted that *North Alamo* was out of step with the prevailing interpretation of section 1926(b) from "every other circuit" to have considered the question, as well as Texas state courts, all of which require some variation of a "physical capability" test. *See Green Valley*, 969 F.3d at 476 & n.31 (citing *Creedmoor-Maha Water Supply Corp. v. Texas Commission on Environmental Quality*, 307 S.W.3d 505, 522 (Tex. App.—Austin 2010, no writ) and collecting federal cases). The Fifth Circuit thus established a new test for evaluating the applicability of section 1926(b) protection. Under *Green Valley*, a utility seeking to invoke section 1926(b) protection "must show that it has (1) adequate facilities to provide service to the area within a reasonable time after a request for service is made and (2) the legal right to provide service." *Green Valley*, 969 F.3d at 476 (citing *Le-Ax Water*, 346 F.3d at 706).

The court declined to "tease out exactly what facilities are necessary or precisely *how nearby* they must be located" to satisfy section 1926(b), but the court cautioned that "[a] utility cannot satisfy that test if it has no nearby infrastructure." *Green Valley*, 969 F.3d at 477 & n.36 (citing *Public Water Supply District No. 3 of Laclede County v. City of Lebanon*, 605 F.3d 511, 523 (8th Cir. 2010); *Lexington–S. Elkhorn Water District v. City of Wilmore*, 93 F.3d 230, 238 (6th Cir. 1996)). Rather, the utility "must have something in place to merit [section] 1926(b)'s protection." *Green Valley*, 969 F.3d at 477.

Also implicated in the *Green Valley* appeal was the Fifth Circuit's prior holding in *Green Valley Special Utility District v. City of Cibolo*, 866 F.3d 339 (5th Cir. 2017), *cert. denied*, 139 S. Ct. 783 (2019), where the Fifth Circuit held that *Green Valley* could rely on federal debt for improvements to the utility's water facilities to invoke section 1926(b) protection of its sewer CCN. The City of Schertz argued in the *Green Valley* appeal discussed here that the court should overrule *Cibolo*. The court declined to do so. The court did, however, vacate and remand for reconsideration a different district court decision in light of *Green Valley*: the district court's ruling in *Crystal Clear Special Utility District v. Walker*, No. A-17-CV-00254-LV, 2018 WL 6242370 (W.D. Tex. Nov. 29, 2018), that Texas Water Code sections 13.245(a–5) and (a–6) were preempted by section 1926(b). See *Crystal Clear Special Utility District v. Marquez*, No. 19-50556 (Oct. 15, 2020), in the U.S. Court of Appeals for the Fifth Circuit (order granting motion to vacate judgment and remand for reconsideration in light of *Green Valley*). The case is currently pending in the district court.

Notably, and as mentioned above, the *Green Valley* court favorably cited the Texas appellate court's decision in *Creedmoor-Maha* in adopting the new "physical ability" test. *Green Valley*, 969 F.3d at 476. In *Creedmoor-Maha*, the court of appeals held that, in addition to showing a legal right to serve, a utility must also show "that it either presently was serving the area or at least presently had the physical means to do so." *Creedmoor-Maha*, 307 S.W.3d at 522. On this issue, then, Fifth Circuit precedent now effectively mirrors the already existing state court interpretation of section 1926(b).

Ongoing urbanization in the state has witnessed increased conflicts between municipalities and rural retail water systems. *See* Emily W. Rogers, *Water and Sewer Certificates of Convenience and Necessity: When and How They Apply to Cities*, *Texas City Attorneys Newsletter* (Spring 2004). Specific concern has been raised that the protection of section 1926(b) for rural water systems prevents municipalities from extending fire protection service to high-density developments. TCEQ regulations do not require fireflow, and rural water systems typically do not provide fireflow to the purely rural areas of their systems, though many systems do provide fireflow to higher density urbanizing areas. Monte Akers, *Water Utility Issues: Conflicts Between Urban and Rural Water Suppliers, The Urban Perspective*, Texas Water Law Institute (2003); *see generally* Scott Hounsel, *Water Associations and Federal Protection Under 7 U.S.C. § 1926(b): A Proposal to Repeal Monopoly Status*, 80 Texas L. Rev. 155 (2001).

Fireflow is discussed at greater detail at section 29.10:7 below.

§ 29.10 Special Matters Involving CCNs

Not all retail public utilities are required to hold a CCN, as explained above. However, many choose to do so to protect their service areas. And utilities and WSCs are required to hold a CCN before providing retail water or sewer service. Once a retail public utility—whether voluntarily or by necessity—obtains a CCN, numerous issues for regulatory authorities, like the PUC, arise. The following sections address some of those regulatory challenges.

§ 29.10:1 Providing Retail Water Utility Service outside the Boundaries of a CCN

Certain entities, including IOUs and WSCs, cannot render retail water or sewer utility service in any way unless they obtain a CCN. *See* Tex. Water Code § 13.242(a). After a CCN has been obtained, however, these entities may extend service outside their CCN to territory contiguous to that already served, as long as the point of ultimate use is within one-quarter mile of the CCN area and does not receive similar service from another retail public utility. Tex. Water Code § 13.243(1). Municipalities and districts generally are not required to obtain a CCN, although they may choose to do so to protect their service areas and investment in facilities and customers. Regardless of whether a retail public utility is required to obtain a CCN for service, all retail public utilities, with few exceptions, must obtain a CCN to provide service to an area where another retail public utility is already lawfully furnishing service. *See* Tex. Water Code § 13.242(a).

The absence of CCN protection can be significant. If a retail public utility that is not required to obtain a CCN chooses not to do so, it does not benefit from the protections a CCN can afford. For instance, a municipality or district that serves outside its corporate limits without a CCN could lose customers because of competition from other nearby retail public utilities. Special utility districts (SUDs) especially should carefully consider whether to provide service without obtaining a CCN. Unlike a municipal utility district, which generally must be annexed by a municipality as a whole, a SUD may be annexed piecemeal. *See* Tex. Loc. Gov't Code § 43.071(e)(3). Thus a SUD without a CCN is particularly vulnerable to a neighboring municipality chipping away at its service territory and associated customers.

§ 29.10:2 Contractual Agreements

The territory covered by a CCN may be altered through contractual agreement. Retail public utilities are authorized to enter into contracts with each other to designate the areas and customers they will serve. Such contracts, when approved by the PUC, are valid and enforceable and are incorporated into the appropriate CCNs. *See* Tex. Water Code § 13.248. To obtain PUC approval, the retail public utilities must file a written request that includes the items listed in 16 Texas Administrative Code section 24.253(b), and the agency will issue notice of the agreement before taking action to approve the terms.

A recent attorney general opinion considered the question of whether a home-rule municipality may agree by contract not to petition to decertify all or part of a SUD's CCN in the future and found that the issue should be decided on a case-by-case basis only. Tex. Att'y Gen. Op. No. KP-0340 (2020). While the Water Code does not address the issue, under the common-law reserved powers doctrine, a political subdivision may "not, by contract or otherwise, bind itself in such a way as to restrict its free exercise of governmental powers, nor [can] it abdicate its governmental functions, even for a 'reasonable time.'" *Clear Lake City Water Authority v. Clear Lake Utility Co.*, 549 S.W.2d 385, 391 (Tex. 1977). There may be circumstances under which a municipality's governmental power could not be exercised without the decertification process. Accordingly, it was determined that the reserved powers doctrine may limit a city's authority to waive decertification petitioning rights depending on a variety of factors, such as the purpose for seeking decertification and the posture of the municipality (for example, as a competing retail public utility or as a landowner). The specific facts at issue in a given case are key in analyzing this issue.

§ 29.10:3 Transfers and Cancellations of CCNs

Retail public utilities can also cancel or transfer all or part of their CCNs. One way a retail public utility can transfer a portion of a CCN is by entering into a contractual agreement with another retail public utility pursuant to Texas Water Code section 13.248. The agreement must be filed with the PUC for approval pursuant to 16 Texas Administrative Code section 24.253, which includes notice and hearing on the matter. The PUC has held, however, that section 13.248 agreements are not appropriate for transferring an entire CCN but only for a portion of a CCN. *See In re the Application from the City of Georgetown, Certificate of Convenience and Necessity (CCN) No. 12369, to Acquire Facilities and Transfer and Cancel CCN No. 11590 Held by Chisholm Trail Special Utility District in Bell, Burnet, and Williamson Counties, Texas*, PUC Docket No. 42861, Preliminary Order (May 1, 2015), https://interchange.puc.texas.gov/Documents/42861_182_847923.PDF. Rather, in a situation where an entire CCN is being transferred, the PUC requires a cancellation of one CCN and amendment of the other. Applications to cancel CCNs and to amend CCNs are available on the PUC's website, www.puc.texas.gov.

In addition, utilities and water supply corporations may sell, assign, or lease their CCNs or any rights obtained under their CCNs; however, the PUC must first determine that the purchaser, assignee, or lessee is capable of rendering adequate and continuous service to every consumer within the certified area. *See* Tex. Water Code § 13.251. Any sale, assignment, or lease of a CCN must be on the conditions prescribed by the PUC. Tex. Water Code § 13.251. If a retail public utility agrees in writing to allow another retail public utility to provide service within its service area (except for an interim period) without amending its CCN, the PUC may amend or revoke the CCN. Tex. Water Code § 13.254(a)(3).

A utility or WSC is required to notify the PUC at least 120 days before the date of a proposed sale, acquisition, lease, rental, or merger of a water or sewer system. A transaction that is subject to this notice requirement and that is not completed pursuant to the provisions of the Water Code is void. *See* Tex. Water Code § 13.301; 16 Tex. Admin. Code § 24.239(o). The PUC has an application process for such transactions, known as sale, transfer, merger (STM) applications, that involves public notice, unless waived by the executive director of the PUC for good cause shown. A person purchasing or acquiring a water or sewer system must demonstrate adequate financial, managerial, and technical capability for providing continuous and adequate service to both the requested area and any areas currently certificated to the entity. If the person cannot, the PUC may require that a bond or other financial assurance be provided. The PUC is required to investigate the proposed transaction to determine whether it will serve the public interest. Any STM transaction that is not completed in accordance with these provisions is void. *See* Tex. Water Code § 13.301(h); 16 Tex. Admin. Code § 24.239(o). Section 13.301 does not apply to a transaction under section 13.255 concerning the transfer of the service area for annexed territory to a municipality. Likewise, a utility may not purchase voting stock in another utility doing business in Texas, and a person may not acquire a controlling interest in such a utility unless the person or utility files a written application with the PUC at least sixty-one days before the date of the proposed transaction. Tex. Water Code § 13.302(a); 16 Tex. Admin. Code § 24.243(a). A "controlling interest" is defined as a person or a combination of a person and the person's family members who possess at least 50 percent of the voting stock of the utility or a person who controls at least 30 percent of the stock and is the largest stockholder. 16 Tex. Admin. Code § 24.243(a). A purchase or acquisition of stock that is not completed in accordance with these provisions is void. *See* Tex. Water Code § 13.302(f); 16 Tex. Admin. Code § 24.243(f).

The PUC rules provide for a fair market valuation process that may be used by a Class A or Class B utility that is acquiring a retail public utility or its facilities, for which approval is required under Texas Water Code section 13.301 and 16 Texas Administrative Code section 24.238. When the utilities agree to use that fair market valuation process, they must file a notice of intent to determine fair market value. The PUC will then select three utility valuation experts from its list of qualified utility valuation experts to determine fair market value. Each of the three experts will perform an independent appraisal and prepare a report. The fair market value is the average of the three appraisals. *See* 16 Tex. Admin. Code § 24.238(b)(3).

A CCN transfer also takes place when a WSC converts into a SUD. *See* Tex. Water Code §§ 65.014–.015. Advantages of converting to a SUD include the ability to issue tax-exempt bonds for financing debt, certain tort claims protection, and exemption from certain taxes. SUD conversions occur in one of two ways—by a special act of the legislature or by filing a petition with the TCEQ pursuant to Water Code chapter 65. An application to the TCEQ must include a legal description of the WSC's service area as that service area appears in the CCN held by the WSC. *See* 30 Tex. Admin. Code § 293.11(h). Any area of the WSC that overlaps another entity's CCN is normally excluded from the SUD boundaries unless the other entity consents in writing to the inclusion of its dually certified area.

§ 29.10:4 Cease and Desist Orders

A retail public utility may seek a cease and desist order from the PUC to protect its infrastructure and service area from competing retail public utilities. Specifically, the PUC may issue a cease and desist order if—

> a retail public utility in constructing or extending a line, plant, or system interferes or attempts to interfere with the operation of a line, plant, or system of any other retail public utility, or furnishes, makes available, renders, or extends retail water or sewer utility service to any portion of the service area of another retail public utility that has been granted or is not required to possess a [CCN] . . . .

Tex. Water Code § 13.252. A cease and desist order may prohibit the construction, extension, or provision of service or may prescribe terms and conditions for providing service or for locating the line, plant, or system affected. A request for a cease and desist order must include the items listed in 16 Texas Administrative Code section 24.255.

In some circumstances, a CCN holder is required to seek a cease and desist order to protect its service area. If a CCN holder becomes aware that another retail public utility is providing service within its service area, the CCN holder has 180 days in which to seek a cease and desist order from the PUC or else it risks the amendment or revocation of its CCN. *See* Tex. Water Code § 13.254(a)(4).

§ 29.10:5 Economically Distressed Areas Program

Financial assistance is available to certain providers of water supply and sewer services to "economically distressed areas" through the Economically Distressed Areas Program (EDAP) administered by the Texas Water Development Board (TWDB). See Chapter 37 of this book for a discussion of the EDAP. *See* Tex. Water Code § 17.922. An economically distressed area is an area in which (1) water supply or wastewater systems are inadequate to meet minimal state standards, (2) financial resources are inadequate to provide services to meet those needs, and (3) an established residential subdivision was located on June 1, 2005. *See* Tex. Water Code § 17.921(1). All political subdivisions, including cities, counties, water districts, and nonprofit water supply corporations, may apply.

The PUC can revoke or amend a CCN in a county that has an economically distressed area with a median household income that is not greater than 75 percent of the median state household income if the cost of providing service by the CCN holder is so prohibitively expensive as to constitute denial of service. *See* Tex. Water Code § 13.254(a)(2).

§ 29.10:6 Regionalization

To obtain a CCN for an area that would require the construction of a physically separate water and sewer system, an applicant must first demonstrate that regionalization is not economically feasible. *See* Tex. Water Code § 13.241(d). Regionalization is the consolidation of the operations or physical systems of two or more existing or proposed water or domestic wastewater systems to achieve the best service at rates that will ensure that the system is maintained for the long term. Texas Health and Safety Code section 341.0315 requires the TCEQ to encourage and promote the development and use of regional and areawide drinking water supply systems. *See* Tex. Health & Safety Code § 341.0315(b).

The PUC requires all applicants for new CCNs and for CCN amendments to provide notice to all cities and neighboring retail public utilities that provide the same utility service within two miles of the proposed boundary for a CCN. *See* 16 Tex. Admin. Code § 24.235(b). In addition, the applicant must list all the public drinking water systems within a one-half mile radius, submit copies of written requests for service and the responses, and explain why connecting to neighboring facilities is not economically feasible. *See* 16 Tex. Admin. Code § 24.227(b). Even if an entity is not required to obtain a CCN, it is still required to satisfy the TCEQ's regionalization requirements in order to operate as a public water system. *See* 30 Tex. Admin. Code § 290.39(c).

As part of the agencies' memorandum of understanding, the PUC and the TCEQ agreed to cooperate regarding demonstrating the economic feasibility of regionalization. The TCEQ's policy is that regionalization is feasible unless (1) no other systems are reasonably close to the proposed system, (2) requests for service from neighboring systems have been denied, or (3) an exception applies based on costs, affordable rates, and financial, managerial, and technical capabilities of the existing system. *See* Texas Commission on Environmental Quality, *The Feasibility of Regionalizing Water and Wastewater Utilities: A TCEQ Policy Statement* (RG-357, Jan. 2003).

§ 29.10:7 Role of "Fireflow" Capabilities

As rural areas have become increasingly urbanized, a growing concern has been the provision of water service of sufficient quantity and pressure to adequately fight fires, known as "fireflow." Texas Water Code chapter 13 does not mandate fireflow as a condition for holding a CCN. Retail water service is defined merely as "potable water service . . . provided by a retail public utility to the ultimate consumer for compensation." Tex. Water Code § 13.002(20). This definition does not encompass fireflow, as the TCEQ made clear in its rulemaking following House Bill 2876: "The commission does not have statutory authority to require CCN holders to have the ability to provide fireflows." 30 Tex. Reg. 8966 (2005). This rulemaking concerned factors to be evaluated in deciding whether to grant a CCN in the first instance. In contrast, an incumbent utility's inability or refusal to provide capacity sufficient for fireflows appears to be a basis for filing a petition for expedited release from the incumbent utility's CCN. *See* Tex. Water Code § 13.254(a–1)(1)(E). In 2013, the Texas legislature authorized municipalities to adopt by ordinance certain fireflow standards that will be established by the TCEQ and apply those standards to utilities and WSCs. Act of May 20, 2013, 83d Leg., R.S., ch. 332 (H.B. 1973) (codified at Tex. Health & Safety Code § 341.0359). However, such an ordinance may not require a utility or WSC to build, retrofit, or improve infrastructure in existence at the time the ordinance is adopted.

IV. Conclusion

§ 29.11 Conclusion

Retail water service is provided by a variety of retail public utilities. As discussed in this chapter, the differences among retail public utilities are driven by differences in the larger purposes for which the utilities are created and to some degree by the profile of the customer population. The level of state supervision varies widely depending on the structure of the retail public utility and has evolved since the inception of state regulation in response to ongoing legislative attention to the need for and cost of providing retail water service. The legislature has also made it clear that landowners are entitled to notice of utility actions affecting their land and, in certain cases, a choice of who will provide retail water or sewer service to the land.

CHAPTER 30

Water Utilities: Protection of Public Health

Angela Moorman[1]

I. Roles and Responsibilities of Water Utilities to Protect Public Health

§ 30.1 Introduction

The average person in the United States uses approximately eighty-two gallons of water per day at home, and the average American family uses more than 300 gallons of water per day at home. *See* Cheryl A. Dieter et al., *Estimated Use of Water in the United States in 2015*, U.S. Geological Survey Circular 1441, 23 at tbl. 6 (2018), https://pubs.usgs.gov/circ/1441/circ1441.pdf [hereinafter *Estimated Use of Water*]; U.S. Environmental Protection Agency, WaterSense, *How We Use Water*, www.epa.gov/watersense/how-we-use-water. As a group, Americans drink more than 1 billion glasses of tap water each day. *See* U.S. Environmental Protection Agency, Office of Water, *Water Facts* 1 (EPA 816-F-04-036, June 2004), http://nepis.epa.gov/Exe/ZyPDF.cgi/3000667W.PDF?Dockey=3000667W.PDF. There are several threats to drinking water quality in the United States.

Public water systems reliably provide high quality drinking water. Throughout the United States, only about 7 to 8 percent of community water systems report at least one health-based violation. *See* Maura Allaire et al., *National Trends in Drinking Water Quality Violations*, Proceedings of the National Academy of Sciences (Feb. 27, 2018), www.pnas.org/content/115/9/2078 [hereinafter *National Trends*]. But drinking water that is not properly treated and disinfected poses a health risk to consumers, as does drinking water that is transported through improperly maintained distribution infrastructure. In addition, potential contamination of source water also poses a health risk to consumers. Each year in the United States, an estimated 16.4 million cases of acute gastroenteritis are attributed to community water systems. *See National Trends*. Laws and regulations have been promulgated at both the federal and state levels to address these threats to drinking water.

As described more fully in part II below, the basis for federal regulation is the Safe Drinking Water Act (SDWA). *See* 42 U.S.C. §§ 300f–300j-27. Under the SDWA, the U.S. Environmental Protection Agency (EPA) has adopted primary and secondary drinking water regulations to ensure the

---

1. Angela Moorman is a partner with Birch, Becker & Moorman, LLP. She has practiced environmental law for over twenty years, assisting clients with permitting, compliance, and enforcement issues related to water quality, stormwater, municipal solid waste, and air quality. Angela received a BA in political science from the University of Oklahoma and a law degree from the Indiana University–Bloomington School of Law. Additionally, Angela has an MS in environmental science from the Indiana University–Bloomington School of Public and Environmental Affairs. She is admitted to the bar in Texas and Oklahoma.

quality of drinking water provided by the more than 148,000 public water systems serving more than 283 million users throughout the United States. *See* U.S. Environmental Protection Agency, *Information About Public Water Systems* (Mar. 26, 2020), www.epa.gov/dwreginfo/information-about-public-water-systems; *See also Estimated Use of Water*.

The SDWA contemplates that states will be the primary authorities for enforcing the drinking water standards. The SDWA identifies how states may receive "primacy" under the statute. Texas has received primacy, making the Texas Commission on Environmental Quality (TCEQ) the primary authority for regulating drinking water quality in Texas. *See* Tex. Health & Safety Code ch. 341, subch. C. The TCEQ has adopted detailed regulations to incorporate and implement the EPA's drinking water regulations. *See* 30 Tex. Admin. Code ch. 290, subchs. D, F.

In addition, both the EPA and TCEQ have adopted regulations recognizing the inherent relationship between drinking water quality and drinking water system supply and delivery capacities. Although the federal and state regulatory authorities address the issue in different manners, their goal is the same: to ensure that public water systems have adequate water source capacity to provide high-quality drinking water to their customers.

The following discussion addresses the history and implementation of drinking water regulation in the United States and Texas.

II. Water Quality under the Federal Safe Drinking Water Act

§ 30.2 Legislative Background

The first federal regulation of drinking water quality dates back to 1914, when the U.S. Public Health Service established standards for certain microbes linked to disease. *See* U.S. Department of Health, Education & Welfare, *Public Health Service Drinking Water Standards 1962* v (rev. 1962); https://law.resource.org/pub/us/cfr/ibr/006/usphs.956.1962.pdf; *see also* Stig E. Regli et al., *Control of Drinking Water Pathogens and Disinfection Byproducts*, *in Drinking Water Regulation & Health* 277, 278 (Frederick W. Pontius ed., 2003). Contemporary regulation of drinking water quality began more than sixty years later with passage of the SDWA in 1974. *See* Safe Drinking Water Act, Pub. L. No. 93-523, 88 Stat. 1660 (1974) (codified at 42 U.S.C. §§ 300f–300j-27). The SDWA was enacted to protect public health by "reclaim[ing] and ensur[ing] the purity of the water" consumed in the United States by regulating the quality of the public drinking water supply. *See* James L. Agee, *Protecting America's Drinking Water: Our Responsibilities Under the Safe Drinking Water Act*, EPA J. (Mar. 1975), https://archive.epa.gov/epa/aboutepa/protecting-americas-drinking-water-our-responsibilities-under-safe-drinking-water-act.html. The requirements of the 1974 SDWA focused on treating raw water as the means of providing the safest drinking water to consumers through the development of federally established primary and secondary drinking water standards that must be met by public water systems. *See* Press Release, U.S. Environmental Protection Agency, *EPA Voices Support for Safe Drinking Water Act* (Mar. 8, 1973), https://archive.epa.gov/epa/aboutepa/epa-voices-support-safe-drinking-water-act.html [hereinafter 1973 Press Release]; *see also* U.S. Environmental Protection Agency, Office of Water, *Drinking Water Monitoring, Compliance, and Enforcement* 1 (EPA 816-F-04-031, June 2004), http://nepis.epa.gov/Exe/ZyPDF.cgi/3000667Q.PDF?Dockey=3000667Q.PDF [hereinafter *Drinking Water Monitoring*].

The SDWA was amended in 1986 and 1996 to expand the protection of drinking water quality. *See* Safe Drinking Water Act Amendments of 1986, Pub. L. No. 99-339, 100 Stat. 642 (1986) (codified at 42 U.S.C. §§ 300f–300j-27); Safe Drinking Water Act Amendments of 1996, Pub. L. No. 104-182, 110 Stat. 1613 (1996) (codified at 42 U.S.C. §§ 300f–300j-27); *see also* Press Release, U.S. Environmental Protection Agency, *President Signs Safe Drinking Water Act Amendments* (June 20, 1986), https://

archive.epa.gov/epa/aboutepa/president-signs-safe-drinking-water-act-amendments.html [hereinafter 1986 Press Release]; Press Release, U.S. Environmental Protection Agency, *President Clinton Signs Legislation to Ensure Americans Safe Drinking Water* (Aug. 6, 1996), https://archive.epa.gov/epa/aboutepa/president-clinton-signs-legislation-ensure-americans-safe-drinking-water.html [hereinafter 1996 Press Release]. The 1986 amendments "greatly increase[d] EPA's responsibilities for protecting the nation's drinking water," requiring the development of drinking water standards for more than eighty then unregulated contaminants and calling for the EPA to impose new monitoring requirements on public water systems. 1986 Press Release. The 1986 amendments also required states to develop programs for protecting areas around wells that supply public drinking water systems. *See* 1986 Press Release.

The 1996 amendments recognized additional methods of ensuring drinking water quality, such as source water protection, operator training, funding for water system improvements, and public information. *See* 1996 Press Release.

In 2002, with the adoption of the Public Health Security and Bioterrorism Preparedness and Response Act, drinking water security provisions were added to the SDWA. *See* Public Health Security and Bioterrorism Preparedness and Response Act of 2002, Pub. L. No. 107-188, 116 Stat. 594 (2002); *see also* Mary Tiemann, Cong. Research Serv., *Safe Drinking Water Act (SDWA): A Summary of the Act and Its Major Requirements* 2 (Mar. 1, 2017), www.hsdl.org/?view&did=799194 [hereinafter *CRS Summary*]. For example, the amendments require community water systems serving a population of greater than 3,300 persons to conduct an assessment of the vulnerability of the system to a terrorist attack or "other intentional acts intended to substantially disrupt the ability of the system to provide a safe and reliable supply of drinking water." 42 U.S.C. § 300i-2(a).

In late 2016, Congress again amended the SDWA to "authorize several grant programs that address lead and other contaminants in public drinking water systems." *See* News Release, The White House, Office of the Press Secretary, *Statement by the Press Secretary on H.R. 710, H.R. 875, H.R. 960, H.R. 1150, H.R. 2726, H.R. 3218, H.R. 3784, H.R. 3842, H.R. 4352, H.R. 4465, H.R. 4618, H.R. 4680, H.R. 4887, H.R. 4939, H.R. 5015, H.R. 5065, H.R. 5099, H.R. 5150* (Dec. 16, 2016), https://obamawhitehouse.archives.gov/the-press-office/2016/12/16/statement-press-secretary-hr-710-hr-875-hr-960-hr-1150-hr-2726-hr-3218. The "Water Infrastructure Improvements for the Nation Act" or the "WIN Act" included provisions specific to "addressing lead in public water systems and increasing compliance assistance for small or disadvantaged communities." *CRS Summary*, at 1; *see also* Water Infrastructure Improvements for the Nation Act, Pub. L. 114-322, 130 Stat. 1628 (2016).

The SDWA was last amended in 2018 with the adoption of America's Water Infrastructure Act of 2018 (AWIA). *See* America's Water Infrastructure Act of 2018, Pub. L. 115-270, 132 Stat. 3765 (2018). Specifically, title II of the AWIA "constitutes the most comprehensive reauthorization of the Safe Drinking Water Act (SDWA) since 1996." Elena H. Humphreys, Cong. Research Serv., R45656 at 2, *America's Water Infrastructure Act of 2018 (P.L. 115-270): Drinking Water Provisions* (Mar. 28, 2019). The AWIA included new requirements for community water systems serving more than 3,300 people, requiring such systems "to develop or update risk assessments and emergency response plans (ERPs)." U.S. Environmental Protection Agency, *America's Water Infrastructure Act of 2018* (AWAI) (Aug. 1, 2019), www.epa.gov/ground-water-and-drinking-water/americas-water-infrastructure-act-2018-awia.

§ 30.3 General Requirements of the SDWA and Regulations

The SDWA applies to every public water system (PWS) in the United States. A PWS is a "system for the provision to the public of water for human consumption through pipes or other constructed conveyances, if such system has at least fifteen service connections or regularly serves at least twenty-five individuals." 42 U.S.C. § 300f(4)(A). A PWS includes (1) any collection, treatment, storage, and distribution facilities under the control of the operator of such system and used primarily in connection with the system, and (2) any collection or pretreatment storage facilities not under such control that are used primarily in connection with the system. *See* 42 U.S.C. § 300f(4)(A). Although all PWSs are regulated, the regulations apply differently depending on the type and size of the PWS. *See* U.S. Environmental Protection Agency, Office of Water, *Understanding the Safe Drinking Water Act* 1 (EPA 816-F-04-030, June 2004), www.epa.gov/sites/production/files/2015-04/documents/epa816f04030.pdf [hereinafter *Understanding SDWA*]. The following terms are important to the applicability of SDWA regulations:

- Community water system: A public water system that supplies drinking water to at least fifteen service connections used by year-round residents of the area served by the system or regularly serves at least twenty-five year-round residents. 42 U.S.C. § 300f(15); *see also* 40 C.F.R. § 141.2.
- Noncommunity water system: A public water system that serves the public but does not serve the same people year round. *See* 42 U.S.C. § 300f(16); *see also* 40 C.F.R. § 141.2; *Understanding SDWA*, at 1. There are two types of noncommunity water systems:
  - Nontransient noncommunity water system (NTNCWS): A noncommunity water system that regularly serves at least twenty-five of the same people over six months per year, but not year round (e.g., a school with its own water supply). *See* 40 C.F.R. § 141.2.
  - Transient noncommunity water system (TWS): A noncommunity water system that serves the public but does not regularly serve at least twenty-five of the same people over six months per year (e.g., a campground with its own water supply). *See* 40 C.F.R. § 141.2.

§ 30.4 Primary and Secondary Drinking Water Regulations

Pursuant to the SDWA, the EPA established national primary drinking water regulations (Primary Standards) that (1) apply to all PWSs; (2) specify contaminants that may have an adverse effect on human health; (3) specify a maximum contaminant level (MCL) for each contaminant if, "in the judgment of the Administrator, it is economically and technologically feasible to ascertain the level of such contaminant in water in public water systems," or if not, a treatment technique that leads to an adequate reduction in the level of such contaminant; and (4) contain criteria and procedures to assure a supply of drinking water "which dependably complies with such maximum contaminant levels; including accepted methods for quality control and testing procedures to insure compliance with such levels and to insure proper operation and maintenance of the system." 42 U.S.C. § 300f(1).

The SDWA, as amended, directed the administrator of the EPA to publish a maximum contaminant level goal (MCLG) and promulgate by rule a Primary Standard, or MCL, for those contaminants for which a national primary drinking water regulation had been promulgated as of August 6, 1996, if the administrator of the EPA determined that (1) the contaminant might have an adverse effect on the health of persons; (2) the contaminant was known to occur or there was a substantial likelihood that the contaminant would occur in PWSs with a frequency and at levels of public health concern; and (3) in the judgment of the administrator, regulation of such contaminant presented a meaningful opportunity for reducing the health risk for persons served by PWSs. 42 U.S.C. § 300g-1(b)(1)(A). The Primary Standards are established to protect against both naturally occurring and man-made contaminants that may be found in drinking water.

To establish Primary Standards, the EPA first determines an MCLG for regulated contaminants. The EPA is to set the MCLG for a contaminant "at the level at which no known or anticipated adverse effects on the health of persons occur and which allows an adequate margin of safety." 42 U.S.C. § 300g-1(b)(4)(A). The MCLG is based on health risks, including risks to the most sensitive consumers, like the elderly and infants. *See Understanding SDWA*, at 3. Available technology is not considered when setting MCLGs. *See* U.S. Environmental Protection Agency, Office of Water,

Drinking Water Standards & Health Effects 2 (EPA 816-F-04-037, June 2004), http://nepis.epa.gov/Exe/ZyPDF.cgi/3000667U.PDF?Dockey=3000667U.PDF [hereinafter *Drinking Water Standards*].

The EPA then sets an MCL, "the maximum permissible level of a contaminant in water which is delivered to any user of a public water system." 42 U.S.C. § 300f(3); *see also Understanding SDWA*, at 3. The MCL is an enforceable standard that is set as close to the MCLG as feasible. *See* 42 U.S.C. § 300g-1(b)(4)(B). The term "feasible" is defined in the SDWA, for purposes of establishing an MCL, as "feasible with the use of the best technology, treatment techniques and other means which the Administrator finds, after examination for efficacy under field conditions and not solely under laboratory conditions, are available (taking cost into consideration)." 42 U.S.C. § 300g-1(b)(4)(D).

After initially determining a proposed MCL that is as close to the MCLG as feasible based on affordable technology, the EPA must complete an economic analysis to determine whether the benefits of that standard justify the costs. "If not, [the] EPA may adjust the MCL for a particular class or group of systems to a level that 'maximizes health risk reduction benefits at a cost that is justified by the benefits.' [The] EPA may not adjust the MCL if the benefits justify the costs to large systems and small systems that are unlikely to receive variances." *Drinking Water Standards*, at 2.

When it is not economically or technically feasible to promulgate an MCL for a particular contaminant or when the EPA determines that there is no reliable or economic method to detect a certain contaminant in the water at very low levels, the EPA is still required to take steps to ensure the safety of the water supply with regard to that contaminant. In that case, instead of setting an MCL, the EPA is required to establish a treatment technique (TT) that identifies a particular way to treat the water to remove contaminants. *See* 42 U.S.C. § 300g-1(b)(7)(A). The SDWA specifically requires the EPA to adopt Primary Standards specifying certain TTs. For example, the EPA is required to adopt Primary Standards that specify criteria under which filtration (including coagulation and sedimentation) would be required as a TT for PWSs supplied by surface water sources. *See* 42 U.S.C. § 300g-1(b)(7)(C)(i). Amendments to the SDWA also specifically require the EPA to promulgate a Primary Standard requiring disinfection as a TT for all PWSs, including both surface water systems and, as necessary, groundwater systems. *See* 42 U.S.C. § 300g-1(b)(8).

The EPA has established Primary Standards for more than ninety contaminants, including microbiological, chemical, radiological, and physical contaminants that can be found in drinking water. *See* U.S. Environmental Protection Agency, *How EPA Regulates Drinking Water Contaminants*, www.epa.gov/dwregdev/how-epa-regulates-drinking-water-contaminants; *see also* U.S. Environmental Protection Agency, *National Primary Drinking Water Regulations* (EPA 816-F-09-004, May 2009), www.epa.gov/sites/production/files/2015-11/documents/howeparegulates_mcl_0.pdf. The Primary Standards are not applicable to the following PWSs: (1) those that consist of only distribution and storage facilities (and do not have collection and treatment facilities); (2) those that obtain all their water from, but are not owned or operated by, a PWS to which the Primary Standards apply; (3) those that do not sell water to any person; and (4) those that are not carriers that convey passengers in interstate commerce. 42 U.S.C. § 300g. Where the Primary Standards are applicable, the PWSs must test for levels of contaminants in their treated drinking water, comparing those levels of contaminants to the MCLs or TTs to ensure that the regulatory requirements are met. *See generally* 42 U.S.C. § 300g-7.

The SDWA outlines the procedures for the EPA to ensure a constant evaluation of the possible effects of other contaminants on PWSs. Every five years the EPA is required to consult with the scientific community and then publish a list of contaminants that are not currently subject to regulation but are known or are anticipated to occur in PWSs. 42 U.S.C. § 300g-1(b)(1)(B)(i)(I). The contaminants on that list are evaluated for possible future regulation through Primary Standards. 42 U.S.C. § 300g-1(b)(1)(B)(ii).

The EPA also establishes secondary drinking water regulations (Secondary Standards). 42 U.S.C. § 300g-1(c). While Secondary Standards also apply to PWSs, they are not enforceable standards. Instead, they specify maximum contaminant levels that, "in the judgment of the Administrator, are requisite to protect the public welfare." *See* 42 U.S.C. § 300f(2). Secondary Standards may apply to a contaminant in drinking water "(A) which may adversely affect the odor or appearance of such water and consequently may cause a substantial number of the persons served by the public water system providing such water to discontinue its use, or (B) which may otherwise adversely affect the public welfare." 42 U.S.C. § 300f(2). Secondary Standards may vary based on geographic region and other site-specific circumstances. 42 U.S.C. § 300f(2). Public water systems are not required to meet the Secondary Standards under federal regulations, but states may choose to adopt and enforce the Secondary Standards. *See Drinking Water Standards*, at 1.

§ 30.5 Monitoring and Reporting Requirements

Regulated PWSs are required to monitor drinking water quality to verify that the drinking water they provide meets all federal and state standards. The EPA has adopted regulations that specify the methods that must be used to analyze drinking water samples. *See* 40 C.F.R. pt. 141, subpt. C. Monitoring and sampling requirements vary depending on the contaminant group, whether the PWS uses groundwater or surface water, and the number of people served by the PWS. *See generally* 40 C.F.R. pt. 141, subpt. C. Certain water systems must also test for particular contaminants that are not currently regulated by the EPA. These data are used to determine which contaminants should be regulated by new standards. *See Drinking Water Monitoring*, at 1.

The 1996 amendments to the SDWA included provisions regarding consumer access to drinking water quality information. *See CRS Summary*, at 2; *see generally* 42 U.S.C. § 300g-3(c)(3). There are several methods through which consumers can obtain information regarding drinking water quality. Each community water system is required to prepare a water quality report, or a consumer confidence report, annually. *See* 42 U.S.C. § 300g-3(c)(4). Every customer of a community water system must have access to the annual report, which provides information on the source of the drinking water supply, the levels of regulated contaminants detected in the drinking water, the health effects of any contaminants that are detected above federal health-based standards, information on the water system's compliance with applicable regulations, and information on the levels of unregulated contaminants for which monitoring is required. *See* 42 U.S.C. § 300g-3(c)(4)(B).

In addition, each state with primacy under the SDWA is required to produce an annual report identifying whether PWSs within the state met drinking water standards during the previous year. *See* 42 U.S.C. § 300g-3(c)(3)(A). The EPA collects information on all PWSs, making much of it available to the public. *See* 42 U.S.C. § 300g-3(c)(3)(B); *see also* U.S. Environmental Protection Agency, Office of Water, *Public Access to Information & Public Involvement* 1 (EPA 816-F-04-039, June 2004), http://nepis.epa.gov/Exe/ZyPDF.cgi/30006610.PDF?Dockey=30006610.PDF.

In addition to annual reports, PWSs are required to provide public notification when there is an emergency with the drinking water supply. The SDWA requires each PWS to notify its customers promptly, using various forms of media, if there is an immediate threat to health due to a violation of a drinking water standard. *See* 42 U.S.C. § 300g-3(c)(1), (c)(2).

§ 30.6 Other SDWA Requirements

An important addition to the SDWA, which occurred with the passage of the 1996 amendments, was the new requirement that all states perform source water assessments. *See* 42 U.S.C. § 300j-13. The first step of this program was for each state to have its Source Water Assessment Program (SWAP) reviewed and approved by the EPA. *See* 42 U.S.C. § 300j-13(a)(3). After approval, each state was to conduct an assessment of each PWS and make those source water assessments available to the public. The SWAPs for various states differ, but each assessment program must address four major elements: (1) delineate or map the source water protection areas; (2) conduct an inventory of potential sources of contamination in those areas; (3) determine the susceptibility of PWSs to those contamination sources;

and (4) release the results of the determinations to the public. *See* 42 U.S.C. § 300j-13(a)(2), (a)(7). Source water protection is not mandated by the SDWA amendments, but the EPA encourages states and communities to use the information obtained from the source water assessments to safeguard source water protection areas from identified sources of contaminants. *See* U.S. Environmental Protection Agency, Office of Water, *Protecting Drinking Water Sources* 2 (EPA 816-F-04-032, June 2004), http://nepis.epa.gov/Exe/ZyPDF.cgi/3000667S.PDF?Dockey=3000667S.PDF.

§ 30.7 Texas "Primacy" under the SDWA

Pursuant to the SDWA, states may receive primary regulatory and enforcement authority—that is, the authority to implement the SDWA within their jurisdiction or "primacy." *See* 42 U.S.C. § 300g-2(a). In fact, the 1974 enactment of the SDWA intended for states to be the primary authorities under the SDWA: "The bill provides that the States shall have primary enforcement authority with regard to the drinking water standards and that [the] EPA will monitor activities of the States and public water systems only to the extent necessary to determine if there is an adequate program to enforce the primary standards." 1973 Press Release. To receive primacy under the SDWA, states must meet certain requirements, including adopting regulations that are at least as stringent as those established by the EPA. *See* 42 U.S.C. § 300g-2(a)(1). In addition, to receive primacy, states are required to demonstrate that they have formal enforcement authority and the authority to assess administrative penalties. *See* 42 U.S.C. § 300g-2(a)(2), (6). Texas has received primacy. *See, e.g.*, 31 Tex. Admin. Code § 354.3(c).

III. Texas Law and Rules for Drinking Water Quality

§ 30.8 Introduction

Texas Health and Safety Code chapter 341, subchapter C, prescribes the duties of the TCEQ with regard to the regulation and control of drinking water systems. *See* Tex. Health & Safety Code ch. 341, subch. C; *see also* 30 Tex. Admin. Code § 290.39. Texas law authorizes the TCEQ to implement the federal SDWA and requires that the TCEQ ensure that PWSs (1) supply safe drinking water in adequate quantities, (2) are financially stable and technically sound, (3) promote the use of regional and area-wide drinking water systems, and (4) review completed plans and specifications and business plans for certain PWSs. *See* 30 Tex. Admin. Code § 290.39(a); *see also* Tex. Health & Safety Code §§ 341.031(a), 341.0315(a).

Texas law provides that public drinking water must be "free from deleterious matter and must comply with the standards established" by the TCEQ or the EPA. Tex. Health & Safety Code § 341.031(a). The TCEQ has adopted drinking water standards that govern the quality of drinking water produced by PWSs and that establish reporting requirements for PWSs. *See* 30 Tex. Admin. Code ch. 290, subch. F. The TCEQ's chapter 290 rules "are written to comply with the requirements of the Federal 'Safe Drinking Water Act,' . . . and the 'Primary Drinking Water Regulations' which have been promulgated by the [EPA]." 30 Tex. Admin. Code § 290.101.

The TCEQ's chapter 290 rules include the same four applicability exceptions discussed above with regard to the federal rules. For example, like the federal rules, the TCEQ's rules do not apply to a PWS that consists only of distribution and storage facilities and that has no production and treatment facilities. *See* 30 Tex. Admin. Code § 290.102(a)(1). In addition, the TCEQ's rules except from the chapter 290 requirements those PWSs that are subject to plumbing restrictions and inspections by the PWS that provides the water. *See* 30 Tex. Admin. Code § 290.102(a)(5).

The chapter 290 rules have been amended repeatedly to implement revisions to federal regulations related to the safety of drinking water. Most recently, the TCEQ amended the chapter 290 rules in March 2017 to ensure that the rules were not less stringent than the federal Revised Total Coliform Rule. *See* 42 Tex. Reg. 1466 (Mar. 24, 2017). In addition, the 2017 amendments provided for consistency with other federal drinking water provisions, addressed the EPA's comments on the federal Ground Water Rule (GWR), and provided clarification to existing state rules. The 2017 amendments ensured that the TCEQ's rules are not less stringent than the federal GWR, in response to the EPA's 2014 primacy review of the TCEQ's previously adopted GWR rules. *See* 42 Tex. Reg., at 1466.

§ 30.9 Summary and Description: Primary Standards—Maximum Contaminant Levels, Maximum Residual Disinfectant Levels, Treatment Techniques, and Action Levels

In compliance with the SDWA and the federal Primary Standards, the TCEQ has adopted MCLs, maximum residual disinfectant levels (MRDLs), TTs, and action levels for a number of drinking water contaminants. *See* 30 Tex. Admin. Code § 290.104(a). The TCEQ has adopted standards for a broad range of contaminants, including inorganic compounds, organic compounds, radionuclides, microbial contaminants, disinfectant residuals, total organic carbon, disinfection by-products, and metals. *See generally* 30 Tex. Admin Code ch. 290, subch. F.

§ 30.9:1 Inorganic Compounds

All PWSs are subject to the regulatory requirements applicable to inorganic compounds, although the "level" of applicability differs based on the type of PWS. *See* 30 Tex. Admin. Code § 290.106. Community water systems and NTNCWSs must comply with the monitoring and reporting requirements and MCLs for all inorganic contaminants identified in TCEQ regulations. *See* 30 Tex. Admin. Code § 290.106(a)(1). TWSs must comply with the monitoring and reporting requirements and MCLs for nitrate, nitrite, and total nitrate and nitrite. *See* 30 Tex. Admin. Code § 290.106(a)(2), (b). PWSs that use groundwater under the direct influence of surface water must meet the inorganic sampling requirements identified for surface water systems. *See* 30 Tex. Admin. Code § 290.106(a)(3). The TCEQ has established MCLs for inorganic compounds, which are found at 30 Texas Administrative Code section 290.106(b).

The TCEQ has adopted detailed monitoring requirements for inorganic compounds. *See* 30 Tex. Admin. Code § 290.106(c). All PWSs are required to monitor at locations identified in the systems' approved monitoring plans. *See* 30 Tex. Admin. Code § 290.106(c). For example, all inorganic compounds, except asbestos, must be monitored at each entry point to the distribution system. *See* 30 Tex. Admin. Code § 290.106(c)(1). If a PWS draws water from more than one source and the sources are combined before distribution, the system must sample at an entry point that is representative of all sources and during periods of normal operating conditions. *See* 30 Tex. Admin. Code § 290.106(c)(1)(A). The executive director of the TCEQ may approve the use of composite samples where such composite sampling meets the requirements established in the TCEQ's rules. *See* 30 Tex. Admin. Code § 290.106(c)(1)(C).

In addition, each PWS is required to monitor at the time designated during each compliance period. *See* 30 Tex. Admin. Code § 290.106(c). A PWS is required to routinely monitor for antimony, arsenic, barium, beryllium, cadmium, chromium, cyanide, fluoride, mercury, selenium, and thallium. *See* 30 Tex. Admin. Code § 290.106(c)(4)(A). For example, each surface water entry point must be sampled annually and each groundwater entry point must be sampled once every three years. *See* 30 Tex. Admin. Code § 290.106(c)(4)(A)(i), (c)(4)(A)(ii). In addition, the executive director can require either reduced or increased monitoring based on the specific situation of the PWS. *See* 30 Tex. Admin. Code § 290.106(c)(4)(B), (c)(4)(C).

There are specific monitoring requirements for asbestos and nitrates and nitrites. *See* 30 Tex. Admin. Code § 290.106(c)(2), (c)(5)–(7). The asbestos sampling requirements provide that a system that is vulnerable to asbestos contamination due to its source of water is required to sample at the entry point to the distribution system, while a system that is vulnerable to asbestos contamination due to corrosion of asbestos-cement pipe is required to sample at a tap served by asbestos-cement pipe under conditions where asbestos contamination is most likely to occur. *See* 30 Tex. Admin. Code § 290.106(c)(2)(A), (c)(2)(B). A system vulnerable to asbestos contamination due to both its source water supply and corrosion of asbestos-cement pipe must sample at a tap served by asbestos-cement pipe under conditions where asbestos contamination is most likely to occur. *See* 30 Tex. Admin. Code § 290.106(c)(2)(C). The executive director may require sampling for asbestos at additional locations based on the size, length, age, and location of asbestos-cement pipe in the distribution system. *See* 30 Tex. Admin. Code § 290.106(c)(2)(D).

Small system compliance technologies (SSCTs) have been established for arsenic. *See* 30 Tex. Admin. Code § 290.106(i). The SSCTs that are set out in 40 Code of Federal Regulations section 141.62(d) may be used with TCEQ approval. Where a point-of-use or point-of-entry device is used for compliance, the PWS must develop a program for long-term operation, maintenance, and monitoring of the devices to ensure adequate performance. *See* 30 Tex. Admin. Code § 290.106(i).

§ 30.9:2 Organic Compounds

All community water systems and NTNCWSs must comply with the TCEQ's regulatory requirements for organic contaminants. *See* 30 Tex. Admin. Code § 290.107(a). Every PWS that uses groundwater under the direct influence of surface water must meet the organic sampling requirements given for surface water. *See* 30 Tex. Admin. Code § 290.107(a). The TCEQ has adopted MCLs for thirty synthetic organic chemical (SOC) contaminants and twenty-one volatile organic chemical (VOC) contaminants, which are found at 30 Texas Administrative Code section 290.107(b)(1) and (b)(2).

As with inorganic compounds, the TCEQ has established detailed monitoring requirements for SOC contaminants and VOC contaminants. *See* 30 Tex. Admin. Code § 290.107(c). All monitoring for SOC contaminants and VOC contaminants must be conducted at sites designated in the PWS's monitoring plan. *See* 30 Tex. Admin. Code § 290.107(c). For SOC monitoring, systems must routinely sample at sample sites representative of each entry point to the distribution system. *See* 30 Tex. Admin. Code § 290.107(c)(1)(A)(i). Each PWS must monitor at the time designated by the executive director within the compliance period. *See* 30 Tex. Admin. Code § 290.107(c)(1)(C)(iv). Community water systems and NTNCWSs are required to take four consecutive quarterly samples for each TCEQ-regulated SOC contaminant during each compliance period beginning with the initial compliance period, although in certain circumstances sampling frequency may be reduced. *See* 30 Tex. Admin. Code § 290.107(c)(1)(C)(i)–(iii). The executive director may require increased SOC monitoring or may waive SOC monitoring. *See* 30 Tex. Admin. Code § 290.107(c)(1)(D), (c)(1)(E).

Every PWS is required to routinely sample for VOC contaminants at sample sites representative of each entry point to the distribution system. *See* 30 Tex. Admin. Code § 290.107(c)(2)(A)(i). For routine monitoring, community water systems and NTNCWSs are required to take four consecutive quarterly samples for each TCEQ-regulated VOC contaminant during each compliance period beginning with the initial compliance period, although in certain circumstances sampling frequency may be reduced. *See* 30 Tex. Admin. Code § 290.107(c)(2)(C)(i), (c)(2)(C)(ii). As with other required monitoring, the executive director can grant waivers from monitoring or require increased monitoring. *See* 30 Tex. Admin. Code §§ 290.107(c)(2)(C)(iv), 290.107(c)(2)(D), (c)(2)(E).

§ 30.9:3 Radionuclides

Radionuclides, other than radon, must be monitored by community water systems. *See* 30 Tex. Admin. Code § 290.108(a). All PWSs that treat groundwater under the direct influence of surface water must comply with the radionuclide requirements for surface water systems. *See* 30 Tex. Admin. Code § 290.108(a).

Maximum contaminant levels have been established for naturally occurring radionuclides as set out in 30 Texas Administrative Code section 290.108(b)(1). Pursuant to TCEQ rules, the MCLs for beta particle and photon radioactivity from man-made radionuclides in drinking water for community water systems are equivalent to the MCLs established in 40 Code of Federal Regulations section 141.66(d). *See* 30 Tex. Admin. Code § 290.108(b)(2).

All PWSs are required to measure the concentration of radionuclides at locations and frequencies specified in the system's monitoring plan. *See* 30 Tex. Admin. Code § 290.108(c). Required monitoring frequencies are specified for both naturally occurring radionuclides and man-made radionuclides. *See* 30 Tex. Admin. Code § 290.108(c)(1), (c)(2). Compliance must be routinely monitored at sampling points representing each entry point to the distribution system. *See* 30 Tex. Admin. Code § 290.108(c)(3)(B). If results from an entry point exceed one-half the MCL, the executive director may require the system to sample all water sources that provide water to that entry point. *See* 30 Tex. Admin. Code § 290.108(c)(3)(B).

Small system compliance technologies have been established for radionuclides. The SSCTs for radionuclides are identified in 40 Code of Federal Regulations section 141.66(h) and may be used with TCEQ approval. 30 Tex. Admin. Code § 290.108(i). Where a point-of-use or a point-of-entry device is used for compliance, the water system must develop a program for the long-term operation, maintenance, and monitoring of the devices to ensure adequate performance. *See* 30 Tex. Admin. Code § 290.108(i).

§ 30.9:4 Microbial Contaminants

All PWSs must comply with the TCEQ's regulatory requirements for microbial contaminants. *See* 30 Tex. Admin. Code § 290.109(a). The TTs and MCL requirements for microbial contaminants are based on the detection of those contaminants or fecal indicator organisms. A PWS is in compliance with the MCL for *Escherichia coli (E. coli)* unless any of the following conditions occur: the PWS has an *E. coli*-positive repeat sample following a total-coliform-positive routine sample; the PWS has a total-coliform-positive repeat sample following an *E. coli*-positive routine sample; the PWS fails to take all required repeat samples following an *E. coli*-positive routine sample; or the PWS fails to test for *E. coli* when any repeat sample tests positive for total coliform. *See* 30 Tex. Admin. Code § 290.109(b)(1).

All PWSs are required to conduct assessments after exceeding particular TT triggers. 30 Tex. Admin. Code § 290.109(c). Level 1 TT triggers include the following: for a PWS that collects at least forty distribution samples per month, the TT is defined as being when more than 5.0 percent of samples collected during the month are total-coliform positive; for a PWS that collects fewer than forty distribution samples per month, the TT is defined as when two or more samples collected in a month are total-coliform positive; and when a PWS fails to collect all required samples after a total-coliform-positive result. *See* 30 Tex. Admin. Code § 290.109(c)(1). Level 2 TT triggers include the following: an *E. coli* MCL violation as specified in section 290.109; and a second Level 1 TT trigger occurring within a rolling twelve-month period. *See* 30 Tex. Admin. Code § 290.109(c)(2). Level 1 and Level 2 assessments are conducted to identify the possible presence of sanitary defects and defects in distribution system coliform monitoring practices. 30 Tex. Admin. Code § 290.109(c)(3). The TT assessments can also indicate that no sanitary defects were identified. 30 Tex. Admin. Code

§ 290.109(c)(3). When conducting Level 1 and Level 2 assessments, the PWS is to ensure that the following items are evaluated: sampling sites, protocol, and processing; atypical events that could affect distributed water quality or indicate that distributed water quality was impaired; changes in distribution system maintenance and operation that could affect distributed water quality; source and treatment considerations that affect distributed water quality; existing water quality monitoring data; and the possible presence of sanitary defects. *See* 30 Tex. Admin. Code § 290.109(c)(3)(B). PWSs are required to correct sanitary defects found through these assessments. *See* 30 Tex. Admin. Code § 290.109(c)(3)(E).

To comply with the microbial contaminants monitoring requirements, all PWSs must collect samples for total coliform, fecal coliform, *E. coli*, or other fecal indicator organisms. *See* 30 Tex. Admin. Code § 290.109(d). As with other contaminants, the TCEQ's rules specify the locations and frequency of monitoring for microbial contaminants. For example, PWSs are to collect routine distribution coliform samples at active service connections that are representative of water quality throughout the distribution system. *See* 30 Tex. Admin. Code § 290.109(d)(1)(A). Other sampling sites may be used if they are located adjacent to active service connections. *See* 30 Tex. Admin. Code § 290.109(d)(1)(A). The monitoring locations must be identified in the system's monitoring plan. *See* 30 Tex. Admin. Code § 290.109(d)(1)(B).

The minimum sampling frequency for community and noncommunity PWSs is based on the population served and the source of the water provided. *See* 30 Tex. Admin. Code § 290.109(d)(2)(A); *see also* 30 Tex. Admin. Code § 290.109(d)(2)(B)–(D). Based on the population, the rules specify the number of samples to be taken per month. *See* 30 Tex. Admin. Code § 290.109(d)(2)(A)(iii). Repeat sampling is required if one or more routine samples is found to contain coliform organisms. *See* 30 Tex. Admin. Code § 290.109(d)(3). The SDWA does not allow small systems to obtain variances from the regulatory requirements applicable to microbial contaminants. *See Drinking Water Standards*, at 2.

§ 30.9:5 Disinfectant Residuals

All PWSs are required to properly disinfect the water before it is distributed to any customers. In addition, PWSs are required to maintain acceptable disinfectant residuals within the distribution system. *See* 30 Tex. Admin. Code § 290.110(a). Both the minimum residual disinfectant concentration and the MRDL apply to PWSs. *See* 30 Tex. Admin. Code § 290.104(f). The MRDL is not to be exceeded. 30 Tex. Admin. Code § 290.110(b). In addition, the disinfection process at a PWS that treats surface water or groundwater under the direct influence of surface water must meet minimum disinfection requirements before the water is supplied to any consumer. *See* 30 Tex. Admin. Code § 290.110(b); *see also* 30 Tex. Admin. Code § 290.111(d). The standards are set out in 30 Texas Administrative Code section 290.104(f)(1)–(4). The disinfection process used by a PWS that treats surface water or groundwater under the direct influence of surface water must achieve minimum microbial inactivation levels as identified in 30 Texas Administrative Code section 290.111(d)(1).

All PWSs are required to monitor the performance of their disinfection facilities to ensure that appropriate disinfectant levels are maintained. *See* 30 Tex. Admin. Code § 290.110(c). Monitoring is to be conducted at sites designated in the PWS's monitoring plan. *See* 30 Tex. Admin. Code § 290.110(c).

§ 30.9:6 Total Organic Carbon

All community water systems and NTNCWSs that treat surface water or groundwater under the direct influence of surface water and use coagulation, flocculation, sedimentation or clarification, or filtration facilities as part of the treatment process must meet specific TCEQ rules applicable to total organic carbon (TOC). *See* 30 Tex. Admin. Code § 290.112(a). Systems must "achieve the Step 1 removal requirements in paragraph (1) of this subsection, meet one of the alternative compliance criteria described in paragraph (2) of this subsection, or apply for the alternative Step 2 removal requirements described in paragraph (3) of this subsection." 30 Tex. Admin. Code § 290.112(b).

For Step 1, section 290.112(b)(1), a water treatment plant's TOC required percent removal is based on the plant's source-water TOC and alkalinity. 30 Tex. Admin. Code § 290.112(b)(1). For example, if the source-water TOC is greater than or equal to 8.0 mg/L and the source-water alkalinity is between 0 and 60 mg/L as calcium carbonate (CaCO3), then 50 percent removal is required. 30 Tex. Admin. Code § 290.112(b)(1).

The alternative compliance criteria described in section 290.112(b)(2)—that is, paragraph (2)—include eight different criteria, alternative compliance criteria numbers 1 through 8, that a system may meet. *See* 30 Tex. Admin. Code § 290.112(b)(2).

If a PWS does not meet the Step 1 TOC removal requirements and does not meet one of the eight alternative compliance criteria, then the system must apply for executive director approval of alternative Step 2 removal requirements. 30 Tex. Admin. Code § 290.112(b)(3).

Systems are required to conduct TOC monitoring during normal operating conditions at sites and at the frequency designated in the system's monitoring plan. 30 Tex. Admin. Code § 290.112(c).

§ 30.9:7 Disinfection By-Products

Disinfection by-products (DBPs) are "[c]hemical compounds formed by the reaction of a disinfectant with the natural organic matter present in water." 30 Tex. Admin. Code § 290.103(8). All community water systems and NTNCWSs are required to meet MCLs for certain regulated DBPs, as addressed below.

TTHM and HAA5: The DBPs total trihalomethanes (TTHM) and haloacetic acids (group of five) (HAA5) are regulated by the TCEQ. *See* 30 Tex. Admin. Code § 290.113. The running annual average concentrations of TTHM and HAA5 are not to exceed 0.080 mg/L for TTHM and 0.060 mg/L for HAA5. 30 Tex. Admin. Code § 290.113(b). All TTHM and HAA5 samples must be taken during normal operation conditions, and monitoring must be done at locations and at frequencies identified in the system's monitoring plan. 30 Tex. Admin. Code § 290.113(c). TCEQ rules include detailed tables defining routine monitoring frequencies and locations and reduced monitoring frequencies and locations for TTHM and HAA5 based on the type of PWS. *See* 30 Tex. Admin. Code § 290.113(c)(3), (c)(4).

Chlorite and Bromate: All public water systems that use chlorine dioxide must comply with an MCL for chlorite of 1.0 mg/L. *See* 30 Tex. Admin. Code § 290.114(a)(1). Monitoring for chlorite concentrations is to be done at locations and intervals specified in the system's monitoring plan. All samples must be collected during normal operating hours. 30 Tex. Admin. Code § 290.114(a)(2). The chlorite concentration of water entering the distribution system must be measured at least once each day. 30 Tex. Admin. Code § 290.114(a)(2)(A). A "three-sample set" must be collected on the same day at the following locations: (1) near the first customer of a plant using chlorine dioxide, (2) at a location representative of the average residence time in the distribution system, and (3) at a location reflecting maximum residence time in the distribution system. 30 Tex. Admin. Code § 290.114(a)(2)(B).

All community water systems and NTNCWSs that use ozone must meet the MCL for bromate of 0.010 mg/L. *See* 30 Tex. Admin. Code § 290.114(b)(1). Bromate concentrations in the water entering the distribution system must be measured at least once each month. *See* 30 Tex. Admin. Code § 290.114(b)(2). Samples are to be collected when the ozonation system is operating under normal conditions and at locations and intervals specified in the system's monitoring plan. *See* 30 Tex. Admin. Code § 290.114(b)(2).

§ 30.9:8 Metals

The TCEQ has established regulatory requirements for lead and copper that apply to community water systems and NTNCWSs, requiring them to control the levels of lead and copper in drinking water by controlling the corrosivity of the water. *See* 30 Tex. Admin. Code § 290.117(a). The TCEQ rules address monitoring, reporting, corrosion control studies and treatment, source water treatment, lead service line replacement, and public education. New PWSs are required to meet the lead and copper requirements when notified by the executive director. 30 Tex. Admin. Code § 290.117(a).

Public water systems must meet action levels for lead and copper in drinking water. 30 Tex. Admin. Code § 290.117(b). The action level for lead is 0.015 mg/L, and it "is exceeded if the '90th percentile' lead level exceeds 0.015 mg/L in any monitoring period. The 90th percentile lead level is exceeded when more than 10% of tap water samples have a concentration over the action level." 30 Tex. Admin. Code § 290.117(b)(1)(A). The action level for copper is 1.3 mg/L. 30 Tex. Admin. Code § 290.117(b)(1)(B). The action level for copper "is exceeded if the concentration of copper in more than 10% of tap water samples collected during any monitoring period is greater than 1.3 mg/L." 30 Tex. Admin. Code § 290.117(b)(1)(B).

Community water systems and NTNCWSs are required to sample at sites and at frequencies approved by the TCEQ executive director and documented in the systems' monitoring plans. *See* 30 Tex. Admin. Code § 290.117(c). Prior to conducting required tap sampling, each PWS must complete a materials survey of its distribution system to identify a pool of tap sampling sites that meet specified requirements. *See* 30 Tex. Admin. Code § 290.117(c)(1)(C)(i). Sample sites are to be representative of the distribution system and must specifically represent areas of the system most vulnerable to corrosion of lead and copper into the water. 30 Tex. Admin. Code § 290.117(c)(1)(C). The material survey is to be submitted to the executive director for review and approval. 30 Tex. Admin. Code § 290.117(c)(1)(C)(i). After completing sample site selection, the system is to submit the Lead and Copper Sample Site Selection form to the executive director for approval. 30 Tex. Admin. Code § 290.117(c)(1)(C)(ii).

The Lead and Copper Rule, a TT established by the EPA, requires optimized corrosion control. *See* 40 C.F.R. pt. 141, subpt. I. TCEQ rules provide that systems may be required to perform corrosion control studies to determine whether treatment is necessary to reduce the corrosivity of the water. *See* 30 Tex. Admin. Code § 290.117(f). Based on the results of the corrosion control study, the system is to recommend to the executive director an optimal water quality parameter (OWQP) range based on normal system operating conditions. 30 Tex. Admin. Code § 290.117(f)(2). The executive director then reviews the corrosion control study and designates OWQPs. 30 Tex. Admin. Code § 290.117(f)(2). In addition, a system that exceeds the action level for lead or copper based on the ninetieth percentile level is required to submit recommendations for optimal corrosion control treatment equipment within six months after the end of the monitoring period during which the exceedance occurred. 30 Tex. Admin. Code § 290.117(f)(3). The executive director is then required to designate the optimal corrosion control treatment method. 30 Tex. Admin. Code § 290.117(f)(3).

Also pursuant to TCEQ rules, all PWSs that serve populations greater than 50,000 are required to conduct monitoring for water quality parameters (WQPs). *See* 30 Tex. Admin. Code § 290.117(e). All systems that serve 50,000 or fewer people that exceed the lead or copper action level are also required to conduct WQP monitoring. 30 Tex. Admin. Code § 290.117(e). WQP monitoring is to be conducted for the following parameters: pH, alkalinity, calcium, conductivity, temperature, total dissolved solids, sodium, sulfate, chloride, hardness, manganese, iron, and orthophosphate or silica. *See* 30 Tex. Admin. Code § 290.117(e)(2). WQP monitoring must be conducted at all entry points and at a number of distribution points, based on the size of the PWS. *See* 30 Tex. Admin. Code § 290.117(e)(2).

Unlike other regulatory requirements discussed above, the TCEQ Lead and Copper Rule includes public education requirements. *See* 30 Tex. Admin. Code § 290.117(k). Public water systems that exceed the lead action level at the ninetieth percentile tap sample are required to deliver public education materials to the public and the executive director. *See* 30 Tex. Admin. Code § 290.117(k); *see also* 40 C.F.R. § 141.85(a). Detailed requirements for public education and notification are set out in the TCEQ's rules. *See* 30 Tex. Admin. Code § 290.117(k).

§ 30.9:9 Surface Water Treatment and Turbidity Treatment Technique Requirements

All PWSs that treat surface water or groundwater under the direct influence of surface water must comply with applicable TCEQ rules, including the TCEQ-adopted turbidity TT requirements. *See* 30 Tex. Admin. Code § 290.104(g); *see also* 30 Tex. Admin. Code § 290.111. The filtration technique used by PWSs must ensure that the system meets the specified TT requirements and performance criteria. Treatment plants that use conventional media filtration must achieve the following turbidity levels: the turbidity level of the combined filter effluent must never exceed 1.0 nephelometric turbidity unit (NTU), and the turbidity level of the combined filter effluent must be 0.3 NTU or less in at least 95 percent of the samples tested each month. 30 Tex. Admin. Code § 290.104(g)(1); *see also* 30 Tex. Admin. Code § 290.111(e)(1). The TCEQ has also established performance criteria for individual filter effluent. The turbidity from each individual filter effluent should never exceed 1.0 NTU, and at a public water system that serves 10,000 people or more, the turbidity from each individual filter effluent should not exceed 0.5 NTU at four hours after the individual filter is returned to service after backwash or shutdown. *See* 30 Tex. Admin. Code § 290.111(e)(2). A PWS that uses unconventional filtration technologies, such as membrane filters or cartridge filters, must meet site-specific TT requirements approved by the executive director. *See* 30 Tex. Admin. Code § 290.111(f)(1).

In addition, a PWS that treats surface water or groundwater under the direct influence of surface water must conduct at least two rounds of special raw surface water monitoring at all surface water intakes and at all wells producing groundwater under the direct influence of surface water. *See* 30 Tex. Admin. Code § 290.111(b). The purpose of such monitoring is to establish minimum TT requirements for *Cryptosporidium* and other pathogens. *See* 30 Tex. Admin. Code § 290.111(b). This monitoring can be waived by the executive director if certain requirements are met. *See* 30 Tex. Admin. Code § 290.111(b).

§ 30.10 Summary and Description: Secondary Standards

The TCEQ has adopted Secondary Standards, or secondary constituent levels, that apply to all PWSs. *See* 30 Tex. Admin. Code § 290.118(a). The maximum secondary constituent levels are listed at section 290.118(b).

If water does not meet the established secondary constituent levels, it cannot be used for public drinking water without written approval from the executive director. 30 Tex. Admin. Code § 290.118(a). Approval by the executive director of drinking water that does not meet the secondary constituent levels is valid only until such time as drinking water of acceptable chemical quality can be made available at "reasonable cost" to the area in question. 30 Tex. Admin. Code § 290.118(a).

Required monitoring for secondary constituent levels is dependent on the source water. For example, each groundwater source must be sampled once every three years at the entry point to the distribution system. 30 Tex. Admin. Code § 290.118(c)(1). Each surface water source must be sampled annually at the entry point to the distribution system. 30 Tex. Admin. Code § 290.118(c)(2).

§ 30.11 Analytical Procedures

All samples that are collected to show compliance with the TCEQ's chapter 290 MCLs, samples that are used to determine compliance with action level requirements and raw groundwater source monitoring requirements, and samples for microbial contaminants must be analyzed at a laboratory accredited by the executive director in accordance with 30 Texas Administrative Code chapter 25. 30 Tex. Admin. Code § 290.119(a)(1). Samples used to demonstrate compliance with the TT requirements and MRDLs must be analyzed by a laboratory approved by the executive director. 30 Tex. Admin. Code § 290.119(a)(2). The methods of analysis that must be used are specified in the Code of Federal Regulations and have been adopted by reference by the TCEQ. *See* 30 Tex. Admin. Code § 290.119(b); *see also* 40 C.F.R. pt. 141, subpt. C. In addition, there are circumstances where TCEQ rules specify analytical methods. For example, with regard to the Primary Standard for disinfectant residuals, TCEQ rules specify the methods to be used to measure and analyze free chlorine or chloramine residual and chlorine dioxide residual. *See* 30 Tex. Admin. Code § 290.110(d). An alternative analytical technique can be specified by the executive director and approved by the administrator of the EPA. 30 Tex. Admin. Code § 290.119(b).

§ 30.12 Monitoring Plans

TCEQ rules specify that all monitoring is to be conducted in the manner and on the schedule approved by the executive director. *See* 30 Tex. Admin. Code § 290.102(e). All PWSs are required to maintain an up-to-date chemical and microbiological monitoring plan that is subject to the review and approval of the executive director. 30 Tex. Admin. Code § 290.121(a). The monitoring plan must identify all sampling locations, frequency, and schedule; the PWS' sample siting plan, which is to include a list of all microbial distribution compliance monitoring sites; the analytical procedures; the laboratories to be used for analysis; the methods used to calculate compliance with all applicable MCLs, MRDLs, and TTs; any groundwater source water monitoring plan to specify well sampling for triggered coliform monitoring; and any raw surface water monitoring plan. *See* 30 Tex. Admin. Code § 290.121(b).

The monitoring plan is required to be very detailed. For example, the monitoring plan must specify the location of each sampling site at a treatment plant or pump station, the origin of any flow stream that is recycled at the treatment plant, any pretreatment that occurs before the recycle stream is returned to the primary treatment process, and the location where the recycle stream is reintroduced to the primary treatment process. 30 Tex. Admin. Code § 290.121(b)(1)(A). Additionally, it must include each entry point to the distribution system (*see* 30 Tex. Admin. Code § 290.121(b)(1)(B)) and the address of each sampling site in the distribution system (*see* 30 Tex. Admin. Code § 290.121(b)(1)(C)).

When one PWS supplies treated water to one or more other PWSs, the executive director may modify the monitoring requirements imposed by chapter 290 to the extent that the interconnection of the systems justifies treating them as a single system for monitoring purposes. 30 Tex. Admin. Code § 290.102(f).

All PWSs are required to maintain a copy of the current monitoring plan at each treatment plant and at a central location, and the monitoring plan must be updated when the PWS's sampling requirements or protocols change. *See* 30 Tex. Admin. Code § 290.121(c).

§ 30.13 Public Notification

The TCEQ's rules identify various required levels of public notification based on different types or degrees of violations. Tier 1 public notification is required for violations of MCLs, MRDLs, or TTs or other situations that pose an acute threat to public health. 30 Tex. Admin. Code § 290.122(a). Tier 2 public notification is required for other violations of MCLs, MRDLs, or TTs or any violations that involve a variance or exemption requirement, which are violations with potential to have serious adverse effects on human health. *See* 30 Tex. Admin. Code § 290.122(b). Tier 3 public notification is required for other violations such as failure to perform required monitoring or comply with required testing procedures. 30 Tex. Admin. Code § 290.122(c).

Situations that pose an acute threat to public health and thus require Tier 1 public notification include a violation of the MCL for *E. coli* or nitrate or nitrite; an acute turbidity issue at a treatment plant that is treating surface water or groundwater under the direct influence of surface water; a violation of the acute MRDL for chlorine dioxide; an occurrence of a waterborne disease outbreak; detection of *E. coli* or other fecal indicators in source water samples as specified (requiring a public notice to be issued within twenty-four hours of notification of the positive sample); other situations that have the potential to have serious adverse effects on health as a result of short-term exposure; and other situations deemed by the executive director based on a threat to public health. *See* 30 Tex. Admin. Code § 290.122(a)(1).

The initial Tier 1 acute public notice or boil-water notice must be issued as soon as possible but no later than twenty-four hours after the violation is identified. *See* 30 Tex. Admin. Code § 290.122(a)(2). The initial acute violation notice for a community water system must be provided to radio and television stations serving the area that is served by the PWS and must be published in a daily newspaper of general circulation in the area served by the PWS, or if the area is not served by such a daily newspaper, notice must be issued by direct delivery, by continuous posting in conspicuous places within the area served by the system, by electronic delivery, or by alert systems (e.g., reverse 911). *See* 30 Tex. Admin. Code § 290.122(a)(2)(B), (a)(2)(C). The owner or operator of a noncommunity water system is to issue a notice of acute violation by direct delivery or by continuously posting the notice in conspicuous places within the area served by the water system, by electronic delivery, or by alert systems. *See* 30 Tex. Admin. Code § 290.122(a)(2)(D). TCEQ-adopted rules also include requirements for additional notices for as long as the violation exists. *See* 30 Tex. Admin. Code § 290.122(a)(3). The other levels, or degrees, of violations require public notice, but generally those notices are not required to be issued as immediately or as broadly. *See* 30 Tex. Admin. Code § 290.122(b), (c). The specifics of public notice are set out in 30 Texas Administrative Code section 290.122(d)(1)–(6). In addition, PWSs must notify customers at sampled taps of the results of any required lead or copper analyses and certify to the executive director that the required notice was provided. *See* 30 Tex. Admin. Code § 290.122(d)(10). Where appropriate, the public notice must be multilingual. *See* 30 Tex. Admin. Code § 290.122(d)(7). Proof of public notice must be provided to the executive director within ten days of its distribution. *See* 30 Tex. Admin. Code § 290.122(f).

Failure to certify that appropriate notice was provided is a violation. *See, e.g.*, 30 Tex. Admin. Code § 290.106(f)(8).

If a PWS has a distribution system separate from other parts of the distribution system with no interconnections, the executive director may allow the PWS to give public notice to only that portion of the system that is out of compliance. *See, e.g.*, 30 Tex. Admin. Code § 290.107(g). A PWS that is required to notify its customers must also provide a copy of the notification to any PWSs that purchase or otherwise receive water from it in the same manner in which it informed its customers. *See* 30 Tex. Admin. Code § 290.122(g).

§ 30.14 Variances and Exemptions

With approval from the EPA, states can grant variances to PWSs that serve 3,301 to 10,000 people. *See* 42 U.S.C. § 300g-4(e)(1)(B). To obtain a variance, the PWS must establish that (1) it cannot meet an MCL, even while using the best available treatment method, because of the characteristics of the raw water; and (2) the variance will not create an unreasonable risk to public health. *See generally* 42 U.S.C. § 300g-4. States may also grant variances from standards for a PWS that serves up to 3,300 people if the system cannot afford to comply with a rule and the PWS installs EPA-approved variance technology. *See generally* 42 U.S.C. § 300g-4.

Exemptions from standards may be granted to allow extra time to seek other compliance options or financial assistance. *See* 42 U.S.C. § 300g-5. To obtain an exemption, the PWS must demonstrate that (1) there are compelling reasons (including economic factors) why it cannot meet the MCL or TT, (2) it was in operation on the effective date of the MCL or TT, and (3) the exemption will not create an unreasonable risk to public health. *See generally* 42 U.S.C. § 300g-5. In granting an exemption, the state must establish a schedule under which the PWS will come into compliance with the MCL or TT. *See generally* 42 U.S.C. § 300g-5.

Pursuant to TCEQ rules, the executive director cannot approve a variance or an exemption from the MCL for total *E. coli*, nitrate, nitrite, or total nitrate and nitrite; the MRDL for chlorine dioxide; the TT requirements for filtration and disinfection; or rules addressing microbial contaminants. *See* 30 Tex. Admin. Code § 290.102(b).

§ 30.15 Compliance and Enforcement

Each of the TCEQ's rules establishing Primary Standards includes provisions to be used in determining whether a PWS is in compliance with the regulatory requirements. *See, e.g.*, 30 Tex. Admin. Code § 290.106(f). For example, the TCEQ's rule for inorganic compounds provides a number of factors to evaluate when determining compliance. These factors include such criteria as the following:

- A PWS that exceeds the level for nitrate, nitrite, or the sum of nitrate and nitrite specified in the TCEQ's rule commits an acute MCL violation. Compliance is to be based on the results of a single sample. If a confirmation sample is collected, compliance is to be based on the average result of the original and confirmation samples. 30 Tex. Admin. Code § 290.106(f)(2).
- A PWS that exceeds the MCL for antimony, arsenic, asbestos, barium, beryllium, cadmium, chromium, cyanide, fluoride, mercury, selenium, or thallium as established in TCEQ rules at any sampling point commits an MCL violation. 30 Tex. Admin. Code § 290.106(f)(3). The frequency of sampling is used to determine whether the violation has occurred. *See generally* 30 Tex. Admin. Code § 290.106(f)(3)(A)–(D).

The other Primary Standards include similar provisions that identify how to determine whether a violation has occurred. *See, e.g.*, 30 Tex. Admin. Code §§ 290.107(f), 290.109(g), 290.110(f), 290.112(f).

Texas statutes establish standards for the enforcement of the applicable drinking water statutes and rules. *See* Tex. Health & Safety Code §§ 341.047–.049. Section 341.049 of the Health and Safety Code provides that the TCEQ may assess an administrative penalty "[i]f a person causes, suffers, allows, or permits a violation" of the applicable statutes, the chapter 290 rules, or a TCEQ order. Tex. Health & Safety Code § 341.049(a). The penalty is defined as not less than $50 and not more than $5,000 for each violation. *See* Act of June 7, 2019, 86th Leg., R.S., ch. 519, § 2 (S.B. 530), eff. Sept. 1, 2019 (amending Tex. Health & Safety Code § 341.049(a)). In determining the amount of an administrative penalty for a violation of the drinking water standards, the TCEQ is to consider the nature of the circumstances and the extent, duration, and gravity of the prohibited acts or omissions; with respect to the alleged violator, the history and extent of previous violations; the degree of culpability, including whether the violation was attributable to mechanical or electrical failures and whether the violation could have been reasonably anticipated and avoided; the person's demonstrated good faith, including actions taken by the person to correct the cause of the violation; any economic benefit gained through the violation; the amount necessary to deter future violation; and any other matters that justice requires. Tex. Health & Safety Code § 341.049(b).

In evaluating the need for an administrative enforcement action against a PWS, the TCEQ relies on its Enforcement Response Policy (ERP), as required by the EPA. *See* Memorandum from Linda

Brookins, Director, Water Supply Division, Texas Commission on Environmental Quality, to Drinking Water Advisory Work Group (June 10, 2011), www.tceq.texas.gov/assets/public/permitting/watersupply/pdw/enforcement/ERPAnnouncement_FINAL.pdf [hereinafter Brookins Memorandum]. The purpose of the ERP is to identify PWSs "with violations that rise to the level of significant non-compliance by focusing on those systems with health-based violations and those that show a history of violations across multiple rules." Brookins Memorandum, at 1. The ERP uses an Enforcement Targeting Tool (ETT) to prioritize PWSs "by assigning each violation a 'weight' or number of points based on the assigned threat to public health." Brookins Memorandum, at 1. The points for each violation are added to provide a total score for that PWS. Unaddressed violations with a score greater than or equal to eleven points will result in a formal enforcement action within six months of the ranking. Brookins Memorandum, at 1. The TCEQ will use the ETT to identify water systems with the highest total noncompliance across all rules, thus allowing the TCEQ to focus its resources to address those water systems with the highest priority problems.

Section 341.048 of the Health and Safety Code addresses civil enforcement, stating that a "person may not cause, suffer, allow, or permit a violation" of the applicable statutes, the chapter 290 rules, or a TCEQ order. Tex. Health & Safety Code § 341.048(a). The civil penalty is to be no less than $50 and not more than $5,000 per violation. Tex. Health & Safety Code § 341.048(b). *See* Act of June 7, 2019, 86th Leg., R.S., ch 519, § 1 (S.B. 530), eff. Sept. 1, 2019 (amending Tex. Health & Safety Code § 341.048(b)). Each day of a continuing violation is considered a separate violation. *See* Tex. Health & Safety Code § 341.048(b). Section 341.048 authorizes the TCEQ, a county, or a municipality to institute a civil suit in district court for injunctive relief or the assessment and recovery of a civil penalty. *See* Tex. Health & Safety Code § 341.048(c). The TCEQ is a necessary and indispensable party if the suit is brought by a county or a municipality. *See* Tex. Health & Safety Code § 341.048(d). The civil suit must be brought in (1) Travis County, (2) the county in which the defendant resides, or (3) the county in which the violation or threat of violation occurs. Tex. Health & Safety Code § 341.048(f).

Health and Safety Code section 341.047 defines the criminal offenses associated with violation of chapter 341. *See* Tex. Health & Safety Code § 341.047. All the offenses identified in section 341.047 are Class C misdemeanors. Tex. Health & Safety Code § 341.047(b).

IV. Addressing "Capacity" to Ensure Drinking Water Quality

§ 30.16 Introduction

Ensuring the adequacy of the quantity of the water supply, as well as the adequacy of infrastructure and technical capacity of a PWS, is intrinsically related to the protection of public health and sanitation. This has been recognized, in different ways, at both federal and state levels.

§ 30.17 Federal Programs

At the federal level, the 1996 amendments to the SDWA created a program focused on maintaining adequate technical, managerial, and financial (TMF) capacity, or ability, for a PWS to meet specified quality levels on a dependable basis. *See* 42 U.S.C. § 300g-9. This capacity development program requires that the EPA publish guidance "describing legal authorities and other means to ensure that all new community water systems and new nontransient, noncommunity water systems demonstrate technical, managerial, and financial capacity with respect to national primary drinking water regulations." 42 U.S.C. § 300g-9(d)(4).

As described by the EPA, "capacity development" is "a process for water systems to acquire and maintain adequate technical, managerial, and financial (TMF) capacity. TMF capacity enables water systems to have the capability to consistently provide safe drinking water to the public." U.S. Environmental Protection Agency, Building the Capacity of Drinking Water Systems, *Learn about Small Drinking Water Systems*, www.epa.gov/dwcapacity/learn-about-small-drinking-water-systems [hereinafter Building Capacity]. Technical capacity includes source water adequacy, infrastructure adequacy (including source, treatment, storage, and distribution), and the ability of personnel to implement requisite technical knowledge. *See* Building Capacity.

Capacity development under the 1996 SDWA amendments has three major components:

1. Under penalty of losing a portion of Drinking Water State Revolving Fund (DWSRF) monies, states must have a program established to "ensure that all new community water systems and new nontransient, noncommunity water systems commencing operation after October 1, 1999, demonstrate technical, managerial, and financial capacity with respect to each national primary drinking water regulation in effect, or likely to be in effect, on the date of commencement of operations." 42 U.S.C. § 300g-9(a).

2. Under penalty of losing a percentage of DWSRF monies, states must develop and implement a "strategy to assist public water systems in acquiring and maintaining technical, managerial, and financial capacity." 42 U.S.C. § 300g-9(c)(1).

3. States may not provide DWSRF loan assistance to systems that lack the technical, managerial, and financial capability to ensure compliance or systems that are in significant noncompliance with any drinking water standard or variance. States may provide assistance if the use of such assistance will ensure compliance and the system has agreed to make the necessary changes in operation to ensure that it has the technical, managerial, and financial capacity to comply over the long term. *See* 42 U.S.C. § 300j-12.

States are required to develop state capacity development programs that include two primary elements: (1) the legal authority to ensure that new PWSs have sufficient technical, managerial, and financial capacity to meet Primary Standards; and (2) a strategy to identify and assist existing PWSs that need to improve managerial, technical, or financial capacity or that need assistance in complying with Primary Standards. *See* 42 U.S.C. § 300g-9(a), (c). The development and implementation of these state programs are directly related to a state's ability to receive funds under the state revolving fund loan program. *See* 42 U.S.C. § 300g-9(a), (c). The EPA has addressed the meaning of the terms "technical capacity," "managerial capacity," and "financial capacity":

- Technical capacity refers to the physical infrastructure of the water system, including but not limited to the adequacy of the source water, infrastructure (source, treatment, storage, and distribution), and the ability of system personnel to implement the requisite technical knowledge.
- Managerial capacity refers to the management structure of the water system, including but not limited to ownership accountability, staffing and organization, and effective linkages to customers and regulatory agencies.
- Financial capacity refers to the financial resources of the water system, including but not limited to revenue sufficiency, creditworthiness, and fiscal controls.

See U.S. Environmental Protection Agency, Office of Water, *Guidance on Implementing the Capacity Development Provisions of the Safe Drinking Water Act Amendments of 1996* 11–13 (EPA 816-R-98-006, July 1998), http://nepis.epa.gov/Exe/ZyPDF.cgi/20002747.PDF?Dockey=20002747.PDF.

To address the capacity-related requirements of the SDWA, Texas law requires the TCEQ to ensure that PWSs supply adequate quantities of safe drinking water and that PWSs are financially stable and technically sound. *See* Tex. Health & Safety Code § 341.0315(a).

§ 30.18 Texas Program

As discussed at section 30.8 above, Texas Health and Safety Code chapter 341, subchapter C, prescribes the duties of the TCEQ with regard to the regulation and control of drinking water systems. *See* Tex. Health & Safety Code ch. 341, subch. C; *see also* 30 Tex. Admin. Code § 290.39. To fully comply with the 1996 amendments to the SDWA, Texas amended both Health and Safety Code chapter 341 and Texas Water Code chapter 13 to incorporate, as appropriate, the phrase "financial, managerial, and technical capacity." *See generally* Act of June 1, 1997, 75th Leg., R.S., ch. 1010 (also known as Senate Bill 1). While the federal SDWA focuses on the capacity to treat and maintain a safe water supply for users, the capacity to maintain a sufficient supply of water to ensure delivery of treated drinking water to the public on a continuous and adequate basis is a Texas initiative. Sufficiency of supply is particularly important in Texas because of climate and the related likelihood of droughts, and the growing population that strains the limited supply of water. Pursuant to TCEQ rules, sources of water supply—both groundwater and surface water—are to have a "safe yield capable of supplying the maximum daily demands of the distribution system during extended periods of peak usage and critical hydrologic conditions." 30 Tex. Admin. Code § 290.41(b). To ensure water delivery, the infrastructure, such as pipelines and pumping capacities, to treatment plants or distribution systems must be adequate. *See* 30 Tex. Admin. Code § 290.41(b).

With regard to capacity, TCEQ rules provide that the total capacity of a PWS's treatment facilities must always be greater than the anticipated maximum daily demand. 30 Tex. Admin. Code § 290.42(a)(1). TCEQ rules also specify very detailed minimum water system capacity requirements. Specifically, 30 Texas Administrative Code section 290.45 identifies certain minimum PWS capacity requirements, including standards for minimum well capacity, pumping capacity, total storage capacity, and treatment capacity for various types of retail water systems and wholesale water providers, and for both surface water and groundwater supplies. *See* 30 Tex. Admin. Code § 290.45.

The importance of sufficient water supply and capacity is further emphasized through enforcement in Texas. The TCEQ's Enforcement Initiation Criteria (EIC) identify certain failures by a community water system to meet minimum water system capacity requirements as Category A violations that require an immediate enforcement action. *See* Texas Commission on Environmental Quality, *Enforcement Initiation Criteria (EIC)* (Rev. 16, eff. Dec. 13, 2018), www.tceq.texas.gov/assets/public/compliance/enforcement/eic/eic-rev16-121318.pdf.

Texas has also addressed additional sources of water such as rainwater harvesting. State law requires the TCEQ to establish recommended standards relating to the domestic use of rainwater, "including health and safety standards for treatment and collection methods for harvested rainwater intended for drinking, cooking, or bathing." Tex. Health & Safety Code § 341.042(a). If a rainwater harvesting structure is connected to a PWS, then it is required to have appropriate cross-connection safeguards. Tex. Health & Safety Code § 341.042(b). The TCEQ has adopted rules regarding the installation and maintenance of privately owned rainwater harvesting systems. *See* 30 Tex. Admin. Code § 290.44(j). For example, any person who intends to connect a rainwater harvesting system to a PWS must give written notice of that intention to the owner of the PWS. 30 Tex. Admin. Code § 290.44(j)(3). Where rainwater harvesting systems are used at residences for potable purposes and there is a connection to a PWS, the PWS must ensure that the rainwater harvesting system is installed by a licensed master or journeyman plumber. 30 Tex. Admin. Code § 290.44(j)(2). In addition, a privately owned rainwater harvesting system with a capacity of more than five hundred gallons that is connected to the PWS is required to have a backflow prevention assembly or an air gap installed at the storage facility to ensure physical separation between the PWS and the rainwater harvesting system. 30 Tex. Admin. Code § 290.44(j)(1). The owner or operator of a PWS may not be held liable for any adverse health effects allegedly caused by the consumption of water collected by a rainwater harvesting system that is connected to the PWS and is used for potable purposes, if the PWS is in compliance with the applicable drinking water standards. Tex. Health & Safety Code § 341.042(b–4).

The TCEQ has also promulgated detailed rules related to source water types, including groundwater sources, springs, and surface water sources, to ensure that all source water is protected from potential contamination. *See* 30 Tex. Admin. Code § 290.41(c)–(e). For example, the rules applicable to groundwater sources and development specify that—

> [g]roundwater sources shall be located so that there will be no danger of pollution from flooding or from unsanitary surroundings, such as privies, sewage, sewage treatment plants, livestock and animal pens, solid waste disposal sites or underground petroleum and chemical storage tanks and liquid transmission pipelines, or abandoned and improperly sealed wells.

30 Tex. Admin. Code § 290.41(c)(1). To ensure compliance with this standard, TCEQ rules restrict the locations of water wells in relationship to possible contaminant sources and define construction standards for such wells. *See* 30 Tex. Admin. Code § 290.41(c)(1)–(3). Similar restrictions are in place for spring water sources and surface water sources. *See* 30 Tex. Admin. Code § 290.41(d), (e).

V. Emerging Threats to Drinking Water

§ 30.19 PFAS

Per- and polyfluoroalkyl substances (PFAS) are a group of man-made chemicals that are persistent in the environment and in the human body and that are now being recognized as being present in drinking water supplies throughout the country. *See* U.S. Environmental Protection Agency, *Basic Information on PFAS* 1 (Jan. 14, 2021), www.epa.gov/pfas/basic-information-pfas#:~:text=PFAS%20manufacturing%20and%20processing%20facilities,including%20sources%20of%20drinking%20water [hereinafter *Basic Information on PFAS*]. There are more than 9,000 known PFAS compounds, of which approximately 600 are currently used in the United States. *See* Annie Sneed, *Forever Chemicals Are Widespread in U.S. Drinking Water*, Scientific American (Jan. 22, 2021), www.scientificamerican.com/article/forever-chemicals-are-widespread-in-u-s-drinking-water/ [hereinafter *Forever Chemicals*]. Scientists refer to PFAS as "forever chemicals" because they do not break down under typical environmental conditions. Current scientific evidence indicates that exposure to PFAS can lead to adverse health outcomes. Studies indicate that some PFAS "can cause reproductive and developmental, liver and kidney, and immunological effects in laboratory animals." *See Basic Information on PFAS*. Human epidemiological studies have shown the following in exposed populations: increased cholesterol levels, effects on the immune system, low infant birth weights, cancer, and thyroid hormone disruption. *See Basic Information on PFAS.*

PFAS include such chemicals as PFOA, PFOS, GenX, and many others, all of which have been manufactured and used in a variety of industries across the United States and around the globe since the 1940s. *See Basic Information on PFAS*. PFAS are found in food, commercial household products, living organisms, and drinking water. Drinking water can be a source of exposure in communities where the chemicals have contaminated the water supply. In fact, scientists have estimated that "more than 200 million people—the majority of Americans—have tap water contaminated with a mixture of PFOA and PFOS at concentrations of one part per trillion (ppt) or higher." *Forever Chemicals*. Such exposure is typically localized and associated with a particular industrial facility.

To begin to address PFAS, the EPA has adopted a PFAS Action Plan. U.S. Environmental Protection Agency, *EPA's PFAS Action Plan* (Feb. 28, 2020), www.epa.gov/pfas/epas-pfas-action-plan. In January 2021, the EPA announced that it was issuing final regulatory determinations for PFOA and PFOS. *See* Press Release, U.S. Environmental Protection Agency, *EPA Delivers Results on PFAS Action Plan* (Jan. 19, 2021), www.epa.gov/newsreleases/epa-delivers-results-pfas-action-plan [hereinafter 2021 Press RElease]. The EPA announced that it was initiating the process to develop a national primary drinking water regulation for PFOA and PFOS and that it would fast-track its evaluation of additional PFAs for future drinking water regulatory determinations. *See* 2021 Press Release. The EPA has also proposed requiring monitoring for twenty-nine PFAS in drinking water. U.S. Environmental Protection Agency, *PFAS Action Plan: Commitments Made, Results Delivered* (Jan. 2021), www.epa.gov/sites/production/files/2021-01/documents/pfas_factsheet_jan2021-v5.pdf.

VI. Conclusion

§ 30.20 Conclusion

Although contemporary regulation of drinking water quality has been evolving for more than thirty years, both federal and state regulatory authorities continue to strive to ensure that there are adequate and appropriate regulations to protect drinking water quality and public health. As demonstrated with the 1996 amendments to the SDWA, appropriate treatment standards and technologies are not the only regulatory tool. Both the EPA and the TCEQ continue to take steps to consider source water protection and capacity development as new methods to ensure drinking water quality.

Modern pressures, such as increasing population, aging infrastructure, impaired or contaminated water sources, and community financing issues, will continue to challenge both regulated PWSs and federal and state authorities as they strive to ensure access to safe drinking water. All available regulatory tools will be necessary to protect drinking water quality and ensure protection of public health in the future.

CHAPTER 31

Wholesale Water Suppliers

Stephen C. Dickman[1]

I. Introduction

§ 31.1 Wholesale Water Suppliers

Although "wholesale water supplier" is not defined in the relevant portions of the Texas Water Code (chapter 11, 12, or 13), here the generally accepted definition is used: any person or entity who provides raw or treated water as a commodity to another person or entity who is not the ultimate consumer of the water. *But see* 31 Tex. Admin. Code § 357.10(44) (defining the term "wholesale water provider" in relation to state water planning). Under Texas law, supplying water on a wholesale basis is distinguished from the conveyance or other transfer of an appropriative water right, which is addressed in Chapters 15 and 18 of this book. The other important distinction is between supplying water on a wholesale basis and supplying potable water to residential or other ultimate consumers on a retail water basis, which is discussed in Chapters 29 and 30.

While supplying potable water to retail customers is strictly regulated to ensure that good quality water is delivered to consumers at a fair and reasonable price, supplying water on a wholesale basis is much less regulated. The trend has been for the state to defer to the right of wholesale water suppliers and customers to freely contract between themselves concerning the terms and conditions under which water will be supplied. As discussed below, the Public Utility Commission of Texas (PUC) and the Texas Commission on Environmental Quality (TCEQ) will undertake to set wholesale water rates only if they have first determined that the rate contracted for between the wholesale water seller and buyer is not in the public interest.

Common examples of wholesale water transactions include—

- a contract by a home rule city to supply raw or treated water to nearby smaller cities, industries, or water districts;
- a contract by a river authority to supply raw water to a city, industrial user, or water district;
- a contract by a water district to provide raw water to a rural water supply corporation; and
- a contract by an irrigation company to provide water to agricultural irrigators.

This chapter first discusses wholesale water supply contracts in general and highlights issues commonly encountered in wholesale water supply contracting. This discussion includes a brief

1. Stephen C. Dickman is a solo law practitioner in Austin, Texas, and formerly was a partner with the firm of Kelly Hart & Hallman L.L.P. in Austin. He has practiced environmental and water law in Texas since 1985, formerly serving at the Texas Water Commission as a hearings examiner and staff attorney. In private practice since 1992, he represents cities, water utilities, and land developers in environmental, water, and water utility law matters. He is certified in the practice of administrative law by the Texas Board of Legal Specialization and has spoken at various Texas water law seminars. He was also a contributing author for the West Texas Practice Series on Environmental Law.

overview of the historical context out of which wholesale water contracting arose and citations to key statutory authority and significant case law (although most of the case law on wholesale water contracting concerns irrigation cases that are no longer of much relevance). Following is a discussion of the PUC and the TCEQ wholesale rate-setting process and rules governing wholesale contract amendments. Next, TCEQ requirements for water conservation and drought contingency planning as they affect wholesale water contracting are reviewed. The chapter concludes with a brief overview of the typical components of a wholesale water contract.

II. Wholesale Water Contracting in General

§ 31.2 Historical Background

The most significant statutory authorities dealing with wholesale water supply issues are Texas Water Code sections 11.036–.041 and 12.013. The provisions in chapters 11 and 12 have antecedents going back to 1913, when the Texas legislature repealed earlier water laws and adopted a new uniform system of water laws for the entire state, including the creation of the TCEQ's original predecessor agency, the Texas Board of Water Engineers, to administer a water rights permitting system. *See Texas Water Rights Commission v. City of Dallas*, 591 S.W.2d 609, 613 (Tex. App.—Austin 1979, writ ref'd n.r.e.). In that era, the courts commonly dealt with wholesale water supply cases involving the rights, obligations, and liabilities of irrigation companies and their agricultural irrigator customers. Accordingly, the statutory scheme adopted in 1913 was oriented in structure and phraseology to address the irrigation water supply issues common in that era. See Chapter 4 of this book for a discussion of these early laws. That structure and phraseology are still reflected in sections 11.036–.041 and 12.013. Modern case law dealing with wholesale water supply issues has largely clarified how these sections apply to current wholesale water supply transactions.

§ 31.3 Parties to a Wholesale Water Contract

In Texas, any person who has a conserved or stored supply of water may contract to supply the water on a wholesale basis to any other legal entity. *See* Tex. Water Code § 11.036(a). In addition, anyone who has a possessory interest in land adjoining a constructed water facility (e.g., a canal, ditch, flume, lateral, dam, reservoir, or lake) and who has secured a right to use water from the facility for any agricultural, industrial, or mining purpose is entitled to be supplied with water in accordance with the terms of the contract. *See* Tex. Water Code § 11.038(a).

The early twentieth century version of Texas Water Code section 11.038(a) generated case law that defined the rights and obligations of irrigation companies and their customers. The principle developed that an irrigation company was a quasi-public corporation that owed a duty, regardless of the existence of a contract, to furnish water that had not been contracted to others and that was needed for the irrigation of crops on land adjoining the irrigation company's canals; failure to meet this duty made the irrigation company liable for resulting damages and subject to mandamus relief. *See, e.g., Lastinger v. Toyah Valley Irrigation Co.*, 167 S.W. 788 (Tex. App.—El Paso 1914, no writ); *Dunbar v. Texas Irrigation Co.*, 195 S.W. 614 (Tex. App.—Galveston 1912, no writ). Such irrigation water was required to be supplied in accordance with the terms of the contract or, if there was no contract, on reasonable terms and conditions. *See American Rio Grande Land & Irrigation Co. v. Mercedes Plantation Co.*, 208 S.W. 904 (Tex. Comm'n App. 1919, judgm't adopted).

§ 31.4 The Price of Water under a Wholesale Water Contract

The price and terms of a wholesale water supply contract must be "just and reasonable and without discrimination," and such contract terms are subject to revision and control as set forth in the rate-setting portions of the Texas Water Code. *See* Tex. Water Code § 11.036(b). However, if a person uses the stored or conserved water without first entering into a contract with the person who stored or conserved it, the user is obligated to pay for the use at a just and reasonable rate determined by the TCEQ. *See* Tex. Water Code § 11.036(d). Similarly, for landowners or tenants adjoining a canal or other surface water supply facility, if the parties cannot agree on a price for the water, then the water facility owner must furnish the needed water at a reasonable and nondiscriminatory price to the extent there is water that has not been contracted to others. *See* Tex. Water Code § 11.038.

Consistent with the above statutory provisions, the holder of a permanent water right (generally, a perpetual contractual right to receive water from a canal adjoining a piece of land; see the discussion of this topic in Chapter 4 of this book) is entitled to use water according to the terms of any contract, but if there is no contract, the water right owner is entitled to use water at a just, reasonable, and nondiscriminatory price. *See* Tex. Water Code § 11.040(c). These concepts were upheld and applied in various irrigation company cases after 1913. *See, e.g., Ball v. Rio Grande Canal Co.*, 256 S.W. 678 (Tex. App.—San Antonio 1923, writ ref'd) (recorded contract under which irrigation company was required to furnish water for irrigation purposes to land had effect of granting easement in favor of land against irrigation company subject to obligation on part of landowner and his successors to pay yearly water charges; such easement was enforceable either as covenant running with the land or, in equity, against subsequent purchasers).

§ 31.5 Other Wholesale Contract Terms

Generally, a water supplier must make and publish reasonable rules regarding the method of supply, the use and distribution of water, and the procedure for applying and paying for the water. *See* Tex. Water Code § 11.037. If a wholesale contract contains "explicit expiration provisions," no continuation of the service obligation will be implied. *See* Tex. Water Code § 11.036(b); *see also* Tex. Gov't Code § 791.026(e). Conversely, however, if a wholesale contract does not contain an explicit expiration provision, a continuing obligation to provide water to the buyer may be implied under the contract. This can result in a determination that a wholesale water rate is being charged "pursuant to a contract," which is a dispositive issue in determining whether the PUC or the TCEQ must first hold a public interest hearing before adjudicating a contested wholesale water rate. See the discussion of this issue at section 31.16 below. Also of note, the terms of a wholesale water contract may expressly require the purchaser to develop alternative or replacement water supplies before the contract expires, and such terms may be enforced by court order. *See* Tex. Water Code § 11.036(c); *see also* Tex. Gov't Code § 791.026(d). Finally, if the delivery method for water supplied on a wholesale basis is through water released down a river or stream channel, a "bed and banks" permit may be required from the TCEQ to authorize such delivery. See the discussion of bed and banks permits in Chapter 10 of this book.

§ 31.6 Distribution of Water during a Shortage

During water shortages because of drought, accident, or any other cause, water must be divided pro rata among all customers based on the amount each customer is entitled to "so that preference is given to no one and everyone suffers alike." *See* Tex. Water Code § 11.039(a). This section applies only to wholesale customers who are not covered by a TCEQ or a Texas Water Development Board (TWDB) water conservation plan. *See* Tex. Water Code § 11.039(a). For wholesale water suppliers operating under a water conservation plan prepared in compliance with TCEQ or TWDB rules, the wholesale provider may base the pro rata distribution of water in times of shortage on the amount of water to which each customer is entitled, less the amount of water the customer would have saved if the customer had operated its water system in compliance with a state-approved water conservation plan. *See* Tex. Water Code § 11.039(b). In any case, however, the wholesale water provider is not precluded from supplying water to any person who has a prior vested right to the water. *See* Tex. Water Code § 11.039(c).

§ 31.7 Transfer of Wholesale Water Ratemaking Jurisdiction from the TCEQ to the PUC

During the 83rd legislative session in 2013, the Texas legislature enacted two bills to transfer the water utility ratemaking authority of the TCEQ to the PUC, including the TCEQ's jurisdiction over wholesale raw or treated water rates as described in section 12.013 of the Texas Water Code. *See* Act of May 14, 2013, 83d Leg., R.S., ch. 170, § 2.07 (H.B. 1600); Act of May 14, 2013, 83d Leg., R.S., ch. 171, § 7 (S.B. 567). The transfer of jurisdiction over wholesale water rates was accomplished by amending sections 12.013 and 13.043 of the Water Code to replace the term "commission," which refers to the TCEQ, with the newly defined term "utility commission," which refers to the PUC. The TCEQ will continue to have jurisdiction over denial-of-water complaints under sections 11.036 through 11.041 of the Water Code, although the PUC is now given express authority to participate in the hearing on a denial-of-water complaint "if necessary to present evidence on the price or rental demanded for the available water." Tex. Water Code § 11.041(f).

The impetus for the transfer of wholesale water ratemaking jurisdiction was a recommendation by the Texas Sunset Advisory Commission that the state could benefit from transferring regulatory functions related to water and wastewater utilities to the PUC. As required by the implementing legislation, on July 31, 2014, the PUC and the TCEQ entered into a memorandum of understanding (MOU) detailing the final plan for transitioning the jurisdiction transfer. The actual transfer of wholesale water ratemaking jurisdiction occurred on September 1, 2014. The TCEQ and the PUC were also directed to adopt rules to implement the statutory changes by September 1, 2015. The TCEQ's existing rules and forms related to water utility ratemaking were adopted by the PUC on an interim basis until the PUC could adopt its own rules by the statutory deadline of September 1, 2015. Therefore, all wholesale ratemaking filings made on or after September 1, 2014, must follow the PUC's procedural rules and the PUC's wholesale water or sewer service rules (now codified at 16 Tex. Admin. Code ch. 24, subch. J, which are essentially the same as those rules adopted by the TCEQ and codified at 30 Tex. Admin. Code ch. 291, subch. I). Moreover, because of the transfer of wholesale ratemaking jurisdiction from the TCEQ to the PUC, the court cases discussed in this chapter that deal with the TCEQ as the regulatory agency may also appropriately be considered to apply to the PUC as the regulatory agency as of September 1, 2014.

§ 31.8 Wholesale Water Contract Price Disputes

Sections 11.041 and 12.013 of the Texas Water Code are the key statutes under which wholesale water supply rates and service issues are regulated in modern-day cases. Under section 11.041, a person who is entitled to use a surface water supply can petition the TCEQ to order the person who owns or controls the water supply to sell water to the petitioner at a just and reasonable price if there is water available and not contracted to others. *See* Tex. Water Code § 11.041(a). If the TCEQ executive director determines that probable grounds exist to support the complaint, a hearing is held and the TCEQ sets a just and reasonable wholesale water rate. As mentioned at section 31.7 above, under the 2013 statutory amendments transferring water utility ratemaking authority from the TCEQ to the PUC, the PUC is now authorized to participate in the hearing if necessary to present evidence on the price or rental demanded for the water. *See* Tex. Water Code § 11.041(c), (f).

Although section 11.041(a) requires the complainant to show that it is "entitled to receive or use the water," a concept originally arising from the rights of landowners adjoining irrigation canals, the courts have not strictly applied that requirement in modern-day wholesale rate cases. When a city supplies water for a number of years without a written contract and is paid for the service, an implied obligation to supply water arises. *See City of Dallas v. Brown*, 150 S.W.2d 129 (Tex. App.—Dallas 1941, writ dism'd). Moreover, in *Texas Water Rights Commission v. City of Dallas*, 591 S.W.2d 609 (Tex. App.—Austin 1979, writ ref'd n.r.e.), the court concluded that even though section 11.041 was originally established as part of the early Texas irrigation laws, the legislature intended for section 11.041 and the other water laws rewritten in 1913 to apply to water supplied for purposes other than irrigation. 591 S.W.2d at 613. The court held that the complainant city of Farmers Branch had a right to be provided with wholesale water from the city of Dallas because Dallas had, over a long period of time, obtained water rights that were so extensive as to afford Dallas control of substantially all municipal water in Dallas County. 591 S.W.2d at 614. Thus, Dallas enjoyed "a substantial monopoly closely resembling that of canal and irrigation entities occupying a monopolistic position." 591 S.W.2d at 614. Moreover, in the Texas Water Rights Commission hearings on its application for its water rights, Dallas had represented that it would use the water to supply water to municipalities in Dallas County. 591 S.W.2d at 611. In support of its ruling, the court cited *City of San Antonio v. Texas Water Commission*, 407 S.W.2d 752, 768 (Tex. 1966), in which the Texas Supreme Court declared that a river authority cannot legally refuse to sell municipal water to any particular municipality because the river authority is under a duty to serve the public without discrimination. Thus, the requirement that a wholesale water rate complainant show that it is "entitled to receive or use the water" can be satisfied by showing a history of being supplied by the seller or by showing some degree of monopoly control by the seller over the source of water supply.

The PUC is given general statutory authority to fix reasonable rates for supplying raw or treated water for any purpose mentioned in chapter 11 or 12. *See* Tex. Water Code § 12.013(a). In reviewing and setting wholesale water rates, the PUC may use any reasonable rate-setting methodology, although the PUC may not set a rate for a political subdivision that is insufficient to meet the debt service and bond coverage requirements of the political subdivision's outstanding debt. *See* Tex. Water Code § 12.013(c). The PUC may establish interim wholesale rates, compel continuing service during the pendency of the wholesale rate case, and order a refund or assess additional charges to make up any difference between the rate charged and the rate ultimately set by the PUC. *See* Tex. Water Code § 12.013(e), (f).

The PUC's rate fixing power under section 12.013 is not limited to instances in which the water supplier appropriates state water as its source of supply, nor is it limited to complaints filed by water purchasers, but rather section 12.013 may also be invoked by wholesale water suppliers who sell water under a contract rate that the seller alleges to be not fair or reasonable. *See Texas Water Commission v. Brushy Creek Municipal Utility District*, 917 S.W.2d 19, 22–23 (Tex. 1996). Moreover, once the PUC's wholesale rate-setting jurisdiction under section 12.013 is invoked, the PUC may set reasonable rates that will apply in future years unless and until the rates are later changed by contract between the seller and buyer or by the PUC pursuant to a subsequent wholesale rate case. *Texas Water Commission v. Boyt Realty Co.*, 10 S.W.3d 334, 340 (Tex. App.—Austin 1993, no writ).

The remaining statutory authority under which the PUC exercises jurisdiction over wholesale rates is Water Code section 13.043(f). This section applies only in cases in which a retail public utility wishes to appeal a water service rate decision (i.e., a rate increase) by another retail public utility or political subdivision. *See* Tex. Water Code § 13.043(f). Another distinction between wholesale contract regulation under section 13.043(f) and wholesale contract regulation under Water Code chapters 11 and 12 is that jurisdiction under chapters 11 and 12 is relevant only to wholesale supplies of surface water; if a wholesale water dispute concerns groundwater supplies, it may be considered by the PUC only under section 13.043(f).

The water purchaser must initiate an appeal under section 13.043(f) by filing a petition with the PUC within ninety days after the date the water purchaser receives notice of the rate change. In such an appeal of a wholesale rate increase, the PUC must ensure that the rate is just and reasonable and not discriminatory. *See* Tex. Water Code § 13.043(j). For wholesale rate disputes between two municipalities, the PUC is required to consider the terms of any wholesale water service agreement. Notwithstanding that the term "wholesale water service" is defined for purposes of Water Code chapter 13 as including only sales of potable water service (*see* Tex. Water Code § 13.002(25)), a wholesale rate case under section 13.043(f) may be brought whether the wholesale rate is being charged for potable or for raw water, and the PUC would accept and process appeals of both potable and raw water rates under section 13.043(f). *See* Susan G. Zachos, *Wholesale Water Rate Cases—Viable or Not?*, *in* Texas Water Law Conference, CLE International, Austin (2004).

The most significant case decided under section 13.043(f) is *Texas Water Commission v. City of Fort Worth*, 875 S.W.2d 332 (Tex. App.—Austin 1994, writ denied). In that case, the Austin court of appeals established the public interest test as a jurisdictional prerequisite in a wholesale rate case. As adopted from prior federal and state natural gas utility cases, the public interest test means that before the PUC or the TCEQ may constitutionally abrogate a contracted wholesale water rate, it must first find that the rate adversely affects the public interest by being unreasonably preferential, prejudicial, or discriminatory. 875 S.W.2d at 336. Indeed, the court emphatically ruled that the public interest test is jurisdictional and that the TCEQ (the wholesale rate-setting agency at that time) may not avoid making the public interest finding even if all parties request that it do so. 875 S.W.2d at 337. The PUC has adopted detailed rules (modeled on those originally promulgated by the TCEQ) that describe the wholesale rate-setting process and how the public interest test is applied in that process. *See* 16 Tex. Admin. Code §§ 24.301–.321. See the discussion at section 31.17 below.

III. Wholesale Supply of Potable Water

§ 31.9 Introduction

Chapter 13 of the Texas Water Code contains various provisions that generally relate to wholesale water service by or to cities, water districts, water supply corporations, and retail public utilities. Because the definition of "wholesale water service" in chapter 13 means potable water service (not raw or untreated water service), the chapter 13 provisions dealing with wholesale water supply issues are generally limited to cases that involve the wholesale supply of potable water, except as discussed at section 31.8 above with respect to section 13.043(f).

§ 31.10 Wholesale Water Sales to a Water District

A city that sells wholesale water to a water district or other special district must determine wholesale water rates on the same basis as for any other of the city's similarly situated wholesale water purchasers. *See* Tex. Water Code § 13.086(a). Thus any differences in wholesale rates charged by a city to a water district must be justified by facts showing that the district is not "similarly situated" to the city's other wholesale customers.

§ 31.11 Notice to the PUC and the TCEQ of a Wholesale Water Supply Contract

Any person or entity that provides wholesale water service to a retail public utility must file a certified copy of the contract with the PUC and the TCEQ within thirty days following contract execution. *See* Tex. Water Code § 13.144. This filing must include the amount of water being supplied, the term of the contract, the consideration being given for the water, the purpose of the water use, the location of the water use, the source of supply, the point of delivery, any limitations on the reuse of water, a disclosure of any affiliated interest between the contracting parties, and any other condition or agreement relating to the wholesale contract. *See* Tex. Water Code § 13.144. The PUC's implementing rules are at 16 Texas Administrative Code section 24.15, and the TCEQ's implementing rules are at 30 Texas Administrative Code sections 295.101 and 297.101. In addition, the TCEQ has promulgated detailed rules describing particular types of contracts for which an amendment of the water supplier's underlying water right is required. *See* 30 Tex. Admin. Code §§ 297.101–.108. See the discussion at section 31.18 below.

§ 31.12 Prohibition on Requiring a Wholesale Purchaser to Obtain a CCN

A water service provider is prohibited from requiring a purchaser to obtain a certificate of convenience and necessity (CCN) if the purchaser is not otherwise required by chapter 13 to obtain the CCN. Tex. Water Code § 13.242(d). As discussed in Chapter 29 of this book, a public utility and a nonprofit water supply corporation must obtain a CCN to provide retail water service, but cities, municipal corporations, water districts, and political subdivisions are excluded from the definition of public utility in section 13.002(23). Therefore, these types of entities are not legally required to obtain a CCN to provide retail water service. Under section 13.242(d), a wholesale water supplier cannot contractually obligate such entities to acquire a CCN as a condition of providing wholesale water service.

§ 31.13 PUC- or TCEQ-Ordered Improvements in Service

The PUC or the TCEQ, after notice and hearing, may order a public utility or water supply corporation that is unable to provide continuous and adequate potable water service to obtain alternative service on a wholesale basis from another consenting utility service provider. *See* Tex. Water Code § 13.253(a)(3).

§ 31.14 Wholesale Water Contracts between Affiliated Interests

A retail utility service provider is prohibited from obtaining its wholesale source of water supply from an affiliated entity except when (1) the wholesale service is provided for not more than ninety days to remedy an emergency condition or (2) the PUC determines that the retail service utility cannot obtain wholesale water service from another source at a lower cost than from the affiliate. Tex. Water Code § 13.343(a). Furthermore, the retail service utility is prohibited from purchasing groundwater if the groundwater source is within a priority groundwater management area and a wholesale supply of surface water is available. Tex. Water Code § 13.343(b).

§ 31.15 Water Conservation Plans

The TCEQ and the TWDB are generally authorized to jointly identify quantified target goals for water conservation and develop model water conservation programs that water suppliers may use as guidelines in preparing water conservation plans. *See* Tex. Water Code § 11.1271(a)–(d). The water conservation programs developed jointly by the TCEQ and the TWDB are to suggest best management practices for achieving the highest practicable levels of water conservation and efficiency achievable for each specific type of water supplier. *See* Tex. Water Code § 11.1271(e). Pursuant to section 11.1271(f), the TCEQ has adopted rules establishing water conservation plan and drought contingency plan requirements specifically for wholesale water suppliers. *See* 30 Tex. Admin. Code §§ 288.5, 288.22. See the discussion at sections 31.19–31.21 below.

IV. Wholesale Rate-Setting Process at the PUC and the TCEQ

§ 31.16 The Two-Tier Hearing Process: The Public Interest Hearing and the Cost-of-Service Wholesale Rate-Setting Hearing

The PUC's and the TCEQ's rules for wholesale rate disputes attempt to strike a balance between protecting the freedom of contract between buyer and seller and protecting the public interest in preventing abuse of monopoly power by the seller. In originally adopting these "public interest" rules, the TCEQ's predecessor agency noted that "the adoption of these rules marks the end of the past policy where the commission essentially automatically cancelled the rate set by contract and set a rate based on cost of service." *See* 19 Tex. Reg. 6229 (1994) (rule adoption preamble). Allowing the parties to freely contract for the terms and conditions of wholesale water service and to rely on those contracts is essential for the types of capital budgeting and facilities planning necessary to secure long-term, dependable sources of water supply. On the other hand, when a seller substantially controls the source of water supply and sets prices and price increases for the water without significant input by the buyer, the potential arises for abuse of monopoly power and harm to the public interest. *See* 19 Tex. Reg. 6227–28 (1994) (rule adoption preamble).

To balance these two competing interests, the PUC rules at 16 Texas Administrative Code sections 24.301–.321 establish a two-tier hearing process: (1) the public interest inquiry and (2) the wholesale rate determination based on the supplier's cost of service. These two phases of the wholesale rate-setting process are described in more detail below.

For wholesale rate cases brought at the PUC under section 12.013 or 13.043(f), on receipt of a petition to set wholesale water rates (typically by the wholesale water purchaser), the PUC makes a preliminary investigation. *See* 16 Tex. Admin. Code § 24.307. If the PUC determines that the petition meets the requirements set forth in 16 Texas Administrative Code section 24.305, the case is forwarded to the State Office of Administrative Hearings (SOAH) for an evidentiary hearing. If the petition is filed as an appeal of a wholesale rate increase under section 13.043(f), the petition must be filed within ninety days of receiving notice of the rate increase.

In a PUC review of a wholesale rate that is charged pursuant to a written contract, SOAH conducts an evidentiary hearing on the public interest that involves issues relating to the existence and abuse of monopoly power by the seller (as described in more detail at section 31.16:1 below). *See* 16 Tex. Admin. Code § 24.307(b). It is only if the PUC determines that the charged wholesale rate is not in the public interest that the dispute can continue to a cost-of-service hearing to determine the appropriate wholesale water rate. However, the parties may agree to consolidate the evidentiary hearing on the public interest and the hearing on the cost of service. *See* 16 Tex. Admin. Code § 24.309(d).

In those (relatively few) wholesale rate petitions or appeals that involve a disputed rate *not* charged pursuant to a written contract, there is no public interest hearing, and the SOAH hearing is a cost-of-service rate-setting hearing inquiring into rate issues typically associated with retail utility rate cases, such as cost of service, rate design, and the setting of a final rate. *See* 16 Tex. Admin. Code § 24.307(c). In those cases where the buyer and seller cannot agree on whether the wholesale rate is charged pursuant to a written contract, the administrative law judge (ALJ) must abate the proceedings so that this issue can be resolved by a court. *See* 16 Tex. Admin. Code § 24.307(d). However, in *City of Dallas v. Sabine River Authority*, No. 03-15-00371, 2017 WL 2536882 (Tex. App.—Austin June 7, 2017, no pet.) (mem. op.), the Austin court of appeals ruled that a city wholesale water buyer's declaratory judgment suit against a wholesale seller river authority to determine that question was barred by the river authority's governmental immunity.

§ 31.16:1 The Public Interest Hearing

As described at section 31.16 above, a public interest hearing is held when the disputed wholesale water rate is charged pursuant to a contract. The purpose of a public interest hearing is to determine whether the protested wholesale rate adversely affects the public interest. 16 Tex. Admin. Code § 24.309(a). In a public interest hearing, discovery and evidence are strictly limited to public interest issues. 16 Tex. Admin. Code § 24.309(b). The hearing does not include a cost-of-service inquiry. The PUC must find that the public interest is adversely affected if any one of the following four public interest criteria has been violated:

1. the protested rate impairs the seller's ability to continue to provide service based on the seller's financial integrity and operational capability;

2. the protested rate impairs the purchaser's ability to provide service to its retail customers based on the purchaser's financial integrity and operational capability;

3. the protested rate evidences the seller's abuse of monopoly power in its provision of water to the purchaser; or

4. the protested rate is unreasonably preferential, prejudicial, or discriminatory compared to the wholesale rates the seller charges other wholesale customers.

16 Tex. Admin. Code § 24.311(a).

The PUC must weigh all relevant factors, including—

- the disparate bargaining power of the parties (including the purchaser's alternative means and costs, environmental impact, regulatory issues, and problems of obtaining alternative water service);
- any failure by the seller to reasonably demonstrate the changed conditions that are the basis for a change in rates;
- the seller's change in ratemaking methodology;
- other valuable consideration received by a party under a rate established by contract;
- incentives necessary to encourage regional projects or water conservation measures;
- the seller's obligation to meet federal or state drinking water standards or wastewater standards;
- the rates charged in Texas by other wholesale water suppliers; and
- the seller's rates charged to its retail customers compared to the retail rates the purchaser charges its retail customers resulting from the wholesale rate demanded by the seller in the present rate case.

16 Tex. Admin. Code § 24.311(a)(3). The PUC rules make clear that a public interest determination may not be based on an analysis of the seller's cost of service. *See* 16 Tex. Admin. Code § 24.311(b).

The wholesale rate petitioner bears the burden of proof in the public interest hearing. 16 Tex. Admin. Code § 24.317. Following receipt of all evidence and closing arguments, the SOAH judge forwards a proposal for decision to the PUC recommending a decision on whether the protested rate adversely affects the public interest. 16 Tex. Admin. Code § 24.309(c). If the PUC determines that the public interest has not been adversely affected, it denies the protest petition and affirms the rate demanded by the seller. 16 Tex. Admin. Code § 24.313(a).

§ 31.16:2 Cost-of-Service Rate Hearing

If the PUC determines that the public interest is adversely affected by the protested rate, the agency issues a remand order, referring the case to SOAH for an evidentiary hearing to determine a just and reasonable wholesale rate. *See* 16 Tex. Admin. Code § 24.313(b). Within ninety days of such referral of the case to SOAH, the seller must file its cost-of-service rate study and other information supporting the protested rate. 16 Tex. Admin. Code § 24.313(c). The seller bears the burden of proof in the cost-of-service rate hearing. 16 Tex. Admin. Code § 24.317.

After the evidentiary hearing, the SOAH judge prepares a proposal for decision and forwards it to the PUC. The PUC determines a cost of service and fixes a rate consistent with the ratemaking mandates of Texas Water Code chapters 12 and 13. *See* 16 Tex. Admin. Code § 24.313(e). The PUC must use any reasonable method set by contract that identifies the costs of providing service or allocates such costs in calculating the cost of service. 16 Tex. Admin. Code § 24.315(a). A change by the seller from one ratemaking method to another must be shown to have a reasonable basis, or the PUC may calculate the cost of service using the former method. If the protested rate is based in part on a change in ratemaking methods, the seller must show in the hearing the calculation of the revenue requirements using both the new and the former methods. When revenue requirements are computed using a new method, the PUC may allow adjustments for past payments. 16 Tex. Admin. Code § 24.315(b).

In those cases in which the PUC has determined that a particular contract rate adversely affects the public interest and has set rates, any rate dispute arising under that contract within three years after the end of the test year period of the initial rate case goes immediately to a cost-of-service rate hearing without a public interest hearing. *See* 16 Tex. Admin. Code § 24.319.

Largely in response to the North Texas Municipal Water District case (discussed in section 31.17 below), in 2021 the Texas legislature enacted Senate Bill 997 to statutorily codify the procedures established by the PUC rules for wholesale contract rate appeals. Effective September 1, 2021, Senate Bill 997 amends section 12.013 of the Texas Water Code and adds new section 13.0431 to clarify the procedures for handling wholesale water contract rate appeals. While Senate Bill 997 for the most part maintains the existing procedures as described above, it did for the first time create a right of judicial appeal of the PUC's determination on the public interest. Under Senate Bill 997, the PUC must determine whether the amount charged under the wholesale contract "harms the public interest," which is slightly different than "adversely affects the public interest" as stated in the PUC's rules. However, it is not anticipated that the PUC will substantially alter its existing rule criteria on the public interest determination in response to this different statutory wording. A party adversely affected by the PUC's ruling on whether the contract rate harms the public interest may seek judicial review of that determination by trial de novo. If such an appeal is filed, the PUC must abate the wholesale rate appeal proceeding until a final judicial determination on the public interest is made. Before commencing a cost-of-service proceeding, the PUC must give the contracting parties sixty days following a final decision on the public interest to amend the amount charged under the contract. If the parties agree on a contract amendment, the rate charged under the amended contract may only be challenged at the PUC five years after the date of the contract amendment or up to twenty-five years after the date of the contract amendment if so agreed by the parties.

§ 31.17 Issues Arising under the Wholesale Rate-Setting Process

Although relatively few wholesale rate cases have been filed since the original adoption of the public interest rules in 1994, one such case highlights several issues under the wholesale rate-setting rules that have yet to be fully resolved. In *Petition of Canyon Regional Water Authority and Bexar Metropolitan Water District to Appeal the Wholesale Water Rate Increase of Guadalupe-Blanco River Authority* (TCEQ Docket No. 2002-1400-UCR; SOAH Docket No. 582-03-1991), two water districts protested the wholesale rate increase charged by the Guadalupe-Blanco River Authority (GBRA) for 2002 under a water purchase contract containing a provision allowing the GBRA to adjust the firm water rate "at any time and from time to time." Because the wholesale customers who protested the rate disagreed that the rate was charged pursuant to a written contract, the ALJ abated the rate case pending at SOAH, as required by TCEQ rules. The parties petitioned the district court of Travis County to make that determination. *GBRA v. Canyon Regional Water Authority, Bexar Metropolitan Water District & the Texas Commission on Environmental Quality*, No. GN400105 (353d Dist. Ct., Travis County, Tex. Aug. 11, 2006). In district court, the rate protestants also raised other issues, such as (1) whether a contract provision authorizing the parties to "apply by appropriate means to [the TCEQ] . . . to establish a just and reasonable adjustment or charge" prevents the parties from using the TCEQ's public interest determination process; (2) whether the GBRA, as a political subdivision of the state, has a contractually protected interest in its wholesale rates; and (3) whether sales of state-owned water are subject to the public interest hearing requirements. The district court ruled on cross-motions for summary judgment that the rate was charged pursuant to a written contract and upheld the TCEQ's public interest rules, which make no exception for rate cases involving state-owned water.

On appeal, the Corpus Christi court of appeals upheld the district court's decision in *Canyon Regional Water Authority v. Guadalupe-Blanco River Authority*, 286 S.W.3d 397 (Tex. App.—Corpus Christi–Edinburg 2008, no pet.). The most significant aspect of the court's decision is its holding that the GBRA water rate was "charged pursuant to a written contract" and thus was subject to the requirement for an initial public interest hearing, notwithstanding the fact that no fixed price for the water was established in the contract. 286 S.W.3d at 403–04. Under the GBRA's wholesale contract with Canyon Regional Water Authority, the contract price was based on the GBRA's firm water rate charged to all of the GBRA's other customers, and such rate could be reset at any time upon sixty days' advance notice. 286 S.W.3d at 401. The court reasoned that such "open term price" provisions were commonly used in business transactions and that Texas courts had specifically upheld the validity of open term price contracts by gasoline refiners. 286 S.W.3d at 403. In rejecting Canyon Regional's claim that the TCEQ's public interest rules effectively establish an unfair and improper barrier to the TCEQ's obligation to set just and reasonable wholesale water rates, the appellate court expressly upheld the validity of the TCEQ's public interest hearing requirement for wholesale water rates. 286 S.W.3d at 406. The *Canyon Regional* case is important not only because it expressly upholds the TCEQ's public interest hearing requirement for wholesale water ratesetting petitions, but also because it means that a fixed contract price for water does not need to be specifically stated in a contract for the PUC to determine that the wholesale water rate is charged pursuant to a written contract.

A 2010 wholesale rate appeal case addressed the question of what constitutes an abuse of monopoly power by a wholesale water provider. In *In re Appeal of Multi-County Water Supply Corporation to Review the Wholesale Water Rate Increase Imposed by the City of Hamilton* (TCEQ Docket No. 2009-0048-UCR; SOAH Docket No. 582-09-2557), the Multi-County Water Supply Corporation (MCWSC) appealed a $0.14 per thousand gallon rate increase imposed by its wholesale supplier, the city of Hamilton, although the city had merely passed through the same rate increase it was charged by its wholesale supplier, the Upper Leon River Municipal Water District. After a SOAH evidentiary hearing concerning whether the protested rate adversely affects the public interest, the ALJ ruled, and the TCEQ agreed, that the city of Hamilton did have monopoly power over MCWSC, but that the city did not abuse that monopoly power. The monopoly power existed because of the forty-year wholesale water supply contract that gave the city the right to unilaterally adjust the rates charged and also limited MCWSC's right to obtain water from a different supplier. However, there was no abuse of that monopoly power under four of the TCEQ criteria: (1) there was no disparate bargaining power between the two contracting entities (instead of entering into the contract, MCWSC could have obtained water from a number of different sources); (2) the rate increase resulted from changed conditions (the rate increase was imposed as a pass-through increase charged by the city's water supplier); (3) the city's rate methodology did not change (the increase was merely a change in one of the city's ratemaking component factors, but not a change in the methodology itself); and (4) there was no other valuable consideration received by the city as wholesale supplier.

In a 2011 wholesale-rate-setting case, the ALJ ruled that a section 13.043(f) appeal was not valid since it was filed by an associational group of wholesale ratepayers rather than by the ratepayers themselves. *See In re Appeal of Navarro County Wholesale Ratepayers to Review the Wholesale Rate Increase Imposed by the City of Corsicana* (TCEQ Docket No. 2009-1925-UCR; SOAH Docket No. 582-10-1944). In that case, the ALJ also determined that all evidence received at the hearing from the remaining ratepayers concerning cost-of-service was irrelevant in the public interest hearing phase of the wholesale rate appeal process. On the main substantive issue, the ALJ determined, and the TCEQ agreed, that the city of Corsicana had not abused whatever monopoly power it possessed in the setting of its wholesale water rates. The primary factors relied on by the ALJ in making this determination were (1) the standard form wholesale water supply contract used by the city of Corsicana was negotiated by an attorney for the city and an attorney who acted in the interests of the wholesale ratepayers, and it was adopted following a public hearing participated in by the wholesale customers; (2) the "sole source" provision of the contract did allow for some degree of choice by the wholesale water customers in obtaining a different supply source; (3) the contracts did have features beneficial to the wholesale water purchasers; and (4) the city's adoption of an inclining block volumetric rate structure for the first time was a change in rate methodology, but the change was not abusive. This TCEQ decision was upheld by the court of appeals in an unreported case. *Navarro County Wholesale Ratepayers v. Covar*, No. 01-14-00102-CV, 2015 WL 3916249 (Tex. App.—Houston [1st. Dist.] June 25, 2015, pet. denied).

Other significant wholesale water rate cases include the following:

PUC Docket No. 42857: *Petition of North Austin M.U.D. No. 1, et al. from the Ratemaking Actions of the City of Austin and Request for Interim Rates in Williamson and Travis Counties.* This was a wholesale water and wastewater rate appeal under Texas Water Code section 13.044 by several special purpose water districts objecting to rates charged by the city of Austin. Under section 13.044, a special purpose water district created by consent of a city in whose corporate limits or extraterritorial jurisdiction the district is located may appeal the wholesale water and wastewater rates charged by the city. *See* Tex. Water Code § 13.044. The PUC decided that it need not conduct a public interest hearing because section 13.044 does not expressly provide for a public interest hearing and because the contract between the parties called for rates to be annually set by city of Austin ordinance so that the rate was not set pursuant to a contract. *See also* PUC Docket No. 48836, in which the PUC similarly ruled that Water Code section 13.044 does not require a public interest inquiry to be conducted.

PUC Docket Nos. 42866 and 43081: *Petition of Travis County M.U.D. No. 12 Appealing Change of Wholesale Water Rates Implemented by West Travis County Public Utility Agency, et al.* These two dockets concern a wholesale water rate appeal under Water Code section 13.043(f). In Docket No. 42866, the PUC dismissed the case following the public interest hearing because no disparate bargaining power as between the wholesale water provider and purchaser had been shown, primarily because the wholesale water purchaser had the alternative of self-service or of reducing the contracted amount of water purchased. The PUC also declined to make a determination about whether the wholesale water provider is a retail public utility notwithstanding the wholesale water purchaser's argument that if the provider was a retail public utility it should be automatically determined to have monopoly power. In Docket No. 43081, which concerned a separate drought surcharge by the wholesale water provider, the parties could not agree whether the surcharge was charged pursuant to a contract, and, therefore, the PUC docket was abated pending a determination of that issue by the district court.

PUC Docket No. 43674: *Petition of the City of Dallas for Review of a Decision by the Sabine River Authority*. In this case, the parties could not agree whether the wholesale water rate was charged pursuant to a written contract, and so the SOAH judge abated the case but without first acting on the city of Dallas's request to set interim rates. The PUC determined that the SOAH judge had authority to set interim rates notwithstanding the PUC rule requirement to abate a wholesale rate case when the parties cannot agree whether the protested rate is charged pursuant to a written contract. The SOAH judge then set an interim rate to be applied until the PUC makes a final decision, which interim rate was the same as the new higher rate, which was protested by the city of Dallas. However, the SOAH judge required that the revenues attributable to the difference between the Sabine River Authority's prior rate and its new higher rate should be escrowed pending a final PUC decision so that any lower rate finally determined by the PUC could be easily refunded to the city of Dallas.

PUC Docket No. 46662: *Petition of the Cities of Garland, Mesquite, Plano and Richardson Appealing the Decision by North Texas Municipal Water District Affecting Wholesale Water Rates*. In this case, filed in late 2016, the petitioning cities were four of thirteen "member cities" who appointed North Texas Municipal Water District (NTMWD) board members. The four petitioning cities claimed that basing the minimum "take-or-pay" amount of water for each member city on the highest historical water usage was unfair to them since they were mostly fully developed and, under recent state water conservation mandates, it was very unlikely that they would ever use such high historical amounts of water again, and thus they were "paying for water never used." The other nine member cities intervened in the case, as any change in the contract method would impact them. After the four petitioning cities filed their wholesale rate review petition with the PUC, the NTMWD, as the wholesale water provider, filed a bond validation suit as well as a declaratory judgment action in Travis County district court objecting to the jurisdiction of the PUC. The NTMWD essentially argued that the PUC had no jurisdiction to set wholesale water rates in this case because the wholesale water contract between the NTMWD and the four petitioning cities was "incontestable" by law, and any PUC hearing on the NTMWD's wholesale water rate would constitute a contest of the contract. The NTMWD was unsuccessful in obtaining a court order to prevent the PUC from proceeding with the wholesale rates case, and the PUC case was referred to SOAH for a public interest hearing. In this case, the PUC issued a twenty-eight-page preliminary order identifying a lengthy list of issues for the "Phase 1" public interest hearing, and many of these issues specifically concerned matters typically adjudicated in a cost-of-service rate hearing, such as—

- What is the seller's cost of debt?
- What is the seller's cost of operating and maintaining its facilities?
- What is the total cost to run the seller's systems?
- What is the seller's annual gross revenues?
- What are the seller's net revenues?

Every wholesale rate case processed by the PUC since this case has featured a similar lengthy list of issues for the public interest hearing that go beyond the PUC rule section 24.311 criteria for determining the public interest. According to the PUC, these kinds of cost-of-service issues are relevant in a public interest hearing as long as the answers to these issues are not used for the purpose of setting rates. This new PUC procedural practice raises the question whether the public interest phase adjudications of these cost-of-service type issues will be binding on the parties in a cost-of-service hearing, and, if not, why the parties should be required to litigate these issues first in a public interest hearing and again in a cost-of-service hearing.

On March 15, 2019, a SOAH ALJ issued a proposal for decision recommending that the PUC find that the NTMWD wholesale water rate adversely affected the public interest and therefore should be referred to a Phase 2 cost-of-service hearing. Almost a year later, the PUC determined that the wholesale rate adversely affected the public interest, but instead of immediately referring the case to SOAH for a cost-of-service hearing, the PUC gave the parties time to attempt to resolve the case by agreement. In late October 2020, the parties announced that they had reached a settlement agreement and asked the PUC to dismiss the case with prejudice. The PUC did so on November 19, 2020, and on the same date dismissed the intervention motions of various wholesale water customer cities who claimed that they would be adversely affected by the parties' settlement. The essential feature of the parties' settlement was that the NTMWD and its member cities would amend their wholesale water contract to gradually (over a twelve-year period) shift from the "highest historical use" to a rolling five-year average of water use to determine their minimum take-or-pay amount.

PUC Docket No. 47742: *Petition of Fort Belknap Water Supply Corp. (WSC), Graham East WSC, City of Bryson, and City of Newcastle Appealing the Decision by the City of Graham to Change Wholesale Water Rates.* In this case, three cities appealed the wholesale water rate increase charged by the city of Graham. The SOAH ALJ determined in the proposal for decision that the three petitioning parties had not established that their wholesale water rate was adverse to the public interest, and the PUC agreed based on the insufficiency of evidence presented by the petitioners. In making this ruling, the PUC stated that there are two public interest standards involved in a wholesale water case: (1) the public interest test under section 13.043(j) of the Texas Water Code (based on the case of *Texas Water Commission v. City of Fort Worth*, 875 S.W.2d 332, 335 (Tex. App.—Austin 1994, writ denied)) and (2) the public interest test established under the PUC's rules at 16 Tex. Admin. Code § 24.311(a). Because the first public interest test expressly requires the PUC to evaluate whether the wholesale rate is just and reasonable and whether it is unreasonably preferential, prejudicial, or discriminatory, evidence that is typically relevant in a cost-of-service hearing is admissible in the public interest phase, notwithstanding the PUC's own rule that prohibits the public interest determination from being based on the seller's cost of service. The PUC clarified this distinction by stating that it cannot consider cost of service during the public interest phase, but that does not preclude the parties from providing evidence of the financial aspects of the wholesale water seller's business.

PUC Docket No. 47814: *Petition of High Point WSC, Talty Special Utility District, and Markout WSC Appealing a Decision by the City of Forney Affecting Wholesale Water Rates.* In this case, filed in late 2017, a key issue is the reasonableness of the cost markup agreed to by all parties during contract negotiations. Under the contract, the city of Forney charges a sixty-one-cent or 63 percent markup, whichever is greater, on water that Forney obtains from the NTMWD to serve the three petitioning wholesale water purchasers. As of the printing of this edition, the parties are still negotiating a possible settlement of the Phase 1 hearing public interest issues. The PUC staff has currently taken the position that the public interest has not been adversely affected by Forney's wholesale water rate charged to the three petitioning wholesale purchasers.

PUC Docket No. 47920: *Petition of the Beeville Water Supply District Appealing the Decision by the City of Corpus Christi to Change Wholesale Raw Water Rates.* In this case, filed in early 2018, the Beeville Water Supply District appealed the wholesale water rate charged by the city of Corpus Christi. The district alleged, among other things, that Corpus Christi's wholesale water rate included recovered costs for facilities that did not benefit the district. After a period of negotiations, the parties settled, and the case was dismissed in late 2019.

PUC Docket No. 48218: *Petition of the City of Hutto Appealing the Decision by Manville WSC to Increase Wholesale Water Rates.* Just prior to filing this case at the PUC in April 2018, Hutto had filed a lawsuit against Manville WSC in Williamson County district court regarding its wholesale water contract. In July of 2018, Manville WSC rescinded its wholesale water rate increase, and the PUC case was dismissed.

PUC Docket No. 50433: *Petition of the City of Star Harbor Appealing the Decision by the City of Malakoff to Increase Wholesale Sewer Rates.* In this case, filed in early 2020, the parties stipulated that the appealed wholesale sewer rate was not charged pursuant to a contract. The parties settled the case in July 2020 in a mediation with a SOAH mediator.

V. Wholesale Water Supply Contractual Amendments and Annual Reporting

§ 31.18 Contractual Amendments and Annual Reporting

To better monitor the use of appropriated state water, the TCEQ has promulgated rules requiring a raw or treated water supplier that possesses a state water right to obtain a TCEQ-approved amendment of that water right before the supplier makes any delivery of water under a new contract. *See* 30 Tex. Admin. Code §§ 297.101–.108. If the contractual water right permit amendment is not obtained as required by TCEQ rules, the TCEQ will not consider the contracted amount of water to be "in perfection" of the supplier's water right (i.e., the water will not be considered to have been beneficially used). *See* 30 Tex. Admin. Code § 297.106(a). The purpose of the water right amendment is to have the water right reflect the contractual arrangements with the buyer. Generally, no contractual water right amendment is needed if the water is sold and used for the purpose and in the place of use stated in the water right. *See* 30 Tex. Admin. Code § 297.101(b).

An applicant for such a water right amendment must file the application information specified in 30 Texas Administrative Code section 295.101 as well as a copy of the contract. If the water supplier is not also the holder of the underlying appropriative water right, the holder of the appropriative right must file the application to amend the water right, either alone or as a coapplicant with the supplier. *See* 30 Tex. Admin. Code § 297.102(c). Sales of up to three years of up to ten acre-feet per year of untreated water from the perimeter of a reservoir for purposes stated in the water right are not required to obtain a contractual water right amendment. *See* 30 Tex. Admin. Code § 297.101(b).

If a contract obligates the supplier to release water from storage (e.g., a reservoir) to a downstream buyer who takes water only from the releases, the supplier is not obligated to make releases when doing so would aggravate existing flooding conditions, and the TCEQ may establish stream flood stages in the permit amendment as limits on such releases. *See* 30 Tex. Admin. Code § 297.103(a). If the contract authorizes the buyer to take purchased water from existing stream flows (i.e., water other than that released from the upstream storage) and neither the seller nor the buyer has a water right authorizing such diversions, then either the buyer or the seller must obtain a regular, term, or temporary permit to appropriate water up to the maximum annual diversions not released from storage. *See* 30 Tex. Admin. Code § 297.103(b). The supplier must bear the transportation and evapotranspiration water losses for water released from an upstream source of supply unless the contract specifies otherwise. *See* 30 Tex. Admin. Code § 297.103(c). If a contract provides for a buyer diverting water upstream of the stored source in a manner that could impair the seller's underlying water right, then either the buyer or the seller must obtain a permit to appropriate water up to the maximum annual diversions of upstream water for the term of the contract. *See* 30 Tex. Admin. Code § 297.104.

Finally, TCEQ rules on annual reporting of state water use require that both the seller and the buyer of state water file annual reports. The buyer must report the amount of water diverted on a weekly and monthly basis, while the seller must report the amount of water used each month and the total amount released downstream each week to each purchaser. *See* 30 Tex. Admin. Code § 295.202(d)(1), (d)(2).

VI. Wholesale Water Supply Conservation and Drought Contingency Planning Requirements

§ 31.19 Introduction

Pursuant to Texas Water Code section 11.1271, the TCEQ rules in 30 Texas Administrative Code sections 288.1–.30 establish the water conservation and drought contingency planning requirements for various types of water users, including wholesale water suppliers. As described in more detail in the following sections, all wholesale water suppliers must prepare and keep updated a water conservation plan and a drought contingency plan. The TCEQ rules contain a definition of the term "wholesale public water supplier":

> An individual or entity that for compensation supplies water to another for resale to the public for human consumption. The term does not include an individual or entity that supplies water to itself or its employees or tenants as an incident of that employee service or tenancy when that water is not resold to or used by others, or an individual or entity that conveys water to another individual or entity, but does not own the right to the water which is conveyed, whether or not for a delivery fee.

30 Tex. Admin. Code § 288.1(25). Although the defined term "wholesale *public* water supplier" appears to be limited to wholesale water resold for public consumption (i.e., potable water), the TCEQ rules at 30 Texas Administrative Code section 288.5 are addressed to "wholesale water suppliers" without limiting applicability to potable water wholesalers. Therefore it is reasonable to conclude that the water conservation planning requirements in section 288.5 apply generally to all wholesale water suppliers, not just potable water resold on a wholesale basis for public consumption.

§ 31.20 Water Conservation Plans for Wholesale Water Suppliers

A water conservation plan for a wholesale water supplier must at a minimum include the following elements:

- a description of the wholesaler's service area, including population and customer data, water use data, and wastewater data;
- specific, quantified five-year and ten-year targets for water savings, including target goals for public water supplies in gallons per capita per day for the wholesaler's service area, maximum acceptable unaccounted-for water, and the basis for development of these goals;
- a description of how the amount of water diverted from the source of supply will be measured and accounted for;
- a monitoring and records management program for determining water sales, deliveries, and losses;
- a metering, leak detection, and repair program for the wholesaler's water storage, delivery, and distribution system;
- a requirement in all water supply contracts that each successive wholesale customer develop and implement a water conservation plan under the TCEQ rules;
- if applicable, a reservoir systems operations plan providing for optimized use of water supplies from all reservoirs;
- a means for implementation and enforcement; and

- documentation that the water conservation plans and goals are consistent with the approved regional water plan.

See 30 Tex. Admin. Code § 288.5(1). See Chapter 20 of this book for a discussion of regional water plans.

The wholesale water supplier can elect to adopt, or the TCEQ can require adoption of, additional water conservation strategies, such as conservation-oriented water rates and water rate structures (e.g., uniform or increasing block rate schedules, seasonal rates), a program to assist agricultural customers in water conservation activities, and a wastewater reuse and recycling program. *See* 30 Tex. Admin. Code § 288.5(2). The wholesale water supplier's conservation plan must be updated every five years to coincide with the supplier's regional water planning group. 30 Tex. Admin. Code § 288.5(3). See Chapter 20 of this book for a discussion of regional water planning groups. See also Chapters 3, 10, and 23 for further discussion of water conservation plans.

§ 31.21 Drought Contingency Plans for Wholesale Water Suppliers

A drought contingency plan for a wholesale water supplier must at a minimum include the following elements:

- provisions to actively obtain public input on preparation of the plan and for informing wholesale customers about the plan (e.g., a noticed public meeting and opportunity to submit comments);
- coordination with regional water planning groups for the service area of the wholesale public water supplier;
- specific criteria for the initiation and termination of drought response stages with an explanation of the rationale or basis for such triggering criteria;
- a minimum of three drought or emergency response stages providing for the implementation of measures for a repeat of the drought of record;
- notification of wholesale customers and other procedures for initiating or terminating drought response stages;
- specific, quantified targets for water use reductions during periods of water shortage and drought;
- specific water supply or water demand management measures to be implemented during each stage of the plan, including (1) pro rata curtailment of water deliveries to wholesale water customers in accordance with section 11.039 of the Texas Water Code, and (2) use of alternative water sources (e.g., interconnection with another water system, temporary use of a nonmunicipal water supply, use of reclaimed water for nonpotable purposes);
- a requirement that every wholesale water contract provide for pro rata curtailments in times of drought;
- procedures for granting variances to the plan; and
- procedures for enforcing any mandatory water use restrictions, including specification of penalties (e.g., liquidated damages, water rate surcharges, discontinuation of service) for violations of such restrictions.

See 30 Tex. Admin. Code § 288.22(a).

The wholesale public water supplier must notify the TCEQ executive director within five business days of the implementation of any mandatory provisions of the drought contingency plan. 30 Tex. Admin. Code § 288.22(b). The wholesale public water supplier must also review and update the drought contingency plan at least every five years based on any new or updated information. 30 Tex. Admin. Code § 288.22(c). See Chapter 22 of this book for further discussion of drought contingency planning.

VII. Wholesale Water Supply Contract Provisions

§ 31.22 Introduction

Wholesale water supply contracts are typically entered into between holders of large state-appropriative water rights and customers such as cities, water districts, nonprofit water supply corporations, industries, and agricultural users. The largest holders of water rights in Texas are generally the major river authorities, large cities, and large municipal water districts. These wholesale water suppliers have tended to develop standard form wholesale contracts for one or more types of their customers or types of water use requested by the customer. Because wholesale water supply contracts and buyer-seller relationships are largely unregulated, however, and because most wholesale contracts deal with a set of facts unique to each wholesale supplier, wide variations exist among the various wholesale water supply contracts used in Texas. A good summary of the similarities and differences among the wholesale water supply contracts of the various river authorities in Texas is found in Sushma Krishnamurthi, Water Supply Aspects of River Authorities in Texas (2006) (unpublished MA thesis, Texas A&M University), http://oaktrust.library.tamu.edu/handle/1969.1/4443 [hereinafter Krishnamurthi]. Nevertheless, some contract provisions are common to most wholesale contracts. The most significant of these provisions are discussed in the following sections.

§ 31.22:1 Term of Agreement

Most wholesale water contracts are intended to help meet the buyer's need for a long-term, dependable source of water supply. Typically, a wholesale contract specifies an initial term of ten to fifty years, with the potential for renewal.

§ 31.22:2 "Take-or-Pay" Volume Provision

Most wholesale contracts specify that the volume of water subject to the contract is supplied on a "take-or-pay" basis so that the buyer is required to pay for a minimum volume of water at a set price regardless of whether the buyer actually takes delivery of the minimum volume. The advantage of a take-or-pay provision in wholesale water contracts is that the buyer is assured of a steady supply at a set price, and the seller is assured of a steady revenue stream while minimizing the risk of future declines in demand. In those cases in which a contract allows a buyer to take more water than the minimum, a price premium on the extra water may be charged by the seller. A good discussion of the authority granted to local governments and state agencies by the Interlocal Co-operative Act (Texas Government Code chapter 791) to enter into take-or-pay contracts for water supply and wastewater treatment can be found in *City of The Colony v. North Texas Municipal Water District*, 272 S.W.3d 699 (Tex. App.—Fort Worth 2008, pet. dism'd).

§ 31.22:3 Diversion Point

A diversion point at which a buyer takes delivery of wholesale water is typically specified in a map or diagram showing the diversion point. The diversion point should be defined with precision to establish the dividing point between seller and buyer concerning liabilities and risk of loss, and also for water rights permitting purposes.

§ 31.22:4 Metering of Water Taken

Typically the buyer bears the cost of installing, operating, and maintaining a meter to accurately measure the amount of water taken. The seller has the right to take meter readings, inspect and test the meter, and require adjustments in the amounts paid in the event any significant meter inaccuracies are discovered. Most wholesale contracts also prescribe a maximum rate of delivery and may require that water flows be mechanically regulated so that the maximum rate is not exceeded. A wholesale water contract also typically provides that any other facilities required by the buyer to divert water and connect to the seller's system must be approved in advance by the seller.

§ 31.22:5 Purpose and Place of Use

To ensure that the provision of water is consistent with the seller's underlying water right, a wholesale contract may limit the buyer to a particular use and place of use of the water.

§ 31.22:6 Water Quality

A wholesale contract for raw or untreated water typically contains only limited commitments by the seller about the quality of the water, or the contract may contain an outright disclaimer of any warranties of fitness for a particular purpose. A contract for the sale of treated water specifies the degree of treatment being provided by the seller.

§ 31.22:7 Water Conservation and Drought Management

As discussed at sections 31.19–31.21 above, Texas law requires a wholesale water supplier not only to have a water conservation and drought contingency plan but also to contractually require its water buyers to have the TCEQ-compliant water conservation and drought contingency plans that the buyer in turn is required to impose on its retail consumers.

§ 31.22:8 Price and Price Adjustments

The pricing provisions of a wholesale water contract are typically very detailed and usually include complex formulas for determining price adjustments under various circumstances. A different base water rate may be set for different uses (municipal/domestic, industrial, or agricultural) and for such water provided on a "firm" basis (uninterruptible even in times of drought) or a "non-firm" basis (interruptible in times of drought). A base water rate charged in a wholesale contract may consist of various components such as a raw water charge, a pumping and transmission charge, a treatment charge, a maximum day (peak) demand charge, or a service charge to cover some portion of the seller's administrative costs. A wholesale contract typically provides for future increases in the base water rate, or components thereof, based on future increases in the seller's cost of providing the water, costs that may or may not be required to be justified by the seller. Some wholesale water sellers providing municipal use water may charge a fee for each new retail customer connection made by the buyer (i.e., a "system access fee" or impact fee). Similarly, some wholesale water sellers may charge a "capital buy-in" fee to help defray the seller's water system capital costs. Different circumstances affect each individual water supplier. These include regional differences in water availability and customer demand, differences in costs that each water supplier attempts to recover in wholesale rates, differences in the legal authority of political subdivisions that act as wholesale water providers (e.g., river authorities, cities, and water districts), and differences in political considerations and economic philosophies among the governing boards of the major water suppliers. One researcher who conducted a survey of wholesale water rates charged by river authorities in Texas found that the per-acre-foot price in 2004 for municipal use water ranged from $25.48 to $140, the per-acre-foot price of industrial use water ranged from $25.48 to $106.50, and the per-acre-foot price of agricultural use water ranged from $9 to $105. Krishnamurthi, at 65–66.

VIII. Conclusion

§ 31.23 Conclusion

Wholesale water supply contracting plays a vital role in the Texas water market because it allows for the transfer of large volumes of untreated or treated water to those entities that have retail customers needing a long-term, dependable source of water. Unlike retail sales of water to end users, which is a highly regulated process, the supply of water on a wholesale basis is largely determined by freely negotiated contracts between the wholesale water supplier and the wholesale water purchaser. The most significant legal control over wholesale water supply is the PUC wholesale water rate-setting process, which is intended to prevent the abuse of monopoly power by wholesale water suppliers over water purchasers. Wholesale water purchasers can be expected to use the PUC wholesale water rate-setting process more frequently as the relatively fixed supply of water available in Texas must meet the ever-increasing demands of the growing Texas economy.

CHAPTER 32

The Endangered Species Act and the Texas Law of Water Resources

Vanessa Puig-Williams[1]

I. Introduction

§ 32.1 The Endangered Species Act in the Context of Water Resources

The Endangered Species Act (ESA) is considered to be one of the most potent federal environmental laws, revered by many for its protection of nonhuman species at all costs, and reviled by many others for exactly the same reason. For the most part, however, the ESA is like many other environmental laws—it demands that humans take into account the effects of economic and social activities on the environment and adjust accordingly. The devil, as always, is in the details of the adjustment: How much, by whom, when, where, and for how long? It has been suggested that the ESA "appears to be having a larger impact on state water laws and private rights than any other piece of federal legislation." Roderick E. Walston, *Water Law Symposium: Keynote Address*, 12 Hastings W. Nw. J. Envtl. L. & Pol'y 125 (2006). The purpose of this chapter is to place the ESA in the context of water resources, where it has had profound impacts, and to guide the reader through the salient details of the statute's administration and enforcement.

In 1973, Congress determined that plants and wildlife are of great value to the nation and its people and enacted the ESA, with the stated purpose to "provide a means whereby the ecosystems upon which endangered . . . and threatened species depend may be conserved." 16 U.S.C. § 1531(b). Fittingly for purposes of this chapter, the true impact of the ESA was revealed in 1978 in a case involving water. In *Tennessee Valley Authority v. Hill*, 437 U.S. 153 (1978), the Supreme Court described the statute as "the most comprehensive legislation for the preservation of endangered species ever enacted by any nation" and ruled that the Tennessee Valley Authority could not complete a dam that was believed at the time to threaten the continued existence of a small fish, the snail darter. 437 U.S. at 180, 194. The Supreme Court found that every section of the ESA makes it plain that the "intent of Congress in enacting [the] statute was to halt and reverse the trend toward species extinction, whatever the cost." 437 U.S. at 184.

In short, the ESA lays out strict prohibitions against "taking" certain species and stiff penalties for individuals who violate its mandates. Though several substantive amendments and various court decisions have tempered somewhat the severity of the ESA, it remains a strong mechanism for protecting and conserving endangered and threatened wildlife and their habitats.

---

1. Vanessa Puig-Williams is an attorney in Austin, Texas, whose practice is focused on land and water conservation in Texas. In addition to advising nonprofits and landowners, Vanessa is a fellow at the Meadows Center at Texas State University. She received her JD from the University of Texas School of Law in 2006 and practiced in the environmental protection division of the Texas Attorney General's Office for several years.

II. Overview of the ESA

§ 32.2 The Endangered Species Act: An Overview

The basic regulatory structure of the law remains divided into five programs administered by the U.S. Fish and Wildlife Service (FWS) for terrestrial and freshwater species and the National Oceanic and Atmospheric Administration Fisheries (also known as the National Marine Fisheries Service (NMFS)) for marine and anadromous species:

- *Species listing:* Section 4 authorizes the FWS and the NMFS to identify "endangered" and "threatened" species, known as the "listing" function, and then to designate "critical habitat" and develop "recovery plans" for the species.
- *Federal agency consultations:* Section 7 requires all federal agencies to consult with the FWS and the NMFS to ensure that actions they carry out, fund, or authorize do not "jeopardize" the continued existence of listed species or "adversely modify" their critical habitat.
- *Take prohibition:* Section 9 and its implementing regulations require that all persons, including all private and public entities subject to federal jurisdiction, avoid committing "take" of listed species of fish and wildlife.
- *Incidental take authorizations:* Sections 7 (for federal actions) and 10 (for actions not subject to section 7) establish a procedure and criteria for the FWS and the NMFS to approve "incidental take" of listed species.
- *Enforcement:* Section 11 establishes enforcement authorities, including a citizen suits provision.

This part of this chapter explores each of these programs in more detail. The later parts focus on the intersection of the ESA and water resources. Indeed, the intersections of the ESA and water have been substantial. Of the 728 animal species with habitat in the United States currently listed as endangered or threatened, 38 are amphibians, 170 are fish, 92 are clams, 51 are snails, and 29 are crustaceans. *See* U.S. Fish and Wildlife Service, *Listed Species Summary (Boxscore)*, https://ecos.fws.gov/ecp/report/boxscore. In other words, almost half of all listed animal species live in water, and for many terrestrial species, water significantly affects their habitat or other essential behavioral functions. Moreover, many species that have been designated by the FWS as candidates for listing under the ESA live in water or count water among their essential habitat requirements. Hence, given the substantial regulatory impact, no discussion of water resources law should proceed without attention to the ESA.

§ 32.3 Purpose and Key Terms

To fully understand the ESA, it is necessary to be familiar with some of its commonly used terms. For example, section 4 of the ESA mandates that the Secretary of the Interior list qualified species as either endangered or threatened. *See* 16 U.S.C. § 1533(c)(1). The term "species" is defined to include any "species or any subspecies of fish or wildlife or plants, and any distinct population segment of any species of vertebrate fish or wildlife which interbreeds when mature." 16 U.S.C. § 1532(16). A species is endangered if it is "in danger of extinction throughout all or a significant portion of its range." 16 U.S.C. § 1532(6). A species is threatened if it is "likely to become an endangered species within the foreseeable future throughout all or a significant portion of its range." 16 U.S.C. § 1532(20). "Foreseeable future" extends only so far into the future as the FWS can reasonably determine that both the future threats and the species' responses to those threats are likely. *See* 50 C.F.R. § 424.11(d); 84 Fed. Reg. 45,020 (Aug. 27, 2019).

The actual list of endangered and threatened species is recorded in the Code of Federal Regulations. *See* 50 C.F.R. §§ 17.11 (fish and wildlife), 17.12 (plants). Hence, threatened and endangered species that appear on the aforementioned list are sometimes collectively referred to as "listed species." Once placed on the list as endangered, species enjoy the full spectrum of protection afforded by the ESA. By contrast, species listed as "threatened" are not automatically afforded protection pursuant to the "take" prohibition found in ESA section 9. Rather, in order for the take prohibition to apply to a threatened species, the FWS must extend the take prohibition to that species through a rulemaking process under ESA section 4(d). 16 U.S.C. § 1533(d). By regulation, however, the FWS has extended the take prohibition to all species listed as threatened, unless a "special" rule otherwise applies. 50 C.F.R. § 17.31.

Section 9 of the ESA and its implementing regulations prohibit any activity that has the potential to "take" a listed species. "Take" is broadly defined as to "harass, harm, pursue, hunt, shoot, wound, kill, trap, capture, or collect, or attempt to engage in any such conduct." 16 U.S.C. § 1532(19). Though these words may seem straightforward on their face, each has a distinct meaning. The term "harm," for example, is defined by FWS regulations as "an act which actually kills or injures wildlife . . . [and] may include significant habitat modification or degradation where it actually kills or injures wildlife by significantly impairing essential behavioral patterns, including breeding, feeding or sheltering." 50 C.F.R. § 17.3. The definition of "harass" extends further protection by covering intentional and negligent acts or omissions that create the likelihood of injury to listed species by annoying the species to such an extent that normal behavioral patterns—such as breeding, feeding, or sheltering—are disrupted. *See* 50 C.F.R. § 17.3. The term "harass" is generally applied to short-term disturbances of a species. Thus, using the foregoing terms as examples, it is easy to see that the ESA can, and often does, have an impact on development and other activities relating to water, especially if that activity could potentially affect the habitat of listed species.

§ 32.4 Listing and Critical Habitat

As described above, section 4 of the ESA includes specific procedures for listing threatened and endangered species and their critical habitat. The Act authorizes the Secretary of the Interior, in the case of freshwater fish and wildlife, and the Secretary of Commerce, in the case of marine and anadromous species (collectively, the Secretary), to designate species as threatened and endangered when their continued existence is at risk by virtually any natural or man-made factor. ESA implementing regulations provide further guidance for determining whether a species should be listed as threatened or endangered. The regulations require that the Secretary make a listing determination "*solely* on the basis of the best available scientific and commercial information regarding a species' status." 50 C.F.R. § 424.11(b) (emphasis added). The agency must use the "best scientific and commercial data available" while examining five criteria for determining whether to list a species: (1) the present or threatened destruction, modification, or curtailment of the species' habitat or range; (2) overutilization for commercial, recreational, scientific, or educational purposes; (3) disease or predation; (4) inadequacy of existing regulatory mechanisms; and (5) other natural or man-made factors affecting the species' continued existence. *See* 16 U.S.C. § 1533(a)(1); 50 C.F.R. § 424.11(c).

Under section 424.11(e), the standard for a decision to delist a species is the same as the standard for a decision not to list the species in the first instance. When reviewing whether to delist a listed species, the FWS must apply the factors in 16 United States Code section 1533(a)(1) and 50 Code of Federal Regulations section 424.11(c).

Once a species is listed, several important duties and prohibitions arise. First, the Secretary must, to the maximum extent prudent and determinable, designate critical habitat for the newly listed species. *See* 16 U.S.C. § 1533(a)(3). As defined by the ESA, "critical habitat" consists of the "specific areas within the geographical area occupied by the species" that are "essential to the conservation of the species and . . . which may require special management considerations or protection" at the time a species is listed. 16 U.S.C. § 1532(5)(A)(i). Areas outside the geographic area currently occupied by the species can also be included as critical habitat, but only if such areas are "essential for the conservation of the species." 16 U.S.C. § 1532(5)(A)(ii).

In November 2018, the U.S. Supreme Court weighed in on the meaning of "critical habitat" that is unoccupied by a listed species in *Weyerhaeuser Co. v. U.S. Fish & Wildlife Service*, 139 S. Ct. 361 (2018), resulting in the FWS revising several regulations related to critical habitat. As defined by the ESA, "critical habitat" may comprise an area that a listed species does not currently occupy, but only if the FWS determines that the area is "essential for the conservation of the species." *See* 16 U.S.C. § 1532(5)(A)(ii). In 2010, the FWS designated critical habitat for the endangered dusky gopher frog, including in the designation a piece of land that had been used as a timber plantation and that the frog had not inhabited for decades. The FWS argued that the land met the statutory definition of "unoccupied critical habitat." *Weyerhaeuser Co.*, 139 S. Ct. at 365–66. The landowner, Weyerhaeuser, sued the FWS, arguing that as a matter of law habitat cannot include areas where the species could not currently survive. The Court issued a unanimous decision, holding that even though the ESA allows the FWS to designate critical habitat in unoccupied areas, to be designated as *critical* habitat under the ESA, the land must be actual habitat. According to the Supreme Court, "Section 4(a)(3)(A)(i) does not authorize the Secretary to designate the area as critical habitat unless it is also *habitat* for the species." *Weyerhaeuser Co.*, 139 S. Ct. at 368.

In response to the Supreme Court's decision, the FWS promulgated new regulations related to critical habitat designations in the August 2019 rulemaking, adding a requirement that, at a minimum, an unoccupied area must have one or more of the physical or biological features essential to the conservation of the species to be considered as potential critical habitat. Additionally, the new rule mandates that the FWS first evaluate areas currently occupied by a species before considering unoccupied areas when making a critical habitat designation. Under the rule, the FWS will only consider unoccupied areas to be essential where a critical habitat designation limited to geographical areas occupied would be inadequate to ensure the conservation of the species. *See* 84 Fed. Reg. 45,020 (Aug. 27, 2019) (amending 50 C.F.R. § 424.12(b)(2)).

Because the ESA does not define "habitat," to provide additional clarity, in December 2020 the FWS revised the regulatory definition of habitat to read as follows: "For the purposes of designating critical habitat only, habitat is the abiotic and biotic setting that currently or periodically contains the resources and conditions necessary to support one or more life processes of a species." 50 C.F.R. § 424.02; *see* 85 Fed. Reg. 81411 (Dec. 16, 2020).

Section 4(b)(2) of the ESA provides the Secretary with discretion to exclude any particular area from a critical habitat designation if the benefits of exclusion outweigh the benefits of inclusion for that area, so long as excluding it will not result in the extinction of the species. In the past, courts afforded the Service discretion in decisions of whether to exclude areas from critical habitat, but in *Weyerhaeuser,* the Court made clear that decisions not to exclude a particular area are judicially reviewable for abuse of discretion. *Weyerhaeuser Co.*, 139. S. Ct. at 371. Therefore, in December 2020, the Service published new rules that provide clarity and transparency on the exclusion process. *See* 85 Fed. Reg. 82376 (Dec. 20, 2020).

§ 32.5 Listing and Critical Habitat—Texas's Response

The Texas legislature also responded to the increase in ESA listing activity by delegating broad authority to the Texas Comptroller of Public Accounts to oversee and involve itself in ESA matters within the state "in a manner consistent with this state's economic development and fiscal stability." Tex. Gov't Code § 403.452(a). The comptroller may develop or coordinate the development of habitat conservation plans or candidate conservation plans, collect funds, and support research into listed species or species proposed for listing. See Tex. Gov't Code § 403.452. After the comptroller facilitated a Texas Conservation Plan for the candidate Dunes sagebrush lizard, the FWS relied on that state conservation effort to withdraw the listing proposal. See 77 Fed. Reg. 36,871, 36,898 (June 19, 2012).

§ 32.6 Species Take (Section 9)

Perhaps the most contested duty arising under the ESA applies not only to federal agencies but also to all persons and entities, both private and public: the duty to comply with section 9 of the ESA and its prohibition of "take." As mentioned above, section 9 of the ESA broadly prohibits the take of endangered species (*see* 16 U.S.C. § 1538(a)(1)), and defines "take" as to "harass, harm, pursue, hunt, shoot, wound, kill, trap, capture, or collect, or attempt to engage in any such conduct." 16 U.S.C. § 1532(19). FWS regulations define "harm" within the "take" definition to encompass not only intentional harm to a listed species but also the destruction or modification of a species' habitat. *See* 50 C.F.R. § 17.3. For listed fish and wildlife, this sweeping prohibition applies to "any person" equally on federal, state, and tribal lands, at sea, and even on private lands. *See* 16 U.S.C. § 1538(a)(1).

For threatened species, the full spectrum of prohibitions applicable to endangered species does not apply. In August 2019, the FWS promulgated new regulations removing the section 4 "blanket rule," which automatically extended the same protections for threatened species as for endangered species under section 9 of the Act. The FWS now drafts regulations for each threatened species listed after September 26, 2019, on a case-by-case basis. *See* 84 Fed. Reg. 44,753 (Aug. 27, 2019) (final rule); 50 C.F.R. §§ 17.31, 17.71.

The breadth of the section 9 take prohibition has created significant controversy and has even merited review by the Supreme Court. The debate often centers on the extent to which the regulatory definition of "harm" applies to habitat modification. The FWS's regulatory definition of "harm" states:

> Harm in the definition of "take" in the Act means an act which actually kills or injures wildlife. Such act may include significant habitat modification or degradation where it actually kills or injures wildlife by significantly impairing essential behavioral patterns, including breeding, feeding or sheltering.

50 C.F.R. § 17.3.

In 1995 the Supreme Court upheld the FWS's inclusion of habitat modification in its regulatory "harm" definition. *See Babbitt v. Sweet Home Chapter of Communities for a Great Oregon*, 515 U.S. 687 (1995) [hereinafter *Sweet Home*] (using the 1981 amendments to the "harm" definition, which is identical to current regulations). In *Sweet Home*, the Court held that Congress's intent was "reasonably construed" by the FWS's regulations, which defined "harm" to include "significant habitat modification or degradation that actually kills or injures wildlife." *Sweet Home*, 515 U.S. at 708. The Court relied not only on the common dictionary definition of "harm," which does not require the application of direct force, but also on the comprehensive nature of the ESA, on Congress's statement in the ESA that the ESA was to conserve the "*ecosystems* upon which endangered and threatened species depend," on the 1982 ESA amendments that added section 10(a)(1)(B) authorizing incidental take permits, and on the ESA's legislative history in which Congress gave examples of prohibited *indirect* harm. *Sweet Home*, 515 U.S. at 697–704 (emphasis added). The Court acknowledged that application of the harm definition, and proximate causation in particular, would depend on individual fact patterns best left to the determination of the lower courts. *Sweet Home*, 515 U.S. at 700 n.13 (Stevens, J.), 713 (O'Connor, J., concurring).

Both before and after the *Sweet Home* decision, various courts weighed in on whether particular cases involving indirect harm constitute take of listed species. For example, the Fifth Circuit Court of Appeals held that the U.S. Forest Services's "even-aged" management practices, which permitted clear-cutting within two hundred feet of "cavity trees" for an endangered woodpecker, impaired the woodpecker's essential behavioral patterns, including sheltering; resulted in take; and were likely to jeopardize the woodpecker's continued existence. *See Sierra Club v. Yeutter*, 926 F.2d 429, 438–39

(5th Cir. 1991). The First Circuit Court of Appeals held that state licensing of fishing and lobstering equipment constituted harm when the equipment led to the entanglement of endangered northern right whales. *See Strahan v. Coxe*, 127 F.3d 155, 164–65 (1st Cir. 1997), *cert. denied*, 525 U.S. 830 (1998). Many courts have followed *Yeutter* and *Strahan*, holding that the section 9 prohibitions apply to actions by state and federal agencies where their regulatory programs approve actions by third parties that contribute to causing the take. *See, e.g., Animal Welfare Institute v. Martin*, 623 F.3d 19 (1st Cir. 2010); *Loggerhead Turtle v. County Council of Volusia County*, 148 F.3d 1231 (11th Cir. 1998); *Defenders of Wildlife v. Administrator, Environmental Protection Agency*, 882 F.2d 1294 (8th Cir. 1989). This line of cases—often called "regulator liability"—is important because in most circumstances the water resources that support the essential habitat requirements for a listed species are regulated by state or federal agencies through comprehensive permitting schemes.

§ 32.7 Section 7 Consultation

Section 7 of the ESA offers protection to listed species by placing on federal agencies the affirmative duty to use their authorities to conserve listed species. *See* 16 U.S.C. § 1536(a)(2). This duty translates into both a substantive and a procedural directive to agencies to engage in "consultation" with either the FWS or the NMFS. Procedurally, federal agencies are required to consult with the FWS on any action that is likely to adversely affect an endangered or threatened species. Substantively, federal agencies must avoid jeopardizing listed species and destroying or adversely modifying their critical habitat. Following is a brief overview of the key provisions of section 7 of the ESA.

§ 32.7:1 Interagency Consultation

Section 7(a)(2) requires that each federal agency—

> in consultation with and with the assistance of the Secretary, insure that any action authorized, funded, or carried out by such agency . . . is not likely to jeopardize the continued existence of any endangered species or threatened species or result in the destruction or adverse modification of [critical habitat].

16 U.S.C. § 1536(a)(2); *see also* 50 C.F.R. § 402.01. The term "action" is read broadly by courts and implementing agencies and includes issuance of licenses and permits, actions intended to conserve listed species or their habitat, promulgation of regulations, and federal funding, among other things. *See* 50 C.F.R. § 402.02. Thus, whenever federal agencies engage in an action that may affect a listed species, the agencies must both consult with the FWS or the NMFS and avoid jeopardizing listed species or destroying or adversely modifying their critical habitat.

For the purposes of section 7(a)(2), "action" includes nonfederal activities that require certain authorization or assistance from one or more federal agencies as a prerequisite to engaging in those activities. *See* 50 C.F.R. § 402.02. Thus, otherwise private activities can be, and often are, subject to consultation under the ESA. For example, if the U.S. Army Corps of Engineers (Corps) were considering issuing a Clean Water Act section 404 permit to a state or local agency constructing a water supply project and the proposed construction activities might affect a listed species, the Corps would be required to consult with the FWS before issuing the permit.

Once an agency determines that an activity is an "action" for section 7 purposes, the agency must determine whether the action "may affect" listed species or designated critical habitat. 50 C.F.R. § 402.14(a). Consultation is not required for federal agency actions that have no effect on listed species. *Marin Audubon Society v. Seidman*, No. 91-2029 (N.D. Cal. Nov. 21, 1991), *aff'd*, 999 F.2d 543 (9th Cir. 1993).

The definition of "effects of the action" includes all consequences of a proposed action, including consequences of any activities caused by the proposed action. Under the definition, a consequence is caused by the proposed action if it would not occur but for the proposed action and it is reasonably certain to occur. *See* 84 Fed. Reg. 44,976 (Aug. 27, 2019) (final rule amending 50 C.F.R. pt. 402).

Consultation can begin as "informal consultation," involving meetings, telephone calls, or other forms of communication between FWS personnel and the action agency, or it can begin as "formal consultation." *See* 50 C.F.R. § 402.02. In informal consultation, project modifications can be suggested to avoid the likelihood of adverse effects. *See* 50 C.F.R. § 402.13(b). To determine the likelihood of adverse effects, the action agency prepares a biological assessment (BA), which evaluates the potential and likelihood of adverse effects of the proposed action on listed or proposed species and designated or proposed critical habitat. *See* 50 C.F.R. § 402.12. The action agency, through the BA, will make one of three calls: (1) the proposed action will have no effect on listed or proposed species or designated or proposed critical habitat; (2) the proposed action may affect, but is not likely to adversely affect, listed or proposed species or designated or proposed critical habitat; or (3) the proposed action is likely to adversely affect listed or proposed species or designated or proposed critical habitat. If the action agency determines the proposed action will have no effect on listed species or critical habitat, the agency has no further obligation under section 7. *See* 50 C.F.R. § 402.12(k). If the action agency decides that the proposed action may affect, but is not likely to adversely affect, a listed species or its critical habitat, and the FWS concurs in that determination, informal consultation is concluded and formal consultation is not necessary. *See* 50 C.F.R. § 402.14(b). If the FWS does not concur with a not likely to adversely affect determination made by the action agency, or if the BA determines that the proposed action is likely to adversely affect listed species or critical habitat, formal consultation is required. *See* 50 C.F.R. § 402.14(a).

Formal consultation begins when the action agency makes a written request to engage in formal consultation with the FWS. *See* 16 U.S.C. § 1536(c)(1); 50 C.F.R. § 402.14(c). Once formal consultation begins, it must proceed in the detailed manner set forth in the ESA and section 7 implementing regulations. *See* 50 C.F.R. § 402.14; *see also* U.S. Fish and Wildlife Service, *Endangered Species Consultation Handbook*, at 4-4–4-7 (Mar. 1998), www.fws.gov/endangered/esa-library/pdf/esa_section7_handbook.pdf [hereinafter *Consultation Handbook*]. Formal consultation must be completed within ninety days of its initiation, unless the FWS and the action agency agree to an extension. *See* 16 U.S.C. § 1536(b)(1)(A); 50 C.F.R. § 402.14(e). At the end of the formal consultation process, a biological opinion (BO) is issued by the FWS. The BO "states the opinion of the [FWS] as to whether or not the . . . action is likely to jeopardize the continued existence of listed species or result in the destruction or adverse modification of critical habitat." 50 C.F.R. § 402.02. If the FWS finds in the BO that the action is likely to jeopardize the continued existence of listed species or the destruction or adverse modification of their critical habitat, then the FWS must suggest reasonable and prudent alternatives (RPAs) to the proposed action. An RPA must be consistent with the intended purpose of the action, within the authority and jurisdiction of the action agency, economically and technologically feasible, and avoid jeopardy or adverse modification or destruction of critical habitat. *See* 50 C.F.R. § 402.02. The action agency may select any RPA that meets the section 7 directive to avoid jeopardy to listed species or destruction or adverse modification to critical habitat. *See Consultation Handbook*, at 4-43. If the BO concludes that the action is likely to result in jeopardy of the species or adverse modification of critical habitat and no RPAs exist, then any incidental take resulting from the proposed action is prohibited. *See Consultation Handbook*, at 4-52.

If the proposed action will take listed species but will not cause jeopardy, or destruction or adverse modification of critical habitat, then the BO will include an "incidental take statement," which specifies the amount or extent of such incidental taking (the "impacts"); specifies reasonable and prudent measures (RPMs) that are necessary to minimize those impacts; sets forth terms and conditions that must be complied with by the action agency or applicant; and specifies procedures to use in the handling or disposal of individuals of species actually taken. *See* 16 U.S.C. § 1536(b)(4); 50

C.F.R. § 402.14(i). "Incidental take" means "takings that result from, but are not the purpose of, carrying out an otherwise lawful activity conducted by the Federal agency or applicant." 50 C.F.R. § 402.02. As a response to previous court rulings, in 2016 the FWS and the NMFS issued a new rule to clarify the meaning of "destruction or adverse modification." *See* 81 Fed. Reg. 7214, 7216 (Feb. 11, 2016) (amending 50 C.F.R. § 402.02 to define "destruction or adverse modification" as "a direct or indirect alteration that appreciably diminishes the value of critical habitat for the conservation of a listed species. Such alterations may include, but are not limited to, those that alter the physical or biological features essential to the conservation of a species or that preclude or significantly delay development of such features").

RPMs cannot serve a general mitigation purpose but must minimize the amount or extent of anticipated take. *Consultation Handbook*, at 4-50. Even though RPMs involve only "minor changes" to the action (those that do not change the action's basic design, location, scope, duration, or timing), if the RPMs are not implemented, any incidental take occurring pursuant to the action is unlawful. *See* 16 U.S.C. § 1536(o); 50 C.F.R. § 402.14(i)(2).

§ 32.7:2 Section 7(a)(1) Duty to Conserve

Section 7(a)(1) imposes on federal agencies the affirmative duty to conserve endangered and threatened species "in consultation with and with the assistance of the Secretary." 16 U.S.C. § 1536(a)(1). Although the duty placed on federal agencies to conserve listed species seems broad, the obligation is poorly defined. No federal agency has promulgated its own rules addressing section 7(a)(1), although the Corps recently published a guidance document regarding ESA section 7. *See* U.S. Army Corps of Engineers, *ESA Guidance* (June 11, 2013), https://planning.erdc.dren.mil/toolbox/library/MemosandLetters/13Jun11-ESA.pdf. Courts have held that section 7(a)(1) creates an affirmative duty not only to protect listed species but also to help the species recover to the point where it no longer requires the protections of the ESA. *See Carson-Truckee Water Conservancy District v. Clark*, 741 F.2d 257, 261–62 (9th Cir. 1984), *cert. denied*, 470 U.S. 1083 (1985). For example, the Fifth Circuit Court of Appeals not only affirmed that federal agencies have an affirmative duty to conserve listed species but also went even further, requiring the U.S. Department of Agriculture (USDA) to adopt or develop conservation programs for listed Edwards Aquifer species. *Sierra Club v. Glickman*, 156 F.3d 606, 616–18 (5th Cir. 1998). In that case, the USDA had not implemented any measures whatever for the conservation of listed species. *Glickman*, 156 F.3d at 616. Other courts have held that ESA section 7(a)(1) imposes no particular mandatory measures on federal agencies. *See Strahan v. Linnon*, 967 F. Supp. 581, 596 (D. Mass. 1997), *aff'd*, 187 F.3d 623 (1st Cir. 1998); *see also Hawksbill Sea Turtle v. FEMA*, 11 F. Supp. 2d 529, 542–43 (D. V.I. 1998). However, in those cases, the defendant agencies had taken some measures to fulfill their section 7(a)(1) duties, and thus the issue was whether the agencies' conservation actions were sufficient. *Strahan*, 967 F. Supp. at 596; *Hawksbill Sea Turtle*, 11 F. Supp. 2d at 543.

§ 32.8 Section 10 Habitat Conservation Plans, Safe Harbors, and Candidate Conservation Agreements

As originally enacted, section 10 authorized exemption from the section 9 take prohibitions only for "scientific purposes or to enhance the propagation or survival of the affected species." Pub. L. No. 93-205, 87 Stat. 896 (1973). In 1982, Congress amended the ESA to include section 10(a)(1)(B), which authorizes the FWS to issue a permit for otherwise prohibited taking of listed species (an "incidental take permit") "if such taking is incidental to, and not the purpose of, the carrying out of an otherwise lawful activity." Pub. L. No. 97-304, 96 Stat. 1422 (1982) (codified at 16 U.S.C. § 1539(a)(1)(B)). This amendment was made to resolve the "concerns of private landowners who

[were] faced with having otherwise lawful activities . . . prevented by [ESA] Section 9 prohibitions against taking." H.R. Conf. Rep. No. 97-835, at 29 (1982), *reprinted in* 1982 U.S.C.C.A.N. 2860, 2870. The purpose of authorizing incidental take permits was not only to allay the fears and concerns of landowners but also to promote the conservation of species by encouraging partnerships between public and private sectors and providing "long-term assurances" to participating landowners. H.R. Conf. Rep. No. 97-835, at 30 (1982), *reprinted in* 1982 U.S.C.C.A.N. 2860, 2871. Today section 10 incidental take permits are a tool often used by landowners to provide for the needs of listed species while at the same time allowing the landowners to engage in land-use activities that would otherwise be prohibited under the ESA. In 2016, the FWS and the NMFS published a revision of their comprehensive *Habitat Conservation Planning and Incidental Take Permit Processing Handbook*, which is available at www.fws.gov/endangered/esa-library/pdf/HCP_Handbook.pdf [hereinafter HCP Handbook].

§ 32.8:1 Habitat Conservation Plans and the "No Surprises" Policy

Formulating a habitat conservation plan (HCP) is a mandatory prerequisite for individuals seeking an incidental take permit. *See* 16 U.S.C. § 1539(a)(2)(A). For an incidental take permit to be issued, the applicant must submit a conservation plan that includes the following:

- the impact that is likely to result from the taking;
- steps the applicant will take to "minimize and mitigate" the impact and the funding that will be available to implement those steps;
- alternatives to the taking the applicant considered and the reasons the alternatives are not being used; and
- other measures the Secretary may require of the applicant as being necessary or appropriate for purposes of the plan.

See 16 U.S.C. § 1539(a)(2)(A)(i)–(iv).

After the FWS receives the permit application along with an HCP that meets the above criteria, and after there has been opportunity for public comment, the Secretary must issue the permit if he finds that (1) the proposed taking will be incidental; (2) the applicant will, to the maximum extent practicable, minimize and mitigate the impacts of such taking; (3) the applicant will ensure that adequate funding for the HCP will be provided; (4) the taking will not "appreciably reduce the likelihood of the survival and recovery of the species in the wild"; and (5) the measures, if any, required by the Secretary of the Interior will be met. *See* 16 U.S.C. § 1539(a)(2)(B)(i)–(v).

The applicant must choose which species to address in the HCP so it is covered for take of those species under the incidental take permit. An HCP may address many different species, or it may focus on specific habitat types and address all species within certain habitat types included in the plan area, but at a minimum it should include all listed species of animals and plants that could be incidentally taken during the life of the project. *See* HCP Handbook, at 7-2, 7-6, 15-7 (stating that, although plants are not the subject of an incidental take permit because section 9 take prohibitions apply only to wildlife, the FWS cannot approve an incidental take permit for an action that would result in jeopardy to a listed species, including a listed plant). If an applicant fails to include a listed species in its HCP and that species is subsequently taken, failure to include that species may result in project shutdowns and delays. *See* HCP Handbook, at 7-4. An applicant is also advised to include unlisted species in its HCP, such as species that are proposed or are candidates for listing and are likely to be listed in the foreseeable future or within the life of the permit. This will protect the applicant from later delays should a species not listed at the time the HCP was approved become subsequently listed. *See* HCP Handbook, at 7-6, 15-6.

The protection afforded by an HCP that includes unlisted species is known as the "no surprises" policy. This "no surprises" policy was formally implemented in February 1998, and its purpose is to provide regulatory, long-term assurances to the holder of an incidental take permit such that—

> no additional land use restrictions or financial compensation will be required of the permit holder with respect to species covered by the permit, even if unforeseen circumstances arise after the permit is issued indicating that additional mitigation is needed for a given species covered by the permit.

63 Fed. Reg. 8859 (Feb. 23, 1998), codified at 50 C.F.R. pt. 17. Thus, for species covered by the permit, if additional mitigation measures are later deemed necessary to provide for the conservation of the species that were otherwise adequately covered under the terms of a properly functioning HCP, then the permittee is not *required* to commit additional resources or funds to remedy unforeseen circumstances, but the permittee is encouraged to work with the FWS to determine an appropriate response within the original resource commitments in the HCP. *See* HCP Handbook, at 1-3 (stating that "a deal is a deal"), 9-40.

The "no surprises" policy applies only for the life of the particular incidental take permit and only with respect to species "adequately covered" by it. *See* 50 C.F.R. §§ 17.22(b)(5), 17.32(b)(5), 222.307(g). For a listed species to be "adequately covered" by the permit, the HCP must satisfy the ESA section 10(a)(2)(B) permit issuance criteria described above. *See* 50 C.F.R. § 17.3 (defining "adequately covered"). For unlisted species to be considered "adequately covered" by the HCP, the HCP must address those species so as to satisfy "the permit issuance criteria under section 10(a)(2)(B) of the ESA that would otherwise apply if the unlisted species covered by the plan were actually listed." *See* 50 C.F.R. § 17.3. As long as a permittee is adequately implementing or has implemented an approved HCP, the FWS will not require additional lands, funds, or restrictions on lands or other natural resources released for development or use under that HCP unless the permittee consents to such additional measures. *See* 50 C.F.R. § 17.22(b)(5)(ii), (b)(5)(iii); HCP Handbook, at 9-38. Simply put, barring "unforeseen circumstances," if the species is covered by a permittee's approved HCP, and the permittee is implementing or has implemented that HCP in good faith, nothing further will be required of the permittee. *See* 50 C.F.R. § 17.22(b)(5)(iii)(C); HCP Handbook, at 9-38.

The ESA implementing regulations and the HCP Handbook include several criteria that the FWS will consider in determining whether and when unforeseen circumstances exist. *See* 50 C.F.R. § 17.22(b)(5)(iii)(C); HCP Handbook, at 9-44. If unforeseen circumstances are found to exist, and the FWS deems it necessary to respond to those circumstances by requiring additional conservation measures, any such measures must be limited to modifications within the "conserved habitat areas," if any, or to the HCP's operating conservation program for the affected species. Additionally, the terms of the original HCP must be maintained to the maximum extent practicable. *See* 50 C.F.R. § 17.22(b)(5)(iii)(C); HCP Handbook, at 9-28. FWS regulations continue to give credence to the broad purpose of the ESA to conserve species by providing that the "no surprises" policy should not be read to limit or constrain any governmental entity, including the FWS, from taking action at its own expense to protect or conserve a species included in an HCP. *See* 50 C.F.R. § 17.22(b)(6).

§ 32.8:2 "Safe Harbor" Permits

ESA section 10(a)(1)(A) permits otherwise prohibited acts when those acts are carried out for the purpose of enhancing the propagation or survival of a listed species. *See* 16 U.S.C. § 1539(a)(1)(A). In 1999, the FWS promulgated new regulations formalizing the use of the "safe harbor agreement" (SHA). *See* 64 Fed. Reg. 32,706 (June 17, 1999), codified at 50 C.F.R. pts. 13, 17. The SHA is a device developed and used in connection with a section 10(a)(1)(A) "enhancement of survival permit" in which a landowner proposes activities that could restore, enhance, or maintain habitat for listed species, thereby potentially increasing numbers of the species on the landowner's property. The SHA thus allows the landowner to provide net conservation benefits to listed species in exchange for the FWS's assurance that any future incidental take of a covered species, back to the baseline population level or habitat condition, will not result in liability for an unlawful taking. SHA-based permits are transferable, and any transferee may avail himself fully of permit protections as long as he is otherwise qualified to hold a permit and provides adequate written assurances that he will fund and implement the permit's terms. *See* 50 C.F.R. § 13.25(b).

An applicant seeking an SHA-based enhancement of survival permit must submit a permit application, which includes the common and scientific names of the listed species to be covered by the permit, a description of the land use or water management activity for which the permit is sought, and an SHA that complies with the SHA policy. *See* 50 C.F.R. §§ 17.22(c)(1)(i)–(iii), 17.32(c)(1)(i)–(iii). According to the Joint Safe Harbor Policy, the FWS will work with prospective applicants to establish the "baseline condition" of the property proposed to be covered by the SHA. 64 Fed. Reg. 32,717, 32,722 (June 17, 1999). "Baseline condition" means the "population estimates and distribution and/or habitat characteristics and determined area of the enrolled property that sustain seasonal or permanent use by the covered species at the time the [SHA] is executed between the [FWS] and the property owner." 64 Fed. Reg. 32,717, 32,722. Once a baseline condition is established, the parties identify certain measures that, when undertaken, will accomplish a "net conservation benefit" relative to the baseline conditions that will contribute to the recovery of the listed species included in the permit and SHA. *See* 50 C.F.R. §§ 17.22(c)(2)(ii), 17.32(c)(1)(i)–(iii); U.S. Fish and Wildlife Service, *Safe Harbor Agreements for Private Landowners* (Oct. 2017), www.fws.gov/endangered/esa-library/pdf/harborqa.pdf. Once the SHA has been developed and the permittee meets the terms of the agreement, the FWS authorizes the incidental take of covered species at a level that allows the permittee to ultimately return the covered property back to the agreed-on baseline conditions. *See* 50 C.F.R. §§ 17.22(c)(2)(ii), 17.32(c)(1)(i)–(iii). The "no surprises" policy applies to SHAs, and thus, once the permit is issued, no additional commitments of land, water, or financial resources will be required. 64 Fed. Reg. 32,717.

§ 32.8:3 Candidate Conservation Agreements with Assurances

When the FWS promulgated regulations formalizing the use of SHAs, it also established standards and procedures for conserving proposed and candidate species through the development of Candidate Conservation Agreements with Assurances (CCAAs). *See* 64 Fed. Reg. 32,726 (June 17, 1999). CCAAs are formal agreements between the FWS and one or more landowners to address the conservation needs of proposed or candidate species or species likely to become candidates for listing in the future. The purpose of CCAAs is to provide landowners an incentive to engage in proactive conservation management, with the ultimate goal being the removal of enough threats to species covered by CCAAs to preclude the need to list those species as threatened or endangered in the future. *See* 64 Fed. Reg. 32,726, 32,733. Specifically, the FWS provides assurances through the CCAA program that, in the event a species covered by the CCAA is listed as endangered or threatened, the FWS will not require additional land, water, or other resource use restrictions above those the landowner voluntarily committed to in the CCAA. *See* 64 Fed. Reg. 32,726, 32,734. Thus, as long as the CCAA is being properly implemented by the landowner, the landowner is responsible only for implementing and maintaining the conservation or management measures agreed to in the CCAA.

§ 32.9 Enforcement

Section 11 imposes stiff penalties for violations of the ESA's take prohibitions in section 9. A person who knowingly violates any section 9 prohibition or implementing regulation with respect to an endangered animal or plant may be faced with a civil penalty of up to $49,676 per violation and a criminal penalty of up to $50,000 per violation and up to one year in prison. *See* 16 U.S.C.

§ 1540(a)(1), (b)(1); 81 Fed. Reg. 41,862, 41,866 (June 28, 2016) (updating statutory civil monetary penalties to adjust for inflation). A person who knowingly violates any other regulation with respect to a threatened animal or plant is subject to a civil penalty of up to $23,744, a criminal penalty of up to $25,000, and up to six months in prison. 81 Fed. Reg. 41,862, 41,866. To be criminally liable under the ESA, a person must knowingly violate the Act. *See* 16 U.S.C. § 1540(b)(1). However, it is no defense that the accused lacked a specific intent to take a listed species. For example, the Fifth Circuit Court of Appeals upheld the conviction of a defendant charged with violating the ESA by possessing a threatened species of turtle. The court held that whether the defendant knew that possessing the turtle was illegal was irrelevant, that it was enough that the defendant knew he was in possession of a turtle, and the government did not need to prove that the defendant knew the turtle was a threatened species or that it was illegal to transport or import it. *See United States v. Nguyen*, 916 F.2d 1016, 1018–20 (5th Cir. 1990).

The ESA also authorizes citizen suits for enjoining persons from violating the ESA or its implementing regulations. *See* 16 U.S.C. § 1540(g)(1)(A). Under the citizen suit provision, citizens may sue federal agencies, state and local governments, and even private individuals, *see* 16 U.S.C. § 1540(g)(1)(A), upon sixty days' written notice to the violator and to the FWS. *See* 16 U.S.C. § 1540(g)(2)(A)–(C). Upon receiving notice, the Secretary may take over the suit, *see* 16 U.S.C. § 1540(g)(2)(A), (g)(2)(B), and if the United States is not a party, then the attorney general may intervene as a matter of right. *See* 16 U.S.C. § 1540(g)(3)(B). Citizen suits may be brought in the judicial district where the violation occurs, *see* 16 U.S.C. § 1540(g)(3)(A), and if the defendant is a federal agency, the plaintiff may choose to bring suit in the district court for the District of Columbia or the district in which the agency's regional headquarters is located. *See* 16 U.S.C. § 1536(n); 28 U.S.C. § 1391(b). The ESA allows courts to award the costs of litigation to any party if the court deems it appropriate. *See* 16 U.S.C. § 1540(g)(4). If a plaintiff in a citizen suit prevails, the court may issue an injunction, and the court may award reasonable costs of the litigation, including attorney's and expert witness fees, to the prevailing party. *See* 16 U.S.C. § 1540(g)(1), (g)(4).

When federal agencies are defendants, certain violations can be pleaded under the ESA citizen suit provision and others must be pleaded under section 702 of the Administrative Procedure Act (APA). *See* 5 U.S.C. § 702; *see also Endangered Species Act: Law, Policy and Perspective* 267–70 (Donald C. Baur & Wm. Robert Irvin eds., American Bar Association 2d ed. 2010). Under the APA, the court must find that the final agency action is unlawful and set such action aside if the court concludes that the action is in violation of one or more of six enumerated standards. *See* 5 U.S.C. § 706. Because the ESA does not contain a standard of review, both ESA and APA claims alleging that an agency's decision is legally or factually wrong, or mistaken as a matter of policy or logic, are reviewed under the APA's "arbitrary and capricious standard," which asks whether the agency's action, findings, or conclusions were "arbitrary, capricious, an abuse of discretion, or otherwise not in accordance with the law." *See* 5 U.S.C. § 706(2)(A); *Bennett v. Spear*, 520 U.S. 154, 174 (1997).

III. The ESA and Texas Groundwater

§ 32.10 The ESA Shapes Groundwater Law and Policy in the Edwards Aquifer

Historically, the most visible clashes between the ESA and the allocation and development of water supplies have occurred in connection with surface water rights and supply projects in western states. In Texas, however, a unique dependence on groundwater has resulted in a clash that has changed the course of water policy and usage in some parts of the state, in particular those overlying portions of the Southern segment of the Edwards Aquifer within the boundaries of the Edwards Aquifer Authority (EAA).

In the early 1990s, a severe drought combined with unregulated pumping of groundwater from the Southern segment of the Edwards Aquifer led to extremely low flows from the two important springs that provide the habitat for several listed species—the Comal Springs and San Marcos Springs. This perfect storm resulted in two significant ESA cases—*Sierra Club v. Lujan*, *sub nom. Sierra Club v. Babbitt*, No. MO-91-CA-069, 1993 WL 151353, at *6 (W.D. Tex. Feb. 1, 1993); and *Sierra Club v. San Antonio*, No. MO-96-CA-097 (W.D. Tex., original petition at 35–37 filed June 11, 1996). Essentially, the Sierra Club argued that the Secretary of the Interior and the FWS caused harm to listed species in the Comal Springs and San Marcos Springs by failing to ensure that water levels in the Edwards Aquifer would sustain a minimum flow level from the springs necessary to protect the species. The litigation resulted in the creation of the first significant regulations on groundwater withdrawals in the area by the EAA, the adoption of a large-scale habitat conservation plan aimed at protecting federally listed species dependent in some way on the water in and discharging from the Edwards Aquifer, and, arguably, an end to the rule of capture for a large area in central Texas.

§ 32.10:1 Court-Mandated Plan to Protect Minimum Spring Flows and Aquifer Levels

Before Sierra Club litigation in 1991, the FWS had listed a total of five species living in the Comal Springs and San Marcos Springs as either threatened or endangered: Texas blind salamander, fountain darter, Texas wild rice, San Marcos salamander, and San Marcos gambusia. In 1980, the FWS also designated the San Marcos Springs and river ecosystem as critical habitat for the San Marcos salamander, San Marcos gambusia, Texas wild rice, and the Fountain darter. See 45 Fed. Reg. 47,355 (July 14, 1980). The other three species—Peck's cave amphipod, Comal Springs dryopid beetle, and the Comal Springs riffle beetle—were all listed after *Sierra Club v. Lujan* was filed in 1991.

In May 1991, the Sierra Club and others filed suit against the FWS to challenge what it described as unchecked pumping that posed a threat to listed species and designated critical habitat. *Lujan*, 1993 WL 151353, at *6. The plaintiffs claimed that by failing to adopt and implement recovery plans for the various endangered species living in Comal Springs and San Marcos Springs, the FWS was not adequately protecting the species. *See Lujan*, 1993 WL 151353, at *6. The court ruled in favor of the plaintiffs and required the state to prepare a plan that would protect minimum continuous spring flows and aquifer levels by limiting withdrawals. *See Lujan*, 1993 WL 151353, at *34.

§ 32.10:2 The Edwards Aquifer Authority

In response to the court's ruling in *Sierra Club v. Lujan*, the Texas legislature passed Senate Bill 1477 on May 30, 1993, which established the EAA to regulate groundwater withdrawals and manage the Aquifer to protect habitat for listed species. Todd H. Votteler, Raiders of the Lost Aquifer? Or, the Beginning of the End to Fifty Years of Conflict over the Texas Edwards Aquifer, 15 Tul. Envtl. L.J. 257, 276 (2002, rev. Aug. 2004), www.edwardsaquifer.net/pdf/raidersofthelostaquifer.pdf.

Senate Bill 1477 resulted in the first significant caps on water withdrawal from the aquifer. The bill created a permit system whereby uncontrolled pumping under the common law was reduced to 450,000 acre-feet per year before December 31, 2007, and then was to be limited to 400,000 acre-feet thereafter. *See* EAA Act § 1.14(b) (repealed 2007), (c) (amended 2007). See Chapter 17 of this book regarding the Edwards Aquifer Authority.

§ 32.10:3 Birth of the EAA and More ESA Litigation

The ESA controversies at Comal Springs and San Marcos Springs were not easily solved, and the EAA was the subject of several rounds of intense litigation. The summer of 1994 brought a dry spell during which flows at Comal Springs decreased so dramatically that the Sierra Club requested, and the court ordered, the preparation of an emergency plan to reduce pumping from the aquifer. *See Sierra Club v. Babbitt*, No. MO-910-CA-069, slip op. at 3–4 (W.D. Tex. June 3, 1994) (order on motion for additional relief). Fall rains and the end of heavy summer pumping eased the drought, and the emergency withdrawal reduction plan was never put into action.

When a more serious drought hit the region in May 1996, debate over the application of the ESA once again stepped to the forefront. In June of that year, the head of the FWS's field office in Austin stated that the FWS would not take action against pumpers to reduce withdrawals from the aquifer. *See* Jerry Needham, *Wildlife Agency Doesn't Plan Suits*, *San Antonio Express-News*, June 7, 1996, at 1C. The Sierra Club subsequently filed a citizen suit to enforce section 9 of the ESA, alleging that aquifer users were causing the take of endangered species. *See Sierra Club v. San Antonio*, No. MO-96-CA-097 (W.D. Tex., original petition at 35–37 filed June 11, 1996). Although the flow of Comal Springs and San Marcos Springs continued at levels below potential "jeopardy" thresholds, the EAA board declined to declare a water use emergency. *See* Todd H. Votteler, The Little Fish That Roared: The Endangered Species Act, State Groundwater Law, and Private Property Rights Collide over the Texas Edwards Aquifer, 28 Envtl. L. 845, 869 (1998), www.edwardsaquifer.net/pdf/the-little-fish-ssrn.pdf. The district judge again ordered that an emergency withdrawal reduction plan be prepared, but the need for the plan was once again eased by fall rains, and the plan was later vacated by the Fifth Circuit Court of Appeals because the *Burford* abstention doctrine requires federal courts to abstain from certain controversies involving comprehensive state regulatory schemes. *See Sierra Club v. City of San Antonio*, 112 F.3d 789, 791–92 (5th Cir. 1997), *cert. denied*, 118 U.S. 879 (1998); see also *Burford v. Sun Oil Co.*, 319 U.S. 315 (1943).

Nevertheless, the continued specter of ESA litigation and regulation had a significant impact on changing water policy in the region. In early 1997 because of drought, the EAA implemented the Irrigation Suspension Program, which paid farmers not to irrigate in times of drought. *See* Keith O. Keplinger et al., *The 1997 Irrigation Suspension Program for the Edwards Aquifer: Evaluation and Alternatives* 5, Texas Water Resources Institute, Report No. TR-178 (Feb. 1998), https://oaktrust.library.tamu.edu/handle/1969.1/6152. By late April 1997, the drought had passed, largely because of heavy winter and spring rains, but the program demonstrated once again just how powerful the ESA can be in shaping the policy, economics, and use of groundwater.

With passage of Senate Bill 3 in 2007, the Texas legislature directed the EAA to, among other things, develop the Edwards Aquifer Recovery Implementation Program (EARIP) to manage the Edwards Aquifer and protect federally listed species dependent on the aquifer, with participation from the FWS, all "interested stakeholders," and relevant state agencies. *See* Act of May 28, 2007, 80th Leg., R.S., ch. 1430, § 12.06. The legislature required that preparation of the plan must be approved and signed by the EAA, the FWS, the Texas Commission on Environmental Quality (TCEQ), the Texas Parks and Wildlife Department, the Texas Department of Agriculture, and the Texas Water Development Board by September 1, 2012. See Act of May 28, 2007, 80th Leg., R.S., ch. 1430, § 12.06 (adding § 1.26A(d)(3) to the EAA Act). The EARIP process included a stakeholder committee and various subcommittees devoted to developing an HCP for the portion of the Southern segment of the Edwards Aquifer within the boundaries of the EAA. The EARIP process culminated with the submittal on June 6, 2012, of the Edwards Aquifer Habitat Conservation Plan (EAHCP) to the FWS as part of the application for an incidental take permit covering take of eight listed species and three petitioned-for species within the Comal and San Marcos springs and rivers ecosystems. The FWS approved the EAHCP on January 29, 2013, and on February 5, 2013, issued a fifteen-year incidental take permit to the copermittees, which include the EAA, the City of San Marcos, the City of New Braunfels, the San Antonio Water System, and Texas State University. See 78 Fed. Reg. 11,218 (Feb. 15, 2013). The copermittees are now implementing the EAHCP. For more information, see the Edwards Aquifer Habitat Conservation Plan website at www.edwardsaquifer.org/habitat-conservation-plan/. See also Chapter 17 of this book.

§ 32.11 The ESA and Groundwater Management Outside of the EAA

The Edwards Aquifer litigation is a prime example of how the ESA can affect laws and policies related to regulation and management of groundwater. Indeed, the ESA influences how other groundwater conservation districts manage aquifers within their jurisdictions across Texas. For a discussion of Texas groundwater management and policy, see Chapters 5 and 16 of this book. For example, in September 2018, the FWS approved a Habitat Conservation Plan (HCP) for the Barton Springs Edwards Aquifer Conservation District (BSEACD), which regulates groundwater withdrawals from the Barton Springs segment of the Edwards Aquifer and from a portion of the Trinity Aquifer in Hays County. The HCP is part of a twenty-year incidental take permit covering certain district activities that could result in the "take" of the Barton Springs salamander or the Austin blind salamander. The HCP incorporates numerous measures designed to protect springflow, such as improving recharge to the aquifer, encouraging permittees to find alternative sources of water, incentivizing permittees to curtail water use, reducing demand on the aquifer through conservation, and restricting groundwater pumping when springflow at Barton Springs declines to certain trigger points.

In the future, more groundwater conservation districts may develop HCPs and apply for incidental take permits as a way to limit their liability for managing groundwater pumping in areas where endangered, groundwater-dependent species reside. In July 2013, the FWS listed six species found in spring systems in West Texas that depend solely on groundwater for survival. *See* 78 Fed. Reg. 41,227 (July 9, 2013). The Pecos amphipod (a freshwater crustacean), Gonzales tryonia snail, and Diamond tryonia snail live in the Diamond Y spring system. *See* 78 Fed. Reg. 41,227. The diminutive amphipod (a freshwater crustacean), Phantom springsnail, and Phantom tryonia snail are located in the San Solomon spring system in West Texas. *See* 78 Fed. Reg. 41,227.

According to the Services, the primary threat to these species' survival is reduced springflow caused by groundwater pumping. The San Solomon Springs and Diamond Y Springs are already home to several endangered species: the Comanche Springs pupfish and the Pecos gambusia, found in the San Solomon Springs, and the Leon Springs pupfish, Pecos gambusia, and Pecos assiminea snail, which live in the Diamond Y Springs. Although the Texas Parks and Wildlife Department and The Nature Conservancy have conserved land around these springs to protect habitat and the FWS included outflow from Diamond Y Springs as critical habitat for the Leon Springs pupfish and Pecos assiminea snail, these conservation measures do not protect springflow, which can be protected only through restrictions on groundwater pumping enforced by a groundwater conservation district. *See* 78 Fed. Reg. 41,227.

The FWS's listing decisions may compel groundwater conservation districts with jurisdiction over affected springs to establish desired future conditions (DFCs) (see Chapter 21 of this book for background on the DFC process) that incorporate minimum levels of springflow necessary to protect newly listed species and to consider applying for an incidental take permit and developing an HCP, as did the BSEACD. A few groundwater conservation districts have already utilized DFCs to protect springflow from springs within their jurisdictions that are home to listed species. For example, the BSEACD has set a DFC that is based on maintaining critical springflow during times of drought—a crucial component of the district's HCP, discussed above. The district measures springflow and aquifer levels and, when certain thresholds are met, requires conditional permittees in the Edwards Aquifer to curtail groundwater production, ensuring that Barton Springs continues to flow. Similarly, in Bell County the Clearwater Underground Water Conservation District manages groundwater in the Northern Edwards Aquifer to ensure that springflow from Salado Springs, where the Salado salamander is located, is protected. The FWS listed both the Salado salamander and Georgetown salamander in Bell and Williamson counties as threatened in 2014. 79 Fed. Reg. 10,236 (Feb. 24, 2014). Clearwater has established a DFC based on springflow and utilizing management tools, such as drought curtailments. The district regulates groundwater production to achieve the DFC.

There are areas of Texas, however, without groundwater conservation districts and, therefore, no entity in place to regulate groundwater production to protect springflow for listed species that depend on groundwater-fed springs for their survival. In February 2014, the FWS listed the Georgetown salamander, which is found in Williamson County, and the Jollyville Plateau salamander, found in Northern Travis County and Williamson County, as threatened. *See* 79 Fed. Reg. 10,235. Both salamanders are found in Northern Edwards Aquifer springs. Currently, no groundwater conservation district exists in these areas to manage groundwater production and to protect springflow, but theoretically pumpers in these unregulated areas are vulnerable to an enforcement action under the ESA if a plaintiff can show that groundwater withdrawals contributed to a reduction in springflow and resulted in a take of a listed species.

In 2015, the FWS published a final 4(d) rule that enables development activities that may otherwise cause an incidental take of the threatened salamanders to continue as long as these activities comply with the city of Georgetown's water quality regulations contained in the city's Unified Development Code (UDC). *See* 80 Fed. Reg. 47,418, 47,419 (Aug. 7, 2015). Chapter 11.07 of the city's UDC describes stream and spring buffers, water quality best management practices, and geologic assessments that are required for property development within the Northern Edwards Aquifer Recharge Zone and the city of Georgetown. *See* 80 Fed. Reg. 47,419. The result is that individual developments no longer need to go through the time and expense of applying for an HCP. This example shows that, when the FWS has the flexibility to craft special 4(d) rules for threatened species, local governments should consider early cooperation with the FWS to develop and adopt local ordinances that are sufficiently protective of the species.

On September 15, 2020, the FWS issued a proposed rule to revise the critical habitat designation for the Georgetown and Salado salamanders in Bell and Williamson counties, proposing an increase in approximately 116 acres of critical habitat to reflect the addition of a new occupied site for the Salado salamander and refined mapping of previously proposed critical habitat units based on more precise spring locations. *See* 85 Fed. Reg. 57,578 (Sept. 15, 2020).

IV. The ESA and Texas Surface Water

§ 32.12 The ESA and Surface Water in Texas

In Texas, as elsewhere, protection of endangered and threatened species and their habitat, and development of water resources and use of water rights, often conflict under the requirements of the ESA and its implementing regulations.

One early significant example of how ESA consultation and permitting requirements affect the development of new surface water resource projects was the O. H. Ivie Reservoir, which was created by the construction of the Stacy Dam near Big Spring. After the hurdles posed by nearly a decade of water rights litigation and legislative struggles were cleared, construction of the dam was held up by a creature that was seemingly much less formidable—the federally listed Concho water snake, which the FWS delisted in 2011. *See* 51 Fed. Reg. 51,412 (Sept. 3, 1986); *see also* 76 Fed. Reg. 66,780 (Oct. 27, 2011).

The Colorado River Municipal Water District (CRMWD) could not build the dam without a permit issued by the Corps, and the Corps could not grant a permit until it concluded consultation with the FWS under section 7 of the ESA. In August 1986, the FWS agreed that it would not object to the dam if the CRMWD built habitat for the Concho water snake. For its part, the CRMWD agreed to spend nearly $4 million on artificial habitat. In April 1987, the Corps issued a permit for the construction of Stacy Dam.

A more recent and far-reaching example of the clash between surface water rights and the ESA is the *Aransas Project v. Shaw* whooping crane litigation. The Aransas Project (TAP) is an organization focused on water management of the Guadalupe River Basin, and in March 2010 it sued the TCEQ, alleging that the TCEQ had violated, and continued to violate, section 9 of the ESA by allowing diversions of water from the Guadalupe and San Antonio river systems, which caused the unpermitted take of the endangered whooping crane. The U.S. District Court for the Southern District of Texas agreed with TAP and ruled that the TCEQ proximately caused an unlawful take of the whooping crane. *See Aransas Project v. Shaw*, 930 F. Supp. 2d 716 (S.D. Tex. 2013), *rev'd*, 756 F.3d 801 (5th Cir. 2014), *opinion amended and superseded*, 775 F.3d 641 (5th Cir. 2014). Specifically, the court held that TAP demonstrated through expert testimony that the TCEQ regulates surface freshwater diversion and use within the state of Texas through its permit system and other regulatory powers. 930 F. Supp. 2d at 744–48. Because there was a severe drought during the 2008–09 winter, there was a reduction in the amount of freshwater inflows to the Aransas National Wildlife Refuge. 930 F. Supp. 2d at 744–48. According to the court, the reduction of freshwater inflows from the drought was exacerbated by the TCEQ's water management practices, which did not consider the needs of the whooping cranes. 930 F. Supp. 2d at 744–48. Less freshwater increased the salinity of the San Antonio Bay, which adversely affected the abundance of blue crabs and wolfberries, the whooping cranes' primary food sources. 930 F. Supp. 2d at 752–54. The whooping cranes became emaciated, exhibited stress behavior, and some left their site territories, which exposed them to increased predation. 930 F. Supp. 2d at 755–56. Out of the approximately 270 individuals that composed the only self-sustaining wild whooping crane population in 2008, at least 23 died at the Refuge and an additional 34 left in the spring but did not return in the fall. 930 F. Supp. 2d at 756–59. The court enjoined the TCEQ from approving or granting new water permits affecting the Guadalupe or San Antonio rivers until the court is assured that such permits will not take whooping cranes. 930 F. Supp. 2d at 789. The court also ordered the TCEQ to seek an HCP that may lead to an incidental take permit. 930 F. Supp. 2d at 789.

The Fifth Circuit granted the Texas Attorney General's motion for emergency stay of final judgment pending appeal and ordered an expedited appeal. *See Aransas Project v. Shaw*, No. 13-40317 (5th Cir. Mar. 26, 2013). The following year, the Fifth Circuit reversed the district court's ruling and, after de novo review, held that the TCEQ was not liable for take of the whooping cranes because proximate cause and foreseeability between TCEQ permitting and crane deaths are "lacking as a matter of law." *Aransas Project v. Shaw*, 775 F.3d 641, 660 (5th Cir. 2014). The Fifth Circuit reasoned that "there is a long chain of causation here between the TCEQ's issuance of permits to take water from the rivers and cranes' mortality." 775 F.3d at 660. The court cited other uncontrollable factors that contributed to the deaths of the whooping cranes, including severe drought, rising salinity levels, and the fact that blue crabs had declined due to overfishing. 775 F.3d at 662.

At least for the Fifth Circuit, the TAP case stretched ESA liability too far. It combined regulatory liability that authorized third parties to conduct activities outside the habitat of the listed species—the upstream water diversions—via proximate causation with a section 9 "harm" take by habitat modification in the coastal marshes. Future ESA cases will further define the contours of the TAP ruling in circumstances where causation is less attenuated, such as suits against those who divert water or against regulators when the impact occurs in the habitat of the species. Although the TAP case is now over, it remains significant because it had the potential to establish diversion or supply limits that would create conflicts between existing and future water rights.

Over the last few years, the FWS has listed several aquatic species that depend on flowing surface water for habitat. In August 2014, the FWS listed the sharpnose shiner and smalleye shiner, two minnows once found throughout the Brazos River and several of its major tributaries, as endangered. *See* 79 Fed. Reg. 45,274 (Aug. 4, 2014). The FWS determined that "the two primary factors affecting the current and future conditions of these shiners are river fragmentation by impoundments and alterations of the natural streamflow regime (by impoundments, drought, groundwater withdrawal, and salt cedar encroachment) within their range." 79 Fed. Reg. 45,274,

45,275. The FWS also designated critical habitat for the shiners, which includes 1,002 river kilometers (623 river miles) of the upper Brazos River basin and the upland areas extending beyond the bankfull river channel by 30 meters (98 feet) on each side. *See* 79 Fed. Reg. 45,242, 45,256 (Aug. 4, 2014).

In February 2018, the FWS listed the Texas hornshell mussel as endangered. The Texas hornshell is found in the Devils River and a segment of the Rio Grande River but historically occupied most of the Rio Grande River watershed. The FWS determined that the primary risk factors for the hornshell are increased fine sediment, water quality impairment, loss of flowing water, and barriers to fish movement. *See* 83 Fed. Reg. 5720, 5725 (Feb. 9, 2018).

In contrast to the Texas hornshell, the FWS predicts a grim future for the Texas fawnsfoot, the Texas pimpleback, and the Texas fatmucket, three federal candidate mussel species that had historically lived throughout riverbeds in central Texas. The FWS has determined that the threats to these species, such as sediment increase and reductions in surface water flow, are of high magnitude. The FWS had also designated two other species of mussels living in central Texas rivers, the golden orb and the smooth pimpleback, as candidate species under review for potential listing under the ESA (*see* 81 Fed. Reg. 87,246, 87,258–260 (Dec. 2, 2016)), but on August 15, 2019, the FWS removed the golden orb and the smooth pimpleback from the candidate species list because genetic studies conducted by the Texas Parks and Wildlife Department and the Texas Comptroller's Office revealed that these two species belong to a more common and wide-ranging species of mussel. *See* 84 Fed. Reg. 41,694, 41,696–698 (Aug. 15, 2019).

Before these listings and in response to potential listing, in 2013 the Bureau of Economic Geology at the University of Texas's Jackson School of Geosciences prepared a report that analyzed the potential economic impacts of listing one or more of the mussel species. The report noted that, because of the law's prohibition on "take," "the [ESA] would require preservation of aquatic habitat. Preserving habitat may necessitate the guarantee of environmental flows . . . in certain streams and rivers, especially in Central Texas, where the highest diversity of mussels is found. Reserving this water for habitat preservation may further constrain the supply of water for human usage." Brad D. Wolaver et al., Bureau of Economic Geology, *Potential Economic Impacts of Environmental Flows Following a Possible Listing of Endangered Texas Freshwater Mussels* 2 (Apr. 2014), www.beg.utexas.edu/research/programs/water-landscape-species.

Most recently, on December 1, 2020, the FWS listed the peppered chub as endangered, a species of minnow that is currently found in the South Canadian River between Ute Reservoir in New Mexico and Lake Meredith in the Texas Panhandle, representing only 6 percent of its historical range. According to the FWS, habitat degradation and fragmentation, which has led to the peppered chub's declining populations, has been primarily a result of water diversion and impoundments. *See* 85 Fed. Reg. 77108 (Dec. 1, 2020).

The effects of these listings and potential listings remain to be seen, but it is possible that water diversions that deplete streamflows or groundwater pumping from aquifers that deplete headwater springs and reduce streamflow could cause take of surface water dependent species, and as the Bureau of Economic Geology report points out, this could collide with the development of water supply infrastructure.

V. Climate Change and the ESA

§ 32.13 The Potential Impact of Climate Change Claims in ESA Litigation on Water Resources

One recent issue in ESA litigation is the impact of climate change on listed species. At least to date, similar claims have not been brought in a case involving ESA-protected species in Texas.

However, a decision from California offers some indication about how these claims may play out in the context of water resources.

In 2007, a federal district court ruled that a BO issued by the FWS, which addressed the effects on a fish population of water diversion operations, was in violation of the APA because it failed to consider the effects of climate change. *See Natural Resources Defense Council v. Kempthorne*, 506 F. Supp. 2d 322 (E.D. Cal. 2007). The case dealt with the Central Valley Project and the State Water Project, which divert large volumes of water from the Sacramento–San Joaquin Delta to central and southern California. *Kempthorne*, 506 F. Supp. 2d at 328. A BO issued by the FWS in 2005 concluded that project operations would not jeopardize the continued existence of the delta smelt even though the smelt's population has declined significantly in recent years. *Kempthorne*, 506 F. Supp. 2d at 328.

A coalition of environmental plaintiffs challenged the BO, alleging that it had violated the APA by assuming that the hydrology of the water bodies affected would follow historical meteorological and hydrologic conditions, and by ignoring data about global climate change that could adversely affect the delta smelt population. *Kempthorne*, 506 F. Supp. 2d at 328–29, 367. The defendants acknowledged that current climate models predict warming scenarios for California, but they argued that "there is no similar consensus regarding the impact of warming on future precipitation." *Kempthorne*, 506 F. Supp. 2d at 369 (internal cites omitted). Nonetheless the court determined that because the BO included no meaningful discussion of climate change at all, it was impossible to determine whether the information was properly discounted or arbitrarily ignored. *Kempthorne*, 506 F. Supp. 2d at 369. The court stated, "At the very least, these studies suggest that climate change will be an important aspect of the problem meriting analysis in the [BO]." *Kempthorne*, 506 F. Supp. 2d at 369 (internal cites omitted). It was therefore held that the FWS's conclusion was arbitrary and capricious and that the BO should have included a discussion of how to deal with climate change. *Kempthorne*, 506 F. Supp. 2d at 370.

The FWS is increasingly citing climate change as one of the threats to species in its listing process decisions. When the FWS listed the Jollyville Plateau salamander and the Austin blind salamander as endangered species and designated critical habitat for both species, the FWS listed climate change as one threat to the salamanders' conservation status. *See* 79 Fed. Reg. 51,278, 51,328 (Aug. 20, 2013). Similarly, the FWS has listed climate change as a threat to the central Texas mussels that are currently under review for proposed listings. See discussion at section 32.12 above. Because the salamanders and mussels are fully aquatic, their listings will likely bring about changes in central Texas development regulations and management of water resources in the near future. Additionally, on December 17, 2020, the Service determined that listing the monarch butterfly was warranted but precluded at this time, citing drought and climate change as two factors contributing to the monarch's decline. *See* 85 Fed. Reg. 81813 (Dec. 17, 2020). Texas is a critical migration pathway for monarchs, and a listing decision could potentially have far-reaching impacts to the state.

VI. Conclusion

§ 32.14 Conclusion

The collision of global climate change, continued legislative oversight on natural resources, and the ongoing use of ESA citizen suits will, no doubt, continue to have a real and lasting impact on the use of water resources not only in Texas but also nationwide. Although Texas has in the past been largely spared federal regulation with respect to its nonfederal water resources, this may not continue to be the case. Current and pending lawsuits, legislation, and new species listings have the potential to complicate and sometimes confound Texas's laws and regulations regarding water resources.

CHAPTER 33

Integrating Water Quality Standards into Water Management Programs

Sara M. Burgin[1] and Paulina Williams[2]

I. Introduction

§ 33.1 Water Supply and Water Quality

Water supply and water quality affect each other in significant ways. Federal law, state law, water law, and environmental law all interact at the intersection of water supply and water quality. It is important for water suppliers and wastewater dischargers alike to understand their rights and obligations at this legally and scientifically complex intersection.

Surface water quality standards are relevant to water supply projects in several respects. First, water quality standards may affect whether a surface water source is suitable for the use to which water from the project can be put. Second, water supply projects may affect whether, or how difficult it is, to attain the surface water quality standards in an affected stream. For example, water supply projects may affect flow in a watercourse, which may, in turn, affect the capacity of the stream to absorb pollutant loads in existing and future point source discharges and nonpoint sources. Reduced stream flow may, therefore, affect whether a watercourse attains the applicable water quality standards and how stringent the effluent limitations on point source discharges must be to attain the applicable water quality standard. Third, if a water supply project requires a federal license or permit, the state must certify under section 401 of the federal Clean Water Act (CWA) that the project will not interfere with attaining the state's surface water quality standards. As part of its certification, the state may impose conditions on the water supply project to ensure that the applicable water quality standard is met.

Pursuant to both the CWA and chapter 26 of the Texas Water Code, the Texas Commission on Environmental Quality (TCEQ) has the primary obligation and authority to establish and implement surface water quality standards in Texas. *See* 33 U.S.C. § 1313(a), (d); Tex. Water Code § 26.023. Thus, both federal and state laws and regulations are cited in this chapter.

This chapter describes how the TCEQ establishes and implements surface water quality standards in Texas. The general background is necessary for understanding how surface water quality standards enter into both the Texas Pollutant Discharge Elimination System (TPDES) and water rights permitting for water supply projects, which is discussed in Chapter 34 of this book. Part II below therefore covers how the TCEQ establishes and implements surface water quality standards under

---

1. Sara Burgin is a partner at Bracewell LLP and has practiced environmental law for more than thirty years. She focuses on issues related to water quality as it relates to permitting.

2. Paulina Williams is a partner at Baker Botts L.L.P. She practices environmental law and works extensively on permitting, enforcement, and other matters related to water quality and water rights.

section 303(a) of the CWA and chapter 26 of the Water Code. Part III discusses how the TCEQ translates these standards into total maximum daily loads (TMDLs) for watercourses that do not attain the applicable standard pursuant to section 303(d) of the CWA.

II. Water Quality Standards

§ 33.2 Introduction

The following sections discuss how the TCEQ establishes and implements surface water quality standards. Section 303(a) of the CWA requires each state to develop surface water quality standards for each body of water in the state. *See* 33 U.S.C. § 1313(a). Surface water quality standards consist of three components: (1) the designated uses of a water body, (2) the water quality criteria needed to protect the designated uses, and (3) an antidegradation policy, which requires that discharges not interfere with the attainment or maintenance of surface water quality standards. *See* 33 U.S.C. §§ 1313(a), (c)(2)(A), (d)(4)(B), 1342(o); Tex. Water Code § 26.003; 40 C.F.R. § 131.12; 30 Tex. Admin. Code § 307.5.

States are required to review water quality standards every three years. *See* 40 C.F.R. § 131.20(a). Every three years, therefore, the state water quality standards are subject to review and modification—including (and especially) site-specific criteria. The most recent revision to the Texas Surface Water Quality Standards (the Standards) became effective on March 1, 2018. *See* 30 Tex. Admin. Code §§ 307.1–.10. The Environmental Protection Agency (EPA) must approve any revisions to the Standards for the revisions to be used for federal permitting programs and other CWA purposes. The TCEQ has initiated a process for the next review and revision of the Standards, which is scheduled to be completed in early 2022. The TCEQ provides updated information on TCEQ-adopted revisions to the Standards, the status of EPA approval of the Standards, and the timeline for revising the Standards at www.tceq.texas.gov/waterquality/standards/WQ_standards_revisions.html.

§ 33.3 Designated Uses

Under the CWA and its implementing regulations, each state must identify the existing uses of its water bodies, defined as the uses actually in existence on or after November 28, 1975. *See* 33 U.S.C. § 1313(a); 40 C.F.R. § 131.3(e). The water quality necessary to support the existing uses as of 1975 must, at a minimum, be maintained, subject to narrow exceptions. *See* 40 C.F.R. § 131.10(h). Designated uses are those uses specified in water quality standards for each water body whether or not they are attained. Designated uses should allow for the protection and propagation of aquatic life and recreation in and on the water, commonly referred to as the "fishable/swimmable" standard. *See* 40 C.F.R. § 131.2. If the fishable/swimmable standard is attainable, it applies regardless of the 1975 existing use, unless the state demonstrates to the EPA that attainment of such use is not feasible. *See* 40 C.F.R. §§ 131.2, 131.10(g).

The Standards define the following use categories:

- recreation: primary contact 1 (PCR 1), primary contact 2 (PCR 2), secondary contact 1 (SCR1), secondary contact 2 (SCR2), or noncontact (NCR), *see* 30 Tex. Admin. Code §§ 307.3(a)(41), (a)(50), (a)(51), (a)(57), (a)(58), 307.7(b)(1);
- domestic water supply: public drinking water supply (PS), sole-source surface drinking water supply and protection zone, or aquifer protection (AP) (i.e., capable of recharging the Edwards Aquifer), *see* 30 Tex. Admin. Code §§ 307.3(a)(53), (a)(63), 307.7(b)(2);

- aquatic life: exceptional (E), high (H), intermediate (I), limited (L), and minimal (M) aquatic life, and oyster waters (o), *see* 30 Tex. Admin. Code §§ 307.3(a)(45), 307.7(b)(3); and
- additional uses: such as navigation (N), agricultural water supply, industrial water supply (IS), wetland water quality functions, and seagrass propagation, *see* 30 Tex. Admin. Code §§ 307.3(a)(56), (a)(86), § 307.7(b)(5).

The criteria that apply to each of these use categories are discussed at section 33.4 below.

The surface water bodies in the state fall into one or more of five general categories: (1) classified segments listed in Appendix A of the Standards; (2) bodies of water classified as sole-source surface drinking water supplies by the TCEQ Drinking Water Protection Team; (3) unclassified segments for which site-specific uses and criteria have been set, listed in Appendix D of the Standards; (4) unclassified segments for which site-specific recreational uses and criteria have been set, listed in Appendix G of the Standards; and (5) other unclassified segments to which only the state's general criteria apply.

The first category of "classified" water bodies includes the major surface waters of the state, which are classified in Appendix A of the Standards by segment for the purpose of water quality management and designation of site-specific standards. *See* 30 Tex. Admin. Code §§ 307.2(c), 307.10 app. A. The geographic extent of each classified segment is described in Appendix C of the Standards. *See* 30 Tex. Admin. Code § 307.10 app. C.

The second group of water bodies includes those surface bodies designated as "sole-source surface drinking water supplies" in compliance with Texas Water Code section 26.0286. The TCEQ Drinking Water Protection Team identifies the water bodies to be included in the classification, and they are listed in Appendix B of the Standards. *See* 30 Tex. Admin. Code § 307.10 app. B.

The third category consists of certain unclassified segments for which site-specific receiving water assessments have been undertaken, allowing an aquatic life use (ALU) designation to be made. These site-specific ALU designations are listed in Appendix D of the Standards. *See* 30 Tex. Admin. Code § 307.10 app. D.

The fourth category consists of certain unclassified segments for which site-specific receiving water assessments have been done, allowing a recreational use designation to be made. Water bodies with this designation are listed in Appendix G of the Standards. *See* 30 Tex. Admin. Code § 307.10 app. G.

The fifth category includes the rest of the surface water bodies in the state (i.e., those not listed in Appendixes A, B, D, or G). These other water bodies are unclassified, and no site-specific receiving water assessment has been made for them. For unclassified segments, the general water quality criteria discussed below generally apply, subject to certain exceptions discussed later in this chapter. *See* 30 Tex. Admin. Code § 307.10.

§ 33.4 Water Quality Criteria

The second component of a water quality standard is the water quality criteria. Water quality criteria are descriptions of the quality necessary to support existing or designated uses in waters of the state. Water quality criteria may be numeric (e.g., milligrams per liter (mg/L)) or narrative (e.g., "essentially free of floating debris and suspended solids"). *See, e.g.*, 30 Tex. Admin. Code §§ 307.4(b) (providing narrative criteria for aesthetic parameters), 307.6 (providing concentrations for toxic materials). Water quality criteria may be general or site-specific. 30 Tex. Admin. Code §§ 307.4 (general criteria), 307.10 (site-specific criteria).

The ecological integrity of a stream or river and its adjacent riparian corridor is a function of both stream flow and water quality. Water quality, however, often dominates aquatic life processes when the water body receives significant pollutant loads from point sources, nonpoint sources, or both. Dissolved oxygen (DO) is a key water quality parameter for aquatic life processes. As water temperature rises, the solubility of oxygen in water decreases. Therefore, the level of DO is particularly important in Texas, where the maintenance of adequate DO for aquatic life is made difficult by the naturally occurring low oxygen levels in warm, slow-flowing (sometimes intermittent) streams and rivers, especially during the summer months. Because water supply projects often involve the impoundment or diversion of surface water, or both, these projects affect stream flow and can also affect the quality of downstream surface water, e.g., total dissolved solids, nutrients, and particularly the concentration of DO available for aquatic life processes. The discussion of water quality criteria below will occasionally focus on the DO criteria.

§ 33.4:1 General Criteria

The general criteria apply to all surface water bodies in the state, subject to certain exceptions discussed later in this chapter and subject to being superseded by site-specific criteria on classified segments. *See* 30 Tex. Admin. Code § 307.4; see also sections 33.4:2 and 33.4:3 below. These general criteria include aesthetic parameters (e.g., taste, odor, appearance, suspended solids, turbidity); nutrient limitations (to prevent overgrowth of undesirable vegetation); temperature; salinity; DO to support aquatic life uses; and pH levels. *See* 30 Tex. Admin. Code § 307.4(b)–(h).

The TCEQ has established numeric criteria for DO concentrations necessary to support each of the subcategories of aquatic life use. *See* 30 Tex. Admin. Code § 307.7(b)(3)(A)(i) tbl. 3.

The general criteria for DO or any other parameter apply only to substances attributed to waste discharges or other human activities. They do not apply to surface water that does not meet the general criteria because of natural phenomena. *See* 30 Tex. Admin. Code § 307.4(a).

During each triennial revision to the Standards, the TCEQ reviews new information and incorporates revisions as appropriate to the toxic materials numeric criteria that apply generally to the surface waters in the state, including criteria for protection of aquatic life and of human health. *See* 30 Tex. Admin. Code § 307.6(c), (d).

§ 33.4:2 Site-Specific Criteria

The site-specific criteria for segments listed in Appendix A supersede the general criteria for surface water. *See* 30 Tex. Admin. Code § 307.4(a).

In addition, for some of the water bodies in the five categories discussed above (classified, sole-source surface drinking water supplies, unclassified with site-specific, unclassified with site-specific recreational uses, and unclassified), permitted dischargers, based on local conditions in the vicinity of the discharge, have undertaken special studies and initiated site-specific procedures to justify different criteria than the general criteria or criteria for classified water bodies established by the TCEQ. These water bodies and their modified criteria are set out in Appendix E of the Standards. *See* 30 Tex. Admin. Code §§ 307.2(d), 307.10 app. E.

In the July 2010 revisions of the Standards, the TCEQ adopted site-specific numeric nutrient criteria related to chlorophyll *a* for seventy-five reservoirs. By letter dated July 2, 2013, the EPA approved chlorophyll *a* criteria for thirty-nine of the reservoirs and disapproved the rest. The thirty-nine reservoirs with EPA-approved chlorophyll *a* criteria are set out in Appendix F of the Standards. *See* 30 Tex. Admin. Code §§ 307.3(a)(42), 307.7(b)(4)(E), 307.10 app. F. The TCEQ is conducting studies and evaluations to develop potential nutrient criteria for selected streams, rivers, and estuaries in Texas.

§ 33.4:3 Exceptions to Applicability

There are exceptions to when the water quality criteria—both general and site-specific—apply to surface waters of the state. Several of these exceptions are potentially relevant to the intersection of water quality and water supply in river basins and coastal basin waters.

Several of the criteria established in the Standards do not apply when stream flow conditions in river basins and coastal basin waters are less than "critical low-flow conditions." The following criteria apply only at and above critical low-flow conditions, not below them:

- numerical criteria for dissolved oxygen;
- numerical criteria for temperature and pH;
- maximum temperature differentials;
- numerical criteria for bacteriological indicators;
- numerical criteria to protect aquatic life from chronic toxicity;
- requirements to preclude total chronic toxicity; and
- dissolved oxygen criteria for unclassified waters.

Numerical criteria to protect aquatic life from acute toxicity do not apply when stream flow is below one-fourth of the critical low flow. *See* 30 Tex. Admin. Code §§ 307.8(a), 307.9(e)(8); *see generally* Texas Commission on Environmental Quality, *Procedures to Implement the Texas Surface Water Quality Standards* 72–82 (RG-194, June 2010), www.tceq.texas.gov/assets/public/permitting/waterquality/standards/docs/june_2010_ip.pdf [hereinafter RG-194]. In addition to the low-flow exemptions, there are exemptions from the water quality standards within the mixing zones of point source discharges. Site-specific criteria do not apply in the mixing zones of point source discharges. *See* 30 Tex. Admin. Code § 307.8(b). Also, as with low-flow conditions, the general criteria continue to apply in the mixing zones, unless specifically exempt under the rules. *See* 30 Tex. Admin. Code § 307.4(a). The mixing-zone exemptions available to point source discharges potentially affected by water resource projects that reduce stream flow include dissolved oxygen, recreation, aquatic life, and temperature criteria. *See* 30 Tex. Admin. Code § 307.8(b)(1)(A)–(H).

As the exemptions discussed above indicate, many of the water quality standards most likely to be affected by water supply projects apply only above the critical low-flow conditions (and only outside of mixing zones in some streams). The critical low-flow conditions for protection of aquatic life criteria are determined, in the absence of site-specific information, based on the 7Q2 flow, which is defined as "[t]he lowest average stream flow for seven consecutive days with a recurrence interval of two years, as statistically determined from historical data," or through the use of alternative low-flow calculations for spring-fed streams. 30 Tex. Admin. Code §§ 307.3(a)(16), (a)(60), 307.8(a)(2).

The TCEQ uses the receiving stream "harmonic mean flow" to evaluate whether a discharge will be protective of human health concentration criteria for toxics in waters of the state that have sustainable fisheries or are designated for use as a public drinking water supply. *See* 30 Tex. Admin. Code §§ 307.6(d)(5), 307.8(a)(4). The harmonic mean flow is calculated by "summing the reciprocals of the individual flow measurements, dividing this sum by the number of measurements, and then calculating the reciprocal of the resulting number." 30 Tex. Admin. Code § 307.3(a)(30). Harmonic mean flows are usually, but not always, greater than the 7Q2 flow. RG-194, at 80. The current 7Q2 and harmonic mean flows are published in RG-194, but the published values are guidelines only and are subject to recalculation as new data become available. *See* 30 Tex. Admin. Code § 307.8(a)(8); RG-194, at 218.

The low-flow criteria in RG-194 are solely for the purpose of defining the flow conditions under which water quality standards apply to a given water body. They are not intended for the purpose of regulating flows in water bodies in any manner or requiring that minimum flows be maintained in classified segments. 30 Tex. Admin. Code § 307.8(a)(5). The Standards, therefore, define requirements for the maintenance of aquatic life and human health but do not provide a remedy by which stream flows can be increased to correct a water quality problem.

Both the 7Q2 and the harmonic mean flow are generally calculated from the most recent thirty years of flow data at U.S. Geological Survey gauge stations. Thus, gradually, as the TCEQ's recalculations of 7Q2 and harmonic mean flows occur using more recent flow data, the diversion of increasing amounts of surface water from a water body may decrease the critical low-flow volume above which the surface water quality standards must be met. Moreover, the TCEQ will calculate the critical low-flow volume based on a shorter period of record use if the thirty-year period of record is unavailable or inappropriate. For example, if a major, permanent hydrologic alteration has occurred, such as upstream reservoir construction, then only the flows recorded after the alteration are used to calculate the 7Q2 and the harmonic mean. *See* RG-194, at 81. Thus, water resource projects that reduce stream flows could cause the critical low-flow condition to decrease. It should be noted, however, that many streams will eventually have environmental flow standards established for them, which could affect the critical low-flow conditions as discussed in Chapter 34 of this book.

The critical low-flow condition is important to dischargers of wastewater in two related ways. First, as discussed above, the critical low-flow condition is the flow above which the Standards must be met. Thus, it is the flow based on which attainment of the Standards will be determined. As this flow decreases, more segments of water bodies may threaten to exceed one or more criteria and require development of TMDLs, as discussed in more detail in part III below. Second, the applicable critical low-flow condition is the condition on which the TCEQ bases water-quality-based effluent limitations (WQBELs) for permits issued under the TPDES program. *See* 30 Tex. Admin. Code § 307.3(a)(16); RG-194, at 75. If the stream flow in a receiving water body decreases over time, more stringent WQBELs may have to be established during renewal cycles of TPDES permitting in order to attain or maintain water quality standards, as discussed in more detail in Chapter 34 of this book.

§ 33.5 Antidegradation

The third component of a water quality standard is an antidegradation policy. The EPA's regulations implementing section 303(a) of the CWA require each state to establish an antidegradation policy as part of its water quality standards. *See* 40 C.F.R. § 131.12; *see also* 33 U.S.C. § 1313(a). As described in section 307.5 of the Standards, the regulations achieve this federal requirement by establishing three antidegradation evaluation tiers:

- Tier 1: Existing uses and water quality sufficient to protect those existing uses will be maintained. Categories of existing uses are the same as for designated uses, as discussed at sections 33.3 and 33.4:2 above (relating to site-specific uses and criteria).
- Tier 2: No activities subject to regulatory action that would cause degradation of waters that exceed fishable/swimmable quality will be allowed unless it can be shown to the TCEQ's satisfaction that the lowering of water quality is necessary for important economic or social development. Degradation is defined as a lowering of water quality by more than a de minimis extent, but not to the extent that an existing use is impaired. Water quality sufficient to protect existing uses will be maintained. Fishable/swimmable waters are defined as waters that have quality sufficient to support the propagation of indigenous fish, shellfish, and wildlife and recreation in and on the water.
- Tier 3: Outstanding national resource waters (ONRWs) are defined as high-quality waters within or adjacent to national parks and wildlife refuges, state parks, wild and scenic rivers designated by law, and other designated areas of exceptional recreational or ecological signifi-

cance. The quality of ONRWs will be maintained and protected. (Currently there are no designated ONRWs in Texas.)

See 30 Tex. Admin. Code § 307.5(b)(1)–(3).

For Tier 1 waters, existing uses are maintained by ensuring that TPDES permits for discharges to water bodies listed pursuant to CWA section 303(d) (i.e., water bodies that do not attain the water quality standard) will not allow an increase in the loading of a listed pollutant that will cause or contribute to the violation of water quality standards. RG-194, at 58. For Tier 2 waters, fishable/swimmable waters are protected by TPDES permits that are subject to antidegradation reviews ensuring that, where water quality exceeds the normal range of fishable/swimmable criteria, such water quality will be maintained unless lowering it is necessary for important economic or social development. RG-194, at 61. When degradation is anticipated, the TCEQ reviews the preliminary determination of potential degradation, the evaluation of alternatives, and economic and social justification. The TCEQ then determines whether a lowering of water quality is expected from the proposed discharge. If it is, the TCEQ determines whether the lowering of water quality is necessary for important economic or social development and whether reasonable alternatives to the lowering of water quality are unavailable. The TCEQ may also refer questions concerning an antidegradation review to the State Office of Administrative Hearings for an administrative hearing. Any proposed TPDES permit that allows degradation is subject to EPA review and approval. RG-194, at 67.

For Tier 3 waters, the quality of ONRWs is maintained and protected by ensuring that no increase in pollution that could cause degradation of water quality is allowed into ONRWs. Such waters must be specifically designated under section 307.5 of the Standards. Currently there are no designated ONRWs in Texas. *See* 30 Tex. Admin. Code § 307.4; RG-194, at 67.

The significance of the antidegradation policy to the intersection of water quality and water supply is that, for Tier 1 and 2 waters, as more surface water is impounded or diverted to meet the water needs of Texas's growing population, there may be less water in the water bodies to absorb pollutant loads in new discharges. More stringent WQBELs may, therefore, be necessary to protect existing uses and attain the fishable/swimmable standard.

III. Total Maximum Daily Load

§ 33.6 Introduction

For water bodies where a Standard is not being attained, pollutant loads can be decreased through the TMDL assessment, planning, and implementation process. The following sections discuss TMDLs and the TMDL process for impaired waters and highlight how the public may be affected and how it can participate in the process.

§ 33.7 List of Impaired Water Bodies under CWA Section 303(d)

TMDLs are part of the state water quality management plans that the TCEQ is required by statute to prepare. *See* Tex. Water Code §§ 26.036, 26.0136, 26.127. The TCEQ executive director prepares, and the commission approves, a comprehensive plan for controlling water quality in the state. *See* Tex. Water Code § 26.012. The list of impaired segments, load and waste load allocations, and implementation plans that make up a completed TMDL are all tools in water quality planning.

These state requirements dovetail with CWA section 303(d), which requires each state to identify water bodies within its boundaries for which technology-based effluent limitations are or threaten to become insufficient to achieve any water quality standard for a given water body and to calculate the maximum amount of the pollutants causing or threatening the impairment allowed to enter the water body so that it will meet and continue to meet the relevant water quality standards. *See* 33 U.S.C. § 1313(d). This list of impaired segments is known as the "303(d) list."

The development of a TMDL for a water segment begins with the initial investigation into the water quality of the segment for the 303(d) list and continues through the integration of TMDL limits in TPDES permits and efforts to implement measures to reduce nonpoint source loading. The development of the 303(d) list is the first step at which the public can be involved by submitting information and data on a particular water body. The EPA requires states to outline their process for developing 303(d) lists in "integrated reports," and states must submit these reports to the EPA under CWA section 305(b) every two years. 33 U.S.C. § 1315(b). The Texas Integrated Report of Surface Water Quality [hereinafter Integrated Report] describes the water quality of all jurisdictional waters in the state and discusses the status and strategies for attaining the ultimate fishable/swimmable goal under the CWA. *See* Texas Commission on Environmental Quality, *2020 Texas Integrated Report of Surface Water Quality for Clean Water Act Sections 305(b) and 303(d)*, www.tceq.texas.gov/waterquality/assessment.

The TCEQ's 2020 Integrated Report Guidance details the TCEQ's methodology for listing a water body and the requirements for data submittals. *See* Texas Commission on Environmental Quality, *2020 Guidance for Assessing and Reporting Surface Water Quality in Texas* (May 12, 2020), www.tceq.texas.gov/assets/public/waterquality/swqm/assess/gawg/2020/2020_guidance.pdf [hereinafter the Guidance]. According to the Guidance, the TCEQ actively solicits and selects acceptable data and information to develop the Integrated Report, including stakeholder input on the assessment guidance and existing methods. Further, stakeholders and the public can comment on the draft Integrated Report. All comments, data, and information must be submitted during the formal public comment period in written form. The Guidance (and federal guidance) directs the TCEQ to include a summary of all public comments and requests along with a response to those comments and requests.

Although listing a water body on the state 303(d) list can trigger the development of a TMDL ultimately affecting a permittee's pollutant loading into the listed water, the TCEQ does not consider the development of the Texas 303(d) list a rulemaking. State agency rulemakings must follow particular processes outlined in the state's administrative procedure act, and final rulemakings are subject to declaratory judgment actions in Travis County district court. *See* Tex. Gov't Code § 2001.038. Instead, the TCEQ posts the draft Integrated Report, including the 303(d) list, on the TCEQ website and alerts the public to opportunities to comment through notices of publication in the *Texas Register*. Comments received during the comment period are considered in the development of the final Integrated Report. A summary of all comments received during the comment period along with TCEQ responses are published with the draft Integrated Report on the TCEQ website. Guidance, at 1–5.

States are required to submit 303(d) lists and TMDLs to the EPA for approval. The EPA requires documentation to support state decisions related to the reliance on particular data and information and decisions to list or not list water segments. *See* 40 C.F.R. § 130.7(b)(6). A decision to remove a water body from a list must also be fully supported. The EPA has thirty days to approve or disapprove the state's submission. *See* 33 U.S.C. § 1313(d)(2). If the EPA disapproves a state's list or TMDL, the EPA is allowed to identify listed water bodies and establish TMDLs. The EPA is required to propose its approval or disapproval and any additions it may have to the 303(d) list in the Federal Register for additional public comment. The EPA's approval or disapproval of a 303(d) list and TMDL constitutes a final agency action that is appealable in federal district court through a CWA citizen suit and potentially under the Administrative Procedure Act. *See* 33 U.S.C. § 1365(a); 5 U.S.C. § 706 (allowing court enforcement for agency action unlawfully withheld or unreasonably delayed). Once the submission is approved, a state must also add TMDLs to its continuous planning process, which is also periodically reviewed by the EPA. *See* 33 U.S.C. § 1313(e).

The most recent EPA-approved 303(d) list for Texas is contained in the 2020 Integrated Report, available at www.tceq.texas.gov/waterquality/assessment/20twqi/20txir. In developing the 2020 Integrated Report, the TCEQ evaluated water quality data from 2,639 sites on 1,644 water bodies, focusing on the major river segments and those segments of water bodies considered at highest risk for pollution. Texas Commission on Environmental Quality, *Biennial Report to the 87th Legislature, FY2019–FY2020*. The 303(d) list is reported at a sub-area level referred to as the assessment unit (AU) for each segment of an assessed water body. A total of 1,009 impairments at the AU level were identified in the 2020 303(d) list, compared to 979 impairments in the 2018 303(d) list. (The number of impairments is greater than the number of impaired water bodies because some water bodies have more than one pollutant for which they do not meet a water quality standard. Each impairment is evaluated and counted.) Impairments because of elevated bacteria represented the highest percentage (33.5 percent). Organics in fish tissue and dissolved oxygen had the next highest percentages (27.5 percent and 12.6 percent, respectively). The draft 2022 Integrated Report is currently under development.

§ 33.8 TMDL Development

In compiling a biennial integrated report, the TCEQ assigns each assessed water body to one of five categories that indicates the status of the water body. Water bodies in Category 5 constitute the 303(d) list and require action by the state, including prioritization of TMDL development. Category 5 water bodies are further divided into 5a (a TMDL is underway, scheduled, or will be scheduled), 5b (a review of the water quality standards for the water body will be conducted before a management strategy is scheduled), or 5c (additional data and information will be collected before a management strategy is scheduled).

Even though a water body may be listed as 5a on the state 303(d) list, there is no set timeline for the state to develop a TMDL. Thus, the first step is the establishment of a schedule to develop the TMDL. Some courts have concluded that a state's persistent failure to submit a TMDL schedule may constitute a "constructive submission" that can be challenged in federal district court. *See Scott v. City of Hammond*, 741 F.2d 992, 996 (7th Cir. 1984). But if a state takes small steps to develop TMDLs, its actions may be sufficient to prevent court mandates. *See San Francisco Baykeeper v. Whitman*, 297 F.3d 877, 882–83 (9th Cir. 2002) (holding that California's submission of some of its required TMDLs demonstrated its progress toward completion); *Hayes v. Whitman*, 264 F.3d 1017, 1023 (10th Cir. 2001) (holding the same for Oklahoma); *but see, e.g., Ohio Valley Environmental Coalition, Inc. v. Pruitt*, 893 F.3d 225, 231 (4th Cir. 2018) (noting that although the constructive submission doctrine would not apply where a state significantly postponed development of TMDLs but has a credible plan to produce them in the future, "[c]ontinued intransigence could change that"); *Environmental Law & Policy Center v. U.S. Environmental Protection Agency*, 415 F. Supp. 3d 775 (N.D. Ohio 2019) (citing low priority ranking and reliance on alternative measures as support for applying constructive submission doctrine); *Columbia Riverkeeper v. Wheeler*, 944 F.3d 1204, 1211 (9th Cir. 2019) (affirming district court application of constructive submission doctrine where Washington and Oregon "clearly and unambiguously" indicated they would not be producing a temperature TMDL for the Columbia and Snake Rivers).

§ 33.8:1 Load Allocation

Once a TMDL schedule is set, states must begin the process of estimating the TMDL of "pollutants" that an impaired water body can receive and still attain the water quality necessary for its designated uses. *See* 33 U.S.C. § 1313(d). For each pollutant causing a water body to be impaired through the TMDL process, the TCEQ—

- determines the maximum amount (or "load") of a particular pollutant that can be added to a water body from all sources, including natural background sources, each day that still permits the water body to both attain and maintain its water quality standards;
- identifies the sources that contribute to the load of the pollutant; and
- allocates the allowable load, and the necessary reductions in it, to the sources in the watershed.

TMDLs must allow for seasonal variations, anticipate future growth, and include a margin of safety to cover uncertainties in the analysis. *See* 33 U.S.C. § 1313(d)(1)(C); 40 C.F.R. § 130.2(e)–(i).

A TMDL has two components: a wasteload allocation (WLA) and a load allocation (LA). The WLA is the portion of a TMDL that is allocated to existing and future point sources. 40 C.F.R. § 130.2(h). The LA is the portion of a TMDL that is allocated to existing and future nonpoint sources, including natural background sources (possibly including atmospheric deposition, according to the EPA). 40 C.F.R. § 130.2(g). Where possible, the LA must distinguish between loadings from natural and nonpoint sources. 40 C.F.R. § 130.2(g). In short, reduced to its simplest form, a TMDL is the sum of the WLAs and LAs, plus a margin of safety and consideration of seasonal variations. *See* 40 C.F.R. § 130.2(i).

Texas emphasizes the inclusion of stakeholder groups in developing the actual TMDL. The TCEQ allows stakeholders to provide public comment on the allocation report, and the TCEQ and the EPA must approve the report. Although the TCEQ does not treat TMDLs as rules in Texas, two state supreme courts have concluded that the final adoption of a TMDL is a final rule that must meet the notice, public comment, and other procedural requirements for formal rulemaking. *See Fairfield County Board of Commissioners v. Nally*, 34 N.E.3d 873, 883 (Ohio 2015) (holding that TMDLs are rules in Ohio); *Asarco Inc. v. State*, 69 P.3d 139, 142 (Idaho 2003) (holding that TMDLs are rules in Idaho).

§ 33.8:2 "Pollutant" vs. "Pollution"

It is important with respect to water supply projects to emphasize that the term "pollutant" is used in CWA section 303(d), rather than "pollution." A "pollutant" subject to the requirement to develop and implement a TMDL is defined as any one of a number of contaminants (e.g., dredged spoil, solid waste, chemical waste, biological materials, heat, and industrial, municipal, and agricultural waste) that is "discharged into water." *See* 33 U.S.C. § 1362(6); 40 C.F.R. § 122.2. The definition of "pollution" is broader. It means any "man-made or man-induced alteration of the chemical, physical, biological, and radiological integrity of water." 33 U.S.C. § 1362(19); 40 C.F.R. § 130.2(c).

Because CWA section 303(d) requires TMDLs only for waters impaired by "pollutants," TMDLs are not required for waters impaired by, for example, flow alterations, habitat alterations, or channelization, since those problems might arguably constitute "pollution" but are not associated with a specific "pollutant." *See* 65 Fed. Reg. 43,586, 43,592–93 (July 13, 2000); 64 Fed. Reg. 46,012, 46,021 (Aug. 23, 1999); *see also Virginia Department of Transportation v. U.S. Environmental Protection Agency*, No. 1:12-CV-775, 2013 WL 53741, at *2, 5 (E.D. Va. Jan. 3, 2013) (rejecting the EPA's TMDL for stormwater flow set as a surrogate for and instead of directly addressing sediment because "[s]tormwater runoff is not a pollutant"). Thus, a state may, subject to its own statutory authorities, promulgate a TMDL for waters impaired by flow alterations and the like, but it is not required to do so by CWA section 303(d). *See* 65 Fed. Reg. 43,586, 43,592–93; 64 Fed. Reg. 46,012, 46,021. The TCEQ adopted such a TMDL for DO applicable to Lake Austin on the Colorado River immediately downstream of the Mansfield Dam. The low DO level was determined to be the result of cold waters released from the bottom of Lake Travis and not the result of the discharge of pollutants. Accordingly, the EPA declined to take action on the TCEQ-approved TMDL.

The distinction between "pollutant" and "pollution" does not restrict the state to limitations on the discharge of "pollutants" when fashioning conditions on the state's CWA section 401 certification for a federally permitted project. The state may also impose flow limitations if necessary to comply with water quality standards. *See PUD No. 1 of Jefferson County v. Washington Department of Ecology*, 511 U.S. 700, 717–20, 723 (1994). Certifications under CWA section 401 for federally permitted projects are discussed in more detail in Chapter 34 of this book.

§ 33.8:3 TMDL Implementation Plan

Once a state has set a TMDL, the state must develop an implementation plan for the TMDL that describes the regulatory and voluntary actions necessary to achieve the water quality standard. *See* Texas Commission on Environmental Quality, *Preserving & Improving Water Quality* 19–20 (GI-351, rev. Aug. 2018). The TMDL implementation plan is developed with further public comment and TCEQ approval. According to the EPA, if a state wants to allocate loads among nonpoint as well as point sources, there must be "reasonable assurances that nonpoint source reduction will in fact be achieved." U.S. Environmental Protection Agency, *Guidance for Water Quality-Based Decisions: The TMDL Process* 15 (Apr. 1991) [hereinafter TMDL Process (EPA 1991)]. According to the EPA, "[w]here there are not reasonable assurances, under the CWA, the entire load reduction must be assigned to point sources." TMDL Process (EPA 1991), at 15. Thus, it is easier for states to impose the pollutant discharge reductions necessary to meet water quality standards on point sources than on nonpoint sources.

§ 33.8:4 Integration of TMDLs into Permits

The waste load allocations adopted in final TMDLs must be integrated into effluent limitations in TPDES permits. The TCEQ can initiate amendments to existing permits to impose new limits, or it can impose new limits during routine renewals and amendments. Since permitted waste loads may be substantially reduced at existing facilities as a result of a TMDL, it is critical for permitted facilities on impaired waters to be vigilant throughout the TMDL development process and not just when the TMDL is finalized and integrated into a permit. One Texas court of appeals has concluded that even while a TMDL is pending development or approval, both existing permittees and those seeking new permits on the impaired watershed could face limits related to the pollutant causing impairment. *See City of Waco v. Texas Natural Resource Conservation Commission*, 83 S.W.3d 169, 177 (Tex. App.—Austin 2002, pet. denied) (concluding that issue of whether loads could be established in permits before a final TMDL was developed was ripe for review). The permit and application process integrating TMDLs into permits is also subject to the TCEQ contested case hearing process. *See* Tex. Gov't Code ch. 2003; 30 Tex. Admin. Code ch. 80.

§ 33.9 Texas TMDL Status

As of October 15, 2021, the TCEQ has adopted 315 TMDLs for 215 waterbody segments, including 431 assessment units (subsets of segments), and the EPA has approved 308 of those TMDLs. The TCEQ has addressed 310 TMDLs through implementation plans. The majority of the completed TMDLs address bacteria or legacy pollutants. The TCEQ has also completed TMDLs on DO; nutrients; certain metals; chloride, sulfates and total dissolved solids; and chlorinated organics. *See* Texas Commission on Environmental Quality, *Summary Table of Completed TMDLs and I-Plans*, www.tceq.texas.gov/waterquality/tmdl/tmdlcompletedsummary.html.

IV. Conclusion

§ 33.10 Conclusion

In summary, the Standards require the attainment and maintenance of designated uses and water quality criteria. The Standards do not, however, provide for regulating stream flows to maintain water quality, only for reducing pollutant loads to attain the water quality standards through WQBELs in wastewater discharge permits and, where applicable, implementation of TMDLs. Water supply projects that may have an impact on the stream flow can affect water quality and cause a ratcheting-down of WQBELs in TPDES permits and increase potential for impairment and 303(d) listing.

CHAPTER 34

Impacts of Water Quality Requirements on Water Supply Projects

Stacie Dowell[1]

I. Introduction

§ 34.1 Introduction

Water quality considerations frequently arise in the permitting of water supply projects. Some water supply projects may result in the discharge of pollutants into state waters. Such discharges are prohibited, except where authorized by a discharge permit issued by the Texas Commission on Environmental Quality (TCEQ). *See* Tex. Water Code §§ 26.027, 26.121; 33 U.S.C. §§ 1311(a), 1342. Such projects may, consequently, require a discharge permit, particularly for the construction phase or if an ongoing effluent discharge is involved. This discharge permit is commonly referred to as a Texas Pollutant Discharge Elimination System (TPDES) permit. *See* 30 Tex. Admin. Code § 305.1(b). Other projects, such as water transfers and dams, do not currently require a TPDES permit, but those exceptions remain in controversy. The applicability or inapplicability of the TPDES permit requirement is discussed in part II below. If a water supply project requires the TCEQ's approval of new or amended water rights under Texas Water Code chapter 11, the TCEQ's review will consider water quality impacts. Tex. Water Code § 11.150.

Discharge permits associated with water supply projects may contain effluent limitations, which may be technology based or water-quality based, or both, as well as other conditions on the concentration, volume, rate, and circumstances of discharges. Effluent limitations are discussed in part III. Protection of water quality is sometimes achieved through instream or environmental flow requirements in diversion permits, which are covered in part IV.

Finally, a water supply project may require a federal permit or license, which may necessitate the state's certification as to impacts on water quality under section 401 of the federal Clean Water Act (CWA). *See* 33 U.S.C. § 1342. The statutory and regulatory background of the CWA 401 certification program, including the certification of dams, is provided in part V. Part VI explains the 401 certification process.

---

1. Stacie Dowell is an Associate Attorney for the Devadoss Law Firm, P.L.L.C. Ms. Dowell served as Associate General Counsel for the Trinity River Authority from 2017 to 2020.

II. TPDES Applicability to Water Supply Projects

§ 34.2 Introduction

The U.S. Environmental Protection Agency (EPA) has delegated its authority over federal CWA permitting and enforcement to the TCEQ for most Texas dischargers other than oil and gas activities. That delegation is realized through the TPDES program. The TCEQ accordingly implements and enforces both the federal and state water quality laws and regulations, and both federal and state water quality laws are relevant to this chapter. The TCEQ's authority to issue TPDES permits is subject to the EPA's right to review and comment on such permits and the TCEQ's obligation to address the EPA's comments. If the TCEQ fails to resolve the EPA's concerns on a permit, the EPA may elect to take over the permitting process for that discharger. *See* Memorandum of Agreement Between the Texas Natural Resource Conservation Commission and the U.S. Environmental Protection Agency, Region 6 Concerning the National Pollutant Discharge Elimination System pt. IV.C.3 (Sept. 14, 1998), www.epa.gov/sites/production/files/2013-09/documents/tx-moa-npdes.pdf.

Texas and federal laws prohibit the discharge of pollutants to "water in the state" and "waters of the U.S.," respectively, except as authorized under a TPDES permit issued by the TCEQ. *See* Tex. Water Code §§ 26.027, 26.121; 33 U.S.C. §§ 1311(a), 1342. Some water supply projects may discharge pollutants to water in the state during the construction phase or on an ongoing basis if project operations require an effluent discharge. The following sections discuss whether and what type of TPDES permit is required, if any, for discharges from water resource projects, including construction stormwater discharges and discharges from water transfers and dams.

§ 34.3 Construction Stormwater Discharges

Many water supply projects involve the construction of dams, water intake structures, water transport pipelines, and similar activities. If a water supply project by itself disturbs one acre or more of land area, or if it is part of a common plan of development or sale (such as a subdivision or other "common plan") that does so, the project requires a TPDES permit for stormwater discharges from construction activities. *See* 30 Tex. Admin. Code § 281.25 (adopting 40 C.F.R. § 122.26).

A TPDES Construction General Permit covers discharges of stormwater from construction activities, construction support activities (such as concrete and asphalt batch plants), and specified nonstormwater discharges associated with construction activities. *See* Texas Commission on Environmental Quality, General Permit to Discharge Under the Texas Pollutant Discharge Elimination System, Stormwater Discharges Associated with Construction Activities TXR150000 (eff. Mar. 5, 2018) pt. II.A, www.tceq.texas.gov/assets/public/permitting/stormwater/txr150000-cgp.pdf [hereinafter TXR150000 (2018)]. If the project will disturb five or more acres of land area (or is part of a common plan that will do so), the project is considered a large construction activity. *See* TXR150000 (2018) pt. I. If the project or common plan disturbs one to five acres, it is considered a small construction activity. *See* TXR150000 (2018) pt. I.

To obtain coverage under the permit, both the owner and operator of a large construction activity must submit notices of intent (NOIs) to the TCEQ seven days before commencing construction or taking over operational control. *See* TXR150000 (2018) pt. II.E.3. However, as permitted by the EPA's rules, the TCEQ does not require an NOI for small construction sites. *See* TXR150000 (2018) pt. II.E.2; *see also* 40 C.F.R. § 122.28(b)(2)(v) (allowing states to forgo NOIs). Small construction sites are automatically authorized by the Construction General Permit (CGP) provided the site owners and operators prepare and implement a Storm Water Pollution Prevention Plan (SWP3), give notice to the operator of the municipal separate storm sewer system (MS4), and meet certain signage and other minor requirements set out in the CGP. *See* TXR150000 (2018) pt. II.E.2. In counties listed in appendix A of the general permit, the SWP3 and NOI requirements are waived for construction that occurs entirely during specified low-erosion periods (although any associated concrete or asphalt batch plant must then be separately authorized). *See* TXR150000 (2018) pt. II.E.1 & app. A.

Discharges that would cause or contribute to a violation of water quality standards, or that would jeopardize or degrade existing designated uses of receiving waters, are not authorized under the CGP. *See* TXR150000 (2018) pt. II.C.3. In addition, construction projects that would discharge constituents of concern (e.g., total suspended solids) to impaired waters that are on the state's 303(d) list are not authorized under the CGP unless there is a completed total maximum daily load (TMDL) for the receiving water body and the project complies with the waste load allocation and implementation plans for that TMDL. *See* TXR150000 (2018) pt. II.C.4. See Chapter 33 of this book for a discussion of section 303(d) and TMDLs. The TCEQ may deny or suspend coverage under the CGP and require ineligible projects to obtain individual permit coverage. *See* TXR150000 (2018) pts. II.C.3, II.H.3.

Conditions of coverage under the CGP include preparation and implementation of a SWP3 and best management practices (BMPs), as well as related inspections and recordkeeping. Local governments may impose more stringent requirements than those in the CGP, with which permittees must also comply. *See* TXR150000 (2018) pt. II.C.7. A notice of termination (NOT) must be submitted upon final stabilization or transfer of operational control for projects with an associated NOI. *See* TXR150000 (2018) pt. II.F.1.

Discharges that occur after construction activities have been completed are not eligible for coverage under the CGP. *See* TXR150000 (2018) pt. II.C.1. Owners and operators of water resource projects must, therefore, consider whether TPDES permit coverage is required for any discharges that might occur after the project is complete, such as discharges from water transfer projects and dams. These discharges are covered in the following sections.

§ 34.4 Water Transfers

Texas law does not currently require discharge permits for discharges of transferred water, whether within or between river basins. Such transfers have been exempted from NPDES/TPDES permitting pursuant to the EPA's Water Transfers Rule. *See* 40 C.F.R. § 122.3(i) [hereinafter the Water Transfers Rule]. That rule took effect in August 2008. *See* 73 Fed. Reg. 33,697 (June 13, 2008) (codified at 40 C.F.R. § 122.3(i)). The CWA's treatment of water transfers and the Water Transfers Rule have given rise to significant litigation nationwide for more than a decade. *See, e.g., Friends of the Everglades v. South Florida Water Management District*, 570 F.3d 1210 (11th Cir. 2009); *ONRC Action v. U.S. Bureau of Reclamation*, No. 97-3090-CL, 2012 WL 3526833 (D. Or. Jan. 17, 2012), *rec. adopted*, 2012 WL 3526828 (D. Or. Aug. 14, 2012).

In January 2017, the Second Circuit court of appeals reversed a federal district court decision that vacated the Water Transfers Rule, the lower court having held that the rule could not stand because it was based on an unreasonable interpretation of the CWA. *Catskill Mountains Chapter of Trout Unlimited, Inc. v. U.S. Environmental Protection Agency*, 846 F.3d 492 (2d Cir. 2017), *rev'g* 8 F. Supp. 3d 500 (S.D.N.Y. 2014), *cert. denied*, 138 S. Ct. 1165 (2018), *and cert. denied*, 138 S. Ct. 1164 (2018). The future of the Water Transfers Rule and its continued vitality seem assured at this time. Nonetheless, without a definitive pronouncement by the Supreme Court, the rule may remain open to additional challenges. Because water transfers are a significant source of both current and future supply for Texas, the fate of the Water Transfers Rule should be of interest to those concerned with water supply planning. *See generally* R.W. Beck, Inc., *Socioeconomic Analysis of Selected Interbasin Transfers in Texas, Final Report*, Texas Water Development Board (Oct. 2007), www.twdb.texas.gov\\publications\\reports\\contracted_reports\\doc\\0604830618_Socioeconomic AnalysisofIBT.pdf.

§ 34.5 Dams

Discharges due to releases of impounded water from dams are not required to obtain a TPDES permit. Although this long-standing interpretation has been criticized by some commentators and also by several courts, the EPA has successfully defended it in two circuits, as discussed in more detail below. *See, e.g., National Wildlife Federation v. Gorsuch*, 693 F.2d 156, 171–74 (D.C. Cir. 1982) (upholding the EPA's position that no permit was needed for dam releases, despite presence of pollutants in released water, because subject pollutants were already present in the water). Recent litigation, however, has focused on instances in which the operation of a dam allegedly does itself add pollutants to water that it releases. *See In re Columbia & Snake River Dams Clean Water Act Litigation*, No. 2:13-md-2494-LRS (E.D. Wash. Aug. 14, 2013) (order granting stipulated motion to dismiss upon settlement); *Columbia Riverkeepers v. U.S. Army Corps of Engineers*, No. 2:19-cv-00126 (E.D. Wash. filed Apr. 15, 2019).

The EPA has long held the view that, although dam releases may result in "pollution," they are not considered "discharges of a pollutant" required to obtain an NPDES permit under CWA section 402 for two reasons. First, the water quality impacts of dams such as low concentrations of dissolved oxygen and dissolved minerals and nutrients, water temperature changes, sediment release, release of entrained fish, and supersaturation, when not caused by the discharge of a listed "pollutant" (such as industrial or municipal waste), are not themselves "pollutants" subject to section 402, according to the EPA. *See National Wildlife Federation v. Consumers Power Co.*, 862 F.2d 580 (6th Cir. 1988); *Gorsuch*, 693 F.2d at 171–74. Second, releases from dams do not constitute the requisite "addition of any pollutant to navigable water" necessary to give rise to an NPDES permit requirement under section 402. *See* 33 U.S.C. §§ 1342(a), 1362(12). According to the EPA in the *Consumers Power* and *Gorsuch* cases (collectively, the "dams cases"), an "addition from a point source occurs only if the point source itself physically introduces a pollutant into water from the outside world." *Consumers Power*, 862 F.2d at 583; *Gorsuch*, 693 F.2d at 175. In the EPA's view, therefore, "the point or nonpoint character of pollution is established when the pollutant first enters navigable water, and does not change when the polluted water later passes through the dam from one body of navigable water (the reservoir) to another (the downstream river)." *Gorsuch*, 693 F.2d at 175.

The U.S. courts of appeal have twice deferred to the EPA's interpretation in the dams cases. *See Consumers Power*, 862 F.2d at 590; *Gorsuch*, 693 F.2d at 181–82. Some commentators and courts of appeal, in dicta, have criticized the EPA's interpretation and suggested that it should be reconsidered in light of more modern standards of agency deference. *See Greenfield Mills, Inc. v. Macklin*, 361 F.3d 934, 949–50 (7th Cir. 2004); Reed D. Benson, *Reviewing Reservoir Operations: Can Federal Water Projects Adapt to Change?*, 42 Colum. J. Envtl. L. 353, 381–82 (2017); M. Rhead Enion, *Rethinking* National Wildlife Federation v. Gorsuch: *The Case for NPDES Regulation of Dam Discharge*, 38 Ecology L.Q. 797, 817 (2011); Alison M. Dornsife, Comment, *From a Nonpollutant Into a Pollutant: Revising EPA's Interpretation of the Phrase "Discharge of Any Pollutant" in the Context of NPDES Permits*, 35 Envtl. L. 175, 192 (2005). Nevertheless, it remains the EPA's interpretation that dam releases are not subject to NPDES permitting requirements, and this long-standing interpretation has not been directly contradicted by any federal appellate court.

III. TPDES Water Quality Considerations—Effluent Limitations

§ 34.6 Introduction

Some types of water supply projects may result in the discharge of pollutants to water in the state, such as projects involving the discharge of desalination concentrate (brine) or treated wastewater effluent.

If a TPDES permit is required for a water supply project, the permit will likely contain effluent limitations, which may be technology based or water-quality based, or both, as well as other conditions on the concentration, volume, rate, and circumstances of the discharge. Effluent limitations, as they would be applied to any discharger (including a water supply project if a permit is required), are the subject of sections 34.7 and 34.8 below.

§ 34.7 Technology-Based Effluent Limitations

Most of the focus under the CWA in the past thirty years has been on promulgating and implementing technology-based limitations on point sources. All TPDES permits contain technology-based effluent limitations. *See* 33 U.S.C. § 1342(a)(1) (referring to 33 U.S.C. § 1311, which requires the EPA to establish effluent limitation guidelines); *see also* 30 Tex. Admin. Code § 305.531(4) (adopting by reference 40 C.F.R. § 122.44). The technology-based effluent limitations in TPDES permits are based on the EPA's national effluent limitations guidelines, which the TCEQ adopts by reference, or on an individual TCEQ permit writer's facility-specific best professional judgment (BPJ), in the event that an effluent limitation guideline has not yet been promulgated. *See* 30 Tex. Admin. Code § 305.541. Technology-based limits reflect what level of control is technologically and economically possible through the use of existing technology and do not consider impacts of the discharge on the receiving stream. *See generally Weyerhaeuser Co. v. Costle*, 590 F. 2d 1011, 1041–42 (D.C. Cir. 1978).

The EPA's technology-based limitations have a variety of acronyms, such as BPT (best practicable control technology currently available), which is the baseline level of control applicable in all circumstances; BAT (best available technology economically achievable), applicable to toxic or nonconventional pollutants by existing sources; NSPS (new source performance standards), applicable to new sources; and a variety of other effluent limitation standards. *See* 33 U.S.C. §§ 1314(b)(1), (b)(2), 1316(b). All permits must comply with a technology-based limit, whether the limit is based on an EPA nationwide effluent limitation guideline or on an individual TCEQ permit writer's facility-specific BPJ, in the event that an effluent limitation guideline has not yet been promulgated. *See E.I. DuPont de Nemours & Co. v. Train*, 430 U.S. 112 (1977) (validating the EPA's ability to establish national technology-based effluent limitations). The EPA's industry-specific, technology-based effluent limitation guidelines are found at 40 C.F.R. pts. 405–471.

Technology-based limits are technology-forcing limits, meaning that they are not based on what is required to protect the quality of the receiving water but on the availability, cost, and effectiveness of wastewater treatment technologies. Technology-based limits may achieve greater than or less than the degree of control necessary to protect the quality of the receiving water body.

§ 34.8 Water-Quality-Based Effluent Limitations

After the TCEQ has applied technology-based limits to a discharge, it must evaluate whether the pollution allowed by the TPDES permit will result in a violation of water quality criteria for the receiving water. 30 Tex. Admin. Code § 305.531 (adopting by reference 40 C.F.R. § 122.44); *see also*

U.S. Environmental Protection Agency, *NPDES Permit Writers' Manual* 6-1 (EPA-833-K-10-001, Sept. 2010), www.epa.gov/sites/production/files/2015-09/documents/pwm_2010.pdf ("[A] permit writer must consider the impact of the proposed discharge on the quality of the receiving water."). All TPDES applications are reviewed "to ensure that permitted effluent limits will maintain instream criteria for dissolved oxygen and other parameters such as bacteria, phosphorus, nitrogen, turbidity, dissolved solids, temperature, and toxic pollutants." Texas Commission on Environmental Quality, *Procedures to Implement the Texas Surface Water Quality Standards* 20 (RG-194, June 2010), www.tceq.texas.gov/assets/public/permitting/waterquality/standards/docs/june_2010_ip.pdf [hereinafter RG-194]. These water-quality-based effluent limits are known by the acronym WQBEL. See Chapter 33 of this book for a detailed discussion of Texas Surface Water Quality Standards. As of the publication date of this edition, the current *Procedures to Implement the Texas Surface Water Quality Standards* is pending EPA approval of the following sections: whole effluent toxicity testing, dechlorination requirements for minor domestic wastewater treatment facilities, and variances. *See* Texas Commission on Environmental Quality, *Implementing the Surface Water Quality Standards in Permitting*, www.tceq.texas.gov/waterquality/standards/WQ_stds.

The Texas Surface Water Quality Standards [hereinafter Standards] dictate WQBELs for classified surface water in Texas and are described in 30 Texas Administrative Code chapter 307. Classified waters are designated as segments in Appendix A of the Standards. *See* 30 Tex. Admin. Code § 307.10. Classified segments have designated uses (such as recreation, aquatic life, and water supply) and associated limits (such as dissolved minerals, dissolved oxygen, pH, bacteria, and temperature). *See* RG-194, at 14. The designated uses and associated criteria are used by the TCEQ to evaluate wastewater permit applications. *See* RG-194, at 14. Unclassified waters are evaluated using site-specific information. As noted in Chapter 33 of this book, the concentration of dissolved oxygen is particularly sensitive to flow conditions and temperature.

IV. Water Rights Permitting and Instream Flow Restrictions

§ 34.9 Pre–S.B. 3 Approach

Chapter 11 of the Texas Water Code requires that a person obtain a water rights permit before appropriating any state water or beginning construction of any work designed for storing, taking, or diverting water, with only limited exceptions. *See* Tex. Water Code § 11.121. In issuing new water rights permits or permit amendments to increase appropriated amounts, the TCEQ must assess the effects of the issuance of the permit on the following parameters:

- bays and estuaries;
- existing instream uses;
- fish and wildlife habitats;
- water quality; and
- groundwater or groundwater recharge.

See Tex. Water Code §§ 11.147(b)–(e), 11.150–.152; 30 Tex. Admin. Code §§ 297.53–.56. Based on these assessments, the TCEQ must include in the permit, "to the extent practicable when considering all public interests," conditions necessary to maintain water quality and other parameters listed above in the stream or river to which the application applies, subject to defined exemptions (e.g., more than two hundred miles from the coast for estuarine considerations; less than 5,000 acre-feet per year for habitat mitigation). *See* Tex. Water Code §§ 11.147(b)–(d), 11.150; 30 Tex. Admin. Code §§ 297.53–.56.

The substantive and procedural requirements for water rights permitting are discussed more fully in Chapter 10 of this book. This section addresses the water quality aspects of the Texas water rights permitting process. One such consideration is the amount of water necessary to support downstream aquatic life and aquatic life in bays and estuaries. Beginning in 2008, the regulation of such flows was the subject of regulatory development in the form of environmental flow standards. The creation of such standards, on a basin-by-basin basis, was required by Senate Bill 3, enacted in 2007 by the 80th Legislature. *See* Act of May 28, 2007, 80th Leg., R.S., ch. 1430, § 1.07 (codified at Tex. Water Code § 11.02362(c)) [hereinafter S.B. 3]. Environmental flows are covered more fully in Chapter 11 of this book.

All the parameters considered by the TCEQ in water rights permitting may be affected to some extent by water quality. With respect to water quality in particular, however, the TCEQ is required to "assess the effects, if any, of the granting of the application on water quality . . . and the need for all existing instream flows to be passed up to that amount necessary to maintain the water quality standards [under chapter 307] for the affected stream." 30 Tex. Admin. Code § 297.54(a); *see also* Tex. Water Code § 11.150 (relating specifically to water quality).

The TCEQ assesses the instream flows necessary to maintain water quality and the other parameters listed above during its technical review of a water rights permit application, in a process known as an "environmental assessment." The TCEQ conducts an environmental assessment on applications for new permits and for amendments requesting an increase in the total appropriative amount, significant upstream new or additional diversion points, a change in the diversion rate, or a significant change in place of use (such as on an application involving an interbasin transfer). *See* Bruce Moulton, *TCEQ—Environmental Flows and Water Rights Permitting* (2004), www.tceq.texas.gov//assets//public//comm_exec//igr//sa_comm//water_rights_perm.ppt [hereinafter Moulton (2004)]. Environmental assessments of amendments requesting merely a "change in purpose of use" are controversial. Such assessments are discussed in more detail in Chapter 10 of this book under the "four corners doctrine."

When available, the TCEQ uses S.B. 3 flow limits or site-specific studies, but in the absence of adopted standards or site-specific data, applications that require an environmental assessment may still undergo a desktop review. *See* Moulton (2004). A desktop review relies on the permit application and related information, such as—

- the stream description and photographs;
- U.S. Geological Survey (USGS) topographic maps;
- geographic information system (GIS) coverages;
- USGS stream gauge data;
- TCEQ water quality integrated report prepared under CWA section 305(b), as mentioned at section 33.7 of Chapter 33 of this book;
- TCEQ list of impaired and threatened segments under CWA section 303(d), as discussed in more detail at section 33.7 of Chapter 33; and
- data from other Texas and federal government agencies.

Following the desktop review, the TCEQ next evaluates whether the permit or amendment should have an instream flow restriction and, if so, at what instream flow instantaneous volume (i.e., cubic feet per second). In developing its instream flow recommendations, in the absence of values established by rule under S.B. 3 or site-specific information, TCEQ staff apply the Lyons method to calculate the minimum recommended flows on perennially flowing waters to protect the aquatic environment and other environmental values the agency must consider. The Lyons method uses 60 percent of the median flow during the warm months (March through September) and 40 percent of the median flow during cool months (October through February). *See* Moulton (2004). The 60 percent values were chosen to provide higher margins of protection during the critical spring and summer months. *See* David Maidment, Water Quality and Bioassessment in Texas Streams and Rivers (Apr. 2004), at 13 (unpublished paper, The University of Texas) [hereinafter Maidment (2004)]. Where the 7Q2 value (i.e., "[t]he lowest average stream flow for seven consecutive days with a recurrence interval of two years") produces a stream flow that is greater than the Lyons method, the 7Q2 is used to set the minimum stream flow, in order to preserve the critical low-flow condition on which TPDES water quality standards attainment and permitted effluent limitations are based. *See* Moulton (2004); see also section 33.4:3 of Chapter 33 (relating to water quality standards) and section 34.8 above (relating to WQBELs).

The desktop review approach will be largely replaced through the implementation of S.B. 3 as described at section 34.10 below, and future permits may provide for diversions below the 7Q2 flow or the Lyons flow. The TCEQ has adopted environmental flow standards for seven major basin and bay systems. *See* 30 Tex. Admin. Code §§ 298.200–.540.

The TCEQ's water rights permitting approach does not completely address the potential, discussed previously, for increases in diversions and impoundments to give rise to more stringent WQBELs in new and renewed wastewater discharge permits for a variety of reasons. There is no environmental review for the mere increased use of existing, permitted water rights, some of which are not subject to instream flow restrictions because their issuance predated the imposition of such restrictions. Therefore, water supply projects that decrease flow could affect the ability of a water body to absorb pollutant loads, in point and nonpoint source discharges. In addition, unlike water quality permits, which are subject to renewal every five years, water rights permits are permanent and not subject to modification by the TCEQ except upon amendment, so there may be no opportunity to impose new instream flow restrictions in existing permits in the absence of a triggering permit amendment. Thus, downstream point source dischargers may see a ratcheting-down of WQBELs when their wastewater discharge permits are issued or amended or renewed every five years.

§ 34.10 Post–S.B. 3 Approach

S.B. 3 has simplified the TCEQ's approach to instream flow requirements in river basins in which the TCEQ has adopted environmental flow standards by rule. S.B. 3, enacted in 2007, requires the TCEQ to adopt environmental flow standards for Texas river basins and bays, beginning with seven priority river basins and associated bays listed in the statute. *See* Act of May 28, 2007, 80th Leg., R.S., ch. 1430, § 1.07 (codified at Tex. Water Code § 11.02362(b), (c), (e)). The TCEQ has adopted S.B. 3 flow standards for those seven basin and bay systems. *See* 30 Tex. Admin Code §§ 298.200–.540. S.B. 3 and environmental flows are discussed in detail in Chapter 11 of this book. The summary below focuses on those aspects of S.B. 3 that may affect the TCEQ's current environmental review process for water rights permits, particularly as that process relates to water quality considerations.

S.B. 3 established a stakeholder-centered process to determine environmental flows or needs for all the major river basins in Texas. The process involved local stakeholders, experts, and the TCEQ. A full exposition on the process is addressed in Chapter 11 of this book. As a first step in the process, S.B. 3 called for the stakeholders and other participants to develop an "environmental flow regime," defined as "a schedule of flow quantities that reflects seasonal and yearly fluctuations that typically would vary geographically, by specific location in a watershed, and that are shown to be adequate to support a sound ecological environment." Tex. Water Code § 11.002(16). Based on regime recommendations, the TCEQ adopted basin-specific "environmental flow standards," which constitute "a schedule of flow quantities, reflecting seasonal and yearly fluctuations that may vary geographically by specific location in a river basin and bay system." Tex. Water Code § 11.1471(c). New permits or permits that increase the authorized diversions must be consistent with established environmental flow standards. Adopted environmental flow standards will not restrict an amendment to an existing water right that does not increase the amount of water authorized to be stored, diverted, or impounded. *See* Tex. Water Code §§ 11.023, 11.1471. Thus, an amendment to change the purpose or place of use should not be subject to an environmental flow standard.

V. The Statutory and Regulatory Background of CWA Section 401 Certification

§ 34.11 Waters of the United States

In 2020, the EPA and the U.S. Army Corps of Engineers (Corps) published a proposed rule that sought to revise the definition and scope for "waters of the United States." *See* 84 Fed. Reg. 56,626 (Oct. 22, 2019). This rule became finalized on April 21, 2020, and modified portions of the CWA. *See* 33 C.F.R. pt. 328. As amended, the term "waters of the United States" now identifies the four categories of waters that may be considered waters of the United States and also identifies those waters that are excluded from the scope of waters of the United States. Waters included within the term "waters of the United States," also known as jurisdictional waters, are the following:

- the territorial seas, as well as waters that are currently used, were used in the past, or may be susceptible to use in interstate or foreign commerce, including waters that are subject to the ebb and flow of the tide;
- tributaries;
- lakes and ponds, as well as impoundments of jurisdictional waters; and
- wetlands adjacent to jurisdictional waters.

See 33 C.F.R. § 328.3(a). Waters outside the scope of the four categories listed above are nonjurisdictional waters and may not be considered waters of the United States. *See* 33 C.F.R. § 328.3(b). Examples of nonjurisdictional waters include the following:

- groundwater, including groundwater drained through subsurface drainage systems;
- ephemeral features that flow only in direct response to precipitation, including ephemeral streams, swales, gullies, rills, and pools;
- diffuse stormwater runoff and directional sheet flow over upland;
- ditches that are not traditional navigable waters or tributaries or that are not constructed in adjacent wetlands, subject to certain limitations;
- prior converted cropland;
- artificially irrigated areas that would revert to upland if artificial irrigation ceases;
- artificial lakes and ponds that are not jurisdictional impoundments and that are constructed or excavated in upland or nonjurisdictional waters;
- water-filled depressions constructed or excavated in upland or nonjurisdictional waters incidental to mining or construction activity and pits excavated in upland or nonjurisdictional waters for the purpose of obtaining fill, sand, or gravel;
- stormwater control features constructed or excavated in upland or nonjurisdictional waters to convey, treat, infiltrate, or store stormwater runoff;

- groundwater recharge, water reuse, and wastewater recycling structures constructed or excavated in upland or nonjurisdictional waters; and
- waste treatment systems.

See 33 C.F.R. § 328.

In addition, the EPA and the Corps also sought to amend the CWA to define jurisdiction based on scientific delineations rather than physical indicators. *See* 33 C.F.R. § 328. For instance, the previous 2015 version of the CWA identified tributaries based on physical indicators such as the tributary's bed and banks and ordinary high water mark. However, the current iteration of the CWA identifies tributaries based on scientific criteria such as ephemeralness, intermittency, and perenniality. *See* 33 C.F.R. § 328.3. By establishing jurisdiction based on the defined terms "perennial," "intermittent," and "ephemeral," the EPA and Corps sought to remove the ambiguity regarding jurisdiction over wetlands and seasonal streams.

For further discussion of "waters of the United States," see Chapter 35 of this book.

§ 34.12 State's Role in the Certification Process

Federal law gives state governments a role in protecting state water quality from potentially adverse impacts of federally permitted activities. Section 401 of the CWA requires certification by the state of any activity conducted under a federal license or permit (or renewal) that "may result in any discharge into the navigable waters" (also known as "waters of the United States"). *See* 33 U.S.C. §§ 1341(a)(1), 1362(7). This certification is commonly referred to as a "401 Certification." 30 Tex. Admin. Code § 279.3(1).

Examples of federal permits that require 401 Certification include—

- permits issued by the Corps for construction of a bridge, causeway, dam, or dike over or in a port, roadstead, haven, harbor, canal, navigable river, or other navigable water under section 9 of the Rivers and Harbors Act of 1899, now codified at 33 U.S.C. § 1341;
- permits issued by the Corps for certain work obstructing or modifying the course or capacity of waters of the U.S. under section 10 of the Rivers and Harbors Act of 1899, now codified at 33 U.S.C. § 1341;
- permits issued by the Corps for discharges of dredged or fill materials into waters of the United States under section 404 of the CWA, 33 U.S.C. § 1344 (discussed in more detail in Chapter 35 of this book);
- permits issued by the U.S. Fish and Wildlife Service to "take" an endangered species under section 10 of the Endangered Species Act, 16 U.S.C. § 1539 (discussed in more detail in Chapter 32 of this book);
- permits issued by the Federal Energy Regulatory Commission (FERC) to construct and operate facilities, including hydropower dams or plants on existing dams, for the development, transmission, or sale of power under the Federal Power Act, 16 U.S.C. § 797(e); 18 C.F.R. § 4.34(b)(5)(i); and
- permits issued by the EPA for the discharge of pollutants into waters of the United States under section 402 of the CWA, 33 U.S.C. § 1342 (in Texas, the TCEQ rather than the EPA issues most permits required under section 402 of the CWA, but the EPA still retains authority to issue NPDES permits for wastewater discharges from oil and gas activities regulated by the Texas Railroad Commission, which unlike the TCEQ has not been delegated NPDES authority by the EPA).

Before a federal agency may issue a permit resulting in discharges to waters of the United States, Texas must certify to the federal authority that the discharge will comply with the applicable provisions of sections 301 and 302 of the CWA, relating to effluent limitations; section 303 of the Act, relating to water quality standards; section 306, relating to new source performance standards; and section 307, relating to toxics. *See* 33 U.S.C. § 1341(a). If the state denies a 401 Certification on an application for a federal permit, the federal licensing or permitting authority cannot issue the requested license or permit. *See* 33 U.S.C. § 1341(a)(1).

Within the state, the TCEQ administers the section 401 water quality certification review process with the exception of oil and gas exploration, which is regulated by the Texas Railroad Commission. *See* Texas Commission on Environmental Quality, *401 Certification Reviews*, www.tceq.texas.gov/permitting/401certification/401certification_definition.html.

Section 401(d) of the CWA allows states to impose effluent limitations as part of a 401 Certification if necessary to comply with sections 301 and 302 (relating to effluent limitations) and sections 306 and 307 (relating to new source performance standards and pretreatment standards), as follows:

> Any certification provided under this section shall set forth any effluent limitations and other limitations, and monitoring requirements necessary to assure that any applicant for a Federal license or permit will comply with any applicable effluent limitations under section [301] or [302] of this title, standard of performance under section [306] of this title, or prohibition, effluent standard, or pretreatment standard under section [307] of this title, and with any other appropriate requirement of State law set forth in such certification, and shall become a condition on any Federal license or permit subject to the provisions of this section.

33 U.S.C. § 1341(d).

Notably missing from section 401(d), quoted above, is an express mention of any authority to impose conditions other than effluent limitations—for example, flow restrictions to ensure compliance with the state's water quality standards established under section 303 of the CWA, 33 U.S.C. § 1313. The U.S. Supreme Court has held, however, that the states are not limited to imposing effluent limitations in a 401 Certification. *See PUD No. 1 of Jefferson County v. Washington Department of Ecology*, 511 U.S. 700 (1994). States may also impose other limitations, specifically minimum stream flows, as long as the purpose of the limitation is to ensure compliance with a water quality standard (composed of a designated use, criteria, and antidegradation policy). 511 U.S. at 707. In *PUD No. 1 of Jefferson County*, the Court rejected the dam operator's argument that section 401 is "only concerned with water 'quality,' and does not allow the regulation of water 'quantity.'" 511 U.S. at 719. The Court found the dam operator's argument to be based on an "artificial distinction" because "water quantity is closely related to water quality" such that "a sufficient lowering of the water quantity . . . could destroy all of its designated uses." 511 U.S. at 719. Thus, the department could impose flow restrictions in its 401 Certification.

§ 34.13 Special CWA Section 401 Applicability Considerations for Dams

The release of water through a dam is enough to make it subject to CWA section 401 Certification, if a federal permit or license is otherwise required. Construction of a dam may require a permit under section 9 or 10 of the Rivers and Harbors Act of 1899, a permit under section 404 of the CWA, or a permit to "take" an endangered species under section 10 of the Endangered Species Act, among others. If such a federal license or permit is required, and if the activity being licensed "may result in any discharge," then 401 Certification is required from the TCEQ. *See* 33 U.S.C. § 1341(a). Not all licensed activities associated with a dam necessarily result in the discharge of a pollutant, however, and until 2006, it was unclear whether the mere pass-through of water through a dam was a "discharge" sufficient to trigger the 401 Certification requirement. In 2006, however, the U.S.

Supreme Court confirmed that dams require 401 Certification because they "may result in a discharge" within the meaning of section 401 of the CWA. *S.D. Warren Co. v. Maine Board of Environmental Protection*, 547 U.S. 370, 386 (2006). This is the case regardless of whether a dam "discharges any pollutant" within the meaning of section 402, thereby requiring an NPDES permit (which, as discussed at section 34.5 above, the federal courts have held they do not).

Although two circuit courts have held that a TPDES permit under CWA section 402 is not required for releases from a dam, the Supreme Court in *S.D. Warren* held that water quality certification under CWA section 401 is required (if the construction or operation of a dam requires a federal permit or license), because while releases from a dam do not constitute the "addition of any pollutant" within the meaning of CWA section 402, they do constitute "discharges" within the meaning of CWA section 401. If a dam otherwise requires a permit or license, then 401 Certification is required. *S.D. Warren*, 547 U.S. at 385.

The Court's ruling in *S.D. Warren* remains unreconciled with a more recent ruling by the same court. In 2013, the Court found that a "discharge" under the CWA does not occur "when polluted water 'flows from one portion of a river that is navigable water of the United States, through a concrete channel or other engineered improvement in the river,' and then 'into a lower portion of the same river.'" *Los Angeles County Flood Control District v. Natural Resources Defense Council*, 568 U.S. 78, 82 (2013). However, the Court did not modify the ruling in *S.D. Warren*, which concluded that the mere pass-through of water through a dam constituted a "discharge" for purposes of CWA section 401 Certification.

VI. TCEQ 401 Certification Process

§ 34.14 Introduction

When 401 Certification is required for a federally licensed activity in Texas, the TCEQ is responsible for making that certification. *See* Tex. Water Code § 26.0136. The TCEQ's rules set out a general procedure applicable to all 401 Certifications and specific procedures applicable to three categories of federal permits: (1) permits issued by the Corps; (2) permits issued by the EPA (no longer widely applicable, since the TCEQ now issues TPDES permits except for oil and gas activities); and (3) other permits. *See* 30 Tex. Admin. Code §§ 279.1–.12. The specific procedures applicable to permits issued by the Corps are directly applicable to many water resource projects and are representative of all three categories of permits. The following sections, therefore, focus on the substance of the TCEQ's review and the TCEQ's general and specific procedures as applied to permits issued by the Corps. See chapter 279 of the TCEQ's rules for specific procedures applicable to other types of permits.

§ 34.15 Substance of Review

The general policy behind the TCEQ's 401 Certification is to ensure that any federally permitted project that "may result in any discharge into the navigable waters" maintains the chemical, physical, and biological integrity of the state's waters and does not cause an overall net loss of the existing wetlands resource base with respect to Texas wetlands functions and values. *See* 33 U.S.C. § 1341; 30 Tex. Admin. Code §§ 279.2, 279.9. The general purposes of certification review are to determine whether a federally permitted project will—

- result in any discharge;
- result in any violation of CWA section 301 or 302 (effluent limitations), 303 (water quality standards), 306 (new source performance standards), or 307 (toxics);

- result in any violation of applicable water quality standards; or
- result in any violation of any other appropriate requirements of state law.

30 Tex. Admin. Code § 279.9. The TCEQ collects the information necessary to complete this review from the underlying applications and from questionnaires given to applicants to complete specifically for 401 Certification review. *See* Texas Commission on Environmental Quality, *State Water Quality Certification of Section 404 Permits* (Apr. 12, 2004), www.tceq.texas.gov/assets/public/permitting/assess/401cert/401cov.pdf [hereinafter TCEQ 401/404 Letter (2004)].

Another purpose of the 401 Certification is to support state and federal efforts to achieve no net loss of existing wetlands resource base with respect to wetlands functions and values. *See* 30 Tex. Admin. Code § 279.2. As a result, "[a]ll activities under the jurisdiction of the [TCEQ] that require a federal license or permit and that may result in any discharge to waters of the United States are subject to review for consistency with the federal CWA and Texas Water Quality Standards." 30 Tex. Admin. Code § 279.2(b).

After certification review, the TCEQ executive director may do one of four things:

- *grant certification* for any activity that will not result in any discharge in violation of water quality standards or any other appropriate requirements as set out above;
- *grant conditional certification* subject to the conditions necessary to prevent any activity that will result in a discharge from violating water quality standards or any other appropriate requirements as set out above;
- *deny certification* for any activity that will result in a discharge in violation of water quality standards or any other appropriate requirements as set out above; or
- *waive certification*, which may be conditioned on the applicant's agreement to include and comply with specific water-quality-related conditions in the applicant's federal permit.

See 30 Tex. Admin. Code § 279.2(b). The TCEQ generally has sixty days from the date it receives the request for 401 Certification to issue a final determination, unless a public meeting is held necessitating an extension. *See* 30 Tex. Admin. Code §§ 279.7(b), 279.10(a), 279.11(a).

§ 34.16 General Procedures

The 401 Certification process is initiated either by the federal agency (specifically, the district engineer in the case of the Corps) or by the applicant submitting a request for 401 Certification to the TCEQ, along with the underlying application for the federal permit, a project description, and a list of adjacent landowners (or a copy of the federal agency's joint public notice with the TCEQ). *See, e.g.*, 30 Tex. Admin. Code § 279.4.

Section 401 of the CWA requires state agencies to establish procedures for public notice in the case of all applications for certification by the state agency and, to the extent the state agency deems appropriate, procedures for public hearings in connection with specific applications. *See* 33 U.S.C. § 1341. The TCEQ's rules require mailed notice of the request for 401 Certification (preferably jointly with the public notice of the relevant federal agency) to—

- adjacent landowners;
- mayor and health authorities of the city or town in which the activity is or will be located;
- county judge and health authorities of the county in which the facility is located;
- Texas Parks and Wildlife Department;
- U.S. Fish and Wildlife Service;
- Texas Water Development Board;

- National Marine Fisheries Service;
- EPA Region 6;
- Texas General Land Office;
- Coastal Coordination Council; and
- applicant.

30 Tex. Admin. Code § 279.5(b).

Persons receiving notice are given at least thirty days to submit comments. *See* 30 Tex. Admin. Code § 279.5(c)(4). The TCEQ must consider all comments related to the impacts of the proposed activity. 30 Tex. Admin. Code § 279.6. Depending on the level of interest in the certification, the TCEQ executive director may, but is not required to, conduct a public meeting (unless requested by a TCEQ commissioner, in which case the meeting is mandatory). *See* 30 Tex. Admin. Code § 279.7(a). A decision to hold a public meeting will prompt a request to the Corps for an extension of the sixty-day deadline for the certification decision. *See* 30 Tex. Admin. Code § 279.7(b).

§ 34.17 Specific Procedures for Corps Permits

The TCEQ has adopted procedures to govern the consideration and issuance of 401 Certifications with specific respect to section 404 permits issued by the Corps. Those procedures have been adopted both by rule and also pursuant to TCEQ guidance documents and a memorandum of agreement between the TCEQ and the Corps. The relevant requirements are described in the following sections.

§ 34.17:1 Avoidance, Minimization, and Compensation Criteria

Section 279.11 of the TCEQ's certification rules sets out procedures specific to permits issued by the Corps. *See* 30 Tex. Admin. Code § 279.11. These regulatory procedures are consistent with the general process described above but contain specific criteria applicable only to 401 Certification reviews of Corps permits. Specifically, with respect to section 404 permits issued by the Corps (and only section 404 permits), the TCEQ's rules state:

- No discharge shall be certified if there is a practicable alternative that would have less of an adverse impact on the aquatic ecosystem, as long as the alternative does not have other more significant adverse environmental consequences. Activities that are not water dependent are presumed to have a practicable alternative, unless the applicant demonstrates otherwise. For the purposes of this rule, compensatory mitigation is not considered an alternative.
- No discharge of dredged or fill material will be certified unless appropriate and practicable steps have been taken that will minimize potential adverse impacts of the discharge on the aquatic ecosystem.
- Certification requires appropriate and practicable compensatory mitigation for all unavoidable adverse impacts that remain after all practicable avoidance and minimization have been completed. Compensatory mitigation requirements will provide for a replacement of impacted functions and values.

30 Tex. Admin. Code § 279.11(c)(1)–(3). These certification criteria for section 404 permits are consistent with the EPA's section 404(b)(1) guidelines, the functional effect of which is to encourage avoidance, then minimization, and, as necessary, compensation for wetlands mitigation, as discussed in Chapter 35 of this book. The TCEQ can deny certification of a section 404 permit if the impacts of the project are so significant that the proposed compensatory mitigation would not accomplish the pur-

pose and policy of Texas Administrative Code title 30, chapter 279, of protecting water quality and wetlands values and functions, discussed in part IV above.

§ 34.17:2 Tier I and Tier II Reviews

Other than the 401/404 criteria discussed at section 34.17:1 above, many of the specific procedures relevant to the TCEQ's certification of section 404 permits are contained in guidance documents and a memorandum of agreement between the TCEQ and the Corps. *See, e.g.*, TCEQ 401/404 Letter (2004); Memorandum of Agreement Between the U.S. Army Corps of Engineers and the Texas Natural Resource Conservation Commission on Section 401 Certification Procedures (Aug. 17, 2000), www.tceq.texas.gov/assets/public/permitting/assess/401cert/MOA2.pdf. All the discussion below comes from one or both of these guidance documents unless otherwise indicated.

The TCEQ and the Corps have developed a tiered system of review for individual section 404 permit applications. Projects fall into one of two tiers based on the size of the project and the amount of state water affected. The extent of 401 Certification review varies depending on the tier into which the project falls and the type of wetland affected. On Tier I projects, the TCEQ waives certification, and a request for certification as well as public notice, opportunity for comment, and public meeting are not required. *See* 30 Tex. Admin. Code §§ 279.5(d), (e), 279.6. Tier II projects are subject to individual certification review by the TCEQ, and the general procedures apply, requiring public notice, opportunity for comment, and a possible public meeting, as discussed at section 34.16 above.

Tier I Waivers: Tier I projects are those that will result in a direct impact to three acres or less of water in the state (including wetlands) or 1,500 linear feet or less of streams. To be eligible for a Tier I waiver, the applicant must complete a Tier I checklist designating the erosion control BMPs the applicant will implement. The checklist is available on the TCEQ website at www.tceq.texas.gov/permitting/401certification/401certification_tier1.html. The applicant must also sign a statement agreeing to incorporate these BMPs into its section 404 permit. If the applicant does not complete the checklist and return the signed agreement to the Corps and the TCEQ before the Corps issues the permit decision document, the project will be considered a Tier II project, and the Corps will request individual certification review by the TCEQ.

Some projects are not eligible for a Tier I waiver. If a project has a combination of impacts that exceeds the three-acre or 1,500-foot threshold or that is submitted after the fact (i.e., after the water in the state has been disturbed), the project does not qualify as a Tier I project. In addition, projects in certain rare or ecologically significant areas identified by the Corps in its nationwide permits are not eligible for Tier I coverage. Texas Commission on Environmental Quality, *Tier II 401 Certification*, www.tceq.texas.gov/permitting/401certification/401certification_tier2.html. Currently the areas ineligible for Tier I coverage in Texas include pitcher plant bogs, swamps dominated by bald cypress and tupelo gum tree species, the area of Caddo Lake within Texas that is designated as a Ramsar Wetland of International Importance, mangrove marshes, and coastal dune swales. TCEQ 401/404 Letter (2004).

Tier II Review: A Tier II project is any project that does not qualify for a Tier I review or for which the applicant elects not to incorporate Tier I criteria or prefers to use alternatives to the BMPs in the Tier I checklist. The Tier II applicant completes a Tier II 401 Certification Questionnaire and Alternatives Analysis Checklist, which the applicant receives from the Corps attached to the TCEQ 401/404 Letter (2004). The checklist is available on the TCEQ website at www.tceq.texas.gov/assets/public/permitting/waterquality/forms/20229.pdf. The TCEQ then undertakes the individual certification review described generally at section 34.16 above.

The Tier II process requires early and significant coordination between the Corps and the EPA. The TCEQ participates in the Corps' preapplication and comment process, and the TCEQ and the Corps share pertinent information with each other throughout the process. The TCEQ and the Corps issue a joint public notice on the permit application and 401 Certification process. The Corps prepares its final permit decision document and gives it to the TCEQ after the close of the public comment process.

Within sixty days of receiving the Corps' final decision document, the TCEQ must deny, grant, or conditionally grant the 401 Certification or request an extension of time for certification review. Otherwise, the certification review is presumed waived under the Corps' waiver rules. *See* 33 C.F.R. § 325.2(b). The Corps (i.e., the district engineer) determines the merit of any time extension requested by the TCEQ and the length of the extension based on the Corps' waiver rules and notifies the TCEQ of its intended decision. The TCEQ has sixty days after receipt of this notice to complete its certification review or have it be presumed waived.

§ 34.18 Specific Procedures for Nationwide and General Permits

Nationwide and general permits are available to cover some activities that require a CWA section 404 permit, as discussed in Chapter 35 of this book. Nationwide and general permits are subject to 401 Certification review by the TCEQ when they are issued by the responsible federal agency, not at the time of each coverage authorization decision. *See* 30 Tex. Admin. Code § 279.12(a)(1), (b)(1). When a federal licensing or permitting agency proposes a nationwide permit for an activity that may result in a discharge or proposes a general permit for an activity that may result in a discharge, the TCEQ mails interagency notice only to the Texas Parks and Wildlife Department, the Texas Water Development Board, and the Texas General Land Office. *See* 30 Tex. Admin. Code § 279.12(a)(2), (b)(2). After considering the comments it receives in response to these notices, the TCEQ may deny, grant, conditionally grant (via "regional conditions"), or waive certification review in the same manner as discussed at section 34.15 above. *See* 30 Tex. Admin. Code § 297.12(a)(3), (b)(3). As noted at section 34.17:1 above, if the TCEQ denies certification or imposes regional conditions not acceptable to the issuing agency, the permit cannot become effective in Texas. *See* 33 U.S.C. § 1341(a)(1).

For nationwide or general permits on which a state has denied 401 Certification, the federal agency can issue provisional nationwide permits (NWPs). However, the applicant must obtain individual 401 Certification from the appropriate state agency before proceeding with work under a provisional NWP. If the federal agency will not issue a provisional NWP, the applicant may have to obtain individual permit coverage (and 401 Certification review) for activities otherwise covered by the nationwide or general permit. The TCEQ is required to maintain a list of all applicable nationwide and general permits and its certification action on each one. *See* 30 Tex. Admin. Code § 279.12(a)(4), (b)(4). This list is available from the TCEQ's 401 Certification coordinator, as well as from the relevant federal agency.

VII. Conclusion

§ 34.19 Conclusion

Water quality considerations come into play in state-permitted water supply projects through the TCEQ's review of applications for TPDES permits and water rights permits. Water quality considerations come into play in federally permitted projects in 401 Certifications made by the TCEQ to the relevant federal permitting authority that the project satisfies applicable effluent limitations and water quality standards.

Parties involved in individual CWA section 404 permits should refer to Chapter 35 of this book, and those involved in actions requiring National Environmental Policy Act documentation should refer to Chapters 3 and 27.

CHAPTER 35

Dredge and Fill Permits under CWA Section 404

Brandon M. Tuck[1]

I. Introduction

§ 35.1 Introduction

The federal government regulates the discharge of dredged or fill material into navigable waters under section 404 of the Clean Water Act (CWA). *See* 33 U.S.C. § 1344. Navigable waters include many more surface water bodies than are actually navigable, and they also include many wetlands. As a result, myriad activities affecting these water features require section 404 authorization—both aquatic-based activities (e.g., the construction of docks, marinas, retaining walls, water intake and control structures, and dams) and activities that are generally associated with work in uplands but that may cross or otherwise affect overlapping aquatic features (e.g., infrastructure projects like roadways, pipelines, transmission lines, water and sewer lines, and other industrial, commercial, or residential developments). The focus of section 404 of the CWA is on the discharge of dredged or fill material into these aquatic features, and not on the discharge of pollutants other than dredged or fill material, which is regulated under section 402 of the CWA, as discussed in Chapter 34 of this book.

Some projects that require authorization under section 404 may also require review and authorization from the U.S. Army Corps of Engineers (Corps) under the Rivers and Harbors Act of 1899 (RHA), which generally applies to a narrower subset of navigable water bodies. For example, section 9 of the RHA, 33 U.S.C. § 401, generally prohibits the construction of any bridge, causeway, dam, or dike over or in any port, roadstead, haven, harbor, canal, navigable river, or other navigable water of the United States without federal authorization. Similarly, section 10 of the RHA, 33 U.S.C. § 403, prohibits the construction, excavation, or deposition of materials in, over, or under navigable waters of the United States or any work that would affect the course, location, condition, or capacity of such waters. In addition, section 14 of the RHA, also known as Section 408, 33 U.S.C. § 408, prohibits the altering of a civil works project (e.g., a sea wall, bulkhead, jetty, dike, levee, wharf, pier, or other work built by the United States) unless permission is granted, in order to ensure that these projects continue to provide their intended benefits to the public.

The Corps issues CWA section 404 permits after notice and opportunity for public hearings and consultation with the U.S. Environmental Protection Agency (EPA) and the states. Importantly, the EPA and the Corps interpret the scope of their authority under section 404 of the CWA to be significantly broader than the Corps' authority under sections 9, 10, and 14 of the RHA. Under the

1. Brandon M. Tuck is an attorney with Vinson & Elkins LLP in Houston, Texas, where he has practiced environmental and natural resource law since 2010. Prior to graduating from the University of Pennsylvania in 2010, Mr. Tuck worked in natural and water resource management for the U.S. Department of the Interior. Mr. Tuck is grateful for the assistance of Kevin Moscon, an associate with Vinson & Elkins, and for the work of this chapter's prior author, Janet McQuaid.

agencies' interpretation, therefore, section 404 of the CWA regulates more activities than sections 9, 10, or 14 of the RHA. A project proponent should not ignore the possible need for authorization under the RHA. Although the Corps issues a single permit under the authority of both CWA section 404 and RHA section 10 when both are required for an activity, and although the Corps may undertake a Section 408 review and grant permission in conjunction with issuance of a section 404 permit, further discussion of RHA authorizations is beyond the scope of this chapter. The balance of this chapter focuses on permits for the discharge of dredged and fill materials under section 404 of the CWA.

II. Overview of Section 404

§ 35.2 Introduction

Section 301 of the CWA prohibits pollutant discharges not in compliance with the various sections of the CWA. *See* 33 U.S.C. § 1311(a). Section 404 of the CWA authorizes the Secretary of the Army, acting through the Corps, to issue permits for the discharge of dredged or fill material into waters of the United States at specified disposal sites. 33 U.S.C. § 1344(a). The Corps maintains its headquarters in Washington, D.C., and divides its U.S. operations into eight geographic divisions. Within each division, there are several districts. The Corps administers its section 404 permitting program through the regulatory branch of each district office, with policy oversight focused at the division and headquarters levels. In Texas, the CWA section 404 permit program is administered and enforced by four Corps district offices: the Galveston District, the Fort Worth District, and the Tulsa District, all in the Corps' Southwestern Division, and the Albuquerque District, in the Corps' South Pacific Division. The Corps provides a map at www.usace.army.mil/locations.aspx that links to additional geospatial data to indicate which Texas counties are within each district's boundaries.

§ 35.3 Dredge and Fill Activities

Typical activities regulated under section 404 include site improvement fill for residential, commercial, or recreational development; construction of breakwaters, levees, dams, and dikes; and placement of fill material for roads, pipelines, and utility lines. Section 404 contains a number of statutory exemptions, which include maintenance of currently serviceable structures; normal farming, silviculture, and ranching activities; construction or maintenance of farm ponds, stock ponds, and irrigation districts; maintenance of drainage ditches; and construction or maintenance of certain farm, forest, and temporary mining roads. *See* 33 U.S.C. § 1344(f). However, as Congress included a recapture provision specifying circumstances where an exemption may not apply, persons intending to operate under a permit exemption should take care to ensure that all relevant conditions are met.

§ 35.4 Agency Roles

Responsibility for administering and enforcing the section 404 permit program is divided between the Corps and the EPA by statute, regulation, and interagency agreement.

§ 35.4:1 U.S. Army Corps of Engineers

The Corps is charged with administering the section 404 permit program, processing applications in accordance with applicable regulatory standards, and issuing permits, where appropriate, after notice and an opportunity for public comment and hearing. When making permitting decisions under section 404, the Corps must evaluate the activities using certain substantive environmental criteria contained in the EPA's regulations. These are known as the "404(b)(1) guidelines," though they are mandatory requirements and not mere "guidelines." The Corps routinely coordinates its review of section 404 permit applications with the EPA to ensure that permit decisions are made in a timely manner, while providing effective protection for human health and environmental quality. Both the EPA and the Corps have enforcement responsibility. See 33 U.S.C. § 1344(n), (s).

The policies and procedures for the Corps' program are found in 33 Code of Federal Regulations parts 320–332. Division and district engineers are authorized to issue individual permits (including standard permits and letters of permission) and general permits (such as regional, nationwide, or programmatic permits). *See* 33 C.F.R. § 325.5. Corps engineers also have the power to modify, suspend, or revoke these permits. *See* 33 C.F.R. § 325.7.

§ 35.4:2 U.S. Environmental Protection Agency

Although the Corps is solely responsible for permit decisions under CWA section 404, Congress reserved for the EPA several significant roles with respect to the section 404 permit program. The first relates to the EPA's promulgating the 404(b)(1) guidelines mentioned above, which contain the substantive environmental criteria the Corps must use when making permit decisions. Congress directed the EPA to develop these criteria in conjunction with the Corps. See 33 U.S.C. § 1344(b)(1).

Next, the EPA reviews proposed Corps permits and may provide comments to the Corps regarding compliance with the section 404(b)(1) guidelines. *See* Clean Water Act Section 404(q) Memorandum of Agreement, Part I [hereinafter 1992 section 404(q) MOA], as supplemented by the EPA's internal memoranda dated October 30, 2006, and May 1, 2008, describing the 1992 section 404(q) MOA's field-level procedures for EPA personnel. The memoranda are available at www.epa.gov/cwa-404/policy-and-guidance-documents-under-cwa-section-404. The Corps must fully consider the EPA's comments when determining compliance with the 404(b)(1) guidelines and other relevant statutes, regulations, and policies, as well as the EPA's views when making a decision to issue, issue with conditions, or deny a permit. If the Corps issues a permit over the EPA's 404(q) objections, the EPA can invoke its veto power over the permit. See 33 U.S.C. § 1344(c). Section 404(q) requires, however, that the EPA and the Corps enter into an agreement assuring that delays in the process are minimized. The 1992 section 404(q) MOA fulfills that requirement by outlining the process for resolving disputes between the EPA and the Corps during the permitting process. The 404(q) process is as follows:

- EPA "may affect" letter: To object during the comment period for the public notice, the EPA regional office must notify the Corps district engineer that the project *may* result in substantial and unacceptable impacts to aquatic resources of national importance.
- EPA "will affect" letter: If the "may affect" letter remains unresolved after the end of the comment period for the public notice, the EPA region may issue a letter signed by the regional administrator within twenty-five days of the end of the comment period stating that the project *will* have substantial and unacceptable impacts to an aquatic resource of national imortance.
- Notice of intent to proceed: Within five days of the Corps district engineer's proposed decision to issue a permit notwithstanding the Corps' receipt of the "will affect" letter, the district engineer must notify the EPA regional administrator and provide a copy of the draft permit and decision document.
- Case elevation: Within fifteen days of receipt of the notice of intent to proceed, the EPA regional administrator must decide whether to elevate review, and must subsequently notify the Corps district of the decision to forward the issue to the EPA assistant administrator with a recommendation to request review by the Assistant Secretary of the Army, Civil Works (ASACW).

- Review of Corps decision: Within twenty days of elevation, the EPA assistant administrator must decide whether to request that the ASACW review the permit decision document.
- Army review: Within thirty days of the EPA assistant administrator's request for review, the ASACW will review the permit decision document and may (1) direct the district engineer to proceed with final action on the permit decision (i.e., to issue the permit), (2) direct the district engineer to proceed with final action in accordance with case-specific policy guidance, or (3) make the final permit decision directly (including potential permit denial). The ASACW notifies the EPA assistant administrator immediately.
- Section 404(c) "veto process": If the Corps decides to issue the permit, the permit may not be issued for ten days in order to allow time for the EPA to decide whether to initiate a section 404(c) "veto" action, although the Corps may issue the permit if it is conditioned on no activity occurring for ten days or in the event that the EPA initiates a section 404(c) proceeding.

See 1992 section 404(q) MOA.

Full-blown "elevation" to the headquarters level under section 404(q) has occurred only twenty times since the 1992 section 404(q) MOA was signed. Of these twenty occurrences, eighteen were in the first fifteen years, and elevation has been sought only twice since 2007. The EPA can, however, exert considerable influence over Corps permits by taking only the initial first or second steps in this process, which can be done at the discretion of EPA regional staff. A negative "may affect" or "will affect" letter from EPA regional staff can influence an applicant to reconsider a project, even if the Corps may not agree with the EPA's views.

In 2002, the EPA issued a memorandum reminding its regional administrators that the elevation of individual permit cases must be limited to those matters that involve aquatic resources of national importance. Then, to make the EPA's role in the 404 permitting process "more consistent and effective," starting in 2006, EPA headquarters required its regional offices to clear "may affect" and "will affect" letters with EPA headquarters before sending these letters to the Corps. *See* U.S. Environmental Protection Agency, Memorandum for the Field, U.S. Environmental Protection Agency (EPA) coordination between Regional offices and Headquarters on Clean Water Act (CWA) Section 404(q) actions (Oct. 30, 2006). The EPA subsequently eliminated that requirement in 2008 for regions that had submitted at least three "may affect" or "will affect" letters to EPA headquarters. The EPA's memoranda are available at www.epa.gov/cwa-404/policy-and-guidance-documents-under-cwa-section-404.

The EPA has finalized a veto under section 404(c) only thirteen times since 1972. *See* U.S. Environmental Protection Agency, *Clean Water Act Section 404(c) "Veto Authority"* 2, www.epa.gov/sites/production/files/2016-03/documents/404c.pdf (listing vetoed permits). In 2014, the EPA proposed a fourteenth section 404(c) veto to preempt permitting for a copper mine in Bristol Bay, Alaska. The applicant sued, however, and following a settlement in May 2017, the EPA initiated a process to withdraw its proposed determination. Although the EPA withdrew the proposed determination in July 2019, the EPA announced in September 2021 its intent to change course and seek to resume efforts to protect those affected waters in the Bristol Bay watershed. *See* U.S. Environmental Protection Agency, *Bristol Bay*, www.epa.gov/bristolbay.

Notably, the EPA can exercise its veto authority to withdraw a previously finalized Corps permit. Section 404(c) provides that the EPA may deny, restrict, or withdraw specification of a site for disposal of dredged or fill material. *See* 33 U.S.C. § 1344(c). The D.C. Circuit Court of Appeals has held that the EPA is authorized to exercise this authority "whenever [the EPA administrator] determines, after notice and opportunity for public hearings, that the discharge of such materials into such area [specified for disposal] will have an unacceptable adverse effect on municipal water supplies, shellfish beds and fishery areas (including spawning and breeding areas), wildlife, or recreational areas." *Mingo Logan Coal Co. v. U.S. Environmental Protection Agency*, 714 F.3d 608, 612 (D.C. Cir. 2013) (quoting 33 U.S.C. § 1344(c)). The court further held that the EPA could exercise this "backstop" authority both prepermit and postpermit; that is, the EPA may prevent the Corps from issuing a section 404 permit specifying a disposal site or it may withdraw specification of a disposal site after the Corps has issued a permit. *See Mingo Logan Coal Co.*, 714 F.3d at 612–14, 616. The D.C. Circuit remanded the matter to the district court to consider Mingo Logan Coal's claims under the Administrative Procedure Act (APA), 5 U.S.C. §§ 500–596, including whether the EPA's withdrawal of approval of the discharge sites was arbitrary, capricious, or an abuse of decision. *Mingo Logan Coal Co.*, 714 F.3d at 616.

On remand, the district court upheld the EPA's withdrawal of approval of the disposal sites. *See Mingo Logan Coal Co. v. U.S. Environmental Protection Agency*, 70 F. Supp. 3d 151, 183 (D.D.C. 2014). While the D.C. Circuit upheld the EPA's withdrawal, it also addressed the standard that the EPA must meet to withdraw a previously issued permit. *See Mingo Logan Coal Co. v. U.S. Environmental Protection Agency*, 829 F.3d 710, 730 (D.C. Cir. 2016). The D.C. Circuit noted that the APA, 5 U.S.C. § 706(2)(A), requires the EPA to offer a satisfactory explanation for a new policy if the prior policy has engendered serious reliance interests on the part of the applicant. Although the court held that the EPA met that standard, the court declined to address the mine operator's arguments that the EPA had failed to consider both costs and benefits before revoking permits under CWA section 404 and that the operator's reliance had triggered a heightened standard for the EPA to do a "more detailed" revocation analysis than a mere "satisfactory explanation." The court held that the mine operator had not previously raised either of the last two arguments to the EPA or the district court, and therefore the mine operator forfeited these arguments at the appellate level. *See Mingo Logan Coal Co.*, 829 F.3d at 719–20, 723–24.

In summary, the *Mingo Logan Coal Co.* decisions mean that, under section 404(c), the EPA can (1) veto disposal sites before the Corps issues a permit or (2) withdraw approval after the Corps issues a permit. The limits on the EPA's postpermit withdrawal powers and standards the EPA must meet to justify such withdrawals have not yet been decided by the courts.

§ 35.4:3 Enforcement

Under a 1989 memorandum of agreement between the Corps and the EPA, the Corps is the lead enforcement agency for violations of Corps-issued permits. *See* U.S. Environmental Protection Agency, *Memorandum Between the Department of the Army and the Environmental Protection Agency* (Jan. 1989), www.epa.gov/cwa-404/federal-enforcement-section-404-program-clean-water-act [hereinafter 1989 Enforcement MOA]. The Corps is also the lead enforcement agency for unpermitted discharge violations that do not meet criteria for forwarding to the EPA as listed in the 1989 Enforcement MOA (e.g., repeat or flagrant violations, cases or classes of cases requested by the EPA, and cases where the Corps recommends that an EPA administrative penalty action may be warranted). The EPA acts as the lead enforcement agency on all unpermitted discharge violations that meet the forwarding criteria. However, if the EPA requests that the Corps take an action on a permit condition violation, and the Corps responds that it will not take an action because of limited staff resources or other reasons, the EPA may choose to take an action on its own. The EPA may not, however, take an enforcement action for an alleged permit violation if the Corps determines that the activity is in compliance with the permit.

The lead enforcement agency is the agency that will complete the enforcement action once an investigation by either agency determines that a violation exists. The lead enforcement agency's decision on any issue in a case, including a decision that no enforcement action will be taken, is final for that case. *See* 1989 Enforcement MOA. As many potential violations are resolved through an applicant's corrective actions and pursuit of an after-the-fact permit, if the Corps determines that legal action is appropriate, the Corps regulations and the 1989 Enforcement MOA provide that the Corps will not accept an after-the-fact permit application until an appropriate enforcement response has been resolved. See 33 C.F.R. § 326.3(e); 1989 Enforcement MOA, at III.G.

Section 404 has specific provisions for both civil and criminal penalties for violations. Civil penalties can be brought administratively or judicially. The agency is empowered to impose administrative penalties directly, and these penalties fall under two classes, depending on the severity. Class I administrative penalties are capped at a lower amount, are generally for less serious violations, and provide only for an informal hearing. Class I penalties may not exceed $22,584 per violation, with the maximum amount of any class I penalty not to exceed $56,460. 33 U.S.C. § 1319(g)(2)(A) (adjusted for inflation by 40 C.F.R § 19.4). Class II penalties are generally reserved for more serious violations and carry higher maximum fines. Because the punishment is more severe, the agency has a higher burden when prosecuting a class II penalty, including following the provisions of the APA. Class II penalties are capped at $22,584 per day, not to exceed $282,293 total. 33 U.S.C. § 1319(g)(2)(B) (adjusted for inflation by 40 C.F.R § 19.4). In addition to the fines, the EPA may also issue an administrative order requiring that specific actions must be taken to bring the party into compliance.

To determine the amount of an administrative penalty, the agency considers the "nature, circumstances, extent and gravity of the violation, or violations, and, with respect to the violator, ability to pay, any prior history of such violations, the degree of culpability, economic benefit or savings (if any) resulting from the violation, and such other matters as justice may require." 33 U.S.C. § 1319(g)(3). Generally, the agency will seek to recover at least the economic benefit received by the violating party. This is viewed as a necessary penalty to level the economic playing field by preventing an unfair financial advantage for noncompliance. The economic benefit analysis includes not only direct cost savings but also delayed and avoided costs, inflation, and the time value of money.

Judicial penalties are imposed by a federal judge and are sought by the agency through the Department of Justice. Penalties can be imposed without proving negligence or fault, but the defendant is entitled to a jury for the determination of liability. This process is more burdensome than that of the administrative penalties, but the associated fines can be much higher. For judicial penalties, the court may assess monetary penalties up to $56,460 per day for each violation. 33 U.S.C. § 1319(d) (adjusted for inflation by 40 C.F.R § 19.4). Penalties can grow to astronomical amounts because these amounts can accrue for each day that unauthorized discharge occurs as well as under the enforcement theory that each day that such discharged material remains in federally jurisdictional waters is a separate violation. The court is also able to issue injunctions to prevent continued violations of the CWA. Violating a court-ordered injunction carries criminal and civil penalties under the CWA and would additionally be considered contempt of court.

There is also criminal enforcement of discharge violations for negligent or knowing violations of a permit or for unauthorized discharges. Violators can be fined up to $50,000 per day of violation and imprisoned up to three years. There are also criminal charges for making false material statements relating to a permit, which could result in a fine of up to $10,000 and two years' imprisonment. Finally, knowing endangerment under the CWA can result in fines up to $250,000 for individuals and $1,000,000 for organizations, along with up to fifteen years' imprisonment for individuals. All of these maximum penalties can be doubled for repeat offenders.

While enforcement of the CWA generally belongs to the Corps and EPA pursuant to the 1989 Enforcement MOA, the CWA also empowers private citizens to bring enforcement actions for certain violations of the CWA. See 33 U.S.C. § 1365. The citizen must be affected by the violation and must provide sixty days' notice to the violator, the state, and the EPA prior to filing the suit. The notice period allows the violator or agencies to act, negating the need for the citizen suit. If the EPA or state are already prosecuting the violation, the citizen suit is not permitted to commence. The citizen suit is also barred if the violator is no longer violating the CWA. Citizen suits carry equivalent fines and injunctions as the agency-prosecuted judicial penalties discussed above; however, in addition to the penalties, the court may also award attorney's fees to the plaintiff.

The Fifth Circuit, which includes Texas, recognizes limitations on the types of citizen suits allowed under the CWA in the context of section 404 permits. The text of the CWA states that "any citizen may commence a civil action on his own behalf . . . against any person . . . who is alleged to be in violation . . . of an effluent standard or limitation under this chapter." 33 U.S.C. § 1365(a). However, the Fifth Circuit interprets the CWA as not allowing citizen suits for violations of a dredge and fill permit. See *Atchafalaya Basinkeeper v. Chustz*, 682 F.3d 356, 359 (5th Cir. 2012). Consequently, within Texas, citizen suits may not be brought against section 404 permit holders for violations of their permits; enforcement of the permit is the primary responsibility of the Corps.

§ 35.4:4 Other Agencies

Federal agencies other than the EPA play advisory and regulatory roles but do not have statutory veto authority over section 404 permit issuance. For example, the U.S. Fish and Wildlife Service (FWS) is specifically granted the opportunity to comment on individual permit applications and proposed section 404 general permits. See 33 U.S.C. § 1344(m), (q). As part of the permit process, the Corps must also complete certain required consultations, including consultation under section 7 of the Endangered Species Act with FWS and the National Marine Fisheries Service (NMFS), as appropriate for species within each agency's jurisdiction, when the Corps determines that the activity may affect listed species or their critical habitat. See 33 C.F.R. § 325.2(b)(5). The Natural Resources Conservation Service (NRCS) administers its own "Swampbuster" program, which is separate from the Corps' section 404 permitting program, to discourage the conversion of wetlands for agricultural purposes. *See* 16 U.S.C. §§ 3801–3862.

§ 35.4:5 States

Congress gave states and certain Native American tribes the opportunity to assume responsibility for administering the section 404 permitting program for some state waters, with the Corps retaining jurisdiction over tidal waters and waters used or susceptible to use as a means of transport in interstate or foreign commerce. See 33 U.S.C. §§ 1344(g), 1377(e). Only Florida, New Jersey, and Michigan have done so. Texas has not applied for the authority to administer its own section 404 permitting program. Even where they have not assumed responsibility, states have other avenues by which they may play a role in the section 404 permitting process. Despite the prominence of federal law and federal agencies in water and wetland regulation, state participation can be substantial, particularly through the certification and consultation requirements imposed on the Corps when it reviews requests for authorization under section 404. These include the following:

- The Texas Commission on Environmental Quality (TCEQ) and the Railroad Commission of Texas, which review applications for section 404 permits that require a state water quality certification under CWA section 401, as discussed in more detail later in this chapter. The TCEQ has jurisdiction over the section 401 certification for most activities, with the Railroad Commission having jurisdiction for section 401 certification activities associated with the exploration, development, or production of oil, gas, or geothermal resources.
- The Texas General Land Office (GLO), which is responsible for state-owned public lands, including coastal wetlands inland to the line of mean high tide and up rivers to the limit of tidal influence. The GLO is also the state's lead agency for coordinating the Coastal Management Plan designed to preserve public beach access, protect coastal wetlands and other coastal natural resources, and respond to beach erosion along the Texas coast. The GLO reviews federal actions along the Texas coastal zone to ensure consistency with the goals and policies of the Coastal Management Plan pursuant to the Coastal Zone Management Act (16 U.S.C. §§ 1451–1466).
- The Texas Historical Commission (serving as the State Historic Preservation Officer), with which section 106 of the National Historic Preservation Act (54 U.S.C. §§ 300101–320303)

requires consultation in order to identify and take into account effects of undertakings on historic properties. This includes the effects of issuing an individual section 404 permit or verifying coverage under general permits.

III. Threshold Jurisdictional Issues

§ 35.5 Introduction

Jurisdiction is an essential inquiry for determining regulatory compliance obligations in Texas. Federal jurisdiction has undergone significant expansion since the passage of the CWA, and the effect of that expansion on private property is most often felt through application of section 404 permitting requirements or the threat of enforcement under section 404. Jurisdiction that formerly extended only to "navigable waters" capable of being used by vessels in interstate commerce was broadened in 1972 when Congress defined that term to mean "waters of the United States, including the territorial seas." *See* 33 U.S.C. § 1362(7). The inquiry to determine whether federal jurisdiction exists over a private landowner seeking to discharge dredged or fill material is (1) whether the discharge is to a "water of the United States" and (2) whether a regulable activity—that is, a "discharge" of dredged or fill material—will occur. Part one of the inquiry is sometimes referred to as a jurisdictional determination (JD).

With respect to the first part of the jurisdictional inquiry, the Corps provides, as a public service, opportunities for applicants or prospective applicants to request the agency's JD, which can come in two forms: a preliminary jurisdictional determination (PJD) or an approved jurisdictional determination (AJD). A PJD may be useful for an applicant who wishes to move ahead expeditiously by assuming that any affected waters are jurisdictional for purposes of computing impacts, determining resource protection measures, and calculating compensatory mitigation requirements. However, a PJD is not binding on the Corps. An AJD, however, is binding on the Corps for a period of five years, and it often requires more time for the Corps to complete. *See* 33 C.F.R. pt. 331. In 2016, the Corps issued a regulatory guidance letter explaining its procedures, particularly in light of Supreme Court authority in *U.S. Army Corps of Engineers v. Hawkes Co.*, discussed in more detail at section 35.11:2 below. *See* U.S. Army Corps of Engineers, *Regulatory Guidance Letter No. 16-01* (Oct. 2016), https://usace.contentdm.oclc.org/utils/getfile/collection/p16021coll9/id/1256.

Because the determination of jurisdiction is the threshold to federal regulation, much controversy has surrounded the test for "navigable waters" (defined to include "waters of the United States" in CWA section 502) and the question whether "incidental fallback" of dredged material is a regulable "discharge." Each of these issues is discussed in more detail below.

§ 35.6 Navigable Waters and "Waters of the United States"

The interpretation of "waters of the United States" is perhaps one of the most controversial topics in environmental law. Interpretation of this phrase governs whether federal law applies to a discharge not only under section 404 but also under the National Pollutant Discharge Elimination System (NPDES) and the Oil Pollution Act programs. The following paragraphs summarize the involved trajectory of the definition of "navigable waters" and the interpretation of "waters of the United States."

Early English common-law tests found navigable waters subject to federal jurisdiction only where the water was subject to the ebb and flow of the tide. *See The Daniel Ball*, 77 U.S. 557, 563 (1871). U.S. courts departed from this test in the nineteenth century and held navigable waters were those waters "navigable-in-fact," or waters that "are used, or are susceptible of being used, in their ordinary condition" for commerce. *The Daniel Ball*, 77 U.S. at 563. Federal statutes from the nineteenth century also adopted this definition. *See, e.g.*, Rivers and Harbors Act of 1899, 30 Stat. 1121, 1151 (codified at 33 U.S.C. § 401). Congress changed the jurisdiction-defining phrase to include interstate or navigable waters under the Water Pollution Control Act of 1948 and the 1961 amendments. In 1972, Congress passed the CWA and redefined navigable waters as "waters of the United States, including the territorial seas." *See* 33 U.S.C. § 1362(7).

As both the Corps and the EPA (collectively, the agencies) administer programs governing federally jurisdictional waters, the agencies have at times worked together to define "waters of the United States" or have taken a common approach. In 1986 and 1988 rulemaking, the Corps and EPA interpreted the phrase to include waters navigable-in-fact and nonnavigable tributaries of traditionally navigable waters, and their adjacent wetlands, as well as isolated waters where the use, degradation, or destruction of such waters "could affect interstate or foreign commerce," and their adjacent wetlands. *See* 53 Fed. Reg. 20,764, 20,774 (June 6, 1988) (defining "waters of the United States" for the EPA in rules then codified at 40 C.F.R. § 232.2(q)(3), (q)(7)); Final Rule for Regulatory Programs of the Corps of Engineers, 51 Fed. Reg. 41,206 (Nov. 13, 1986) (defining "waters of the United States" for the Corps in a rule then codified at 33 C.F.R. § 328.3(a)(3), (a)(7)). In 2008, the Corps and EPA issued guidance following the Supreme Court's decision in *Rapanos v. United States* (discussed at section 35.6:1 below) regarding application of the 1986 definition. *See* Environmental Protection Agency, *2008 Rapanos Guidance and Related Documents under CWA Section 404*, www.epa.gov/cwa-404/2008-rapanos-guidance-and-related-documents-under-cwa-section-404.

In 2015, the agencies went through a new rulemaking (2015 Rule) that expanded the definition of "waters of the United States" to the limits of the "significant nexus" test described in Justice Kennedy's concurring opinion in *Rapanos* and arguably beyond that test. Jurisdiction under the 2015 Rule included waters that are (1) categorically jurisdictional or (2) deemed jurisdictional by having a significant nexus with other jurisdictional waters. *See* Clean Water Rule: Definition of "Waters of the United States," 80 Fed. Reg. 37,053 (June 29, 2015). However, the 2015 Rule was suspended by preliminary injunctions in several district courts, leaving it ineffective in twenty-eight states, including Texas. It was replaced by the Navigable Waters Protection Rule (NWPR), which largely adopted the definition offered by Justice Scalia's plurality opinion in *Rapanos* (discussed in section 35.6:1 below), scaling back federal CWA jurisdiction by, for example, including only relatively permanent waters and wetlands abutting or having a direct hydrological surface connection to those waters. *See* 85 Fed. Reg. 22,250, 22,251–52 (Apr. 21, 2020). The rule is currently being litigated in several states and was remanded back to the Corps and EPA with vacatur on August 30, 2021. *See Pasqua Yaqui Tribe v. U.S. Environmental Protection Agency*, No. cv-20-00266-TUC-RM, 2021 WL 3855977 (D. Az. Aug. 30, 2021). Following this vacatur, the Corps and EPA halted their implementation of the NWPR and have reverted to applying the 1986 definition in accordance with the 2008 *Rapanos* guidance while the agencies initiate a new rulemaking process to develop a more "durable" definition. *See* Environmental Protection Agency, *About Waters of the United States*, www.epa.gov/wotus/about-waters-united-states.

§ 35.6:1 Supreme Court Decisions Interpreting Waters of the United States

When an agency engages in the rulemaking process, it cannot contradict Supreme Court precedent. Therefore, reviewing the Supreme Court's interpretation of the CWA's definitions of "waters of the United States," prior to analyzing the agencies' rules, is instructive.

- 1985 decision in *United States v. Riverside Bayview Homes*: The Court unanimously held that the Corps acted reasonably when it required permits for discharge of fill materials into wetlands adjacent to "waters of the United States," because adjacent wetlands are "inseparably bound up with the 'waters' of the United States." 474 U.S. 134, 139 (1985).

- 2001 decision in *Solid Waste Agency of Northern Cook County v. U.S. Army Corps of Engineers (SWANCC)*: The water at issue in *SWANCC* collected in isolated, permanent and seasonal ponds from a former sand and gravel operation that were visited by migratory birds. 531 U.S. 162 (2001). At the time giving rise to the litigation, the EPA had issued guidance extending section 404 to intrastate waters that could be used by migratory birds (called the "migratory bird rule"). The Court held, however, that the use of the ponds by migratory birds was independently insufficient for federal jurisdiction under the CWA. The significant nexus between the wetlands and the navigable water in *Riverside* was not a factor in *SWANCC. See* 531 U.S. at 167.
- 2006 decision in *Rapanos v. United States* and *Carabell v. U.S. Army Corps of Engineers* (collectively, *Rapanos*): In a plurality opinion, which has caused circuit splits due to its lack of binding precedent, the Court attempted to define "waters of the United States" in the context of wetlands near ditches or man-made drains that discharge into traditional navigable water. *Rapanos*, 547 U.S. 715, 729 (2006). Justice Scalia, joined by three other justices, adopted a narrow test for jurisdiction, where only wetlands with a "continuous surface connection" to "waters of the United States" would be jurisdictional. *Rapanos*, 547 U.S. at 742. In contrast, Justice Kennedy's concurrence advanced federal jurisdiction to wetlands and waters with a "significant nexus" to traditionally navigable waters, where there is a "reasonable inference of ecological interconnection." *Rapanos*, 547 U.S. at 779–80.

§ 35.6:2 Post-*Rapanos* Circuit Court Case Law

Many federal circuit courts have opined on the effect of the *Rapanos* plurality, but with inconsistent results. Commentators and the courts continue to debate whether the split decision in *Rapanos* establishes a legal standard that binds the lower courts, because it is difficult to discern common elements on which the plurality and the concurring opinions in *Rapanos* agree to find a holding on the "narrowest grounds" of a plurality opinion. *See Marks v. United States*, 430 U.S. 188, 193 (1977). The present outcomes in the circuits currently favor Justice Kennedy's concurrence, which also served as the fundamental basis for the 2015 Rule. However, when the NWPR was in force, there was renewed attention on Justice Scalia's plurality opinion.

The circuit courts have split on whether any *Rapanos* standard establishes binding precedent and, if so, which standard controls. Some circuits have avoided the issue by finding, under the facts of the cases before them, that all of the *Rapanos* standards are met. In particular, the Seventh, Ninth, and Eleventh Circuits have held that Justice Kennedy's concurrence contains the controlling standard. *See United States v. Gerke Excavating, Inc.*, 464 F.3d 723, 725 (7th Cir. 2006) (Kennedy's test "must govern the further stages of this litigation"); *Northern California River Watch v. City of Healdsburg*, 496 F.3d 993, 995 (9th Cir. 2007) ("In a 4-4-1 decision, the controlling opinion is that of Justice Kennedy who said that to qualify as a regulable water under the CWA the body of water itself need not be continuously flowing, but that there must be a 'significant nexus' to a waterway that is in fact navigable."); *United States v. Robison*, 505 F.3d 1208, 1221 (11th Cir. 2007) ("[W]e join the Seventh and the Ninth Circuits' conclusion that Justice Kennedy's 'significant nexus' test provides the governing rule of *Rapanos*.").

The First, Third, and Eighth Circuits have held that there is jurisdiction as long as either Justice Kennedy's or the plurality's test is satisfied. *See United States v. Johnson*, 467 F.3d 56, 60 (1st Cir. 2006) ("We conclude that the United States may assert jurisdiction over the target sites if it meets either Justice Kennedy's legal standard or that of the plurality."); *United States v. Donovan*, 661 F.3d 174, 184 (3d Cir. 2011) ("We hold that federal jurisdiction to regulate wetlands under the CWA exists if the wetlands meet either the plurality's test or Justice Kennedy's test from *Rapanos*."); *United States v. Bailey*, 571 F.3d 791, 799 (8th Cir. 2009) ("[W]e join the First Circuit in holding that the Corps has jurisdiction over wetlands that satisfy either the plurality or Justice Kennedy's test.").

The Second, Fourth, and Sixth Circuits have declined to state which standard is controlling. *See, e.g., Catskill Mountains Chapter of Trout Unlimited, Inc. v. U.S. Environmental Protection Agency*, 8 F. Supp. 3d 500, 565–66 (S.D.N.Y. 2014) (finding that the definition of "navigable waters" in *Rapanos* "is binding on this Court and on the EPA" but using all three *Rapanos* tests to evaluate the term "navigable waters"); *Precon Development Corp. v. U.S. Army Corps of Engineers*, 633 F.3d 278, 288 (4th Cir. 2011) (noting that because the parties agreed that the Kennedy "significant nexus" test would apply, the court did "not address the issue of whether the plurality's 'continuous surface connection' test provides an alternate ground upon which CWA jurisdiction can be established"); *United States v. Cundiff*, 555 F.3d 200, 210 (6th Cir. 2009) ("[J]urisdiction is proper here under both Justice Kennedy's and the plurality's tests, so we leave ultimate resolution of the *Marks*-meets-*Rapanos* debate to a future case that turns on which test in fact controls.").

The Fifth Circuit (which includes Texas, Louisiana, and Mississippi) has generally refrained from taking an expansive view of CWA jurisdiction, requiring in contexts other than wetlands that, to be jurisdictional, the waters in question must be "truly adjacent to navigable waters" or at least have a "significant measure of proximity." *See In re Needham*, 354 F.3d 340, 345–46, 347 n.12 (5th Cir. 2003); *see also Rice v. Harken Exploration Co.*, 250 F.3d 264, 269 (5th Cir. 2001) (relating to discharges to groundwater). Since *Rapanos*, the Fifth Circuit has not clearly stated which test it would follow. It has avoided the question in specific cases both by mentioning *Rapanos* without further analysis or by acknowledging that evidence presented at trial was sufficient to satisfy either test, absolving the court of the need to pick a side. *See United States v. Lipar*, 665 Fed. Appx. 322, 325 (5th Cir. 2016); *Gulf Restoration Network v. McCarthy*, 783 F.3d 227, 230 n.3 (5th Cir. 2015) (noting in dicta that "[t]he outer limit of the phrase 'waters of the United States' remains fuzzy"); *United States v. Lucas*, 516 F.3d 316, 327 (5th Cir. 2008) ("[T]he evidence presented at trial supports all three of the *Rapanos* standards."); *compare United States v. Chevron Pipe Line Co.*, 437 F. Supp. 2d 605, 614–25 (N.D. Tex. 2006) (reasoning that *Rapanos* did not establish binding legal precedent to hold that the government did not have jurisdiction over an oil spill to an intermittent tributary), *with Smith v. The Abandoned Vessel*, 610 F. Supp. 2d 739, 749 (S.D. Tex. 2009) (noting that navigable waters include those waters that meet the *Rapanos* plurality's two-element test).

Separately, discharges into groundwater may be considered discharges into waters of the United States when the discharge has the "functional equivalence" of a traditional point source discharge. *County of Maui v. Hawaii Wildlife Fund*, 140 S. Ct. 1462 (2020). In *Maui*, the Court rejected "a more absolute position" and adopted a fact-intensive approach to determine whether a discharge into groundwater has the equivalence of a discharge into waters of the United States. The "functional equivalence test" requires a court to consider a multitude of factors when establishing whether CWA jurisdiction applies to a groundwater discharge. While the Court expounded seven factors that might be considered, including distance and time, it did not mandate any specific consideration requirements. *County of Maui*, 140 S. Ct. at 1476–77. Instead, the Court noted that further guidance and boundary shaping will have to develop from cases brought in the lower courts and from EPA guidance. *County of Maui*, 140 S. Ct. at 1477. The result is uncertainty for all nonpermitted discharges—both those into jurisdictionally indeterminant waters and those into groundwater. In Texas, *Maui* complicates existing case law that previously held discharges into groundwater were not discharges into waters of the United States under the CWA. *Rice*, 250 F.3d at 271. Since *Maui*, the federal courts in Texas have not had the opportunity to apply the "functional equivalence" test to a live controversy, so it remains unclear how the new test will affect jurisdiction of groundwater discharges in the state.

§ 35.6:3 "Waters of the United States" Rule Currently in Effect in Texas

The current definition of "waters of the United States" in effect in Texas has recently been in flux, as it has been across the nation. The NWPR had gone into effect in 2020 but was vacated in August 2021. Before the NWPR, Texas had obtained an injunction preventing enforcement of the 2015 Rule within the state. *See Texas v. U.S. Environmental Protection Agency*, No. 3:15-CV-00162, 2018 WL 45182230 (S.D. Tex. Sept. 12, 2018) (order granting preliminary injunction); No. 3:15-CV-00162, 2019 WL 2272464 (S.D. Tex. May 28, 2019) (memorandum opinion and order). Under the injunction and prior to the NWPR, practitioners in Texas relied on the 1986/1988 rules and the Supreme Court precedent in *Riverside*, *SWANCC*, and *Rapanos* discussed above. It is to these rules that the agencies have returned following the August 2021 vacatur of the NWPR. The following sections provide the various definitions that have been promulgated over the last few decades, beginning with rulemaking in 1986 and 1988, and then on to the 2015 Rule and the NWPR. These provide not only a historical perspective, but they also add insight into what definitions may apply in the future as courts continue to wrestle with challenges to rulemaking and as the agencies undertake additional rulemaking efforts.

1986/1988 Rules: In the 1986/1988 version of the rules, the EPA and the Corps interpreted the term "waters of the United States" to include not only waters susceptible to use in interstate commerce—the traditional understanding of the phrase "navigable waters of the United States"—but also tributaries of those waters, including intermittent and ephemeral streams, as well as wetlands adjacent to those waters or their tributaries. Specifically, the 1986/1988 rules defined "waters of the United States" in relevant part to mean—

(1) All waters which are currently used, or were used in the past, or may be susceptible to use in interstate or foreign commerce, including all waters which are subject to the ebb and flow of the tide;

(2) All interstate waters including interstate wetlands;

(3) All other waters such as intrastate lakes, rivers, streams (including intermittent streams), mudflats, sandflats, wetlands, sloughs, prairie potholes, wet meadows, playa lakes, or natural ponds, the use, degradation or destruction of which could affect interstate or foreign commerce including any such waters:

 (i) Which are or could be used by interstate or foreign travelers for recreational or other purposes; or

 (ii) From which fish or shellfish are or could be taken and sold in interstate or foreign commerce; or

 (iii) Which are used or could be used for industrial purposes by industries in interstate commerce;

(4) All impoundments of waters otherwise defined as waters of the United States under this definition;

(5) Tributaries of waters identified in paragraphs (s)(1) through (4) of this section;

> (6) The territorial seas;
>
> (7) Wetlands adjacent to waters (other than waters that are themselves wetlands) identified in paragraphs (s)(1) through (6) of this section; waste treatment systems, including treatment ponds or lagoons designed to meet the requirements of CWA (other than cooling ponds as defined in 40 CFR 423.11(m) which also meet the criteria of this definition) are not waters of the United States.
>
> Waters of the United States do not include prior converted cropland. Notwithstanding the determination of an area's status as prior converted cropland by any other federal agency, for the purposes of the Clean Water Act, the final authority regarding Clean Water Act jurisdiction remains with EPA.

53 Fed. Reg. 20,765, 20,774 (June 6, 1988) (defining "waters of the United States" for the EPA in rules then codified at 40 C.F.R. § 232.2(q)(3), (q)(7)); Final Rule for Regulatory Programs of the Corps of Engineers, 51 Fed. Reg. 41,206 (Nov. 13, 1986) (defining "waters of the United States" for the Corps in a rule then codified at 33 C.F.R. § 328.3(a)(3), (a)(7)).

2008 Jurisdictional Guidance: On December 2, 2008, the Corps and the EPA issued joint guidance entitled "Clean Water Act Jurisdiction Following the U.S. Supreme Court's Decision in *Rapanos v. United States* & *Carabell v. United States*" [hereinafter 2008 Guidance]. The 2008 Guidance is available on the EPA's and the Corps' websites at www.epa.gov/sites/production/files/2016-02/documents/cwa_jurisdiction_following_rapanos120208.pdf and https://usace.contentdm.oclc.org/utils/getfile/collection/p16021coll5/id/1411, respectively. The 2008 Guidance interpreted the 1986/1988 rules and supplemented an earlier joint memorandum issued by the Corps and the EPA, which rescinded the migratory bird rule in January 2003. *See* Advance Notice of Proposed Rulemaking on the Clean Water Act Regulatory Definition of "Waters of the United States," 68 Fed. Reg. 1991, 1995 app. A (Jan. 15, 2003) (reprinting prior guidance superseding the migratory bird rule in light of the Supreme Court's decision in *SWANNC*, 531 U.S. 159 (2011)).

§ 35.6:4 Discussion of the 2015 Rule

The 2015 Rule revised the definition of "waters of the United States" throughout all CWA regulation sections. *See* 33 C.F.R. pt. 328 (Corps permits under section 404), 40 C.F.R. pt. 230 (EPA guidelines for specified disposal sites under section 404), 40 C.F.R. pt. 232 (EPA section 404 exemptions); *see also* 40 C.F.R. pt. 110 (discharge of oil), pt. 112 (oil pollution prevention), pt. 116 (designation of hazardous substances under the CWA), pt. 117 (reportable quantities under the CWA), pt. 122 (NPDES permits), pt. 300 (CERCLA National Contingency Plan), pt. 302 (CERCLA reportable quantities), pt. 401 (CWA effluent limitation guidelines).

The 2015 Rule enlarged the seven categories of "waters of the United States" from the 1986/1988 rules. This expansion had the effect of broadening the coverage of the CWA to waters not previously within federal jurisdiction. The 2015 Rule outlines three overarching categories of water: (1) waters categorically jurisdictional, (2) waters deemed jurisdictional on a case-by-case basis by having a "significant nexus" with other jurisdictional waters, and (3) waters categorically excluded from jurisdiction.

Categorically Jurisdictional Waters: The 2015 Rule included these same categorically jurisdictional waters as the 1986/1988 rules:

> (1) All waters which are currently used, were used in the past, or may be susceptible to use

in interstate or foreign commerce, including all waters which are subject to the ebb and flow of the tide;

(2) All interstate waters, including interstate wetlands;

(3) The territorial seas;

(4) All impoundments of waters otherwise identified as waters of the United States under this section;

(5) All tributaries, as defined in paragraph (c)(3) of this section, of waters identified in paragraphs (a)(1) through (3) of this section.

80 Fed. Reg. 37,054, 37,104 (June 29, 2015).

Notably, the 2015 Rule defined "tributary" for the first time. Only those tributaries that met the definition and flowed directly or indirectly to waters listed above were "waters of the United States." *See* 80 Fed. Reg. 37,105–06. The rule defined "tributary" to require the presence of the physical indicators of a bed and banks and an ordinary high-water mark. *See* 80 Fed. Reg. 37,105–06. The rule stated that a tributary may be natural, man-altered, or man-made water and included waters such as rivers, streams, canals, and ditches not excluded under the specific exclusions from the definition of "waters of the United States," discussed in more detail later in this chapter. *See* 80 Fed. Reg. 37,105–06. Unlike the 1986/1988 rule, the preamble to the 2015 Rule stated that tributaries were always jurisdictional waters, as long as they met the definition, even if they are perennial, ephemeral, or intermittent. *See* 80 Fed. Reg. 37,068.

The 2015 Rule revised category (6) of the jurisdictional categories of waters. The 1986/1988 rules defined category (6) to include "adjacent wetland." The 2015 Rule revision included "all waters" adjacent to a jurisdictional water identified in categories (1) through (5), including "wetlands, ponds, lakes, oxbows, impoundments, and similar waters." 80 Fed. Reg. 37,104. Thus, the 2015 Rule expanded this category to include other waters, not only wetlands. Further expansion occurred in the 2015 Rule's definition of "adjacent." The 2015 Rule preserved the definition of adjacent, meaning "bordering, contiguous, or neighboring," but expanded that definition to also include waters laterally adjacent to jurisdictional waters under categories (1) through (5) and water adjacent to the headwaters of those jurisdictional waters. *See* 80 Fed. Reg. 37,105. Importantly, the 2015 Rule did not require adjacent waters to have a significant nexus to jurisdictional waters. The rule also defined "neighboring" to mean within 100 feet of the ordinary high-water mark (OHWM) of a type (1) through (5) water or within the one-hundred-year floodplain and not more than 1,500 feet from the OHWM, or within 1,500 feet of the high tide line of a type (1) through (3) water. If any part of a water is "neighboring," all of the water would be considered jurisdictional. *See* 80 Fed. Reg. 37,105.

Jurisdictional Waters on a Case-by-Case Basis: The second category of "waters of the United States" under the 2015 Rule was found under subsections (7) and (8) and adopted a version of Justice Kennedy's test espoused in *Rapanos*. This included certain waters defined under (7)(i) through (v) and having a "significant nexus" with other waters under subsections (1) through (3), which are waters used for interstate commerce or subject to the ebb and flow of the tide, interstate waters and wetlands, and territorial seas. In addition to the five types of waters listed in 33 C.F.R. § 328.3(a)(7), the significant nexus test applied to waters in paragraph (a)(8), which included the one-hundred-year floodplain of traditionally navigable waters, interstate waters and wetlands, and the territorial seas, and to all waters within 4,000 feet of the high tide line of these types of waters (if tidal) or their tributaries or impoundments. *See* 80 Fed. Reg. 37,105 (codified at 33 C.F.R. § 328.3(a)(8)). If waters in these areas were also "adjacent waters" under paragraph (a)(6), then they were covered adjacent waters and no case-specific significant nexus analysis was required for jurisdiction to attach.

"Significant nexus" under the 2015 Rule was defined to mean "that a water, including wetlands, either alone or in combination with other similarly situated waters in the region, significantly affects the chemical, physical, or biological integrity of a water identified in paragraphs (a)(1) through (3) of this section." 80 Fed. Reg. 37,106. For an effect to be significant, it must have been more than speculative or insubstantial. The rule listed nine water quality functions considered to be relevant to a "significant nexus" evaluation, including sediment trapping; nutrient recycling; pollutant trapping, transformation, filtering, and transport; retention and attenuation of flood waters; runoff storage; contribution of flow; export of organic matter; export of food resources; and provision of life cycle–dependent aquatic habitat. *See* 80 Fed. Reg. 37,106. Additional details on the "significant nexus" evaluation are provided in the rule.

Categorically Nonjurisdictional Waters: Waters listed under this third category were excluded from CWA jurisdiction, including waste treatment systems; prior converted cropland; certain ditches with ephemeral or intermittent flow and ditches that do not flow directly into "waters of the United States"; artificial features such as areas that would revert to dry land should application of water to that area cease; constructed lakes and ponds created in dry land for uses such as farm and stock watering ponds, irrigation ponds, settling basins, fields flooded for rice growing, log cleaning ponds, or cooling ponds; reflecting pools or swimming pools created in dry land; small ornamental waters created in dry land; water-filled depressions created in dry land incidental to mining or construction activity, including pits excavated for obtaining fill, sand, or gravel that fill with water; erosional features, including gullies, rills, and other ephemeral features that do not meet the definition of tributary, non-wetland swales, and lawfully constructed grassed waterways; puddles, groundwater, stormwater-control features constructed to convey, treat, or store stormwater that are created in dry land; and, finally, wastewater recycling structures constructed in dry land such as detention and retention basins, groundwater recharge basins, percolation ponds, and water distributary structures. *See* 80 Fed. Reg. 37,105.

§ 35.6:5 Litigation and Replacement of the 2015 Rule

As stated previously, as a result of challenges to the rule brought at the district court level, the 2015 Rule was previously enjoined in twenty-eight states, including Texas, Louisiana, and Mississippi (*Texas v. U.S. Environmental Protection Agency*, No. 3:15-CV-00162, 2018 WL 45182230 (S.D. Tex. Sept. 12, 2018)). For a time, the 2015 Rule was effective in twenty-two states. Opponents to the rule brought challenges in both federal district and appellate courts, and the Supreme Court ruled that under the CWA, the challenges are properly first brought in district courts. *See National Ass'n of Manufacturers v. Department of Defense*, 138 S. Ct. 617 (2018).

In accordance with a Trump administration executive order in 2017, the EPA and the Corps proposed a two-step process to replace the 2015 Rule. *See* U.S. Environmental Protection Agency, *Navigable Waters Protection Rule: About Waters of the United States*, www.epa.gov/nwpr/about-waters-united-states. "Step one" rulemaking repealed the 2015 Rule in October 2019 and returned the definitions of jurisdiction to the 1986/1988 rules. 84 Fed. Reg. 56,626 (Oct. 22, 2019). "Step two" rulemaking replaced the 1986/1988 rule in April 2020 (85 Fed. Reg. 22,250 (Apr. 21, 2020)) with the NWPR, a narrowed definition of "waters of the United States."

§ 35.6:6 Navigable Waters Protection Rule

The Navigable Waters Protection Rule replaces the 2015 Rule and scales back the scope of federal jurisdiction under the CWA. Under the NWPR, "waters of the United States" exclusively consists of four definitional categories:

(1) territorial seas and traditional navigable waters;

(2) perennial and intermittent tributaries of the territorial seas and navigable waters;

(3) certain lakes, ponds, and impoundments of jurisdictional waters; and

(4) wetlands adjacent to jurisdictional waters.

85 Fed. Reg. 22,250, 22,251 (Apr. 21, 2020).

These categories intentionally follow the definition proposed by Justice Scalia in the plurality decision for *Rapanos*. Under that definition, "'waters of the United States' includes only those relatively permanent, standing or continuously flowing bodies of water 'forming geographic features' that are described in ordinary parlance as 'streams[,] . . . oceans, rivers, [and] lakes,'" and ''wetlands with a continuous surface connection'' to a ''relatively permanent body of water connected to traditional interstate navigable waters.'' *Rapanos v. United States*, 547 U.S. 715, 739, 742 (Scalia, J., plurality) (quoting *Webster's New International Dictionary* 2882 (2d ed. 1954)).

The NWPR explicitly excludes all other waters and provides further clarifications of the above terms. The rule makes the following key changes to the 2015 Rule:

- Removes CWA coverage of "ephemeral waters" that flow or pool only in response to precipitation and certain ditches that contain ephemeral flows or are "upland" from other jurisdictional waters.
- Requires water to flow continuously year-round (perennial waters) or during certain times of the year (intermittent waters) for CWA coverage.
- Includes only lakes and ponds that are traditionally navigable waters subject to federal jurisdiction or that are connected to such waters through tributaries.
- Removes interstate waters—or waters that form part of a state's boundary—as an independent category of waters subject to the CWA.
- Narrows wetland coverage to include only wetlands that abut jurisdictional waters or that have a direct hydrological connection to such waters, and excluding wetlands separated by a berm, dike, or other barrier.
- Requires jurisdictional determinations to be made based on "typical year" conditions, which are based on precipitation, drought, and other climatic factors over the previous thirty years of data.

See U.S. Environmental Protection Agency, *Fact Sheet: Navigable Waters Protection Rule*, www.epa.gov/sites/production/files/2020-01/documents/nwpr_fact_sheet_-_overview.pdf.

§ 35.6:7 Outlook on the NWPR and Waters of the United States

The Navigable Waters Protection Rule was in effect nationwide but was vacated in August 2021. Other lawsuits targeting the NWPR have included those that claim that the new rule is too expansive and others that claim it is too restrictive; these provide a model for likely litigation over any new rulemakings that may emerge, such as the one the Biden administration's EPA and Corps are currently commencing. *See, e.g., Conservation Law Foundation v. Environmental Protection Agency*, No. 1:20-cv-10820-DPW (D. Mass. 2020) (environmental groups claim the rule adopts an unreasonably narrow interpretation of the CWA); *New Mexico Cattle Grower's Ass'n v. Environmental Protection Agency*, No. 1:19-cv-00988-RB-SCY (D. NM 2020) (ranchers seek to remove federal jurisdiction over intermittent water); *S.C. Coastal Conservation League v. Wheeler*, No. 2:20-cv-01687 DCN (D.S.C. 2020) (environmental groups claim the rule is unintelligible, inconsistent, detached from science, and inconsistent with the CWA). Colorado was briefly successful at obtaining an injunction to halt application of the NWPR within the state's boundaries, but the district court's decision was overturned on appeal. *Colorado v. U.S. Environmental Protection Agency*, 445 F. Supp. 3d 1295, 1303 (D. Colo. 2020), *rev'd and vacated*, No. 20-1238, 2021 WL 790999 (10th Cir. Mar. 2, 2021). Seventeen other states and two cities sought a nationwide injunction based on claims that the new rule violated federal law and failed to follow the intent of the CWA, but these states have been unsuccessful. *California v. Wheeler*, 467 F. Supp. 3d 864, 871 (N.D. Cal. 2020) (motion for preliminary injunction denied).

In the meantime, a JD is dependent on the rule defining "waters of the United States" that is in effect at the time of the JD. *See* 33 C.F.R. § 325.9 (Corps engineers authorized to determine jurisdictional area by the terms "navigable waters" and "waters of the United States"); *see also* 80 Fed. Reg. 37,054, 37,074 (June 29, 2015) ("As a general matter, the agencies' actions are governed by the rule in effect at the time the agency issues a jurisdictional determination or permit authorization."); U.S. Army Corps of Engineers, *Jurisdictional Determination Form Instructional Guidebook* 1 n.1 (May 30, 2007), www.nap.usace.army.mil/Portals/39/docs/regulatory/jdjd_guidebook_051207final.pdf (decisions on a water will be based on applicable statutes, regulations, and case law). At present, JDs in Texas are governed by the 1986/1988 rules.

§ 35.7 Identifying the Presence of a Wetland

Regardless of which definition of "waters of the United States" is considered, all include wetlands to one degree or another. Thus, it is necessary to consider how the Corps and the EPA evaluate whether an area is a wetland.

The Corps and the EPA define "wetlands" as those areas that are "inundated or saturated by surface or groundwater at a frequency and duration sufficient to support, and that under normal circumstances do support, a prevalence of vegetation typically adapted for life in saturated soil conditions. Wetlands generally include swamps, marshes, bogs, and similar areas." 33 C.F.R. § 328.3(c)(16); 40 C.F.R. § 120.2(3)(xvi).

Three characteristics are required to consider an area a wetland: hydrophytic vegetation, hydric soil, and wetland hydrology. All three wetland characteristics must be present during some portion of the growing season for an area to be considered a jurisdictional wetland. *See* U.S. Army Corps of Engineers, *Corps of Engineers Wetlands Delineation Manual* pt. II, § 26 (Environmental Laboratory Jan. 1987), www.lrh.usace.army.mil/Portals/38/docs/USACE%2087%20Wetland%20Delineation%20Manual.pdf [hereinafter *Delineation Manual*]. Recognizing the importance of developing regional revisions to the *Delineation Manual*, the Corps has developed region-specific, supplemental procedural guidance for delineating wetlands. In Texas, practitioners should refer to Regional Supplements for the Arid West, the Great Plains, or the Atlantic and Gulf Coastal Plains, according to the geographic location of the project. These Regional Supplements may replace or supersede the contents of the *Delineation Manual*, as the supplements provide the latest updated guidance for wetland delineation.

§ 35.7:1 Vegetation Indicators

The vegetation characteristic is determined by the presence of hydrophytic plants (e.g., cattails, bulrushes, cordgrass, sphagnum moss, bald cypress, and willows). Absent specific identification of hydrophytic plants, some readily visible situations indicate a strong possibility that an area is a wetland. These include the presence of trees with shallow root systems, swollen trunks, or roots found growing from the trunk above the soil surface. See *Delineation Manual* pt. III, §§ 29–35, for a discussion of hydrophytic vegetation.

Approximately 5,200 plant types may occur in wetlands in the United States. The FWS published a "National List of Plant Species that Occur in Wetlands" in 1988, and it has been used extensively in wetland delineations and related projects as the National Wetland Plant List. In 2006, the FWS transferred administration of the National Wetland Plant List to the Corps, and the Corps began a collaborative and ongoing process to update the list. The Corps' current National Wetland Plant List is available at https://wetland-plants.usace.army.mil/nwpl_static/v34/home/home.html.

§ 35.7:2 Soil Indicators

The soil characteristic is determined by the presence, as judged by the Corps, of hydric soil. The NRCS maintains a list of hydric soils occurring in the United States. *See* U.S. Department of Agriculture, Natural Resources Conservation Service, *Hydric Soils*, www.nrcs.usda.gov/wps/portal/nrcs/main/soils/use/hydric/. The *Delineation Manual* discusses hydric soils in pt. III, §§ 36–45, and it notes the importance of referring to other reference materials in making these determinations.

§ 35.7:3 Hydrology Indicators

The wetland hydrology characteristic is judged by the presence of water at or above the soil surface for a sufficient period of time during the growing season. Although the best evidence of wetland hydrology may be provided by a gauging station or groundwater well data, other visual indicators are often present. These include standing or flowing water during some portion of the growing season; waterlogged soil during the growing season; or water marks, drift lines, flood debris, or sedimentary deposits on leaves or other objects. *See Delineation Manual* pt. III, §§ 46–49.

§ 35.8 Determining the Scope of "Discharge": Incidental Fallback

As the foregoing discussion illustrates, whether the EPA or the Corps has jurisdiction over certain waters that may be affected by an activity may, in many cases, be far from settled. Even when a project developer addresses that difficult jurisdictional question, there is yet another jurisdictional issue to be evaluated: whether the *activity* in question results in a "regulable discharge."

Mechanized equipment working to excavate material from "waters of the United States" has the potential to discharge dredged and fill material into those waters, and section 404 of the CWA allows the Corps to issue permits for that "discharge of dredged or fill material." The Corps and the EPA have long sought to define this phrase to assert jurisdiction over excavation activities. The following sections discuss the history of the agencies' regulatory efforts and implications of court decisions regarding the scope of federal jurisdiction over excavation activities that may result in incidental fallback of dredged or fill material.

§ 35.8:1 Corps' Initial Rule

Initially, in 1986, the Corps promulgated a rule that would exempt incidental fallback from the requirement for a section 404 permit by defining the phrase "discharge of dredged material" as "[a]ny addition of dredged material into the waters of the United States" except "*de minimis*, incidental soil movement occurring during normal dredging operations," commonly referred to as "incidental fallback." *See* 51 Fed. Reg. 41,206, 41,232 (Nov. 13, 1986).

§ 35.8:2 Tulloch Rule

Environmental groups challenged the Corps' 1986 definition in *California Wildlife Federation v. Tulloch* (Civ. No. C90-713-CIV-5-BO (E.D.N.C. 1992)). This challenge led to a settlement that resulted in a zero-discharge definition of "discharge of dredged material": "[A]ny addition of dredged material into, including redeposit of dredged material within, the waters of the United States." 58 Fed. Reg. 45,008, 45,035 (Aug. 25, 1993). This rule was commonly referred to as the "Tulloch Rule."

Industry groups succeeded in having this rule overturned, as ultimately affirmed by the D.C. Circuit Court of Appeals in *National Mining Ass'n v. U.S. Army Corps of Engineers*, 145 F.3d 1399 (D.C. Cir. 1998). The D.C. Circuit Court held that "the straightforward statutory term 'addition' cannot reasonably be said to encompass the situation in which material is removed from the waters of the United States and a small portion of it happens to fall back." *National Mining*, 145 F.3d at 1404. The court noted, however, that since the statute "sets out no bright line between incidental fallback on the one hand and regulable redeposits on the other, a reasoned attempt by the agencies to draw such a line would merit considerable deference." *National Mining*, 145 F.3d at 1405. The court therefore affirmed the judgment of the district court and enjoined the Corps and the EPA from enforcing the Tulloch Rule. *National Mining*, 145 F.3d at 1401, 1410.

§ 35.8:3 Interim Rule (1999)

In 1999, in response to the *National Mining* decision, the Corps and the EPA promulgated an interim rule that removed the word "any" before "redeposit" and excluded "incidental fallback" from the definition of discharge of dredged material, as follows: "Any addition, including redeposit other than incidental fallback, of dredged material, including excavated material, into waters of the United States which is incidental to any activity, including mechanized landclearing, ditching, channelization, or other excavation." 64 Fed. Reg. 25,120, 25,123 (May 10, 1999). The agencies did not define the term "incidental fallback" but promised to expeditiously undertake further rulemaking to "enhance clarity, certainty, and consistency in determining what activities are subject to section 404 in light of the [*National Mining*] decision." 64 Fed. Reg. 25,121. In the meantime, the agencies would decide whether a discharge of dredged material was regulable on a "case-by-case basis." *See* 64 Fed. Reg. 25,121.

After the D.C. Circuit affirmed the lower court's overturning of the Tulloch Rule, the lower court subsequently had occasion to review the interim rule. In *American Mining Congress v. U.S. Army Corps of Engineers*, 120 F. Supp. 2d 23 (D.D.C. 2000), the court found the interim rule facially consistent with the court's prior injunction of the Tulloch Rule, noting in particular that "the [interim] rule makes clear that the agencies may not exercise § 404 jurisdiction over redeposits of dredged material to the extent that the redeposits involve only incidental fallback." *American Mining Congress*, 120 F. Supp. 2d at 29. The court noted that the agencies planned to make a "reasoned attempt to more clearly delineate the scope of CWA jurisdiction over redeposits of dredged material" through notice and comment rulemaking. *American Mining Congress*, 120 F. Supp. 2d at 27. In the meantime, the district court approved the agencies' interim approach of determining jurisdiction on a case-by-case basis about whether a particular redeposit constitutes incidental fallback. *American Mining Congress*, 120 F. Supp. 2d at 27. The agencies contend that the 1999 "interim rule" is currently in effect.

§ 35.8:4 Tulloch II Rule (2001)

In 2001, the Corps and the EPA published the "Tulloch II Rule." This rule defined the phrase "discharge of dredged material" to mean—

> the use of mechanized earth-moving equipment to conduct landclearing, ditching, channelization, in-stream mining or other earth-moving activity in waters of the United States as resulting in a discharge of dredged material unless project-specific evidence shows that the activity results in only incidental fallback. This paragraph does not and is not intended to shift any burden in any administrative or judicial proceeding under the CWA.

66 Fed. Reg. 4550, 4575 (Jan. 17, 2001). The Tulloch II Rule also defined the term "incidental fallback":

> Incidental fallback is the redeposit of small volumes of dredged material that is incidental to excavation activity in waters of the United States when such material falls back to substantially the same place as the initial removal. Examples of incidental fallback include soil that is disturbed when dirt is shoveled and the back-spill that comes off a bucket when such small volume of soil or dirt falls into substantially the same place from which it was initially removed.

66 Fed. Reg. 4575.

Industry groups challenged this definition in the D.C. district court. The district court initially dismissed the appeal for lack of ripeness on the merits, but this dismissal was reversed and remanded on appeal. *See National Ass'n of Home Builders v. U.S. Army Corps of Engineers*, 440 F.3d 459, 464 (D.C. Cir. 2006). On remand, the district court disapproved the agencies' reliance in the Tulloch II Rule solely on "small volumes" to define incidental fallback, suggesting that larger volumes might also be considered incidental fallback, depending on the length of time the material is held before being dropped and the distance between the place collected to the place dropped. *National Ass'n of Home Builders v. U.S. Army Corps of Engineers*, No. 01-0274 (JR), 2007 WL 259944, at *3 (D.D.C. Jan. 30, 2007) [hereinafter *NAHB*]. The district court indicated an expectation that the Corps and the EPA would try again to refine the distinction between regulable "discharges of dredged material" and nonregulable "incidental fallback," but it warned that the agencies "cannot require 'project-specific evidence' from projects over which they have no regulatory authority." *NAHB*, 2007 WL 259944, at *3. The district court therefore enjoined the agencies from enforcing the Tulloch II Rule. *NAHB*, 2007 WL 259944, at *4.

§ 35.8:5 Current Rule

In 2008, the Corps and the EPA responded to the district court's decision in the *NAHB* case by abandoning the Tulloch II Rule and publishing a joint rule at 73 Fed. Reg. 79,641 (Dec. 30, 2008). The agencies stated that the *NAHB* court's decision on the Tulloch II Rule effectively reinstated the text of the 1999 interim rule, and the joint rule therefore attempts to ensure that the language in the Code of Federal Regulations conforms to the court's decision. This latest rule thus restores the 1999 definition of "discharge of dredged material" and deletes both the narrowly defined term "incidental fallback" and the presumption that use of mechanized earthmoving equipment results in a regulated discharge.

The 2008 joint rule provides no guidance about which activities result in the discharge of dredged or fill material and which activities merely result in incidental fallback and are unregulable. As a result, whether an activity is regulable will be decided on a case-by-case basis. Thus, after several rounds of litigation and multiple efforts at rulemaking, predictions concerning whether an activity results in a regulable discharge still lack certainty.

IV. Obtaining CWA Section 404 Authorization

§ 35.9 Introduction

Applicants seeking CWA section 404 authorization for an activity may have several options. One is to apply for a standard permit, also known as an individual permit. As discussed further below, when processing an individual permit, the Corps will issue a public notice, undertake National Environmental Policy Act (NEPA) analysis, conduct a public interest review, determine compliance with the EPA's 404(b)(1) guidelines, comply with other requirements outside the CWA (such as requirements relating to protected species or historic resources), and ultimately prepare a decision memorandum to support the Corps' decision to issue or deny the permit. This process can take many months and even years.

However, some minor and routine actions may qualify for streamlined review or coverage under general permits where the individual and cumulative impacts of the activity are no more than minimal. Potential applicants have the option of meeting with Corps officials before determining what authorization to seek or before applying for a permit. The consultation is not mandatory, but an applicant can use the consultation to understand what information will be required in the application process and the factors the Corps will consider in making its decision. *See* 33 C.F.R. § 325.1(b).

§ 35.10 Authorization Options

§ 35.10:1 General Permits: Nationwide Permits

The Corps has the authority to issue general permits, each valid for no longer than five years, on a state, regional, or nationwide basis for categories of discharges that are similar in nature and will have only minimal adverse environmental effects individually and cumulatively. *See* 33 U.S.C. § 1344(e)(1). One advantage of general permits is that the Corps prepares a NEPA analysis associated with issuance of the general permit itself, which means that the Corps need not prepare additional NEPA documents each time the general permit is used. For decades, the Corps has issued and re-issued a suite of nationwide permits (NWPs) for many common activities, and applicants can sometimes obtain coverage under an NWP with little delay or paperwork. *See* 33 C.F.R. § 330.1(b). Examples of common activities authorized under NWPs include maintenance for serviceable structures; bank stabilization; utility line installation and maintenance; residential, commercial, and industrial development; and facilities to manage stormwater. Some activities may fit into more than one NWP. Currently available NWPs are listed at www.usace.army.mil/Missions/Civil-Works/Regulatory-Program-and-Permits/Nationwide-Permits/.

Each NWP specifies the circumstances where it may apply, which are in addition to general conditions that apply to all NWPs, as well as additional regional conditions that may be imposed by Corps districts and other conditions that may be imposed by states as part of section 401 water quality certification. In some circumstances, an applicant may be able to self-verify that an activity qualifies for authorization under an NWP, without the applicant's needing to submit any documents to the Corps or await any action by the Corps. This is often referred to as a "non-reporting" use of an NWP. As a matter of best practice, applicants obtaining non-reporting NWP coverage should fully document how the activity complies with all of the NWP's specific limitations and conditions and retain that documentation as the applicant would any materials necessary to support other environmental permits.

The conditions of some NWPs require that an applicant submit a preconstruction notification (PCN) to the Corps in order to give the Corps an opportunity to evaluate the proposed use of the NWP and verify that the activity complies. This is often referred to as a "reporting" use of an NWP. The NWP program gives the Corps only a limited period of time to act—generally forty-five days, unless certain circumstances stop the running of that forty-five-day clock. If that time runs out without any Corps action on the PCN (e.g., a verification letter from the Corps stating that the activity complies with the NWP, which may impose additional conditions, or a letter denying the use of the NWP), the applicant's use of the NWP is verified by rule.

A PCN is always required in certain circumstances, such as if species protected under the Endangered Species Act might be affected by the activity or are in the vicinity (see general condition 18), or if the activity may affect a historic resource protected under the National Historic Preservation Act (see general condition 20). In these circumstances, the forty-five-day clock is also paused. In such a case, the applicant may not begin the activity until receiving written notification from the Corps that there is "no effect" on listed species or "no potential to cause effects" on historic properties, or that any consultation required under section 7 of the Endangered Species Act or section 106 of the National Historic Preservation Act is completed. The Corps' framework for complying with the Endangered Species Act through compliance with general condition 18 has been the subject of continued litigation. For example, in a challenge to the Keystone pipeline, a Montana federal district court held that the Corps' framework for Endangered Species Act compliance in its administration of NWP 12 (which is used for utility lines) was unlawful. See Northern Plains Resource Council v. U.S. Army Corps of Engineers, No. 4:19-cv-44-BMM (D. Mont. filed May 11, 2020). The court enjoined the use of NWP 12 nationwide as applied to new oil and gas pipelines, though the Supreme Court stayed that injunction except as to the Keystone pipeline pending appeal. Army Corps of Engineers v. Northern Plains Resource Council, No. 19A-1053 (July 6, 2020). If the district court's holding that the Corps' general condition 18 framework violates the Endangered Species Act is upheld, it would affect the viability of all of the Corps' NWPs and likely require extensive programmatic consultation under the Endangered Species Act before such activities could be authorized.

Along with basic information regarding the identity of the applicant and the general nature of the proposed activity, all PCNs must include the project's purpose, direct and indirect adverse environmental effects, a discussion regarding its impact on endangered species and historic properties, a mitigation plan when impacts to wetlands are greater than a one-tenth acre, and other permit-specific items. When an activity does not qualify for coverage under a general permit (e.g., the activity cannot comply with limitations and conditions of the permit, or the Corps district engineer exercises discretion to deny use of the general permit, such as in circumstances where the effects of the activity may be more than minimal), the applicant must usually proceed under an individual permit.

Prospective users of an NWP should read the general NWP conditions, regional conditions, and any section 401 water quality certification conditions, and assess whether a particular NWP authorizes a specific project and whether the project meets all conditions of the NWP. The Corps issued fifty NWPs in 2017 and a subset of NWPs in 2021. Those NWPs issued in 2017 that were not replaced as part of the 2021 issuance will expire on March 18, 2022. The 2021 issuance included twelve NWPs that replace counterparts from the 2017 issuance and four new NWPs. These will expire on March 15, 2026. However, the Corps may modify or revoke any NWP before it expires.

The various Corps websites contain links to available NWPs, as well as resources regarding permit conditions, conditions imposed by the TCEQ (or the Texas Railroad Commission, as applicable) as part of the state's CWA section 401 water quality certification, Corps procedural guidance, forms, and instructions for each of the Corps district offices applicable to Texas projects. Links to each of the Corps' permitting websites relevant to Texas are provided below.

- Tulsa District of the Corps' Southwestern Division: www.swt.usace.army.mil/Missions/Regulatory.aspx
- Fort Worth District of the Corps' Southwestern Division: www.swf.usace.army.mil/Missions/Regulatory/Permitting/General-Permits/

- Galveston District of the Corps' Southwestern Division: www.swg.usace.army.mil/Business-With-Us/Regulatory/Permits/
- Albuquerque District of the Corps' South Pacific Division: www.spa.usace.army.mil/Missions/Regulatory-Program-and-Permits/

Practitioners and potential applicants should refer to these websites to check for more details on the nationwide and regional general permits potentially applicable to their projects as well as conditions on any such permits they hope to use for their projects.

§ 35.10:2 Other General Permits

The Corps may issue general permits on a state or regional basis. The Corps websites provided above also contain details on available general permits in Texas, such as regional general permits that individual or groups of Corps districts may issue for use in their district boundaries or in the state. The Corps may also issue state programmatic general permits (SPGPs) based on an existing state, local, or other federal agency program so as to avoid duplication with that program. For state regulatory programs that are as protective or more protective of the waters regulated by the Corps pursuant to section 404, SPGPs offer a route to increased state oversight of wetlands without the burden of administering the entire program. *See* 33 C.F.R. § 325.5(c)(3).

§ 35.10:3 Letters of Permission

In some circumstances, the Corps may issue a letter of permission (LOP) in lieu of an individual permit. For authorization under section 404, the Corps may develop categories of activities that may qualify for simplified LOP procedures after consulting with state fish and wildlife agencies, the EPA, and the state agencies responsible for section 401 water quality certification and Coastal Zone Management Act consistency determinations. In cases subject to section 10 of the Rivers and Harbors Act, the Corps may issue an LOP when the proposed work would be minor, have insignificant impact on environmental values, and encounter no appreciable opposition. *See* 33 C.F.R. § 325.2(e)(1).

§ 35.10:4 Individual Permit

An individual permit is a permit granted on a case-by-case basis for potentially significant impacts that cannot fall under the umbrella of a general permit or qualify for an LOP. *See* 33 C.F.R. § 322.2(e). A party seeking an individual permit will be required to undergo the standard review process delineated below. This process is much more time consuming and complicated than the process for obtaining a general permit or LOP.

Submitting the Application: The first required step in the permitting process is the submittal of the standard application form, including drawings, sketches, or plans, as well as payment of fees and submittal of other information necessary to enable the Corps to issue a public notice. *See* 33 C.F.R. § 325.1(c)–(f). The Corps district office then has fifteen days to determine whether the application is incomplete (and alert the applicant to the missing information) or, if complete, to proceed with issuing a public notice. *See* 33 C.F.R. § 325.2(a)(2).

Public Notice: The public notice is the primary method of advising interested parties of the proposed activity and of soliciting comments necessary to evaluate the probable impact on the public interest. *See* 33 C.F.R. § 325.3(a). The notice must include sufficient information to give a clear understanding of the nature and magnitude of the activity. *See* 33 C.F.R. § 325.3(a). The district engineer then gathers all comments received and furnishes the applicant with a summary of the comments, the actual letters or portions thereof, or representative comments—allowing the applicant the opportunity to respond. *See* 33 C.F.R. § 325.2(a)(3). The Corps normally provides a thirty-day comment period. *See* 33 C.F.R. § 325.2(d)(2). The district engineer will also evaluate the application to determine the need for a public hearing. *See* 33 C.F.R. § 325.2(a)(5).

Corps Decision Making—Public Interest Review: The Corps decides whether to issue a permit after evaluating the probable impacts, including cumulative impacts, of the proposed activity and its intended use on the public interest. *See* 33 C.F.R. § 320.4(a)(1). The Corps balances various factors, which may include conservation, economics, aesthetics, wetlands, historic properties, navigation, water supply, water quality, and other issues important to the needs and welfare of the public. *See* 33 C.F.R. § 320.4(a)(1). The weight given to any one factor will vary based on the nature and circumstances of each individual project application. *See* 33 C.F.R. § 320.4(a)(3). Since the primary responsibility for determining zoning and land use matters rests with state, local, and tribal governments, during this phase of the process, the district engineer will normally accept decisions by such governments on those matters unless there are significant issues of overriding national importance. *See* 33 C.F.R. § 320.4(j)(2). The Corps will not issue a permit when the Corps determines it would be contrary to the public interest. *See* 33 C.F.R. § 320.4(a)(1).

Corps Decision Making—Alternatives Analysis (Compliance with 404(b)(1) Guidelines): Along with the general balancing test applied to the public interest review, the Corps must determine that the proposed activity adheres to the EPA's 404(b)(1) guidelines.

The 404(b)(1) guidelines state that, "[e]xcept as provided under section 404(b)(2), no discharge of dredge or fill material shall be permitted if there is a practicable alternative to the proposed discharge that would have less adverse impact on the aquatic ecosystem, so long as the alternative does not have other significant adverse environmental consequences." 40 C.F.R § 230.10(a). When an activity is not considered water dependent (meaning that the activity does not depend on proximity, siting, or access to an aquatic site to fulfill its basic purpose), the Corps will presume that practicable alternatives that do not involve special aquatic sites are available. *See* 40 C.F.R. § 230.10(a)(3). A "special aquatic site" means wetlands, mud flats, vegetated shallows, coral reefs, riffle and pool complexes, and sanctuaries and refuges, which possess special ecological characteristics of productivity, habitat, wildlife protection, or other important and easily disrupted ecological values. *See* 40 C.F.R. § 230.3(m).

Under the guidelines, except as provided under section 404(b)(2), no discharge of dredge or fill material will be permitted that will cause or contribute to significant degradation of the "waters of the United States," including significant adverse effects on human health or welfare, aquatic ecosystems, and recreational, aesthetic, and economic values. *See* 40 C.F.R § 230.10(c)(1), (c)(4).

Additionally, except as provided under section 404(b)(2), the discharge of dredge or fill material will not be permitted unless appropriate and practicable steps have been taken to minimize adverse effects on the aquatic ecosystem. *See* 40 C.F.R. § 230.10(d). Such appropriate and practicable steps are outlined at 40 C.F.R. §§ 230.70–.77.

Additionally, the guidelines address compensatory mitigation requirements, which align with the Corps' own compensatory mitigation regulations. *See* 40 C.F.R. §§ 230.91–.98; 33 C.F.R. pt. 332. The rules and guidance for compensatory mitigation are available at www.epa.gov/cwa-404/background-about-compensatory-mitigation-requirements-under-cwa-section-404#recent. The functional result of the section 404(b)(1) guidelines is that a burden rests on the applicant for a section 404 permit to show efforts to (1) avoid impacts on aquatic resources, (2) minimize potential impacts on aquatic resources, and (3) provide compensation for any remaining unavoidable impacts.

Corps Decision Making—Compliance with Provisions Outside the Scope of Section 404: The Corps also evaluates applications for compliance with the requirements of other laws, including the following:

- Endangered Species Act, 16 U.S.C. §§ 1531–1544: The Corps reviews applications for potential impact on threatened or endangered species pursuant to section 7 of the Endangered Species Act. If the district engineer finds that the proposed activity may affect a protected species or its critical habitat, the Corps will consult with the FWS or the NMFS. *See* 33 C.F.R. § 325.2(b)(5). See Chapter 32 of this book for a discussion of the Endangered Species Act.

- National Historic Preservation Act, 54 U.S.C. §§ 300101–320303: If the proposed activity would involve any property listed or eligible for listing in the National Register of Historic Places, the district engineer will proceed in accordance with Corps' National Historic Preservation Act implementing regulations. *See* 33 C.F.R. § 325.2(b)(3).
- National Environmental Policy Act, 42 U.S.C. §§ 4321–4347: A decision on an individual permit application will require either an environmental assessment or an environmental impact statement unless it is included within a categorical exclusion. *See* 33 C.F.R. § 325.2(a)(4). See Chapters 3 and 27 of this book.
- Coastal Zone Management Act (CZMA), 16 U.S.C. §§ 1451–1466: If the proposed activity is in a statutory coastal zone, the district engineer must obtain certification from the applicant that the proposed activity complies with the approved state CZMA program. *See* 33 C.F.R. § 325.2(b)(2).
- CWA section 401 water quality certification: If the district engineer determines that water quality certification for the proposed activity is necessary under the provisions of section 401 of the CWA, the district engineer must obtain a copy of that certification from the applicant or the certifying agency. *See* 33 C.F.R. § 325.2(b)(1). No permit will be granted until the required certification has been obtained or waived. *See* 33 C.F.R. § 325.2(b)(1)(ii). See Chapter 34 of this book for a discussion of section 401 certification.

The CWA section 401 certification is the primary means by which state authorities review any federal permit that may result in discharge to wetlands or other waters under state jurisdiction. In Texas, the TCEQ is responsible for providing 401 certification to the Corps for section 404 activities with one exception: activities associated with oil and gas operations covered by section 404 are certified by the Railroad Commission of Texas rather than the TCEQ. *See* Tex. Nat. Res. Code § 91.101; Tex. Water Code §§ 26.011, 26.131. Section 404 permits cannot be issued in Texas unless applicable TCEQ or Railroad Commission certification has been obtained or waived.

§ 35.10:5 Issuance of Decision and Permit

After considering the completed application, the district engineer determines whether the permit should be issued based on the record and applicable regulations. *See* 33 C.F.R. § 325.2(a)(6). The district engineer prepares a statement of findings or, where an environmental impact statement has been prepared, a record of decision. *See* 33 C.F.R. § 325.2(a)(6). If a permit is issued, the permit decision document includes a discussion of the environmental impacts of the project, the findings of the public interest review process, and any special evaluation required by the type of activity, such as compliance determinations with the section 404(b)(1) guidelines. *See* 33 C.F.R. § 325.2(a)(6). The applicant must sign the permit to accept the conditions, and the permit is not valid until signed by the issuing officer. *See* 33 C.F.R. § 325.2(a)(7). If the application is denied, the Corps will provide the reasons for the denial in writing. *See* 33 C.F.R. § 325.2(a)(7).

§ 35.11 Recourse for Dissatisfied Applicants

There are various decision points in the section 404 permitting processes at which applicants may be dissatisfied with the Corps' permitting decisions. The following sections discuss potential recourse for dissatisfied applicants.

§ 35.11:1 Administrative Appeal

For applicants who are dissatisfied with a Corps decision, regulations provide for a process of administrative appeal. Applicants can appeal the following decisions to a superior Corps official: (1) approved jurisdictional determinations; (2) permit applications denied with prejudice; and (3) declined permits. *See* 33 C.F.R. § 331.1. In 2016, the Corps also issued a regulatory guidance letter explaining its procedures, particularly in light of Supreme Court authority in *U.S. Army Corps of Engineers v. Hawkes Co.*, discussed in more detail at section 35.11:2 below. *See* U.S. Army Corps of Engineers, *Regulatory Guidance Letter No. 16-01* (Oct. 2016), https://usace.contentdm.oclc.org/digital/collection/p16021coll9/id/1262/.

§ 35.11:2 Suit in Federal Court

If administrative appeal procedures are unavailing, legal action in federal court against the Corps, the EPA, or both may be an option. While the CWA contains limited provisions for judicial review of Corps or EPA rulings, judicial review is authorized when the EPA or the Corps imposes, or threatens to impose, administrative or civil penalties. *See, e.g.*, 33 U.S.C. § 1319(g)(8) (providing a statutory basis for federal judicial review when the EPA or the Corps imposes administrative penalties). The Administrative Procedure Act (APA) provides another avenue to challenge these decisions. For example, the Supreme Court has held that the APA allows pre-enforcement review of an EPA-issued compliance order under the CWA that required respondents to restore property and threatened penalties if they did not comply. *See Sackett v. Environmental Protection Agency*, 566 U.S. 120, 130 (2012). The Supreme Court extended *Sackett* to include approved jurisdictional decisions of the Corps. *See U.S. Army Corps of Engineers v. Hawkes Co.*, 136 S. Ct. 1807, 1816 (2016).

An applicant aggrieved by agency action should be aware that there are often legal prerequisites to a judicial challenge, including filing deadlines and exhaustion requirements. Corps regulations require the exhaustion of administrative remedies before seeking relief in federal courts. *See* 33 C.F.R. § 331.12.

In any event, the viability of any suit depends on many factors, including the grounds for the complaint, the government agencies named as defendants, and the specificity of the applicable administrative regulations regarding administrative appeals and judicial review.

V. Conclusion

§ 35.12 Conclusion

As with many projects governed by environmental laws, regulations aimed at protecting "waters of the United States" can significantly impact an existing or proposed activity or development project. The regulations applicable to "waters of the United States," including wetlands, are particularly controversial and have been under nearly continuous judicial review and regulatory change since their inception. Persons developing projects that rely on or affect these aquatic resources must stay apprised of existing statutes, regulations, guidance, and judicial decisions affecting their current projects as well as laws on the horizon that may affect future projects.

CHAPTER 37

Financing Water Projects

Jeffrey A. Leuschel[1]

I. Introduction

§ 37.1 Public Financing of Water Projects

The importance attached to the public financing of water projects in the state of Texas is readily apparent in the Texas Constitution. The constitution contains at least fifteen provisions that directly or indirectly relate to the creation of state, regional, and local entities to provide for the conservation and development of the water resources of the state. Twelve constitutional provisions relate specifically to programs administered by the Texas Water Development Board, and two relate to the conservation and development of the state's natural resources, including water, by regional and local districts. State law has long granted cities the authority to own, operate, and finance water and sewer utility systems. This chapter describes the law as it pertains to financing water projects at the state, regional, and local levels.

II. State Financial Assistance

§ 37.2 Texas Water Development Board

In 1957, in response to the drought conditions that affected the state in the 1950s, the Texas Constitution was amended and article III, section 49–c, was added. This section authorizes the creation of the Texas Water Development Board (TWDB) to aid in the conservation and development of the water resources of the state, including the control, storage, and preservation of its stormwaters and flood waters and its rivers and streams by the construction of dams and reservoirs. It also grants the board the authority to issue state general obligation bonds to finance water projects.

The TWDB is the state agency primarily responsible for water planning and for administering water financing. Tex. Water Code § 6.011. The board has primary jurisdiction over the development of the state water plan, the administration of the state's various water assistance and financing programs,

---

1. Jeff Leuschel is a partner with McCall, Parkhurst & Horton L.L.P. Jeff has practiced public finance law for over twenty-five years. Jeff advises the Texas Water Development Board and the Oklahoma Water Resources Board on financing water projects, as well as cities including Austin, Dallas, and Fort Worth on financing water and wastewater projects. Jeff is a frequent speaker on public finance law issues. He was bond counsel on the Texas Water Development Board State Water Implementation Revenue Fund for Texas Revenue Bonds, Series 2015A and Taxable Series 2015B, that was recognized by *The Bond Buyer* as the Southwest Region Deal of the Year in 2016. This chapter was significantly influenced by the counsel and friendship of Suzanne Schwartz, formerly the General Counsel to the Texas Water Development Board and currently the Environmental Program Director, Center for Public Policy Dispute Resolution at the University of Texas School of Law. Without Suzanne's encouragement and gifts of persuasion, Jeff would not have undertaken this effort.

including those created by the constitution, and other duties as may be assigned to the board by law. Tex. Water Code § 6.012(a)(1), (a)(2), (a)(4). Under the provisions of House Bill 4, passed by the Texas legislature during the 2013 regular session, several changes to the composition of the board were enacted. Effective September 1, 2013, the board consists of three members, appointed by the governor with the advice and consent of the Texas Senate. One member must have experience in the field of engineering, one member must have experience in the field of public or private finance, and one member must have experience in the field of law or business. The governor must make appointments to the board in such a manner that the members reflect the diverse geographic regions and population groups of the state and do not have any conflicts of interest prohibited by federal or state law. *See* Tex. Water Code § 6.052. A person is not eligible for appointment to the board if the person served on the board on or before January 1, 2013. Tex. Water Code § 6.053. Board members are appointed to serve staggered terms of six years, with the term of one member expiring February 1 of each odd-numbered year. A person appointed to the board may not serve for more than two six-year terms. Tex. Water Code § 6.056. The governor names a member to serve as chair at the will of the governor, and the board elects a vice-chair every two years. Tex. Water Code § 6.059. The board shall hold regular meetings and all hearings at times specified by board order and entered in its minutes. Tex. Water Code § 6.060.

Each member of the board shall serve on a full-time basis. Tex. Water Code § 6.061. House Bill 4 also required the board to appoint an executive administrator by October 1, 2013. The person appointed as executive administrator could not be the person who served as executive administrator on January 1, 2013. *See* Tex. Water Code § 6.103.

§ 37.2:1 General Obligation Bond Programs

Exercising its constitutional authority, the TWDB issues general obligation bonds and uses the bond proceeds to make loans to eligible political subdivisions. Because the state's general obligation bonds are backed by its full faith and credit, the bonds bear the credit rating of the state of Texas. The credit rating of Texas has been at or near triple-A, the highest credit rating for municipal securities issued by municipal bond rating agencies. As a result, when issued, the general obligation bonds pay interest at the lowest rates in the public debt markets. The board uses the bond proceeds to make loans to eligible political subdivisions by purchasing bonds issued by the political subdivisions. The board is able to purchase the political subdivision bonds at interest rates lower than those the subdivisions could obtain if they had attempted to sell their bonds in the public debt markets. This provides significant debt service savings to the political subdivisions.

Before 1985, the primary focus of the TWDB was to provide financial assistance by purchasing bonds from political subdivisions that were not able to access the public debt markets in an economical manner. These political subdivisions generally did not possess strong creditworthiness and therefore found it a hardship to borrow funds in the public debt markets. Beginning in 1985, amendments to the Texas Constitution and legislative changes expanded the authority of the board to purchase bonds from all political subdivisions of the state, not just from "hardship" political subdivisions. Article III, section 49–d–5, of the constitution was added in 1985, permitting the legislature to extend benefits to nonprofit water supply corporations, entities that are not political subdivisions of the state. In addition, the board was given the authority to issue revenue bonds, secured not by the full faith and credit of the state but from the repayments of loans made to political subdivisions through the purchase of their bonds by the board.

Texas Water Development Fund: Article III, section 49–c, of the Texas Constitution established the Texas Water Development Fund. The original constitutional amendment authorized the issuance of $200 million in general obligation bonds, known as Texas Water Development Bonds, secured by the full faith and credit of the state, to finance water projects. Subsequent amendments to the constitution expanded the authority of the board to finance projects through the issuance of general obligation bonds for wastewater conveyance and treatment (article III, section 49–d–1), flood control (article III, section 49–d–2), and agricultural water conservation projects (article III, section 50–d). Authorization for the state to acquire an interest in water and wastewater facilities is provided in article III, section 49–d.

Texas Water Code chapter 17, particularly subchapter B, provides the statutory framework for the issuance of Texas Water Development Bonds under the constitutional authority granted to finance water projects, payable from moneys on deposit in the Texas Water Development Fund (including, if necessary, the first moneys coming into the treasury in each fiscal year, not otherwise appropriated by the constitution). *See* Tex. Water Code ch. 17, subch. C.

Since the enactment in 1997 of article III, section 49–d–8, of the constitution, creating the Texas Water Development Fund II (also referred to as "Development Fund II"), the TWDB has declared its intent not to issue bonds to augment the Texas Water Development Fund, although it reserves the right at its discretion to do so.

Texas Water Development Fund—Economically Distressed Areas Program: In 1989, the Texas Constitution was amended to add section 49–d–7 to article III. This provision permits the TWDB to issue general obligation bonds to provide wholesale and retail water and wastewater facilities to economically distressed areas of the state, as defined by law. The ability of the board to provide financial assistance to fund projects to benefit economically distressed areas represents a significant public policy change in how the general obligation bond program is administered. General obligation bonds issued by the board are secured by the full faith and credit of the state, and they are payable from the first moneys coming into the state treasury in each fiscal year, not otherwise appropriated by the constitution. *See* Tex. Const. art. III, § 49–d–7; *see also* Tex. Water Code § 17.080. The lending program is structured so that the repayments from political subdivisions received by the board must be sufficient in whole to retire the general obligation bonds issued by the board.

However, proceeds from Texas Water Development Bonds issued to fund the economically distressed areas program are intended to provide financial assistance in the form of grants as well as loans. Therefore, the state expects to appropriate general revenue for payment of the bonds issued to fund the economically distressed areas program. These are referred to as EDAP bonds. Water Code sections 17.0111 and 17.0112 limit the principal amount of EDAP bonds that can be issued in a fiscal year. *See* Tex. Water Code §§ 17.0111, 17.0112. A separate "economically distressed areas program interest and sinking fund" was established within the Texas Water Development Fund, and money deposited in this fund is reserved solely for the payment of EDAP bond debt service. *See* Tex. Water Code § 17.0741. This separate interest and sinking fund serves to distinguish the traditional self-supporting general obligation programs of the board from the economically distressed areas program.

Water Code section 17.921 first defined economically distressed areas as those in which (1) water supply or sewer services were inadequate to meet minimal needs of residential users as defined by board rules, (2) financial resources were inadequate to provide water supply or sewer services to satisfy those needs, and (3) an established residential subdivision was located on June 1, 1989, as determined by the board. The initial focus for the economically distressed areas program was to serve communities known as *colonias* in the Rio Grande Valley.

Section 17.921 was amended in 2005 to expand the established residential subdivisions eligible to be treated as economically distressed areas to those areas in which an established residential subdivision was located on June 1, 2005. *See* Act of May 25, 2005, 79th Leg., R.S., ch. 927, § 5. Most of the funding to political subdivisions provided under the economically distressed areas program has been in the form of grants, and repayment is not expected. As of January 1, 2008, the board has issued approximately $238 million in EDAP bonds and the state has appropriated funds from the general fund to make debt service payments on the EDAP bonds. EDAP bonds are not considered on a parity with the outstanding Texas Water Development Bonds, and the program is governed by separate statutory and contractual arrangements, set forth in Water Code chapter 17, subchapter K.

When adopted, article III, section 49–d–7, limited the issuance of EDAP bonds to $250 million. In November 2007, the constitution was amended to add section 49–d–10 to article III, granting to the TWDB the authority to issue an additional $250 million in EDAP bonds as general obligation bonds of the state. *See* Tex. S.J. Res. 20, 80th Leg., R.S. (2007).

See discussion below regarding the transition of this program into Development Fund II.

Texas Water Development Fund—State Participation Program: The economically distressed areas program is not the only state funding program administered by the TWDB in which there is no expectation of the recipient's immediately repaying the state for the costs of constructing the project. The "state participation" program is designed to provide funds to encourage optimal regional development of projects including the design, acquisition, lease, construction, reconstruction, development, or enlargement of reservoirs and stormwater retention basins for water supply, flood protection, and groundwater recharge, facilities for the transmission and treatment of water, and treatment works. *See* Tex. Const. art. III, § 49–d; *see also* Tex. Water Code § 16.131.

There is one critical distinction between the state participation program and the EDAP bond program: the state has the expectation of recovering its investment in the projects funded through the state participation program. Before the TWDB can acquire a facility or an interest in a facility, it must affirmatively find that (1) it is reasonable for the state to recover its investment in the facility, (2) the cost of the facility exceeds the current financing capabilities of the area involved and optimal regional development could not be achieved without state participation, (3) the public interest will be served by the acquisition of the facility, and (4) the facility contemplates the optimal regional development reasonably required under existing circumstances. Tex. Water Code § 16.135. Local participation also is required for the board to fund the state's share of the costs of a facility. The board may acquire all or part of any authorized facility to the extent that it finds that a political subdivision (1) is willing and reasonably able to finance that portion of the cost of the facility not acquired by the board, (2) has obtained all necessary permits, (3) has proposals that are consistent with the state's water plan, and (4) has a water conservation program for the more efficient use of water. Tex. Water Code § 16.136.

Water Code chapter 16, subchapter F, establishes the authority of the TWDB to sell or lease facilities acquired through the state participation program, which enables the state to recover its initial investment made through the initial financing of the facilities. The sale of facilities is consistent with the state's intention not to permanently acquire water and wastewater facilities but to provide financial assistance to local and regional political subdivisions to construct the facilities.

See discussion below regarding the transition of this program into Development Fund II.

Texas Water Development Fund II: As the Texas Water Development Fund grew and the bond authority granted to the TWDB expanded, elements governing the operation and administration of the Texas Water Development Fund became more burdensome. Article III, section 49–c, of the Texas Constitution requires the board to deposit sufficient money into the interest and sinking fund to pay the interest and principal becoming due during the ensuing year and to establish and maintain a reserve in the interest and sinking fund equal to the average annual principal and interest requirements on all outstanding Texas Water Development Bonds. This section further requires the board to notify the comptroller of public accounts no later than the fifteenth day after the end of each fiscal year of the amounts needed to pay the interest on and principal of all Texas Water Development Bonds coming due during the fiscal year and the average annual principal and interest requirements on all outstanding bonds. The comptroller then makes transfers as necessary to pay these amounts as well as all collection charges and exchanges on the bonds.

The funding requirements of this section result in money well in excess of current debt service requirements being deposited to the credit of the Texas Water Development Fund. During the early years of the general obligation bond program, this approach was prudent as a means to avoid using general revenues to pay debt service on the bonds, but as the programs administered by the board matured, the repayments received by the board resulted in the accumulation of a large surplus. Money in the interest and sinking fund may be used only to pay debt service on Texas Water Development Bonds. Financial assistance programs cannot be funded with this accumulated surplus.

Other constitutional restrictions also affected the ability of the board to administer the financial assistance programs. Water quality enhancement projects funded under article III, section 49–d, of the Texas Constitution cannot be funded with the proceeds of bonds issued under article III, section 49–c, to fund water supply projects, or vice versa. When the proceeds to fund water quality enhancement projects were expended, the board could not use unexpended water supply project proceeds to fund water quality enhancement projects. This resulted in the board's issuing bonds to fund water quality enhancement projects while unspent proceeds remained from bonds issued to fund water supply projects.

In 1997, the constitution was amended and article III, section 49–d–8, was added. This section established a new fund called Texas Water Development Fund II (also referred to as "Development Fund II"). Development Fund II is separate and distinct from the Texas Water Development Fund. It may be used for any one or more of the purposes currently or formerly authorized by article III, sections 49–c, 49–d, 49–d–1, 49–d–2, 49–d–5, 49–d–6, and 49–d–7, of the constitution. Pursuant to the requirements of article III, section 49-d-8, three accounts are established within Development Fund II: the "state participation account" (*see* Tex. Water Code §§ 17.956, 17.957), the "economically distressed areas program account" (*see* Tex. Water Code §§ 17.956, 17.958), and the "financial assistance account" (*see* Tex. Water Code §§ 17.956, 17.959). Pursuant to article III, section 49–d–8, the TWDB is authorized, at its discretion, to issue general obligation bonds for one or more accounts of Development Fund II in an aggregate principal amount equal to the amount of bonds previously authorized under applicable sections of the constitution less the amount of bonds issued under those sections to augment the Texas Water Development Fund.

The amendment gives flexibility to the TWDB in administering the water projects in the state and provides the mechanism for the eventual transfer of the moneys and assets on deposit in the Texas Water Development Fund to the credit of Development Fund II. The funding requirements of the interest and sinking fund contained in article III, section 49–c, applicable to Texas Water Development Bonds are not included in article III, section 49–d–8, and do not apply to bonds issued to augment Development Fund II. Money to pay debt service on bonds issued to augment Development Fund II is deposited as needed into the appropriate account to pay debt service when due. *See* Tex. Water Code § 17.963.

In addition, under article III, section 49–d–8, the board may enter "bond enhancement agreements" to provide additional security for its general obligation bonds and have the payment obligations under the bond enhancement agreements be treated as a general obligation of the state. Water Code section 17.954(c) defines bond enhancement agreements to include agreements to obtain a letter of credit or line of credit and agreements to provide a hedge or interest rate management, such as interest rate swap agreements or other cash flow exchange agreements.

Article III, section 49–d–8, also declares that since it was intended only to establish a basic framework and not to be a comprehensive treatment of Development Fund II, the legislature is granted full power to implement the amendment, including the power to delegate authority to the TWDB as it believes necessary. This provides the legislature the authority to grant the board greater flexibility to administer the financial assistance programs than was available to administer the Texas Water Development Fund.

Subchapter L was added to chapter 17 of the Water Code to implement the provisions of this section. Moneys on deposit in the state participation account and the economically distressed areas program account of Development Fund II are to be used for the parallel programs originally administered under the Texas Water Development Fund. *See* Tex. Const. art. III, § 49–d–8(a); *see also* Tex. Water Code § 17.971. Moneys on deposit in the financial assistance account, however, may be used by the TWDB for any one or more of the purposes described in article III, section 49–d–8, other than for state participation or economically distressed areas program purposes. This allows the board to use bond proceeds flexibly to fund water supply, water quality enhancement, and flood control projects in the manner the board determines necessary for the administration of Development Fund II and to implement the stated objectives of the constitutional framework governing the board.

General obligation bonds issued to augment Development Fund II are known as "Water Financial Assistance Bonds." Tex. Water Code § 17.952. Consistent with the constitutional provisions supporting Texas Water Development Bonds, Water Financial Assistance Bonds also are supported, if necessary, from the first moneys coming into the treasury each fiscal year, not otherwise appropriated by the constitution. *See* Tex. Water Code § 17.963.

Unlike Water Development Bonds, Water Financial Assistance Bonds may be sold at either a public (or competitive) or private (or negotiated) sale. The bonds may be in the form and denominations provided by the board and issued in the manner and under the terms, conditions, and details provided by board resolution. Tex. Water Code § 17.953. In addition, rather than specifying a time frame for coordinating transfers with the comptroller of public accounts, Water Code section 17.963(a) provides that the board shall cooperate with the comptroller to develop procedures for the payment of debt service on Water Financial Assistance Bonds, thereby providing the legal authority to streamline the transfer and payment process and eliminating the need to provide for additional reserves to make payments on Water Financial Assistance Bonds.

In 2006, completing a process that began in 1997, the TWDB provided for the retirement of the last outstanding Texas Water Development Bonds payable from money in the interest and sinking funds in the Texas Water Development Fund and transferred the final remaining moneys and assets in the Texas Water Development Fund to Development Fund II.

In 2001, article III, section 49–d–9, was added to the constitution. This section authorizes the TWDB to issue general obligation bonds, at its discretion, for one or more accounts of Development Fund II, in an amount not to exceed $2 billion. Of this additional general obligation bond authorization, $50 million shall be used for the "Water Infrastructure Fund."

In November 2011, the constitution was amended to add section 49–d–11 to article III, granting to the board the authority to issue general obligation bonds, on a continuing basis, for one or more accounts of Development Fund II, in amounts such that the aggregate principal amount of bonds issued under this section at any time does not exceed $6 billion. *See* Tex. S.J. Res. 4, 82nd Leg., R.S. (2011). As of January 1, 2019, there exists authority to issue approximately $5,937,000,000 in bonds under authority of article III, section 49–d–11.

Agricultural Water Conservation Fund: Article III, section 50–d, of the Texas Constitution authorizes the TWDB to issue up to $200 million in general obligation bonds to provide moneys for deposit into the Agricultural Water Conservation Fund. Water Code chapter 17, subchapter J, provides for the issuance of Agricultural Water Conservation Bonds and the administration of the funding program. Proceeds of the bonds are to be used to make loans and grants to fund conservation programs or conservation projects. *See* Tex. Water Code §§ 17.897–.899. Conservation programs include technical assistance, research, and educational programs relating to agricultural water use and conservation. Tex. Water Code § 17.897. Conservation projects include projects that improve water use, prepare irrigated land for conversion to dryland conditions, and prepare dryland for more efficient use of natural precipitation. Tex. Water Code § 17.898. As of January 1, 2008, the board has issued $35,160,000 in bonds to fund conservation programs and conservation projects.

§ 37.2:2 Revenue Bond Programs

In addition to general obligation bonds, which are secured by and payable from the full faith and credit or taxing power of the issuer, state agencies and political subdivisions issue revenue bonds, which are secured by and payable from a designated revenue source. Utility system revenues are one example of a designated revenue source used to secure and pay revenue bonds. Before 1987, the TWDB possessed the legal authority to issue only general obligation bonds. In 1987, subchapter I was added to chapter 17 of the Texas Water Code, and a new fund, the Texas Water Resources Fund, was created.

Texas Water Resources Fund: Revenue bonds may be issued by the board to provide money for the Texas Water Resources Fund; to acquire interests in water supply projects, treatment works, and flood control projects; and to provide financial assistance to political subdivisions, state agencies, or nonprofit water supply corporations. Money in the Texas Water Resources Fund may be used only to provide state matching funds for federal funds provided to any state revolving loan fund created under Water Code chapter 15, subchapter J; to provide financial assistance to water supply corporations; to provide financial assistance for the construction of water supply projects and treatment works; and to provide financial assistance for water supply corporations in economically distressed areas to the extent the board can make that assistance without adversely affecting the current or future integrity of the Texas Water Resources Fund or of any other financial assistance program of the board. *See* Tex. Water Code § 17.853(c).

State Water Pollution Control Revolving Fund: The granting of authority to the TWDB to issue revenue bonds was in part in response to the enactment by Congress of the Water Quality Act of 1987 (33 U.S.C. §§ 1251–1327). This federal law authorized the creation of a loan program to provide financial assistance to state agencies and political subdivisions within the states for publicly owned wastewater treatment works, including stormwater and nonpoint source pollution projects. The Act authorized the U.S. Environmental Protection Agency to make grants to states that had established perpetual revolving loan funds to provide financial assistance as described in the Act. Pursuant to 33 U.S.C. section 1382(b)(2), the federal government provides 80 percent of the funds for deposit into the state revolving fund, to be matched by a 20 percent state contribution. Under the Act, the revolving fund established by a state is maintained in perpetuity, and repayments from loans remaining after the payment of debt service on board bonds issued to fund the revolving fund are to be loaned to new borrowers.

In 1987, the TWDB established the State Water Pollution Control Revolving Fund, commonly known as the Clean Water State Revolving Fund (CWSRF), and provided the initial state matching funding through the issuance of Texas Water Development Bonds. Since 1992, the board has issued revenue bonds to provide funds for the CWSRF, providing funding for low-interest loans to Texas political subdivisions to finance improvements to publicly owned wastewater treatment works. *See* Tex. Water Code ch. 15, subch. J. The federal funds made available under the Water Quality Act of 1987 enable the board to subsidize the lending rate on the obligations it purchases from participating political subdivisions. Those subdivisions realize significant savings through the CWSRF program through interest rates that are as much as 170 basis points (1.70 percent) lower than the political subdivision's alternative cost of funds if it sold its bonds in the public debt market.

The TWDB uses repayments of these loans by political subdivisions to pay the debt service on the revenue bonds that the board issued to provide funding to the CWSRF, as well as to make future loans to participating political subdivisions and pay the administrative costs of the program. *See* Tex. Water Code § 15.604. Since the inception of the CWSRF, and capitalizing on the ability to leverage the grants from the Environmental Protection Agency, the board has made more than $8.7 billion in loans to political subdivisions throughout the state.

Drinking Water State Revolving Fund: A similar federal funding program was established in 1996 for providing federal capitalization grants to the states for the purpose of assisting communities to comply with federal drinking water regulations. *See* 42 U.S.C. §§ 300f–300j-27 (Safe Drinking Water Act as reauthorized in 1986 and amended in 1996 and 2016). As a condition for receiving a federal capitalization grant, a state is required to establish a drinking water state revolving fund into which the capitalization grant must be deposited. The state also must provide state matching funds equal to at least 20 percent of the capitalization grant for deposit into the drinking water state revolving fund and comply with certain other requirements of the Safe Drinking Water Act. Money in the drinking water state revolving fund may be used to provide financial assistance to community water systems and nonprofit community water systems in a number of ways, including making direct loans, retiring existing debt through refinancing, and providing loan guarantees for expenditures that facilitate compliance with the primary national drinking water regulations.

Under the Act, no less than 15 percent of the money credited to the drinking water state revolving fund must be provided to public water systems that serve fewer than 10,000 persons, to the extent such funds can be obligated for eligible projects. As much as 30 percent of the federal capitalization grant may be used for loan subsidies (including forgiveness of principal) for disadvantaged communities. Additional set-asides may be made for source water protection loans, programs for capacity development, and state administration of the Act. Pursuant to the Act, the term of a loan cannot exceed twenty years from the completion of a project, except that loans to disadvantaged communities may have a term not to exceed thirty years. As is the case with the CWSRF, the drinking water state revolving fund is to be created in perpetuity to fulfill the purposes outlined in the Act. Texas established a safe drinking water state revolving fund (DWSRF) under the authority of Water Code chapter 15, subchapter J, and since 1998 has provided low-interest loans to communities of interest in an aggregate amount in excess of $2.7 billion.

Cross-Collateralization of CWSRF and DWSRF: In 2018, the TWDB established a new financing approach to borrow funds to provide financial assistance to political subdivisions for eligible projects under both the CWSRF and the DWSRF. The board exercised authority under the federal Safe Drinking Water Act and state law (*see* Tex. Water Code § 15.6042) to "cross-collateralize" the assets of both the CWSRF and the DWSRF to provide a source of revenue for the payment of revenue bonds issued by the TWDB to fund both clean water and drinking water projects. The new financing approach also provides state matching funds required to receive federal capitalization grants for both programs. The proceeds of the TWDB State Revolving Fund Revenue Bonds, New Series 2018, were used to fund $240 million in clean water projects, $49 million in drinking water projects, $20 million in state matching funds for the CWSRF, and $21 million in state matching funds for the DWSRF. Repayments of political subdivision obligations acquired by the TWDB with bond proceeds provide the primary source of security to repay the New Series 2018 bonds.

§ 37.2:3 Other Texas Water Development Board Assistance Programs

The TWDB administers other assistance programs targeted to specific political subdivisions or for specific water projects through its issuance of general obligation bonds. Two of those programs, administered through the Rural Water Assistance Fund and the Water Infrastructure Fund, are discussed below.

Rural Water Assistance Fund: In 2001, the legislature established the Rural Water Assistance Fund. *See* Tex. Water Code § 15.993. The fund is administered by the TWDB. It was created to provide low-interest loans to rural political subdivisions for water or water-related projects and for water quality enhancement projects, including the purchase of well fields, the purchase or lease of rights to produce groundwater, onsite or wetland wastewater treatment facilities, and interim financing of construction projects. Rural political subdivisions are nonprofit water supply or sewer service corporations, water districts, or municipalities that have a service area of less than 10,000 population or that otherwise qualify for financing from a federal agency; or a county in which no urban area exceeds 50,000 population. Tex. Water Code § 15.992(4). The Rural Water Assistance Fund has been funded with proceeds from Water Financial Assistance Bonds issued under authority of article III, section 49–d–8, of the Texas Constitution.

Water Infrastructure Fund: In 2001, the legislature established the Water Infrastructure Fund. *See* Tex. Water Code § 15.973. Article III, section 49–d–9, of the Texas Constitution requires that $50 million of the $2 billion of the bonds therein authorized must be used for the Water Infrastructure Fund. In addition to funding traditional water and wastewater projects, money in the Water Infrastructure Fund may be used to provide financial assistance to an eligible political subdivision to fund loans and grants for projects that conserve and develop the water resources of the political subdivision for the ultimate benefit of the public and that develop and diversify its local economy, consistent with the terms and conditions set forth in a program adopted by the governing body of the political subdivision. Tex. Water Code § 15.979. An eligible political subdivision may establish economic development programs and make loans and grants of public funds to assist in providing projects within the political subdivision that conserve and develop the water resources of the political subdivision for the ultimate benefit of the public. Tex. Water Code § 17.980. The authority granted to a political subdivision to make loans and grants constitutes a program in furtherance of the public purposes provided by article III, section 52–a, of the constitution. Financial assistance received by an eligible political subdivision from the Water Infrastructure Fund may be used to make loans or grants to persons for projects that the political subdivision finds will conserve and develop the water resources of the political subdivision for the ultimate benefit of the public and assist in diversifying and developing the economy of the political subdivision and the state. *See* Tex. Water Code § 15.974. In creating the Water Infrastructure Fund, the legislature recognized the vital role a reliable water supply plays in attracting and maintaining business activity in the state. *See* Tex. Water Code § 15.972. In the 2007 legislative session, General Appropriations Act money was appropriated to the board to support the issuance of approximately $450 million in Water Financial Assistance Bonds in the 2008–2009 biennium to initiate and augment the Water Infrastructure Fund, in furtherance of implementing the state water plan and its objectives.

Miscellaneous Texas Water Development Board Financial Assistance Programs: In addition to the programs described above, the TWDB administers numerous grant programs, dealing with such diverse water issues as regional water facility planning (*see* Tex. Water Code § 15.406), community self-help programs (*see* Tex. Water Code ch. 15, subch. P), and water research programs (*see* Tex. Water Code § 15.404). Through funds made available by the federal government, the board administers the *colonia* plumbing loan program to enable low-income residents of *colonias* to connect their homes with existing water and sewer systems. *See* Tex. Water Code ch. 15, subch. L. The board works with the Federal Emergency Management Agency to develop flood mitigation programs to reduce or eliminate the long-term risk of flood damage to buildings, manufactured homes, and other structures insurable under the National Flood Insurance Program.

§ 37.2:4 Financial Assistance Application Process

The TWDB has established an application procedure for eligible political subdivisions to seek financial assistance. Financial assistance made to eligible political subdivisions takes the form of loans, through the purchase of bonds and other obligations, and grants. Each financing program administered by the board is governed by rules that address the receipt and review of applications for financial assistance. Information about the different financial assistance programs is provided on the TWDB's website at www.twdb.texas.gov/financial/programs/index.asp. The TWDB has divided the state into six regions (Panhandle/West, Brazos, Northeast, East, Central, and South) administered by teams responsible for each region.

The board may purchase bonds or other obligations of eligible political subdivisions with a maturity date of not more than fifty years from their date of issuance (*see* Tex. Water Code § 17.175), bearing interest at rates determined by the board (*see* Tex. Water Code § 17.176). The political subdivision bonds may be secured by the net revenues of the project to be financed, ad valorem taxes levied by the political subdivision, a combination of taxes and net revenues, and revenues from other available sources. The board may further require that the security for the political subdivision bonds it purchases be a combination of taxes and revenues as the board considers necessary to fully secure the investment. *See* Tex. Water Code § 17.179.

No acquisition of political subdivision bonds is permissible unless the political subdivision has approved the application for financial assistance at an open meeting of the governing body of the political subdivision. *See* Tex. Water Code § 17.1765. All political subdivision bonds to be purchased by the board must be approved by the attorney general and registered by the comptroller of public accounts. Tex. Water Code § 17.177.

The rules of the board detail the requirements of the application for financial assistance. *See* 31 Tex. Admin. Code § 363.12. Under section 363.12, general, legal, and fiscal information must be included in an application. Required information includes the total cost of the project, the amount of financial assistance being requested, a description of the project, the source of repayment of the financial assistance, the financing plan for repaying the total cost of the project, and the most recent annual financial statements and latest monthly and year-to-date reports for the general fund and utility fund of the applicant. 31 Tex. Admin. Code § 363.12(2)(A). The application must contain a preliminary engineering feasibility report in accordance with section 363.13, an environmental assessment in accordance with section 363.14, and a required water conservation plan in accordance with section 363.15. *See* 31 Tex. Admin. Code § 363.12(2)(D); *see also* 31 Tex. Admin. Code § 363.15.

The preliminary engineering feasibility report must include the following: (1) a description and purpose of the project, (2) the entities to be served and current and future populations, (3) the cost of the project, (4) a description of alternatives considered and reasons for the selection of the proposed project, (5) sufficient information to evaluate the engineering feasibility of the project, and (6) maps and drawings sufficient to locate and describe the project area. 31 Tex. Admin. Code § 363.13.

If the state or federal government prepares or requires an environmental assessment (EA) or an environmental impact statement (EIS) for substantially the same project, the applicant for financial assistance must file the EA or the EIS with the TWDB. 31 Tex. Admin. Code § 363.14(d). The rules also require an applicant, before or concurrently with the submission of an application, to submit preliminary data on any known environmental, social, and permitting issues that may affect the alternatives considered for implementation of the project or that may impact the existing environment in a manner that is the subject of any environmental regulation. 31 Tex. Admin. Code § 363.14(e)(3). This requirement is designed to provide sufficient information to the executive administrator for a determination of the necessary level of review for the proposed project. 31 Tex. Admin. Code § 363.14(e).

The levels of review are as follows: categorical exclusion review, mid-level review, or full review. 31 Tex. Admin. Code § 363.14(f). If the executive administrator determines that the project would not appear to cause significant environmental impacts under any environmental regulation, a categorical review will be performed. If the project would cause only significant environmental impacts that are limited in number or scope or that may be readily avoided, minimized, or mitigated, the executive administrator must do a mid-level review. Only if the project would appear to cause extensive, significant impacts that are not readily avoided, minimized, or mitigated, or would appear to involve a probable or known significant public controversy relating to environmental or social impacts, is a full review under section 363.14 required. *See* 31 Tex. Admin. Code § 363.14(f).

Under the successive rounds of state water planning (see Chapter 20 of this book for a detailed discussion of state and regional water planning), conservation of water resources is taking on greater significance in the review of applications by the board. See Chapters 3 and 23 of this book for discussions of water conservation. For example, water conservation efforts are taken into consideration when the TWDB has limited resources for financial assistance. *See* 31 Tex. Admin. Code § 363.19. This emphasis on water conservation is also reflected in 31 Tex. Admin. Code § 363.15, requiring an applicant for financial assistance to submit two copies of its water conservation plan with the application (although there are some exceptions to this requirement). Generally, the water conservation plan must include an evaluation of the applicant's water and wastewater system and consumer water use characteristics, identify water conservation opportunities, and set goals to be accomplished. *See* 31 Tex. Admin. Code § 363.15(b). Minimum elements of the plan are established in section 363.15(b)(1) and include a utility profile including data on population, consumers, water use, water supply system, and wastewater system; quantified five-year and ten-year targets for water savings; a schedule for achieving the targets; water loss; a water rate structure that is not "promotional" of water use; how the implementation and enforcement of the conservation is effected; and a current drought contingency plan that includes specific water supply or water demand management measures. *See* 31 Tex. Admin. Code § 363.15(b)(1).

TWDB regulations also set the procedures regarding loan closings, including the purchase of bonds from political subdivisions. Instruments required at the time of closing include (1) proof that the applicant authorized the issuance of debt; (2) information about the applicant's water conservation program; (3) the approving opinion of the attorney general; (4) bond counsel's unqualified opinion that the bonds are valid and binding obligations of the political subdivision, and that the interest on the bonds is exempt from federal income taxation; and (5) an executed escrow agreement. *See* 31 Tex. Admin. Code § 363.42(a).

The TWDB may request the attorney general in the event of a default to seek a writ of mandamus to compel a "financial assistance program recipient" (a recipient or beneficiary of funds administered by the TWDB under the Water Code) or its officers, agents, and employees to cure the default or any other legal or equitable remedy that TWDB and the attorney general consider necessary and appropriate. Default is defined to include the following: defaults in the payment of debt service on obligations acquired by the TWDB; the failure to perform any covenant related to obligations acquired by the TWDB; the failure to perform any term of a loan, grant, or financing agreement; or any other failure to perform an obligation, breach of a term of an agreement, or default as provided by any proceeding or agreement evidencing an obligation or agreement of a recipient, beneficiary, or guarantor of financial assistance provided by the TWDB. *See* Tex. Water Code § 6.114.

In addition, if a financial assistance program recipient is not a municipality or county, or a district or authority created under article III, section 52, or article XVI, section 59, of the Texas Constitution, at the request of the TWDB the attorney general shall bring suit in a district court in Travis County for the appointment of a receiver to collect the assets and carry on the business of the financial assistance program recipient. The receiver would have the power or duty to perform audits, raise rates, fund reserves, make payments on obligations acquired by the TWDB, and take other actions necessary to prevent or remedy the default. *See* Tex. Water Code § 6.115. This power would principally apply to actions against nonprofit water supply corporations who receive financial assistance from the TWDB.

§ 37.3 Constitutional Amendment of November 5, 2013: SWIFT and SWIRFT

On November 5, 2013, Texas voters approved adding sections 49–d–12 and 49–d–13 to article III of the Texas Constitution. Section 49–d–12 created the State Water Implementation Fund for Texas (SWIFT). Section 49–d–13 created the State Water Implementation Revenue Fund for Texas

(SWIRFT). Both SWIFT and SWIRFT will be administered by the TWDB, or its successor, for the purpose of implementing the state water plan.

In accordance with House Bill 1025, adopted by the Texas legislature in its 2013 regular session, $2 billion was appropriated from the state's economic stabilization fund for transfer to SWIFT.

House Bill 4, adopted by the Texas legislature in its 2013 regular session, addressed how SWIFT and SWIRFT may be administered and how projects to implement the state water plan may be prioritized. Texas Water Code chapter 15 was amended to add subchapters G and H, which pertain to SWIFT and SWIRFT, respectively.

Funds in SWIFT shall be held and invested by the Texas Treasury Safekeeping Trust Company (Trust Company). Payments to the TWDB pursuant to a bond enhancement agreement may be made no more often than twice per fiscal year. *See* Tex. Water Code § 15.433. Bond enhancement agreements may be used to support the payment of debt service on bonds if the proceeds of the sale of the bonds have been or will be deposited to the credit of SWIRFT, the Water Infrastructure Fund, the Rural Water Assistance Fund, the State Participation Account within Development Fund II, or the Agricultural Water Conservation Fund. *See* Tex. Water Code § 15.435(b).

At the direction of the TWDB, the Trust Company shall make disbursements from the SWIFT to another fund or account pursuant to a bond enhancement agreement in amounts the TWDB determines are needed for debt service payments on or security provisions of the TWDB's general obligation bonds or revenue bonds, after considering all other sources available for those purposes in the respective fund or account. Disbursements may be made under a bond enhancement agreement to the TWDB for the support of bonds the proceeds of which are used to provide financial assistance in the form of a loan bearing an interest rate of not less than 50 percent of the then-current interest rate available to the TWDB; a loan to finance a facility with a term not to exceed the lesser of the expected useful life of the facility or thirty years; a deferral of loan repayments; incremental repurchase terms for an acquired facility; or a combination of the above-described methods. *See* Tex. Water Code § 15.435(c).

Limitations are imposed on the types of projects to be supported from SWIFT; the TWDB shall undertake to apply not less than 10 percent to support projects that are for rural political subdivisions or agricultural water conservation, and 20 percent to support projects, including agricultural irrigation projects, that are designed for water conservation or reuse. *See* Tex. Water Code § 15.434.

House Bill 4 created the State Water Implementation Fund for Texas Advisory Committee. The committee consists of seven persons: the comptroller, or a person designated by the comptroller; three members of the senate appointed by the lieutenant governor, including a member of the committee of the senate having primary jurisdiction over matters relating to finance and a member of the committee of the senate having primary jurisdiction over matters relating to natural resources; and three members of the house of representatives appointed by the speaker of the house, including a member of the committee of the house having primary jurisdiction over matters relating to appropriations and a member of the committee of the house having primary jurisdiction over matters relating to natural resources. The committee shall submit comments and recommendations to the TWDB regarding the use of money in SWIFT for use by the TWDB in adopting rules and policies and procedures. *See* Tex. Water Code § 15.438.

The TWDB shall adopt rules providing for the use of money in SWIFT that are consistent with Water Code chapter 15, subchapter G, including rules establishing standards for determining whether projects meet the criteria for rural political subdivision projects and water conservation or reuse projects, and specifying the manner for prioritizing projects included in the state water plan for the purpose of providing financial assistance under subchapter G. *See* Tex. Water Code § 15.439.

The TWDB shall adopt policies and procedures for the purpose of mitigating or minimizing the adverse effects, if any, of federal laws and regulations relating to income taxes, arbitrage, rebates, and related matters that may restrict the TWDB's ability to freely invest all or part of SWIFT or to receive and retain all the earnings from SWIFT. *See* Tex. Water Code § 15.441.

SWIRFT may be used by the TWDB only for the purpose of providing financing for projects included in the state water plan that are authorized by Water Code chapter 15, subchapter Q or R; Water Code chapter 16, subchapter E or F; or Water Code chapter 17, subchapter J. *See* Tex. Water Code § 15.474.

Moneys in SWIRFT consist of moneys transferred or deposited to the credit of SWIRFT by law; the proceeds of any fee or tax imposed by the state that by statute is dedicated for deposit to the credit of SWIRFT; any other revenue that the legislature by statute dedicates for deposit to SWIRFT; investment earnings on amounts credited to SWIRFT; bond proceeds, including proceeds from revenue bonds issued by the TWDB under Water Code chapter 15, subchapter H, that are designated by the TWDB for the purpose of providing money for SWIRFT; repayments of loans made from SWIRFT; money from the sale, transfer, or lease of a project acquired, constructed, reconstructed, developed, or enlarged with money from SWIRFT; and money disbursed to SWIRFT from SWIFT. *See* Tex. Water Code § 15.472.

The TWDB may issue revenue bonds for the purpose of providing money for SWIRFT and to refund revenue bonds or bonds and obligations issued or incurred in accordance with other provisions of law. Revenue bonds do not constitute indebtedness of the state as prohibited by the constitution. *See* Tex. Water Code § 15.475. The terms and conditions relating to the issuance of revenue bonds are set forth in Water Code section 15.475(g).

Since SWIFT and SWIRFT were established, the TWDB has issued eight series of revenue bonds: two series issued in 2015, one series issued in 2016, two series issued in 2017, and three series issued in 2018. These bond series aggregated over $5 billion in principal amount, enabling the TWDB to make approximately $5.55 billion in financial assistance available to political subdivisions to finance state water plan projects.

§ 37.4 Flood Infrastructure Fund

On November 5, 2019, Texas voters approved a state constitutional amendment establishing the Flood Infrastructure Fund (FIF). The FIF is administered by the TWDB or its successor.

Money in the FIF is used to provide financing for drainage, flood mitigation, or flood control projects, including planning and design activities; work to obtain regulatory approval to provide nonstructural and structural flood mitigation or drainage; or construction of structural flood mitigation and drainage infrastructure. *See* Tex. H.R.J. Res. 4, 86th Leg., R.S. (2019).

Two bills were adopted by the Texas legislature in its 2019 regular session, Senate Bill 7 and Senate Bill 8, addressing a variety of issues relating to planning for flood infrastructure and the financing of flood projects throughout the state. Article 2 of S.B. 7, which addresses the uses and funding of and financing made available to eligible political subdivisions from the FIF, took effect on January 1, 2020. *See* Act of May 25, 2019, 86th Leg., R.S., ch. 947, § 5.01(b) (S.B. 7), eff. June 13, 2019.

S.B. 8 directs the TWDB to prepare and adopt no later than September 1, 2024, and before the end of each successive five-year period after that date, a comprehensive state flood plan. *See* Act of May 26, 2019, 86th Leg., R.S., ch. 565, § 1 (S.B. 8), eff. June 10, 2019 (adding Tex. Water Code § 16.061(a)). See also Chapter 39 of this book discussing flood management.

S.B. 7 adds subchapter I to chapter 15 of the Texas Water Code. *See* S.B. 7, § 2.01. A "flood project" is defined to mean a drainage, flood mitigation, or flood control project, including planning and design activities, work to obtain regulatory approval to provide nonstructural and structural flood mitigation and drainage, construction of structural flood mitigation and drainage infrastructure, and construction and implementation of nonstructural projects, including projects that use nature-based features to protect, mitigate, or reduce flood risk. *See* Tex. Water Code § 15.531(2). An "eligible political subdivision" includes a district or authority created under section 52, article III, or section 59, article XVI, of the constitution, a municipality, or a county. *See* Tex. Water Code § 15.531(1).

The FIF consists of legislative appropriations, proceeds of general obligation bonds issued for a purpose of the FIF, fees and other sources of revenue the legislature dedicates for deposit to the FIF, repayments of loans made from the FIF, interest earned on money credited to the FIF, money raised from revenue bonds or other sources designated by the TWDB for deposit to the FIF, and depository interest and money from gifts, grants, or donations. *See* Tex. Water Code § 15.533(c).

S.B. 7 creates a split set of rules governing the uses of the FIF. Prior to the adoption of the first state flood plan, section 15.534 of the Water Code controls. Upon the adoption of the first state flood plan, section 15.534 of the Code expires, and section 15.5341 of the Code controls. *See* S.B. 7, § 2.03.

S.B. 7 authorizes the TWDB to use the FIF (1) to make a loan to an eligible political subdivision at or below market interest rates for a flood project; (2) to make a grant or loan at or below market interest rates to an eligible political subdivision for a flood project to serve an area outside a metropolitan statistical area as defined by Water Code section 15.531(4); (3) to make a loan at or below market interest rates for planning and design costs, permitting costs, and other costs associated with state or federal regulatory activities with respect to a flood project; (4) to make a loan or grant to provide matching funds to enable an eligible political subdivision to participate in a federal program for a flood project; (5) to make a grant to an eligible political subdivision for a flood project if the TWDB determines that the eligible political subdivision does not have the ability to repay a loan; (6) as a source of security or revenue for the payment of bonds issued by the TWDB if the proceeds of the bonds are to be deposited into the FIF; (7) to pay necessary and reasonable expenses of the TWDB in administering the FIF; and (8) to make transfers to the research and planning fund created by Water Code section 15.402. *See* Tex. Water Code § 15.534(a).

S.B. 7 authorizes the TWDB to defer the principal and interest payments on loans made under section 15.534(a)(3) for not more than ten years or until construction of the flood project is completed, whichever is earlier. *See* Tex. Water Code § 15.534(b).

Section 15.5341 of the Water Code becomes effective upon the adoption of the first state flood plan. *See* S.B. 7, § 2.03. Under section 15.5341 of the Code, the TWDB may use the FIF only to provide financing for flood projects included in the state flood plan. *See* S.B. 7, § 2.03. This creates several gaps in what may or may not be eligible to be financed, and calls into question whether the TWDB may provide for the deferral of principal and interest payments on loans, because the terms of S.B. 7 specifically state that on the date the first state flood plan is adopted by the TWDB, section 15.534 of the Code expires. It is uncertain whether a state flood plan adopted by the TWDB can address deferrals of loan repayments. Because a flood project is defined in such a manner that subsections 15.534(a)(6), (a)(7), or (a)(8) may not carry forward, as those subsections identify costs that fall outside the scope of the definition of flood project, legislation may be needed prior to the adoption of the first state flood plan in order to address these matters.

III. Regional Authorities and Districts: Financing Water Projects

§ 37.5 How Regional Authorities and Districts Finance Water Projects

This part discusses laws relating to the powers of regional authorities and districts to develop the water resources of the state and how water projects can be financed by regional authorities and districts. Those powers include storing the water supply, treating and transporting water, conserving and developing water and hydroelectric power, and navigating the inland and coastal waters of the state.

§ 37.6 Constitutional Authority

Article III, section 52, and article XVI, section 59, of the Texas Constitution provide the authority for the creation of conservation and reclamation districts, as well as the ability of cities and other political subdivisions to develop and conserve the water resources of the state. Conservation and reclamation districts are created through the passage of general laws and special laws that address their powers, rights, privileges, and functions. General law districts are created by action of the Texas Commission on Environmental Quality (TCEQ) (*see* Tex. Water Code ch. 54), by a commissioners court (*see* Tex. Water Code chs. 53, 55, 56, 57), or, depending on the size of the district, by the TCEQ or commissioners court (*see* Tex. Water Code chs. 51, 58). See Chapter 8 of this book for a discussion of water districts.

Districts created under the constitution include river authorities, regional water districts, water control and improvement districts, municipal utility districts, and flood control districts. Some of the districts serve wide geographic expanses of the state—for example, the Brazos River Authority, within whose jurisdiction lie the watershed counties of the Brazos River. Some serve distinct geographic areas within a county—for example, Travis County Water Control and Improvement District No. 17.

State laws enacted after the adoption of these constitutional amendments provide the authority for conservation and reclamation districts, cities, and other political subdivisions to finance water and wastewater projects. This section focuses on the authority granted to conservation and reclamation districts.

Article XVI, section 59, was added to the constitution in 1917. Subsection (b) authorizes the legislature to create conservation and reclamation districts. The districts are to promote the conservation and development of the natural resources of the state, as described in subsection (a). Their functions include the control, storage, preservation, and distribution of the state's stormwaters and flood waters and the waters of its rivers and streams and the conservation and development of water and hydroelectric power. Other purposes are irrigation, the reclamation of land, and the preservation and conservation of all natural resources of the state.

Under subsection (d) of this constitutional provision, the legislature may not create a conservation and reclamation district unless notice of the intention to introduce a bill is published at least thirty days and not more than ninety days before its introduction. The notice must be published in a newspaper having general circulation in the county or counties in which the district will be located. A newspaper must meet the requirements of Texas Government Code section 2051.044.

Subsections (d) and (e) also provide that no law creating a conservation and reclamation district may be passed unless, at the time notice is published, a copy of the bill is delivered to the commissioners court and to the governing body of each incorporated city or town in whose jurisdiction the district will be located. A copy of the notice and the bill must be delivered to the governor, who must submit the notice to the TCEQ. The TCEQ must file its recommendation on the bill with the governor, lieutenant governor, and speaker of the House of Representatives within thirty days after it receives the notice.

Article XVI, section 59, of the constitution also authorizes the legislature to permit a district to levy and collect ad valorem taxes for the maintenance of the district and the payment of debt service on bonds. The legislature may not authorize a district to issue bonds payable from ad valorem taxes unless the bonds are approved at the election held by the district. Bonds may be issued to provide for improvements within the district and the maintenance of the improvements.

Article III, section 52, of the constitution authorizes the legislature to permit any city, county, or other political subdivision of the state to lend its credit, and issue bonds and levy and collect taxes to pay debt service, for specified purposes. Those purposes include the improvement of rivers, creeks, and streams to prevent overflows and the construction and maintenance of pools, lakes, reservoirs, dams, canals, and waterways for the purposes of irrigation, drainage, or navigation.

§ 37.7 Statutory Authority

Conservation and reclamation districts may be created either by special law or under the general laws of the state. Many of these special laws are codified in the Texas Special District Local Laws Code. The Special District Local Laws Code was enacted in 2003 and became effective April 1, 2005, as part of the state's continuing statutory revision program. Title 6 of the Code contains special laws for water and wastewater districts. These special laws describe the district's boundaries, its organization, and the particular powers of the district, including the ability to finance projects within its statutory authority and purpose.

In addition to special laws creating conservation and reclamation districts, general laws provide authority for the districts to be created. Title 4 of the Texas Water Code contains general laws for water districts. Chapters 49 and 50 of the Water Code apply generally to all water districts, including those created by special law. *See* Tex. Water Code § 49.002; *see also* Tex. Water Code § 50.107. Specific chapters of the Water Code apply to the creation and functions of designated districts. For example, chapter 51 applies to a water control and improvement district, chapter 53 to the creation and functions of a fresh water supply district, chapter 54 to the creation and functions of a municipal utility district, and chapter 65 to the creation and functions of a special utility district. See Chapter 8 of this book for a discussion of the functions and powers of these districts. Each chapter provides specific authority to finance water projects and must be reviewed in order to determine whether a project may be financed under the chapter and the steps necessary to ensure the lawful issuance of obligations to finance water projects.

The powers granted to these districts are similar, but each Water Code chapter addresses issues unique to each type of district. The laws authorizing these districts were enacted at different times, and the distinctions between the powers and responsibilities of the districts often are a source of confusion. For example, each of the districts has the authority to issue bonds, but the projects that can be financed with bonds differ from entity to entity. The particular chapter of the Water Code governing an entity must be reviewed carefully to confirm that the authority exists to finance a specific type of project, just as the enabling statute must be carefully reviewed for special law districts.

Chapter 51A of the Water Code authorizes the TCEQ to create subdistricts over designated territory within the boundaries of a conservation and reclamation district that (1) is created by general or special law pursuant to article XVI, section 59, of the constitution; (2) is governed by chapter 51 of the Water Code to the extent the provisions of that chapter are not inconsistent with the provisions of any special law creating the district; and (3) contains at least 10,000 acres after all exclusions of land have occurred. *See* Tex. Water Code § 51A.001(3). Pursuant to an election, the subdistrict may impose ad valorem taxes on property within the subdistrict. *See* Tex. Water Code § 51A.003.

§ 37.8 Texas Commission on Environmental Quality Oversight

Water projects may be financed by districts upon review and approval by the TCEQ. The following sections discuss the statutory oversight the TCEQ may assert over water projects and the approvals that may be required before a district may finance a water project.

§ 37.8:1 Statutory Authority over District Projects

Chapter 49 of the Texas Water Code gives the TCEQ jurisdiction over projects undertaken by districts, including the financing of the projects. A district may not issue bonds to finance projects unless the TCEQ (1) determines that the project to be financed by the bonds is feasible and (2) issues an order approving the issuance of the bonds. The issuance of refunding bonds, or bonds purchased by federal or state agencies such as the United States Department of Agriculture, the Farmers Home Administration, and the TWDB, are exempt from TCEQ approval. *See* Tex. Water Code § 49.181(a).

Numerous districts, however, are exempt from TCEQ jurisdiction. *See* Tex. Water Code § 49.181(h). The result of the exemptions is to focus TCEQ jurisdiction on districts that exist primarily as development tools created to encourage residential development. Generally, water control and improvement districts, fresh water supply districts, municipal utility districts, and special utility districts are subject to TCEQ jurisdiction. River authorities and regional water districts generally are not subject to TCEQ jurisdiction.

A district under TCEQ jurisdiction must submit to the TCEQ a written application for investigation of feasibility. An engineer's report describing the project must be submitted with the application. *See* Tex. Water Code § 49.181(b). Upon examination, the TCEQ determines whether the project is feasible. An order is issued either approving or disapproving, as appropriate, the issuance of the bonds to finance the project. *See* Tex. Water Code § 49.181(c)–(f).

The TCEQ may approve the issuance of bonds of a district without the submission of plans and specifications of the improvements to be financed with the bonds. Money must be placed in escrow until the plans and specifications have been submitted to and approved by the TCEQ. *See* Tex. Water Code § 49.181(g).

§ 37.8:2 TCEQ Rules for Financing Projects

Familiarity with the rules of the TCEQ is essential to determine whether a project is feasible, what costs of a project may be financed or reimbursed from bond proceeds, and the conditions to be met for the approval of bonds. The rules of the TCEQ governing the issuance of bonds are contained in 30 Texas Administrative Code chapter 293, subchapter E (referred to throughout this discussion as the Rules). The Rules address the financing of projects where developer assistance is expected (see Tex. Water Code § 49.052(d) for a definition of "developer").

A developer incurs the construction costs of facilities with the expectation that the money will be reimbursed from bond proceeds. The Rules provide that the feasibility of construction projects depends on a developer's paying some portion of the costs. Increases in the property values within the district are necessary for the developer to be repaid for the initial costs. Under section 293.47 of the Rules, the developer must pay not less than 30 percent of the district construction costs. The Rules generally define what costs are eligible to be reimbursed with bond proceeds. Section 293.47, however, exempts numerous districts from this requirement. The exemptions relate to such factors as ratio of debt to assessed valuation, credit ratings on bonds, and contracts with other political subdivisions pledging revenues in consideration of the district's development of water or wastewater facilities. *See* 30 Tex. Admin. Code § 293.47.

To the extent that improvements included in the bond issue are needed to produce values sufficient to support the bonds, and that improvements have not been completed, the developer must enter into an agreement with the district to secure payment of the costs. An escrow of funds, a letter of credit, or similar security may be established in the name of the district to secure the payment of costs. The agreement must be entered before the bond sale is advertised. The agreement is to ensure that the district may draw on the financial guarantee to pay the developer's share of construction and engineering costs. *See* 30 Tex. Admin. Code §§ 293.47(g), 293.56. Section 293.59 of the Rules expands on the statutory requirement that the TCEQ determines the economic feasibility of each proposed bond issue. The TCEQ reviews land values, existing improvements, and projected improvements in the district to determine economic feasibility. A reasonable tax rate for debt service payments must result while competitive utility rates are maintained from the facilities to be financed. *See* 30 Tex. Admin. Code § 293.59(b). The TCEQ examines both a "no-growth debt service tax rate" and a "combined projected tax rate" in its review. *See* 30 Tex. Admin. Code § 293.59(e), (f). The approval of tax-supported bonds is subject to satisfying additional requirements affecting the levy and collection of ad valorem taxes.

A no-growth tax rate is the tax rate required to meet projected annual debt service requirements using the current assessed value and a 100 percent tax collection rate. This calculation is used to determine whether sufficient cash flow is available to the district to support indebtedness. A 90 percent tax collection rate is used in determining the projected tax rate collections, unless the district demonstrates that its historical collection rate is higher. *See* 30 Tex. Admin. Code § 293.59(k)(2). The TCEQ requires that at least 25 percent of the projected value of houses and other improvements shown in the projected tax rate calculations must be completed before the bonds may be issued. *See* 30 Tex. Admin. Code § 293.59(k)(7). A written agreement must be executed between the district and the developer and other parties receiving bond proceeds that permanently waives the right to claim any agricultural, open-space, timberland, or inventory valuation for any land, homes, or buildings that the developer or other parties own in the district. The agreement is binding for thirty years, unless such exemptions were in effect at the time of the TCEQ approval of the bond issue and were shown in the projected tax rate calculations. *See* 30 Tex. Admin. Code § 293.59(k)(8).

The 25 percent value requirement is also subject to exceptions. *See* 30 Tex. Admin. Code § 293.59(k)(11). The exceptions are extensive, and it is important to review them before submitting an application to the TCEQ.

The first bond issue and subsequent bonds issues of a district are treated differently under the Rules. Section 293.59(k) of the Rules governs the first bond issue of a district, while section 293.59(*l*) governs the subsequent bond issues. The Rules treat developer projects differently than projects in which there is no developer.

In subsequent bond issues, houses or buildings equal to 75 percent of the projected buildout used in the projected tax rate calculations contained in all prior bond issues must be completed and located on the area developed from the proceeds of prior bond issues, the proposed bond issue, and future bond issues. *See* 30 Tex. Admin. Code § 293.59(*l*)(4). A district may request, and the TCEQ may waive, this requirement. The waiver may be granted on the basis of sufficient assessed values existing in the district, the credit rating issued for the bonds, or the debt-to-assessed value ratio in the district. *See* 30 Tex. Admin. Code § 293.59(*l*)(5).

Applicants must submit all required data at one time in one package. The TCEQ may grant expedited treatment under section 293.42 of the Rules. Section 293.44 addresses developer projects. A developer project is one that provides water, wastewater, drainage, or recreational facility service for property owned by a developer of property in the district. 30 Tex. Admin. Code § 293.44(a)(1). Restrictions on financing oversized facilities are set forth in section 293.44(a)(8) of the Rules. This section also addresses whether certain costs are subject to the 30 percent developer contribution requirements. *See* 30 Tex. Admin. Code § 293.44(a)(8).

An independent appraisal is required before a district can purchase existing facilities from a developer. An appraisal, however, is not required in every instance. Section 293.44 addresses the circumstances in which an appraisal is not required.

A developer may proceed with financing the construction of water, wastewater, drainage, and recreational facilities before TCEQ approval under the conditions described in section 293.46 of the Rules. Failure to comply with the conditions set forth in this rule could result in the denial of reimbursement to the developer of construction costs. *See* 30 Tex. Admin. Code § 293.46.

Decisions need to be made early in the development process by both the district and the developer to determine the most economical method to finance improvements. Developers in particular should analyze whether it is more cost-effective to fund the construction costs up front or seek reimbursement once the projects are completed. It is more likely that credit enhancement can be obtained to support the payment of debt service on district bonds if the improvements have been completed. Improvements in the ground are more likely to result in the construction of homes, giving credit providers comfort that the valuation needed to support the payment of debt service will exist throughout the term of a district bond issue.

§ 37.9 Contract Revenue Bonds

River authorities and regional districts finance the construction of facilities to provide water supply or wastewater treatment. The water supply or wastewater treatment services are sold to cities and other political subdivisions. To support the payment of debt service on bonds issued by river authorities and regional districts, contracts are executed with cities and other political subdivisions. Texas Government Code chapter 791 and Texas Local Government Code chapter 552 provide the contracting authority necessary to support this method of finance.

Government Code chapter 791 is commonly known as the Interlocal Cooperation Act. Tex. Gov't Code § 791.002. The Act generally provides authority to a local government to contract with another local government or a state agency to perform governmental functions and services. The Act defines local government to include a county, municipality, special district, junior college district, or other political subdivision of the state. Tex. Gov't Code § 791.003(4). Governmental functions and services are defined at Tex. Gov't Code § 791.003(3). Political subdivision is defined to include any corporate and political entity organized under state law. Tex. Gov't Code § 791.003(5).

Section 791.026 addresses the authority under the Act for certain local governments to contract for water supply and wastewater treatment facilities. A municipality, district, or river authority of the state may contract with another municipality, district, or river authority of the state to obtain or provide part or all of (1) water supply or wastewater treatment facilities or (2) a lease or operation of water supply facilities or wastewater treatment facilities. Tex. Gov't Code § 791.026(a). The contract may provide that the party obtaining services may not obtain those services from a source other than a contracting party unless otherwise provided in the contract, and, if the contract so provides, payments made under the contract are the paying party's operating expenses for its water supply system, wastewater treatment facilities, or both. Tex. Gov't Code § 791.026(b), (c). The contract may contain terms and extend for any period on which the parties agree and may provide that the contract will continue in effect until bonds specified by the contract and any refunding bonds issued to pay those bonds are paid. Tex. Gov't Code § 791.026(d). Tax revenue may not be pledged to the payment of amounts agreed to be paid under the contract. Tex. Gov't Code § 791.026(f).

The authority granted by section 791.026 enables contracting parties to structure contracts to provide and finance water supply and wastewater treatment facilities on a "take-or-pay" basis. Since the payments to be made by the contracting party to receive the services are the sole source of funds available to the contracting party to provide the services to pay debt service on its bonds, the contracts are structured so that the receiving party will pay for the service to be provided regardless of whether it actually receives the service. In addition, the contract typically will provide for the payment of operation and maintenance expenses relating to the system constructed by the providing party. See Chapter 31 of this book for a discussion of take-or-pay wholesale water contracts.

A good discussion of the authority granted by the Act to enter into contracts for water supply and wastewater treatment can be found in *City of The Colony v. North Texas Municipal Water District*, 272 S.W.3d 699 (Tex. App.—Fort Worth 2008, pet. dism'd). The City of The Colony entered into a contract with the City of Frisco and the North Texas Municipal Water District, under which the District was to provide wastewater treatment services to the two cities. The District issued bonds to construct a regional wastewater treatment system. The contract provided that it was the sole responsibility of each city to transport, or cause to be transported, at no cost to the other participants, its wastewater to its points of entry. The Colony never constructed transmission lines to its point of entry to the wastewater treatment system and never received wastewater treatment services. The Colony made payments under the contract in support of the debt service and operation and maintenance expenses of the system. After several years of not making payments under the contract, The Colony sued to invalidate the contract.

The contract provided that the cities "shall be obligated unconditionally, and without offset or counterclaim, to make . . . payments . . . in the manner provided in this Contract, regardless of whether or not the District actually provides such facilities and services, or whether or not any [city] actually receives or uses such facilities and services, and regardless of the validity or performance of the other parts of this or any other contract." *The Colony*, 272 S.W.3d at 714. The contract also stated that the payments by the two cities were the "only source available to the District to provide" for the payment of debt service on bonds issued by the District. *The Colony*, 272 S.W.3d at 714.

The court also addressed whether the contract violated public policy. The court found that the "government code expressly allows for this particular type of contract," citing Government Code section 791.026(a)(1), and that "the government code reflects a public policy that permits the execution of this particular type of agreement." *The Colony*, 272 S.W.3d at 730. The validity of the contract was upheld by the court.

The contract language cited above is the classic language of a take-or-pay contract. The obligation of the contracting party to make payments under the contract to the party providing the facilities and services is unconditional, regardless of whether the facilities or services are actually provided, received, or used. The take-or-pay feature of the contract is also sustained by the provisions of Government Code section 791.026(g), which states that the powers granted by section 791.026 prevail over a limitation contained in another law. Tex. Gov't Code § 791.026(g).

Local Government Code chapter 552 also provides contracting authority to support this method of finance. Local Government Code section 552.014 authorizes municipalities to enter into contracts with districts created under article XVI, section 59, of the Texas Constitution. The district will acquire for the benefit of the city and then convey to the city a water supply or treatment system, a water distribution system, a sanitary sewage collection or treatment system, or related improvements. The contract may provide for purchase of the system by the municipality through periodic payments to the district in amounts sufficient to pay the principal of and interest on the bonds of the district. The contract must be approved by the governing body of the municipality. Municipalities are provided with similar authority to contract with water districts under sections 552.012, 552.019, 552.020, and 552.022 of the Local Government Code.

The contract may provide that any payments due are payable from and are secured by a pledge of specified revenues (including revenues from municipal sales and use taxes), an ad valorem tax levied to make the payments due, or both. Tex. Loc. Gov't Code § 552.014(c). Contracts between cities and the districts generally are structured as take-or-pay contracts. The contract also will require that the district prepare an annual budget. The budget will set forth the payments to be made for debt service and operation and maintenance expenses, for costs of administration of the system, and for related costs for capital repairs and replacements. Provisions relating to review of the budget and dispute resolution are also common features in these contracts. The payments made for the acquisition of the services received, both for debt service and operation and maintenance expenses, are treated as expenses of the city's waterworks system or wastewater system, either combined or separate, as the case may be. This is consistent with the statutory provisions of Local Government Code sections 552.019(b) and 552.020(e) and Government Code section 1502.056.

§ 37.10 Texas Government Code Chapter 1371

Texas Government Code chapter 1371 provides broad powers to eligible issuers to finance a wide array of projects defined in Government Code section 1371.001(2) and (8). Government Code section 1371.001(4) defines an issuer to include a conservation and reclamation district organized or operating as a navigation district under article III, section 52, or article XVI, section 59, of the Texas Constitution, and a district organized or operating under article XVI, section 59, that has all or part of two cities within its boundaries.

An issuer may issue obligations secured by any revenue that an issuer is authorized by the constitution, a statute, or a home-rule charter to pledge to the payment of an obligation (defined in Government Code section 1371.001(5)). An issuer may adopt proceedings providing the terms and conditions relating to the sale of obligations. The proceedings may authorize one or more designated officers or employees of the issuer to act on behalf of the issuer in selling and delivering the obligation and setting the procedures relating to the obligation. Tex. Gov't Code § 1371.053(c).

The ability of an issuer to delegate the authority to an authorized representative to set the terms of the sale of the obligations is a significant power and provides flexibility in pricing and selling a bond issue. Government Code section 1371.004 provides that a finding by the authorized representative has the same force and effect as if made by the governing body of the issuer.

An issuer also may enter into credit agreements to provide additional security for obligations. A credit agreement includes numerous types of agreements executed in connection with the sale of an obligation issued under Government Code chapter 1371. *See* Tex. Gov't Code § 1371.001(1). Letters or lines of credit, reimbursement agreements, and interest rate management agreements are a few of the agreements authorized by section 1317.001(1). The payment obligation of the issuer incurred under a credit agreement may be paid from any source, including the proceeds of an obligation to which the credit agreement relates, revenues of the issuer that are available to pay the obligation, and ad valorem taxes, to the extent permitted by Government Code chapter 1371. *See* Tex. Gov't Code § 1371.056(c). The credit agreement must contain the terms and be for the period as approved by the issuer. *See* Tex. Gov't Code § 1371.056(b). An issuer may enter into a credit agreement at any time before, after, or concurrently with the issuance of obligations. *See* Tex. Gov't Code § 1371.056(a).

Government Code section 1371.001(3–a) defines "interest rate management agreement." An interest rate management agreement provides a hedge for managing interest rates. An interest rate swap agreement, where one party agrees to pay a fixed rate of interest and the counterparty agrees to pay a variable rate of interest tied to an index, is one example of an interest rate management agreement.

Interest rate management agreements generally follow a format wherein the parties enter into a "master agreement," which contains the common terms governing transactions, and a "confirmation," which is specifically designed for a particular transaction executed under the master agreement. *See* Tex. Gov't Code § 1371.001(3–a). There are limits on the ability of an issuer to enter into interest rate management agreements. Government Code section 1371.056(j) restricts issuers who may enter into an interest rate management agreement transaction to those that have either entered into at least three interest rate management transactions before November 1, 2006, or entered into one or more transactions with an aggregate notional amount of at least $400 million before November 1, 2006. *See* Tex. Gov't Code § 1371.056(j). Issuers who do not satisfy the restriction of section 1371.056(j) may enter into an interest rate management transaction if it complies with the provisions of Government Code section 1371.056(k). Under this section, the governing body of the issuer must adopt a risk management policy. This policy must address the conditions under which an issuer may enter into an interest rate management agreement without independent advice from a financial advisor. *See* Tex. Gov't Code § 1371.056(k). Government Code chapter 1371, subchapter D, sets forth the requirements governing the eligibility of an entity to serve as a financial advisor for an issuer as well as which issuers are exempt from the requirements of the subchapter.

The policy must address the pricing of the transactions that may be entered under the agreement. Either the governing body of the issuer or its authorized representative must confirm that a transaction conforms to the requirements of the policy. The issuer must review and ratify or modify its risk management policy at least biennially. *See* Tex. Gov't Code § 1371.056(*l*).

A designated officer of the issuer is required to monitor interest rate management agreement transactions. *See* Tex. Gov't Code § 1371.061. The designated officer must provide a report to the issuer describing the terms of transactions and how the transactions were valued. The designated officer also must state whether continuing transactions under the agreement comply with the issuer's risk management policy. The reporting requirements do not apply to issuers who have either entered into at least three interest rate management transactions before November 1, 2006, or entered into one or more transactions with an aggregate notional amount of at least $400 million before November 1, 2006.

The powers granted to issuers under Government Code chapter 1371 have broad application and are used not only by regional issuers, such as river authorities, but also by state agencies, such as the TWDB, and designated local units of government. *See* Tex. Gov't Code § 1371.001. The powers exercised by cities in financing water projects under chapter 1371 are discussed in greater detail in part IV below. The authority granted by this statute is limited to those issuers the legislature deems to be sophisticated and with broad financial strength. Many water districts operating under Texas Water Code chapters 49, 51, and 54 are not eligible to act as an issuer under Government Code chapter 1371 and are not authorized to use the powers granted by this statute; however, see Government Code section 1371.001(e) and (p).

IV. Local Financial Assistance

§ 37.11 Introduction

Cities are the unit of local government principally responsible under Texas law to finance local water projects. Counties, water supply corporations, and special purpose districts also are authorized by Texas law to finance water projects.

§ 37.12 Cities

Cities are the primary local unit of government responsible for financing water projects in Texas. Cities derive the authority to own and operate utility systems, including waterworks and sewer systems, from Texas Local Government Code chapter 552, Texas Government Code chapter 1502, and, in the case of home-rule cities, their city charter. As discussed at section 37.9 above, Local Government Code chapter 552 authorizes cities to enter into contracts with water districts to obtain water supply and water treatment services. Cities possess the legal authority under Government Code chapter 1502 to acquire, purchase, construct, improve, enlarge, equip, operate, or maintain any property, interests in property, buildings, structures, activities, services, operations, or other facilities, with respect to a utility system. *See* Tex. Gov't Code § 1502.002(a). Government Code section 1502.051 also provides cities with the authority to issue revenue bonds to finance extensions and improvements to a utility system. Government Code chapter 1371 provides additional authority to home-rule cities with a population of 50,000 or more to finance utility system improvements. *See* Tex. Gov't Code § 1371.001(4).

§ 37.12:1 Revenue Bonds

A city may issue public securities and incur contractual obligations under Texas Government Code chapter 1502 to provide funds to acquire, purchase, or otherwise obtain any interest in property, including additional water or riparian rights, as well as to acquire and construct utility system improvements. *See* Tex. Gov't Code § 1502.051. A city may pledge all or any part of the revenue of the utility system to secure the payment of the public securities. *See* Tex. Gov't Code § 1502.052. The city can determine the priority of liens granted to secure the payment of public securities; however, a statutory first lien against that revenue is preserved for the payment of each expense of operation and maintenance of the utility system, including all salaries, labor, materials, interest, repairs, and extensions necessary to provide efficient service. *See* Tex. Gov't Code § 1502.056. As a result, the revenue bonds are secured by a pledge of "net revenues" of the utility system. A city may enter into a contract with a water district to acquire water supply or other services and provide a superior lien on the utility system revenues that precedes the lien on revenues granted to secure the payment of revenue bonds. *See* Tex. Gov't Code § 1502.056(c).

Public securities issued under Government Code chapter 1502 may not have a maturity of greater than fifty years. *See* Tex. Gov't Code § 1502.062. As additional security for public securities issued or obligations incurred, the city by the terms of the encumbrance may grant a purchaser under sale or foreclosure a franchise to operate the encumbered utility system for a term not to exceed twenty years from the date of purchase, subject to all laws regulating the operation of the utility system in force at the time of the sale or foreclosure. *See* Tex. Gov't Code § 1502.053.

Government Code section 1502.054 provides that public securities issued under chapter 1502 are not debt of the city. It also requires that utility system revenue bonds bear a statement that the holder of the revenue bonds is not entitled to demand payment out of money raised by taxation. *See* Tex. Gov't Code § 1502.054. The revenues pledged to the payment of the public securities may not be used to pay any other debt or obligation of the municipality, except as permitted under Government Code section 1502.059 or Local Government Code section 271.052. *See* Tex. Gov't Code § 1502.058(a). Notwithstanding Government Code section 1502.058(a), or a similar law or municipal charter provision, a city may transfer to its general fund and use for general or special purposes revenue of any municipally owned utility system in the amount and to the extent authorized in the indenture, deed of trust, or ordinance providing for and securing payment of public securities issued under this chapter or similar law.

It is critical, therefore, to carefully draft the authorizing indenture, deed of trust, or ordinance to preserve the ability to use "surplus revenues" for any lawful purpose unrelated to the operation of the utility system. Government Code section 1502.059 does not provide sufficient authority to enable a city to use surplus utility system revenues for a purpose unrelated to the operation of a utility system. Rather, this authority is coupled with the terms of the instrument authorizing the issuance of public securities.

In the public security debt markets, revenue bonds are considered less creditworthy than general obligation bonds because the sole source of security for the revenue bonds is the revenues produced by the enterprise. General obligation bonds are backed by the full faith and credit of the city, and as a result are afforded higher credit ratings.

To protect the interests of bondholders, a city must impose and collect charges for services provided by a utility system in amounts at least sufficient to (1) pay all operating, maintenance, depreciation, replacement, improvement, and interest charges in connection with the utility system; (2) provide for an interest and sinking fund sufficient to pay any public securities issued or obligations incurred under chapter 1502 of the Government Code; and (3) pay any outstanding obligations against the system. Tex. Gov't Code § 1502.057(a). The rates charged for utility system services must be equal and uniform, and a city may not allow any free utility system service except for municipal public schools or buildings and institutions operated by the city. Tex. Gov't Code § 1502.057(b).

In addition to the revenues pledged to the payment of revenue bonds, reserves are created and pledged to the payment of the debt service on the revenue bonds. The reserves can take the form of cash or a credit agreement and can be funded from the proceeds of public securities issued under Government Code chapter 1502. Government Code section 1502.064 defines a credit agreement to have the same meaning given that term in Government Code section 1371.001. The need for reserves reflects the fact that the obligations are secured solely by the net revenues of the utility system, and not by the city's full faith and credit. If the volume of sales decreased, a deficiency in anticipated revenue collections would result. Reserves available to pay debt service reduce the potentially adverse consequences of reduced revenue collections.

Proceeds from the issuance of public securities also may be used to pay interest on the public securities during the period of the acquisition or construction of any facilities to be provided through the issuance of the public securities, and for one year after completion of the acquisition or construction of the facilities. Tex. Gov't Code § 1502.060(b); *see also* Tex. Gov't Code § 1201.042(a).

The facilities being financed are necessary to generate the revenues needed to pay debt service; if the facilities are not operative, they cannot provide services and thus generate revenues.

The proceedings authorizing the issuance of public securities under Government Code chapter 1502 may reserve to the city the right to issue additional obligations secured on a parity with, or by a lien on the revenues of the utility system subordinate to, the lien on revenues securing outstanding public securities previously issued by the city. *See* Tex. Gov't Code § 1502.061(a). This right, however, is not automatic; a city may issue additional public securities on a parity and of equal dignity with the outstanding public securities only if the ordinance, deed of trust, or indenture of trust authorizing or securing the outstanding public securities provides for the subsequent issuance of additional parity public securities. *See* Tex. Gov't Code § 1502.061(c). The issuance of additional public securities also is subject to conditions contained in the ordinance, deed of trust, or indenture of trust. Government Code section 1502.065 authorizes a city to issue public securities to refinance any obligation incurred under this chapter to which revenues have been pledged. A city may issue refunding bonds under Government Code chapter 1207 for the same purpose.

§ 37.12:2 Certificates of Obligation

In addition to revenue bonds, cities also may issue public securities known as "certificates of obligation" to finance utility system improvements. *See* Tex. Loc. Gov't Code ch. 271, subch. C. Certificates of obligation are public securities that may be issued by a city or county to finance the construction of any public work and the purchase of materials, supplies, equipment, machinery, buildings, land, and rights-of-way for authorized needs and purposes. *See* Tex. Loc. Gov't Code § 271.045(c). Specifically, a city may issue certificates of obligation to pay all or part of the contractual obligations incurred for interests in and rights to water or sewer treatment capacity in connection with a water supply and transmission project or sewer treatment or collection project constructed on behalf of the city by another governmental entity or political subdivision under a written agreement expressly authorized under Texas Local Government Code section 552.014 or Texas Government Code section 791.026. Tex. Loc. Gov't Code § 271.045(c).

Certificates of obligation are treated as "debt" within the meaning of article XI, sections 5 and 7, of the Texas Constitution. *See* Tex. Loc. Gov't Code § 271.053. In addition to ad valorem taxes, certificates of obligation may be secured by other revenues if the issuer is authorized by the constitution or other statutes to secure or pay any general or special obligation by or from those revenues. *See* Tex. Loc. Gov't Code § 271.052(a).

Before certificates of obligation may be issued, the city must publish a notice of intention to issue them. The notice must be published once a week for two consecutive weeks in a newspaper, as defined by Government Code chapter 2051, subchapter C, that is of general circulation in the area of the issuer. *See* Tex. Loc. Gov't Code § 271.049.

Amendments adopted in the 86th regular session of the Texas legislature provide that the date of the first publication must be before the forty-fifth day before the date tentatively set for the passage of the order or ordinance authorizing the issuance of the certificates of obligation. If the issuer maintains an Internet website, the notice must be continuously on the website for at least forty-five days before the date tentatively set for passage of the action authorizing the issuance of the certificates of obligation. The notice must state (1) the time and place tentatively set for the passage of the order or ordinance authorizing the issuance of the certificates of obligation; (2) the maximum amount and purpose of the certificates to be authorized; (3) the manner in which the certificates of obligation will be paid for, whether by taxes, revenues, or both; (4) the then-current principal of all outstanding debt obligations of the issuer, the then-current combined principal and interest required to pay all outstanding debt obligations of the issuer on time and in full, the maximum principal amount of the certificates of obligation to be authorized, and the estimated combined principal and interest required to pay the certificates of obligation to be authorized, on time and in full; (5) the estimated interest rate for the certificates of obligation to be authorized or that the maximum interest rate for the certificates may not exceed the maximum legal interest rate; and (6) the maximum maturity date for the certificates of obligation to be authorized. *See* Act of May 26, 2019, 86th Leg., R.S., ch. 728, § 5 (H.B. 477), eff. Sept. 1, 2019 (amending Tex. Loc. Gov't Code § 271.049).

The notice requirement allows the residents of the city to present a petition to require that a referendum be held to permit the issuance of the certificates of obligation. Should the city receive a petition signed by at least 5 percent of the qualified voters of the city protesting the issuance of the certificates of obligation, the city may not authorize the issuance of the certificates of obligation unless the issuance is approved at an election ordered, held, and conducted in the manner provided for bond elections under Government Code chapter 1251. *See* Tex. Loc. Gov't Code § 271.049. Local Government Code section 271.056 provides for the issuance of certificates of obligation without notice under limited circumstances, such as public calamity.

Certificates of obligation may be sold for cash or in exchange for work provided. A city must limit the principal amount of certificates to an amount equal to (1) the aggregate of the contractual payments or the total costs allocated or attributed, under generally accepted accounting principles, to the capital costs of the project, as opposed to any maintenance or operating costs to be paid under the written agreement; or (2) the total cost of the project multiplied by the percentage of the nameplate capacity of the project acquired or conveyed by the written agreement to the city, whichever limitation is applicable to the contractual interests or rights being conveyed or identified in the written agreement. Tex. Loc. Gov't Code § 271.045(d).

The city may pay or pledge to the payment of the certificates of obligation all or any portion of the revenues of its utility system. *See* Tex. Gov't Code § 1502.058. The city also may determine the provisions governing the issuance of certificates of obligation. *See* Tex. Loc. Gov't Code § 271.047(b). This enables the city to structure a certificate of obligation issue so that the security is a combination of ad valorem taxes and utility system revenues. The levy of ad valorem taxes to pay the certificates of obligation can be made subject to the budgeting of revenues for the payment of debt service, under current standards of interpretation of the law by the state attorney general. This effectively allows an issuer to issue an ad valorem tax–supported obligation but never have to pay that obligation from ad valorem taxes if the revenues budgeted to pay debt service are sufficient to pay the debt service.

The rating agencies treat certificates of obligation secured by ad valorem taxes as the equivalent of full faith and credit general obligations of the issuer, which typically have higher credit ratings than an obligation secured solely by utility system revenues. This financial structure can be a significant advantage to communities whose utility systems are not able to support the rates and charges needed to have obligation ratings match those of ad valorem tax–supported obligations. Many Texas communities structure certificates of obligation in this manner and sell those certificates of obligation to the TWDB under the various financing programs operated by the board.

A pledge of revenues lawfully available to secure other indebtedness is required for an issuer to sell certificates of obligation for cash. *See* Tex. Loc. Gov't Code § 271.052. It is not uncommon for a minimum pledge of revenues, not to exceed $1,000, to be made to secure the payment of the certificate of obligation to effect the sale of certificates of obligation for cash.

Section 26.012, Tax Code, was amended in the 87th regular session of the Texas legislature to constrain political subdivisions from issuing nonvoted ad valorem tax-supported obligations to finance public improvements. Acts 2021, 87th Leg., R.S., ch. 674, § 1 (H.B. 1869), eff. Sept. 1, 2021. The issuance of nonvoted obligations would require the obligations to be treated not as "debt," but rather as financing an operation and maintenance expense, which would subject the debt service paid on the nonvoted obligations to the voter-approved tax rate cap of three and one-half percent for cities and counties. The definition of "debt" was amended in the legislation to clarify that debt includes obligations evidencing a loan under a state or federal financial assistance program (e.g., loans made by the TWDB) and obligations issued to finance "designated infrastructure." Debt is defined in a manner that includes infrastructure, including a facility, equipment, rights-of-way, or land, as part of any utility system, water supply project, water plant, wastewater plant, water and wastewater distribution or conveyance facility, or flood control and drainage project. *See* Tex. Tax Code § 26.012. The impact on issuing nonvoted ad valorem tax-supported obligations to finance water projects should be minimal as a result of the amended definition of debt.

§ 37.12:3 Texas Government Code Chapter 1371

Texas cities with populations above 50,000, and cities that have a principal amount of at least $100 million in outstanding long-term indebtedness, in long-term indebtedness proposed to be issued, or a combination of the two, and some amount of long-term indebtedness outstanding or proposed to be outstanding in one of the four highest rating categories for long-term debt instruments by a nationally recognized rating agency, without regard to the effect of any credit agreement or other form of credit enhancement entered into in connection with an obligation, may exercise the authority under Texas Government Code chapter 1371. Chapter 1371 authorizes an issuer to execute "credit agreements" in connection with or related to the authorization, issuance, security, purchase, payment, sale, resale, redemption, remarketing, or exchange of an obligation. A credit agreement is an agreement for professional services and must contain the terms and be for the period of time approved by the issuer. The cost of a credit agreement may be paid from any source, including the proceeds from the sale of the obligation to which the credit agreement relates, the revenue of the issuer that is available to pay the obligation, any interest on the obligation or that may otherwise be legally used, or ad valorem taxes to the extent permitted by chapter 1371. *See* Tex. Gov't Code § 1371.056.

An additional tool to finance water projects is to structure commercial paper programs. Commercial paper is a public security that is a short-term obligation, with a maturity of 270 days or less. Commercial paper provides interim financing for eligible projects. Eligible projects include public works such as property or facilities for the conservation, storage, supply, treatment, or transmission of water and the treatment, collection, or disposal of water-carried wastes or solid wastes. *See* Tex. Gov't Code § 1371.001. Because commercial paper notes have a short maturity, interest rates borne by the notes are significantly lower than the interest rates borne by long-term, fixed-rate obligations.

Frequent maturities of commercial paper notes require that a market be continuously maintained. When a commercial paper note matures, the issuer may not want to pay the maturing principal coming due on the commercial paper note from available funds. The issuer may want the then-current holder to purchase a new commercial paper note of like principal amount, having a new maturity period and new interest rate. For this to occur, the issuer must have legal authority to enter into agreements with the makers of the market, known as commercial paper dealers (typically investment banking firms), to facilitate this type of market and market activity. If the holder of a commercial paper note does not want to roll over its note (i.e., it wants to be paid the principal and interest due and owing upon maturity), and the commercial paper dealer cannot find other market participants to purchase a new commercial paper note, then the issuer must have sufficient funds available to pay the maturing noteholder its principal and interest, issue bonds to refinance the notes, or have other resources available to pay the noteholder. Therefore, the issuer must have legal authority to enter into agreements with lenders to provide credit or liquidity support, in the form of a line or letter of credit, to generate funds sufficient to pay noteholders should efforts to find new purchasers of the issuer's commercial paper notes fail.

Commercial paper notes must meet the definition of "obligation" set forth in Government Code section 1371.001(5). Obligations may bear interest at no interest or at any rate not to exceed the maximum net effective interest rate allowed by law. *See* Tex. Gov't Code ch. 1204. Interest rates may be fixed, variable, or otherwise. Interest rates may be determined by a formula, index, or other arrangement. *See* Tex. Gov't Code § 1371.054. An obligation, including accrued interest, or a credit agreement may be refinanced by the issuance of another obligation or credit agreement. *See* Tex. Gov't Code § 1371.060.

Government Code chapter 1371 provides authority unique to the issuers of public securities. An issuer, in the proceedings authorizing commercial paper notes, must provide the maximum principal amount of notes that may be outstanding at any one time and from time to time, and a maximum term the notes may be outstanding. *See* Tex. Gov't Code § 1371.053(b).

Unlike the proceedings that authorize the issuance of bonds, new commercial paper notes may be issued once outstanding commercial paper notes have been retired. For example, an issuer authorizes the issuance of up to $100 million in commercial paper notes that may at any time and from time to time be outstanding. The issuer issues $100 million in notes and subsequently pays off $50 million of the outstanding notes. The authority to issue $50 million in commercial paper notes is then restored. This characteristic of a commercial paper program affords an issuer significant flexibility in managing a large-scale capital improvement program, such as those associated with large waterworks and sewer systems, and differs from that under bonds. Once bonds are retired, the ability does not exist under the proceedings authorizing their issuance to issue "new" bonds.

Most municipal utility system commercial paper programs are structured as "bond anticipation notes." The commercial paper notes are not secured by utility system revenues; they are secured by the issuance of commercial paper notes, revenue bonds, or funds provided under a credit agreement. This is the result of historical accident rather than conscious drafting. The authority to issue commercial paper notes in Texas did not exist before 1983, and then-existing utility system revenue bond covenants did not provide for the issuance of variable-rate obligations, the execution of credit agreements, or the pledge of revenues to secure obligations incurred under credit agreements. These limitations made the operation of a commercial paper program impractical, if not impossible to accomplish.

The revenues of the utility system are pledged to support the payment of obligations incurred under a credit agreement, if and when such obligations are incurred. In a typical utility system commercial paper program, a bank provides a line or letter of credit for the possibility of a failed remarketing of maturing commercial paper notes. The noteholder is due principal and interest upon maturity, and if the noteholder no longer wants to own commercial paper notes, and the commercial paper dealer is unable to find a new purchaser for the commercial paper notes, the issuer draws on the line or letter of credit to pay the noteholder whose notes have matured. This results in the issuer incurring a loan from the bank. The credit agreement will provide the terms and conditions under which this loan is to be repaid. The issuer has incurred a lawful obligation and must ensure that covenants regarding debt service coverage that are contained in utility system revenue bond proceedings or the proceedings authorizing the commercial paper program are satisfied.

Contemporary funds management stresses that an issuer with a large debt portfolio must maintain a certain percentage of its debt in variable-rate instruments. An issuer of commercial paper notes is able to achieve this because the commercial paper notes mature frequently and interest rates change upon the new issuance of the notes. Commercial paper notes are an effective tool for an issuer to provide for variable-rate financing at relative low cost.

§ 37.12:4 Anticipation Notes

Other forms of debt instruments are available under Texas law to finance water projects. Texas Government Code chapter 1431 authorizes cities and counties to issue "anticipation notes" to finance the construction of public works and the purchase of materials, supplies, equipment, machinery, buildings, lands, and rights-of-way for authorized purposes. *See* Tex. Gov't Code §§ 1431.002–.004. Anticipation notes may be secured by a pledge of ad valorem taxes, revenues, or a combination of ad valorem taxes and revenues. *See* Tex. Gov't Code § 1431.007. Anticipation notes that are payable from bonds secured by an ad valorem tax may not be issued unless the proposition authorizing the issuance of the bonds is approved at an election held by the issuer and the proposition states that anticipation notes may be issued. *See* Tex. Gov't Code § 1431.008. Anticipation notes issued for the purposes described above cannot have a maturity in excess of the seventh anniversary of the date the attorney general approves the anticipation notes. *See* Tex. Gov't Code § 1431.009.

Counties with a population of three million or more may issue anticipation notes with a maximum maturity of fifteen years from the date the attorney general approves the anticipation notes. *See* Tex. Gov't Code § 1431.009(b). Refunding bonds under Government Code chapter 1207 may be issued to refinance outstanding anticipation notes, and the maximum maturity for refunding bonds, forty years from their date of issue, applies to refunding bonds issued to refinance anticipation notes. *See* Tex. Gov't Code § 1431.009(d). Anticipation notes may be sold at public or private sale for cash. *See* Tex. Gov't Code § 1431.010.

Unlike certificates of obligation, which require that a notice of intention be published as a condition of issuance, anticipation notes can be issued without publishing a notice of intention. Although the seven-year maximum maturity is a constraint on the issuance of anticipation notes, the ability to refinance the anticipation notes with refunding bonds with a maximum maturity of forty years may provide an issuer with an effective alternative to issuing public securities to finance utility system improvements.

§ 37.12:5 General Obligation Bonds

Utility system improvements also can be financed by a city through the issuance of general obligation bonds. *See* Tex. Gov't Code § 1331.001(a). A city may not issue bonds that are to be paid from ad valorem taxes unless the issuance is first approved by the qualified voters of the city. Tex. Gov't Code § 1251.001.

As a result of amendments to the Texas Election Code, the requirements for bond elections have become confusing. An issuer must take into account both the provisions of Texas Government Code section 1251.003 and the general provisions of the Election Code. Bond elections must be held on one of the two uniform election dates provided in Election Code section 41.001. Notice provisions for bond elections in the Government Code also differ from, but need to conform to, applicable provisions of the Election Code. Election Code chapter 3 governs when an election can be called. A carefully drafted bond proposition will provide for a maximum amount of bonds and that the interest rates for the bonds when issued will not exceed the maximum lawful rate permitted when the bonds are issued. The details that must be included in the authorizing instrument calling the election are set out in Election Code section 3.009. *See* Tex. Elec. Code § 3.009.

General obligation bonds seldom are issued to finance water or wastewater improvements. Most cities finance these improvements with revenue bonds or with certificates of obligation secured by a combination of ad valorem taxes and utility system revenues. If a city presents to its citizens a proposition to approve general obligation bonds for water or wastewater improvements and the proposition is not approved by a majority of the citizens voting in the election, the city may not issue certificates of obligation for the same project for a period of three years following the election. *See* Tex. Loc. Gov't Code § 271.047(d).

§ 37.13 Local Financing: Other Entities

Although cities are the principal government entities that own, operate, and manage water and sewer systems, other entities can provide for the financing of such system improvements. Water supply corporations are nonprofit corporations that may be created to provide water and sewer services. Counties may own and operate water and sewer systems. Special-purpose districts, such as tax increment reinvestment zones, public improvement districts, and municipal management districts, possess similar powers. Cities and counties can form, individually or jointly, local government corporations to perform any public purpose, which includes the ownership and operation of water and sewer systems. The following sections discuss the legal authority under Texas law granted to these entities.

§ 37.13:1 Water Supply Corporations

Texas Water Code chapter 67 governs the organization and powers of water supply or sewer service corporations. See Chapter 29 of this book for a more detailed discussion. A water supply corporation may be organized to provide water supply, sewer service, or both for a municipality, a private corporation, an individual, or a military camp or base and flood control and a drainage system for a political subdivision, private corporation, or another person. Tex. Water Code § 67.002.

A water supply corporation has the powers of a general nonprofit corporation. *See* Tex. Water Code § 67.004. It also has the power to construct, acquire, lease, or maintain the facilities or equipment necessary to provide more adequate sewer service, flood control, or drainage for a political subdivision. Tex. Water Code § 67.009. A water supply corporation may contract with any political subdivision, federal agency, or other entity for an authorized purpose. Tex. Water Code § 67.010(a). It may issue bonds and other obligations to finance improvements. *See* Tex. Water Code § 67.010(c). The Securities Act, Texas Revised Civil Statutes articles 581–1 to –43, does not apply to the issuance of bonds or other obligations issued by a water supply corporation. *See* Tex. Water Code § 67.015.

§ 37.13:2 Counties

Texas Local Government Code sections 562.015 and 562.016 extend to counties certain powers to operate water and sewer utilities. Local Government Code section 412.015 provides the authority to an "affected county," as defined in Texas Water Code section 16.341, to own, operate, and maintain a water or sewer utility in the same manner as a city under Local Government Code chapter 552. Local Government Code section 562.016 provides that a county may acquire, own, operate, or contract for the operation of a water or sewer utility system to serve an unincorporated area of the county in the same manner and under the same regulations as a municipality under Local Government Code chapter 552. Section 562.016 further provides for the issuance of bonds for water or sewer systems. A county may issue bonds payable solely from the revenue generated by the water or sewer utility system. The bonds issued are not a debt of the county but are only a charge on the revenues pledged. The issuance of general obligation bonds payable from ad valorem taxes to finance a water or sewer utility system is not authorized by section 562.016; however, a county with a population of two million or more and any adjoining county may issue general obligation bonds with the approval of qualified voters. *See* Tex. Loc. Gov't Code § 562.016(b). Counties also have the authority to issue certificates of obligation. *See* Tex. Loc. Gov't Code § 271.043(7).

§ 37.13:3 Economic Development Entities

Texas law provides that a variety of special entities can be created to foster and encourage economic development. Entities such as tax increment reinvestment zones, public improvement districts, and municipal management districts assist in economic development within a community, whether that be industrial or commercial development or residential development. Water and sewer services funded by these entities often are not the primary reason the entities were created, but the revenues generated by these entities can provide funds to pay for these services. Texas Tax Code chapter 311, the Tax Increment Financing Act, authorizes cities and counties to create tax increment reinvestment zones. A base property value of real property within the boundaries of the zone is established, and tax revenues generated as a result of the increased values of real property within the zone above the base property value are captured and used to pay for project costs within the zone or, in limited circumstances, for facilities functionally related to facilities within the zone that may fall outside the boundaries of the zone. Project costs include the costs of public works or public improvements, including water and sewer utility system improvements.

Texas Local Government Code chapter 372, subchapter A, the Public Improvement District Assessment Act, authorizes cities and counties to create public improvement districts to undertake improvement projects. *See* Tex. Loc. Gov't Code § 372.003. The city or county that creates a public improvement district shall determine assessments to be paid by property owners within the district that will benefit from the improvement projects to be undertaken within the district. A public improvement district can include property within the extraterritorial jurisdiction of the city. *See* Tex. Loc. Gov't Code § 372.015. Costs of improvement projects may be paid in accordance with the provisions of Local Government Code section 372.023, and general obligation bonds and revenue bonds may be issued to finance improvement projects as provided in section 372.024. The creation and use of public improvement districts has increased since 2010, as using assessments in districts to finance water and wastewater improvements within residential areas in a district has helped defray local government costs in providing this infrastructure.

Local Government Code chapter 375 authorizes municipalities to create municipal management districts. The legislature found that the creation of a municipal management district is essential for accomplishing the purposes of article III, section 52, article XVI, section 59, and article III, section 52–a, of the Texas Constitution to promote, develop, encourage, and maintain employment, commerce, and economic development. *See* Tex. Loc. Gov't Code § 375.001. A district has the rights conferred by the general laws of Texas applicable to conservation and reclamation districts created under article XVI, section 59, including those conferred by Texas Water Code chapter 54. *See* Tex. Loc. Gov't Code § 375.091.

§ 37.14 Attorney General Review of Bond Issuance

The role of the TWDB in accepting and reviewing applications for financial assistance under its many loan programs, and the role of the TCEQ in accepting and reviewing applications for financing projects by water districts, are discussed above. A transcript of proceedings regarding the issuance of public securities must be submitted to the Texas attorney general for legal review. Texas Government Code chapter 1202 addresses the submission process.

Government Code section 1202.001 defines "issuer," "public securities," and "record of proceedings." The definition of issuer is broad: any state agency or political subdivision, or a nonprofit corporation acting on behalf thereof, is an issuer. That section also broadly defines public securities to include any bond or other instrument that evidences an interest in payments due to be paid by an issuer. *See* Tex. Gov't Code § 1202.001.

Before the issuance of a public security, unless otherwise excepted from the submission process (*see* Tex. Gov't Code § 1202.007), the issuer must submit the public security and the record of proceedings to the attorney general. If the attorney general finds the issuance of the public security is authorized, the attorney general must (1) approve the public security and (2) deliver to the comptroller of public accounts (a) a copy of the attorney general's legal opinion stating that approval and (b) the record of proceedings. A public security must be issued in compliance with Government Code chapter 1202, unless otherwise exempted by section 1202.007.

The provisions of Government Code section 1202.004 require that the issuer submit with the record of proceedings a nonrefundable fee to the attorney general for the review of the transcript of proceedings.

A public security and any contract the proceeds of which are pledged to the payment of the public security are valid and incontestable in a court or other forum and are binding obligations for all purposes (1) after the public security is approved by the attorney general and registered by the comptroller and (2) on issuance of the public security. *See* Tex. Gov't Code § 1202.006(a).

V. Federal Financial Assistance

§ 37.15 Introduction

Three federally administered financial assistance programs provide funding for water and wastewater projects. The U.S. Department of Agriculture administers Rural Utilities Service Water and Environmental Programs (WEP) to enable rural communities to obtain financing necessary to develop water and waste disposal systems. The U.S. Department of the Interior administers two programs: long-term, low-cost supplemental loans for regionally and nationally significant water, wastewater, and water recycling projects, under the Water Infrastructure Finance and Innovation Act of 2014 (WIFIA); and a program to provide financial assistance for new water recycling and reuse projects, as part of the Water Infrastructure Improvements for the Nation (WIIN) Act.

§ 37.16 WEP

Rural areas and towns with populations of 10,000 or less may apply for funding as part of the WEP water and waste disposal loan and grant program. This program provides funding for clean and reliable drinking water systems; sanitary sewage disposal, sanitary solid waste disposal, and storm water disposal; and storm water drainage. Funds may be used to finance the acquisition, construction, or improvement of drinking water sourcing, treatment, storage, and distribution and sewer collection, transmission, treatment, and disposal. The rules governing this federal program are located at 7 C.F.R. pt. 1780 and section 306 of the Consolidated Farm and Rural Development Act (7 U.S.C. § 1926).

§ 37.17 WIFIA

WIFIA, incorporated into the Water Resources Reform and Development Act of 2014 (Pub. L. No. 113-121, tit. 5, § 5021, 128 Stat. 1332, June 10, 2014), established a water infrastructure lending program to provide financial assistance for projects that are eligible for CWSRF and DWSRF funding. Financial assistance is also provided for desalination, water recycling, drought prevention and reduction, and aquifer recharge projects. Minimum funding of $5 million is available for small communities (populations of 25,000 or less) and $20 million is available for large communities. The maximum portion of eligible project costs that WIFIA can fund is 49 percent of the project's eligible costs. Financial assistance can be provided either by a secured loan funded either by the Department of the Interior or the administrator of the U.S. Environmental Protection Agency, or by a loan guarantee authorized by WIFIA. The total federal assistance available may not exceed 80 percent of a project's eligible costs.

Project selection is determined through an application process. Creditworthiness of the applicant, readiness to proceed to construction, and the project's ability to meet the strategic outlines of WIFIA are considered. Applicants are ranked and approved applications are invited to apply for a WIFIA loan. The first project loans made under WIFIA were funded in 2018.

WIFIA has been amended by both the Fixing America's Surface Transportation Act of 2015 (Pub. L. No. 114-94, 129 Stat. 1312, Dec. 4, 2015) and WIIN.

§ 37.18 WIIN

The Water Infrastructure Improvements for the Nation Act (Pub. L. No. 114-322, 130 Stat. 1628, Dec. 16, 2016), amended 43 United States Code sections 390h through 390h-39 to authorize the secretary of the interior to review feasibility studies of reclamation and reuse projects for municipal, industrial, domestic, and agricultural wastewater or impaired ground or surface waters.

VI. Public-Private Participation in Financing

§ 37.19 Introduction

In recent years, public entities providing water and wastewater services have explored alternatives to providing these services. The alternatives include purchasing water supply from private entities, selling or leasing operations to private entities, and contracting with private entities to manage the public facilities and to provide these services. In considering undertaking any of these alternatives, a public entity must consider legal constraints, both statutory and contractual. Does existing state law permit any of these alternatives to be exercised? Do existing contracts, particularly proceedings governing the issuance of bonds, permit the public entity to undertake an alternative? Also, financial considerations must be taken into account, including such issues as valuing the assets to be purchased or sold, the terms by which a management relationship may be completed, and how rates and charges for services to be provided after a sale are to be determined.

This part of this chapter explores how existing statutes impact the analysis of contracting with a private entity in the purchase of water, the sale or lease of facilities, or the management of facilities. As governmental entities on all levels are confronted with budgetary constraints, exploration of private alternatives to providing traditionally public services is likely to increase in the years to come.

For water districts, this part focuses on Texas Water Code chapter 49. In addition, either enabling legislation pertaining specifically to a water district, or chapters in the Water Code relating to specific types of water districts, must be reviewed to determine whether those statutes impact the sale or lease of real or personal property or the management of existing facilities.

§ 37.20 Public Entity Purchase of Water from a Private Entity

As discussed earlier in this chapter, public entities traditionally obtain their water supply from municipalities, river authorities, and regional districts. Nothing in Texas law, however, prevents a private person or entity from obtaining groundwater rights and conveying the water developed through those rights to public entities. In this discussion, the term "convey" refers to changing ownership rather than the physical transportation of the water from one place to another. As discussed in Part C of this book, particularly in Chapters 16 and 18, a landowner has a right to pump and convey groundwater from under the owner's land, while regulatory agencies, particularly groundwater conservation districts, can regulate the transfer of water beyond the boundaries of the district. How that water may be conveyed, rather than whether that water can be conveyed, becomes the issue a public entity must analyze.

§ 37.20:1 Purchases by a Water District

Texas Water Code section 49.213 provides that a water district may contract with a person or any public or private entity for the joint construction, financing, ownership, and operation of any works. Water districts may enter into contracts, which may be of unlimited duration, with persons or any public or private entity on the terms and conditions the board of the water district may consider desirable, fair, and advantageous. Such contracts may be for the purchase or sale of water; the transportation of the district's domestic, industrial, and communal wastes; the maintenance and operation of any works of the district or of another person or public or private entity; and the exercise of any other rights, powers, and duties granted to the district.

An important consideration for a private entity seeking to sell water supply to a district is economic: How will the district pay for the water purchased? The transportation of water from its source to the end user is costly. Similar to the situation confronted by a district when it enters into agreements with municipalities to construct reservoirs and transport water, a private entity seeking to access credit markets most certainly would want similar assurances that the obligation of the purchaser of water to the private entity would be on a take-or-pay basis. Section 49.213 provides a water district with statutory authority to enter into a take-or-pay contract with a private entity, because it authorizes the district to enter into a contract with terms the board of the district considers "desirable, fair, and advantageous" to the district and the goals to be accomplished under the contract. Tex. Water Code § 49.213(c).

§ 37.20:2 Purchases by a Municipality

There appears to be no clear statutory authority for municipalities to enter into a take-or-pay contract with a private entity on a basis similar to the basis under Texas Government Code chapter 791. As discussed at section 37.9 above, the contracting authority language in section 791.026, which covers contracts between political subdivisions, including municipalities, is both broad and specifically applicable to water contracts. A municipality's authority under section 791.026 to enter into take-or-pay contracts for water from other political subdivisions has been affirmed in *City of The Colony v. North Texas Municipal Water District*, 272 S.W.3d 699 (Tex. App.—Fort Worth 2008, pet. dism'd). See the discussion at section 37.9 above. However, Government Code section 1502.002(b), which authorizes municipalities to contract with private entities, does not clearly allow for take-or-pay contracts. Under section 1502.002(b), the governing body of a municipality may "authorize the execution and delivery of contracts between the municipality and any person to" acquire, construct, improve, operate, or maintain any property, services, operations, or other facilities with respect to a utility system. Tex. Gov't Code § 1502.002(b). Unlike Government Code section 791.026, no reference is made about how and under what conditions a municipality may contract to purchase water from a private entity, leading to the question whether a municipality can enter directly into a take-or-pay contract with a private entity. So, while statutory authority exists for a municipality to contract to purchase water from a private entity, it is uncertain whether that contract may be structured as a take-or-pay contract.

Likewise, Texas Local Government Code section 552.018, another source of authority for municipal contracting, is not as broad as Government Code section 791.026. Section 552.018 provides that a municipality may "contract with an individual, firm, or corporation that operates without profit to make available for delivery to and use by the municipality all or part of the raw or treated water to be used for the municipal water distribution system." Tex. Loc. Gov't Code § 552.018(a). The statute does not address contracting powers; it does provide that a contract is limited to "any duration to which the parties agree and may provide for renewal or extension." Tex. Loc. Gov't Code § 552.018(b). The question whether the legislature, by authorizing contracts with corporations operating without profit, has precluded the municipality from entering into such a contract with a for-profit corporation, must be addressed before proceeding.

If a municipality seeks to purchase water from a private entity and the private entity requires a take-or-pay contract, one possible method to accomplish this would be as follows: an arrangement where the private entity and a water district enter into a take-or-pay contract under authority of Texas Water Code section 49.213, and the district and the municipality enter into a take-or-pay contract under authority of Government Code section 791.026. The water would be conveyed, and could also be transported, to the municipality from the private entity through the water district. The board of directors of the water district would make a finding in its contract with the private entity that the take-or-pay term of the contract with the private entity was desirable, fair, and advantageous for the purchase of water, and the district and the municipality would provide in their contract a take-or-pay provision consistent with the authority granted by Government Code section 791.026.

§ 37.20:3 Public Utility Agency

Texas Local Government Code chapter 572 permits two or more public entities (defined in section 572.001(3) of the Local Government Code to include a county, municipality, or district or authority created under article III, section 52, or article XVI, section 59, of the Texas Constitution) that have the authority to engage in the conservation, storage, transportation, treatment, or distribution of water to join together as cotenants or co-owners to plan, finance, acquire, construct, own, operate, or maintain facilities. Tex. Loc. Gov't Code § 572.011.

Local Government Code chapter 572, subchapter C, permits two or more public entities to create a public utility agency. The agency is created through adoption by each public entity of a concurrent ordinance (as defined in Code section 572.051(1)). The concurrent ordinance must contain identical provisions, define the boundaries of the agency to include the territory within the boundaries of each participating public entity, designate the name of the agency, and designate the number, place, initial term, and manner of appointment of directors. Tex. Loc. Gov't Code § 572.055.

The agency may enter into a contract, lease, or agreement with departments or agencies of the United States; departments, agencies, or municipalities or other political subdivisions of Texas; or a public or private corporation or person. Tex. Loc. Gov't Code § 572.058(b)(2). The agency may contract, under terms the agency's board of directors considers appropriate, with private entities for the conservation, storage, transportation, treatment, or distribution of water or the collection, transportation, treatment, or disposal of sewage. Tex. Loc. Gov't Code § 572.060. Private entities are defined in section 572.001 to include an entity, other than a public entity, involved solely in financing, constructing, operating, or maintaining water and sewer facilities. Tex. Loc. Gov't Code § 572.001(2). An example is Alliance Water, formerly the Hays Caldwell Public Utility Agency, formed in January 2007. Its members are the city of San Marcos, the city of Kyle, the city of Buda, and the Canyon Regional Water Authority. Information regarding the Hays Caldwell Public Utility Agency can be found at its website, www.hcpua.org.

§ 37.21 Public Entity Sale or Lease of Water and Wastewater Facilities to a Private Entity

Whether to reduce the burdens of government, raise cash, or a combination of the two, governmental entities may explore the possibility of selling or leasing assets to a private entity. Facilities that provide water and wastewater treatment services, or the rights to water supply itself, are assets that have immense value, both in the short and long term, and governmental entities exploring this alternative must analyze numerous issues before implementing this alternative. The issues include the legal authority to sell or lease facilities; the consequences raised by a sale or lease if the facilities were financed with obligations, the interest on which is exempt from federal income taxation; and consequences that may result under existing contracts with other governmental entities providing goods and services, specifically contracts relating to the purchase of water supply or wastewater treatment services.

§ 37.21:1 Sale or Lease by a Water District

For water districts subject to Texas Water Code chapter 49, the provisions of law relating to the sale or lease of real and personal property are found generally in Code sections 49.225, 49.226, and 49.2261. But see, for example, section 49.002, regarding the application of chapter 49 to all general and special law districts (e.g., groundwater conservation districts are not subject to chapter 49).

Section 49.225 states that a district may lease any of its property, real or personal, to any person. The lease may contain terms and provisions that the board of the district determines to be advantageous to the district. Tex. Water Code § 49.225.

Section 49.226 addresses the sale or exchange of real or personal property. Any surplus personal property valued at more than $300, or any land or interest in land owned by the district, may be sold at either public or private sale, or the land or interest in land may be exchanged for other land or interest in land or personal property needed by the district. Such sales or exchanges must be for fair market value, as determined by the district. Tex. Water Code § 49.226(a). The fair market value requirement does not apply to property dedicated to or acquired by the district without expending district funds, or property of the district that is abandoned, released, exchanged, or transferred to another district, municipality, county, countywide agency, or authority. In such cases, the property may be conveyed on terms and conditions deemed necessary or advantageous to the district. Tex. Water Code § 49.226(b). Before a public sale of real property, the district shall give notice of the intent to sell by publishing notice once a week for two consecutive weeks in one or more newspapers with general circulation in the district. Tex. Water Code § 49.226(c).

If the district has outstanding bonds secured by a pledge of tax revenues, the proceeds of the sale of property originally acquired with bond proceeds must be applied to retire the outstanding bonds or held and treated as surplus bond proceeds and spent only as provided by the rules of the TCEQ relating to surplus bond proceeds. Tex. Water Code § 49.226(d).

The sale of nonsurplus real property is not clearly addressed by the statute. The statute distinguishes between holding a private sale and a public sale, but it appears that unless one of the exceptions in section 49.226(b) applies, the sale must be of surplus property and must be conducted by a public sale. The district must seek bids, which significantly affects the ability of a district to negotiate a sale of assets to a private entity or the price at which the assets could be sold.

§ 37.21:2 Sale or Lease by a Municipality

Texas Government Code section 1502.055 restricts the ability of a municipality to sell a utility system. The municipality may not sell a utility system unless authorized by a majority vote of qualified voters, and the governing body of the municipality must hold an election in the manner provided for bond elections in the municipality. Tex. Gov't Code § 1502.055(a), (b). The only exception to the election requirement is the sale of an unencumbered natural gas system owned by a municipality with a population of 100,000 or more. Tex. Gov't Code § 1502.055(c). Section 552.016 of the Texas Local Government Code imposes a similar election requirement in respect to a sale or lease of a water system and plant owned by a Type A general-law municipality. Tex. Loc. Gov't Code § 552.016. (See Local Government Code chapters 7 and 9 for definitions and authority to create a Type A general-law municipality). Government Code chapter 1502 is silent on the question of whether a lease of a utility system requires an election. The lease of a utility system involving an initial payment of consideration and the transfer of rights to a lessee normally associated with ownership could be construed as a sale and may be subject to the election requirement under Government Code section 1502.055. A long-term lease, where a significant upfront payment is made to the municipality by the lessee for consideration to enter the lease, may be treated as a sale, and the election requirement would impact the decision to enter into a long-term lease.

§ 37.21:3 Existing Covenants in Contracts or Bond Proceedings

Governmental entities typically finance the acquisition and construction of utility system facilities through the issuance of bonds or other obligations secured by the revenues of the utility system. Those obligations generally have been issued as obligations, the interest on which is excludable, for federal income tax purposes, from gross income of the holders. The bond proceedings will contain covenants relating to ownership of the facilities and maintaining a prescribed level of revenues. The revenues must be sufficient to operate and maintain the system. Additionally, revenues must be sufficiently in excess of annual debt service sufficient to pay annual debt service, maintain debt service and other reserves, and pay other costs reasonably expected to be paid from the revenues of the utility system. The proceedings will also contain covenants requiring the governmental entity to preserve the tax-exempt status of the interest on the obligations issued. Municipalities that have entered into take-or-pay contracts must review the contracts to determine if covenants that could impact the ability of the municipality to sell facilities, assign interests in the supply or services purchased, or the continued treatment of any obligations issued by the water district as tax-exempt obligations, are included in the contract.

Proceedings relating to the issuance of obligations typically contain a covenant that restricts the ability to sell, lease, or otherwise dispose of utility system property, except for replacing or substituting for such property. The covenant requires that, to the extent that the proceeds from such sale, lease, or disposition of property are not used to acquire replacement or substitution property, they will be used to acquire other improvements to the utility system, retire obligations issued to finance utility system improvements, or purchase or redeem outstanding obligations. The proceedings also contain a covenant to set rates sufficient to pay operation and maintenance expenses, to pay other obligations of the utility system, and to produce revenues of a specified percentage at least equal to 100 percent of the debt service requirements of outstanding obligations secured by the revenues of the utility system.

Governmental entities that have issued or incurred obligations secured by different pledges of security must also consider rights granted to other participants that have made financial commitments in respect to the obligations issued or incurred by the governmental entity. For example, consent from a bank that issued a credit facility or liquidity facility in support of the payment of debt service on commercial paper notes may be required before the governmental entity may enter an agreement for the sale or lease of the facilities. If obligations have a municipal bond insurance policy issued in support of payment of debt service on the obligations, the policy and related proceedings must be reviewed to determine if a sale or lease of facilities may occur, and under what conditions (e.g., whether consent of the insurer is required).

Because the outstanding obligations typically are issued as tax-exempt obligations, the provisions of the federal Internal Revenue Code relating to tax-exempt obligations also must be considered in connection with the sale of utility system assets. The sale or lease of utility system facilities to a private entity will constitute a "change in use" for purposes of federal income tax law. The Internal Revenue Code, and the regulations and rulings relating to tax-exempt obligations, are designed to inhibit the financing of privately owned or managed facilities with tax-exempt obligations. The sale or lease of facilities financed with tax-exempt obligations to a private entity must be analyzed to determine if the sale or lease can satisfy the covenants relating to maintaining the tax-exempt status on the outstanding obligations. Given the perspective of the Internal Revenue Code and the rationale for the treatment of obligations as tax-exempt obligations, the burden will be on the governmental entity selling tax-exempt obligations to satisfy the covenants to maintain the tax-exempt treatment of the interest on the obligations.

This is especially the case where a water district and a municipality or another governmental entity have entered into a contract to provide water supply or wastewater treatment services and the water district has issued tax-exempt obligations to finance the improvements to provide the services. Were the municipality or other governmental entity to sell or lease its facilities to a private entity, this might adversely affect the tax-exempt status of the bonds issued by the water district, since the result would be that the services provided would no longer be to a governmental entity, but to a private entity for use in its trade or business.

The contract may not allow the assignment of the right to receive services, whether through an explicit prohibition of the right to assign, being silent on the right to assign, or by limitations to the right to assign, such as consent by the other party or parties to the contract.

§ 37.21:4 Governmental Immunity

In 2006, the Texas Supreme Court provided a clear roadmap for parties to determine whether a governmental entity can assert immunity from suit. In *Tooke v. City of Mexia*, 197 S.W.3d 325 (Tex. 2006), the court held that words in statutes such as "sue and be sued" do not, in and of themselves, effect a waiver of governmental immunity. Immunity is waived only by clear and unambiguous language. A statute that purports to waive immunity must do so beyond doubt; ambiguities in a statute that purports to waive immunity will be resolved by retaining immunity.

In 2016, the Supreme Court ruled in *Wasson Interests, Ltd. v. City of Jacksonville*, 489 S.W.3d 427, 439 (Tex. 2016), that sovereign immunity does not imbue a city with derivative immunity when it performs proprietary, as opposed to governmental, functions in respect to contracts executed by a city. Texas jurisprudence has generally held that proprietary functions are those conducted by a city in its private capacity, for the benefit only of those within its corporate limits, and not as an arm of the government or under the authority or for the benefit of the state.

Governmental immunity has two components: immunity from liability and immunity from suit. By entering into a contract, a governmental entity necessarily waives immunity from liability, but entering a contract does not, in and of itself, waive immunity from suit. Both governmental and private entities must look to a specific statutory grant of the ability to waive governmental immunity to determine what the risks are in entering a contract for the sale or lease of facilities or the acquisition of goods and services.

There are many examples in Texas statutes that show that the Texas legislature knows how to grant authority to permit the waiver of governmental immunity. Section 1371.059 of the Texas Government Code provides that an issuer "may agree to waive sovereign immunity from suit or liability for the purpose of adjudicating a claim to enforce the credit agreement or obligation or for damages for breach of the credit agreement or obligation." Tex. Gov't Code § 1371.059(c). This ability to waive, however, does not apply to an issuer that is a state agency (including an institution of higher education) or a county with a population of 1.5 million or more. Tex. Gov't Code § 1371.059(c). Texas Local Government Code chapter 271, subchapter I, provides that a local governmental entity that is authorized by statute or the Texas Constitution to enter into a contract and that enters a contract subject to the subchapter waives sovereign immunity to suit for the purpose of adjudicating a claim for breach of the contract. Tex. Loc. Gov't Code § 271.152. A local governmental entity means a political subdivision of the state, other than a county or a unit of state government. Tex. Loc. Gov't Code § 271.151(3). A contract subject to the subchapter means a written contract for providing goods or services to the local governmental entity. Tex. Loc. Gov't Code § 271.151(2).

Parties to a contract must examine the nature of the contract, the statutory authority to enter into the contract, and the goods or services provided under the contract to determine if a governmental entity that is a party to the contract has the statutory authority to agree to a waiver of governmental immunity.

§ 37.21:5 Other Issues

In a sale or lease of water or wastewater facilities from a political subdivision to a private entity, once the legal issues have been analyzed, the next step is to determine the fair market value of the property. Making such a determination raises additional questions: Would the amount of funds needed to retire outstanding obligations constitute fair market value if the appraised value of the facilities exceeds the amount needed to retire outstanding obligations secured by the revenues of the utility system? Can the entity accept an offer to purchase the facilities priced at the amount necessary to retire outstanding bonds in this instance? Can the future value of revenues be taken into consideration in determining fair market value? Compare section 1502.059 of the Texas Government Code, which allows a municipality to transfer revenues to its general fund, with section 272.001(f) of the Texas Local Government Code, which provides that an appraisal is determinative of the fair market value of land, an easement, or other real property interest. *See* Tex. Gov't Code § 1502.059; Tex. Loc. Gov't Code § 272.001(f).

Other issues not specifically related to the sale or lease of facilities must be considered. Can the private entity that provides water and wastewater services to a municipality be compelled to provide those services to areas annexed into the municipality after the sale or lease of facilities has taken effect? Would the governing body of the selling entity or the end users of the services have any rights to input if a future rate increase is proposed? Could the governmental entity retain the right to receive service without compensation? If condemnation is necessary to effect improvements for the benefit of the private entity providing the services, would the condemnation constitute "public use" under article I, section 17, of the Texas Constitution, since it is arguable that the taking may result in transferring property to the private entity for the primary purpose of economic development or enhancing tax revenues? The sale or lease of governmentally owned facilities raises many issues that will come from both expected and unexpected sources, and all must be considered with care.

In 2011, Senate Bill 1048 was enacted, adding chapters 2267 and 2268 to the Government Code and providing a detailed procedure for governmental entities and other persons to enter into public-private partnership agreements for qualified projects. Chapter 2267 defines a qualified project in a manner that includes water supply and waste treatment facilities. S.B. 1048 was enacted to meet a public need to acquire, construct, expand, operate, or install qualifying projects, to encourage public entities and private entities and other persons to enter into partnerships to develop and effect qualified projects, and to authorize private entities and other persons to develop or operate qualifying projects to serve the public safety, benefit, and welfare by making the projects available to the public in a more timely or less costly fashion. *See* Tex. Gov't Code § 2267.002. Chapter 2267 provides a detailed process for developing guidelines and negotiating interim and final agreements regarding the development of a qualified project.

Chapter 2268 authorizes the creation of the Partnership Advisory Commission to advise governmental entities on proposals received under chapter 2267. The Partnership Advisory Commission consists of the chair of the House Appropriations Committee or the designee thereof, the chair of the Senate Finance Committee or the designee thereof, three representatives appointed by the Speaker of the House, three senators appointed by the lieutenant governor, and three representatives of the executive branch appointed by the governor. Legislative members serve on the commission until the expiration of their terms or until their successors qualify. The members appointed by the governor serve at the will of the governor.

Before negotiating an agreement, the governmental entity must provide copies of a proposal to the presiding officer of the commission and the chairs of the House Appropriations Committee and the Senate Finance Committee or their designees. Certain proposals are not required to be submitted to the commission. *See* Tex. Gov't Code § 2268.058(b). Not later than the tenth day after the date the commission receives a detailed proposal for a qualifying project, the commission shall determine whether to accept or decline the proposal for review and notify the governmental entity of its decision.

If the commission accepts the proposal for review, the commission shall provide its findings and recommendations not later than the forty-fifth day after the date the commission receives complete copies of the detailed proposal. Acceptance of a proposal is a condition to a governmental entity commencing negotiations of agreements.

The powers granted by chapters 2267 and 2268 may be helpful in those circumstances where other existing statutory authority is uncertain or not adequate to pursue a specific project.

§ 37.22 Management of Public Entity Water and Wastewater Facilities by a Private Entity

A governmental entity may consider contracting with a private entity to manage and operate the facilities owned by the governmental entity. Similar legal issues as discussed above with respect to the sale or lease of facilities must be considered when a public entity is negotiating with a private entity to provide management services. This is especially the case when obligations, the interest on which is excluded from gross income for purposes of federal income taxation, have been issued by the governmental entity to finance the improvements comprising the utility system.

§ 37.22:1 Water Districts

A water district, as defined in Texas Water Code section 49.001(a)(1), has the functions, powers, authority, rights, and duties to allow it to accomplish the purposes for which it was created or the purposes authorized by the constitution, the Water Code, or any other law. Tex. Water Code § 49.211(a). Water districts possess broad powers to contract. As discussed at section 37.20:1 above, Water Code section 49.213 authorizes a district to enter into contracts with any person or any public or private entity for the performance of any purpose or function permitted by a district. *See* Tex. Water Code § 49.213.

As in the case of a sale or lease of facilities to a private entity, bond covenants and contracts must be reviewed to determine if there are any contractual constraints on the ability of the water district to contract with a private entity to manage or operate its facilities. As discussed at section 37.22:3 below, one such constraint may be covenants relating to maintaining the tax-exempt status of obligations issued by the water district to finance the facilities.

§ 37.22:2 Municipalities

Municipalities are confronted by a potential statutory conflict relating to their ability to contract with a private entity to provide management services. While section 1502.002(b) of the Texas Government Code provides that a municipality may authorize the execution of contracts between it and any person to accomplish enumerated purposes, section 1502.070 of the Code provides that management and control of a utility system may be vested in the municipality's governing body or a board of trustees named in the proceedings adopted by a municipality. *See* Tex. Gov't Code §§ 1502.002(b), 1502.070. The issue raised by section 1502.070 is whether the legislature, in enacting section 1502.070, meant to limit or restrict the ability of a municipality to manage its utility system to either its governing body or a board of trustees named in proceedings adopted by the municipality. In considering entering into a management agreement with a private entity, the municipality must determine whether section 1502.070 preempts or restricts its ability to contract with a private entity for management services.

Two other statutes provide municipalities contracting authority regarding management and control of water and wastewater facilities. Under Texas Local Government Code section 552.142, a municipality by ordinance may transfer management and control of two or more of its water, wastewater, storm water, or drainage systems to a board of trustees consisting of seven members, one of whom must be the presiding officer of the municipality. Government Code chapter 791 authorizes a municipality to contract with another municipality, county, or water district to provide governmental services, including those related to obtaining water supply or wastewater treatment facilities under Government Code section 791.026.

Home rule municipalities possess powers under their city charters, which include general contracting powers, and may include specific contracting powers related to their ownership or operation of a utility system. Article XI, section 5, of the Texas Constitution provides that no city charter shall contain any provision inconsistent with the constitution or the general laws enacted by the legislature. As discussed above, the authority of a municipality appears to be limited in its management and control of its utility system. The question arises whether these statutes restrict the ability of a municipality to contract with a private entity to provide management services for its utility system. A municipality must determine whether sufficient legal authority exists in considering entering into a management contract with a private entity.

§ 37.22:3 Covenants in Bond Proceedings to Maintain Tax-Exempt Status of Bonds

Hiring a private entity to operate or manage a utility system owned by a public entity gives rise to "private business use" under the federal Internal Revenue Code relating to the issuance of tax-exempt obligations. A safe harbor is provided by Revenue Procedure 97-13, where a management agreement has been negotiated that demonstrates that beneficial use of the facilities has not been passed to the manager.

Under Revenue Procedure 97-13, the primary focus on a management agreement is compensation to the manager. The compensation must be reasonable, and not based, in whole or in part, on net profits that would accrue to the manager. The management contract must contain a periodic fixed fee arrangement that requires that at least 50 percent of annual compensation be based on a predetermined fee. The term of the agreement may not exceed five years, and the agreement must be cancellable by the governmental entity at the end of two years. Exceptions to term length of the agreement are dependent on the basis of the fixed fee arrangement. A maximum term of fifteen years is permissible if the periodic fixed fee determines 95 percent of annual compensation. The challenges of providing services efficiently and economically will cause public entities to explore all options, including privatization. Entering into contracts with private entities is subject to the public entity's having the legal authority to enter such contracts, and public entities must proceed with care in determining whether the legal authority exists. Once determined, other issues must be considered carefully to ensure that the objective of providing efficient and economical services can be satisfied.

VII. Conclusion

§ 37.23 Conclusion

The importance of water, and the ability of political subdivisions to finance water and wastewater improvements, is affirmed by the number and scope of Texas constitutional provisions and statutes to finance water improvements. The state, acting through the Texas Water Development Board, uses its full faith and credit to enable political subdivisions to access funds at low cost to conserve and develop the water resources of the state. Regional water authorities and districts serve not only to conserve and develop the water resources of the state, providing wholesale water supply and wastewater services to other public entities, but also provide retail services to residents of the state. Local governments have authority to issue obligations secured not only by revenues of their utility systems but also by securing the obligations with their full faith and credit, through ad valorem tax pledges. Public entities, in response to budget concerns or administrative burdens, are looking to partner with private entities to provide water supply, wastewater treatment, or management services in fulfilling their responsibilities to their citizens to provide water and wastewater services efficiently and economically.

CHAPTER 38

Water for a Public Purpose: Governmental Acquisition of Water by Involuntary Means

Steve Kosub[1]

I. Introduction

§ 38.1 Introduction

Anticipated growth in the population of Texas over the next fifty years will place an unprecedented demand on the state's water supply. Texas municipalities and various other governmental and quasi-governmental entities are ultimately responsible for ensuring the health, safety, and welfare of their residents, and nothing is more fundamental to the public's health than water. Recognition of this fact is reflected in the Texas Water Code. *See* Tex. Water Code § 11.024(1) (noting the primary preference given to domestic and municipal use in the appropriation of state water).

Historically, local governments have been able to satisfy their water supply needs through a combination of available surface water rights and unregulated groundwater. Local government use of the power of eminent domain for acquiring water rights has been spare or nonexistent because of cost or political volatility. However, the evolution of Texas water law and planning during the last decade has forced local government officials to examine the adequacy of their future public water supplies. Many local governments have come up short, which may result in the more frequent use of eminent domain power to acquire water and water rights.

The Texas Commission on Environmental Quality and the Texas Water Development Board anticipate that the population of Texas will increase more than 70 percent between 2020 and 2070, growing from 29.5 million to 51 million. Even with dramatic conservation measures, the water needs of municipalities, industries, and some aspects of agriculture will also expand by approximately 17 percent. Approximately 17 million acre-feet of water were available in 2000. That availability exceeded the overall demand of 16.9 million acre-feet. However, availability will actually decrease from 16.8 million acre-feet in 2020 to 13.8 million acre-feet in 2070 as a result of reservoir silting and groundwater depletion, and it will substantially lag behind the expected demand of 19.2 million acre-

---

1. Steve Kosub is of counsel to Sprouse Shrader Smith PLLC. His practice focuses on the development and distribution of groundwater and other water resources. His work has encompassed groundwater transactions, project negotiations, permitting activities, infrastructure agreements, intergovernmental agreements, water planning, and innovative water strategies. He received his BA in political science from Texas A&M University in 1974 and his JD from the University of Texas School of Law in 1977. Mr. Kosub is certified in administrative law by the Texas Board of Legal Specialization. He is a past chair of the Environmental and Natural Resources Law Section of the State Bar of Texas and a frequent writer and speaker on water law, regulatory takings, and development issues.

feet. *See* Texas Water Development Board, *Water for Texas 2022* (2022), www.twdb.texas.gov/waterplanning/swp/2022 [hereinafter 2022 State Water Plan].

This chapter begins with a discussion of eminent domain and condemnation in general. Next it examines condemnation in the context of water rights, both surface water and groundwater. It highlights certain 2011 amendments to chapter 2206 of the Texas Government Code and chapter 21 of the Texas Property Code governing eminent domain, and also highlights certain 2003 amendments to chapter 21 that specifically relate to the condemnation of water rights. The chapter then examines federal and state legal theories of inverse condemnation, including physical and regulatory takings, in the context of Texas water rights, and the Texas Private Real Property Preservation Act. Finally, it discusses what constitutes property in the context of water rights and takings law.

II. Eminent Domain

§ 38.2 Eminent Domain

Eminent domain is the power to take private property for public use. The right of eminent domain is the right of the state to reassert, either temporarily or permanently, its dominion over any portion of the soil of the state on account of public exigency and for the public good. *See Black's Law Dictionary* 637 (10th ed. 2014). This right is balanced against the constitutional protection of private property, found in both the United States and Texas Constitutions. The Fifth Amendment to the U.S. Constitution concludes with the following statement: "nor shall private property be taken for public use, without just compensation." U.S. Const. amend. V.

Article I, section 17, of the Texas Constitution provides in part as follows:

> No person's property shall be taken, damaged, or destroyed for or applied to public use without adequate compensation being made, unless by the consent of such person, and . . . [w]hen . . . taken . . . , except for the use of the State, compensation . . . shall be first made, or secured by a deposit of money . . . .

Tex. Const. art. I, § 17. See section 38.9 below for a discussion of the effect of the difference in language between the state and federal constitutional protections.

Throughout much of our judicial history, the great majority of governmental takings occurred in the straightforward context of land occupation or acquisition. Thus, much of the law of eminent domain has developed for the purpose of providing the procedural structure for governmental takings and the determination of just compensations. See *Hendler v. United States*, 952 F.2d 1364, 1371–73 (Fed. Cir. 1991), for an excellent and concise discussion of this history, citing Julius L. Sackman, *Nichols' the Law of Eminent Domain* § 8 (1991).

The Texas legislature in 2011 enacted Senate Bill 18 relating to the use of eminent domain authority. *See* Act of May 6, 2011, 82d Leg., R.S., ch. 81, eff. Sept. 1, 2011. This legislation made significant amendments to chapters 552 and 2206 of the Texas Government Code, chapters 251, 261, 263, and 273 of the Texas Local Government Code, chapter 21 of the Texas Property Code, chapter 202 of the Texas Transportation Code, chapter 54 of the Texas Water Code, and certain special laws governing nonprofit charitable corporations. The legislation generally imposes new procedural requirements that must be satisfied before initiating eminent domain proceedings and creates new procedural challenges for attorneys and both private and governmental entities engaged in eminent domain practice. The 84th Legislature added a new subchapter D to Government Code chapter 2206, directing the comptroller to create and make accessible on a website maintained by the comptroller an eminent domain database with extensive information that may be useful to the practitioner. *See* Act of May 30, 2015, 84th Leg., R.S., ch. 1218, eff. June 19, 2015.

§ 38.3 Condemnation

Condemnation is the legal process by which the government exercises the right of eminent domain to take the property of a private owner for public use, without consent, but upon the payment of just compensation. *Hubler v. City of Corpus Christi*, 564 S.W.2d 816, 820 (Tex. App.—Corpus Christi–Edinburg 1978, writ ref'd n.r.e.). Condemnation proceedings are governed by Texas Property Code chapter 21. Notably, chapter 21 establishes only the *procedure* by which the power of eminent domain is exercised when that power has been delegated. Nothing in chapter 21 constitutes a delegation of the power itself. Additional procedures required to initiate eminent domain proceedings are found in chapter 2206, subchapter B, of the Texas Government Code (Truth in Condemnation Procedures Act). Chapter 2206 also includes significant limitations on the use of eminent domain if the taking (1) confers a private benefit on a particular private party through the use of the property, (2) is for a public use that is merely a pretext to confer a private benefit on a particular private party, (3) is for primarily economic development purposes, or (4) is not for a public use. Tex. Gov't Code § 2206.001(b). However, this section does not affect the authority of an entity authorized by law to take private property through the use of eminent domain for most traditional governmental purposes as enumerated in Government Code section 2206.001(c).

An eminent domain proceeding is not within the general jurisdiction of a court; rather, any power to act is special and depends on the particular eminent domain statute. *In re Tarrant Regional Water District*, 495 S.W.3d 296 (Tex. App.—Tyler 2015, no pet.); *Gulf Energy Pipeline Co. v. Garcia*, 884 S.W.2d 821, 822 (Tex. App.—San Antonio 1994, no writ). District courts and county courts at law have concurrent jurisdiction in eminent domain cases. A county court has no jurisdiction in eminent domain cases. Tex. Prop. Code § 21.001.

The object of a condemnation proceeding is to ascertain what would be just compensation to the owner of the land sought to be taken under the circumstances of the particular case. Essentially, the process involves negotiations between the condemnor and condemnee, filing of a condemnation petition in the appropriate court, a commissioners' hearing to assess damages, and potentially a trial de novo on damages and jurisdictional issues.

In Texas, the power of eminent domain must be conferred by the legislature either expressly or by necessary implication and will not be gathered from doubtful inferences. *See Texas Rice Land Partners, Ltd. v. Denbury Green Pipeline-Texas, LLC*, 363 S.W.3d 192 (Tex. 2012). Because the exercise of the power of eminent domain is in derogation of the rights of citizens, statutes that confer such power are strictly construed in favor of the landowner and against those corporations and subdivisions of the state vested with such power. *See Burch v. City of San Antonio*, 518 S.W.2d 540 (Tex. 1975). A governmental entity that has eminent domain power may exercise such authority exclusively through Property Code sections 21.012 through 21.016. *See* Tex. Prop. Code § 21.011. In condemnation proceedings, the requirements of the statutes are strictly followed. *See City of Bryan v. Moehlman*, 282 S.W.2d 687 (Tex. 1955).

Where the power of eminent domain is granted, a determination by the condemnor of the necessity for acquiring certain property is conclusive unless the condemnor's decision was fraudulent, in bad faith, or arbitrary and capricious. *City of Austin v. Whittington*, 384 S.W.3d 766, 777 (Tex. 2012); *FKM Partnership, Ltd. v. Board of Regents of the University of Houston System*, 255 S.W.3d 619, 629 n.9 (Tex. 2008).

III. Condemnation of Water Rights

§ 38.4 Condemnation of Water Rights

Most legal practitioners have at least passing familiarity with the government's use of condemnation to acquire real property. The power of eminent domain is regularly invoked for the construction of highways, streets, pipelines, drainage improvements, electric transmission lines, and other public facilities. A water treatment plant or storage tank may need to be located on property that is otherwise unavailable for purchase at a fair price. Condemnation may be necessary to acquire the site. But what about the water itself? How is it acquired for public use?

As discussed more fully elsewhere in this book and chapter, waters in the rivers and navigable streams of Texas belong to the state, while groundwater is the property of the owner of the surface estate. Until the middle of the twentieth century, supplies of both were readily available and adequate for the state's needs. A period of record drought in the 1950s, however, and the state's subsequent rapid urbanization led to a regulatory system for use of the state's surface water rights by municipalities, industry, agriculture, and recreational interests. Permits for the use of water rights from the state's rivers and reservoirs are issued by the state and generally transferrable for value, but reliable supplies are now for the most part fully used in the river basins where they are most in demand. See Chapter 4 of this book.

Groundwater supplies, once seemingly unlimited, were historically unregulated and inexpensively produced by simply purchasing a small parcel of land and drilling a well. However, management of groundwater resources has now been entrusted by the state to a growing number of local groundwater districts created under chapter 36 of the Texas Water Code. These districts may regulate and limit groundwater production through a variety of means. See Chapter 5 of this book.

With water supplies now limited and demand for water increasing, water utilities must increasingly turn to the market to satisfy their raw water needs. Just as in the case of real property, the market may not willingly make water available for purchase. The use of condemnation to acquire water rights will likely become more common.

Professor Corwin W. Johnson explored the condemnation of water rights in a 1968 *Texas Law Review* article. *See* Corwin W. Johnson, *Condemnation of Water Rights*, 46 Texas L. Rev. 1054 (1968). As the last thorough scholarly analysis of the issue in this state, the article should be a starting point of reference for any practitioner anticipating a water rights condemnation action. At the time the article was prepared, the rule of capture for groundwater was unquestioned and groundwater supplies could be acquired through the acquisition of a tract of land large enough to accommodate a public well. As a result, there was little need for condemnation to acquire groundwater rights. Thus, not surprisingly, the article focuses on the acquisition of surface water rights. Because it predates significant changes in the Water Code, it must be qualified accordingly.

The article, however, includes an excellent analysis of the statutory authority (or lack thereof) of a local government in Texas to condemn water rights. The analysis is a helpful primer on the legal fine points that distinguish general law cities, home-rule cities, and other governmental entities in Texas. Understanding the analysis is critical to understanding the distinction noted earlier in this chapter: that Texas Property Code chapter 21 is a mechanism for condemnation only when the right to exercise the power of eminent domain is afforded by another statute. In the absence of an express statement of eminent domain authority, the authority does not exist. Counsel for both condemnor and condemnee should therefore begin their work with a careful analysis of the condemnor's constitutional foundation, statutory framework, and corporate powers.

The right to exercise the power of eminent domain in the context of water is found in multiple statutes. With regard to surface water rights, two of the most notable are Texas Water Code section 11.033 and, for municipalities, Texas Local Government Code chapter 251.

Water Code section 11.033 states:

> The right to take water necessary for domestic and municipal supply purposes is primary and fundamental, and the right to recover from other uses water which is essential to domestic and municipal supply purposes is paramount and unquestioned in the policy of the state. All political subdivisions of the state and constitutional governmental agencies exercising delegated legislative powers have the power of eminent domain to be exercised as provided by law for domestic, municipal, and manufacturing uses and for other purposes authorized by this code, including the irrigation of land for all requirements of agricultural employment.

Tex. Water Code § 11.033.

Water Code section 11.040(a) provides that "[a] permanent water right is an easement and passes with the title to the land." Tex. Water Code § 11.040(a). This characterization helps place condemnation of water rights squarely within traditional notions of the use of eminent domain. Vested water rights cannot be taken without compensation, without due process, or retroactively. *In re Water Rights of Cibolo Creek Watershed of San Antonio River Basin*, 568 S.W.2d 155, 156 (Tex. App.—San Antonio 1978, no writ). Both sections 11.033 and 11.040 relate to surface water rights by virtue of their placement in Water Code chapter 11. Chapter 11 defines "water right" as a "right acquired under the laws of this state to impound, divert, or use state water." Tex. Water Code § 11.002(5).

A careful analysis of section 11.033 as undertaken by Professor Johnson suggests that it might be read more restrictively than its sweeping language implies. *See* Johnson, at 1062. However, Local Government Code chapter 251 provides as follows:

> (a) When the governing body of a municipality considers it necessary, the municipality may exercise the right of eminent domain for a public use to acquire public or private property, whether located inside or outside the municipality, for any of the following uses:
>
> (1) the providing, enlarging, or imposing of a . . . water works system, including reservoirs, other water supply sources, watersheds, and water storage, drainage, treatment, distribution, transmission, and emptying facilities; . . .
>
> (2) the determining of riparian rights relative to the municipal water works;
>
> (3) the straightening or improving of the channel of any stream, branch, or drain;
>
> (4) the straightening, widening, or extending of any alley, street, or other roadway; and
>
> (5) any other municipal public use the governing body considers advisable.
>
> (b) A municipality condemning land under this section may take a fee simple title to the property if the governing body expresses the intention to do so.

Tex. Loc. Gov't Code § 251.001.

The Code goes on to say that an exercise of the power of eminent domain granted by chapter 251 is governed by Property Code chapter 21. Tex. Loc. Gov't Code § 251.002.

By contrast, the eminent domain authority of a groundwater conservation district is specifically limited. It may not be used for the condemnation of land for the purpose of acquiring rights to groundwater, surface water, or water rights, or the production, sale, or distribution of groundwater or surface water. Tex. Water Code § 36.105(b).

Similarly, the eminent domain authority of a general law district or water supply corporation is specifically restricted by the following language: "The power of eminent domain may not be used for the condemnation of land for the purpose of acquiring rights to underground water or of water or water rights." Tex. Water Code § 49.222(c). See also Chapter 7 of this book.

Interestingly, and significantly for the South Central Texas region, section 1.11(g) of the Edwards Aquifer Authority Act contains the following language with regard to the condemnation of water rights: "The authority has the power of eminent domain. The authority may not acquire rights to underground water by the power of eminent domain." Act of May 30, 1993, 73d Leg., R.S., ch. 626, § 1.11, *as amended by* Act of May 16, 1995, 74th Leg., R.S., ch. 524; Act of May 29, 1995, 74th Leg., R.S., ch. 261; Act of May 6, 1999, 76th Leg., R.S., ch. 163; Act of May 25, 2001, 77th Leg., R.S., ch. 1192; Act of May 28, 2001, 77th Leg., R.S., ch. 966, §§ 2.60–.62, 6.01–.05; Act of June 1, 2003, 78th Leg., R.S., ch. 1112, § 6.01(4); Act of May 23, 2007, 80th Leg., R.S., ch. 510; Act of May 28, 2007, 80th Leg., R.S., ch. 1351, §§ 2.01–.12; Act of May 28, 2007, 80th Leg., R.S., ch. 1430, §§ 12.01–.12; Act of May 21, 2009, 81st Leg., R.S., ch. 1080; and Act of May 20, 2013, 83d Leg., R.S., ch. 783 [hereinafter Edwards Aquifer Act]. See also Chapter 17 of this book.

The Edwards Aquifer Authority (EAA) is thus limited notwithstanding its statutory mandate to manage withdrawals of groundwater from the Edwards Aquifer in order to protect endangered species while also protecting historic groundwater use. The EAA is required to achieve its mandate by entirely voluntary or regulatory means. Whether that regulation has itself constituted a taking or acquisition of the water is a question that is explored below.

The foregoing enumeration of statutory provisions is by no means exclusive. A wide variety of water regulatory entities exist by special-purpose legislation and other statutory frameworks. Although historically there have been few successful jurisdictional challenges in condemnation proceedings, the unique nature of water law may provide opportunities for challenging the authority of a condemnor of water rights.

§ 38.5 House Bill 803, 78th Legislature (2003)

Notwithstanding the wholesale changes in Texas water law and water policy during the last thirty-five years, the scope and application of the various statutory provisions discussed above have until recently received relatively little attention or clarification from the Texas legislature. In 2003, however, the 78th Legislature adopted a bill that bolstered eminent domain authority for the acquisition of water rights but also dramatically limited the availability and increased the potential cost of this remedy. House Bill 803 made two amendments to Texas Property Code chapter 21 relating to water rights in the context of condemnation. First, the bill added a new section 21.0121 (Condemnation to Acquire Water Rights) that requires a political subdivision in a condemnation proceeding for purposes of acquiring water rights to plead and prove that it has—

(1) prepared a drought contingency plan;

(2) developed and implemented a water conservation plan that will result in the highest practicable levels of water conservation and efficiency achievable in the political subdivision's jurisdiction;

(3) made a bona fide good faith effort to obtain practicable alternative water supplies to the water rights the political subdivision proposes to condemn;

(4) made a bona fide good faith effort to acquire the rights to the water the political subdivision proposes to condemn by voluntary purchase or lease; and

(5) made a showing that the political subdivision needs the water rights to provide for the domestic needs of the political subdivision within the next 10-year period.

Tex. Prop. Code § 21.0121(a). Second, the new section provides that a court shall deny the right to condemn unless the political subdivision proves to the court that the political subdivision has met the requirements of subsection (a). Tex. Prop. Code § 21.0121(b).

With regard to the valuation of such water rights, H.B. 803 did not change the valuation of surface water rights found in Texas Water Code section 11.0275:

> Whenever the law requires the payment of fair market value for a water right, fair market value shall be determined by the amount of money that a willing buyer would pay a willing seller, neither of which is under any compulsion to buy or sell, for the water in an arms-length transaction and shall not be limited to the amount of money that the owner of the water right has paid or is paying for the water.

Tex. Water Code § 11.0275. Contrast this more traditional valuation standard for surface water rights with the new Property Code section 21.0421 (Assessment of Damages: Groundwater Rights) under H.B. 803.

Under section 21.0421, evidence relating to the market value of groundwater rights as property apart from the land in addition to the local market value of the real property must be admitted if (1) the political subdivision proposes to condemn the fee title of real property and (2) a finding is made that the real property may be used by the political subdivision to develop or use the rights to groundwater for a public purpose. Such evidence of market value must be based on generally accepted appraisal methods and techniques, including the methods of appraisal under Texas Tax Code chapter 23, subchapter A. *See* Tex. Prop. Code § 21.0421(a), (b).

The damages must be assessed based on "(1) the local market value of the real property, excluding the value of the groundwater in place, at the time of the hearing; and (2) the market value of the groundwater rights as property apart from the land at the time of the hearing." *See* Tex. Prop. Code § 21.0421(c). In making such a finding, the special commissioners or other fact finder must consider:

(1) the amount of groundwater the political subdivision can reasonably be expected to produce from the property on an annual basis;

(2) the number of years the political subdivision can reasonably be expected to produce groundwater from the property;

(3) the quality of the groundwater;

(4) the location of the real property in relation to the political subdivision for conveyance purposes;

(5) any potential environmental impact of producing groundwater from the real property;

(6) whether or not the real property is located within the boundaries of a political subdivision that can regulate the production of groundwater from the real property;

(7) the cost of alternative water supplies to the political subdivision; and

(8) any other reasonable factor that affects the market value of a groundwater right.

Tex. Prop. Code § 21.0421(d).

Section 21.0421 clarifies that its terms do not affect the appraisal of such property for tax appraisal purposes. Groundwater rights appraised separately from the real property under this section may not be appraised separately from real property for property tax appraisal purposes, and real property condemned for the purpose described by section 21.0421(a) is not subject to an additional tax as provided by Tax Code section 23.46 or 23.55. *See* Tex. Prop. Code § 21.0421(e).

These statutory changes pose significant new obstacles to the condemnation of water rights. To the extent that they articulate a statutory vehicle for such condemnation, they may be seen as a helpful tool in any debate over condemnation authority. However, that benefit comes at a high price.

Section 21.0121 applies to the acquisition of both groundwater and surface water rights. The first two requirements for a drought contingency plan and water conservation plan "that will result in the highest practicable levels of water conservation and efficiency achievable" will almost certainly have been addressed to some degree by any local government resorting to condemnation to secure a water supply. *See* Tex. Prop. Code § 21.0121(a)(1), (a)(2). However, the substance and adequacy of those plans may provide rich ground for jurisdictional litigation, particularly in an effort to define "highest practicable levels . . . achievable."

The requirement that the political subdivision must make "a bona fide good faith effort to obtain practicable alternative water supplies to the water rights [which it] proposes to condemn" may be a very high hurdle. *See* Tex. Prop. Code § 21.0121(a)(3). It raises many questions. In the widely divergent world of municipal finances, what is "practicable"? How much effort is required? How much must the political subdivision spend? What is a good-faith effort? What if each alternative itself requires condemnation of water rights? A planning effort to obtain alternative supplies will almost certainly take many years. In addition, subsection (5) requires a showing of need within the next ten-year period. *See* Tex. Prop. Code § 21.0121(a)(5). What if the need is short term in order to facilitate alternative planning? Are the alternative supplies not practicable if they would cost more than the rights to be condemned?

Section 21.0121(a)(4) requires the political subdivision to have made a bona fide, good-faith effort to acquire the rights to the water by voluntary purchase or lease. *See* Tex. Prop. Code § 21.0121(a)(4). This requirement reflects and expands the underlying requirement of section 21.012 that the condemnor is "unable to agree with the owner of the property on the amount of damages." *See* Tex. Prop. Code § 21.012(a). But is a "bona fide good faith effort" under section 21.0121 different from the good-faith effort already imposed by Texas courts that have interpreted section 21.012? *See State v. Hipp*, 832 S.W.2d 71 (Tex. App.—Austin 1992), *rev'd in part sub nom. State v. Dowd*, 867 S.W.2d 781 (Tex. 1993); *Hubenak v. San Jacinto Gas Transmission Co.*, 141 S.W.3d 172 (Tex. 2004); and consolidated cases.

The language of Property Code section 21.0421 is even more problematic for the condemning authority. The language of the section raises not only imposing cost issues but also new procedural questions as well. Furthermore, the process for valuation of groundwater rights is established in the context of the ongoing uncertainty about the legal nature of such rights. See discussion below and Chapter 5 of this book.

Before H.B. 803, a political subdivision wishing to acquire a groundwater supply might simply acquire a well site outside the boundaries of a groundwater district and rely on the rule of capture for virtually unlimited production. The cost of the acquisition would be the surface value of the amount of land required for the public well. If the groundwater source fell within the boundaries of a groundwater district that regulates production through correlative rights, it would have also been necessary for the condemnor to acquire sufficient surface acreage to accommodate production limitations imposed by the district's regulations. Even in that event, however, the acreage would have been acquired at a nominal surface valuation.

Section 21.0421 now provides from the outset that the special commissioners or court must admit evidence relating to the market value of groundwater rights *as property apart from the land* in addition to the local value of the real property under the conditions outlined in the statute. *See* Tex. Prop. Code § 21.0421(a). Those conditions include a finding by the special commissioners or court based on evidence submitted at the hearing that the real property may be used by the political subdivision to develop or use the rights to groundwater for a public purpose. Tex. Prop. Code § 21.0421(a)(2). By placing this threshold finding in the hands of the special commissioners, the statute thrusts a new fact-finding role on the commissioners, whose work was previously limited to a determination of value in condemnation proceedings.

Section 21.0421(b) first directs that evidence submitted on the market value of groundwater as property apart from the land must be based on generally accepted appraisal methods and techniques. Tex. Prop. Code § 21.0421(b). However, if the commissioners or court finds that the real property may be used by the condemnor to develop or use the rights to groundwater for a public purpose, the special commissioners' court may assess damages to the property owner based on (1) the value of the real property excluding the value of the groundwater and (2) the value of the groundwater rights as property apart from the land. Tex. Prop. Code § 21.0421(c). The use of "may" suggests that this additional standard for damages is discretionary, but the statute offers no guidance on when it would be appropriately applied.

Section 21.0421(d) enumerates criteria that the special commissioners or court must consider in assessing damages based on the market value of groundwater rights under subsection (c)(2). *See* Tex. Prop. Code § 21.0421(d). Those criteria may create a measure of damages that is wholly inconsistent with long-standing condemnation law and may render the availability of condemnation proceedings meaningless in the groundwater context. As noted above, damages in all other condemnation proceedings are assessed in accordance with the criteria set forth in Property Code section 21.042. Those criteria revolve entirely around the local market value of the property taken at the time of the special commissioners' hearing and the extent of injury and benefit to the remainder if only a portion of the property has been condemned. Pursuant to section 21.041, the special commissioners must admit evidence on (1) the value of the property being condemned, (2) the injury to the property owner, (3) the benefit to the property owner's remaining property, and (4) the use of the property for the purpose of condemnation. Tex. Prop. Code § 21.041.

By contrast, section 21.0421(d) essentially formulates a measure of damages based on the value of the property taken to the condemnor as a consequence of the condemnation, rather than the value of the property taken at the time of the taking. The valuation criteria assumes that the groundwater has the same value in the ground before the condemnation as it will have as a result of the condemnor's development efforts. Even more problematic for the condemnor, subsection (d) requires the commissioners to consider the "cost of alternative water supplies to the political subdivision." Tex. Prop. Code § 21.0421(d)(7). The cost of these alternative supplies may be very high and will probably be the motivation for the condemnation in the first place.

Such a measure of damages may afford a windfall to the property owner far in excess of the groundwater's local market value in the ground. In determinations of the market value of condemned land, it is a well-settled principle that a fact finder should not take into consideration any increase or decrease in value that might have accrued to property due to the location of the project for which the property is being condemned. *DeWitt & Rearick, Inc. v. State*, 531 S.W.2d 862, 865–66 (Tex. App.—El Paso 1975, no writ) (citing *City of Fort Worth v. Corbin*, 504 S.W.2d 828 (Tex. 1974)). A condemnee must be paid for what it has lost, not for what the condemnor has gained. *State v. Ware*, 86 S.W.3d 817, 825 (Tex. App.—Austin 2002, no pet.). The legislature has also authorized the commissioners or court to consider "any other reasonable factor that affects the market value of a groundwater right." Tex. Prop. Code § 21.0421(d)(8).

The changes made by H.B. 803 have not been interpreted by the appellate courts; however, they were placed squarely before the third court of appeals in the case of *State v. 7KX Investments*, No. 03-10-00069-CV (Tex. App.—Austin, filed Feb. 5, 2010), on appeal from Bell County Court at Law No. 1. In that case, the Texas Department of Transportation invoked Property Code chapter 21 to acquire 27.7 acres of real property fronting Interstate 35 for a highway rest stop. The state offered to pay approximately $500,000 for the land to be acquired. The land included six large groundwater wells. Based largely on the value of the groundwater beneath the land, and the requirements of sections 21.0121 and 21.0421, a jury awarded the property owners $5.8 million for the condemned tract of land. The case was settled before the court of appeals issued an opinion.

As highlighted by *7KX Investments*, condemnation of water rights in compliance with the requirements of H.B. 803 will pose many challenges for governmental entities. These challenges will translate into delays, uncertainty, and cost. Nonetheless, the use of condemnation for water supply development is likely to occur more frequently in the future. The state must develop new water supplies for its growing population. Landowners are increasingly sophisticated about the value of water resources and reluctant to sell water on terms acceptable to governmental entities. The enormous cost of infrastructure for a water supply project requires that large volumes of water be available for the project. Restrictions imposed by groundwater districts and other governmental entities encourage low-impact production spread over a large geographic area. Securing rights for such production requires successful negotiations with many different owners in a predictable period of time. Many landowners have no interest in selling their water on any terms.

These are the circumstances that underlie the historic exercise of eminent domain authority. Condemnation will be an essential tool in the acquisition of water rights for public use, as it has been essential for other government initiatives.

IV. Inverse Condemnations or "Takings"

§ 38.6 Inverse Condemnation

The exercise of eminent domain authority through condemnation is seldom well received by landowners. Unfortunate condemnees may view it as an oppressive incursion by government onto the private property of citizens, which the citizens are largely powerless to prevent. Condemnation is, nonetheless, a straightforward, time-honored, legislatively established process by which the government acquires property for a public purpose and pays fairly for what it receives. Government could hardly function without this authority. Due process and fair compensation are the keys.

However, the exercise of eminent domain is not the only governmental action that involves impacts on private property. Takings may be categorized as either statutory (if the government compensates the owner for the taking) or inverse (if the owner must file suit because the government took, damaged, or destroyed the property without paying compensation). *Kopplow Development, Inc. v. City of San Antonio*, 399 S.W.3d 532, 536 (Tex. 2013) (citing *Westgate, Ltd. v. State*, 843 S.W.2d 448, 452 (Tex. 1992)). By imposing regulations on private property or restricting its use, government may effectively acquire the property for its own purposes, while rendering it without value to its nominal owner. Examples of such government action abound. Overly burdensome land use restrictions, required dedications, and outright seizure of property all can lead to a governmental taking without payment of compensation as required by the U.S. and Texas Constitutions. This is commonly known as inverse condemnation. Such conduct by government may be actionable and has been a rich source of federal and state litigation.

It is expected that the rapid proliferation of groundwater districts in Texas and their evolving efforts to manage or limit the production of groundwater will add to this jurisprudence. Landowners throughout the state are finding that their historic access to groundwater beneath their land has been reduced by newly adopted groundwater district regulations. From the perspective of the affected landowner, this water has been acquired by the government for public use as surely as if it had been condemned and transported away by a distant water utility. However, unlike under the exercise of eminent domain, no compensation has been paid.

Inverse condemnation is a "cause of action against a governmental defendant to recover the value of property which has been taken in fact by the governmental defendant, even though no formal exercise of the power of eminent domain has been attempted by the taking agency." *Hearts Bluff Game Ranch, Inc. v. State*, 381 S.W.3d 468, 475 (Tex. 2012) (quoting *United States v. Clarke*, 445 U.S. 253, 257 (1980)); *see also State v. Brownlow*, 319 S.W.3d 649, 652 (Tex. 2010). Inverse condemnation occurs when property has been taken, damaged, or destroyed for public use without due process or without proper condemnation proceedings, forcing the property owner to seek compensation through the courts. *See City of Dallas v. Stewart*, 361 S.W.3d 562, 567 (Tex. 2012); *City of Houston v. Trail Enterprises*, 300 S.W.3d 736 (Tex. 2009); *City of Abilene v. Burk Royalty Co.*, 470 S.W.2d 643, 646 (Tex. 1971). In an inverse condemnation action, the traditional condemnation roles of the parties are reversed. The property owner, having already lost a property interest, must take the role of plaintiff to recover compensation for his loss. The government, having already taken the property, becomes the defendant. It is well settled that the Texas Constitution waives government immunity with respect to inverse condemnation claims. *City of Houston v. Carlson*, 451 S.W.3d 828, 830 (Tex. 2014) (citing *City of Dallas v. VSC, LLC*, 347 S.W.3d 231, 236 (Tex. 2011)). Nevertheless, such a claim is predicated on a viable allegation of taking. *Carlson*, 451 S.W.3d at 830 (citing *Hearts Bluff Game Ranch, Inc.*, 381 S.W.3d at 476).

Inverse condemnation generally occurs in one of two contexts: physical or nonphysical invasion of the property by the government or regulatory restrictions imposed by the government on the property's use. A subset of this regulatory category may take the form of an exaction by the government in exchange for issuance of a permit to which the property owner is otherwise entitled. The U.S. Supreme Court has defined inverse condemnation as a "shorthand description of the manner in which a landowner recovers just compensation for a taking of his property when condemnation proceedings have not been instituted." *Clarke*, 445 U.S. at 257.

There are three elements of an inverse condemnation action under article I, section 17, of the Texas Constitution. *See* Tex. Const. art. I, § 17. They are (1) the governmental entity intentionally performed an act in the exercise of its lawful authority, (2) that resulted in the taking, damaging, or destruction of the plaintiff's property, (3) for public use. *Comunidad Balboa, LLC v. City of Nassau Bay*, 402 S.W.3d 479, 483 (Tex. App.—Houston [14th Dist.] 2013, pet. denied).

First, a property owner must prove that the governmental entity intentionally performed certain acts in the exercise of its lawful authority. *Steele v. City of Houston*, 603 S.W.2d 786, 790 (Tex. 1980). Mere negligence on the part of the government does not suffice. *Kopplow Development, Inc.*, 399 S.W.3d at 537; *Tarrant Regional Water District v. Gragg*, 151 S.W.3d 546, 554–55 (Tex. 2004). A governmental entity may be liable if it "(1) knows that a specific act is causing identifiable harm; or (2) knows that the specific property damage is substantially certain to result from an authorized governmental action"—that is, that the damage is necessarily an incident to, or necessarily a consequential result of, the government action. *City of Arlington v. State Farm Lloyds*, 145 S.W.3d 165, 168 (Tex. 2004) (quoting *City of Dallas v. Jennings*, 142 S.W.3d 310, 314 (Tex. 2004)). "When the government acts pursuant to colorable contract rights, it lacks the necessary intent to take under its eminent-domain powers and thus retains its immunity from suit." *State v. Holland*, 221 S.W.3d 639, 643 (Tex. 2007).

Second, the property owner must show that the government's action resulted in a taking or damage to the property within the meaning of the Texas Constitution. *Woodson Lumber Co. v. City of College Station*, 752 S.W.2d 744, 746 (Tex. App.—Houston [1st Dist.] 1988, no writ). The distinction between a "taking" and a "damaging" is largely an evidentiary matter, and a single pleading will often suffice for both claims. *Hubler v. City of Corpus Christi*, 564 S.W.2d 816, 822 (Tex. App.—Corpus Christi–Edinburg 1978, writ ref'd. n.r.e.).

Third, the owner must prove that the taking or damaging was "for or applied to public use." "Public use" has been variously defined. One court suggested that a "public use" might be found if the governmental entity intended to accomplish an eminent domain objective under the guise of police power; if the governmental entity was attempting to gain a benefit for the public at large; or if, as a result of the governmental action, a benefit would inure to the general public. *Woodson Lumber Co.*, 752 S.W.2d. at 746.

The issue of public use received intense scrutiny at the federal level in the case of *Kelo v. City of New London*, 545 U.S. 469 (2005). In that case, the city undertook a straightforward condemnation action for urban renewal purposes, with the goal of transferring the acquired property to private developers. The U.S. Supreme Court reaffirmed a broad deference to local governmental determinations of "public use." This decision, although determined under the federal constitution, may be expected to guide the Texas Supreme Court in light of the Texas court's past deference to federal takings jurisprudence. *See Sheffield Development Co. v. City of Glenn Heights*, 140 S.W.3d 660 (Tex. 2004). Partially in response to the *Kelo* decision, the Texas legislature adopted Texas Government Code chapter 2206, which places limitations on the use of eminent domain if the taking will confer a private benefit on a private party or if it is for certain economic development purposes.

See also the extensive discussion of "public use" in *City of Austin v. Whittington*, 384 S.W.3d 766, 777 (Tex. 2012), and *FKM Partnership, Ltd. v. Board of Regents of the University of Houston System*, 255 S.W.3d 619, 629 (Tex. 2008).

The elements of a federal inverse condemnation cause of action are substantially similar to those for a state action, except, as noted, the additional "damaged or destroyed" language under the Texas Constitution is not found in the Fifth Amendment.

§ 38.7 What Constitutes a Taking

The most difficult federal and state jurisprudence arising from inverse condemnation claims focuses on the second element of proof: Did the governmental action result in a compensable taking within the meaning of the state or federal constitution? In both federal and state jurisprudence, takings can be classified as either physical or regulatory. The government commits a physical taking when it uses its power of eminent domain to formally condemn and acquire title to property. *United States v. General Motors Corp.*, 323 U.S. 373, 374–75 (1945). Physical takings occur when the government authorizes an unwarranted physical occupation of an individual's property. *Mayhew v. Town of Sunnyvale*, 964 S.W.2d 922, 933 (Tex. 1998). The government also commits a physical taking when it takes possession of property without acquiring title. "When the government physically takes possession of an interest in property for some public purpose, it has a categorical duty to compensate the former owner . . . ." *Tahoe-Sierra Preservation Council, Inc. v. Tahoe Regional Planning Agency*, 535 U.S. 302, 322 (2002) (citing *United States v. Pewee Coal Co.*, 341 U.S. 114, 115 (1951)). The government may also physically take property by occupation of the property, as in the case of recurring flooding caused by the construction or operation of a dam. "These sorts of physical appropriations constitute the 'clearest sort of taking,' and we assess them using a simple, *per se* rule: The government must pay for what it takes." *Cedar Point Nursery v. Hassid*, 141 S. Ct. 2063, 2071 (2021) (quoting *Palazzolo v. Rhode Island*, 533 U.S. 606, 617 (2001)).

The growth of the regulatory state at all levels of government in the twentieth century resulted in a wide variety of governmental restrictions on private property other than outright occupation or purchase. Physical possession is a taking for which compensation is constitutionally mandated under both Texas and federal law, but under both jurisprudence a restriction in the permissible uses of property or a diminution in its value resulting from regulatory action within the government's police power may or may not be a compensable taking. *Sheffield Development Co. v. City of Glenn Heights*, 140 S.W.3d 660, 669–70 (Tex. 2004). All property is held subject to the valid exercise of the police power, and thus not every regulation is a compensable taking. *Sheffield Development Co.*, 140 S.W.3d at 670 (citing *City of College Station v. Turtle Rock Corp.*, 680 S.W.2d 802, 804 (Tex. 1984)); *see also In re Adjudication of the Water Rights of Upper Guadalupe Segment of Guadalupe River Basin*, 642 S.W.2d 438 (Tex. 1982).

"Government could hardly go on . . . if to some extent values incident to property could not be diminished [by government regulation] without paying for every such change in the general law." *Sheffield Development Co.*, 140 S.W.3d at 670 (quoting *Pennsylvania Coal Co. v. Mahon*, 260 U.S. 393, 413 (1922)). Yet, "a strong public desire to improve the public condition is not enough to warrant achieving the desire by a shorter cut than the constitutional way of paying for the change. . . . The general rule at least [is] that while property may be regulated to a certain extent, if regulation goes too far it will be recognized as a taking." *Sheffield Development Co.*, 140 S.W.3d at 670 (quoting *Mahon*, 260 U.S. at 415–16).

As reflected earlier in this chapter, the takings clauses of the Texas and U.S. Constitutions are different. Nonetheless, the Texas Supreme Court has repeatedly demonstrated its inclination to look to federal jurisprudence for guidance when analyzing a takings claim. *Sheffield Development Co.*, 140 S.W.3d at 668; *City of Austin v. Travis County Landfill Co.*, 73 S.W.3d 234, 238–39 (Tex. 2002); *Mayhew*, 964 S.W.2d at 932. Prosecution of a takings claim therefore requires some understanding of the federal analysis.

§ 38.8 Federal Analysis of What Constitutes a Taking

For several decades after the U.S. Supreme Court decision in *Pennsylvania Coal Company v. Mahon*, a landowner's relief in a federal constitutional challenge based on a land use regulation that went too far was limited to the court's invalidation of the regulation. In 1978, the fight to preserve air space over New York's Grand Central Station introduced a new era of Supreme Court attention to regulatory takings. *See Penn Central Transportation Co. v. New York City*, 438 U.S. 104 (1978).

In a series of opinions over the following twenty years, the Court clearly established the right to compensation for a regulatory taking under the federal constitution, but obscured the analysis of when such a taking occurs. *See Agins v. City of Tiburon*, 447 U.S. 255 (1980); *San Diego Gas & Electric Co. v. City of San Diego*, 450 U.S. 621 (1981); *Loretto v. Teleprompter Manhattan CATV Corp.*, 458 U.S. 419 (1982); *Williamson County Regional Planning Commission v. Hamilton Bank of Johnson City*, 473 U.S. 172 (1985); *First English Evangelical Lutheran Church of Glendale v. Los Angeles County*, 482 U.S. 304 (1987); *Nollan v. California Coastal Commission*, 483 U.S. 825 (1987); *Keystone Bituminous Coal Ass'n v. DeBenedictis*, 480 U.S. 470 (1987); *Lucas v. South Carolina Coastal Council*, 505 U.S. 1003 (1992); *Concrete Pipe & Products of California, Inc. v. Construction Laborers Pension Trust for Southern California*, 508 U.S. 602 (1993); *Dolan v. City of Tigard*, 512 U.S. 374 (1994); *Suitum v. Tahoe Regional Planning Agency*, 520 U.S. 725 (1997).

These cases were collectively described by one land-use practitioner as "intellectual chaos." Gideon Kanner, *Hunting the Snark, Not the Quark: Has the U.S. Supreme Court Been Competent in Its Effort to Formulate Coherent Regulatory Takings Law?*, 30 Urb. Law. 307, 309 (1998). In the words of the federal circuit court:

> The Supreme Court itself likes to point out that no set formula exists to determine whether compensation is constitutionally due for a government restriction of property; instead the court must engage in "essentially ad hoc, factual inquiries." But at bottom what emerges is at least the basic notion that the government, under the guise of regulation, cannot take from a property owner the core economic value of the property, leaving the owner with a mere shell of shambled expectations.

Hendler v. United States, 952 F.2d 1364, 1373 (Fed. Cir. 1991) (citation omitted).

Between 1997 and 2002, the Court issued three additional major regulatory takings opinions in the cases of *City of Monterey v. Del Monte Dunes at Monterey, Ltd.*, 526 U.S. 687 (1999); *Palazzolo v. Rhode Island*, 533 U.S. 606 (2001); and *Tahoe-Sierra Preservation Council, Inc. v. Tahoe Regional Planning Agency*, 535 U.S. 302 (2002). These cases generally reflect that the Court takes a dim view of regulatory zeal by local governments. However, only in the *City of Monterey* case did the Court affirm a takings judgment for the plaintiff.

Notwithstanding their length and complexity, the foregoing cases reflected a discernible federal takings analysis. The analysis relies heavily on case-specific facts and a sense of fairness to justly apportion the burdens of government regulation. Three broad rules emerge from the cases:

1. A taking occurs when the government physically occupies property. No matter how small the intrusion, a permanent physical occupation of private property requires compensation *per se*. *See Loretto*, 458 U.S. 419.

2. A taking occurs when the government regulation deprives the owner of all economically beneficial use of the property. *See Lucas*, 505 U.S. 1003.

3. If a landowner has been deprived of less than all economically viable use, the court must determine whether the regulation unreasonably interferes with the owner's right to use and enjoy the property. In that event, the takings inquiry will focus on the multifactor balancing test articulated in *Penn Central*, 438 U.S. 104. That test requires the court to determine on an ad hoc basis whether fairness and justice have been served by balancing the following factors: (a) the character or nature of the governmental conduct, (b) the economic impact on the landowner, and (c) the degree to which the regulation has affected the reasonable, investment-backed expectations of the land. *Penn Central*, 438 U.S. at 124.

In considering the character of the action, the court may in turn consider whether (1) the interference can be characterized as an invasion, (2) the interference arises from a public program adjusting the benefits and burdens of economic life to promote the public good, or (3) the action is against the economic interest of an owner for the government's own advantage. *Penn Central*, 438 U.S. at 124. These factors are neither mathematically precise nor a *per se* rule. They are instead elements in a "complex of factors" leading to the ultimate determination of whether compensation is required.

In *Bridge Aina Le'a, LLC v. Hawaii Land Use Commission*, 141 S. Ct. 731 (2021), the U.S. Supreme Court denied a petition for writ of certiorari to the U.S. Court of Appeals for the Ninth Circuit. The court of appeals had overturned a district court decision that a regulatory taking had occurred in a land use dispute. *Bridge Aina Le'a, LLC v. State Land Use Commission*, 950 F.3d 610 (9th Cir. 2020). Dissenting from the denial of certiorari, Justice Thomas strongly criticized the U.S. Supreme Court's regulatory takings jurisprudence and the three-part *Penn Central* test:

> As one might imagine, nobody—not States, not property owners, not courts, not juries—has any idea how to apply this standardless standard. This case illustrates the point. After an 8-day trial and with the benefit of jury instructions endorsed by both parties, the jury found a taking. The District Court, in turn, concluded that there was an adequate factual basis for this verdict. But the Ninth Circuit on appeal reweighed and reevaluated the same facts under the same legal tests to conclude that *no reasonable jury* could have found a taking. These starkly different outcomes based on the application of the same law indicate that we have still not provided courts with a "workable standard." . . . A know-it-when-you-see-it test is no good if one court sees it and another does not.
>
> Next year will mark a "century since *Mahon*," during which this "Court for the most part has refrained from" providing "definitive rules." It is time to give more than just "some, but not too specific, guidance." If there is no such thing as a regulatory taking, we should say so. And if there is, we should make clear when one occurs.

Bridge Aina Le'a, LLC, 141 S. Ct. 731 (internal citations omitted).

There are several distinctions between physical takings and regulatory takings. The former "are relatively rare, easily identified, and usually represent a greater affront to individual property rights," whereas the latter "are ubiquitous and most of them impact property values in some tangential way." *Lowenberg v. City of Dallas*, 168 S.W.3d 800, 801 (Tex. 2005) (citing *Tahoe-Sierra Preservation Council, Inc.*, 535 U.S. at 324). As a result, it is often inappropriate to treat cases involving one as controlling precedent for the other. However, the distinction between a *per se* physical taking and a regulatory use restriction that goes "too far" may not always be clear. In *Cedar Point Nursery v. Hassid*, 141 S. Ct. 2063, 2071 (2021), the U.S. Supreme Court was asked to decide if a California regulation allowing labor organizations a right to access an agricultural employer's property in order to solicit support for a unionization resulted in a *per se* taking. The Court concluded that the regulation granted labor organizations a right to invade the grower's property and therefore constituted a *per se* physical taking. *Cedar Point Nursery*, 141 S. Ct. at 2083.

> Government action that physically appropriates property is no less a physical taking because it arises from a regulation. . . . The essential question is not . . . whether the government action at issue comes garbed as a regulation (or statute, or ordinance, or miscellaneous decree). It is whether the government has physically taken property for itself or someone else—by whatever means—or has instead restricted a property owner's ability to use his own property. See *Tahoe-Sierra*, 535 U.S. at 321–323. Whenever a regulation results in a physical appropriation of property, a *per se* taking has occurred, and *Penn Central* has no place.

Cedar Point Nursery, 141 S. Ct. at 2072.

In *Lingle v. Chevron U.S.A., Inc.*, 544 U.S. 528 (2005), the Court reconsidered and disavowed a fourth takings test that was first articulated twenty-five years earlier in *Agins*, 447 U.S. 255. In the context of a challenge to a municipal zoning ordinance, the *Agins* court declared that a regulation effects a taking if it does not substantially advance a legitimate state interest. *See Agins*, 447 U.S. at 260. However, a regulation that does not advance the public interest is not a valid regulation and may be challenged under the Due Process Clause:

> Instead of addressing a challenged regulation's effect on private property, the "substantially advances" inquiry probes the regulation's underlying validity. But such an inquiry is logically prior to and distinct from the question whether a regulation effects a taking, for the Takings Clause presupposes that the government has acted in pursuit of a valid public purpose. The Clause expressly requires compensation where government takes private property "for public use." It does not bar government from interfering with property rights, but rather requires compensation "in the event of *otherwise* proper interference amounting to a taking." Conversely, if a governmental action is found to be impermissible—for instance because it fails to meet the "public use" requirement or is so arbitrary as to violate due process—that is the end of the inquiry. No amount of compensation can authorize such action.

Lingle, 544 U.S. at 543 (emphasis added) (citation omitted).

By confusing the effectiveness of a regulation in accomplishing its purpose with the impact of the regulation on private property, the *Agins* court badly confused takings jurisprudence for the next quarter century. As noted by Justice O'Connor in her *Lingle* opinion, the test tells us nothing about the actual burden imposed on property rights or how that burden is allocated. A regulation that effectively advances a legitimate state interest may nonetheless unfairly burden a private property interest. Similarly, an ineffective regulation may not burden private property rights at all. The court recognized that the effectiveness of the regulation may be a factor in a due-process analysis of its validity, but it has no place in takings jurisprudence and is not a valid method by which to identify regulatory takings for which the Fifth Amendment requires compensation. *Lingle*, 544 U.S. at 540.

As a subset of the three categorical takings rules, the Court has articulated a two-part takings test for the "special context" of land use exactions. In both *Nollan*, 483 U.S. 825, and *Dolan*, 512 U.S. 374, governmental entities demanded that landowners dedicate an easement allowing public access to or through their property as a condition of obtaining necessary development permits. Simple appropriation of the easement in each case would have been a compensable physical taking. As described by Justice O'Connor, the question was whether the government could, without paying the compensation that would otherwise be required, demand the easement as a condition for granting a development permit the government was to some degree entitled to deny. *Nollan* and *Dolan* collectively articulated a two-part test for determining whether the exaction constituted a compensable taking. The test holds that an exaction is not a taking if (1) an essential nexus exists between the exaction and a legitimate state interest and (2) the exaction is roughly proportional to the public consequences of the requested land use for which a permit is required. *Nollan*, 483 U.S. at 837; *Dolan*, 512 U.S. at 391.

Justice O'Connor stresses that, although *Agins* language is quoted in both *Nollan* and *Dolan*, the rule established by those cases is entirely distinct from the "substantially advance" test addressed and disavowed in *Lingle*. *Lingle*, 544 U.S. at 540. For its clarity and holding, the *Lingle* opinion should be early reading in preparation for a takings claim.

The U.S. Supreme Court was asked to conclude that a decision by the Florida Supreme Court had effected a taking of private property. *See Stop the Beach Renourishment, Inc. v. Florida Department of Environmental Protection*, 560 U.S. 702 (2010). The case arose from certain planned beach restoration activity by two local governments. The local governments applied for and were issued permits for the beach restoration by the state of Florida. Adjoining beachfront property owners asserted that issuance of the permits deprived the owners of certain littoral property rights without just compensation.

The Florida Supreme Court concluded that the state activity did not effect a taking of private property because the right to accretions is not a vested property right, and there is no littoral right to contact with the water independent of the right of access. That decision was challenged in the federal courts. In a majority opinion by Justice Scalia, the U.S. Supreme Court concluded that if a court declares that what was once an established right of private property no longer exists, that is a taking of that property, no less than if the state had physically appropriated it or destroyed its value by regulation. *Stop the Beach Renourishment, Inc.*, 560 U.S. at 714. However, the Court also concluded that no taking had occurred based on the facts of the case. *Stop the Beach Renourishment, Inc.*, 560 U.S. at 731.

In 1985, the Court held that a property owner whose property had been taken by a local government could not bring a federal takings claim in federal court until a state court had denied his claim for just compensation under state law. *See Williamson County Regional Planning Commission*, 473 U.S. 172; *see also San Remo Hotel, L.P. v. City & County of San Francisco*, 545 U.S. 323 (2005). In June 2019, however, the Court overruled the state-litigation requirement of *Williamson County* and held that a property owner may bring a takings claim under 42 U.S.C. § 1983 upon the taking of his property without just compensation by a local government. *See Knick v. Township of Scott, Pennsylvania*, 139 S. Ct. 2162 (2019).

§ 38.9 State Analysis of What Constitutes a Taking

Similar to the Fifth Amendment to the U.S. Constitution, article I, section 17, of the Texas Constitution provides that property shall not be taken, damaged, or destroyed without adequate compensation being made. Tex. Const. art. I, § 17. This provision, like its federal counterpart, "was designed to bar government from forcing some people alone to bear public burdens, which, in all fairness and justice, should be borne by the public as a whole." *Steele v. City of Houston*, 603 S.W.2d 786, 789 (Tex. 1980) (quoting *Armstrong v. United States*, 364 U.S. 40, 49 (1960)). Earlier Texas constitutions made no provision for damage as distinguished from appropriation. *See* Tex. Const. art. I, § 17 interp. commentary.

The "damaged or destroyed" language in the Texas Constitution represents a remarkable distinction from the comparable federal provision. The additional language has been largely ignored in Texas case law in recent decades. The distinction, however, was well recognized by earlier Texas courts. "Damage," as distinguished from property taken, signifies that the property has been injuriously affected without any appropriation or intrusion on the land itself. *See Fort Worth*

Improvement District No. 1 v. City of Fort Worth, 158 S.W. 164 (Tex. 1913). Under Texas law, since compensation must be paid when property is taken, destroyed, or damaged, the distinction between an appropriation and damage without any appropriation is no longer important in the question of liability to pay compensation. *See McCammon & Lang Lumber Co. v. Trinity & B.V. Railway Co.*, 133 S.W. 247 (Tex. 1911).

The distinction was noted again by the Texas Supreme Court in *Sheffield Development Co. v. City of Glenn Heights*, 140 S.W.3d 660, 669 (Tex. 2004), as follows: "As the court of appeals noted, it could be argued that the differences in the wording of the two provisions are significant, but neither Sheffield nor the City makes this argument." In light of this invitation by the appellate courts, the enhanced relief apparently afforded by the Texas Constitution may be more aggressively explored in the future.

The Texas Supreme Court has issued a number of important opinions in the last twenty-five years addressing inverse condemnation or regulatory takings in the general context of land use. *See Harris County Flood Control District v. Kerr*, 499 S.W.3d 793 (Tex. 2016); *Porretto v. Texas General Land Office*, 448 S.W.3d 393 (Tex. 2014); *Hearts Bluff Game Ranch, Inc. v. State*, 381 S.W.3d 468 (Tex. 2012); *Hallco Texas, Inc. v. McMullen County*, 221 S.W.3d 50 (Tex. 2006); *Lowenberg v. City of Dallas*, 168 S.W.3d 800 (Tex. 2005); *City of Dallas v. Jennings*, 142 S.W.3d 310 (Tex. 2004); *Sheffield Development Co.*, 140 S.W.3d 660; *Town of Flower Mound v. Stafford Estates Ltd. Partnership*, 135 S.W.3d 620 (Tex. 2004); *Mayhew v. Town of Sunnyvale*, 964 S.W.2d 922 (Tex. 1998); *City of Tyler v. Likes*, 962 S.W.2d 489 (Tex. 1997); *Taub v. City of Deer Park*, 882 S.W.2d 824 (Tex. 1994), *cert. denied*, 513 U.S. 1112 (1995); *State v. Biggar*, 873 S.W.2d 11 (Tex. 1994); *Religious of Sacred Heart of Texas v. City of Houston*, 836 S.W.2d 606 (Tex. 1992); and *Westgate, Ltd. v. State*, 843 S.W.2d 448 (Tex. 1992). Two other significant Supreme Court regulatory takings pronouncements in the recent past are *City of Austin v. Teague*, 570 S.W.2d 389 (Tex. 1978), and *City of College Station v. Turtle Rock Corp.*, 680 S.W.2d 802 (Tex. 1984).

The opinions by Justice Hecht in *Sheffield* and *Town of Flower Mound* offer guidelines for a takings analysis in a zoning challenge and in the "special context" of land use exactions. In *Sheffield*, the court drew heavily on federal jurisprudence to conclude that a zoning regulation did not effect a compensable taking of the plaintiff developer's property. The court methodically restates and endorses the federal analysis of when a taking occurs:

1. A taking occurs when regulation compels the property owner to suffer a physical invasion of his property.

2. A taking occurs when regulation denies all economically beneficial use of land.

3. When a regulation denies less than all economically viable use, the court must carefully analyze how the regulation affects the balance between the public interest and that of the landowner; in other words, has it "gone too far"? In determining whether a regulation went too far, the court may look to the *Penn Central* factors as guideposts: (a) the economic impact of the regulation on the claimant, (b) the extent to which the regulation has interfered with distinct, investment-backed expectations, and (c) the character of the governmental action.

These *Penn Central* factors are not exclusive, but rather only considerations in a "careful examination and weighing of all the circumstances" in applying "a fact-sensitive test of reasonableness." *Sheffield Development Co.*, 140 S.W.3d at 671–74.

The court concluded that the zoning ordinance in question "substantially advanced a legitimate state interest" under the *Agins* test (which was subsequently rejected by the U.S. Supreme Court in *Lingle*). The city, citing *City of Monterey v. Del Monte Dunes at Monterey, Ltd.*, 526 U.S. 687 (1999), argued that (even before *Lingle*) the U.S. Supreme Court had begun to equivocate on its *Agins* rule. In what may prove to be a significant portent of things to come, Justice Hecht wrote that the Texas

Supreme Court was "not . . . bound to follow *Agins* in this case since Sheffield makes no claim under the United State Constitution, but" it looks to "federal takings cases for guidance in applying [the Texas] constitution." *Sheffield Development Co.*, 140 S.W.3d at 674. The court concluded, therefore, that "*Agins* remains authoritative" and "the statement in *Agins* is correct: that whether regulation substantially advances legitimate state interests is an appropriate test for a constitutionally compensable taking, at least in some situations." *Sheffield Development Co.*, 140 S.W.3d at 674.

In *Town of Flower Mound*, the Supreme Court again drew almost exclusively on federal jurisprudence to analyze a state constitutional takings claim arising from imposition of a development exaction. The court restated the rule of *Nollan* and *Dolan* as follows: "[C]onditioning government approval of a development of property on some exaction is a compensable taking unless the condition (1) bears an essential nexus to the substantial advancement of some legitimate government interest and (2) is roughly proportional to the projected impact of the proposed development." *Town of Flower Mound*, 135 S.W.3d at 634. Applying this test, the court concluded that the exaction imposed by the Town of Flower Mound was a taking for which the developer was entitled to be compensated.

The clear, unified guidance propounded by the Supreme Court in *Sheffield* and *Town of Flower Mound* was badly fractured in the 2006 decision of *Hallco Texas, Inc. v. McMullen County*. That case involved a regulatory takings challenge arising from a land use restriction. The majority opinion by Justice O'Neill resolved the case by concluding that it was barred on res judicata grounds following an exhaustive thirteen-year procedural journey through state and federal courts.

Justice Hecht's dissent in *Hallco* reflects the same grasp of regulatory takings principles that characterized his earlier opinions for a unanimous court. *Hallco* is a grim reminder of the challenges presented when a plaintiff must straddle both federal and state courts while properly exhausting administrative remedies and still preserving its claim. In the words of Justice Hecht:

> This case illustrates how the government can use this ripeness requirement to whipsaw a landowner. The government can argue either that there was no request for a variance when there should have been, or that the request was not specific enough, or that it was not reasonable enough, or that there was insufficient time to consider it—and therefore the landowner's regulatory-takings claim is premature, unripe, and should be dismissed. Or else it can argue that a request for a variance would be a waste of time, or that none was authorized, or that the landowner should have known his ridiculous proposal would never be seriously considered—and therefore his claim is late, barred, and should be dismissed. One way or the other, the result is the same. Ripening a regulatory-takings claim thus becomes a costly game of "Mother, May I", in which the landowner is allowed to take only small steps forward and backwards until exhausted.

Hallco Texas, Inc., 221 S.W.3d at 63. The game of "Mother, May I" was again at issue but resolved unfavorably for the government in *City of Lorena v. BMTP Holdings, L.P.*, 409 S.W.3d 634, 640 (Tex. 2013).

These opinions should be read in conjunction with the U.S. Supreme Court decisions in *Knick v. Township of Scott, Pennsylvania*, 139 S. Ct. 2162 (2019), and *San Remo Hotel, L.P. v. City & County of San Francisco*, 545 U.S. 323 (2005), discussed at section 38.8 above, for a better understanding of the current interplay between state and federal courts in the takings arena. The newly available choice between state and federal recourse creates both opportunities and challenges for the takings plaintiff in Texas.

Inverse condemnation is also prohibited by Texas Government Code chapter 2007 (Private Real Property Rights Preservation Act), which creates a statutory cause of action in Texas for certain governmental actions that affect private real property rights. It also establishes certain requirements that a governmental entity must satisfy to identify and evaluate governmental actions within the meaning of the Act that may result in a taking. *See City of Houston v. Guthrie*, 332 S.W.3d 578 (Tex. App.—Houston [1st Dist.] 2009, pet. denied). The Act's definition of "private real property" includes a groundwater or surface water right of any kind. The relief afforded by the Act may lead to invalidation of the governmental action or damages. The relief is not exclusive and is cumulative to the relief afforded under article I, section 17, of the Texas Constitution. A real property owner who prevails in a suit or contested case filed under the chapter is entitled to receive attorney's fees and court costs. However, a defendant governmental entity that prevails in a suit or contested case filed under the chapter is also entitled to receive attorney's fees and court costs. Similar relief is not available to either party in a takings claim filed under the state or federal constitution. In *Edwards Aquifer Authority v. Bragg*, 21 S.W.3d 375 (Tex. App.—San Antonio 2000), *aff'd*, 71 S.W.3d 729 (Tex. 2002), certain regulatory actions of the EAA were challenged as violating the Act. The court concluded that such actions were excepted from the Act because they were reasonably taken to fulfill an obligation mandated by state law. *Bragg*, 21 S.W.3d at 379–80.

§ 38.10 Inverse Condemnation and the Edwards Aquifer Authority

In the specific context of groundwater rights, the Texas Supreme Court sustained the Edwards Aquifer Authority Act against a takings claim in *Barshop v. Medina County Underground Water Conservation District*, 925 S.W.2d 618 (Tex. 1996). In *Barshop*, the plaintiffs asserted that the Act, on its face, constituted an unconstitutional taking of their property. The case was filed immediately after the Act's adoption by the legislature and before any rules were adopted or permits issued by the EAA. The Texas Supreme Court declined to conclude that the mere adoption of the Act effected an unconstitutional taking of property. "Assuming without deciding" that the plaintiff landowners possessed a vested property right in the water beneath their land, the *Barshop* court also declined to address the essential question of when water regulation unconstitutionally invades the property rights of landowners. *Barshop*, 925 S.W.2d at 626.

Justice Abbott articulated the legal challenge posed by this growing regulatory regime in *Barshop*:

> The State concedes that Plaintiffs have significant rights to the water under their land. In the [Edwards Aquifer Authority] Act, the Legislature specifically recognized the ownership and rights of the landowner in the underground water and that action taken pursuant to the Act may not be construed as depriving or divesting the owner of these ownership rights.
>
> At the same time, however, the State relies on our opinions which have long recognized the necessity of legislation that conserves and preserves our limited water resources. . . .
>
> While our prior decisions recognize both the property ownership rights of landowners in underground water and the need for legislative regulation of water, we have not previously considered the point at which water regulation unconstitutionally invades the property rights of landowners. The issue of when a particular regulation becomes an invasion of property rights in underground water is complex and multi-faceted. The problem is further complicated in this case because Plaintiffs have brought this challenge to the Act before the Authority has even had an opportunity to begin regulating the aquifer.
>
> Despite these problems and competing interests, this case involves only a facial challenge to the Act. Because Plaintiffs have not established that the Act is unconstitutional on its face, it is not necessary to the disposition of this case to definitively resolve the clash between property rights in water and regulation of water.

Barshop, 925 S.W.2d at 626 (citations omitted).

In light of the fact-specific nature of regulatory takings claims, the "complex and multi-faceted" issue posed by Justice Abbot may never be definitively resolved. However, the San Antonio court of appeals concluded that the implementation of the Act resulted in a taking in the context of a commercial pecan orchard. *See Edwards Aquifer Authority v. Bragg*, 421 S.W.3d 118 (Tex. App.—San Antonio 2013, pet. denied). The court of appeals also concluded that the statute of limitations for takings challenges to the EAA's permit decisions is ten years. For those who timely filed their permit application, limitations began to run on the date of final action by the EAA on a permit application. In a subsequent case, the United States District Court for the Western District of Texas concluded that, for late filers of permit applications, limitations began to run on December 30, 1996, when limitations on withdrawals from the Aquifer under the Act became effective. *See GG Ranch, Ltd. v. Edwards Aquifer Authority*, No. SA-14-CV-00848, 2015 WL 4698851 (W.D. Tex. 2015), *aff'd*, 639 F. App'x 269 (5th Cir. 2016). The historic right of Texas landowners to pump groundwater without limitation pursuant to the rule of capture is being rapidly curtailed by the rules of groundwater districts around the state as it was curtailed in the Edwards Aquifer region by the Edwards Aquifer Authority Act. These districts do not provide for compensation to a landowner in exchange for limitation of access to groundwater.

§ 38.11 Property

The foregoing federal and state takings analyses are predicated on a claim that property has been taken, damaged, or destroyed. If no property is lost, then no compensation can be due. Therefore, prosecution of a takings claim under either the federal or state constitution must begin with an analysis of the property interest affected by the government action. Such an analysis is difficult in a case involving water. What, after all, is the property that has been taken, damaged, or destroyed, and who owns it?

The U.S. Supreme Court has concluded that takings claims in the federal context should be analyzed by reference to units of property as defined by state law. *See Lucas v. South Carolina Coastal Council*, 505 U.S. 1003, 1016 (1992); *Keystone Bituminous Coal Ass'n v. DeBenedictis*, 480 U.S. 470, 519 (1987). Where the estate defined by state law is both severable and of value in its own right, it is appropriate to consider the effect of regulation on that particular property interest. *See Keystone Bituminous Coal Ass'n*, 480 U.S. at 520. The essential character of property is that it is made up of mutually reinforcing understandings that are sufficiently well grounded to support a claim of entitlement. *Kaiser Aetna v. United States*, 444 U.S. 164, 179 (1979).

Texas courts have defined property in broad terms. "Property," as used in article I, section 17, of the Texas Constitution, means not only the tangible thing owned but also every right and incident that accompany ownership. *Gulf, C. & S.F. Railway Co. v. Fuller*, 63 Tex. 467 (1885). For purposes of inverse condemnation, property susceptible of legal injury and a corresponding right to compensation includes incorporeal property as well as tangible property. *See State v. Biggar*, 873 S.W.2d 11 (Tex. 1994).

Texas law recognizes a property interest in water. The nature of that interest varies depending on whether it is surface water or groundwater. Surface water in Texas is held by the state in trust for the people. *Motl v. Boyd*, 286 S.W. 458, 468 (Tex. 1926); *In re Adjudication of the Water Rights of Upper Guadalupe Segment of Guadalupe River Basin*, 642 S.W.2d 438, 444 (Tex. 1982); *see also* Tex. Water Code § 11.021(a). Unless and until surface water is made the subject of a water right recognized by the state, it is not private property that can be taken by the state, or for which compensation must be paid by the state. See Chapter 4 of this book for discussion of surface water rights. Once recognized by the state, however, a water right becomes private property protected by the state and federal constitutions. The water right, and the right of a property owner to the use of water flowing by his land, are identified with the realty and are a real and incorporeal hereditament. *Lakeside Irrigation Co. v. Markham Irrigation Co.*, 285 S.W. 593, 596 (Tex. 1926). A matured appropriation right to water is a vested right subject to beneficial and nonwasteful use. *Texas Water Rights Commission v. Wright*, 464 S.W.2d 642, 647 (Tex. 1971).

For authoritative discussions of surface water rights, see Frank F. Skillern, *Texas Water Law* (1988), and Wells A. Hutchins, *The Texas Law of Water Rights* (1961). See also the following cases: *Lower Colorado River Authority v. Texas Department of Water Resources*, 689 S.W.2d 873 (Tex. 1984); *Board of Water Engineers v. McKnight*, 229 S.W. 301 (Tex. 1921); *Board of Water Engineers v. Slaughter*, 382 S.W.2d 111 (Tex. App.—San Antonio 1964, writ ref'd n.r.e.), *aff'd*, 407 S.W.2d 467 (Tex. 1966); and *Clark v. Briscoe Irrigation Co.*, 200 S.W.2d 674 (Tex. App.—Austin 1947, writ dism'd).

The legislature amended Texas Water Code section 36.002 in 2011 to clearly recognize that a landowner owns the groundwater below the surface of the landowner's land as real property. *See* Act of May 27, 2011, 82d Leg., R.S., ch. 1207, § 1, eff. Sept. 1, 2011. However, the amendment also scrupulously recognizes the ability of groundwater districts to regulate groundwater production as authorized by Water Code chapter 36. It also recognizes the ability of the Edwards Aquifer Authority and the Harris-Galveston and Fort Bend Subsidence Districts to regulate groundwater pursuant to their respective enabling acts. *See* Edwards Aquifer Act, Act of May 30, 1993, 73d Leg., R.S., ch. 626, § 1.07; Tex. Spec. Dist. Code ch. 8801 (Harris-Galveston Subsidence District); Tex. Spec. Dist. Code ch. 8834 (Fort Bend Subsidence District). Uniquely for the Edwards Aquifer, the legislature by the Edwards Aquifer Authority Act effectively decreed the amount of water available in the aquifer and created a marketplace for permitted withdrawal rights.

The legislature's explicit recognition of groundwater ownership followed several years of evolving debate among Texas water and real estate lawyers about the exact nature of a landowner's ownership interest. Landowners and property rights advocates argued that more than one hundred fifty years of Texas law recognizes a property right in the groundwater beneath a landowner's property. Advocates of strong groundwater regulation argued that Texas cases that seem to confirm such a property right in groundwater beneath a landowner's property do so only as dicta, and that no protected property interest exists in groundwater until that groundwater has been reduced to personal possession in accordance with any applicable regulatory restrictions. See Chapter 5 of this book.

This issue was resolved by the Texas Supreme Court in the case of *Edwards Aquifer Authority v. Day*, 369 S.W.3d 814 (Tex. 2012), in which the court held that land ownership includes an interest in groundwater in place that cannot be taken for public use without adequate compensation guaranteed by article I, section 17(a), of the Texas Constitution. The court did not resolve the issue of whether the Authority's denial of a groundwater withdrawal permit in the amount requested by Day constitutes a taking and remanded the case to the trial court for further proceedings. The case was subsequently settled.

Groundwater conveyances are critical to the development of new, badly needed groundwater supplies in Texas. Practitioners around the state are drafting conveyance and financing documents to facilitate the transfer of groundwater and groundwater withdrawal rights for value. These documents, and the transactions that they memorialize, involve millions of dollars and thousands of acre-feet of underground water supplies. Perhaps more important, from the public perspective at least, municipalities and other water utilities are relying on these transactions to supply new water projects and meet the state's future water needs. See Chapter 6 of this book.

In the context of regulatory takings, the explicit recognition by the Texas legislature and Texas Supreme Court of groundwater ownership will require that essential government regulation of this precious resource be undertaken with respect for property rights long assumed by Texas landowners. It is the same essential balance recognized by the U.S. Supreme Court in the *Mahon* case in 1922: that governments must regulate, but the regulation cannot go too far.

§ 38.12 Relevant Parcel of Property

A determination that landowners possess a vested property right in the water beneath their land does not end the property component of a takings analysis. Next, the "relevant parcel" or "denominator" issue must be addressed in determining the property interest affected by a given regulation. The issue was articulated in *Lucas v. South Carolina Coastal Council*, 505 U.S. 1003 (1992), as follows:

> Regrettably, the rhetorical force of our "deprivation of all economically feasible use" rule is greater than its precision, since the rule does not make clear the "property interest" against which the loss of value is to be measured. When, for example, a regulation requires a developer to leave 90% of a rural tract in its natural state, it is unclear whether we would analyze the situation as one in which the owner has been deprived of all economically beneficial use of the burdened portion of the tract, or as one in which the owner has suffered a mere diminution in value of the tract as a whole.

Lucas, 505 at 1016 n.7.

Must a regulation prohibit all pumping of groundwater to be a compensable taking? If not, how much? Is the groundwater distinct from the land itself, or simply part of the larger estate? What if the real property retains substantial value even without groundwater withdrawal rights? What property interest has been taken or damaged by the regulatory action?

Since *Lucas*, the U.S. Supreme Court has held that a "claimant's parcel of property could not first be divided into what was taken and what was left for the purpose of demonstrating the taking of the former to be complete and hence compensable." *Concrete Pipe & Products of California, Inc. v. Construction Laborers Pension Trust for Southern California*, 508 U.S. 602, 644 (1993). This is known as the "parcel as a whole" rule. *See Tahoe-Sierra Preservation Council, Inc. v. Tahoe Regional Planning Agency*, 535 U.S. 302, 327 (2002). As the Court stated in *Penn Central*:

> "Taking" jurisprudence does not divide a single parcel into discrete segments and attempt to determine whether rights in a particular segment have been entirely abrogated. In deciding whether a particular governmental action has effected a taking, this Court focuses rather both on the character of the action and on the nature and extent of the interference with rights in the parcel as a whole . . . .

Penn Central Transportation Co. v. New York City, 438 U.S. 104, 130–31 (1978).

It is thus critical to ascertain whether the property affected by a government action constitutes a separate property right apart from the underlying property interest. This issue was addressed at length by the Court in *Murr v. Wisconsin*, 137 S. Ct. 1933 (2017). In an opinion by Justice Kennedy, a divided court (with Justice Gorsuch not participating) concluded that two separate but adjoining property parcels must be evaluated as a single parcel in determining whether land use restrictions effected a compensable regulatory taking. However, the dissenting opinion by Justice Roberts suggests that a different outcome might be anticipated under the court's new membership. The analysis may be less important in the context of the unique "damage" language of the Texas Constitution, which is not a factor in the extensive federal case law and commentary. Its significance is also mitigated in the water rights context by the "rich tradition of protection" afforded to water rights as a separate estate in Texas. *See Lucas*, 505 U.S. at 1016.

In the case of *Elliff v. Texon Drilling Co.*, 210 S.W.2d 558 (Tex. 1948), the Texas Supreme Court restated the law regarding ownership of oil and gas in place as follows:

> In our state the landowner is regarded as having absolute title in severalty to the oil and gas in place beneath his land. The only qualification of that rule of ownership is that it must be considered in connection with the law of capture and is subject to police regulations. The oil and gas beneath the soil are considered a part of the realty. Each owner of land owns separately, distinctly and exclusively all the oil and gas under his land and is accorded the usual remedies against trespassers who appropriate the minerals or destroy their market value.

Elliff, 210 S.W.2d at 561 (internal citations omitted).

In its opinion in *Edwards Aquifer Authority v. Day*, the court held that this language correctly states the common law regarding the ownership of groundwater in place. *Edwards Aquifer Authority v. Day*, 369 S.W.3d 814, 832 (Tex. 2012). The courts have not yet explored the implications of this language to the "relevant parcel" analysis in a takings case. Nor have the courts explored the relationship of the language to the mandate of Texas Property Code section 21.0421(a) that groundwater rights be treated "as property apart from the land" for purposes of assessing condemnation damages.

V. Conclusion

§ 38.13 Conclusion

The population of Texas is expected to grow at a rapid pace in the next fifty years. This growth will place enormous demand on water supplies and require the movement of water from regions of plenty to regions of need. Cities and water utilities will ultimately take whatever lawful action is necessary to secure healthy water for their constituents. A wide variety of political, legal, and financial considerations encourage governmental entities to acquire water in the marketplace. Although many governmental entities have condemnation authority to acquire water supplies without landowner consent upon payment of fair compensation, the Texas legislature has made the use of this authority burdensome and expensive.

Condemnation does not pose the only risk to landowners' water rights. Regulatory restrictions on water use imposed by groundwater districts and other governmental entities may effectively take the water from landowners for public use without any compensation at all. In such circumstances, landowners may find relief in the takings clauses of the state and federal constitutions and the Private Real Property Rights Preservation Act.

CHAPTER 39

Flood Management

Reem J. Zoun, P.E., CFM,[1] and Christopher Smith[2]

I. Introduction

§ 39.1 Importance of Flood Management

Since Hurricane Harvey dumped 34 trillion gallons of rain over Texas, affecting 30 percent of the Texas population and causing $125 billion in damages, there has been a lot of positive momentum to work toward reducing the risk and impact of flooding in the state. Virtually no one would disagree that Texas needs additional water resources. But, like the rule of toxicology that "the dose makes the poison," in a state that too often experiences water shortages, severe storms can turn lands desperate for water into areas of uncontrolled flooding. Perhaps this principle has never been more aptly demonstrated than during the period of 2010 to 2018—a period that began with a record-setting drought, including the second-driest year in Texas history in 2011, and ended with five years of extremely high rainfall, including the wettest year in Texas history in 2015. Then, as if to put an exclamation point on the extremes that nature can produce, Hurricane Harvey made landfall on the Texas Gulf Coast just before 10:00 P.M. on August 25, 2017, subjecting Texans to arguably the most significant rainfall and flooding event in U.S. history.

The silver lining in these otherwise dark storm clouds is that extreme weather events often drive significant progress in Texas water policy. The physical and economic devastation caused by Harvey, and the extraordinary challenges experienced by Texas communities during response and recovery efforts, sparked the passage of several landmark pieces of legislation during the 2019 legislative session. This chapter briefly documents the impacts of Hurricane Harvey and examines several of the resulting new laws related to flood management and considers how they will reshape Texas flood policy.

This chapter also examines issues of surface drainage, liability for flooding, statutes and rules regulating floodplain management, and standards for dam construction. First discussed are claims for flooding brought under section 11.086 of the Texas Water Code and court decisions that have narrowed the applicability of this statute by limiting its use to flooding that arises from diffused surface waters. Also included is a discussion of how sovereign immunity decisions have further narrowed the class of persons liable under the statute, the types of damages recoverable from flooding, and distinctions between temporary and permanent damages.

Because flood damage can arise from the actions of governmental entities, this chapter includes a discussion of inverse condemnation claims, including recent cases in which flooding resulted from the construction of a dam and from the development and subdivision of land.

---

1. Reem J. Zoun is the Director of Flood Planning at the Texas Water Development Board.

2. Chris Smith is a partner at Smith Jolin LLP where his practice focuses on environmental and administrative litigation.

The Texas legislature has obligated cities and counties to adopt ordinances as necessary to participate in the Federal Emergency Management Agency's (FEMA's) National Flood Insurance Program, and this chapter includes a brief discussion of FEMA's programs and regulations addressing floodplain management. Cities typically implement such programs through the municipal zoning and platting process, which is also discussed.

Finally, this chapter discusses the regulations applicable to owners and operators of dams, including permits, safety reviews, and design standards established by the Texas Commission on Environmental Quality (TCEQ).

§ 39.1:1 Hurricane Harvey

On August 25, 2017, Hurricane Harvey made landfall along the Texas Gulf Coast just northeast of Corpus Christi as a Category 4 hurricane with sustained winds of 115 knots. Over the next four days, the storm slowly moved northeastward along the coast, repeatedly moving offshore and then back onshore, dropping unprecedented amounts of rainfall across the upper Gulf Coast all the way to Louisiana. On August 30, Harvey finally made its final landfall near Cameron, Louisiana, and eventually dissipated over Kentucky two days later. *See* Eric S. Blake & David A. Zelinsky, National Hurricane Center, *Tropical Cyclone Report: Hurricane Harvey, 17 August–1 September 2017* 1–3 (May 9, 2018), www.nhc.noaa.gov/data/tcr/AL092017_Harvey.pdf [hereinafter *Tropical Cyclone Report*].

When considering every major rainfall event in Texas or even American history—storms like Allison, Amelia, Beulah, and Claudette—Harvey dwarfed them all both in terms of rainfall totals and areal extent. The *Washington Post* stated that Harvey "is on an entirely different scale than what we've seen before in the United States," and went on to point out that Harvey exceeded a thousand-year flood event over an area of Texas equal to the size of the state of New Jersey. *See* Jason Samenow, *Harvey Is a 1,000-year Flood Event Unprecedented in Scale*, *Washington Post* (Aug. 31, 2017), www.washingtonpost.com/news/capital-weather-gang/wp/2017/08/31/harvey-is-a-1000-year-flood-event-unprecedented-in-scale/?noredirect=on&utm_term=.6379d2f6d1b6.

Rainfall totals during Harvey were literally off the then-existing charts. During the event, the National Weather Service announced that it was adding additional colors to its color scale for rainfall amounts because it could not fully capture the magnitude of rainfall in southeast Texas. *See* National Weather Service (@NWS), Twitter (Aug. 28, 2017, 7:21 A.M.), https://twitter.com/NWS/status/902174274571689984. The highest rainfall at a single location occurred near Nederland, Texas, with a reported total of 60.58 inches. Groves, Texas, reported a total of 60.54 inches. The previously accepted U.S. rainfall record was 52 inches at Kanalohuluhulu Ranger Station in Hawaii. *See Tropical Cyclone Report*, at 6. What makes Harvey truly unique, however, is not just the individual rainfall totals but the enormous areal extent of the heavy rainfall. The U.S. Geological Survey compared Hurricane Harvey to other historic tropical rainfall events and found that while some events like Allison (2001) and Beulah (1967) had significant rainfall totals over relatively large areas, for any total over 15 inches, Hurricane Harvey far exceeded other storms in terms of areal extent. *See Tropical Cyclone Report*, at 7. Harris County Flood Control District meteorologist Jeff Lindner noted that for a 120-hour duration over 10,000 square miles, "Harvey exceeded the previous record from June 1899 by 13.33 inches or 62 percent." *See* Memorandum from Jeff Lindner, Director of Hydrologic Operations, & Steve Fitzgerald, Chief Engineer, to Harris County Flood Control District Flood Watch/Partners, at 4 (June 4, 2018), www.hcfcd.org/Portals/62/Harvey/immediate-flood-report-final-hurricane-harvey-2017.pdf.

The flooding and devastation inflicted by Harvey were as unparalleled as the storm itself. Harvey caused catastrophic flooding across southeast Texas, including in some of the most densely populated areas of the U.S. Gulf Coast. Over 300,000 structures and up to 500,000 cars were flooded. An estimated 780,000 citizens evacuated their homes, with over 40,000 being housed in local shelters.

Approximately 336,000 customers lost power. Approximately 30,000 rescues were conducted, and 68 direct deaths resulted from Hurricane Harvey. Damages resulting from Hurricane Harvey are estimated at $125 billion, second only to Hurricane Katrina. *See Tropical Cyclone Report*, at 8, 9.

Despite the devastating impacts of Hurricane Harvey, and beginning even before the storm had completely passed, Texans were already rebuilding and looking for ways to be better prepared for future storms, including through the development of significant policy changes in the area of flood management. On September 7, 2017, Governor Greg Abbott announced the creation of the Governor's Commission to Rebuild Texas and appointed Texas A&M Chancellor John Sharp to lead the effort. The purpose of the commission was to "oversee the response and relief effort between the state and local governments" and to be "involved in the rebuilding process." Governor's Commission to Rebuild Texas, *Eye of the Storm* 5 (Nov. 2018), www.rebuildtexas.today/wp-content/uploads/sites/52/2018/12/12-11-18-EYE-OF-THE-STORM-digital.pdf. The commission's report documents not only the impacts of Hurricane Harvey but also the lessons learned, and it makes numerous recommendations intended to help Texas citizens and communities be more resilient and better able to withstand future storms. Many of the recommendations from the report led directly to legislation that was ultimately passed by the 86th Legislature. In addition, numerous water industry experts provided input and recommendations to guide policy makers. *See, e.g.*, Texas Water Conservation Association, Flood Response Committee, *Flooding in Texas: Preparation and Response* (Nov. 6, 2018), www.texenrls.org/wp-content/uploads/2020/08/Howard-S.-Slobodin.pdf.

Another project making progress since Hurricane Harvey is the cornerstone project for the Institute of Disaster Resilient Texas (IDRT): the Texas Disaster Information System (TDIS). This project is currently in the planning phase, but it is intended to be an interactive, analytical, and visual web-based spatial data system designed to support more resilient disaster decision making at the state level. More information is available at https://idrt.tamug.edu/tdis/.

§ 39.1:2 Flood Legislation from 86th Legislature

Going into the 2019 legislative session, lawmakers were eager to undertake truly landmark legislation relating to all aspects of flood management. Policy recommendations such as those mentioned above contributed to extensive interim reports with detailed recommendations related to flood preparation, management, and response. *See* Senate Committee on Agriculture, Water & Rural Affairs, *Interim Report: 2017 Hurricane Harvey Response to the 86th Legislature* (Nov. 2018), https://senate.texas.gov/cmtes/86/c700/c505.Harvey.InterimReport2018.pdf; House Committee on Natural Resources, *Interim Report to the 86th Texas Legislature* (Dec. 2018), https://house.texas.gov/_media/pdf/committees/reports/85interim/Natural-Resources-Committee-Interim-Report-2018.pdf.

Numerous measures were eventually adopted and signed into law. The more significant measures can be loosely grouped into the following subject-matter categories. First are bills related to funding for flood planning, flood mitigation, and Harvey-related projects. This topic is briefly addressed below and in more detail in Chapter 37 of this book. Second are bills related to state and regional flood planning (RFP), which is discussed below. The final category is bills related to emergency communications, response, and recovery, including public notification systems, debris management, critical infrastructure resilience and restoration, and training for emergency managers and local officials. This topic is not discussed in this chapter and is beyond the scope of this book.

Flood Funding: Flood funding has a significant impact on flood management and planning activities, and such funding almost always comes from property taxes. This makes sense given that the goal of flood management is to protect the life and property of citizens. It is a core function of local taxing entities such as cities, counties, and special districts such as flood control and levy districts. However, the source of a flood event is often hundreds of miles and numerous counties away from the area that is damaged by flooding. In some cases, a local city or county would need to implement a project in another county in order to mitigate its local flood problem. Policymakers recognize that there is a need to manage flooding on a larger-scale basis, such as across entire river basins or watersheds, but river authorities and other regional water districts, with only one or two exceptions, have no taxing authority. These agencies typically have the necessary legal authority but no funding. Cities and counties have the legal authority and funding but may not have the ability to implement the necessary projects. This challenge presented a considerable impediment to local and state officials, but the 86th Legislature took a major step toward addressing this problem through an infusion of state funding from the state's Economic Stabilization Fund (or "Rainy Day Fund"). Senate Bill 7, House Joint Resolution 4, and Senate Bill 500 together appropriated and authorized the use of approximately $1.7 billion of state funds for various purposes related to flood management and mitigation. The funds were appropriated through numerous grant and loan programs that led to opportunities for cities and counties to partner with regional entities and implement watershed-wide flooding solutions. *See* Act of May 25, 2019, 86th Leg., R.S., ch. 947 (S.B. 7), eff. June 13, 2019; Tex. H.J. Res. 4, 86th Leg., R.S., May 28, 2019; Act of May 27, 2019, 86th Leg., R.S., ch. 465, §§ 74–77, 85, 86 (S.B. 500), eff. June 6, 2019. These new laws are addressed in more detail in Chapter 37 of this book.

Flood Planning: Another landmark bill related to flood management is Senate Bill 8. *See* Act of May 26, 2019, 86th Leg., R.S., ch. 565 (S.B. 8), eff. June 10, 2019. S.B. 8 contains three major initiatives: (1) it establishes a process for the creation of a state flood plan compiled from regional flood plans; (2) it requires the Texas State Soil and Water Conservation Board (TSSWCB) to prepare a plan for the repair and maintenance of certain dams within the board's jurisdiction; and (3) it creates a State Flood Plan Implementation Advisory Committee to assist the Texas Water Development Board (TWDB) in the regional and state flood planning process.

The flood planning provisions in S.B. 8 are modeled after the highly successful water planning program managed by the TWDB. According to the bill, the TWDB will first create flood planning regions across the state based on hydrologic boundaries such as river basins. Individuals representing defined stakeholder interests will be selected to serve on the regional flood planning groups (RFPGs). The TWDB will provide guidance and financial assistance to the regional stakeholders, who will then develop regional flood plans. The flood plans are required to include a description of existing flood control infrastructure; flood projects currently under development; information on land use and population; a description of flood-prone areas and related mitigation strategies; and a notation of any strategies that meet an emergency need, utilize federal funds, or also qualify as a water supply strategy. Regional flood plans are subject to requirements for public notice and comment prior to being submitted to the TWDB for approval. The TWDB designated fifteen flood planning regions on April 9, 2020, and adopted final rules to implement a new regional and state flood planning process for Texas on May 21, 2020. The first regional flood plans will be due in 2023, and the first state flood plan will be due September 1, 2024. *See* Texas Water Development Board, *TWDB Flood Programs*, www.twdb.texas.gov/flood/index.asp; Tex. Water Code § 16.062.

Following the submittal of regional flood plans, the TWDB is then required to adopt a comprehensive state flood plan that incorporates the regional plans. The state flood plan must "provide for orderly preparation for and response to flood conditions to protect against the loss of life and property," "be a guide to state and local flood control policy," and "contribute to water development where possible." *See* Tex. Water Code § 16.061(a). The state flood plan will include a statewide, ranked list of flood control strategies, an analysis of previous flood control strategies, a discussion of development in flood-prone areas, and legislative recommendations. The initial state flood plan is due September 1, 2024, and the bill then creates a five-year planning cycle similar to that used for water supply planning. *See* Tex. Water Code § 16.061(a), (b).

The next major provision in S.B. 8 relates to the TSSWCB. The board is required to adopt a ten-year dam repair, rehabilitation, and maintenance plan addressing the needs of certain defined flood control dams that fall under its jurisdiction. The plan will be delivered to the TWDB and must be updated and resubmitted every ten years. Each year, the board is required to deliver a report to the TWDB regarding progress made on the items listed in the plan. *See* Tex. Agric. Code § 201.0227.

The final major provision of S.B. 8 was the creation of a State Flood Plan Implementation Advisory Committee to assist the TWDB in the regional and state flood planning process. The committee was composed of the chair of the senate committee having primary jurisdiction over water resources; the chair of the house committee having primary jurisdiction over natural resources; a member of the senate committee on finance, appointed by the lieutenant governor; a member of the house committee on appropriations, appointed by the speaker; a representative of the Texas Division of Emergency Management (TDEM); and a representative of the TSSWCB. The advisory committee's purpose was to review the development of the state flood plan and the rules adopted by the TWDB to implement the plan. The advisory committee was dissolved on September 1, 2021. *See* Act of May 26, 2019, 86th Leg., R.S., ch. 565, § 3.

The sweeping changes to flood funding and planning made by the 86th Legislature took time to implement, but their impact on flood management will undoubtedly be significant. Notably absent from the list of new laws promulgated in the first session after Hurricane Harvey were any laws affecting liability for flooding. This topic is addressed in part II of this chapter.

The Texas Water Code provides that a regional flood plan must—

(1) use information based on scientific data and updated mapping; and

(2) include:

> (A) a general description of the condition and functionality of flood control infrastructure in the flood planning region;
>
> (B) flood control projects under construction or in the planning stage;
>
> (C) information on land use changes and population growth in the flood planning region;
>
> (D) an identification of the areas in the flood planning region that are prone to flood and flood control solutions for those areas; and
>
> (E) an indication of whether a particular flood control solution:
>
> > (i) meets an emergency need;
> >
> > (ii) uses federal money as a funding component; and
> >
> > (iii) may also serve as a water supply source.

Tex. Water Code § 16.062(e). Similarly, the Code provides that a state flood plan must—

(1) provide for orderly preparation for and response to flood conditions to protect against the loss of life and property;

(2) be a guide to state and local flood control policy; and

(3) contribute to water development where possible.

Tex. Water Code § 16.061(a). The state flood plan must include—

(1) an evaluation of the condition and adequacy of flood control infrastructure on a regional basis;

(2) a statewide, ranked list of ongoing and proposed flood control and mitigation projects and strategies necessary to protect against the loss of life and property from flooding and a discussion of how those projects and strategies might further water development, where applicable;

(3) an analysis of completed, ongoing, and proposed flood control projects included in previous state flood plans, including which projects received funding;

(4) an analysis of development in the 100-year floodplain areas as defined by the Federal Emergency Management Agency; and

(5) legislative recommendations the board considers necessary to facilitate flood control planning and project construction.

Tex. Water Code § 16.061(b).

As mentioned above, S.B. 8 established the framework for the TWDB to institute a new program of regional and state flood planning for the state of Texas reflected in regulations quoted just above. The overarching goal of the RFP program is for regions to develop bottom-up plans for their regions and for the state to then compile those regional plans into one statewide plan. On April 9, 2020, the TWDB designated fifteen flood planning regions based on river basins. At the May 21, 2020, board meeting, the TWDB board approved the final administrative rules for 31 Texas Administrative Code chapter 361 and 31 Texas Administrative Code chapter 362. The rules became effective June 10, 2020.

Each RFPG must maintain at least one voting member from each of the following interest categories: the public, counties, municipalities, industry, agriculture, environment, small business, electric-generating utilities, river authorities, water districts, water utilities, and flood districts. Definitions for these interest categories can be found in 31 Texas Administrative Code section 361.11(e)(1)–(13). Regional flood planning group members are expected to be capable of adequately representing their assigned interest category in the region for which they serve. The RFPGs may add voting or nonvoting positions to ensure adequate representation from interests in its unique region.

The RFPGs are also statutorily required to include nonvoting members, as ex officio representatives, from seven state agencies: the TWDB, TCEQ, General Land Office (GLO), Texas Parks and Wildlife Department, Texas Department of Agriculture, TSSWCB, and TDEM.

II. Liability from Impoundment or Diversion of Surface Water

§ 39.2 Introduction

Texas law allows the owner of higher ground a right to have surface waters flow naturally from his land onto the land of lower owners. Correspondingly, the owner of a lower property has no right to unnaturally force back surface waters onto a higher owner's land. The principle of protecting the higher ground owner's water rights was described by the court in *Miller v. Letzerich*, 49 S.W.2d 404, 408 (Tex. 1932):

> These rights of the owners of estates under the civil law are appurtenant to and a part of the land itself, and passed to them with the grants. The right of the owner of the upper estate to have the surface waters falling thereon to pass in their natural condition on to the lands of the lower estate is a servitude or natural right in the nature of an easement over the lower estate of his neighbor.

This legal principle is now codified in section 11.086 of the Texas Water Code, which traces its origins back as early as 1915, when the legislature adopted a statutory cause of action for damages arising from the wrongful diversion or impounding of surface waters. Acts 1915, 34th Leg., 1st C.S., ch. 7. Consistent with the description in *Miller*, the effect of the current statute is to impose an easement on the lower landowner to receive the natural flow of surface water.

Section 11.086 quite succinctly states a person's liability for diversion or impoundment of the natural flow of surface waters:

> (a) No person may divert or impound the natural flow of surface waters in this state, or permit a diversion or impounding by him to continue, in a manner that damages the property of another by the overflow of the water diverted or impounded.
>
> (b) A person whose property is injured by an overflow of water caused by an unlawful diversion or impounding has remedies at law and in equity and may recover damages occasioned by the overflow.

Tex. Water Code § 11.086(a), (b). The statute creates a form of strict liability, as the injured landowner is not required to provide proof of negligence or intentional harm by the offending person. *See Kraft v. Langford*, 565 S.W.2d 223, 229 (Tex. 1978) (listing elements of cause of action); *Bily v. Omni Equities, Inc.*, 731 S.W.2d 606, 611 (Tex. App.—Houston [14th Dist.] 1987, writ ref'd n.r.e.) (liability under Water Code section 11.086 does not require a finding of negligence).

Section 11.086 usually becomes relevant when land is subdivided or developed in a manner that concentrates or increases the natural flow of water off the land by, for example, the increase or change in water flow as a result of the addition of rooftops, building of retaining walls, paving of streets, and construction of other impervious covers. In the absence of the construction of a detention pond or other structure to capture and regulate the rate of release of water from the subdivision, owners of lower lands may be flooded by the increased flows from runoff or by a change in the predevelopment drainage pattern or discharge point. The statute creates a cause of action in favor of the lower property owner if his property is injured by an increase or change in the natural flows. The statute is not an exclusive remedy but complements common-law remedies that may be applicable to interferences with the interests in real property. *Kraft*, 565 S.W.2d at 229 (predecessor to current Water Code section 11.086 not an exclusive remedy). See also Chapter 40 of this book, which discusses the effects of land use practices on water resources and flooding.

In urban areas, drainage issues are typically addressed as part of the municipal subdivision platting process. Indeed, a municipal code may require a developer to comply with the city drainage ordinance to manage drainage with a detention pond designed to control flooding from a specific design event, such as a hundred-year storm, so that the new development avoids increasing the volume or velocity of water discharged to lower properties. *See City of Keller v. Wilson*, 168 S.W.3d 802, 808 (Tex. 2005). Importantly, however, compliance with a municipal ordinance does not automatically excuse a concurrent Water Code violation. *See Bily*, 731 S.W.2d at 611 (holding that if it is possible to comply with both a municipal ordinance and section 11.086 a landowner has a duty to do so). In some cases the developer may be required to purchase a drainage easement from a lower landowner of sufficient width and distance to convey increased flows to a state watercourse. Additionally, a developer may be required to make improvements to an existing channel to widen or deepen the channel, so as to prevent the increased flows from flooding onto a neighbor's property.

§ 39.3 A Neutered Statute

At first reading, Texas Water Code section 11.086 is appealing in its simplicity. However, court decisions, such as those limiting the application to only diffused surface runoff and those broadly applying sovereign immunity, have dramatically narrowed the circumstances in which the statute will provide relief to an injured landowner. A review of cases reported under section 11.086 reveals that the statute has been, in the words of one court, "effectively neutered by many years of judicial construction." *Dietrich v. Goodman*, 123 S.W.3d 413, 418 (Tex. App.—Houston [14th Dist.] 2003, no pet.); *see also Michaelski v. Wright*, 444 S.W.3d 83, 93 (Tex. App.—Houston [1st Dist.] 2014, no pet.).

As early as 1936, the Texas Supreme Court hinted that this type of statutory cause of action would have limited application. In *Turner v. Big Lake Oil Co.*, 96 S.W.2d 221, 228 (Tex. 1936), the court found that the predecessor statute to section 11.086 was inapplicable to the escape of produced oil-field saltwater from artificial earthen ponds. The court noted that the plaintiff did not plead that the injury arose from the wrongful impounding or diversion of "surface waters" and hence could not recover under the statute. *Turner*, 96 S.W.2d at 228. The narrow construction of section 11.086 announced in *Turner* has continued to be applied by courts.

§ 39.4 Judicially Narrowed Definition of "Surface Water" in Texas Water Code Section 11.086

Section 11.086 states that "[n]o person may divert or impound the natural flow of surface waters in this state, or permit a diversion or impounding by him to continue, in a manner that damages the property of another by the overflow of the water diverted or impounded." Tex. Water Code § 11.086(a). A number of courts have concluded that the term "surface water" in section 11.086 is limited to "diffused surface water" rather than the broader, more common use of the term "surface water," which is used to describe the water flowing in streams, rivers, and lakes. *Dietrich v. Goodman*, 123 S.W.3d 413, 419 (Tex. App.—Houston [14th Dist.] 2003, no pet.) (defining "surface water" as water that is diffused over the ground from falling rains or melting snows); *see also Kozak v. LeFevre Development, Inc.*, No. 09-18-00369-CV, 2019 WL 2220305, at *5 (Tex. App.—Beaumont May 23, 2019, no pet.) (mem. op.) (holding that channeled water flowing through a creek into a canal and then into a lake does not qualify as surface waters); *Michaelski v. Wright*, 444 S.W.3d 83 (Tex. App.—Houston [1st Dist.] 2014, no pet.); *Salazar v. Sanders*, 440 S.W.3d 863, 873 (Tex. App.—El Paso 2013, pet. denied), *cert. denied*, 135 S. Ct. 1433 (2015); *Jefferson County Drainage District No. 6 v. Lower Neches Valley Authority*, 876 S.W.2d 940, 950 (Tex. App.—Beaumont 1994, writ denied) (holding that surface waters do not remain surface waters once they enter a channel that has been modified by man); *Dalon v. City of DeSoto*, 852 S.W.2d 530, 538 (Tex. App.—Dallas 1992, writ denied) (holding that when rainfall is under control by ditches, tanks, ponds, or pipes, it is no longer "surface water"); *Stoner v. Dallas*, 392 S.W.2d 910, 911–12 (Tex. App.—Dallas 1965, writ ref'd n.r.e.) (finding no liability in the case of the widening and deepening of an existing creek that flooded a neighboring homeowner).

According to these decisions, a distinguishing feature of the term "surface water" as used in section 11.086 is that it is never found in a natural watercourse. Thus, the term "surface water" is merely a shortened form of the phrase "diffused surface water"—for example, natural precipitation diffused over the surface of the ground until it evaporates, is absorbed by the land, or reaches the bed or channel of a watercourse. *Dietrich*, 123 S.W.3d at 418–19. Indeed, one court has suggested that a landowner might divert the entire flow of the Brazos River across his neighbor's property without subjecting himself to liability under section 11.086. *Dietrich*, 123 S.W.3d at 419.

Diffused surface water is also distinct from floodwaters, which are "waters that have overflowed a natural water course but remain a continuous part of that original part of the water course."

Michaelski, 444 S.W.3d at 93; *see also Vien v. Del Buono*, No. 10-09-00318-CV, 2010 WL 5117248, at *3 (Tex. App.—Waco Dec. 15, 2010, pet. denied) (mem. op.) (floodwaters are those that "have overflowed a river, stream or natural water course and have formed a continuous body with the water flowing in the ordinary channel").

There is some split in authority regarding when diffused surface water becomes floodwaters. In 1994, the Beaumont court of appeals stated that diffused surface water changes character when it "enter[s] into a channel that has been touched or modified by the hands of man." *Jefferson County Drainage District No. 6*, 876 S.W.2d at 950; *see also Salazar*, 440 S.W.3d at 873 (holding that once water flowed through a man-made ditch controlled by a floodgate, it was no longer diffused surface water). However, more recent cases from the first court of appeals have rejected the argument that water loses the designation of diffused surface water simply because it is "touched by the hands of man." *Texas Woman's University v. The Methodist Hospital*, 221 S.W.3d 267, 281–82 (Tex. App.—Houston [1st Dist.] 2006, no pet.); *Michaelski*, 444 S.W.3d at 96–97. Instead, these cases have concluded that the critical inquiry is whether water comes under the control of a defined waterway, and thus loses its designation as diffused surface water. *Texas Woman's University*, 221 S.W.3d at 281; *Michaelski*, 444 S.W.3d at 96–97.

§ 39.5 Sovereign Immunity

Section 11.086 allows suits against "persons" who divert or impound the natural flow of surface waters. *See* Tex. Water Code § 11.086(a). Court decisions have narrowed the class of persons who may be held liable under Texas Water Code section 11.086. *But see Konark Ltd. Partnership v. BTX Schools, Inc.*, No. 04-17-00558-CV, 2018 WL 5808325, at *17 (Tex. App.—San Antonio Nov. 7, 2018, pet. filed) (holding that a claimant has a cause of action against a charter school under section 11.086 and finding that the Water Code defines "person" to include corporations). The Texas Supreme Court has stated that the statute is a rule of property that creates easements and limits their use and therefore has "no application to persons or entities who are not proprietors of land." *Kraft v. Langford*, 565 S.W.2d 223, 229 (Tex. 1978). For example, where defendants did not own or control the adjacent properties that were the alleged sources of water, a court of appeals held that the defendants were improper parties under section 11.086. *See City of Magnolia v. Smedley*, No. 09-15-00334-CV, 2018 WL 2246533, at *8–9 (Tex. App.—Beaumont 2018, no pet.) (mem. op.); *see also Fairfield Estates L.P. v. Griffin*, 986 S.W.2d 719, 722 (Tex. App.—Eastland 1999, no pet.) (holding that although section 11.086 requires that the violator be a proprietor of land, there is no requirement that the injured property be adjacent to the property of the "person" who violated the statute).

Applying section 11.086 to municipalities adds another wrinkle for the courts. Courts have reached conflicting decisions on whether the statute also holds a municipality liable for flood damage, given the apparent breadth of the term "person" as used in the statute. *See City of Brady v. Cox*, 48 S.W.2d 511, 514 (Tex. App.—Austin 1932, no writ) (statute applicable to municipality); *Meier v. Thompson*, 248 S.W.2d 493 (Tex. App.—Waco 1952, writ ref'd n.r.e.) (statute applicable to municipality); *City of Houston v. Renault*, 431 S.W.2d 322 (Tex. 1968) (statute not applicable to municipality).

In recent decisions, courts have dismissed section 11.086 claims against municipalities on the basis that the claims were barred by sovereign immunity. *City of Midlothian v. Black,* 271 S.W.3d 791, 795–98 (Tex. App.—Waco 2008, no pet.); *see also Gilliam v. Santa Fe Independent School District*, No. 01-14-00186-CV, 2016 WL 828055, at *8 (Tex. App.—Houston [1st Dist.] Mar. 3, 2016, no pet.) (mem. op.); *Church v. City of Alvin*, No. 01-13-00865-CV, 2015 WL 5769998, at *4 (Tex. App.—Houston [1st Dist.] Sept. 29, 2015, no pet.); *City of Leon Valley v. Wm. Rancher Estates Joint Venture*, No. 04-14-00542-CV, 2015 WL 2405475, at *3 (Tex. App.—San Antonio May 20, 2015, no pet.). The *Black* court noted that a statutory waiver of sovereign immunity must be made by clear and unambiguous language, following the principles set forth by the Texas Supreme Court in *Tooke v. City* *of Mexia*, 197 S.W.3d 325, 343 (Tex. 2006). Accordingly, the court rejected the plaintiff's argument that the Code Construction Act's definition of "person" to include a municipality was sufficient to support a conclusion that the legislature intended to waive such immunity in section 11.086, given the use therein of the term "person." *Black*, 271 S.W.3d at 798. Nevertheless, as discussed at section 39.7 below, a landowner may still have a cause of action for inverse condemnation against a city or other political subdivision of the state, even absent the benefits of section 11.086.

§ 39.6 Damages

Assuming a plaintiff navigates the complexities of Texas Water Code section 11.086, damages awards for impoundment or diversion of surface water are dictated by whether the injury to the property is temporary or permanent. These two type of injuries are "mutually exclusive and damages for both may not be recovered in the same action." *Houston Unlimited, Inc. Metal Processing v. Mel Acres Ranch*, 443 S.W.3d 820, 826 (Tex. 2014) (*quoting Kraft v. Langford*, 565 S.W.2d 223, 227 (Tex. 1978)); *see also Coastal Transport Co. v. Crown Central Petroleum Corp.*, 136 S.W.3d 227, 235 (Tex. 2004) (holding that temporary damages were appropriate where otherwise a plaintiff would be overcompensated if it were allowed to recover both loss of use and for the cost to rebuild a facility).

If the injury is temporary, the measure of damages is the reasonable cost of repairs necessary to restore the property to its condition immediately before the injury. *City of Princeton v. Abbott*, 792 S.W.2d 161, 164 (Tex. App.—Dallas 1990, writ denied); *Planet Plows v. Evans*, 600 S.W.2d 874, 876 (Tex. App.—Amarillo 1980, no writ); *Weaver Construction Co. v. Rapier*, 448 S.W.2d 702, 703 (Tex. App.—Dallas 1969, no writ). Future damages are not allowed. *City of Princeton*, 792 S.W.2d at 164. Also included in temporary injury damages is any loss as a result of not being able to use the property. *Crosstex North Texas Pipeline, L.P. v. Gardiner*, 505 S.W.3d 580, 610 (Tex. 2016); *Weaver Construction Co.*, 448 S.W.2d at 703; *City of Princeton*, 792 S.W.2d at 164; *see also Lakeside Village Homeowners Ass'n v. Belanger*, 545 S.W.3d 15, 43 (Tex. App.—El Paso 2017, pet. denied) (holding that loss of rentals is an appropriate measure of damages for the temporary loss of use of land). In instances where the cost to repair an injury exceeds the loss in the land's value due to the injury, only the loss in value is recoverable under the "economic feasibility exception." *ExxonMobil Corp. v. Lazy R Ranch, LP*, 511 S.W.3d 538, 540 n.5 (Tex. 2017) (listing cases discussing the "economic feasibility exception," which limits the owner to the lesser amount of damages when necessary to avoid overcompensation).

Permanent injury is measured by the difference between the reasonable market value of the property immediately before and immediately after the injury. *Weaver Construction Co.*, 448 S.W.2d at 703; *Kraft*, 565 S.W.2d at 227; *see also Crosstex*, 505 S.W.3d at 610 (holding that when nuisance is permanent, claimant may recover lost market value); *Schneider National Carriers, Inc. v. Bates*, 147 S.W.3d 264, 276 (Tex. 2004).

Whether an injury to property is temporary or permanent also determines when the statute of limitations accrues, and thus when an injured party's claims are barred. When a limitation accrues is a question of law. *Schneider*, 147 S.W.3d at 274–75. A two-year statute of limitations applies in both instances; however, if the injury is permanent, suit must be brought within two years of the first actionable injury, while if the injury is temporary, suit may be brought within two years of any injury, not just the first actionable injury. *See Yalamanchili v. Mousa*, 316 S.W.3d 33, 38 (Tex. App.—Houston [14th Dist.] 2010, pet. denied); *Graham v. Pirkey*, 212 S.W.3d 507, 512 (Tex. App.—Austin 2006, no pet.); *Anders v. Mallard & Mallard, Inc.*, 817 S.W.2d 90, 95 (Tex. App.—Houston [14th Dist.] 1991, no writ); *see also* Tex. Civ. Prac. & Rem. Code § 16.003(a).

§ 39.6:1 Distinguishing between Permanent and Temporary Injuries

Schneider National Carriers, Inc. v. Bates, 147 S.W.3d 264, 273 (Tex. 2004), established boundary lines between permanent and temporary injury. This decision focused on nuisances, but applies the permanent/temporary distinction to injuries as a result of flooding as well. *Schneider*, 147 S.W.3d at 273–74. Defining a nuisance as "temporary" or "permanent" turns on how long it lasts and "whether it is 'infrequent' or 'continuous' or how often it occurs." *Schneider*, 147 S.W.3d at 273. A nuisance is temporary if it is uncertain "that any future injury will occur." *Schneider*, 147 S.W.3d at 272. It has also been defined as "occasional, intermittent or recurrent" or "sporadic and contingent upon some irregular force such as rain." *Schneider*, 147 S.W.3d at 272 (citing *Bayouth v. Lion Oil Co.*, 671 S.W.2d 867, 868 (Tex. 1984), and *Kraft v. Langford*, 565 S.W.2d 223, 227 (Tex. 1978), respectively). *Schneider* synthesized this to the basic rule that it must be so "irregular or intermittent over the period leading up to filing and trial that future injury cannot be estimated with reasonable certainty." *Schneider*, 147 S.W.3d at 281.

Without overturning the above descriptions, the Texas Supreme Court "reformulated" this permanent/temporary distinction by stating that permanent injuries are unrepairable or, even with repair, will continually and predictably occur, while temporary injuries cannot be repaired and any recurrence is unpredictable:

> An injury to real property is considered permanent if (a) it cannot be repaired, fixed, or restored, *or* (b) even though the injury can be repaired, fixed, or restored, it is substantially certain that the injury will repeatedly, continually, and regularly recur, such that future injury can be reasonably evaluated. Conversely, an injury to real property is considered temporary if (a) it can be repaired, fixed, or restored, *and* (b) any anticipated recurrence would be only occasional, irregular, intermittent, and not reasonably predictable, such that future injury could not be estimated with reasonable certainty. These definitions apply to cases in which entry onto real property is physical (as in a trespass) and to cases in which entry onto real property is not physical (as with a nuisance).

Gilbert Wheeler, Inc. v. Enbridge Pipelines (East Texas), L.P., 449 S.W.3d 474, 480 (Tex. 2014); *Ray-Max Management, L.P. v. American Tower Corp.*, No. 02-15-00298-CV, 2016 WL 4248041, at *5 (Tex. App.—Fort Worth Aug. 11, 2016, pet. denied), *cert. denied*, 137 S. Ct. 2131 (2017) (mem. op.) (holding that "[w]hether the land is permanently damaged is not the proper inquiry . . . [it] is whether the alleged injury is sufficiently constant such that the future impact of the trespass can be reasonably evaluated even though the injury can be repaired, fixed, or restored").

A nuisance is permanent if it is "constant and continuous" and if the "injury constantly and regularly recurs." *Schneider*, 147 S.W.3d at 272 (citations omitted). It does not have to be eternal, nor does it have to occur daily to be "constant and continuous," but only with enough regularity as to be predictive with regard to market value. *Schneider*, 147 S.W.3d at 276. Material factual disputes about the frequency, duration, and extent of the nuisance conditions are decided by jurors. *Schneider*, 147 S.W.3d at 275, 281; *Premium Valve Services, LLC v. Comstock Oil & Gas, LP*, No. 01-15-00108-CV, 2016 WL 4253896, at *4 (Tex. App.—Dallas Aug. 11, 2016, no pet.) (mem. op.) (holding a trial court's failure to submit the factual disputes regarding temporary/permanent distinction to be harmful and worthy of remand). *Schneider* succinctly stated that a nuisance is permanent if it is "sufficiently constant or regular (no matter how long between occurrences) that future impact can be reasonably evaluated." *Schneider*, 147 S.W.3d at 281; *Mitchell v. Timmerman*, No. 03-08-00320-CV, 2008 WL 5423268, at *6 (Tex. App.—Austin Dec. 31, 2008, no pet.) (mem. op.) (holding that a drainage system causing damage to property every time there was a significant rainfall was sufficiently "constant or regular" to find the injury permanent); *Pope v. John Kiella Homes*, No. 07-06-0146-CV, 2008 WL 1903332, at *4 (Tex. App.—Amarillo Apr. 30, 2008, no pet.) (mem. op.) (holding that flooding twice was sufficient to demonstrate the injury was recurrent, thus permanent).

Like the market value measure of permanent damages, the time frame for designating a nuisance as temporary or permanent should be measured in future years. *Schneider*, 147 S.W.3d at 277. However, even if "exact dates, frequency, or extent of future damage" may remain unknown, if the future impact can be reasonably evaluated, it should be treated as permanent. *Schneider*, 147 S.W.3d at 280; *RayMax Management*, 2016 WL 4248041, at *5 (holding where a claimant was able to estimate its future injury from the alleged injury with reasonable certainty, the injury was permanent). Finally, the determination of whether a nuisance is permanent can be made by showing that either the plaintiff's injuries or the defendant's operations were permanent. *Schneider*, 147 S.W.3d at 283.

§ 39.6:2 Additional Damages Rules

Damages claims under Texas Water Code section 11.086 are limited to property damage and do not extend to survival actions, personal injuries, or wrongful death. *Raburn v. KJI Bluechip Investments*, 50 S.W.3d 699, 704 (Tex. App.—Fort Worth 2001, no pet.). Exemplary damages may be awarded if there is evidence of an intentional violation of section 11.086 in which the defendant was knowingly indifferent to the plaintiff's rights or if there is evidence of fraud, malice, or gross negligence. *Vaughn v. Drennon*, 202 S.W.3d 308, 321 (Tex. App.—Tyler 2006, no pet.); *Bily v. Omni Equities, Inc.*, 731 S.W.2d 606, 613–14 (Tex. App.—Houston [14th Dist.] 1987, writ ref'd n.r.e.); *compare Solomon v. Steitler*, 312 S.W.3d 46, 54–55 (Tex. App.—Texarkana 2010, no pet.) (holding a defendant's conscious indifference to the claimant's rights, safety, or welfare in violating section 11.086 supported the imposition of exemplary damages), *with Dietrich v. Goodman*, 123 S.W.3d 413, 420–21 (Tex. App.—Houston [14th Dist.] 2003, no pet.) (holding a defendant's lack of awareness of an extreme degree of risk or the magnitude of the potential harm to the claimants did not support an imposition of exemplary damages).

Where flooding causes damage to a home, the owner may be able to obtain "stigma damages" if the market value of the property has been damaged due to the stigma that may attach to a flooded home. *Royce Homes, L.P. v. Humphrey*, 244 S.W.3d 570, 576 (Tex. App.—Beaumont 2008, pet. denied). However, the supreme court noted that "[e]ven when it is legally possible to recover stigma damages, it is often legally impossible to prove them," because "[e]vidence based on conjecture, guess or speculation is inadequate to prove stigma damages." *Houston Unlimited, Inc. Metal Processing v. Mel Acres Ranch*, 443 S.W.3d 820, 827 (Tex. 2014) (internal quotations omitted). If there are multiple responsible parties, damages should be apportioned among the responsible parties if it can be determined for what percentage of injury the parties were liable. *Planet Plows v. Evans*, 600 S.W.2d 874, 876 (Tex. App.—Amarillo 1980, no writ).

As discussed above, the ability to recover damages for flooding is limited. Typically, an owner of higher ground may allow the natural flow of surface water to pass onto the property of a lower landowner without liability, and court decisions have substantially limited the extent to which a lower landowner may recover for property damage resulting even from an upper landowner's impoundment or diversion of water. *See Miller v. Letzerich*, 49 S.W.2d 404, 408 (Tex. 1932); *Bishop v. Harris*, 669 S.W.2d 859, 860 (Tex. App.—Tyler 1984, writ dism'd). The next section discusses inverse condemnation, a cause of action that may be available when the party responsible for causing flooding is a governmental entity.

§ 39.7 Inverse Condemnation Claims

When a governmental entity's actions cause or change the character of flooding on private property, a "taking" of the property may result. The type of taking at issue in flooding cases is a physical taking, which is a taking that occurs when the government physically appropriates or invades private property or unreasonably interferes with the landowner's right to use and enjoy the property. *Tarrant Regional Water District v. Gragg*, 151 S.W.3d 546, 554 (Tex. 2004). The Texas Constitution protects landowners from takings by obligating payment of adequate compensation: "[n]o person's property shall be taken, damaged or destroyed for or applied to public use without adequate compensation being made, unless by the consent of such person." Tex. Const. art. I, § 17. The taking, damaging, and destruction of property are three distinct claims under article I, section 17, although the term "taking" is used as shorthand to refer to all three types of claims. *City of Dallas v. Jennings*, 142 S.W.3d 310, 313 n.2 (Tex. 2004). See also Chapter 38 of this book.

If property has been taken or damaged for public use without compensation, the property owner may obtain compensation through an inverse condemnation or "taking" action. *Westgate, Ltd. v. State*, 843 S.W.2d 448, 452 (Tex. 1992). Although sovereign immunity generally protects governmental entities from lawsuits for monetary damages, it offers no shield against a taking claim brought under the constitution. *Steele v. City of Houston*, 603 S.W.2d 786, 791 (Tex. 1980). The determination of whether a taking has occurred is ultimately a question of law. *Harris County Flood Control District v. Kerr*, 499 S.W.3d 793, 806 (Tex. 2016).

To establish a taking claim, the claimant must prove that the governmental entity intentionally performed certain acts that resulted in a taking of property for public use. *General Services Commission v. Little-Tex Insulation Co.*, 39 S.W.3d 591, 598 (Tex. 2001) (citing *Steele*, 603 S.W.2d at 788–92). Thus, to defeat a governmental entity's plea to the jurisdiction, a claimant must raise a fact issue as to (1) intent, (2) causation, and (3) public use. *See Little-Tex Insulation Co.*, 39 S.W.3d at 598. Intent requires that the claimant show the governmental entity "intentionally took or damaged their property for public use, or was substantially certain that would be the result," and "knows that a specific act is causing identifiable harm or knows that the harm is substantially certain to result." *Kerr*, 499 S.W.3d at 799. There must be "objective indicia of intent." *City of Keller v. Wilson*, 168 S.W.3d 802, 830 (Tex. 2005). The governmental entity's knowledge at the time it acted, not with the benefit of hindsight, is relevant in determining the entity's intent. *Kerr*, 499 S.W.3d at 806.

The requisite intent element for a taking requires that the governmental entity has made (1) some affirmative conduct, (2) with specificity, (3) for a public use. Under the affirmative conduct prong, intent is more than mere negligent conduct by a government. *Kerr*, 499 S.W.3d at 799–800. Also, the governmental entity cannot be liable if it committed no intentional act; thus, the law does not recognize takings liability for failure to act. *Kerr*, 499 S.W.3d at 799–800; *City of Mason v. Lee*, No. 04-18-00275-CV, 2018 WL 58082600, at *3 (Tex. App.—San Antonio 2018, no pet.) (mem. op.). For example, in *Running v. City of Athens*, No. 12-18-00047-CV, 2019 WL 625972, at *6 (Tex. App.—Tyler Feb. 14, 2019, no pet.) (mem. op.), when a claimant's factual bases for the taking claim centered on a city's negligence in failing to prevent overflow that flooded his property, the court found that a taking did not occur. The court held that even though evidence illustrated that the city intended the water's release, it was not sufficient to show the city intended the harm. *Running*, 2019 WL 625972, at *6–7; *see also City of Magnolia v. Smedley*, 533 S.W.3d 1, 4 (Tex. App.—Beaumont 2016), *rev'd on other grounds*, 533 S.W.3d 297 (Tex. 2017) (holding evidence that flooding occurred on the claimant's property after a city built a walkway was insufficient to show the city's intent).

Under the specificity prong, intent ordinarily requires that the governmental entity knows which property it is taking. *Kerr*, 499 S.W.3d at 800; *see also San Jacinto River Authority v. Burney*, 570 S.W.3d 820, 834–35 (Tex. App.—Houston [1st Dist.] 2018, pet. granted). The court will not recognize government liability where someday, somewhere, its performance of a governmental function will result in some damage to some unspecified parcel. Instead, the claimant must show that the governmental entity knew "a specific act is causing identifiable harm" or that "specific property damage is substantially certain to result from an authorized government action." *Kerr*, 499 S.W.3d at 800; *see also Burney*, 570 S.W.3d at 834 (pleading that river authority "intentionally, knowingly, affirmatively, and consciously flooded" particular properties identified by street address met intent prong).

Finally, intent requires a showing that the government is using its powers of eminent domain with designs to use the claimant's particular property to accomplish a public use. For example, in *City* *of Rollingwood v. Brainard*, No. 03-17-00077-CV, 2017 WL 2417388, at *4 (Tex. App.—Austin May 31, 2017, no pet.) (mem. op.), when a governmental entity diverted water out of the street and onto the claimant's property, the court held that the city, in alleviating the street flooding, intended a "benefit" for public use purposes.

To establish a taking, the claimant must also prove a second element: causation. For example, in *Waller v. Sabine River Authority*, No. 09-18-00040-CV, 2018 WL 6378510, at *5 (Tex. App.—Beaumont Dec. 6, 2018, no pet.) (mem. op.), the court held that the claimants were required, and failed, to establish that the governmental entity's affirmative conduct was a proximate cause of the damage to their property, when the water released from the governmental entity mixed with water from other tributaries and rainwater before flowing onto the claimants' property.

Finally, to establish a taking, the claimant must also prove a third element: that the governmental entity took for a public use. For example, the public-use element is met when a governmental entity takes property for the public benefit or if an injury results from either the "construction of public works or their subsequent maintenance and operation." *Kerr*, 499 S.W.3d at 801. In contrast, the element of public use is doubtful when a governmental entity merely approves private development and is not substantially certain the approval will damage specific property. *Kerr*, 499 S.W.3d at 804; *cf. Brainard*, 2017 WL 2417388, at *4 (holding a sufficient fact question was raised regarding public use to deny the city's plea to the jurisdiction where there was evidence not just that a city approved of a private party's construction but also that the city itself altered a curb on a street that increased flooding onto claimant's property).

Not all flooding caused by governmental actions rises to the level of a taking under article I, section 17, of the Texas Constitution. In flooding cases, recurrence is a probative factor to determine the extent of a taking and whether it is necessarily incident to authorized governmental activity and, therefore, substantially certain to occur. *Gragg*, 151 S.W.3d at 555. Although nonrecurrent flooding may cause damage, a single flood event generally does not rise to the level of a taking. There is a split, however, in the Texas courts of appeals on this issue. In a recent decision, the El Paso court of appeals held that, in the context of a plea to the jurisdiction, a single flood event could be sufficient to satisfy the requirement for intent. *City of Socorro v. Campos*, 510 S.W.3d 121 (Tex. App.—El Paso 2016, pet. granted). In reaching this decision, the court noted its opinion could be viewed as in conflict with a 2007 decision of the first court of appeals in Houston. *See City of Socorro*, 510 S.W.3d at 131–32 (discussing *Toomey v. Texas Department of Transportation*, No. 01-05-00749-CV, 2007 WL 1153035 (Tex. App.—Houston [1st Dist.] Apr. 19, 2007, no pet.)).

This distinction between a taking by flooding and mere temporary damage is best illustrated by *Brazos River Authority v. City of Graham*, 354 S.W.2d 99 (Tex. 1961). In that case, the Brazos River Authority's construction of a dam caused siltation that resulted in a steady increase in the upstream water elevation over time. As a result, the city's sewage treatment plant and water treatment plant, both of which were upstream from the dam, eventually flooded. Because the dam's construction would subject the city's sewage treatment plant to repeated flooding and render its operation impossible, the court held that a taking had occurred. In contrast, the water treatment plant, which was at a higher elevation than the sewage treatment plant, had flooded only once. Although the court found the water treatment plant might flood more frequently in the future as siltation increased, it held that a taking had not yet occurred. The court observed that until a plaintiff is in a position "to establish the repetitious nature of the injury, he should be confined in his demand for damages to those flowing directly from the single injury or flooding." *Brazos River Authority*, 354 S.W.2d at 108.

Similarly, a taking does not occur when a governmental action is a mere proposal that threatens to cause flooding. Although the proposed action may result in a *future* loss of property, its proposal alone does not give rise to a present cause of action for a taking, in the absence of a current, direct restriction on the property's use. *See, e.g., Howard v. City of Kerrville*, 75 S.W.3d 112, 117 (Tex. App.—San Antonio 2002, pet. denied) (stating that construction of a dam increased the base flood elevation on the claimant's property but no flooding had yet occurred); *Allen v. City of Texas City*, 775

S.W.2d 863, 865 (Tex. App.—Houston [1st Dist.] 1989, writ denied) (determining that construction of a rainwater levee increased the property's susceptibility to flooding and diminished the market value of the property but no flooding had yet occurred); *Hubler v. City of Corpus Christi*, 564 S.W.2d 816 (Tex. App.—Corpus Christi–Edinburg 1978, writ ref'd n.r.e.) (stating that a proposed drainage system, if implemented, would increase flooding on the property but no flooding had yet occurred).

A governmental entity also is not responsible for a taking when mere negligence contributes to property damage. *Gragg*, 151 S.W.3d at 554; *Kerr*, 499 S.W.3d at 799–800. The constitution requires compensation only if property is damaged or appropriated for public use. When damage is merely the accidental result of the government's actions, there is no public benefit and the property cannot be said to be taken or damaged for public use. *Jennings*, 142 S.W.3d at 313. If no taking has occurred, there will likely be no recovery of damages because governmental entities generally have immunity from negligence actions.

Gragg addressed the distinction between a taking and mere negligent governmental conduct. In that case, a water district argued that the increased flooding of a downstream landowner's ranch was due to mere negligence in operating the dam's floodgates, and if the dam were properly operated, the amount of water passing downstream would be the same as occurred naturally. The supreme court observed, however, that the landowner's complaint did not concern the amount of water passing downstream but rather the changed *character* of the water, which after construction of the dam arrived sooner, flowed faster, and was deeper, longer lasting, and more forceful. Although the gate-release operations contributed to these effects, there was evidence that the reservoir's physical characteristics, such as its limited excess storage capacity, were significant and inevitably changed the characteristics of floods at the downstream ranch and that the district's releases resulted in unnatural surges of water. The court concluded there was sufficient evidence that the extensive damage suffered by the ranch was the inevitable result of the reservoir's construction and of its operation as intended, and the district's actions were therefore a taking rather than mere negligence. *Gragg*, 151 S.W.3d at 555; *Burney*, 570 S.W.3d at 837 (rejecting river authority's argument that release of water during Hurricane Harvey was not for a public purpose because the river authority's government-mandated powers did not include flood control); *but see Running*, 2019 WL 625972, at *6–7 (holding that a city's mere intent to release water, without intent to harm, did not amount to a taking).

The damages a property owner may recover for a taking vary depending on whether the taking is permanent or temporary. *See Gragg*, 151 S.W.3d at 558; see also section 39.6:1 above. A permanent taking occurs when the damage is ongoing and will continue in the future. *Gragg*, 151 S.W.3d at 558. A temporary taking occurs when the damage is intermittent. *Brazos River Authority*, 354 S.W.2d at 125. For permanent takings, such as those due to recurrent flooding, a property owner is entitled to recover the diminished value of the property—that is, the difference in the property's value before and after the taking. *Gragg*, 151 S.W.3d at 558. For temporary takings, such as those due to a single flooding event, the property owner may recover damages only for injuries that resulted from the specific flood. *Gragg*, 151 S.W.3d at 558. Under temporary takings, loss of rentals or lost profits are also appropriate measures of damages for the temporary loss of use of land. *Austin v. Teague*, 570 S.W.2d 389, 394 (Tex. 1978) (loss of rentals); *San Antonio v. Guidry*, 801 S.W.2d 142, 150 (Tex. App.—San Antonio 1990) (lost profits and expenses).

Although options may exist to hold governmental entities accountable when their actions cause flooding, the recovery of monetary damages is a poor substitute for avoiding flooding in the first place. In this regard, local governmental entities often play a significant role in preventing or reducing flooding-related damage by developing and implementing strategies to manage development within the floodplain. Floodplain management and drainage are addressed in the next part.

III. Floodplain Management and Drainage

§ 39.8 Introduction

A floodplain is any normally dry land area that is susceptible to being inundated by water from any natural source. Local communities often adopt regulations to promote the wise use of floodplains and to reduce damages caused by flooding. Floodplain management is defined in 31 Texas Administrative Code section 361.10 as "the operation of an overall program of corrective and preventative measures for reducing flood damage." These measures can take a variety of forms and generally include building, subdivision, zoning, land use, or other special-purpose ordinances such as flood damage prevention ordinances. Floodplain management can include the minimum requirements necessary to comply with the National Flood Insurance Program (NFIP) but may also include a variety of standards higher than NFIP minimums that local entities may choose to adopt. See Chapter 40 of this book for further discussion of the NFIP. In Texas, local governments have the primary responsibility for establishing and enforcing floodplain management programs; however, state and federal entities play an important role through incentive-based programs and technical and financial assistance.

The following sections describe the influence of the federal government and FEMA on floodplain management, assistance provided by the Natural Resources Conservation Service to local communities for flood control projects, the involvement of municipalities in implementing floodplain management guidelines through the platting and permitting process, and the use of state watercourses to manage the movement of water.

§ 39.9 Role of the Federal Government and FEMA

One federal program has had an essential role in shaping state and local floodplain management: the National Flood Insurance Program (NFIP), administered by FEMA. *See* 42 U.S.C. §§ 4001–4129. The NFIP is an incentive-based program that coordinates floodplain management with the availability of flood insurance. Unless a community participates in the NFIP, federally backed flood insurance is not available to residents and business owners in the community. To participate, communities must adopt and enforce minimum floodplain management regulations designed to minimize damage to homes and businesses in "special flood hazard areas" (SFHAs). These areas have the greatest risk of flooding and are defined as those areas of land that would be inundated by a flood that has a 1 percent or greater chance of occurring in any given year (also referred to as the base flood or hundred-year flood). 44 C.F.R. § 59.1. In 1999, the Texas legislature obligated Texas cities and counties to adopt any ordinances or orders necessary to be eligible to participate in the NFIP. Tex. Water Code § 16.3145.

FEMA provides the data that participating communities must use to establish floodplain management regulations. The data available for each community vary. In some communities, the available maps show only the approximate boundaries of SFHAs, while in others, FEMA has undertaken detailed flood insurance studies and published flood insurance rate maps indicating base flood elevations, flood risk zones, and floodways. SFHAs are designated on the flood insurance rate maps as A Zones and V Zones. *See* 44 C.F.R. § 59.1 (defining "areas of special flood hazard").

Occasionally a flood insurance rate map inadvertently includes property within an SFHA even though the property is at or above the base flood elevation. In such cases, the owner or lessee of the property may submit mapping and survey information to FEMA and request a "letter of map amendment," which officially removes a structure or lot from the SFHA. 44 C.F.R. §§ 70.1–.9. To remove a structure from the SFHA, the applicant must demonstrate that the lowest ground touching the structure is at or above the base flood elevation; to remove an entire lot, the applicant must show that the lowest point on the lot is at or above the base flood elevation. *See* Federal Emergency Management

Agency, *Letter of Map Amendment & Letter of Map Revision-Based on Fill Process*, www.fema.gov/letter-map-amendment-letter-map-revision-based-fill-process. In most cases, the applicant will need to hire a licensed land surveyor or a registered professional engineer to prepare an elevation certificate for the property.

More extensive changes to the maps may be requested by the community participating in the NFIP. Procedures are available to request that FEMA revise SFHA boundaries, base flood elevations, and floodways. *See* 44 C.F.R. §§ 65.1–.17. If FEMA agrees to a change, it will issue a "letter of map revision," which is an official revision to an effective NFIP map. 44 C.F.R. § 65.9.

Procedures also exist for obtaining comments from FEMA concerning proposed projects. A "conditional letter of map amendment" is FEMA's comment on whether a proposed project would be excluded from the SFHA shown on the effective NFIP map. 44 C.F.R. § 70.9. A "conditional letter of map revision" is FEMA's comment on whether a proposed project that affects the hydrologic or hydraulic characteristics of a flooding source would necessitate modifying the existing regulatory floodway or effective base flood elevations. 44 C.F.R. § 65.8. Neither of these conditional letters revises an effective NFIP; rather, they indicate how FEMA will recognize a particular project if it is built as proposed.

The minimum floodplain management standards for flood-prone areas are set out in 44 C.F.R. § 60.3. Communities participating in the NFIP must require property owners to obtain permits for all proposed construction or other development in SFHAs. In addition, communities must review subdivision proposals and other proposed new development to determine whether they will be reasonably safe from flooding and whether the utilities and facilities servicing them will be constructed to minimize or eliminate flood damage. Other requirements vary depending on the type of flood risk data FEMA has provided to the community. *See* 44 C.F.R. § 60.3. In general, communities must require that all new construction or substantially improved existing buildings have their lowest floor (including basement) elevated to or above the base flood elevation. Communities that fail to enforce the minimum floodplain management requirements may be placed on probation and eventually suspended from the NFIP. 44 C.F.R. § 59.24(b), (c).

Communities may adopt floodplain management standards that are more stringent than the minimum NFIP requirements, and the NFIP encourages them to do so through its community rating system. *See* 42 U.S.C. § 4022(b). Communities are rated on a scale from one to ten, and those with a lower rating can secure lower premiums for policyholders in the community. *See* Federal Emergency Management Agency, *National Flood Insurance Program Community Rating System*, www.fema.gov/national-flood-insurance-program-community-rating-system.

In each state, a "state coordinating agency" may be designated to assist with implementation of the NFIP in that state. 44 C.F.R. §§ 59.1, 60.25. In 2007, the Texas legislature transferred responsibility for coordinating the NFIP from the TCEQ to the TWDB. *See* Act of May 26, 2007, 80th Leg., R.S., ch. 1323. The board is tasked with aiding, advising, and coordinating the efforts of present and future political subdivisions endeavoring to qualify for participation in the NFIP. Tex. Water Code § 16.316(a).

Under executive order (EO) 11988, Floodplain Management, federal agencies funding and/or permitting critical facilities are required to avoid the 0.2 percent (500-year) floodplain or protect the facilities to the 0.2 percent chance flood level. 42 Fed. Reg. 26,951 (May 24, 1977). Executive order 13990, signed January 2021, reinstated the Federal Flood Risk Management Standard (FFRMS) established by EO 13690 in 2015 that modified the original 1977 EO 11988 with increased requirements for federal funds and flood risk requirements. 86 Fed. Reg. 7037 (Jan. 20, 2021).

A good Texas source for higher standards is from the Texas Floodplain Management Association (TFMA), which performs occasional surveys of Texas communities to assess higher freeboard standards. *See* Texas Floodplain Management Association, *TFMA Documents and Reposts*, www.tfma.org/page/documents-reports. *See also* Texas Floodplain Management Association, *A Guide for Higher Standards in Floodplain Management* (May 2018), https://cdn.ymaws.com/www.tfma.org/

resource/resmgr/documents_smc/tfma_higher_standards_guide0.pdf. FEMA also encourages communities to adopt higher standards and offers discounts for all flood insurance policies in the community that adopt those higher standards through the Community Rating System (CRS) program. *See* Federal Emergency Management Agency, *National Flood Insurance Program Community Rating System*, www.fema.gov/floodplain-management/community-rating-system.

The *Natural Hazard Mitigation Saves: 2019 Report* provides estimates of mitigation savings from adopting current residential and building codes, exceeding those codes, and addressing retrofits. *See* K. Porter et al., *National Hazard Mitigation Saves: 2019 Report* (National Institute of Building Sciences, Dec. 2019), www.nibs.org/projects/natural-hazard-mitigation-saves-2019-report. The summary of findings in the 2019 report depicts that the overall benefit-cost ratio for adopting current residential and building codes, exceeding those codes, and adding retrofits for riverine flooding ranges from 5:1 to 8:1.

With a riverine flood, for example, if codes regulating floodplain development were adopted that did not previously exist within a certain community, those codes would create compliance costs (staff to administer the codes, higher construction costs, etc.). However, the benefits of reduced future flood damages are estimated to be significantly higher.

Neither S.B. 8 nor 31 Texas Administrative Code chapter 361 rules grant the RFPGs or political subdivisions any additional regulatory power or authority. If an RFPG finds that there are legal, regulatory, or other barriers to implementation of standards, the RFPG may choose to make related legislative, regulatory, administrative, or other recommendations that they consider necessary to facilitate floodplain management and flood mitigation planning and implementation. Regardless of such recommendations, the authority of existing regulatory bodies may remain limited under current statutory law.

§ 39.10 USDA Natural Resources Conservation Service Dams

Another federal program that addresses flood management is the Watershed and Flood Prevention Operations Program, which provides local government sponsors with technical and financial support to implement conservation practices and works of improvement, including floodwater-retarding dams and reservoirs. *See* 16 U.S.C. §§ 1001–1012. This program is administered by the Natural Resources Conservation Service (NRCS), which is an agency of the U.S. Department of Agriculture. A crucial aspect of the program is local involvement. Project sponsors must demonstrate strong local support by agreeing to obtain land rights, contribute to the cost of construction, and perform operation and maintenance. 7 C.F.R. § 622.11(a)(7). Authorized project purposes include watershed protection, conservation and proper use of land, flood prevention, agricultural water management including irrigation and drainage, public recreation, public fish and wildlife, municipal and industrial water supply, hydropower, water quality management, groundwater supply, agricultural pollution control, and other water management. 7 C.F.R. § 622.2(c).

The focus is generally on small projects in upstream tributary watersheds. Projects are eligible only if they do not exceed 250,000 acres and do not include any single structure providing more than 12,500 acre-feet of floodwater detention capacity or more than 25,000 acre-feet of total capacity. 16 U.S.C. § 1002. Any project involving federal contributions in excess of $5 million or construction of any single structure with a capacity in excess of 2,500 acre-feet requires congressional approval. 16 U.S.C. § 1002. At least 20 percent of the total benefits of the project must be directly related to agriculture, including rural communities. 16 U.S.C. § 1002.

Participation in the NRCS program does not obviate the need for obtaining a state water rights permit from the TCEQ. As a condition to providing federal assistance for the installation of works of improvement, local organizations must acquire, or provide assurance that landowners or water users have acquired, such water rights, pursuant to state law, as may be needed in the installation and operation of the work of improvement. 16 U.S.C. § 1004(4).

§ 39.11 Municipal Authority and Land Development

Municipalities typically implement floodplain management guidelines through the platting and permitting processes. The specific procedures of each municipality vary, but most follow a similar format. In general, no permit for a structure or development may be issued, and no plat may be approved, unless the applicant demonstrates that the permit or plat satisfies the city's flood prevention and drainage requirements. The standards set by most municipalities are based on the requirements for participation in the NFIP, discussed at section 39.9 above. As a result, the focus is on determining whether the property under consideration is in a "special flood hazard area" or floodway. The regulations generally require that buildings be constructed in a way that will minimize damage from flooding and will not impair a floodway's ability to pass floodwaters.

§ 39.12 Use of State Watercourses

Developers may address the increased runoff created by a development project by directing the runoff to a designated location on the property and then into a natural watercourse. Texas has long recognized that landowners may use ditches, drains, and artificial streams to accumulate surface water and direct it into a natural watercourse. *Jefferson County Drainage District No. 6 v. Langham*, 76 S.W.2d 484, 488 (Tex. Comm'n App. 1934, judgm't adopted). This right, however, is not unlimited. The water added to the watercourse may not exceed what the watercourse has the natural capacity to carry. *Langham*, 76 S.W.2d at 488; *Coleman v. Wright*, 155 S.W.2d 382, 383 (Tex. App.—Waco 1941, no writ). In addition, before reaching the watercourse, the water may not be diverted or impounded in a manner that damages the property of another by overflow of the diverted or impounded water. Tex. Water Code § 11.086; *see also Payne v. J. Baker Corp.*, No. 02-12-00181-CV, 2013 WL 2091774, at *3 (Tex. App.—Fort Worth May 16, 2013, no pet.) (mem. op.).

Because natural watercourses may be used for flood control and drainage, the definition of a "watercourse" is significant. To constitute a watercourse, there must be something more than mere surface drainage over the entire face of a tract of land. *Hoefs v. Short*, 273 S.W. 785, 787 (Tex. 1925). A watercourse has (1) a well-defined bed and banks, (2) a current of water, and (3) a permanent source of supply. *Hoefs*, 273 S.W. at 787. While these three requirements must be met, they are not rigorously applied. The bed and banks may be "slight, imperceptible, or absent" in some instances without the stream losing its character as a watercourse. *Hoefs*, 273 S.W. at 787. The source must be permanent, but it need not be continuous, and a watercourse may be dry for long periods of time. *Hoefs*, 273 S.W. at 787. Permanent source "merely means that the stream must be such that similar conditions will produce a flow of water, and that these conditions recur with some degree of regularity, so that they establish and maintain a running stream for considerable periods of time." *Hoefs*, 273 S.W. at 788. The watercourse may shift positions over time as long as it presently has a defined course. *Domel v. City of Georgetown*, 6 S.W.3d 349, 356 (Tex. App.—Austin 1999, pet. denied).

As discussed above, a variety of programs exist to manage the development of land within the floodplain. Although the approaches may vary, the goal is to reduce the damage that results when the floodplain inevitably is inundated by water. This risk of flooding may also be managed with flood control dams, which can be used and operated to accumulate floodwaters and slow their release downstream. The regulation of dam owners and operators is discussed below.

IV. Regulation of Dams

§ 39.13 Introduction

Any discussion of the topic of flooding would not be complete without explaining the role of dams. Dams provide several economic and social benefits, including flood control, water supply, hydroelectric power, navigation, recreation, and wildlife habitat. However, in the event of failure, dams also present a risk of severe flooding that can result in loss of life and property damage. See Chapter 27 of this book for a discussion of reservoirs formed by dams. The state of Texas manages this risk by regulating the construction, alteration, and removal of dams. The regulations apply to nearly all dams, including many dams on private land. For a detailed discussion of requirements for dams, see Greg Graml, *Flooding Challenges: Reservoir Operations and Liability*, *in The Changing Face of Water Rights in Texas* (State Bar of Texas 2017).

§ 39.14 Dams on State Watercourses

With few exceptions, before a person can begin constructing any work that is designed to store, take, or divert state water, the person must obtain a permit from the TCEQ to impound and appropriate the water. Tex. Water Code § 11.121. State water is property of the state of Texas and includes "[t]he water of the ordinary flow, underflow, and tides of every flowing river, natural stream, and lake, and of every bay or arm of the Gulf of Mexico, and the storm water, floodwater, and rainwater of every river, natural stream, canyon, ravine, depression, and watershed in the state." Tex. Water Code § 11.021. An applicant seeking a permit to construct a storage reservoir must apply to the TCEQ for a water rights permit and comply with the public notice and permitting requirements of the agency.

§ 39.15 Dams on Private Land

There are few exceptions to the permit requirement; however, a person may construct on the person's own property a dam or reservoir with normal storage of not more than two hundred acre-feet of water for domestic and livestock purposes without obtaining a permit. Tex. Water Code § 11.142(a), (b). More than two hundred acre-feet of water may be stored temporarily in such a privately owned dam or reservoir if the dam or reservoir has not stored more than two hundred acre-feet of water on average in any twelve-month period. Tex. Water Code § 11.142(a). An exempt reservoir may be on-channel, adjacent to the stream, or on a contiguous piece of property through which the water flows. 30 Tex. Admin. Code § 297.21(b). A dam constructed under this exemption may not be located on a navigable stream. 30 Tex. Admin. Code § 297.21(c). The state of Texas owns the lands underlying navigable streams. *State v. Bradford*, 50 S.W.2d 1065, 1069 (Tex. 1932). Thus, a dam constructed on a navigable stream is not considered to be on the person's "own property." *Garrison v. Bexar-Medina-Atascosa Counties Water Improvement District No. 1*, 404 S.W.2d 376, 377 (Tex. App.—Austin), *writ ref'd n.r.e.*, 407 S.W.2d 771 (Tex. 1966). By statute, any stream that has an average width of thirty feet from its mouth up is considered legally navigable regardless of whether it is navigable in fact. *See* Tex. Nat. Res. Code § 21.001(3); *Diversion Lake Club v. Heath*, 86 S.W.2d 441, 445–46 (Tex. 1935); *Texas River Barges v. City of San Antonio*, 21 S.W.3d 347, 352 (Tex. App.—San Antonio 2000, pet. denied).

§ 39.16 Permits and Construction

The TCEQ is charged with adopting and enforcing rules and orders that are necessary for the safe construction, maintenance, repair, and removal of dams. Tex. Water Code § 12.052(a). As part of this charge, the TCEQ has implemented the Dam Safety Program, which monitors and regulates both public and private dams in Texas. *See* 30 Tex. Admin. Code §§ 299.1–.72. Under the Dam Safety

Program, the TCEQ performs safety evaluations of existing dams, reviews plans and specifications for dam construction and major rehabilitation work, inspects construction work on new and existing dams, and reviews and approves emergency action plans.

As discussed in this and the following sections, the Dam Safety Program underwent significant changes effective January 1, 2009, when the TCEQ adopted new, updated rules for the program. *See* 33 Tex. Reg. 10,465 (Dec. 26, 2008). The Texas legislature made further changes to the program in 2011 by directing the TCEQ to "focus on the most hazardous dams in the state" (*see* Act of May 27, 2011, 82d Leg., R.S., ch. 1021, § 1.07, eff. Sept. 1, 2011 (amending Tex. Water Code § 12.052)) and creating additional exemptions for certain dams (*see* Act of June 14, 2013, 83d Leg., R.S., ch. 641, §§ 1, 2, eff. Sept. 1, 2013 (amending Tex. Water Code § 12.052)). In 2019, the Texas legislature again made changes to the Dam Safety Program by requiring owners of dams with spillways to notify downstream communities when spillway releases are made to regulate floodwater (*see* Act of June 9, 2019, 86th Leg., R.S., ch. 1020, eff. Sept. 1, 2019 (amending Tex. Water Code § 12.052(a–1)–(a–4))) and by requiring the TCEQ to provide a biannual report to municipal emergency management directors identifying each dam with a "significant" or "hazardous" classification (*see* Act of June 10, 2019, 86th Leg., R.S., ch. 709, eff. Sept. 1, 2019 (amending Tex. Water Code § 12.052(e–3)–(e–5))).

§ 39.16:1 Dams Subject to Regulation

The TCEQ defines a "dam" as "[a]ny barrier or barriers, with any appurtenant structures, constructed for the purpose of either permanently or temporarily impounding water." 30 Tex. Admin. Code § 299.2(14). Despite this broad definition, the TCEQ's dam safety rules apply only to a subset of dams. The rules originally applied to all structures with a height greater than six feet. However, the TCEQ revised its dam safety rules effective January 1, 2009, to apply only to dams that (1) have a height greater than or equal to twenty-five feet and a maximum storage capacity greater than or equal to fifteen acre-feet; (2) have a height greater than six feet and a maximum storage capacity greater than or equal to fifty acre-feet; (3) are classified as a high- or significant-hazard dam, regardless of height or maximum storage capacity; or (4) are used as a pumped storage or terminal storage facility. 30 Tex. Admin. Code § 299.1(a). The rule change effectively removed certain smaller, lower-risk dams from regulation. Nevertheless, the legislature further revised the applicability of the Dam Safety Program in both 2011 and 2013 by amending section 12.052 of the Texas Water Code to exempt dams of low and significant hazard storing less than five hundred acre-feet of water if they are located in a county with a population of less than 350,000 and are not within the corporate limits of a municipality. *See* Tex. Water Code § 12.052.

Under the TCEQ's dam safety rules, the following types of dams are also exempt: dams designed by, constructed under the supervision of, and owned and maintained by federal agencies; embankments constructed for roads, highways, and railroads, including low-water crossings, that may temporarily impound floodwater; dikes or levees designed to prevent inundation by floodwater; certain off-channel impoundments; and aboveground water storage tanks made of steel, concrete, or plastic. 30 Tex. Admin. Code § 299.1(c). A process is also available to obtain an exception to the dam safety requirements if the physical conditions involved or consequences of potential failure, when evaluated using accepted engineering practices, make the requirements unnecessary. 30 Tex. Admin. Code § 299.5.

§ 39.16:2 Design and Flood Evaluation

The design standard used for dams is the "probable maximum flood." The probable maximum flood is the flood magnitude that may be expected from the most critical combination of meteorologic and hydrologic conditions that are reasonably possible for a given watershed. 30 Tex. Admin. Code

§ 299.2(47). Dams must be constructed to safely handle an appropriate percentage of the probable maximum flood. The percentage varies based on the dam's size and downstream hazard potential. The dam's size—small, intermediate, or large—is based on the dam's maximum height or maximum reservoir storage capacity. *See* 30 Tex. Admin. Code § 299.13. The hazard classification—low, significant, or high—is based not on any condition of the dam itself but on the potential loss of human life and property damage in the event of a failure or malfunction of the dam or its appurtenant facilities. *See* 30 Tex. Admin. Code § 299.14. All large dams and all high-hazard dams must be designed to safely pass the full probable maximum flood; other dams are required to safely pass only a percentage of the probable maximum flood. *See* 30 Tex. Admin. Code § 299.15. Safely passing a flood for an existing dam means discharging the flood without a failure of the dam or one of its critical elements. As a supplement to its regulations, the TCEQ published *Hydrologic and Hydraulic Guidelines for Dams in Texas*, which contains detailed instructions, standards, and accepted procedures for the hydrologic and hydraulic analysis of existing and proposed dams. *See* Texas Commission on Environmental Quality, *Hydrologic and Hydraulic Guidelines for Dams in Texas* (GI-364, Jan. 2007), www.tceq.texas.gov/assets/public/comm_exec/pubs/gi/gi-364.pdf.

§ 39.16:3 Dam Safety Review

The TCEQ is involved at all stages of a dam's life. The construction of a dam or the enlargement, repair, or alteration of an existing dam may not begin without the written approval of the TCEQ's executive director unless the work is ordinary maintenance or emergency repair. 30 Tex. Admin. Code § 299.22. The TCEQ has issued *Design and Construction Guidelines for Dams in Texas*, which describes the design and construction requirements for the construction of a proposed dam or the reconstruction, modification, enlargement, rehabilitation, alteration, or repair of an existing dam. *See* Texas Commission on Environmental Quality, *Design and Construction Guidelines for Dams in Texas* (RG-473, Aug. 2009), www.tceq.texas.gov/assets/public/comm_exec/pubs/rg/rg-473.pdf.

A licensed professional engineer must prepare all plans and specifications for dams subject to the TCEQ's review unless the executive director waives this requirement. 30 Tex. Admin. Code § 299.4. If the plans and specifications for a dam are submitted to the TCEQ as part of an application for a water rights permit, the executive director will not issue written approval until after the water rights permit is issued. 30 Tex. Admin. Code § 299.22(e)(2)(A). Approval must be obtained before water is deliberately impounded in a partly or newly completed reservoir that will impound more than one thousand acre-feet at normal storage capacity. 30 Tex. Admin. Code § 299.28. After approval, the executive director may make periodic inspections of the construction to determine if the dam is in compliance with the approved plans and specifications. 30 Tex. Admin. Code § 299.25(b). If a project is not being constructed in accordance with the approved plans and specifications, the executive director will notify the owner of the deficiencies or violations and direct the owner to take the necessary action to bring the project into compliance within thirty days. 30 Tex. Admin. Code § 299.25(b).

After completion, the owner is responsible for operating and maintaining the dam and appurtenant structures in a safe manner. 30 Tex. Admin. Code § 299.41(a). The owner must develop and implement an operation and maintenance plan and, if the dam is an intermediate- or large-size dam with a gated spillway, must also implement a gate operation plan. 30 Tex. Admin. Code §§ 299.43–.44. In addition, owners of high-hazard dams that are notified by the TCEQ of the need for increased security must develop a security plan that includes measures to prevent unauthorized operation or access and backup power requirements to ensure operation. 30 Tex. Admin. Code § 299.62.

The TCEQ will perform periodic engineering inspections of dams, with the frequency of inspections determined by the dam's hazard classification. 30 Tex. Admin. Code § 299.42(a). The executive director may reclassify a dam's hazard classification at any time based on an inspection and downstream hazard evaluation, a breach analysis, or a review of current aerial photography and topographic maps, along with information obtained in the field. 30 Tex. Admin. Code § 299.12(b). If the owner of a dam is required to reevaluate the adequacy of an existing dam or spillway, the TCEQ may enter into an agreement with the owner that includes timelines to achieve compliance with the TCEQ's design criteria and that authorizes deferral of compliance with the criteria, as appropriate. Tex. Water Code § 12.052(b–1).

The TCEQ may issue an emergency order directing a dam's owner to repair, modify, maintain, dewater, or remove an unsafe dam if the dam's existing condition is creating or will cause extensive or severe property damage or economic loss to others, or is posing an immediate and serious threat to human life or health, and if other procedures available to remedy or prevent the occurrence of the situation will result in unreasonable delay. Tex. Water Code § 12.052(d). The emergency order may be issued without notice to the dam owner or with notice that is practicable under the circumstances. Tex. Water Code § 12.052(d). If the commission issues an emergency order without notice to the dam owner, the commission must hold a hearing as soon as practicable to affirm, modify, or set aside the emergency order. Tex. Water Code § 12.052(e). If the owner of a dam willfully fails or refuses to comply within thirty days of the TCEQ's final, nonappealable order requiring the owner to construct, reconstruct, repair, or remove the dam, the owner may be subject to a penalty for each day the violation continues. *See* Tex. Water Code § 12.052(c). The owner also may be subject to a daily penalty for willfully failing to comply with any rule or other order issued by the TCEQ pursuant to its dam safety authority. *See* Tex. Water Code § 12.052(c). See Chapter 13 of this book for a discussion of enforcement.

§ 39.16:4 Removal of Dams

The owner of a dam eventually may opt to remove the dam. Removal may be motivated by dam deterioration and risk of failure or simply by a desire to return the waterway to its original condition. The decision to remove a dam is made primarily by the owners and stakeholders of the structure. However, the executive director of the TCEQ may require the removal of deficient dams that fail to comply with the TCEQ's dam safety rules and pose a significant threat to human life or property. *See* 30 Tex. Admin. Code §§ 299.2(16), 299.51(a). Owners proposing to remove or breach a dam, or owners ordered to remove a deficient dam, must submit final plans and specifications to the executive director for review and approval before the start of work to remove or breach the dam. 30 Tex. Admin. Code § 299.51. The liability associated with the dam remains with the owner throughout the removal process.

The TCEQ publishes *Dam Removal Guidelines* that provide guidance to dam owners who are considering removing or breaching a dam. *See* Texas Commission on Environmental Quality, *Dam Removal Guidelines* (GI-358, Sept. 2006), www.tceq.texas.gov/assets/public/comm_exec/pubs/gi/gi-358.pdf. The guidelines state that before removing a dam, the owner should submit a dam removal plan to the TCEQ's Dam Safety Program for approval. *Dam Removal Guidelines*, at 3. The plan should include a schedule for conducting the phases of work, a description of the method to be used to dewater the reservoir, drawings showing the location and size of the breach, a rationale for the sizing and placement of the breach, a plan for preventing erosion and sediment loss, and an emergency action plan to address the risks associated with removal. *Dam Removal Guidelines*, at 3. The guidelines also contain a list of additional actions, approvals, and permits that may be required from both state and federal agencies. For instance, if the project will disturb more than one acre of land, the owner must develop and implement a Storm Water Pollution Prevention Plan. *Dam Removal Guidelines*, at 4. If the project will disturb more than five acres of land or is part of a larger common plan of development, the owner must also secure a Construction General Permit. *Dam Removal Guidelines*, at 4. Projects that involve the use of federal funds or that affect wetlands or waters of the United States may need approval from the U.S. Army Corps of Engineers. *Dam Removal Guidelines*, at 4.

§ 39.16:5 Public Notice Requirements for Flood Releases

In 2019, the Texas legislature enacted requirements for owners and operators of state-regulated dams with spillway gates used to regulate floodwaters to notify local emergency operations centers in downstream communities when spillway releases are made to regulate floodwaters. See Tex. Water Code § 12.052(a–1). The local emergency operation centers, in turn, are required to provide notice to the public when a release may contribute to flooding that may result in damage to life and property. See Tex. Water Code § 12.052(a–2). The notice must identify the dam and reservoir, the downstream communities potentially impacted, the expected duration of the release, and the level of potential flooding. See Tex. Water Code § 12.052(a–2). The notice required by section 12.052(a–2) may not be construed as an admission of liability and is not admissible as evidence in any lawsuit related to a release of floodwaters that is the subject of the notice. See Tex. Water Code § 12.052.

V. Conclusion

§ 39.17 Conclusion

Flooding is an inevitability for much of the state of Texas. As discussed in this chapter, some of the key issues presented by flooding include determining who, if anyone, is responsible for damage caused by flooding and the importance of preventing or minimizing the risk of damage by properly managing land development within the floodplain. Since Hurricane Harvey, flood management has become an even more critical issue even as the state must plan for how to meet the water supply needs of its growing population. The regional and state flood plan will focus on both identification and reduction of the flood risk and impact to life and property that already exist and prevention of additional flood risk in the future.

CHAPTER 40

Land Use and Water

Roel Lopez,[1] Forrest Cobb,[2] Allison W. Elder,[3] Jim D. Bradbury,[4] and Tiffany Dowell Lashmet[5]

I. Relationship of Land Use and Water

§ 40.1 Introducing the Relationship between Land Use and Water

Texas rivers, reservoirs, aquifers, and other bodies of water are influenced by their surrounding lands or watersheds and associated land uses. Understanding the relationship between land use (the primary economic and cultural human use of a piece of land) and water supplies (both quantity and quality) is essential for those wishing to manage water resources effectively. While the basic water cycle involves many factors, this chapter focuses on describing the general relationship of land use to water supplies in terms of development intensity, land use type, and management practices. Many local, state, and federal programs and policies serve to maintain healthy and sustainable water resources by protecting and enhancing the natural resource benefits from public and private lands. In this chapter, we hope to provide an overview of the land-water connection and some key approaches to improving our state's water supplies through natural resource management and common land use practices.

Texas is composed of nearly 171 million acres of land. Those lands make up our watersheds—the land area that channels rainfall or snowmelt into Texas streams, rivers, and lakes. Additionally, many of those lands also serve as contributing or recharge zones—areas where water flows into aquifers. The majority of that land base, approximately 82 percent, consists of *rural, working lands* (i.e., farms, ranches, and forest lands). *See* Addie Smith et al., Texas A&M Natural Resources Institute, *Status Update and Trends of Texas Working Lands 1997–2017* (Dec. 2019), https://

---

1. Roel Lopez is the Texas A&M Natural Resources Institute director and a professor in the Department of Rangeland, Wildlife, and Fisheries Management at Texas A&M University.

2. Forrest Cobb is a senior research associate at the Texas A&M Natural Resources Institute.

3. Allison W. Elder is the director of legal services at the San Antonio River Authority, where her practice focuses on real estate and conservation.

4. Jim D. Bradbury is an attorney in private practice with Austin and Fort Worth offices focusing on agricultural law, water, and land conservation.

5. Tiffany Dowell Lashmet is an associate professor and extension specialist in agricultural law in the Department of Agricultural Economics at Texas A&M University.

The authors gratefully acknowledge the contributions of Jewel Uzquiano and Alison Lund for providing a review of this chapter. Ms. Uzquiano is a research technician, and Ms. Lund is a program coordinator for the Texas A&M Natural Resources Institute.

nri.tamu.edu/media/2707/texas-land-trends_status-update-and-trends-of-tx-working-lands.pdf [hereinafter Smith et al. 2019]. These rural, working lands provide many public benefits, often referred to as "ecosystem services," including supplying the state's water needs. *See* U.S. Environmental Protection Agency, *Basic Information about Nonpoint Source (NPS) Pollution*, www.epa.gov/nps/basic-information-about-nonpoint-source-nps-pollution. Since 82 percent of Texas lands are farms, ranches, and forest lands, 82 percent of the state's annual rainfall falls on these private lands. The quality and quantity of water that makes its way into our water supply are dependent on the condition of that land base. As development intensity increases within a watershed from undeveloped lands to residential or industrial development, the ecosystem services provided by those lands are generally reduced and water resources degraded. *See* Mark Brown & M. Benjamin Vivas, *Landscape Development Intensity Index*, 101 Env. Mon. & Assess. 289 (2005). Therefore, the condition of rural lands is a crucial component to maintaining Texas water resources. Three primary ways rural lands influence water supply include (1) water capture, (2) flooding and water storage, and (3) water filtration and purification.

§ 40.1:1 Water Capture

One of the most significant factors in the conversion of rural, working lands within watersheds is the increase in impervious surfaces. See Chester L. Arnold, Jr. & C. James Gibbons, Impervious Surface Coverage: The Emergence of a Key Environmental Indicator, 62 J. Am. Plan. Ass'n 243 (1996); Elizabeth Brabec et al., Impervious Surfaces and Water Quality: A Review of Current Literature and Its Implications for Watershed Planning, 16 Journl of Plan. Lit. 499 (2002). As the proportion of impervious surfaces such as concrete, pavement, and roof surfaces increases within a watershed, infiltration of rainfall decreases and runoff increases. See Figure 1. Runoff picks up sediments and pollutants and moves quickly over ground surfaces, eventually entering a water body. This process can degrade the quality of the water supply and increase the risk of flooding. Impervious surfaces also prevent rainfall and surface waters from infiltrating or flowing into aquifers. The Edwards Aquifer is emblematic of both the challenges and possible solutions for maintaining water supply despite land conversion and development.

The Edwards Aquifer is one of the most productive aquifers in the United States and supplies water for more than 2 million Texans, being nearly the sole source of drinking water for the City of San Antonio. See City of San Antonio, Edwards Aquifer, www.sanantonio.gov/EdwardsAquifer. The contributing and recharge zones of the Edwards Aquifer, however, are located in the Texas Hill Country, which is being rapidly converted from rural, working lands to low-density housing and commercial uses. The unique characteristics of this area—the large sinkholes, sinking streams, and extensive cave networks—make the aquifer recharge rapid and the aquifer productive enough to serve San Antonio's large and growing population. See City of San Antonio, Edwards Aquifer. For example, one sinkhole located on private property was found to provide recharge of up to 1,770 gallons per second to the aquifer. See W. Hammond, Enhanced Recharge and Karst, Edwards Aquifer, South Central Texas, 25 Geol. Soc. of America, Absts. with Prog. (1993). The closing of such sinkholes through development on even just one property can have a significant impact on recharge potential. To protect its water supply, San Antonio funded the Edwards Aquifer Protection Program (EAPP) using a sales tax. This program established conservation easements on properties over the recharge zone to protect the city's primary source of drinking water. The program succeeded in conserving approximately 27 percent of the recharge zone before funding for the program was halted by the San Antonio City Council in 2020. Although plans to find alternative funding are currently underway, the future of the program remains in doubt. For more information on the EAPP, other Edwards Aquifer protection efforts, and conservation easement programs, see section 40.7:3 below. See also Chapter 17 of this book.

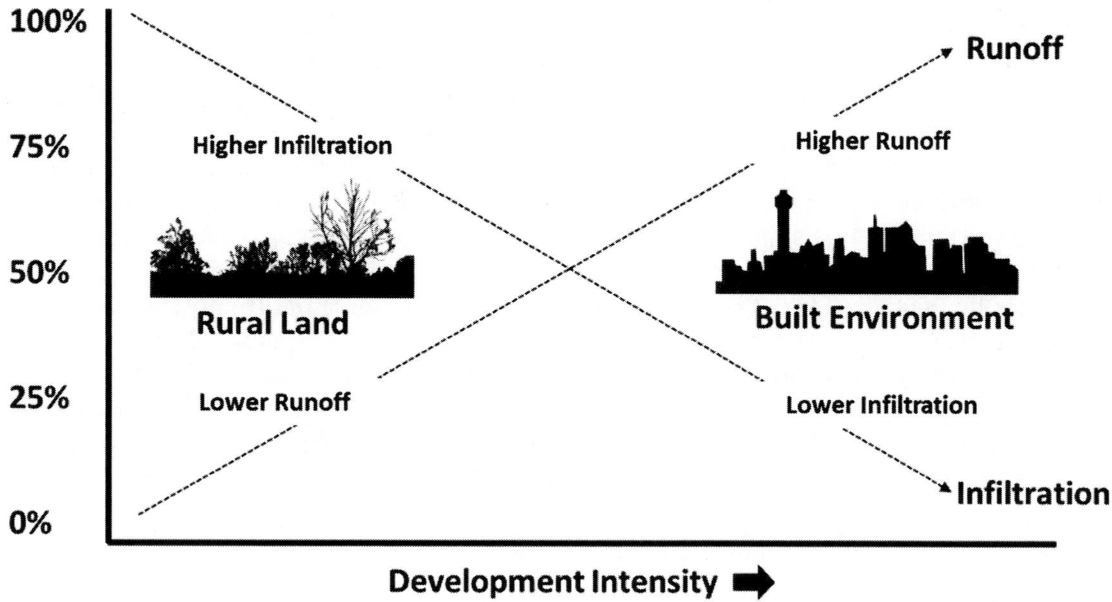

Figure 1. General relationship between land uses/cover types to water infiltration and runoff rates. Image created by Roel Lopez.

§ 40.1:2 Flooding and Water Storage

Undeveloped rural lands also play an important ecological function in flooding and water storage. Research has found soil infiltration and landscape water retention are crucial to reducing peak storm flows and flooding. A study by the U.S. Geological Survey reported that urbanization could increase water volume in peak flows by up to 250 percent in 100-year flood events, 300 percent in 10-year flood events, and 600 percent in 2-year flood events. See C.P. Konrad, Effects of Urban Development on Floods, U.S. Geological Survey Fact Sheet 076-03 (2003), http://pubs.usgs.gov/fs/fs07603/. The loss of natural storage areas such as wetlands, open spaces, and agricultural land often results in higher peak flow runoff volumes. For example, two Texas coastal studies reported higher property damage from floods where natural hydrological systems are fragmented, resulting in increased runoff. *See* Samuel Brody et al., *Examining the Impacts of Development Patterns on Flooding on the Gulf of Mexico Coast*, 50 Urb. Stud. 789 (2013); Samuel Brody et al., *Examining the Influence of Development Patterns on Flood Damages along the Gulf of Mexico*, 31 J. Plan. Educ. & Res. 438 (2011).

These processes are illustrated by flood prevention and mitigation challenges experienced by the City of Houston. After the unprecedented 1 trillion gallons of rainwater that Harris County (where Houston is located) received from Hurricane Harvey, the extensive damage and loss of life have spurred an even deeper conversation about flood prevention. See Jeff Lindner & Steve Fitzgerald, Memorandum: Hurricane Harvey—Storm and Flood Information, Harris County Flood Control District (June 4, 2018). Part of that conversation focuses on land fragmentation and development around Houston, which eliminates working lands and removes the remaining native coastal prairie ecosystem. A few defining features of the region's coastal prairies are surface depressions, referred to as prairie potholes, and deep-rooted grass species, both of which retain water, encourage water infiltration, and slow down overland water flow. See Waggonner & Ball, Living with Water Houston (Jan. 2020), https://reduceflooding.com/wp-content/uploads/2020/02/Living-With-Water.pdf; Morgan

Garner, Understanding the Impact of Changes to Coastal Prairie Landscapes on Watershed Response and Urban Flood Mitigation (Jan. 2020) [hereinafter Garner 2020]. In one estimate, the Katy Prairie Conservancy lands, which are 17,000 acres of preserved coastal prairie outside of Houston, retain as much as 0.6 acre-feet/acre of rainfall runoff, or approximately 10,200 acre-feet during a 100-year flood event. See Garner 2020. Organizations like the Katy Prairie Conservancy (KPC) are attempting to protect Houston from further loss of these lands by expanding their efforts. More information about the KPC is available at www.katyprairie.org/. Recently, the U.S. Department of Agriculture (USDA) Natural Resources Conservation Service (NRCS) awarded the KPC $7 million in funding from its Regional Conservation Partnership Program (RCPP) to conserve larger, contiguous areas of coastal prairie as a flood prevention and mitigation strategy. See Katy Prairie Conservancy and Partners awarded $7 million for The Texas Coastal Prairie Initiative to Conserve the Highly Imperiled Coastal Prairie Ecosystem in Texas, The Katy News (Apr. 28, 2021), https://thekatynews.com/2021/04/28/katy-prairie-conservancy-and-partners-awarded-7-million-for-the-texas-coastal-prairie-initiative-to-conserve-the-highly-imperiled-coastal-prairie-ecosystem-in-texas/. For more information on flood prevention programs, see section 40.7:2 below and Chapter 39 of this book, and for more on the NRCS and RCPP programs, refer to sections 40.6:1 and 40.8:1 below.

§ 40.1:3 Water Filtration and Purification

Finally, rural, working lands provide benefits to water quality through naturally occurring filtration and purification. These services are often complex and are expensive to replace. Several studies report that replacing these natural ecosystem services would cost the United States billions of dollars once lost. See James Salzman et al., Protecting Ecosystem Services: Science, Economics, and Law, 20 Stan. Env. L.J. 309 (2001). Texas wetlands are essential ecosystem service providers that benefit water quality. In the Dallas/Fort Worth area, leaders in water management have invested in the natural filtration and storage capacity of wetlands by incorporating natural and artificial wetlands into their water treatment system. In partnership with many state and private entities, the Tarrant Regional Water District and the North Texas Municipal Water District have created three wetland projects: the George Shannon Wetlands Project, the East Fork Water Reuse Project, and the John Bunker Wetland Center. See Texan by Nature, Constructed Wetlands—North Texas Municipal Water District and Tarrant Regional Water District (2018), https://texanbynature.org/wp-content/uploads/2018/06/Constructed-Wetlands-Project-Overview-2018-CW.pdf [hereinafter Texan by Nature 2018]. These projects aim to naturally treat and store wastewater before it is diverted to surrounding lakes and reservoirs. One of these projects, the George Shannon Wetlands Project, removes up to 95 percent of sediment loads and 50 to 60 percent of phosphorus and nitrogen from up to 92 million gallons of wastewater per day while also providing wildlife habitat and recreational hunting, fishing, and birding opportunities to the local community. See Plummer, Tarrant Regional Water District George W. Shannon Wetlands Water Reuse Project, www.plummer.com/projects/tarrant-regional-water-district-george-w-shannon-wetlands-water-reuse-project; Texan by Nature 2018. These projects supply raw water to approximately 3.8 million people in North Texas, are more cost-effective, and occupy a smaller footprint than additional reservoir investments. See Texan by Nature 2018. Because they operate on the same ecological principles, constructed wetland projects illustrate the importance of protecting existing native wetlands on rural lands that serve as natural infrastructure for maintaining water quality.

The types of activities and management practices employed on working lands can also have large effects on water quality. For example, detrimental impacts, such as the hypoxic or "dead" zones, in the Mississippi River and Gulf of Mexico require adjustment in land management rather than a shift in land use. This zone is the result of increased algae growth from nitrogen levels in runoff from surrounding lands. The excess nitrogen comes from many anthropogenic sources, including animal wastes and sewage, but evidence points to excessive use of nitrogen fertilizer within the Mississippi River Basin as the primary source. See G. Philip Robertson & Peter M. Vitousek, Nitrogen in Agriculture: Balancing the Cost of an Essential Resource, 34 Ann. Rev. of Env. and Res. 97 (2009).

Many state and federal programs work with private landowners to implement best management practices and prevent excess fertilizer runoff to improve water quality. One successful example of this type of program is on the Lower San Antonio River. In 2000, the Lower San Antonio River was added to the Clean Water Act section 303(d) list of impaired waters due to high levels of bacteria. See Environmental Protection Agency (EPA), Implementing Practices Through Cooperative Conservation Improves Water Quality in the Lower San Antonio River, Texas Success Stories, EPA 841-F-17-001Y (2017) [hereinafter EPA 2017]. This watershed is made up mostly of rural, working lands. The most significant contributors to bacteria were from runoff containing wildlife (primarily feral hogs), cattle, and to a lesser extent human fecal matter and sewage. See Steve Raabe, A Case Study in Watershed Conservation: Implementing Watershed Scale Best Management Practices in the San Antonio River Basin (San Antonio River Authority 2017) [hereinafter Raabe 2017]. Through a collaborative effort of many agencies, local governmental organizations, and community associations, watershed management plans were created and implemented across the Lower San Antonio River watershed. Management measures included feral hog trapping, restoration of riparian vegetation, stream bank restoration, and implementation of agricultural best management practices (Raabe 2017; EPA 2017). After fourteen years of program implementation, water quality in the Lower San Antonio River has improved, and portions of the river have been removed from the 303(d) list. For additional information on watershed protection programs, see section 40.8:2 below.

In our introduction of the relationship between land use and water, we recognize that undeveloped lands, which in Texas are primarily rural, working lands, are providing essential ecosystem services in maintaining water quantity and quality in the state. Rapid land use changes in Texas threaten these ecological benefits. In our next section, we review factors that are spurring land use change and increasing development and loss of rural, working lands.

§ 40.2 Changing Land Use in Texas

Understanding the current unprecedented changes in Texas land use and development are vital to water protection and watershed planning. Texas is currently comprised of approximately 141 million acres of rural, working lands, leading the nation in land area devoted to privately owned farms, ranches, and forestlands that support agricultural systems in addition to wildlands and wildlife habitat. *See* Smith et al. 2019. However, rural lands in Texas are being converted and lost at an astonishing rate. In their analysis of national land use trends, the American Farmland Trust found that nationally over 11 million acres of agricultural land had been fragmented, paved over, or converted to uses that jeopardize agriculture in a fifteen-year time period. *See* Julia Freedgood et al., *Farms Under Threat: The State of the States* (American Farmland Trust 2020). In that same study, the threat to Texas agricultural lands from fragmentation and conversion was ranked as the highest in the nation. Sections 40.3 and 40.4 below detail changes in Texas that are driving some of the land development–water conflicts discussed in section 40.1 above. A resource for further examining Texas land use trends, and the data used for those sections, can be found at the Texas A&M Natural Resources Land Trends Database. *See* Smith et al. 2019.

§ 40.3 Increase in Human Population

As previously mentioned, rural lands account for 82 percent of the state's entire land area and provide substantial economic, environmental, and recreational resources. *See* Smith et al. 2019. From 1997 to 2017, the population of Texas grew from 19 million to 29 million, an increase of 48 percent or approximately 470,000 new residents annually. The majority of this increase (86 percent) occurred within the state's top twenty-five highest population growth counties. *See* Smith et al. 2019. While these counties represent only 10 percent of the total land area of the state, 74 percent of all Texans reside within them. The state's increasing population has put pressure on rural lands surrounding those urban centers and has resulted in their continued fragmentation and conversion.

Looking ahead, between 2020 and 2070, the Texas population is expected to increase more than 70 percent from 29.7 million to 51 million. *See* Texas Water Development Board, *Water for Texas 2022* 47 (2022), www.twdb.texas.gov/waterplanning/swp/2022/ [hereinafter 2022 State Water Plan]. This growth will create significant water supply shortages in key regions of the state. Concentrated increases in human population are also an early predictor of land fragmentation, along with or often leading to the conversion of working lands to nonagricultural, higher intensity development uses. Current estimates are that Texas loses approximately 640 acres per day, which is even higher in and around these urban centers *See* Smith et al. 2019.

§ 40.4 Fragmentation and Conversion

An increase in the human population is generally followed by a demand for rural land to be converted to developed land. Rural land market values typically increase with this demand, which in turn results in an increased risk of fragmentation and conversion. Like traditional home real estate values, rural land market values vary by location, land use, property size, and other characteristics. The average appraised market value for Texas working lands has increased by 291 percent since 1997. *See* Smith et al. 2019. Changes in market value are closely tied to the growth of major metropolitan growth areas. The average land value in Texas within the top twenty-five fastest growing counties was nearly four times higher than the remaining 229 counties. *See* Smith et al. 2019. An increase in market value thus results in an increased risk of land fragmentation and conversion to nonagricultural uses. See Figure 2. The end result is an increase in land fragmentation (i.e., breaking up a larger farm into smaller parcels) or land conversion (i.e., converting a farm or ranch to subdivision or strip mall). In Texas, approximately six million acres of rural lands have been fragmented in addition to the more than two million acres of land conversion in the last twenty years. *See* Smith et al. 2019. Land use conversion rarely ever works in the opposite direction, to decrease development intensity and restore ecological functioning. Once lost, ecological services are very difficult, if not impossible, to fully restore.

Land fragmentation and conversion trends signal greater challenges or issues beyond the direct impacts due to changes in land uses. These other challenges include (1) greater demand for water resources with increasing human populations (*see* 2022 State Water Plan ch. 4); (2) challenges in managing smaller tracts of land due to incompatible and competing land uses and diverse ownership philosophies; and (3) higher levels of development intensity and conversion of highly permeable, undeveloped land surfaces to impervious areas that reduce water quantity and quality and increase runoff for a given area. In reviewing the projected future land ownership and use trends for the state compared to projected water needs from the state's water plan, the degree of the challenge becomes apparent. See Figure 3. Population increases are driving land use fragmentation and conversion with the potential to degrade water resource quality and quantity, while at the same time increasing demand for those water resources. This is especially apparent along the I-35 corridor, including over the Edwards Aquifer recharge zone, as well as in the counties surrounding Houston and Dallas. An exception to this can be seen in the Texas panhandle where high water demand is more likely associated with groundwater withdrawal for crop irrigation or for oil and gas development than with population increases.

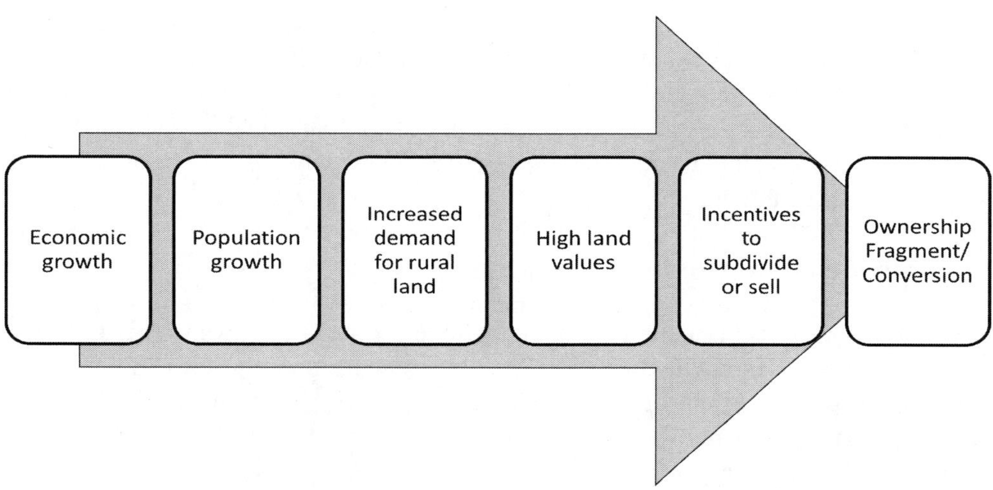

Figure 2. Process of land fragmentation and conversion driven by increasing population and land market value. *See* Smith et al. 2019.

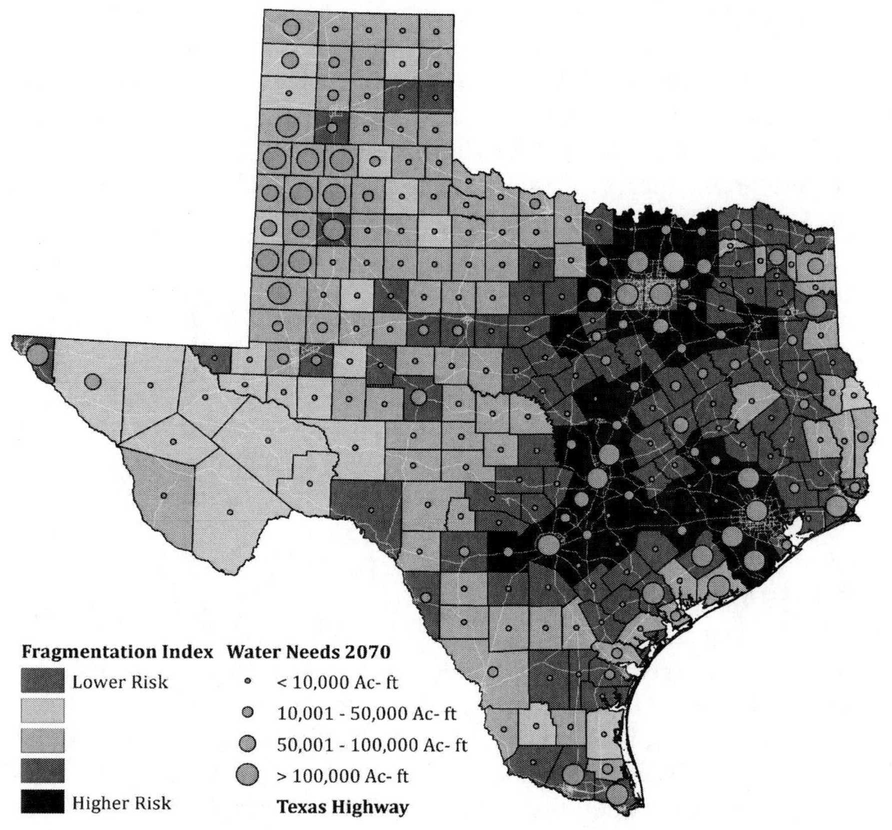

Figure 3. Risk of future land fragmentation and projected water needs in 2070. Texas fragmentation risk index created using market value percent change (1997 to 2017), operator age greater than 65 (2017), average operation size (2017), future population growth (2020 to 2070). Image created by Roel Lopez and Addie Smith based on data from Smith et al. 2019 and Texas Water Development Board, *Water for Texas 2017* (2017), www.twdb.texas.gov/waterplanning/swp/2017/.

II. Land Use Policy and Programs for Improving Watersheds

In part I of this chapter, we reviewed the relationship between land use and water supply. We also discussed the likely future trends and land uses moving forward in the state, which will continue to challenge our ability to effectively manage water supplies in a sustainable manner. In the next few sections, we will review some basic land use policies and stewardship programs that serve to counteract these future land trends.

§ 40.5 Overview of Conservation Programs

Certain land management practices can be beneficial for improving water quality and quantity in a given watershed. From a landowner perspective, such practices or activities can be encouraged and/or enforced through combinations of regulatory and incentive-based strategies designed to guide development and achieve balance between economic, social, and environmental forces within a landscape. In sections 40.6 through 40.8:3 below, we provide examples of programs that are managed and executed by federal, state, local, and nongovernmental organizations (NGOs) for the improvement of watersheds. In many cases, there may be overlap in terms of the organizations that are responsible for program execution. For example, you may have a federal agency that provides program funds that are executed in turn by a state agency, and in some cases, many federal programs require that state or local governments contribute funding to the project. This "local match" requirement can be a challenge in Texas. Most local jurisdictions have few resources devoted to property acquisition and often contend with state legislatures or constituencies that oppose taxes or fees that could generate the needed revenue to stretch conservation-oriented project dollars. *See* Mihir Zaveri, *Harris County Judge Ed Emmett Takes Aim at State Leaders in County Address*, *Houston Chronicle* (Nov. 28, 2017), www.chron.com/news/politics/houston/article/Harris-County-Judge-Ed-Emmett-takes-aim-at-state-12388878.php. The programs addressed below are organized within three broad categories: landowner incentives, zoning and permanent protections, and community partnerships.

§ 40.6 Landowner Incentives

The first group of programs are designed to encourage private landowner stewardship by incentivizing behaviors and practices that protect natural resources on private lands. Watershed management on private lands often involves incentivizing private landowners to manage their natural resources to their benefit and the benefit of the public at large. Incentive programs allow federal and state agencies to encourage sustainable use of these ecosystem services by providing financial and technical assistance to landowners.

§ 40.6:1 Farm Bill Overview

A landmark piece of legislation supporting conservation on private lands is the Agriculture Improvement Act of 2018, Pub. L. No. 115-334, www.congress.gov/bill/115th-congress/house-bill/2/text, also known as the 2018 Farm Bill, which is an $867 billion, five-year agricultural policy bill. The 2018 Farm Bill is a continuation of the 2008 Farm Bill and follows a long history of agricultural subsidies in energy, conservation, nutrition, and rural development. One of the major components of the Farm Bill is providing baseline funding for conservation and working lands programs ($60 billion in 2018). The majority of these programs are managed by the USDA NRCS as well as the Farm Service Agency (FSA).

Originally called the Soil Conservation Service, the NRCS was established by Congress in 1935 with the mission of conserving natural resources on private lands. The NRCS has since expanded to provide landowners technical and financial assistance to improve soil, water, and air conditions, which assists plant and animal life, for productive lands and healthy ecosystems. Common agency programs under the conservation and working lands umbrella are outlined and further described below (Table 1). Generally, Farm Bill conservation programs from a watershed protection perspective can be grouped as land retirement, working land enhancements, conservation easements (see section 40.8:3 below), and landowner partnerships (see section 40.9 below).

Table 1: USDA Natural Resources Conservation Service and Farm Service Agency Conservation Programs by Category, 2018

Program*	Category	Description
ACEP	Permanent Financial Incentives	Helps landowners, land trusts, and other entities protect, restore, and enhance wetlands, grasslands, and working farms and ranches through conservation easements.
AMA	Short-term Financial Incentives, Technical Assistance	Helps agricultural producers manage financial risk through diversification, marketing, or natural resource conservation practices. NRCS administers the conservation provisions while USDA's Agricultural Marketing Service and Risk Management Agency implement the production diversification and marketing provisions.
CIG	Technical Assistance	Awards competitive grants that drive innovation and develop the tools, technologies, and strategies for next-generation conservation efforts on working lands. Grantees leverage the federal investment through matching requirements. Through CIG's new On-Farm Trials, partners provide incentive payments to producers to offset the risk of implementing innovative approaches.
CRP	Short-term Financial Incentives	Protects soil, water quality, and habitat by removing highly erodible or environmentally sensitive land from agricultural production through long-term rental agreements.
CREP	Short-term Financial Incentives	Encourages landowners to sell or lease long term to beginning, socially disadvantaged, and veteran farmers and ranchers willing to implement sustainable practices or transition to organic production by providing two years of additional payments for expiring CRP-enrolled land.
CSP	Short-term Financial Incentives	Helps agricultural producers maintain and improve their existing conservation systems and adopt additional conservation activities to address priority natural resource concerns. Participants earn CSP payments for conservation performance—the higher the performance, the higher the payment.
EQIP	Short-term Financial Incentives, Technical Assistance	Provides financial and technical assistance to agricultural producers to address natural resource concerns and deliver environmental benefits, such as improved water and air quality, conserved groundwater and surface water, reduced soil erosion and sedimentation, and improved or created wildlife habitat.

HFRP	Permanent Financial Incentive	Helps landowners restore, enhance, and protect forestland resources on private lands through easements and financial assistance. Through HFRP, landowners promote the recovery of endangered or threatened species, improve plant and animal biodiversity, and enhance carbon sequestration.
RCPP	Landowner Partnerships Short-term Financial Incentives	Promotes coordination between NRCS and its partners to deliver conservation assistance to producers and landowners. Under partnership agreements, NRCS and its partners leverage and target their respective resources to deliver conservation assistance to producers and landowners to address priority natural resource concerns.
VPA-HIP	Short-term Financial Incentives	Provides state and tribal governments with funding or incentives to expand or improve habitat in existing public access programs.

*Note that most programs require the development of a conservation plan. For program descriptions and further specifics regarding plan requirements and eligible practices, visit www.nrcs.usda.gov. Acronyms defined as follows: ACEP = Agricultural Conservation Easement Program; AMA = Agricultural Management Assistance Program; CIG = Conservation Innovation Grants; CRP = Conservation Reserve Program; CREP = Conservation Reserve Enhancement Program; CSP = Conservation Stewardship Program; EQIP = Environmental Quality Incentives Program; HFRP = Healthy Forest Reserve Program; RCPP = Regional Conservation Partnership Program; and VPA-HIP = Voluntary Public Access and Habitat Incentive Program.

§ 40.6:2 Conservation Reserve Program

Land retirement programs authorize the USDA to make payments to private landowners to voluntarily retire land from production for less resource-intensive uses. The primary land retirement program in this category is the Conservation Reserve Program (CRP). The CRP pays producers annual rental payments under ten- to fifteen-year contracts to set aside previously cropped land that is marginally productive or highly erodible. In return for establishing and maintaining conservation practices that address soil erosion, water quality, wetland and forest enhancement, and wildlife management, landowners receive annual rental payments or cost-share assistance (not to exceed 50 percent of the eligible costs). Land must meet eligibility requirements to qualify for the CRP, which includes the following four programs: general CRP signup, continuous CRP, Conservation Reserve Enhancement Program, and the Farmable Wetlands Program (see Table 1). The CRP and continuous CRP practices include establishing vegetation cover or trees on erodible cropland, planting native grasses, or placing buffer strips along stream banks to reduce pollution. The primary benefit of this group of land retirement programs is enhancing the ecological functions of overall rural working lands in improving water quality or water quantity within the watershed. *See* U.S. Department of Agriculture, *Conservation Reserve Program Fact Sheet* (Dec. 2019), www.fsa.usda.gov/programs-and-services/conservation-programs/conservation-reserve-program/.

§ 40.6:3 Working Land Conservation Programs

Another category of land-based programs within the 2018 Farm Bill is "working land" conservation programs that allow private land to remain in production, while implementing various conservation practices to address specific natural resource concerns. Generally, program participants receive some form of conservation planning and technical assistance to find appropriate practices to apply given the natural resource concerns and land condition. The two main working lands programs are the Conservation Stewardship Program (CSP) and the Environmental Quality Incentives Program

(EQIP). Combined, both programs account for more than half of all conservation program funding. *See* U.S. Department of Agriculture, *Conservation Stewardship Program*, www.nrcs.usda.gov/wps/portal/nrcs/main/national/programs/financial/csp/; U.S. Department of Agriculture, *Environmental Quality Incentives Program*, www.nrcs.usda.gov/wps/portal/nrcs/main/national/programs/financial/eqip/.

The CSP differs from land retirement programs in that it rewards farmers and ranchers for maintaining existing conservation practices as well as undertaking additional conservation activities and improvements. Through five-year contracts, the program offers payments to producers who maintain a high level of conservation on their land and who agree to adopt higher levels of stewardship. It provides two possible types of payments. An annual payment is available for installing new conservation activities (e.g., no-till farming) and maintaining existing practices, and a supplemental payment is available for also adopting a resource-conserving crop rotation (e.g., planting soybeans every third year to add nitrogen back to the soil). Eligible lands include cropland, grassland, native prairie, improved pastureland, rangeland, nonindustrial private forest land, and agricultural land under the jurisdiction of an indigenous American tribe. The NRCS makes the CSP available on a nationwide basis through a continuous sign-up process.

Similar to the CSP, the EQIP provides technical assistance, incentive payments, and cost sharing to farmers and ranchers to implement, in many cases, longer-term conservation practices on their lands. Contracts can be up to ten years in duration, and allowable practices are based on a set of national priorities that are adapted to each state. These priorities range from reduction of point and nonpoint source pollution to watersheds and groundwater to the improvement of wildlife habitat for at-risk species.

§ 40.7 Zoning and Permanent Protections

The second group of land-based programs focuses on changes to landowner or property owner behaviors based on zoning restrictions or programs that afford permanent protection. Here we describe strategies promoting Low Impact Development as well as longer-term permanent protection such as the use of conservation easements.

§ 40.7:1 Low Impact Development

There are several approaches to encouraging what can collectively be described as Low Impact Development (LID). For example, municipal ordinances can be used to designate open spaces or passive recreation sites for flood detention, require LID practices, encourage density where appropriate, create conservation subdivision bonuses to incentivize density and conservation through unconventional land development, implement impervious cover limitations, and require a consideration of impacts on downstream communities, even if they lie outside the community's regulatory jurisdiction. All of these practices are considered LID.

Regional governmental entities may also encourage LID by funding beneficial land practices. For example, the San Antonio River Authority (SARA) has an active LID rebate program. This program provides rebates to reimburse a property owner for construction costs incurred installing qualifying LID measures such as permeable pavement, rain catchment systems, or bioswales. *See* San Antonio River Authority, *Low Impact Development*, www.sara-tx.org/be-river-proud/flood-risk/low-impact-development-lid. The SARA also maintains a LID manual and provides regular training to the development community. *See* San Antonio River Authority, *San Antonio River Basin Low Impact Development Technical Guidance Manual* (2d ed. May 2019), www.sariverauthority.org/sites/default/files/2019-08/SARB%20LID%20Technical%20Design%20Manual%202nd%20Edition.pdf.

Protected open space as part of a LID strategy also creates sites for flood detention by returning chronically flooded properties to a more "natural" state. Public purchases of flood-prone properties designed to remove residents from harm's way while compensating them financially are usually called "buyouts." *See* Governor's Commission to Rebuild Texas, *Eye of the Storm* (Nov. 2018), www.rebuildtexas.today/wp-content/uploads/sites/52/2018/12/12-11-18-EYE-OF-THE-STORM-digital.pdf [hereinafter Eye of the Storm]. The purchased property can then be returned to its natural flood function while creating open-space amenities for nearby residents. This provides an opportunity to use open-space protection to meet multiple objectives including flood risk reduction. Buyouts and open-space protection in vulnerable areas are important components of any effective flood risk reduction strategy in Texas. *See* Eye of the Storm. This is a slow process that can take more than two years. After the property has been purchased, an open-space use deed restriction is placed on the property, and the property cannot be developed again. *See* Rice University Kinder Institute for Urban Research, *Case Studies in Floodplain Buyouts: Looking to Best Practices to Drive the Conversation in the Houston Region* 8, 20 (Feb. 2018), https://kinder.rice.edu/sites/default/files/documents/KI%202018%20Buyout%20Report%20.pdf.

Another practice that is considered to be a LID strategy is the protection and restoration of existing wetlands and creation of wetlands around structures or on vacant parcels, which also helps accommodate flood waters. *See* Eye of the Storm. Regulations that prevent development along waterways and wetlands (setbacks) are particularly useful for creating areas that collect stormwater runoff while promoting public access. One national study found that communities that protect open spaces avoid an average of about $200,000 annually in insured flood losses. Multiple studies have found that preventing development near river systems also protects natural wetlands that absorb and store flood waters. *See* William J. Mitsch & James G. Gosselink, *Wetlands* (John Wiley & Sons, 5th ed. 2015); Samuel D. Brody et al., *Examining the Relationship between Wetland Alteration and Watershed Flooding in Texas and Florida*, 40 Nat. Hazards Rev. 413 (2007); Andy Bullock & Mike Acreman, *The Role of Wetlands in the Hydrological Cycle*, 7 Hydr. & Earth Sys. Sci. 358 (2003); William M. Lewis, Jr., *Wetlands Explained: Wetland Science, Policy, and Politics in America* (Oxford University Press 2001).

§ 40.7:2 National Flood Insurance Act

A major program that oftentimes is used in promoting LID is the National Flood Insurance Act, codified at 42 U.S.C. §§ 4001–4131, which created the National Flood Insurance Program (NFIP) to guide development away from flood hazard areas and to require that buildings be constructed in ways that would minimize or prevent flood damage (similar to the state's Texas Flood Funding Program). *See* Federal Emergency Management Agency, *National Flood Insurance Program (NFIP) Floodplain Management Requirements: A Study Guide and Desk Reference for Local Officials* 2–3 (Feb. 2005), https://arkansasfloods.org/wp-content/uploads/2014/06/FEMA-480.pdf. [hereinafter NFIP Floodplain Requirements]. The NFIP is a voluntary protection program administered by the Federal Emergency Management Agency (FEMA). More information is available at www.floodsmart.gov/.

The NFIP provides federally backed flood insurance to communities that agree to regulate development in their mapped floodplains to standards that meet or exceed NFIP criteria. As long as communities continue to develop the floodplains to the standards set by the NFIP, the whole community will be provided with federally backed insurance through the NFIP. This federally backed insurance benefits property owners who may be at risk of flooding by providing an affordable flood insurance product to mitigate their individual risk of loss due to flood damage. Local, state, and federal governments, together with private insurance companies, share roles and responsibilities in meeting the goals of the NFIP.

Both counties and cities have roles to play under the NFIP. Counties, unlike cities, do not have zoning authority. However, counties do have authority to establish and enforce subdivision ordinances and floodplain ordinances created under the NFIP. A city's zoning authority is an essential tool used to implement a comprehensive flood plan along with subdivision regulations, infrastructure planning, and economic strategies. *See* William Dahlstrom, *Zoning Regulations in Texas* 137, *in A Guide to Urban Planning in Texas Communities* (American Planning Association, Texas Chapter, 2013). A city's zoning authority is derived from chapter 211 of the Texas Local Government Code.

Enacting planning and zoning ordinances that establish standards and techniques to encourage or require low impact development and other types of beneficial land use is essential to protecting an urban watershed. The City of Austin and Cameron County are two examples of government entities that have adopted watershed protection ordinances. Austin's watershed protection ordinance focuses on environmental concerns and floodplain management. More than 400 miles of stream buffers were adopted to maintain natural drainage systems and block development in floodways. *See* Eye of the Storm. Cameron County created a Coastal High Hazard Zone with a 200-foot buffer landward of the FEMA-defined V-zone (a coastal area subject to inundation by a 100-year flood and storm-induced waves). *See* Eye of the Storm.

In some cases, the implementation of beneficial land uses may require that developed properties are converted back to an undeveloped state. As discussed above, some federal funding supports voluntary acquisition of properties that are at a high risk of repetitive flooding, often termed "buyout." The FEMA Hazard Mitigation Grant Program (HMGP) provides this type of funding. *See* www.fema.gov/grants/mitigation/hazard-mitigation. The agency collaborated with private, public, and academic sectors to develop an Environmental Benefits Analysis Report that identified benefits produced by deed-restricted open space and estimated the benefits communities gain from open space preservation, including flood hazard reduction, erosion control, habitat preservation, and recreation, at $2.57 per square foot annually for open green space and $12.29 annually for land near waterways. *See* Federal Emergency Management Agency, *Consideration of Environmental Benefits in the Evaluation of Acquisition Projects under the Hazard Mitigation Assistance Programs* 5 (June 18, 2013), https://salishsearestoration.org/images/d/d5/FEMA_2013_environmental_benefits_acquisition_hazard_mitigation.pdf.

The primary objectives of the HMGP are to "prevent or reduce future loss of lives and property through the identification and funding of cost-effective mitigation measures" and to "minimize the costs of future disaster response and recovery." *See* Texas Division of Emergency Management, *Hazard Mitigation Grant Program (HMGP)* (rev. Apr. 1, 2020), https://tdem.texas.gov/wp-content/uploads/2020/04/HMGP-Fact-Sheet_TDEM_04.01.2020-1.pdf. The HMGP provides federal funds for hazard mitigation projects such as the acquisition, demolition, or elevation of flood-prone structures and small-scale structural hazard control or protection projects. Limited funds are also available for public awareness projects and mitigation action plans such as flood studies. Land acquired through an HMGP buyout cannot be developed again but instead must be used for one of several purposes specified by FEMA, such as wetland restoration, wildlife refuges, gardens, and campgrounds.

§ 40.7:3 Conservation Easements

Permanent private land conservation can be accomplished through the use of a conservation easement. A conservation easement is a voluntary agreement, negotiated between a landowner and the easement holder, often a governmental entity or a nonprofit land trust. Some conservation easements are donated by property owners, and some conservation easements are purchased. Conservation easements are often used to protect natural areas to keep them in their undeveloped, natural, and open-space condition. Land trusts are NGOs whose mission is land and water conservation and that often employ or administer conservation easements. There are roughly thirty land trusts in Texas. Some operate statewide, and some are specific to a geographic location or environmental resource. They are uniquely positioned to partner with governmental entities, private foundations, and landowners to hold development rights in order to protect the ecosystem service benefits of open space. In some parts of the country, land trusts play a significant role in protecting clean drinking water sources locally or even preserving upstream lands that provide clean water protection benefits to downstream users that may be miles away.

The USDA's Agricultural Conservation Easement Program (ACEP) is a major funding program that provides financial and technical assistance to help conserve agricultural lands and wetlands through the purchase of conservation easements. *See* U.S. Department of Agriculture, Natural Resources Conservation Service, *Agricultural Conservation Easement Program,* www.nrcs.usda.gov/wps/portal/nrcs/main/national/programs/easements/acep/. Zoning is not required to create a conservation easement. The land trust or governmental entity seeking to acquire a conservation easement can purchase some property rights on a subject property, while allowing the landowner to retain many of the other property rights. A donated conservation easement could still retain the right to build a house and raise cattle while limiting other development rights. The landowner may continue its current use of the property, provided the resources the conservation easement is intended to protect are sustained and the limitations agreed to are followed. *See* Texas Land Trust Council, *What Is a Conservation Easement?*, www.texaslandtrustcouncil.org/index.php/about/what-is-a-conservation-easement.

The Texas Farm and Ranch Lands Conservation Program (TFRLCP) is an excellent example of a state-led conservation easement program, which is administered by the Texas Parks and Wildlife Department (TPWD). The TFRLCP funding can be used as matching dollars with federal programs like USDA's ACEP, and may include private landowner contributions as well. The TFRLCP seeks to conserve natural resources by protecting working lands from fragmentation and development through agricultural conservation easements, by leveraging monies to fund high-quality projects, and by highlighting the ecological, economic values of working lands. *See* Texas Parks and Wildlife Department, *Texas Farm and Ranch Lands Conservation Program*, https://tpwd.texas.gov/landwater/land/private/farm-and-ranch/.

As discussed in section 40.1 above, an example of a municipality using conservation easements to protect groundwater is the City of San Antonio's EAPP. The city used conservation easements to preserve the natural condition of lands that overlie the Edwards Aquifer Recharge and Contributing Zones to help ensure protection of the quantity and quality of water entering the aquifer. Beginning in 2000, voters approved a tax increase to identify and protect properties that are over the Edwards Aquifer Recharge Areas. *See* City of San Antonio, *Edwards Aquifer*, www.sanantonio.gov/EdwardsAquifer. Since that time, voters in San Antonio have authorized the investment of $225 million through four sales tax ballot measures. This program targets undeveloped land over the recharge zone and purchases conservation easements, which limit topographical change, subdivision, and impervious cover. Purchasing conservation easements instead of purchasing property in fee allows the City of San Antonio to stretch its dollars, protecting significantly more land than it could through fee simple acquisitions. The land remains in private ownership, under private management, and on the local tax rolls. The city protects its investment by monitoring its conservation easements annually and holds rights of enforcement in the event that a conservation easement is violated. *See* City of San Antonio, *Conservation Easement FAQs*, www.sanantonio.gov/ParksAndRec/Parks-Facilities/All-Parks-Facilities/Gardens-Natural-Areas/Edwards-Aquifer#280391501-protected-properties.
Currently, San Antonio has conservation easements over 156,081 acres. *See* City of San Antonio, *Protected Properties*, www.sanantonio.gov/ParksAndRec/Parks-Facilities/All-Parks-Facilities/Gardens-Natural-Areas/Edwards-Aquifer#280391501-protected-properties.

The City of Austin's bond program is a similar program managed by a municipality. Austin's program has funded the purchase of conservation easements and fee title to protect water resources in the community. In 1998, Austin initiated a program to purchase land and development rights from property owners. Today, the almost 30,000 protected acres include 25 percent of the Barton Springs recharge zone. *See* Jessi Devenyns, *After 20 Years the City Protects 25 Percent of the Barton Springs Recharge Zone*, *Austin Monitor* (Sept. 18, 2018), www.austinmonitor.com/stories/2018/09/after-20-years-the-city-protects-25-percent-of-the-barton-springs-recharge-zone/. Austin continues to expand its acquisition of environmentally significant land, conservation easements, and development rights for the protection of sensitive areas, including floodplains, riparian areas, wetlands, and land that supports recharge of the Edwards Aquifer. *See* City of Austin Planning and Zoning Department, *2018 Annual Report* 61 (Aug. 2018), http://austintexas.gov/sites/default/files/files/Imagine_Austin/DRAFT_IAannualreport_full.pdf.

Texas county governments also have the ability to fund conservation easement purchases. The Travis County Conservation Easement Program provides for the retention of open space and protection of natural resources through conservation easements with landowners. *See* Travis County, *Conservation Easement Program*, www.traviscountytx.gov/tnr/nr/conservation-easement. In 2014, the Travis County Commissioners Court unanimously approved the Land, Water, and Transportation Plan to protect land and water resources, build a comprehensive transportation system, and deliver related services in unincorporated Travis County. The plan includes a conservation map detailing conservation priorities for the county, which was developed from stakeholder feedback during the planning process. Potential conservation easements that support the implementation of the plan are given priority. *See* Travis County, *Land Water and Transportation Plan*, www.traviscountytx.gov/tnr/lwtp.

§ 40.8 Community Partnerships

The third and final group of land-based programs presented in this chapter focuses on landowner-community partnerships that result in the conservation of rural, working lands. This final group of programs can include both financial and technical assistance to include training, funding, or other resources such as personnel or equipment to assist land managers in implementing beneficial land use practices. Some examples of assistance programs in Texas are reviewed briefly below.

§ 40.8:1 NRCS Regional Conservation Partnership Program

The USDA NRCS RCPP is a major source of funding support for efforts that promote coordination between NRCS and its partners to deliver conservation assistance to producers and landowners (see Table 1). Under partnership agreements, NRCS and its partners leverage and target their respective resources to deliver conservation assistance to producers and landowners for addressing priority natural resource concerns. The Texas Gulf Coast Stream and Wetland Initiative, which NRCS RCPP selected in 2014 for funding, is an example partnership that targeted the Texas Gulf Coast region that was experiencing rapid growth and development, putting pressure on the aquatic resources of the region and contributing to the degradation of the Gulf of Mexico. The restoration and protection of headwater stream and wetland systems on agriculture lands are the focus of the project in order to improve function and provide protection against future impacts caused by development. The initiative seeks to achieve this through education and outreach and by increasing the number of landowners and land managers using conservation practices on their land. *See* U.S. Department of Agriculture, Natural Resources Conservation Service Texas, *Regional Conservation Partnership Program*, www.nrcs.usda.gov/wps/portal/nrcs/main/tx/programs/farmbill/rcpp/.

§ 40.8:2 EPA Watershed Protection Plans

The EPA is responsible for overseeing broad environmental protections to include clean water. Watershed protection plans are implemented by the EPA through state cooperators as part of the Clean Water Act. The Clean Water Act of 1972 (CWA; 33 U.S.C. § 1251) is a federal law that regulates the discharge of pollutants into the nation's surface waters, including lakes, rivers, streams, wetlands, and coastal areas. The EPA provides states with a comprehensive guide for developing watershed plans in the 2008 *Handbook for Developing Watershed Plans to Restore and Protect our Waters*, available at www.epa.gov/sites/production/files/2015-09/documents/2008_04_18_nps_watershed_handbook_handbook-2.pdf. The Handbook also provides guidance on how to incorporate the nine minimum elements from the Clean Water Act Section 319 Nonpoint Source Program. See Chapter 33 of this book for further discussion.

The Texas State Soil and Water Conservation Board (TSSWCB) is a state agency that administers soil and water conservation law and coordinates conservation and nonpoint source water pollution abatement programs throughout the state. Such programs include nonpoint source pollution plans (mandated) and watershed protection plans (voluntary/local stakeholder driven process). *See* Texas State Soil and Water Conservation Board, www.tsswcb.texas.gov/tsswcb-home-page.

For nonpoint source pollution plans, the federal CWA requires the state to identify lakes, rivers, streams, and estuaries failing to meet or not expected to meet water quality standards for their designated uses (i.e., swimming, drinking, aquatic life). This list of impaired waterbodies is known as the Texas 303(d) List and is submitted to the EPA for review and approval every two years. In response, the state then establishes a Total Maximum Daily Load (TMDL) for those water bodies on the 303(d) List. A TMDL defines the maximum daily amount of a pollutant that a waterbody can assimilate. The reduction goal set by the TMDL is necessary to restore attainment of the designated use of the impaired waterbody. An Implementation Plan (I-Plan) is then developed that prescribes the measures necessary to meet the TMDL standard. The I-Plan specifies limits for point source dischargers, recommends best management practices for nonpoint sources, and outlines a schedule for implementation. The TMDL and the I-Plan are intended to function together to restore the full use of the waterbody, and remove it from the 303(d) List. *See* Texas State Soil and Water Conservation Board, *Total Maximum Daily Load Program*, www.tsswcb.texas.gov/programs/texas-nonpoint-source-management-program/total-maximum-daily-load-program. See also Chapter 33.

In contrast, Watershed Protection Plans (WPPs) are a coordinated framework for implementing prioritized and integrated water quality protection and restoration strategies (primarily outlined by EPA's Handbook) driven by environmental objectives. Through the watershed planning process, the state encourages stakeholders to develop WPPs that address sources and causes of impairments to both surface and ground water resources within a watershed. Developed and implemented through diverse and integrated partnerships, a WPP assures the long-term health of a watershed. Adaptive management is used to modify the WPP based on science that involves monitoring, evaluating strategies, and incorporating new knowledge into decision-making. The TSSWCB and the Texas Commission on Environmental Quality provide technical and financial assistance to stakeholder groups to develop and implement WPPs. *See* Texas State Soil and Water Conservation Board, *Watershed Protection Plan Program*, www.tsswcb.texas.gov/programs/texas-nonpoint-source-management-program/watershed-protection-plan-program. See also Chapter 33.

§ 40.8:3 Innovative Watershed Partnerships and Funding Sources

Flood resiliency was a critical focus in the 2019 state legislative session, due in large part to Hurricane Harvey in 2017. In response to this need, the 86th Texas Legislature passed Senate Bill 7, Acts 2019, 86th Leg., R.S., ch. 947 (S.B. 7), eff. June 13, 2019, marking the first time the state had a significant role in funding flood mitigation infrastructure. *See* Taylor Landin, *86th Legislative Session Summary* (June 20, 2019), www.houston.org/news/86th-legislative-session-summary. Senate Bill 7 amended the Texas Water Code to create both a Flood Infrastructure Fund (FIF) and a Texas Infrastructure Resiliency Fund (TIRF) to be administered by the Texas Water Development Board (TWDB). *See* Acts 2019, 86th Leg., R.S., ch. 947 (S.B. 7), eff. June 13, 2019. See also Chapter 37 of this book. The bill outlined the purposes of both funds, application requirements, and appropriate uses. The definition of a "flood project" for the FIF included the "construction and implementation of nonstructural projects, including projects that use nature-based features to protect, mitigate, or reduce flood risk." Tex. Water Code § 15.531(2)(D). Similarly, the TIRF defined "flood project" as "a drainage, flood mitigation, or flood control project, including . . . nonstructural or natural flood control strategies." Tex. Water Code § 16.451(3)(D). This recognition of the functionality of the natural environment as a flood mitigation strategy should provide a source of local match dollars in Texas and an opportunity for local jurisdictions to secure federal dollars in order to implement conservation projects in flood-prone areas. In Texas, additional local match dollars are made available through several programs including the Clean Water State Revolving Fund administered by the TWDB and the Texas Farm and Ranch Land Conservation Program administered by the TPWD. Chapter 37 of this book provides additional information regarding the TWDB's Clean Water State Revolving Fund.

As an example of state funding outside of Texas, the state of Minnesota has a well-established and successful state program for water resource protection, the Reinvest in Minnesota Reserve Program (RIM). Minnesota has invested more than $200 million to help improve water quality, wildlife habitat, and flood attenuation on private lands. Under RIM, landowners are compensated for granting conservation easements on economically marginal, flood-prone, environmentally sensitive, or highly erodible agricultural lands. In partnership with the NRCS, the county soil and water conservation districts, land trusts, and other conservation organizations, the state of Minnesota has purchased more than 6,000 conservation easements covering more than 250,000 acres since the program began. *See* Minnesota Board of Water and Soil Resources, *Reinvest in Minnesota Overview*, www.bwsr.state.mn.us/reinvest-minnesota-overview.

Finally, some NGOs have contributed funding for beneficial land practices that protect water resources, and several water-dependent industries have voluntarily invested significant dollars in the evaluation and implementation of water conservation methods. These investments often involve collaboration with nonprofits, such as The Nature Conservancy or Ducks Unlimited, with private foundations with a focus on environmental protection, or with governmental entities such as the TPWD. One example of this type of collaborative effort is the One Water initiative of the Mitchell Foundation. The goal of One Water is to ensure that the water quantity and quality needs of the Texas environment are met, now and into the future. This initiative engaged leaders from governmental, nonprofit, and for-profit industries to develop a collaborative approach to statewide water management. *See* Rachel Cardone & Carol Howe, *Advancing One Water in Texas* (Feb. 2018), https://cgmf.org/graphics/cgmf_one_water_report_02_14_18_final.pdf?eType=EmailBlastContent&eId=c64dd049-19fc-41e2-b93c-517ec4b863d9.

Examples of innovative partnerships outside of Texas are the New York City Watershed Protection Program and the Chesapeake Bay Watershed Agreement. For the former, New York City was faced with an enormous requirement of building a water treatment plant to address watershed impairment issues within the watershed that services the city's water supply. The municipal water supply system provides about one billion gallons of drinking water a day to over 9.5 million people in New York City and nearby Westchester, Putnam, Ulster, and Orange counties with a total storage capacity of approximately 580 billion gallons. Instead of building a multimillion-dollar water treatment plant, the city chose to work with private landowners and other communities in developing the Watershed Protection Program to maintain and enhance the quality of these surface water sources. The program was extremely successful. *See* National Academies of Sciences, Engineering, and Medicine, *Review of the New York City Watershed Protection Program* (Nov. 2020), www.nap.edu/resource/25851/NYC%20Watershed%20-%204%20Pager.pdf.

Similarly, the Chesapeake Bay Watershed Agreement was a watershed-scale effort that included multiple federal agencies and departments, six states, the District of Columbia, and the Chesapeake Bay Commission. Through this agreement, stakeholders agreed on common goals and outcomes for the watershed. The agreement was created in response to degradation of water quality in the Chesapeake Bay caused by a systemic overabundance of human-introduced nitrogen and phosphorus. These poor conditions feed algae blooms that block sunlight to underwater grasses and contribute to the formation of "dead zones"—areas in the bay and tidal waters lacking healthy oxygen levels. The Chesapeake Bay program brought together these participants, along with academic and local watershed organizations, to build and adopt policies that support the restoration of the bay. The Chesapeake Bay Watershed Agreement represents the first time representatives from an entire watershed signed onto a watershed-scale restoration agreement. *See* Chesapeake Bay Program, *Chesapeake Bay Watershed Agreement*, www.chesapeakebay.net/what/what_guides_us/watershed_agreement.

III. Conclusion

§ 40.9 Conclusion

Water resources in Texas are influenced by their surrounding land uses and land users. Undeveloped lands, especially wildlands in their natural condition, provide numerous ecosystem services that benefit water resources. Rural, working lands can benefit water resources when best management practices are implemented that lead to the retention of functional ecosystem services such as water storage, water filtration, and flood mitigation. As the population of Texas grows, land market pressures will continue to increase in rural areas, resulting in increased ownership fragmentation, land use conversion, and increased development intensities. The resulting changes in land use can degrade water quality and quantity; however, some tools are available to Texas communities and landowners to address these pressures and mitigate these risks. These tools include incentivizing land and water protection, preventing incompatible development through conservation easements, and encouraging beneficial management strategies. Communities wishing to conserve their natural resources for the well-being of their citizens and the environment should consider land use and land management as major components of future planning and proactively develop a suite of strategies to protect undeveloped wild and working lands, conserve productive and functional ecosystems, and ensure quality of life for the future.

IV. References

Arnold, C. L., Jr., and C. J. Gibbons. 1996. *Impervious surface coverage: The emergence of a key environmental indicator*. Journal of the American Planning Association, v. 62, pp. 243–58.

Brabec, E., Schulte, S., and P.L. Richards. 2002. *Impervious surfaces and water quality: A review of current literature and its implications for watershed planning*. Journal of Planning Literature, v. 16(4), pp. 499–514.

Brody, S.D., Highfield, W.E., Ryu, H.C., and L. Spanel-Weber. 2007. *Examining the relationship between wetland alteration and watershed flooding in Texas and Florida*. Natural Hazards, v. 40, pp. 413–28.

Brody, S.D., Zahran, S., Highfield, W.E., Grover, H., and A. Vedlitz. 2008. *Identifying the impact of the built environment on flood damage in Texas*. Disasters, v. 32, pp. 1–18.

Brody, S.D., Gunn, J., Peacock, W., and W.E. Highfield. 2011. *Examining the influence of development patterns on flood damages along the Gulf of Mexico*. Journal of Planning Education and Research, v. 31, pp. 438–48.

Brody, S.D., Kim, H., and J. Gunn. 2013. *Examining the impacts of development patterns on flooding on the Gulf of Mexico coast*. Urban Studies, v. 50, pp. 789–806.

Brown, M.T., and M.B. Vivas. 2005. *Landscape Development Intensity Index*. Environmental Monitoring and Assessment, v. 101, pp. 289–309.

Bullock, A., and M. Acreman. 2003. *The role of wetlands in the hydrological cycle*. Hydrology and Earth System Sciences, v. 7, pp. 358–89.

Garner, M. 2020. *Understanding the impact of changes to coastal prairie landscapes on watershed response and urban flood mitigation*. Thesis, Rice University.

Hammond, W.W., Jr. 1993. *Enhanced recharge and karst, Edwards Aquifer, South Central Texas*. Geological Society of America, Abstracts with Programs, v. 25:1; Conference 27. Annual GSA South-Central Section meeting, Fort Worth, TX.

Lewis, W.M., Jr., 2001. *Wetlands explained: Wetland science, policy, and politics in America*. Oxford University Press.

Mentens, J., Raes, D., and M. Hermy. 2006. *Green roofs as a tool for solving the rainwater runoff problem in the urbanized 21st century*. Landscape and Urban Planning, v. 77, pp. 217–26.

Mitsch, W.J. and J.G. Gosselink. 2015. *Wetlands*. Fifth edition. John Wiley & Sons.

Robertson, G.P., and P.M. Vitousek. 2009. *Nitrogen in agriculture: Balancing the cost of an essential resource*. Annual Review of Environment and Resources, v. 34, pp. 97–125.

Salzman, J., Thompson, B.H., Jr., and G.C. Daily. 2001. *Protecting ecosystem services: Science, economics, and law*. Stanford Environmental Law Journal, v. 20, pp. 309–32.

CHAPTER 41

Water-Energy Nexus

Holly Heinrich[1]

I. Introduction

§ 41.1 Introduction

Texas is an energy powerhouse, both in fossil fuel and renewable energy resources. However, the Texas energy sector also has an Achilles' heel. Texas periodically experiences both severe drought and severe flooding, creating potential long-term vulnerability in an energy sector that relies heavily on water to extract energy resources and generate power. Understanding this nexus between water and energy is important for understanding—and shaping—the future of Texas.

In most respects, Texas's energy future is bright. More than a fifth of the nation's domestically produced primary energy (the energy harvested directly from natural resources) is produced here in the Lone Star State, and Texas leads the nation in crude oil reserves and production, as well as in crude oil refining and natural gas production. *See* U.S. Energy Information Administration, *Texas State Profile and Energy Estimates, Profile Analysis* (Mar. 19, 2020), www.eia.gov/state/analysis.php?sid=TX [hereinafter EIA State Profile for Texas]; *see also* U.S. Energy Information Administration, *State Energy Production Estimates 1960 through 2018* 6 tbl. P4, www.eia.gov/state/seds/sep_prod/pdf/P4.pdf; Jason Donev et al., University of Calgary, *Primary Energy*, https://energyeducation.ca/encyclopedia/Primary_energy (defining primary energy).

Texas also generates more electric power than any other U.S. state, accounting for twice the electric power generation of the next highest-producing state, Florida. *See* U.S. Energy Information Administration, *Texas State Profile and Energy Estimates, Profile Overview* (Mar. 19, 2020), www.eia.gov/state/?sid=TX#tabs-2 [hereinafter EIA Energy Estimates for Texas]. In 2019, Texas led the nation in wind power generation, providing over a quarter of national wind generation. Texas also has some of the most significant solar potential in the United States, as discussed in section 41.6 below.

Water scarcity and flooding, however, pose a threat to the Texas energy sector, as well as to other areas of the state economy. Texas is prone to extreme cycles of drought and flood. Climate change research indicates that these extremes are likely to intensify over time. Population growth, as well as growth in energy resource extraction, may also strain Texas water supplies, unless adequate steps are taken to conserve and use water efficiently.

Water is essential to both the extraction of fossil fuels and the generation of thermoelectric power. Severe water scarcity can compel power generation facilities to reduce or shut down generation, potentially causing rolling brownouts or blackouts. Water scarcity can also limit fossil fuel extraction or refining activities.

---

1. Holly Heinrich is an assistant city attorney in the Utilities Division of the City of Austin Law Department. The views expressed in these materials do not necessarily represent those of the City of Austin.

Energy is also needed to extract, treat, and distribute water. Reductions in electric power generation can thus prevent public water supply systems from supplying water to their customers, as Texans witnessed during a brutal, days-long winter storm and frigid cold spell in February 2021. During that storm, ice and subfreezing temperatures knocked nearly 50 percent of available generation offline across the state, while demand for power surged to near summer-peak levels as Texans struggled to keep warm. Water utilities struggled to supply customers with safe drinking water—and to supply some customers with any water at all—because of power failures, low water pressure, and reduced water supply caused by line breaks and high water demand. (Few buildings in Texas have water pipes insulated to withstand the Arctic temperatures that plagued the state in February 2021, and water pipes across the state froze and burst as a result.)

The power failures of February 2021, and Texans' subsequent loss of access to safe drinking water—and in some cases any running water—demonstrate that the water-energy nexus is far from a mere academic concept. The connections between water and energy affect almost all the activities that make up our daily lives. Maintaining these critical linkages is essential to preserving public health, sanitation, the economy, and a functioning society.

This chapter explores the interconnections between water and energy issues in Texas and demonstrates how supply disruptions in one resource can impact the availability of the other. The water-energy nexus concept is introduced in section 41.2 below. Part II of this chapter discusses how rising water and power demand, the booming Texas energy sector, climate change, technological advances, federal policy, and other new developments are affecting Texas water and energy resources. Part III describes how the water-energy nexus has been applied as a concept at the international, national, and state levels. Part IV provides a detailed discussion of how water is used for energy resource extraction and electric power generation, while part V explains how energy is used to extract, treat, and distribute water.

§ 41.2 Defining the Water-Energy Nexus

The "water-energy nexus" describes the interdependent relationship between energy and water resources. The nexus concept recognizes that water is often needed to extract energy resources and generate electrical power, while energy is needed to extract, treat, and distribute water. Thus, water scarcity can limit power generation and energy resource extraction, while reduced power generation can prevent water suppliers from withdrawing, treating, and distributing water.

There are numerous examples of the water-energy nexus in Texas. Water is a key component in hydraulic fracturing, or "fracking," as energy companies have been able to extract previously inaccessible reserves of oil and natural gas by injecting a mixture of water, chemicals, and other substances into underground rock formations containing hard-to-reach reserves, causing oil and natural gas to escape when the rock fractures. This is discussed in depth at section 41.14 below. Water is also used to cool thermal power generation facilities and refine raw oil, natural gas, and other resources into usable fuels, while energy is needed to treat drinking water and pump water to users throughout the state. In Texas, the nation, and around the world, some policymakers increasingly recognize that decisions about water and energy resources would be better formed if governments considered how decisions about one resource impact the other. However, many governments have no comprehensive strategy for coordinating the development of water and energy policy.

§ 41.3 Limitations of This Chapter

This chapter has several limitations. First, while efforts have been made to ensure uniformity in the data provided, much of the data cannot be directly compared. The data here is drawn from a range of governmental, quasi-governmental, and private sources located in Texas, the United States, and throughout the world. This data was also collected over different time periods and for different purposes. Therefore, the data in this chapter should be used as a reference point for understanding various water and energy topics but not for the purposes of comparison.

In addition, water quality is not a major focus of this chapter, although the use of energy for water treatment is discussed. Water availability, use, and consumption are the main water issues addressed here. "Use" is distinguished from "consumption" throughout the chapter. Water that is "used" may be used again in the short term, perhaps immediately or after treatment. In contrast, water is "consumed" by processes that render it unavailable for reuse in the short term—as when irrigation water becomes part of a crop, or when energy extraction or manufacturing methods render water too polluted to reuse or recycle. Thus, in this chapter, water quality issues are primarily discussed when a process renders water so polluted that it is "consumed" by that use.

Lastly, while many sources cited in this chapter periodically update their findings and figures, there are instances where the most comprehensive and recently available data was collected as long as ten to twenty years ago. Thus, this data may not reflect the current state of the energy and water sectors in Texas and the United States and may not provide an accurate understanding of the circumstances we can expect to see in the future.

II. The Water-Energy Nexus in Texas: Present and Future

§ 41.4 Current and Predicted Demand for Water and Energy

Texas not only produces more energy than any other U.S. state but also consumes more energy. *See* EIA Energy Estimates for Texas. Texas consumed 14,227.4 trillion Btu of energy in 2019. U.S. Energy Information Administration, *Table C11: Energy Consumption Estimates by End-Use Sector, Ranked by State, 2019* (2019), www.eia.gov/state/seds/sep_sum/html/pdf/rank_use.pdf. The industrial sector accounted for most of the statewide energy consumption, constituting 52.7 percent. *See* EIA Energy Estimates for Texas. Transportation accounted for 23.4 percent, residential for 12.4 percent, and commercial for 11.4 percent. *See* EIA Energy Estimates for Texas.

The water demand patterns for various sectors of the Texas economy differ widely, although it is difficult to compare estimates from the U.S. Energy Information Administration (EIA) and the Texas Water Development Board (TWDB) because they separate users into different categories. Total Texas water use was approximately 14.66 million acre-feet (AF) in 2018. *See* Texas Water Development Board, *Historical Water Use Estimates, 2018 Water Use Estimates Summary* 1 (June 15, 2020), www.twdb.texas.gov/waterplanning/waterusesurvey/estimates/ [hereinafter 2018 Water Use Estimates Summary]. Agricultural irrigation used more water than any other sector, accounting for 54 percent of statewide water use (7.97 million AF). Municipal water use was the second highest, constituting 30 percent (4.66 million AF). Manufacturing accounted for 7 percent of total Texas water use, while the power and mining sectors accounted for 3 and 1 percent, respectively. Livestock accounted for the remaining 2 percent. *See* 2018 Water Use Estimates Summary, at 1.

The demand for water and energy in Texas is only expected to rise. Texas's recent increases in water and energy demand—as well as predicted future increases—are due, in part, to the state's growing population. Between 2010 and 2020, Texas gained approximately 4 million new residents, more than any other U.S. state. *See* U.S. Census Bureau, *Texas: 2020 Census*, www.census.gov/library/stories/state-by-state/texas-population-change-between-census-decade.html [hereinafter U.S. Census 2020]. *See also* Alexa Ura et al., *People of Color Make Up 95% of Texas' Population Growth, and Cities and Suburbs Are Booming, 2020 Census Shows*, *Texas Tribune*, Aug. 12, 2021, www.texastribune.org/2021/08/12/texas-2020-census/ [hereinafter Ura et al.]. Major cities such as Austin, San Antonio, Dallas, and Houston have absorbed much of this population growth, requiring utilities in these areas to figure out how to meet rising demand. *See* U.S. Census 2020; *see also* Ura et al. From 2020 to 2070, the state population is expected to nearly double, from 29.7 million to 51.5 million. *See* Texas Water Development Board, *Water for Texas 2022* 3 (2022), www.twdb.texas.gov/waterplanning/swp/2022 [hereinafter 2022 Texas State Water Plan].

Water demand is rising with the growing population, which will impact the demand for energy needed to produce, treat, and distribute water. Municipal water demand is expected to increase more than demand from any other sector. According to the TWDB, municipal demand will increase by 63 percent over the next five decades, from 5.2 million AF per year in 2020 to 8.5 million AF in 2070. *See* Texas Water Development Board, *2021 Regional Water Plan, Water Demand Projections for 2020–2070, Texas State Summary in Acre-Feet* (Mar. 28, 2019), https://www3.twdb.texas.gov/apps/reports/Projections/2022%20Reports/demand_state [hereinafter 2021 TWDB Water Demand Projections]; *see also* Memorandum from Temple McKinnon, Director, Water Use, Projections & Planning, Texas Water Development Board, & Yun Cho, Manager, Economic and Demographic Analysis, Texas Water Development Board, to Texas Water Development Board Members 4 (Apr. 5, 2018), www.twdb.texas.gov/waterplanning/rwp/planningdocu/2021/doc/board_memos/2018-04_Brd12.pdf [hereinafter 2018 TWDB Water Demand Projections]. Beginning in 2060, municipal demand is expected to become the largest water demand category in Texas, displacing agricultural irrigation as the sector with the greatest water use. *See* 2021 TWDB Water Demand Projections.

By 2070, Texas could experience a water shortfall of approximately 5.6 million AF during a drought if no measures are taken to curb statewide water demand and better manage state water supplies. This shortfall would occur because water demand is expected to reach 19.2 million AF by 2070—but it is estimated that as little as 13.6 million AF of water would be reliably available during a drought by 2070. *See* 2018 TWDB Water Demand Projections, at 3; 2022 Texas State Water Plan, at 3. This means that the reliable water supply during a drought in 2070 would be 18 percent lower than the 16.8 million AF expected to be reliably available if a drought occurred in 2020. *See* 2022 Texas State Water Plan, at 3. This shortfall could negatively impact the energy sector activities that rely on the availability of an adequate water supply.

Rising energy demand, changing generation capacity, and extreme weather also affect Texas's ability to supply power to the state's growing population. Millions of Texans experienced this personally in February 2021, when a series of Arctic storms swept across Texas and knocked approximately 48.6 percent of the state's power generation capacity offline. *See* Jozelyn Escobedo & Tanya Eiserer, *'This Was a Devastating Event,' CEO Says in ERCOT Board Meeting After Millions Lost Electricity Last Week*, *Dallas Business Journal*, Feb. 24, 2021, www.bizjournals.com/dallas/news/2021/02/24/ercot.html. Millions of Texans were without power for days. Nearly two-thirds of Texans also found themselves without safe drinking water—or without water altogether—as power outages shut down water treatment plants and subfreezing temperatures caused water pipes to burst in buildings not designed to withstand the extreme cold. Loss of power at water treatment plants, low water pressure, and surging demand left water utilities across the state temporarily unable to supply their customers. The winter storm thus serves as a stark reminder of the critical nexus between water and energy. The sudden loss of power and safe drinking water thrust millions of Texans into conditions of life reminiscent of the frontier days. *See* Jack Healy, Richard Fausset & James Dobbins, *Cracked Pipes, Frozen Wells, Offline Treatment Plants: A Texan Water Crisis*, *New York Times*, Feb. 18, 2021, www.nytimes.com/2021/02/18/us/texas-water-crisis-winter-storm.html.

Such a polar storm was rare but not unforeseen. After a severe winter storm almost exactly ten years prior in February 2011, the Federal Energy Regulatory Commission (FERC) and the North American Electric Reliability Corporation (NERC) warned the Electric Reliability Council of Texas (ERCOT), the state's nonprofit electric grid operator, that Texas power generators and pipeline operators needed to winterize their infrastructure and the state needed to increase its reserve margin to withstand severe winter storms. *See* Federal Energy Regulatory Commission & North American Electric Reliability Corporation, *Outages and Curtailments During the Southwest Cold Weather Event of February 1–5, 2011: Causes and Recommendations* (Aug. 2011), www.ferc.gov/sites/default/files/

2020-04/08-16-11-report.pdf [hereinafter 2011 FERC/NERC Report]. (The reserve margin is the excess capacity that an electric system expects to have at peak demand. For instance, a 15 percent reserve margin means that an electric system has excess capacity of 15 percent above expected peak demand. *See* U.S. Energy Information Administration, *Reserve Electric Generating Capacity Helps Keep the Lights On* (June 1, 2012), www.eia.gov/todayinenergy/detail.php?id=6510.) The report concluded that "the majority of the problems experienced by the many generators . . . during the [February 2011 winter storm] were attributable, either directly or indirectly, to the cold weather itself." 2011 FERC/NERC Report, at 8. The FERC and the NERC noted that while "all preventative measures entail some cost . . . in many cases, the needed fixes would not be unduly expensive." 2011 FERC/NERC Report at 10.

Ten years later, as Texas reeled in the aftermath of a far more severe February storm, emerging evidence suggests that ERCOT failed to heed federal warnings to compel generators to winterize their systems. *See* Tanya Eiserer & Jason Trahan, *30 Years of Warnings to Winterize Texas Power Plants, Yet Still They Froze. Will Austin Finally Require It?* WFAA, Feb. 18, 2021, www.wfaa.com/article/news/local/investigates/30-years-of-warnings-to-winterize-texas-power-plants-yet-they-still-froze-will-austin-finally-require-it/287-20540908-dbce-4e17-90a3-19aa4f4f4690; *see also* Erin Douglas, Kate McGee & Jolie McCullough, *Texas Leaders Failed to Heed Warnings that Left the State's Power Grid Vulnerable to Winter Extremes, Experts Say*, *Texas Tribune*, Feb. 19, 2021, www.texastribune.org/2021/02/17/texas-power-grid-failures/. (Since ERCOT is not federally regulated, the FERC/NERC report served as mere guidance that ERCOT was not legally required to implement.) At the peak of the storm, approximately half of the state's power generation capacity was knocked offline. At one point during the storm, ERCOT was four minutes and thirty-seven seconds away from a catastrophic grid "trip," which would have caused certain circuits to automatically shut down. This would have required generators to perform a "black start" on generation facilities, essentially restarting those facilities after a complete shutdown. Restoring power after such a black start could have taken weeks. *See* Keaton Fox, *Texas Power Grid Was Four Minutes from Catastrophic Failure: ERCOT*, ABC 13 Eyewitness News, Feb. 25, 2021, https://abc13.com/ercot-grid-blackout-power-fail-in-texas-outages/10367289/ [hereinafter Fox].

The February 2021 storm, known as Storm Uri, crippled Texas's natural gas, nuclear, and coal power plants, which provide the bulk of the state's winter power generation. *See* Veronica Penney, *How Texas' Power Generation Failed During the Storm, in Charts*, *New York Times*, Feb. 19, 2021, www.nytimes.com/interactive/2021/02/19/climate/texas-storm-power-generation-charts.html. Additionally, about half of the installed wind power generation capacity in Texas went offline during the storm as turbines froze. *See* Brandon Mulder, *Frozen Wind Turbines Hamper Texas Power Output, State's Electric Grid Operator Says*, *Austin-American Statesman*, Feb. 14, 2021, www.statesman.com/story/news/2021/02/14/historic-winter-storm-freezes-texas-wind-turbines-hampering-electric-generation/4483230001/. While some state politicians suggested that wind generation was to blame for the widespread power outages, subsequent analysis shows that both thermal and renewable generation sources failed in the bitter cold, as much of Texas's generation infrastructure was not sufficiently winterized. *See* Erin Douglas & Ross Ramsey, *No, Frozen Wind Turbines Aren't the Main Culprit for Texas' Power Outages*, *Texas Tribune*, Feb. 16, 2021, www.texastribune.org/2021/02/16/texas-wind-turbines-frozen/. ERCOT has acknowledged that natural gas facilities accounted for most of the power capacity that went offline; the "loss in wind power was significantly less, though elevated." *See* Fox. State leaders have subsequently called for generators to winterize their infrastructure.

Texas more commonly faces the risk of rolling blackouts when summer temperatures soar along with customer use of air-conditioning. In May 2019, when ERCOT had a low planning reserve margin, the grid operator reported that there was a heightened risk that emergency action would be needed to maintain system reliability if energy demand exceeded the grid's capacity. *See* News Release, Electric Reliability Council of Texas, *ERCOT Expects Record Electric Use, Increased Chance of Energy Alerts* (May 8, 2019), www.ercot.com/news/release?id=cb38c5f5-ed50-3071-93b7-07a09b0b14ae

[hereinafter ERCOT News Release May 2019]. During an August 2019 heatwave, ERCOT issued two Energy Emergency Alerts (EEA1), calling on all available power supplies to be brought online and calling for customers to conserve. *See* Robert Walton, *ERCOT Calls 2 Energy Emergencies in One Week, 3rd in 5 Years*, *Utility Dive*, Aug. 16, 2019, www.utilitydive.com/news/ercot-calls-2nd-energy-emergency-this-week-3rd-in-5-years/561065/. Power prices briefly soared to $9,000/MWh, which is ERCOT's systemwide offer cap price; Texas also reached this cap price during the February 2021 winter storm. *See Texas Power Prices Briefly Soar to $9,000/MWh as Heat Wave Bakes State*, *Reuters*, Aug. 14, 2019, www.reuters.com/article/us-texas-power-demand/texas-power-prices-briefly-soar-to-9000-mwh-as-heat-wave-bakes-state-idUSKCN1V41HV; Mark Watson, *Texas Regulators Keep Prices Near $9,000/MWh Cap During Rotating Outages*, *S&P Global*, Feb. 16, 2021, www.spglobal.com/platts/en/market-insights/latest-news/natural-gas/021621-texas-regulators-keep-prices-near-9000mwh-cap-during-rotating-outages.

ERCOT's tight reserve margin in summer 2019 was attributed to "above-normal growth in electric demand" and delays and cancellations of planned generation projects that would have helped replace generation from retiring power plants. *See* ERCOT News Release May 2019; *see also* News Release, Electric Reliability Council of Texas, *New Report Shows Tightening Electricity Reserve Margins* (Dec. 4, 2018), www.ercot.com/news/release?id=4e9670d5-6c77-38d6-bdbb-40b0914cef29. ERCOT has predicted that the planning reserve margin will be higher in 2020–2023, as more planned utility-scale wind and solar projects are connected to the grid. *See* ERCOT News Release May 2019; *see also* News Release, Electric Reliability Council of Texas, *ERCOT Report Shows Increasing Reserves in Coming Years* (Dec. 16, 2020), www.ercot.com/news/release?id=0c4de0d7-577f-3334-b750-abd13ad18b63 [hereinafter ERCOT News Release December 2020]. The ERCOT region continues to experience rising customer demand, although increased home energy efficiency is believed to have helped mitigate the growth in residential customer demand. *See* ERCOT News Release December 2020; *see also* Jim Malewitz, *ERCOT: Growth in Texas Energy Demand Slows*, *Texas Tribune*, Feb. 28, 2014, www.texastribune.org/2014/02/28/ercot-growth-texas-energy-demand-slows/. In 2019, electric demand growth was especially strong in West Texas due to oil and gas development and along the Gulf Coast where new industrial facilities were being constructed. *See* ERCOT News Release May 2019.

As predictions from both the TWDB and ERCOT demonstrate, demand is increasing for both water and energy in Texas. Both the public and private sectors will have to find solutions to satisfy these growing demands—perhaps through conservation, increased efficiency, or the development of new sources.

§ 41.5 Update to Texas Water Development Board's Planning Methodology

In 2018, TWDB analysts adopted a new methodology for predicting water demand for manufacturing and steam-electric power generation. This change in methodology caused the TWDB to revise the state's estimated water demand for 2070 downward from 21.6 million to 19.2 million AF per year. *See* 2018 TWDB Water Demand Projections, at 3. Under this new methodology, the TWDB estimates that water demand for steam-electric power will remain constant from 2022 to 2070. *See* Yun Cho, Manager, Economic and Demographic Analysis, Texas Water Development Board, Presentation at the Texas Demographic Conference, *Methods & Data for Developing Projections for the 2021 Regional Water Plans and 2022 State Water Plan* (May 24, 2018), demographics.texas.gov/Resources/Presentations/DDUC/2018/2018_05_24_MethodsandDataforDevelopingProjectionsforthe2021.pdf. The new methodology will apply to predictions in the 2022 State Water Plan.

In the new methodology, the TWDB rejects its historical method of calculating future water use for power generation by evaluating various scenarios involving factors that could affect water use over a fifty-year period. *See* Texas Water Development Board, *Methodologies for Developing Draft Irrigation, Manufacturing, and Steam-Electric Water Demand Projections* 13 (Feb. 2017), www.twdb.texas.gov/waterplanning/data/projections/methodology/doc/2022/2022IrrManuSEMethodology.pdf?d=4236.514999996871 [hereinafter TWDB Projection Methodologies]. These factors formerly included electrical power demand, fuel prices, weather conditions, and the cooling design of power plants. *See* TWDB Projection Methodologies, at 13. Additional factors included power facility replacement schedules, anticipated generation efficiency and cooling systems, carbon capture activities, and environmental and regulatory policies. The TWDB decided that using these many factors to predict water demand for power generation was "resource-prohibitive." *See* TWDB Projection Methodologies, at 16.

Now, the TWDB plans to base demand projections for each county on (1) the highest county water use in the most recent five years for steam-electric power providers (based on results from the TWDB's annual survey), (2) the retirements and near-term additions of power generation facilities, and (3) a constant volume of water demand through 2070. *See* TWDB Projection Methodologies, at 13. The TWDB determined that projections should be based on the highest county water use in the most recent five years because this ensures that the TWDB "will be planning for water use that has already occurred in the recent past." *See* TWDB Projection Methodologies, at 15.

The TWDB has decided to hold demand constant because a projected increase in wind and solar generation may help meet the state's rising electrical power demand without causing water demand for electric power to increase as much as it would have if only traditional power plants (with water cooling systems) were available to meet demand. *See* TWDB Projection Methodologies, at 16. The TWDB also assumed that even if new power plants are constructed to meet rising power demand or to replace old plants, the new plants are likely to be more water efficient, as they typically either use less water or produce more power with a similar volume of water. *See* TWDB Projection Methodologies, at 16.

Additionally, the TWDB decided not to predict where new power plants will be built (which would increase the water demand for steam-electric power in a county), as these predictions are likely to be inaccurate. The locations of new power plants cannot be identified unless they are listed in government reports, and distributing anticipated increases in water use to counties that already have power plants would cause the TWDB to overestimate future water demand in some counties and underestimate it in others. *See* TWDB Projection Methodologies, at 16. Instead, the TWDB plans to hold steam-electric water demand constant and update water demand projections in each planning cycle, ensuring that the projections are as current as possible, without making potentially flawed predictions about where new generation will be built. *See* TWDB Projection Methodologies, at 16.

§ 41.6 Technology's Impact on Water and Energy Demand

Texas's rising water demand for power generation is expected to be curbed, at least to some degree, by more water-efficient technology in power plants. *See* TWDB Projection Methodologies, at 16. Increased generation from wind and solar also has the potential to decrease water demand for power in Texas, especially if a cost-effective battery is made widely available that enables large-scale storage of wind and solar energy. Companies such as Tesla, which has plans for a new Gigafactory in the Austin area, are developing and manufacturing innovative technologies that would enable more widespread solar power generation and storage.

In contrast to many other generation sources—including traditional thermal power plants—wind turbines and solar photovoltaic (PV) panels consume minimal amounts of water. *See* Edward S. Spang et al., *The Water Consumption of Energy Production: An International Comparison*, 9 Envtl. Res. Letters 1, 5 (2014), https://iopscience.iop.org/article/10.1088/1748-9326/9/10/105002/pdf. The little water they do require is typically used to wash solar PV panels and wind turbine blades. The Solar Energy Industries Association (SEIA) estimates that "[i]n general, all solar power technologies use a modest amount of water (approximately twenty gallons per megawatt hour, or gal/MWh) for cleaning solar collection and reflection surfaces like mirrors, heliostats, and photovoltaic (PV) panels." Solar Energy Industries Association, *Water Use Management*, www.seia.org/initiatives/water-use-management#:~:text=In%20general%2C%20all%20solar%20power,and%20photovoltaic%20(PV)%20panels [hereinafter SEIA Water Use Management]. (Water use in manufacturing these technologies is a separate matter that is not reached in this chapter.) Concentrating solar power plants do not offer the same water conservation benefits as solar PV, as they consume approximately the same amount of water (500 to 800 gal/MWh) as other thermal power plants, such as coal and nuclear plants. *See* SEIA Water Use Management.

The renewable energy sector remained resilient in 2020, despite construction delays and supply chain disruptions caused by the global COVID-19 pandemic, which slowed the progress of renewable energy projects in the first six months of 2020. The International Energy Agency predicted that renewable electric power generation would grow by almost 7 percent in 2020, even though global energy demand was expected to decline by 5 percent. *See* International Energy Agency, *Renewables 2020: Analysis and Forecast to 2025* (Nov. 2020), www.iea.org/reports/renewables-2020.

Renewables are already playing an important role in the Texas energy market, and renewable generation capacity is expected to increase. Texas generates more wind power than any other state, supplying almost three-tenths of U.S. wind power in 2020. *See* EIA State Profile for Texas. By the end of 2019, Texas had approximately 28,800 MW in installed wind capacity. *See* EIA State Profile for Texas. Texas was fourth in the nation for installed solar capacity in September 2020, with approximately 5,577 MW. *See* Solar Energy Industries Association, *State Solar Spotlight—Texas* (Sept. 2020), www.seia.org/sites/default/files/2020-09/Texas.pdf [hereinafter *Solar Spotlight—Texas*]. High levels of direct solar radiation in West Texas provide some of the most significant solar potential in the United States; in a September 2020 report, the SEIA predicted that Texas would add nearly 15,000 MW in installed solar capacity over the next five years. *See* EIA State Profile for Texas; *Solar Spotlight—Texas*. In terms of solar power generation, Texas ranked sixth among U.S. states in 2019. *See* EIA State Profile for Texas.

However, Texas is still far from achieving its full potential solar power capacity and generation. For instance, Texas still has far less total installed solar capacity than Germany, even though Texas is geographically twice as large and enjoys a far sunnier climate with higher levels of direct solar radiation. (Germany's solar potential has been compared to that of some regions of Alaska. *See* U.S. Department of Energy, Office of Indian Energy Policy and Programs, *Solar Energy Prospecting in Remote Alaska* 1–2, (Feb. 11, 2016), www.energy.gov/indianenergy/downloads/solar-energy-prospecting-remote-alaska.) However, due to substantial governmental support, Germany's total installed solar capacity reached approximately 49 gigawatts (GW), or 49,000 MW, in 2019, far exceeding Texas's 15,000 MW. *See* Benjamin Wehrmann, *Solar Power in Germany—Output, Business, & Perspectives*, *Clean Energy Wire*, Apr. 16, 2020, www.cleanenergywire.org/factsheets/solar-power-germany-output-business-perspectives.

§ 41.7 Impact of Climate Change on Water and Energy Resources

Climate change is expected to have significant impacts on water and energy in Texas. Hotter temperatures and more frequent severe droughts are likely to periodically diminish surface water supplies across the state, increasing demand for groundwater, which requires more energy to extract than surface water. While Texas will experience less precipitation overall, flooding events will become more extreme, increasing the risk of damage to energy and water infrastructure. The heightened demand for cooling that comes with hotter summers and more intense droughts is likely to strain electric utility operations unless utilities can rely more on generation that requires little water. Additionally, on the Texas coast, sea level rise may threaten the infrastructure of both electric utilities and energy producers, as well as groundwater sources like the Gulf Coast Aquifer. *See* Kevin Kloesel et al., *Chapter 23, Southern Great Plains, in 2 Impacts, Risks, and Adaptation in the United States: Fourth National Climate Assessment* (U.S. Global Change Research Program 2018), https://

nca2018.globalchange.gov/downloads/NCA4_Ch23_Southern-Great-Plains_Full.pdf [hereinafter *Fourth National Climate Assessment*].

If no reductions in global greenhouse gas emissions occur, then the *Fourth National Climate Assessment* predicts that, by the end of the twenty-first century, the Southern Great Plains (encompassing Texas, Oklahoma, and Kansas) will experience thirty to sixty additional days per year of temperatures above 100°F. *See Fourth National Climate Assessment*, at 995. By the middle of the century, average annual temperatures in this region are expected to be 3.6°F to 5.1°F higher than the averages from 1976 to 2005. By the end of the twenty-first century, average annual temperatures are predicted to be 4.4°F to 8.4°F higher. *See Fourth National Climate Assessment*, at 995. The region will see a decline in extreme cold events and an increase in the frequency, duration, and intensity of extreme heat events. High temperatures like those seen during Texas's summer 2011 drought will become more likely to recur. *See* Michael E. Mann et al., *Projected Changes in Persistent Extreme Summer Weather Events: The Role of Quasi-Resonant Amplification*, 4 J. Sci. Advances No. 10 (Oct. 31, 2018), http://advances.sciencemag.org/content/4/10/eaat3272. Higher temperatures will generally cause the use of more electrical power for cooling and thus will increase the demand for water required for energy generation, at the same time as drought conditions decrease the supply of water.

Climate change is likely to strain the operations of utilities and power plants. Longer, hotter summers increase air-conditioning demand—which, in turn, increases water demand for power generation unless a greater share of Texas electric power is generated from sources with minimal water requirements, such as wind and solar. Because of the urban heat island effect, the rate of temperature increase is likely to be especially high in large urban centers. *See* U.S. Environmental Protection Agency, *Climate Change and Heat Islands*, www.epa.gov/heat-islands/climate-change-and-heat-islands. Population growth, greater density, and urban expansion intensify this effect, increasing cooling demand. As the *Fourth National Climate Assessment* notes, "[i]f prolonged power failure occurs during high heat conditions, the impact to human health and comfort is projected to be notably more detrimental in a warmer climate." *Fourth National Climate Assessment*, at 1004.

Hotter temperatures and longer dry periods are also likely to diminish available surface water supplies. During past droughts, surface water supplies have declined, causing higher groundwater use. *See Fourth National Climate Assessment*, at 1004. In some instances, this water scarcity has compelled affected areas to import water and build new water pipelines. Water pipelines that are aging or operating above their recommended capacity can also pose a threat to the Texas water supply during droughts. *See Fourth National Climate Assessment*, at 1004. During the 2011 drought, Fort Worth had over two hundred water main breaks in a single month, while over one thousand occurred in a month in Houston, as the local clay soil shrank in the dry conditions. *See Fourth National Climate Assessment*, at 1004. Soil shrinkage can damage water infrastructure, such as water and sewer lines, as well as roads and building foundations.

While projections show that the Southern Great Plains states will generally experience hotter and drier summers, the region is also likely to experience more frequent and intense episodes of heavy precipitation, creating greater risk of floods (especially because soil will be drier due to longer periods between rains). *See Fourth National Climate Assessment*, at 996. Regional weather in recent decades may foreshadow what is to come. Over the past thirty years, record-breaking flood events have increased in the Southern Great Plains, even as overall flood frequency declines, perhaps due to lower total precipitation over the same period. *See Fourth National Climate Assessment*, at 994; *see also* National Oceanic and Atmospheric Administration, *NOAA Updates Texas Rainfall Frequency Values* (Sept. 27, 2018), www.noaa.gov/media-release/noaa-updates-texas-rainfall-frequency-values.

Furthermore, although Texas is expected to experience warmer summers and winters on average, some climate scientists believe that warmer temperatures in the Arctic may cause atmospheric disruptions in the polar vortex, causing more frequent severe cold-weather events in places like the southern United States. These polar storms would likely remain rare but would be part of an overall pattern of more frequent extreme weather events, such as hurricanes, heat waves, and wildfires *See*

Benjamin Storrow & Chelsea Harvey, *Texas Power Outage Underscores Looming Climate Tests*, *Scientific American*, Feb. 17, 2021, www.scientificamerican.com/article/texas-power-outage-underscores-looming-climate-tests/.

Both electric utilities and energy producers in coastal Texas will have to invest in protecting their infrastructure from sea level rise, especially in the Galveston–Texas City area, which is home to a critical oil refining and transport hub. *See Fourth National Climate Assessment*, at 1005; *see also* U.S. Global Change Research Program, *Houston-Galveston, Texas: Observed Trends and Projected Future Conditions for Climate Change Preparedness and Resilience* (Oct. 2014), www.globalchange.gov/sites/globalchange/files/CCPR_HOU_brochure-final.pdf [hereinafter Houston-Galveston Climate Trends and Projections]. Climate change also threatens the Gulf Coast region's freshwater sources. The Gulf Coast Aquifer, which provides water to approximately eight million people, has already experienced saltwater intrusion because of intensive water extraction. The aquifer is "vulnerable to further saltwater intrusion resulting from [sea level rise] and storm surge exacerbated by climate change." *Fourth National Climate Assessment*, at 1006; *see also* Houston-Galveston Climate Trends and Projections. In short, the *Fourth National Climate Assessment* predicts that the Texas economy will be severely and negatively impacted by climate change unless appropriate measures are taken, in both the public and private sectors, to reduce greenhouse gas emissions and adapt to a changing climate. See Chapter 2 of this book.

§ 41.8 Federal Policy Impact on Water-Energy Nexus

The 2021 transition from the administration of President Donald J. Trump to the administration of President Joseph R. Biden will significantly impact federal energy policy, and thus water supply and water demand, over the next four years, including through new climate and environmental policies.

President Biden has established a federal goal of achieving 100 percent clean electricity by 2035 and net-zero greenhouse gas emissions by 2050. *See* The White House, *Executive Order on Tackling the Climate Crisis at Home and Abroad* (Jan. 27, 2021), www.whitehouse.gov/briefing-room/presidential-actions/2021/01/27/executive-order-on-tackling-the-climate-crisis-at-home-and-abroad/ [hereinafter January 27, 2021 Executive Order]. The Biden climate action plan would also "impose stricter gas mileage standards, fund investments to weatherize millions of homes and commercial buildings, and upgrade the nation's transportation system." John Muyskens & Juliet Eilperin, *Biden Calls for 100 Percent Clean Electricity by 2035. Here's How Far We Have to Go*, *Washington Post*, July 30, 2020, www.washingtonpost.com/climate-environment/2020/07/30/biden-calls-100-percent-clean-electricity-by-2035-heres-how-far-we-have-go/?arc404=true [hereinafter Muyskens & Eilperin]. President Biden's executive orders demonstrate that his administration will shift federal support away from fossil fuel extraction and toward clean energy generation, including by supporting job creation in the clean energy sector. *See* The White House, *Executive Order on Protecting Public Health and the Environment and Restoring Science to Tackle the Climate Crisis* (Jan. 20, 2021), www.whitehouse.gov/briefing-room/presidential-actions/2021/01/20/executive-order-protecting-public-health-and-environment-and-restoring-science-to-tackle-climate-crisis/; *see also* January 27, 2021 Executive Order. The Biden administration has also recommitted the United States to the global Paris Agreement on climate change.

Biden staffers have cautioned that there will be obstacles to achieving presidential climate goals, as the administration will have to rebuild the EPA's workforce (which is believed to have lost approximately 600 staffers during the Trump administration) and will have to address Trump-era regulations that would hinder federal action to reduce greenhouse gas emissions and conduct climate research. *See* Adam Aton, *Biden Climate Team Says It Underestimated Trump's Damage*, *Scientific American*, Jan. 6, 2021, www.scientificamerican.com/article/biden-climate-team-says-it-underestimated-trumps-damage/. President Biden's climate and environmental actions are also expected to face legal challenges from industry and some state attorney generals, including Texas

Attorney General Ken Paxton. *See* Alison Durkee, *Texas Governor Vows to Sue Biden Over Climate Change Orders*, *Forbes*, Jan. 28, 2021, www.forbes.com/sites/alisondurkee/2021/01/28/texas-governor-abbott-vows-to-sue-biden-over-climate-change-orders/?sh=5316eb792db5.

President Biden's plans to reduce carbon emissions may also reduce the energy sector's water consumption, if lessons can be drawn from predictions relating to the Obama administration's Clean Power Plan. The Obama-era plan is considered less ambitious than the Biden climate plan, as it called for the electricity sector to cut carbon pollution by merely 32 percent by 2030 and did not lay out a trajectory for phasing out oil, coal, or natural gas production. In contrast, the Biden plan aims to achieve 100 percent clean electricity by 2035 and net-zero greenhouse gas emissions by 2050. *See* Muyskens & Eilperin.

A 2014 study found that, between 2019 and 2029, the Texas power sector would have reduced its water usage by 20 percent in complying with the Clean Power Plan's emissions reduction requirements, assuming the power sector reduced its reliance on coal and increased its use of natural gas and wind energy. *See* Paul Faeth, *The Impacts of EPA's Clean Power Plan on Electricity Generation and Water Use in Texas: Additional Analysis* iii (CNA Analysis & Solutions, Mar. 2015), www.researchgate.net/publication/290190286 [hereinafter CNA CPP Analysis]. The same study found that the Texas energy sector's water consumption was expected to decline by only 5 percent without the Clean Power Plan. *See* CNA CPP Analysis, at iii. Decreases in the energy sector's water consumption were not expected in all states, as the Clean Power Plan did not include water conservation goals. *See* Sarah Ladin, Note, *Energy-Water Nexus, the Clean Power Plan, and Integration of Water Resource Concerns into Energy Decision-Making*, 7 Mich. J. Envtl. & Admin. Law 205, 220 (2017), https://repository.law.umich.edu/cgi/viewcontent.cgi?article=1073&context=mjeal.

Federal interest in the water-energy nexus is discussed further in section 41.10 below.

III. Interest in the Water-Energy Nexus

§ 41.9 International Interest in Water-Energy Nexus

International institutions have identified the water-energy nexus (often discussed more broadly as the water-food-energy-climate nexus) as a risk facing the global community. The World Economic Forum (WEF) identified the water-food-energy nexus as one of the three most significant risks facing the international community in its Global Risks 2011 report. *See* World Economic Forum, *Global Risks 2011* 7, 28 (6th ed. 2011), http://reports.weforum.org/wp-content/blogs.dir/1/mp/uploads/pages/files/global-risks-2011.pdf [hereinafter *Global Risks 2011*]. The WEF found that widespread insecurity in the areas of water, food, and energy can chronically impede economic growth and social stability—both nationally and when national problems ripple out to broader regions. *See Global Risks 2011*, at 28.

Since 2011, the WEF has not identified the water-energy-food nexus as a top risk to global security. However, "water crises" have been listed as a top-five global risk in terms of impact each year from 2014 to 2020. *See* World Economic Forum, *The Global Risks Report 2020* Fig. I (15th ed. 2020), http://www3.weforum.org/docs/WEF_Global_Risk_Report_2020.pdf [hereinafter *Global Risks Report 2020*]. Catastrophes that impact water and energy resources—including climate change, climate action failure, extreme weather, and natural disasters—have also been listed as top-five global risks during this period. *See Global Risks Report 2020*, at Fig. I. In 2020, WEF predicted that "[t]he next 10 years will shape the outlook for climate risk for the rest of the century," and cautioned that "to avoid the worst consequences, global emissions need to peak almost immediately and decline precipitously—by 7.6% each year between 2020 and 2030." *Global Risks Report 2020*, at 36.

The International Energy Agency (IEA), an independent organization linked to the Organization for Economic Cooperation and Development (OECD), has also produced considerable research on the water-energy nexus, beginning with its annual World Energy Outlook report in 2012. *See* International Energy Agency, *World Energy Outlook 2012* (2012), www.iea.org/reports/world-energy-outlook-2012. The IEA addressed water-energy nexus issues most recently in 2016 as part of its World Energy Outlook report. The IEA found that globally, over the past few decades, the rate of growth in water demand has been double the rate of population growth. *See* International Energy Agency, *Water-Energy Nexus: Excerpt from the World Energy Outlook 2016* 11 (2016), iea.blob.core.windows.net/assets/e4a7e1a5-b6ed-4f36-911f-b0111e49aab9/WorldEnergyOutlook2016ExcerptWaterEnergyNexus.pdf [hereinafter IEA Water-Energy Nexus 2016]. Irrigated agriculture is responsible for the bulk of global water use and consumption, although municipal water demand is rising, especially in India, Africa, and developing countries in Asia (excluding China). *See* IEA Water-Energy Nexus 2016, at 11.

The IEA report emphasizes that policy in the energy and water sectors would be far more effective if formed in an integrated manner and warns that "inter-dependencies between energy and water are set to intensify in the coming years, as the water needs of the energy sector rise." IEA Water-Energy Nexus 2016, at 5–6. The IEA believes that an increase in demand for biofuels and the greater deployment of nuclear power will increase both water withdrawal and consumption levels. *See* IEA Water-Energy Nexus 2016, at 5. The IEA has noted that adopting energy sources with lower carbon emissions will not necessarily reduce water consumption. Increased reliance on biofuels and nuclear power would increase water use and consumption, while renewables like wind and solar would reduce the volume of water required for power generation. The IEA also notes that, conversely, energy consumption in the water sector could be reduced by up to 15 percent by 2040 if the water sector used more energy recovery and energy-efficient technologies. The greatest energy savings are possible in wastewater treatment, desalination, and water supply operations. *See* IEA Water-Energy Nexus 2016, at 6.

In 2020, the IEA reported that "[w]ater scarcity is already having an impact on energy production and reliability," potentially endangering the economic and environmental viability of power sources around the world, such as China's coal-power plants and African hydropower dams. *See* International Energy Agency, *Introduction to the Water-Energy Nexus* (Mar. 23, 2020), www.iea.org/articles/introduction-to-the-water-energy-nexus [hereinafter IEA Water-Energy Nexus Introduction]. The agency also noted that conversely, "diminished freshwater resources can lead to a greater reliance on energy-intensive sources of water supply such as desalination," as has occurred in the Middle East. By 2040, the water sector's energy use is projected to more than double. *See* IEA Water-Energy Nexus Introduction. Desalination is expected to be the greatest driver of that increased energy use, followed by large-scale water transfers and rising demand for wastewater treatment (as well as higher levels of treatment). However, there is significant unrealized potential to save energy in the water sector, as "[w]astewater contains significant amounts of embedded energy that, if harnessed, could cover more than half of the electricity needs of municipal wastewater utilities." Reduction of water losses caused by leaks, line bursts, and theft could also reduce the water sector's usage of both water and energy. *See* IEA Water-Energy Nexus Introduction.

The IEA also noted that energy will be essential to meet global demand for clean drinking water and sanitation. *See* IEA Water-Energy Nexus Introduction. The agency has determined that "achieving universal access to clean water and sanitation . . . would add less than 1% to global energy demand . . . by 2030." The IEA notes that many households that lack clean water also lack electricity, and "[a]s a result, considering water supply needs when planning electricity provision" could potentially lower the cost of providing electricity. *See* IEA Water-Energy Nexus Introduction.

§ 41.10 U.S. Interest in Water-Energy Nexus

The federal government has also demonstrated interest in the water-energy nexus. In December 2018, the U.S. Department of Energy (DOE) announced plans to use $100 million to establish an Energy-Water Desalination Hub that will focus on early-stage research and development for desalination technologies. The Hub will fund research and development on low-cost options for treating "non-traditional" water sources such as seawater, brackish water, and produced water. *See* News Release, U.S. Department of Energy, *Department of Energy Announces $100 Million Energy-Water Desalination Hub to Provide Secure and Affordable Water* (Dec. 13, 2018), www.energy.gov/articles/department-energy-announces-100-million-energy-water-desalination-hub-provide-secure-and. See sections 41.14:1 and 41.14:2 below for further discussion in produced water as a water source.

In 2019, the DOE announced a Solar Desalination Prize competition with a $9 million award, which is intended to "accelerate the development of systems that use solar-thermal energy to produce clean water from salt water." *See* U.S. Department of Energy, *U.S. Department of Energy Solar Desalination Prize*, www.energy.gov/eere/solar/american-made-challenges-solar-desalination-prize. The competition is part of the federal government's Water Security Grand Challenge to promote technological innovation that will help meet water demand. Other goals in the DOE's Water Security Grand Challenge include achieving a near-zero water impact for new thermoelectric power plants (and significantly reducing freshwater use by existing plants); developing small, modular energy-water systems that will work in a variety of settings (including urban, rural, and disaster relief settings); finding uses for produced water resulting from fossil fuel extraction; and doubling resource recovery from municipal wastewater. *See* U.S. Department of Energy, *About the Water Security Grand Challenge*, www.energy.gov/water-security-grand-challenge/water-security-grand-challenge.

The federal government has conducted considerable research on the water-energy nexus. This began in 2004, when Congress asked the secretary of energy to prepare a report on the interdependence of water and energy, which was published in 2006. *See* U.S. Department of Energy, *Energy Demands on Water Resources: Report to Congress on the Interdependency of Energy and Water* (Dec. 2006). In 2005, Congress established the National Energy-Water Roadmap Program for the purpose of assessing efforts by the DOE and other federal agencies to address energy-water policy issues. This program published a report in March 2007. *See* Sandia National Laboratories, U.S. Department of Energy, *Energy-Water Roadmap Process* (2007). From 2009 to 2012, the U.S. General Accounting Office published the following six reports on water-energy nexus issues:

- *Energy-Water Nexus: Improvements to Federal Water Use Data Would Increase Understanding of Trends in Power Plant Water Use* (Report No. GAO-10-23, Oct. 16, 2009).
- *Energy-Water Nexus: Many Uncertainties Remain about National and Regional Effects of Increased Biofuel Production on Water Resources* (Report No. GAO-10-116, Nov. 30, 2009).
- *Energy-Water Nexus: A Better and Coordinated Understanding of Water Resources Could Help Mitigate the Impacts of Potential Oil Shale Development* (Report No. GAO-11-35, Oct. 29, 2010).
- *Energy-Water Nexus: Amount of Energy Needed to Supply, Use, and Treat Water Is Location-Specific and Can Be Reduced by Certain Technologies and Approaches* (Report No. GAO-11-225, Mar. 23, 2011).
- *Energy-Water Nexus: Information on the Quantity, Quality, and Management of Water Produced during Oil and Gas Production* (Report No. GAO-12-156, Jan. 9, 2012).
- *Energy-Water Nexus: Coordinated Federal Approach Needed to Better Manage Energy and Water Tradeoffs* (Report No. GAO-12-880, Oct. 15, 2012).

As the titles indicate, each report focused on water-energy nexus issues in specific sectors. Each report outlined the sector's effect on water and energy resources, the factors driving the sector's energy and water consumption, and future projections for water and energy consumption.

In 2014, the DOE published another report on the water-energy nexus. That report addressed (1) climate change's impact on U.S. temperature and precipitation patterns; (2) population growth in arid parts of the United States, like the Southwest, driven by regional migration patterns; (3) the predicted impact of new technologies on water and energy demand; and (4) the effect of policies that address the water impacts of energy production. *See* U.S. Department of Energy, *The Water-Energy Nexus: Challenges and Opportunities* (June 2014), www.energy.gov/sites/prod/files/2014/07/f17/Water%20Energy%20Nexus%20Full%20Report%20July%202014.pdf.

The recently enacted Energy Act of 2020 directs the DOE to incorporate water and energy considerations into the agency's research and development (R&D) and demonstration programs and establishes an interagency committee, led by the secretary of energy and secretary of the interior, which will coordinate and collaborate on energy-water nexus activities. *See* Consolidated Appropriations Act of 2021, Pub. L. No. 116-260, § 1010(a)(3), 134 Stat. 1182 (2020). Noting that the states have "primacy over allocation and administration of water resources (except in specific instances where preempted under Federal law)," the Act directs federal agencies to "maximize coordination and consultation" with state and local governments in "all energy-water nexus management activities." *See* Consolidated Appropriations Act of 2021, Pub. L. No. 116-260, § 1010(a)(3), 134 Stat. 1182 (2020).

§ 41.11 Texas Interest in Water-Energy Nexus

The Texas Water Development Board (TWDB) has taken a leading role in examining the connection between energy and water demand in Texas. The TWDB has commissioned studies on water-energy nexus issues, such as a 2008 report prepared by the University of Texas Jackson School of Geosciences that focused on the current and projected water demand for electric power generation from various sources (including fossil fuel–fired thermoelectric power plants, wind, nuclear, solar photovoltaic, and concentrated solar power projects). *See* Carey King et al., Bureau of Economic Geology, *Water Demand Projections for Power Generation in Texas* (Texas Water Development Board 2008), www.twdb.texas.gov/publications/reports/contracted_reports/doc/0704830756Thermoelectric WaterProjection.pdf [hereinafter 2008 Texas Water Demand Projections].

In 2011, the TWDB published another study on water use in the mining industry and the oil and gas industry, prompted by an increase in shale gas production. This study was commissioned to aid the agency in its next water planning cycle. *See* Jean-Phillippe Nicot et al., Bureau of Economic Geology, *Current and Projected Water Use in the Texas Mining and Oil and Gas Industry* (Texas Water Development Board 2011), www.twdb.texas.gov/publications/reports/contracted_reports/doc/0904830939_MiningWaterUse.pdf [hereinafter 2011 Mining Water Use Report]. In 2012, this study was updated to reflect (1) the industry's shift from gas to oil production and (2) the rapid technological advances that have increased the industry's water reuse, as well as the use of brackish water. *See* Jean-Phillippe Nicot et al., Bureau of Economic Geology, *Oil & Gas Water Use in Texas: Update to the 2011 Mining Water Use Report* i (Texas Oil & Gas Association 2012), www.twdb.texas.gov/publications/reports/contracted_reports/doc/0904830939_2012Update_MiningWaterUse.pdf [hereinafter 2012 Mining Water Use Report Update]. The results of these studies are discussed at sections 41.14:1 and 41.14:2 below.

IV. Water for Energy in Texas: Power Generation, Fossil Fuels, Uranium, and Biofuels

§ 41.12 Introduction

The energy sector uses a relatively small share of Texas water. In 2018, the TWDB estimated that total state water use was 14.66 million AF per year, up from the previous estimate of 14.02 million AF in 2017. The power sector (which in the context of TWDB water planning includes electric generation) accounted for only 3 percent of Texas water use in 2018, while the mining sector (which in the context of TWDB water planning includes oil and gas production) accounted for 1 percent. *See* 2018 Water Use Estimates Summary, at 1.

§ 41.13 Water Use for Thermoelectric Power Plant Generation

Historically, power generation has been primarily centralized, and this model largely exists today. In a centralized power system, power plants and other large generation facilities distribute power through a system of transmission and distribution lines to customers over a large geographic area. In Texas, most electric power is generated by thermoelectric power plants, which are powered by fuels such as natural gas, coal, and uranium. Water is typically used to cool these plants, as it is readily available, can be reused, and has a low cost relative to other cooling mediums.

Different types of power plants have different water use and consumption requirements. Natural gas-fired power plants typically use less water than coal-fired power plants. Renewable generation sources such as wind and solar PV have relatively low water requirements, creating the possibility that water use and consumption for power generation will decline if these generation sources become a greater share of Texas's energy mix. Currently, most renewable energy in Texas is generated by utility-scale wind and solar installations, suggesting that the bulk of renewable power generation may continue to come from utility-scale generators rather than rooftop solar and other decentralized generation.

In thermoelectric power generation, most water is used, rather than consumed, so cooling water can often be reused relatively soon after treatment. In 2015, the USGS estimated that approximately 133 billion gallons of water per day were withdrawn for thermoelectric power generation. *See* Cheryl A. Dieter et al., *Estimated Use of Water in the United States in 2015* 1, U.S. Geological Survey Circular 1441 (2018) (supersedes USGS Open-File Report 2017-1131), https://pubs.usgs.gov/circ/1441/circ1441.pdf [hereinafter 2015 U.S. Water Use]. Only 3 percent of this water (4.31 billion gallons per day) was consumed rather than used, indicating that most of the withdrawn water was likely returned to its source (typically a cooling reservoir) after use. *See* 2015 U.S. Water Use, at 1.

The USGS has determined that an average of fifteen gallons of water were used to produce one kilowatt-hour (kWh) of electrical power in 2015, compared to almost nineteen gallons per kWh in 2010. *See* 2015 U.S. Water Use, at 42. (Note that these figures refer to water *use*, not consumption. As explained in section 41.3 above, water is considered "used" if it may be reused again in the short term, perhaps immediately or after treatment. Water is "consumed" by processes that render it unavailable for reuse in the short term, such as evaporation.) Rates of water consumption for thermoelectric power appear in Table 1 below. Texas has the largest total withdrawals for thermoelectric power of any U.S. state (10,400 million gallons per day). *See* 2015 U.S. Water Use, at 42.

Water consumption rates vary by the type of fuel and power plant technology used, as shown in Table 1 below. In 2008, coal or natural gas-fired power plants with steam turbines consumed approximately 0.35 to 0.70 gallons of water per kWh. *See* 2008 Texas Water Demand Projections, at 25. Nuclear steam turbine plants consumed an average of 0.60 gallons per kWh. Natural gas combined-cycle units equipped with cooling towers consumed 0.23 gallons per kWh, while natural gas-fired plants with gas turbines consumed only 0.05 gallons per kWh. *See* 2008 Texas Water Demand Projections, at 25. Water consumption rates for these plant types may be lower now because of technological advancement.

Table 1: TWDB Default Water Consumption Rates, by Fuel/Technology

Fuel	Prime mover	Once-through or cooling tower	Water consumption rate (gal/kWh)
Natural gas	Combined cycle	Cooling tower	0.23
Natural gas	Gas turbine	Cooling tower	0.05
Natural gas	Steam turbine	Cooling tower	0.70
Natural gas	Combined cycle	Once-through	0.23
Natural gas	Gas turbine	Once-through	0.05
Natural gas	Steam turbine	Once-through	0.35
Coal	Steam turbine	Cooling tower	0.60
Coal	Steam turbine	Once-through	0.35
Nuclear	Steam turbine	Any	0.60

Source: Carey King et al., Bureau of Economic Geology, *Water Demand Projections for Power Generation in Texas* 25 tbl. 1.5 (Texas Water Development Board 2008), www.twdb.texas.gov/publications/reports/contracted_reports/doc/0704830756ThermoelectricWaterProjection.pdf.

Note that these figures represent water consumption under normal climatic conditions. A power plant's water consumption can vary during periods of abnormal weather, especially when higher temperatures cause cooling demand to spike.

Water consumption also varies depending on whether a power plant uses a closed-loop or open-loop cooling system. In open-loop cooling, also referred to as once-through cooling, water is circulated through the facility once before it is discharged back to its source, which serves as a heat sink. Closed-loop systems, on the other hand, are equipped with cooling towers that recirculate water, most of which is not returned to the source. Open-loop systems typically use forced evaporation, allowing most of the withdrawn water to be returned to the source. Closed-loop systems, in contrast, use direct evaporation in the cooling tower, so only a small portion of this water is returned to the source (to maintain acceptable dissolved solids levels), while the rest is recirculated within the cooling tower. Thus, more water is consumed by closed-loop systems because less water is returned to the source. *See* Brian L. Sledge & W. Greg Carter, *Power Generation Water Use in Texas for the Years 2000 through 2060* (Texas Water Development Board 2003), www.twdb.texas.gov/publications/reports/contracted_reports/doc/2001483396.pdf. However, although closed-loop cooling systems consume up to 80 percent more water than open-loop cooling systems do, they withdraw 95 percent less water, as the closed-loop systems recirculate water. *See* Natural Resources Defense Council, *Power Plant Cooling and Associated Impacts: The Need to Modernize U.S. Power Plants and Protect Our Water Resources and Aquatic Ecosystems* 3 (Apr. 2014), www.nrdc.org/sites/default/files/power-plant-cooling-IB.pdf. (Open-loop cooling systems also return water to the source at a higher temperature, which can have negative environmental effects on aquatic life in that water source. *See* U.S. Energy Information Administration, *Many Newer Power Plants Have Cooling Systems that Reuse Water* (Feb. 11, 2014), www.eia.gov/todayinenergy/detail.php?id=14971.)

Power plants may also have dry cooling systems that use air instead of water. However, these systems are less efficient and often have higher capital and operating costs. Their use is not expected to increase in Texas, although they use about 95 percent less water than water cooling systems. *See* William "Skip" Mills et al., Texas A&M University, *Viability and Impacts of Implementing Various Power Plant Cooling Technologies in Texas* 2–6 (Electric Power Research Institute, Aug. 2012); *see also* U.S. Energy Information Administration, *Some U.S. Electricity Generating Plants Use Dry Cooling* (Aug. 29, 2018), www.eia.gov/todayinenergy/detail.php?id=36773 [hereinafter EIA Dry Cooling]. In 2017, Texas had 2.8 GW of dry cooling capacity, more than any other state. *See* EIA Dry Cooling.

Most Texas power plants use surface water for cooling, making surface water very important to statewide electric reliability. Interest in this issue increased in 2011, when a severe drought raised concerns that reduced water in power plant reservoirs could lead to shutdowns or reductions in generation. Higher temperatures during the 2011 drought caused a 6 percent increase in statewide electric power demand. *See* Bridget R. Scanlon et al., Bureau of Economic Geology, *Drought and the Water-Energy Nexus in Texas*, Envtl. Res. Letters 8, 5 (Dec. 20, 2013), https://iopscience.iop.org/article/10.1088/1748-9326/8/4/045033/pdf. The drought also increased water demand or consumption (evaporation) of cooling water by 9 percent. *See* Scanlon et al., at 5. Stored water in power plant reservoirs fell by 30 percent from October 2010 to November 2011. Scanlon et al., at 5. However, Texas power plants "were flexible enough at the plant level" to adapt by adopting less water-intensive technologies that ensured continued operation. To use water more efficiently, some utilities stocked reservoirs with reclaimed water, rather than relying on water that would be needed for municipal or other potable uses. *See* Scanlon et al., at 1.

Studies commissioned by ERCOT found that single-year droughts do not impact generation capacity because of improvements in water storage. However, multiyear droughts are expected to affect capacity, as they impact long-term water availability. *See* Black & Veatch, *Water Use and Availability in the ERCOT Region* 25 (July 11, 2013), www.ercot.com/files/docs/2013/09/30/ercot_water_use_and_availablility___drtrpt_1df.pdf; *see also* Black & Veatch, *Drought in the ERCOT Region* 13 (Oct. 12, 2012), www.ercot.com/files/docs/2012/10/10/drought_rpg_101212.pdf. These studies used projections through 2035 that assumed that future climate variations will mimic those from 1900 to 2012. However, if future climate variations deviate substantially from historical patterns—as many climate change studies have predicted—then these studies will not reliably predict how Texas generation capacity may be impacted by future droughts.

§ 41.14 Water Use in Recovery of Oil and Gas

There are three general methods for recovering oil or natural gas: primary, secondary, and tertiary. These methods require the use of differing amounts of water. Primary recovery relies on pumpjacks or the natural pressure in a formation to extract oil. In 2011, primary recovery required an estimated 0.2 gallons of freshwater per gallon of crude oil recovered. Secondary recovery involves injecting gas or water into the formation to displace the oil. Secondary recovery methods include thermal recovery, chemical injection, gas injection, and water flooding. The water requirements of secondary recovery vary depending on the method used. Lastly, tertiary recovery—also known as enhanced recovery or EOR—involves using chemical reactions or heat to either (1) thin the oil so that it flows more freely or (2) change the properties of the underground rock so oil adheres less tightly. *See* May Wu & Yiwen Chiu, *Consumptive Water Use in the Production of Ethanol and Petroleum Gasoline—2011 Update* 6 (Center for Transportation Research, Argonne National Laboratory, July 2011), https://greet.es.anl.gov/publication-consumptive-water [hereinafter 2011 Consumptive Water Use Update].

Oil and gas operators' decisions about whether to use surface or groundwater, and whether to use fresh, brackish, or recycled water, are influenced by factors such as the formation's oil or gas content, its geographical location (including whether water scarcity creates a need for conservation and reuse), and other site-specific requirements. *See* The Academy of Medicine, Engineering and Science of Texas, *Environmental and Community Impacts of Shale Development in Texas* 117 (2017), http://tamest.org/wp-content/uploads/2017/07/Final-Shale-Task-Force-Report.pdf [hereinafter TAMEST Report]. For instance, in arid areas such as West Texas's Permian Basin and South Texas's Eagle Ford Shale, groundwater is primarily used for hydraulic fracturing because surface water supplies are limited. In contrast, more surface water is used for production in North Texas's Barnett Shale and East Texas's Haynesville Shale because more surface water is available in the regions where those plays are located.

§ 41.14:1 Current and Predicted Water Use in Hydraulic Fracturing

In 2018, hydraulic fracturing, or "fracking," was used to extract approximately 60 percent of the crude oil produced in the United States. *See* U.S. Energy Information Administration, *EIA Adds New Play Production Data to Shale Gas and Tight Oil Reports* (Feb. 15, 2019), www.eia.gov/todayinenergy/detail.php?id=38372. Hydraulic fracturing has grown in importance as conventional oil and natural gas reserves have become depleted and extraction technologies have improved, allowing the industry to tap into unconventional reserves. There are multiple types of unconventional gas, but shale gas is the major unconventional gas play in Texas. (A play is an area where hydrocarbons such as oil or natural gas have accumulated. *See* Schlumberger, *Oilfield Glossary*, www.glossary.oilfield.slb.com/Terms/p/play.aspx.)

Although mining accounts for a small percentage of overall Texas water use, as mentioned above, hydraulic fracturing in oil and gas production can have a significant impact on local water resources in dry regions. *See* U.S. Environmental Protection Agency, *Hydraulic Fracturing for Oil and Gas: Impacts from the Hydraulic Fracturing Water Cycle on Drinking Water Resources in the United States* (Dec. 2016), https://cfpub.epa.gov/ncea/hfstudy/recordisplay.cfm?deid=332990. Hydraulic fracturing uses high volumes of water, especially as energy companies seek to reach oil and gas reserves at increasingly greater depths. A rapid increase in population and development in regions that are rich with shale gas and oil can also increase local water demand. *See* Andrew J. Kondash et al., *The Intensification of the Water Footprint of Hydraulic Fracturing*, 4 J. Sci. Advances 8, 4–5 (2018), www.science.org/doi/10.1126/sciadv.aar5982 [hereinafter Kondash et al.]; *see also* Andrew J. Kondash et al., *Quantity of Flowback and Produced Waters from Unconventional Oil and Gas Exploration*, 574 J. Sci. Total Env't 314, 320 (2017), https://sites.nicholas.duke.edu/avnervengosh/files/2011/08/Quantity-and-source-of-unconventional-wastewater.pdf.

In hydraulic fracturing, fluid (typically water combined with a high-viscosity additive) is injected at high pressure from a wellbore into a rock formation until the rock fractures. When the rock fractures, a propping agent (typically sand) is pumped into the fractures to prevent them from sealing when the pressure releases. When the pressure does release, the fluid travels back into the fracture, through the well, and up to the surface. This process loosens the rock formation and allows oil or natural gas to escape into the well.

In all regions with unconventional oil and gas plays, the volume of water used in hydraulic fracturing has steadily increased over time. *See* Kondash et al., at 4. Water use increases as wells are refractured and as both the length and depth of the wells grow. Early in the hydraulic fracturing boom, operators in North Texas's Barnett Shale would inject approximately 1.2 to 3.5 million gallons of water into a gas well during each fracturing operation. *See* James Bené et al., *Northern Trinity/Woodbine Aquifer GAM Assessment of Groundwater Use in the Northern Trinity Aquifer Due to Urban Growth and Barnett Shale Development* 2 (Texas Water Development Board 2007), www.twdb.texas.gov/groundwater/models/gam/trnt_n/TRNT_N_Barnett_Shale_Report.pdf. By 2014, it was estimated that, on average, 5 million gallons of water were used per well in each operation. *See*

Jean-Philippe Nicot et al., *Source and Fate of Hydraulic Fracturing Water in the Barnett Shale: A Historical Perspective*, 48 Envtl. Sci. Technol. 9 (Jan. 2014), http://pubs.acs.org/doi/abs/10.1021/es404050r [hereinafter Barnett Shale Fracturing Water Study]. A 2018 analysis by the *San Antonio Express-News* found that the amount of water used to produce a well in West Texas's Permian Basin rose from an average of 2.7 million gallons in 2014 to 5.4 million gallons in 2015, and subsequently to 10.5 million gallons in 2016. *See* Jennifer Hiller, *Bigger Wells, But More Water*, *San Antonio Express-News*, Jan. 20, 2018, www.expressnews.com/business/eagle-ford-energy/article/Bigger-wells-but-more-water-12512262.php [hereinafter Hiller]. In the Eagle Ford Shale in South Texas, an estimated average of 9.7 million gallons was required to produce a well in 2016, up from 4.5 million gallons in 2013. *See* Hiller. The increase in water use has been more extreme in some regions than others. For instance, from 2011 to 2016, water use per well increased by 770 percent in the Permian Basin but only by 20 percent in Pennsylvania's Marcellus Shale. *See* Kondash et al., at 2.

Most water injected for hydraulic fracturing is retained within the shale formation. Only a small fraction returns as flowback water, which makes it potentially available for recycling or reuse. *See* Kondash et al., at 4–5. However, flowback and produced water have been increasing as volumes of injected water increase. For instance, from 2011 to 2015, flowback and produced water volumes increased by up to 1,440 percent in the natural gas–bearing section of the Eagle Ford Shale and by 610 percent in the oil-bearing section. *See* Kondash et al., at 3.

Flowback and produced water can provide oil and gas companies with an opportunity to reuse or recycle water. For instance, the combined use of water recycling, water reuse, and brackish water increased by 21 percent from 2008 to 2011 in Texas hydraulic fracturing operations (although there was still a total increase in water use and consumption for hydraulic fracturing, which was not entirely offset using recycling, reuse, and brackish water). *See* 2012 Mining Water Use Report Update, at i–ii. Whether water is recycled typically depends on the economics of the oil and gas play. This is influenced by factors such as trucking and disposal costs, freshwater costs, treatment costs, and recycled water's proximity to future wells. *See* House Committee on Natural Resources, *Interim Report to the 83rd Texas Legislature* 69 (Jan. 2013), www.house.state.tx.us/_media/pdf/committees/reports/82interim/House-Committee-on-Natural-Resources-Interim-Report.pdf [hereinafter 2013 Interim Report]. The Railroad Commission of Texas, the state's oil and gas regulator, has sought to incentivize water recycling for hydraulic fracturing by adopting rules that eliminate the requirement for a recycling permit when operators recycle fluid on their own leases or transfer fluid to be recycled on another operator's lease. *See* 16 Tex. Admin. Code § 3.8(d)(7)(B); *see also* 16 Tex. Admin. Code § 3.8(a)(41); Railroad Commission of Texas, *Recycling*, www.rrc.state.tx.us/oil-and-gas/applications-and-permits/environmental-permit-types/recycling/.

The interest in recycling produced water is reflected in the State Water Plan, a recent legislative interim report, and recently introduced Senate Bill 601. The TWDB reported that in 2014 nearly 37 percent of mining water consumption that year occurred in the top ten oil-producing counties driven by fracking. In these counties, which all lie in the Eagle Ford and Permian Basin, mining water use accounted for an average of 40 percent of total water consumption, highlighting the material impact the shale boom exerts on local water conditions. *See* Gabriel Collins, *Oilfield Produced Water Ownership in Texas: Balancing Surface Owners' Rights and Mineral Owners' Commercial Objectives* (Feb. 2017), www.bakerinstitute.org/media/files/files/23bd889f/CES-pub-ProdWaterTX-020817.pdf.

Currently, Region F in West Texas is the only regional water planning group using recycled produced water as a management strategy to address demand in the mining industry in all thirty-two of its covered counties. The latest Region F Plan shows that demands in the mining industry in the region have doubled since the 2017 State Water Plan. *See* Texas Water Development Board, *2021 Region F Water Plan* 2–19 (Nov. 2020), www.twdb.texas.gov/waterplanning/rwp/plans/2021/F/RegionF_2021 RWP_V1.pdf. In fact, the TWDB is looking at produced water as a possible contribution for aquifer storage and recovery projects and to increase water supply throughout the state. *See Interim Report of the Senate Committee on Water and Rural Affairs* 10 (Dec. 16, 2020) [hereinafter SCWRA Interim Report].

The SCWRA Interim Report recommended creation of the Texas Produced Water Consortium with industry stakeholders to pool research and innovation in one spot. This group would create policy recommendations, share technology, and create economically viable solutions for produced water use. The main purpose of the consortium would be to create a pilot program sponsored by the state for a large scale, interconnected produced water facility in the Permian Basin. The report further recommended formally tracking produced water data. Further, in a recommendation that succinctly illustrates the nexus between water and energy, the report suggested regulations for the capture and use of flaring to be used as an energy source to desalinate the produced water and noted that the consortium could use this form of energy to power the pilot project. *See* SCWRA Interim Report, at 30–31.

In the 87th Texas legislative regular session, Senator Perry filed Senate Bill 601, which implemented the SCWRA Interim Report recommendations on this issue. The bill created the Texas Produced Water Consortium by adding subchapter E to chapter 109 of the Education Code. The agency advisory council is comprised of representatives of the Department of Agriculture, General Land Office, Parks and Wildlife Department, Texas Railroad Commission, the State Energy Conservation Office, the TCEQ, the Texas Economic Development and Tourism Office of Governor's Office, and the TWDB. A report is due by September 1, 2022, and will address the pilot project for state participation in a produced water facility. There are public and private stakeholders in the work of the consortium; sponsorship will buy access to data in proportion to sponsorship level. *See* Tex. Educ. Code §§ 109.202–.206.

There is also increased interest in the use of brackish water for hydraulic fracturing, as lower freshwater use and consumption can help oil and gas companies adapt to arid climates in regions such as South and West Texas. *See* 2012 Mining Water Use Report Update, at i. The use of both fresh and brackish water for oil and gas extraction is expected to increase through 2020 and then plateau from 2020 to 2030 at a rate of approximately 180,000 AF per year. *See* 2012 Mining Water Use Report Update, at 65. By 2060, this use is predicted to decline to 60,000 AF per year. *See* 2012 Mining Water Use Report Update, at 65. The industry's freshwater consumption is expected to peak at approximately 100,000 AF per year by 2020, ultimately declining to a few tens of thousands of AF by the middle of the century. *See* 2012 Mining Water Use Report Update, at 65. The increased use of brackish water is an effective solution for reducing freshwater consumption, but the potential increase in storage and truck transportation of brine water increases the risk that accidental brine water releases will occur, causing contamination. *See* TAMEST Report at 120 tbl. 6-2.

§ 41.14:2 Water Flooding as Method of Oil and Gas Extraction

Before the expansion of hydraulic fracturing, water flooding was the most common method in the United States for extracting onshore crude oil. The method is still commonly used in U.S. oil production. In 2014, approximately 42 percent of onshore U.S. oil was recovered using water flooding. *See* May Wu & Hui Xu, *Consumptive Water Use in the Production of Ethanol and Petroleum Gasoline—2018 Update* 8 (Argonne National Laboratory 2018), https://publications.anl.gov/anlpubs/2019/01/148043.pdf [hereinafter 2018 Consumptive Water Use Update]. This method's water requirements are high, as the technique involves pumping water into an oil-producing reservoir to replace oil removed by primary production. The water requirements vary with the age and characteristics of the individual well and formation. In this method, injected water fills the void left by extracted oil, either maintaining or increasing reservoir pressure so that the remaining oil can be extracted. *See* 2011 Consumptive Water Use Update, at 47 fig. 27. The Argonne National Laboratory estimates that water flooding requires an average of 15.7 gallons of water per gallon of crude oil recovered, sharply contrasting with the mere 0.2 gallons of water per gallon of crude oil used in primary recovery. In 2014, the water flooding method of recovery accounted for 94 percent of the water injected into onshore wells for oil recovery. Use of the method appears to be on the decline, as it decreased by 25 percent from 2006 to 2014. *See* 2018 Consumptive Water Use Update, at 8.

Water flooding typically requires 100 percent new water in the initial operation. Demand for new water declines as the well operations progress further. As a well produces more water, operators can reuse much of the water extracted from that well-produced water. In situations where water flooding is used as a method of extracting oil and gas, the produced water is typically composed of free water, oil-water emulsion, and oil and suspended solids—a combination known in the industry as basic sediment and water, or BS&W. Produced water is extracted at a wellhead and pumped to gathering points known as satellites. From each satellite, that water is pumped to a production facility, or battery, where it is separated from oil. Once final filtration is complete, the water is reinjected into a producing formation or discharged into injection wells and evaporation ponds. *See* 2011 Consumptive Water Use Update, at 6.

§ 41.15 Water for Nuclear Power Generation and Uranium Mining

The development of new nuclear power generation in Texas, with its associated use of large volumes of water, is not expected soon. Although NRG Energy and its partners received licenses in 2016 from the U.S. Nuclear Regulatory Commission to build two new nuclear reactors at the South Texas Project, a nuclear facility located southwest of Houston, it was reported that NRG was unlikely to build the reactors soon because of the project's significant cost (estimated at $14 billion in 2011) and low Texas power prices. *See* Jordan Blum, *Regulators Approve New Nuclear Reactors near Houston*, *Houston Chronicle,* Feb. 6, 2016, www.houstonchronicle.com/business/energy/article/Regulators-approve-new-nuclear-reactors-near-6819187.php; *see also* James Osborne, *Nuclear Power Woes Extend to Texas*, *Houston Chronicle*, Mar. 23, 2019, www.houstonchronicle.com/business/article/Nuclear-power-woes-extend-to-Texas-13709604.php.

Historically, water for in situ leach uranium mining has represented a small share of Texas water use. *See* 2011 Mining Water Use Report, at 236. Water demand for uranium mining, however, may rise in the long term and thus increase water demand. Texas has significant untapped uranium reserves, and global uranium demand is expected to increase over the next few decades. In 2015, there were an estimated 220 million pounds of recoverable uranium oxide in South Texas, well above the 60 million pounds that the federal agency had previously estimated. *See* U.S. Geological Survey, *Assessment of Undiscovered Sandstone-Hosted Uranium Resources in the Texas Coastal Plain, 2015* (Nov. 2015), https://pubs.usgs.gov/fs/2015/3069/fs20153069.pdf. As of February 2021, there were six current state-issued permits for uranium exploration. *See* Railroad Commission of Texas, *Texas Uranium Exploration Permits*, www.rrc.state.tx.us/surface-mining/programs/uranium-exploration/texas-uranium-exploration-permits/.

While demand for nuclear power has declined in many developed countries including the United States, global uranium demand is predicted to increase over the next several decades, particularly in developing countries seeking to provide electric power to their growing populations. *See* Nuclear Energy Agency & International Atomic Energy Agency, *Uranium 2018: Resources, Production and Demand* 14 (2018), www.oecd-nea.org/ndd/pubs/2018/7413-uranium-2018.pdf. The Uranium Energy Corporation, which processes uranium in the Eagle Ford Shale, predicts that its use of a method like hydraulic fracturing will create a South Texas uranium boom. *See* Christopher Helman, *Energy's Latest Battleground: Fracking for Uranium*, *Forbes*, Jan. 23, 2013, www.forbes.com/sites/christopherhelman/2013/01/23/fracking-for-uranium/#4c4533417c5b. Thus, demand for Texas uranium (and water use for uranium mining and processing) might rise with global uranium demand, even if there is no heightened domestic demand for nuclear power.

Future trends in this area are still uncertain, but some market watchers became bullish on uranium by early 2020. *See* Christopher Collins, *Trump Has Kneecapped Another Environmental Safeguard. Could That Spur Expanded Uranium Mining in South Texas*?, *Texas Observer*, Jan. 10, 2020, texasobserver.org/trump-has-kneecapped-another-environmental-safeguard-could-that-spur-expanded-uranium-mining-in-south-texas/. In 2020, the Trump administration recommended a rollback of federal regulations on uranium mining, including environmental reviews conducted pursuant to the National Environmental Policy Act (NEPA). This would have allowed for uranium mining on federal lands, including near Grand Canyon National Park. *See* U.S. Department of Energy, *Restoring America's Competitive Nuclear Energy Advantage* 18 (2020), www.energy.gov/sites/prod/files/2020/04/f74/Restoring%20America%27s%20Competitive%20Nuclear%20Advantage_1.pdf. While few federal lands are in Texas, this could have signaled a change in direction for the industry.

However, during his presidential campaign, President Biden announced that he would shut down the plans for uranium mining near the Grand Canyon and on certain other federal lands. *See* Rebecca Beitsch, *Biden Vows Reversal as Trump Eyes Mining Near Grand Canyon, Bristol Bay*, *The Hill*, Aug. 10, 2020, https://thehill.com/policy/energy-environment/511303-biden-vows-reversal-as-trump-eyes-mining-near-grand-canyon-bristol. The Trump-era plans to allow new uranium mining on federal lands thus appear unlikely to proceed.

§ 41.16 Water Use for Biofuel Production

Biofuels are derived from living matter, such as plants and animals. They are thus considered renewables because they can be regenerated. However, this does not mean that they use little water, in contrast to wind and solar PV power. In fact, growing some biofuel crops can require considerable volumes of water. Irrigation accounts for the greatest share of biofuel water consumption. Additional water consumption is involved in converting feedstock into fuel. Water consumption varies dramatically depending on the type of biofuel produced and the crop (or other feedstock) used. The most common types of biofuel are ethanol and biodiesel.

§ 41.16:1 Water Use for Ethanol Production

Ethanol (grain alcohol) is a renewable fuel used in gasoline-powered vehicles and other internal combustion engines. Ethanol accounted for 94 percent of U.S. biofuel production in 2012. *See* U.S. Department of Agriculture, *U.S. Bioenergy Statistics*, www.ers.usda.gov/data-products/us-bioenergy-statistics/. In the United States, ethanol is mostly made from corn, and over 95 percent of fuel consumed by gasoline-powered vehicles is petroleum gasoline blended with 10 percent ethanol. *See* U.S. Energy Information Administration, *Almost All U.S. Gasoline Is Blended with 10% Ethanol* (May 4, 2016), www.eia.gov/todayinenergy/detail.php?id=26092. In January 2020, fuel ethanol production capacity in the U.S. was 17.3 billion gallons per year, or 1.1 million barrels per day. *See* U.S. Energy Information Administration, *U.S. Fuel Ethanol Production Capacity Increased by 3% in 2019* (Sept. 29, 2020), www.eia.gov/todayinenergy/detail.php?id=45316#:~:text=In%20the%20September%202020%20Short,13%25%20lower%20than%202019%20levels.&text=EIA%20forecasts%20that%20fuel%20ethanol,b%2Fd%20in%20December%202020 [hereinafter U.S. Fuel Ethanol Production Capacity]. Actual U.S. ethanol production totaled 15.8 billion gallons in 2019 (or 1.03 million barrels per day). *See* U.S. Fuel Ethanol Production Capacity. The EIA projects that U.S. biofuel production will grow slowly through 2050 because a predicted decline in U.S. consumption of ethanol-blended gasoline is expected to be offset by rising U.S. ethanol exports. *See* U.S. Energy Information Administration, *EIA Projects U.S. Biofuel Production to Slowly Increase through 2050* (Mar. 9, 2020), www.eia.gov/todayinenergy/detail.php?id=43096.

Researchers at the Lawrence Berkeley National Laboratory have estimated that, depending on climate conditions, corn-based ethanol requires between 2,500 and 29,000 gallons of water per million

Btu of energy produced. *See* James E. McMahon & Sarah K. Price, *Water and Energy Interactions* 5 (U.S. Department of Energy 2011), www.osti.gov/servlets/purl/1171537. This water is primarily used for irrigation. The Argonne National Laboratory has determined that "producing a gallon of corn ethanol can consume as little as 10 or as much as 324 gallons of water," depending on the volume of water used to irrigate the corn. The extreme variation in water requirements is due to geographical and climate differences in areas where corn is grown. *See* 2011 Consumptive Water Use Update, at 71.

The United States had 197 ethanol plants in operation in January 2021. *See* U.S. Energy Information Administration, *U.S. Fuel Ethanol Plant Production Capacity* (Sept. 3, 2021), www.eia.gov/petroleum/ethanolcapacity/index.php. Most ethanol production plants in the United States are in the Midwest, especially in Iowa, Nebraska, and Illinois, which together contain half of the nation's total ethanol production capacity. *See* U.S. Fuel Ethanol Production Capacity. Texas ethanol production is limited in comparison. In 2021, only four ethanol production facilities were operating in Texas, all in the Panhandle, with a combined production capacity of approximately 390 million gallons per year. *See* Ethanol Producer Magazine, *U.S. Ethanol Plants*, www.ethanolproducer.com/plants/listplants/US/Operational/All/.

§ 41.16:2 Water Use for Biodiesel Production

Biodiesel is made from animal or vegetable materials and can be used in diesel engines. The United States produced approximately 1.65 billion gallons of biodiesel in 2020. *See* U.S. Energy Information Administration, *Monthly Biodiesel Production Report* 4 tbl. 1 (Jan. 2021), www.eia.gov/biofuels/biodiesel/production/biodiesel.pdf [hereinafter EIA Biodiesel Report]. In November 2020, the nation's total production capacity for biodiesel was about 2.45 billion gallons per year. *See* EIA Biodiesel Report, at 4 tbl. 1. Texas has eight biodiesel plants that have a combined manufacturing capacity of 375 million gallons per year. *See* EIA Biodiesel Report, at 8 tbl. 4.

Water is required both to produce biodiesel feedstock and to convert that feedstock into the final product. Estimating the exact volume of water consumption associated with feedstock production is complicated. Some biodiesel feedstocks, such as recycled oils and fats, do not involve any water consumption. These feedstocks would otherwise require disposal, which could burden wastewater collection or treatment systems. Water consumption can also vary dramatically depending on whether a feedstock is produced from a crop requiring irrigation. Most biodiesel feedstock comes from non-irrigated crops. Even oilseed crops that are grown specifically for biodiesel—such as jatropha, camelina, or algae—consume relatively little water, as, globally, water consumption is a key selection factor for these crops. In other instances, biodiesel may be produced as a coproduct of plants, like peanuts and soybeans, which already have their own markets. *See* EIA Biodiesel Report, at 3. Thus, it can be challenging to estimate the true water consumption of biodiesel feedstocks, as many either have a low water footprint or are not produced specifically for use as biodiesel. In Texas, a diverse array of feedstocks is used for biodiesel, and information on their water consumption is not readily available.

V. Energy for Water in Texas: Extraction, Treatment, and Distribution

§ 41.17 Introduction: Energy Required for Water Supply

Water supply—the process of taking water from its original source to its final use—has three primary components: (1) extraction, (2) treatment, and (3) distribution. These components—and subsequently collecting and treating wastewater—are energy-intensive processes. Compared to other sectors, however, public drinking water and municipal wastewater systems use a small share of the nation's electricity. In 2013, the Electric Power Research Institute (EPRI) determined that public drinking water systems and municipal wastewater systems account for approximately 1 and 0.8 percent of total electricity use in the United States, respectively, or about 39.2 billion kWh and 30.2 billion kWh per year. *See* S. Pabi et al., *Electricity Use and Management in the Municipal Water Supply and Wastewater Industries* 4-16 (Electric Power Research Institute 2013) [hereinafter EPRI Electricity Use]. In Texas, the processes of water extraction, distribution, and treatment are thought to account for 0.8 to 1.3 percent of total statewide electric power demand. *See* Ashlynn S. Stillwell et al., University of Texas at Austin & Environmental Defense Fund, *Energy-Water Nexus in Texas* 1 (Apr. 2009), www.edf.org/sites/default/files/Energy_Water_Nexus_in_Texas_1.pdf [hereinafter Stillwell et al.].

However, researchers face limitations in assessing how much energy is used to operate municipal water and wastewater systems. In 2002, EPRI estimated that about 4 percent of the nation's electricity was used to extract, treat, and distribute water and to collect and treat wastewater. *See* Electric Power Research Institute, 4 *Water and Sustainability: U.S. Electricity Consumption for Water Supply & Treatment—The Next Half Century* 1–2 (2002), www.circleofblue.org/wp-content/uploads/2010/08/EPRI-Volume-4.pdf [hereinafter EPRI Water and Sustainability]. In 2017, the Congressional Research Service found that the estimate and EPRI's projections of the water sector's future energy use were likely flawed, as the 2002 EPRI study (1) relied on secondary source data; (2) did not include future projections of the electric power requirements for water in the thermoelectric sector (as it was assumed that this energy use would decline); (3) did not consider on-site heating, cooling, pumping, and softening of water for end-use as part of water sector's energy demand; and (4) did not consider that, in the future, a larger proportion of water demands will likely be met with sources that have higher energy demands, such as desalinated water or groundwater pumped from greater depths. *See* Claudia Copeland & Nicole T. Carter, *Energy-Water Nexus: The Water Sector's Energy Use* 2 (Congressional Research Service 2017), https://fas.org/sgp/crs/misc/R43200.pdf [hereinafter Congressional Research Service Report]. The Congressional Research Service found that the EPRI estimate was "a good starting place for understanding the magnitude" of energy required to provide public drinking water and to treat wastewater but cautioned that the data on energy use for water processes are "fragmentary and not well documented." Congressional Research Service Report, at 2. It is also difficult to draw generalized conclusions about overall energy use for water in the United States, because energy use for water can vary significantly due to geographical and other regional differences. *See* Congressional Research Service Report, at 4.

Electric power demand for procuring and treating water can vary depending on several factors, as shown in Table 2 below. These factors are discussed in more detail at section 41.19 below.

Table 2: Factors that Influence Electric Power Demand for Water
• **Water Source: Groundwater vs. Surface Water.** Pumping groundwater requires approximately 30 percent more electric power on a per unit basis than withdrawing surface water. EPRI Water and Sustainability, at 1-2. The electric power requirements for extracting groundwater increase as the depth at which groundwater is located increases. For instance, only 540 kWh/Mgal is required to pump water from a 120-foot well, while 2,000 kWh/Mgal is required to pump water from a 400-foot well. Stillwell et al., at 20. Electric power requirements for extracting groundwater are likely even higher in Texas, as the average depth of Texas groundwater is nearly 700 feet. Stillwell et al., at 20.
• **Distribution Distance.** Electric power requirements increase with the distance of the water source from its intended end use. Major elevation changes can also increase electrical power requirements, as water suppliers may have to pump (rather than use gravity) to transport water across changing elevations.
• **Level of Treatment Required.** Higher levels of treatment require more electric power. Thus, treating water to drinking quality requires more electric power. Desalination also requires a great deal of power, so treating brackish or saline water is more energy-intensive than treating freshwater.

• **Leakage and Evaporation Loss.** Leakage and evaporation loss in a system can also raise electric power requirements, as more water must be pumped to make up for these losses.
Source: Claudia Copeland & Nicole T. Carter, *Energy-Water Nexus: The Water Sector's Energy Use* 3 (Congressional Research Service 2017), https://fas.org/sgp/crs/misc/R43200.pdf. This source is used in Table 2 unless otherwise stated.

§ 41.18 Comparing Water Demand for Public Water Supply Systems and End-User Suppliers

Public water supply systems (which may also be referred to as public water supply agencies) handle and control the process of taking water from its original source to its final use for most private individuals and some industries. In contrast, rural residential users and non-residential users (including the commercial, farming, industrial, and power generation sectors) typically control this process themselves. This is known as self-supply or end-user supply. All data are national, except where Texas-specific data are identified.

As shown in Table 3 below, most U.S. water demand is for power generation and agricultural irrigation, generally self-suppliers. Public water supply systems are the primary providers of water for domestic use, supplying approximately 85 percent of total domestic demand while meeting about 20 percent of industrial demand and providing little to no water for agricultural irrigation, livestock, mining, and electric power generation. *See* EPRI Water and Sustainability, at 4-1.

Table 3: Estimated Use and Source of Water Withdrawals in the U.S. (2015) (Million Gallons Per Day)

Sector	**Freshwater**	**Saline Water**	**Total**
Public Supply	N/A	N/A	39,000
Self-Supplied Domestic	3,260	N/A	3,260
Irrigation	118,000	N/A	118,000
Livestock	2,000	N/A	2,000
Aquaculture	N/A	N/A	7,550
Industrial	14,000	786	14,786
Mining	1,880	2,120	4,000
Power Generation	95,100	37,800	132,900
Total U.S. Water Use	**281,000**	**41,000**	**322,000**

Source: Cheryl A. Dieter et al., Estimated Use of Water in the United States in 2015 10, U.S. Geological Survey Circular 1441 (2018) (supersedes USGS Open-File Report 2017-1131), https://pubs.usgs.gov/circ/1441/circ1441.pdf.

Note that the values in Table 3 may not sum to totals because of independent rounding. Values for public water supply and aquaculture include fresh and saline water withdrawals.

The amount of electric power required to treat water depends on whether the water is publicly or privately provided and on the ultimate use. A comparison of estimated power consumption by different water providers and for different uses appears in Table 4 below:

Table 4: Summary of Nationwide Electricity Consumption Projections for Water Supply and Wastewater Treatment

Year	2000	2005	2010	2015	2020	2050
Public Supply and Treatment—Million kWh						
Public water supply	30,632	31,910	33,240	34,648	36,079	45,660
Publicly owned treatment works (POTW)	21,006	24,512	24,895	25,277	26,039	29,820
Private Supply and Treatment—Million kWh						
Domestic supply	894	930	965	1,001	1,038	1,274
Commercial supply	476	499	525	553	581	780
Industrial supply	3,341	3,793	4,236	4,731	5,284	10,255
Mining supply	490	509	528	548	569	713
Irrigation supply	23,607	25,639	27,909	30,453	33,314	60,646
Livestock supply	992	1,047	1,095	1,144	1,192	1,510
Privately operated wastewater treatment (see note)	42,012	49,025	49,790	50,555	52,078	59,641
Total electricity	**123,450**	**137,864**	**143,182**	**148,910**	**156,174**	**210,299**

Source: Electric Power Research Institute, 4 *Water and Sustainability: U.S. Electricity Consumption for Water Supply & Treatment—The Next Half Century* 1-5 tbl. 1-2 (2002), www.circleofblue.org/wp-content/uploads/2010/08/EPRI-Volume-4.pdf. EPRI notes that "[i]t was not possible to make electricity consumption projections for privately operated wastewater treatment facilities. . . . The figure shown here is a surrogate representing twice the electricity consumption of POTWs. This estimate was used because there are about 50 percent more privately operated wastewater treatment facilities in the U.S. as POTWs, and their unit electricity consumption is estimated to be about 50 percent greater than that of POTWs because of loss of economies of scale and different treatment regimens."

See section 41.17 above, which discusses why the EPRI data does not provide a conclusive answer to the question of how much electric power is required for the extraction, treatment, and distribution of water in the United States. It does, however, offer a useful starting point.

§ 41.19 Public Water Supply Systems: Electricity Demand

Public water supply systems account for approximately 1 percent of overall U.S. electric power use. *See* EPRI Electricity Use, at 4-16. This means that American public water supply systems use about 0.11 TWh of electrical energy per day, or 39.2 TWh per year. *See* EPRI Electricity Use, at 4-16. In 2011, University of Texas researchers estimated that Texas alone uses 2.1 to 2.7 TWh of electrical power for water supply systems annually, and an additional 1.1 to 2.2 TWh for wastewater systems. *See* Stillwell et al., at 1.

Municipalities often find that energy usage by water and wastewater utilities accounts for approximately 30 to 40 percent of their total energy bills. *See* Congressional Research Service Report, at 6. For municipal water and wastewater utilities, energy is often the second-highest budget item after labor costs. *See* Congressional Research Service Report, at 6.

Why do public water supply systems have such high energy requirements? Supplying clean water to the public involves treatment and distribution costs that do not exist for self-suppliers in most other sectors. This section primarily discusses energy needed for public water supply systems distribution and treatment requirements.

In the United States, about 80 to 85 percent of electric power consumption for providing treated surface water is used to pump that water through the supplier's distribution system. *See* EPRI Water and Sustainability, at 2-2. Energy requirements can increase—sometimes dramatically—whenever additional pumping is required, such as when water must be piped over long distances or changing elevations. In California, where municipal water is often pumped across vast distances and over changing elevations, energy usage for water distribution can range from 1,330 kWh/Mgal to 9,930 kWh/Mgal. *See* California Energy Commission, *California's Water-Energy Relationship, Final Staff Report* 25 (2005), http://large.stanford.edu/courses/2012/ph240/spearrin1/docs/CEC-700-2005-011-SF.PDF [hereinafter *California's Water-Energy Relationship*]. As a result, as much as 19 percent of California electric power is consumed to pump, treat, collect, and discharge water and wastewater. *See California's Water-Energy Relationship*, at 8.

Under the Safe Drinking Water Act (42 U.S.C. §§ 300f–300j-27), public water supply agencies must generally treat drinking water before supplying it to users. See Chapter 30 of this book for a discussion of the Safe Drinking Water Act. Treatment costs are typically lower for groundwater than for surface water, as groundwater generally has fewer contaminants. In some instances, groundwater treatment requires only chlorination, involving minimal cost and energy use. *See* EPRI Water and Sustainability, at 2-2, 2-3. (However, providing groundwater to customers still requires more energy overall due to pumping requirements. *See* EPRI Water and Sustainability, at 2-3.) At most, surface water treatment typically accounts for no more than 15 percent of a public water supply system's total electric power consumption. *See* Stillwell et al., at 22–23.

Multiple processes are used to treat surface water, including but not limited to screening raw water to remove debris; preoxidation with chlorine or ozone to kill bacteria and other organisms; processes that clarify water and remove turbidity; and a final round of disinfection to kill remaining organisms. A more detailed explanation of surface water treatment appears in EPRI Water and Sustainability, at 2-1.

In Texas, most municipal holders of surface water rights are concentrated in the central and northeastern parts of the state, reflecting both higher population and greater surface water availability, as rainfall levels in Texas tend to be higher in the eastern half of the state, and Texas rivers typically flow from west to east. *See* Stillwell et al., at 28 fig. 3.3; *see also* Texas Aquatic Science, 8 *Texas Aquatic Science Textbook: Streams and Rivers*, https://texasaquaticscience.org/streams-rivers-aquatic-science-texas/. As this situation indicates, surface water is an important water source for much of the Texas population, as most of the state's major population centers (including Houston, Austin, San Antonio, and Dallas-Fort Worth) are in the central or eastern regions of Texas. Groundwater, however, is also an important municipal water supply source. Groundwater met about 36 percent of Texas municipal water demand in 2011. *See* Peter G. George et al., *Aquifers of Texas: Report 380* 3 (Texas Water Development Board July 2011), www.twdb.texas.gov/publications/reports/numbered_reports/doc/R380_AquifersofTexas.pdf?d=83142.85499999824.

An increasing number of Texas municipalities are also looking to desalination as a new source of water supply, although the desalination process is highly energy intensive. In the United States, desalinating brackish groundwater can require 3,900 to 9,700 kWh per million gallons of water. *See* Stillwell et al., at 22. Energy requirements for desalinating seawater are much higher. Seawater desalination can require 9,700 to 16,500 kWh per million gallons of water. *See* Stillwell et al., at 22.

Texas aquifers are estimated to contain more than 2.7 billion AF (879,797 billion gallons) of brackish groundwater. *See* Texas Water Development Board, *The Future of Desalination in Texas: 2016 Biennial Report on Seawater and Brackish Groundwater Desalination, 85th Legislative Session* 8 (Dec. 2016), www.twdb.texas.gov/innovativewater/desal/doc/2016_TheFutureofDesalination

inTexas.pdf [hereinafter Desalination Report]. In 2016, Texas had enough municipal desalination capacity to desalinate up to 159,060 AF of water annually. *See* Texas Water Development Board, *Desalination Facts*, www.twdb.texas.gov/innovativewater/desal/facts.asp. Most of that capacity is available for desalination of brackish groundwater (up to 95,212 AF annually), followed by brackish surface water (up to 60,488 AF annually).

Cost has been an impediment to the development of seawater desalination. *See* Desalination Report, at 9. Factors such as permitting, treatment, brine disposal, and transmission pipelines have made seawater desalination more expensive than desalinating brackish water or developing other water supplies. *See* Desalination Report, at 9. However, in the Corpus Christi area, a seawater desalination plant is in the initial planning stages of construction, and it may become the first seawater desalination plant in the state. *See* Paul Cobler, *Seawater Desalination Plant Proposed for Corpus Christi Area*, *Texas Tribune*, May 16, 2018, www.texastribune.org/2018/05/16/port-corpus-christi-seeking-permission-construct-seawater-desalination/ [hereinafter Corpus Christi Seawater Desalination Plant]. The facility's output will be treated for industrial use only, but the plant will be located close to a municipal water treatment facility where the output can be further treated to drinking water standards. The development of this facility is discussed at section 41.21 below, along with other predicted developments in energy use for supplying water in Texas. See also Chapter 25 of this book.

§ 41.20 End-User Suppliers: Electricity Demands

As discussed above, end-user suppliers meet their water demands without public water supply systems. End users can include individuals, typically in rural areas, who supply their own water for domestic use. However, most end users are in the industrial, mining, thermal power generation, livestock, and agricultural irrigation sectors, as shown at Table 4 above. Eighty percent of industrial and mining water, for instance, is supplied by end users. *See* EPRI Water and Sustainability, at 4-8. End users also meet all water demand for agricultural irrigation and livestock, and virtually all water demand for power generation. *See* EPRI Water and Sustainability, at 4-1, 4-13, 4-18.

End users typically use less electric power to supply water for a given volume than public water supply systems do. This is because their treatment costs are often low or nonexistent, as end users rarely need to treat water for agricultural irrigation, thermal power generation, industry, and mining. Even domestic end users often have low treatment costs, as they often use groundwater that generally requires little treatment. End-user suppliers often have lower extraction and distribution costs as well. Extraction often involves simply bringing water to the surface using relatively small, uncomplicated pumps. *See* EPRI Water and Sustainability, at ch. 4. End users often transport their water over shorter distances than public water supply systems do, and distribution may be gravity-assisted, as end users water is often stored in elevated tanks near the source. As a result, end-user suppliers typically use 300 kWh/Mgal to supply surface water and 700 to 800 kWh/Mgal to supply groundwater, while public water supply systems average 1,406 kWh/Mgal for surface water and 1,824 kWh/Mgal for groundwater. *See* EPRI Water and Sustainability, at 1-4.

§ 41.21 Predicted Electric Power Use for the Water Supply Sector

In 2002, the EPRI estimated that total U.S. consumption of electric power for supplying water will rise more than 50 percent from 2000 to 2050, while electric power consumption for agricultural and industrial water users specifically will more than double. *See* EPRI Water and Sustainability, at 1-2. See Table 5 below. The amount of electrical power used to supply water for thermoelectric power generation is likely to remain flat as new technologies decrease water consumption in that sector. *See* EPRI Water and Sustainability, at 1-2.

Table 5: Electricity Consumption Projections for Water Supply		
Water supply	**2010 (million kWh)**	**2050 (million kWh)**
Public	33,240	45,660
Domestic	965	1,274
Commercial	525	780
Industrial	4,236	10,255
Mining	528	713
Irrigation	27,909	60,646
Livestock	1,095	1,510
Total	**68,498**	**120,838**
Source: Electric Power Research Institute, 4 *Water and Sustainability: U.S. Electricity Consumption for Water Supply & Treatment—The Next Half Century* 1-5 (2002), www.circleofblue.org/wp-content/uploads/2010/08/EPRI-Volume-4.pdf. Please see the source for estimates of electric power consumption by privately operated wastewater treatment facilities, as these estimates are not included here.		

The EPRI has predicted that the water supply sector's energy requirements will increase overall. However, numerous factors will influence future energy usage for supplying water. More energy-efficient technologies in the water supply sector could reduce power demand. (Replacing aging infrastructure with modern, energy-efficient systems would likely lower energy consumption.) Water conservation, as well as water reuse and recycling, could also help lower energy demand, although both reuse and recycling have their own energy requirements. Additionally, if Texas population growth causes a significant increase in water demand, water may have to be transported over longer distances, as urban centers and other communities may decide to obtain water from more distant sources if local supplies prove to be insufficient. The San Antonio Water System, for instance, constructed a 142-mile pipeline to bring water to San Antonio from the Carrizo/Simsboro Aquifer in Burleson County. *See* Jessica Corso, *SAWS Turns on Tap of $900M Vista Ridge Project*, *San Antonio Business Journal*, May 6, 2020, www.bizjournals.com/sanantonio/c/saws-turns-on-tap-of-900m-vista-ridge-project.html. The $930 million pipeline was completed in 2020.

Desalination is another avenue that some Texas cities are considering enhancing their reliable water supply. In 2012, Texas had forty-six municipal desalination plants, which generally treat either brackish groundwater or brackish surface water. *See* Desalination Report, at 8. However, in the Corpus Christi area, there are plans to build what may become the state's first seawater desalination plant. The plant will make processed seawater available for industrial and possibly municipal use. *See* Corpus Christi Seawater Desalination Plant. Its predicted output will be up to 19.1 million gallons of water per day, making it one of the larger desalination facilities in Texas. (The largest is the Kay Bailey Hutchinson Desalination Plant in El Paso, which produces 27.5 million gallons of desalinated water per day.) In 2020, the Corpus Christi City Council voted to approve a financing agreement with the TWDB that will enable the City to issue nearly $11.5 million in bonds to fund a municipal desalination project. City of Corpus Christi, Resolution 20-0980, approved Aug. 25, 2020, https://corpuschristi.legistar.com/LegislationDetail.aspx?ID=4618144&GUID=A48F3999-CCA3-47D2-90E5-90ABF5B9D409.

The high cost of seawater desalination has been an impediment to constructing seawater desalination plants, but this cost is less of an obstacle to industrial users, as these users are willing to pay far more for water than municipal or agricultural users. The Corpus Christi-area plant is considered a "drought-proof" water source that will help industrial users ensure that their production processes are not interrupted by water scarcity. *See* Corpus Christi Seawater Desalination Plant. While the plant's output will be treated for industrial use, it will be located close to a municipal water treatment plant, so the facility may also be available to support the municipal water supply. *See* Corpus Christi Seawater Desalination Plant.

VI. Conclusion

§ 41.22 Conclusion

Both water and energy have been influential in shaping Texas's past and present. These resources will also shape the state's future. Ensuring that Texas has enough water will be essential to the state's economy and energy sector. Providing sufficient electric power generation will likewise be necessary to ensure that Texans have reliable access to water, especially safe drinking water. Developments such as rapid population growth and climate change will present challenges to policymakers, businesses, and others who manage or rely on the state's water and energy resources. However, these challenges also create opportunities for innovation, as has been evidenced by the increasing use of renewable power generation, desalination, water recycling, and energy-efficient technologies in Texas. Innovative solutions in technology, government, business, and at home will be important for helping Texans meet the state's water-energy nexus challenges. Many sectors will be able to develop more effective, creative solutions if they treat water and energy issues as interlinked—in other words, as a nexus.

Statutes and Rules Cited

[Decimal references are to chapter section numbers.]

TEXAS

Texas Constitution

Texas Revised Civil Statutes

Texas Agriculture Code

Texas Civil Practice & Remedies Code

Texas Education Code

Texas Election Code

Texas Government Code

Texas Health & Safety Code

Texas Local Government Code

Texas Natural Resources Code

Texas Occupations Code

Texas Parks & Wildlife Code

Texas Property Code

Texas Special District Local Laws Code

Texas Tax Code

Texas Transportation Code

Texas Utilities Code

Texas Water Code

Texas Administrative Code

Texas Attorney General Opinions

United States

United States Constitution

United States Code

Code of Federal Regulations

Federal Rules of Civil Procedure

Cases Cited

[Decimal references are to chapter section numbers.]

A

B

C

D

E

F

G

H

I

J

K

L

M

N

T

U

V

W

Y

Subject Index

[Decimal references are to chapter section numbers.]

B

C

D

F

G

H

I

J

K

L

M

N

O

P

R

S

T

U

V

W

How to Download This Book

To install this book's digital download—

1. go to **https://manage.texasbarpractice.com**;
2. if prompted to log in, do so; and
3. in the "Downloadables" column, click the download button for this book's title.

For details, see the section below titled "Downloading and Installing."

DIGITAL DOWNLOAD DOCUMENTATION

Essentials of Texas Water Resources, 7th Ed.
Digital Download 2022

The downloadable version of *Essentials of Texas Water Resources, 7th Ed.*, contains the entire text of the printed book. If you have questions or problems with this product not covered in the documentation available via the URLs below, please contact Texas Bar Books at 800-204-2222, ext. 1499 for technical support or ext. 1411 for orders and accounts, or at **books@texasbar.com**.

Additional and Entity Licenses

The current owner of this book may purchase additional and entity licenses for the digital download. Each additional license is for one additional lawyer and that lawyer's support team only. Additional and entity licenses are subject to the terms of the original license concerning permitted users of the printed book and digital download. Please visit **www.texasbarpractice.com/knowledgebase/article/how-to-get-access-for-other-lawyers** for details.

Usage Tips and Other Information

For information on digital download licensing, installation, and usage, visit the Texas Bar Practice Knowledge Base at **www.texasbarpractice.com/knowledgebase**.

Downloading and Installing

Use of the digital download is subject to the terms of the license and limited warranty included in this documentation and on the digital download web pages. By accessing the digital download, you waive all refund privileges for this publication.

To install this book's complete digital download, follow the instructions below.*

1. Go to **https://manage.texasbarpractice.com**:

   If the site prompts you to log you in, do so using the email address associated with this purchase.

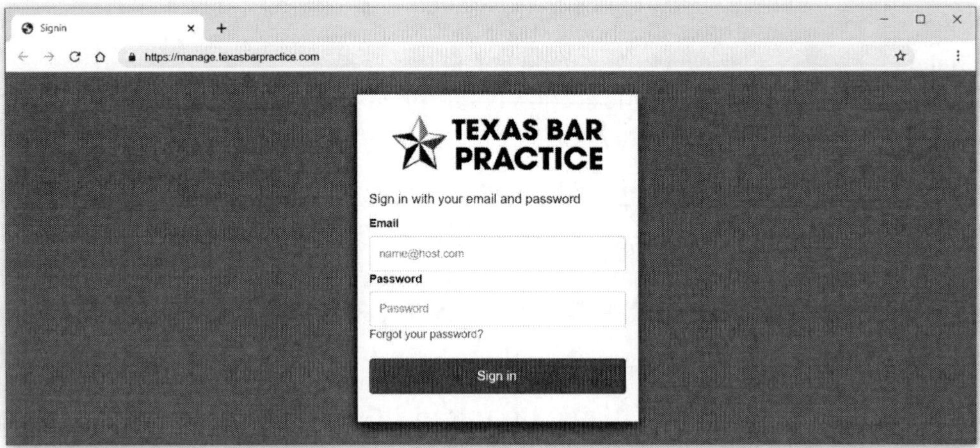

   Once logged in, you should see the user icon in the upper right-hand corner of the page.

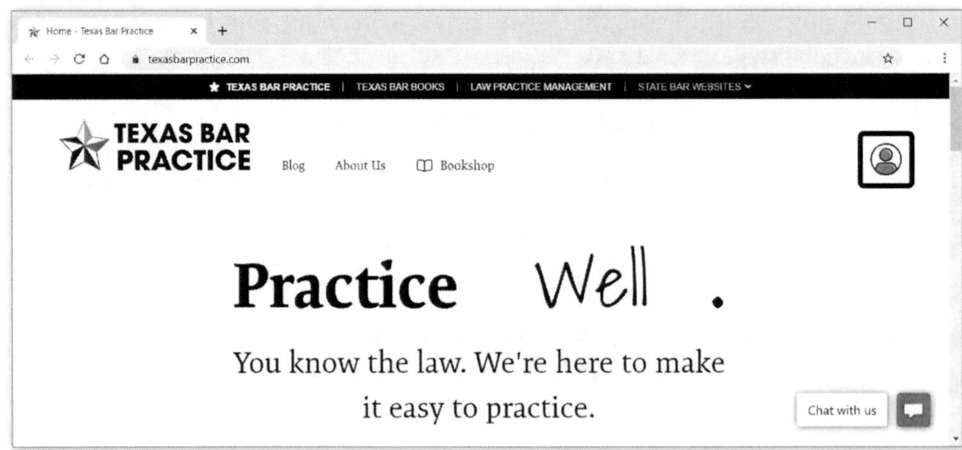

2. Go to your account:

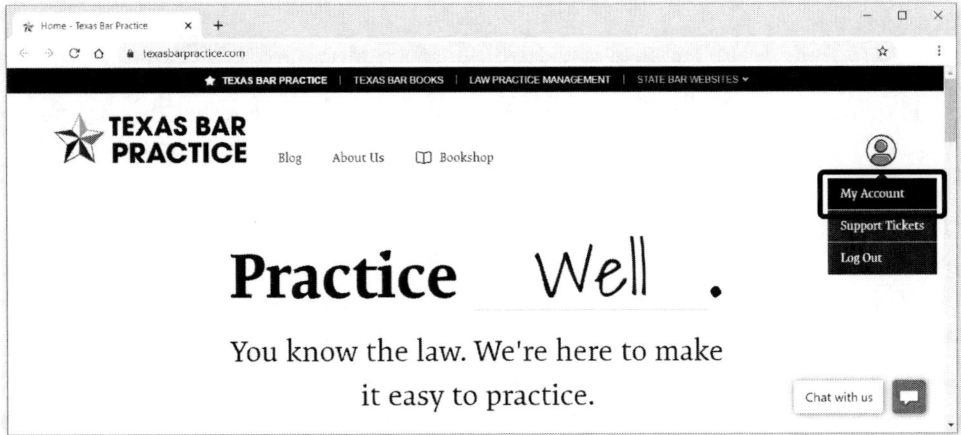

3. Select the library of the individual or organization associated with this download, and click the download button next to the book's title.

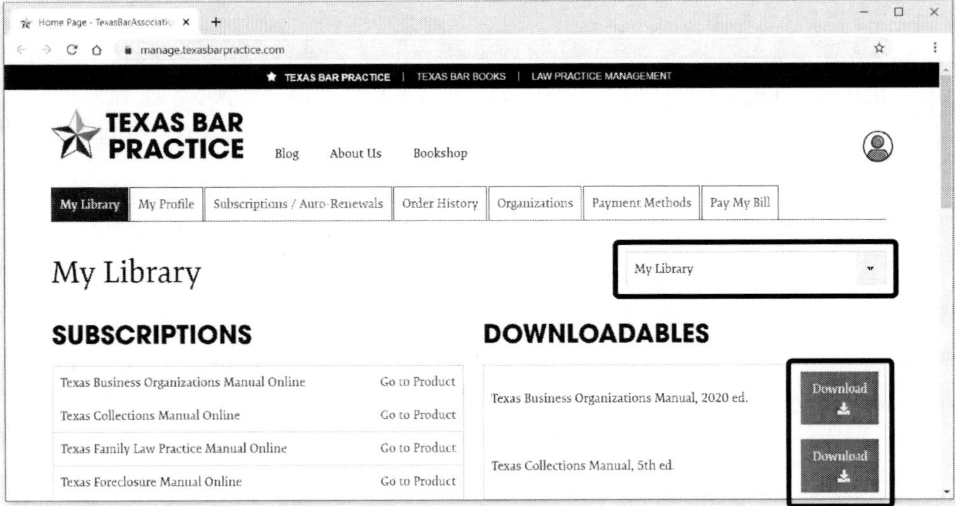

***Notes:**

- If you have never logged in to our site, the purchaser of this book should follow the instructions at **www.texasbarpractice.com/knowledgebase/article/already-a-customer**.
- If you purchased the book as an organization, see **www.texasbarpractice.com/knowledgebase/texas-bar-practice-accounts**.

If you need any assistance, you may chat with us online or email us at **books@texasbar.com**.

USE OF THE MATERIAL IN THE DIGITAL DOWNLOAD IS SUBJECT TO THE FOLLOWING LICENSE AGREEMENT.

License and Limited Warranty

Grant of license: The material in the digital product and in the documentation is copyrighted by the State Bar of Texas ("State Bar"). The State Bar grants you a nonexclusive license to use this material as long as you abide by the terms of this agreement.

Ownership: The State Bar retains title and ownership of the material in the files and in the documentation and all subsequent copies of the material regardless of the form or media in which or on which the original and other copies may exist. This license is not a sale of the material or any copy. The terms of this agreement apply to derivative works.

Permitted users: The material in these files is licensed to you for use by one lawyer and that lawyer's support team only. At any given time, the material in these files may be installed only on the computers used by that lawyer and that lawyer's support team. That lawyer may be the individual purchaser or the lawyer designated by the firm that purchased this product. You may not permit other lawyers to use this material unless you purchase additional licenses. **Lawyers, law firms, and law firm librarians are specifically prohibited from distributing these materials to more than one lawyer. A separate license must be purchased for each lawyer who uses these materials.** For information about special bulk discount pricing for law firms, please call 1-800-204-2222, ext. 1402, or 512-427-1402. Libraries not affiliated with firms may permit reading of this material by patrons of the library through installation on one or more computers owned by the library and on the library's network but may not lend or sell the files themselves. The library may not allow patrons to print or copy any of this material in such a way as would infringe the State Bar's copyright.

Copies: You may make a copy of the files for backup purposes. Otherwise, you may copy the material in the files only as necessary to allow use by the users permitted under the license you purchased. Copyright notices should be included on copies. You may copy the documentation, including any copyright notices, as needed for reference by authorized users, but not otherwise.

Transfer: You may not transfer any copy of the material in the files or in the documentation to any other person or entity unless the transferee first accepts this agreement in writing and you transfer all copies, wherever located or installed, of the material and documentation, including the original provided with this agreement. You may not rent, loan, lease, sublicense, or otherwise make the material available for use by any person other than the permitted users except as provided in this paragraph.

Limited warranty and limited liability: **THE STATE BAR MAKES NO WARRANTIES, EXPRESS OR IMPLIED, CONCERNING THE MATERIAL IN THESE FILES, THE DOCUMENTATION, OR THIS AGREEMENT. THE STATE BAR EXPRESSLY DISCLAIMS ALL IMPLIED WARRANTIES, INCLUDING THE IMPLIED WARRANTIES OF MERCHANTABILITY AND OF FITNESS FOR A PARTICULAR PURPOSE. THE MATERIAL IN THE FILES AND IN THE DOCUMENTATION IS PROVIDED "AS IS."**

THE STATE BAR SHALL NOT BE LIABLE FOR THE LEGAL SUFFICIENCY OR LEGAL ACCURACY OF ANY OF THE MATERIAL CONTAINED IN THESE FILES. NEITHER THE STATE BAR NOR ANY OF THE CONTRIBUTORS TO THE MATERIAL MAKES EITHER EXPRESS OR IMPLIED WARRANTIES WITH REGARD TO THE USE OR FREEDOM FROM ERROR OF THE MATERIAL. EACH USER IS SOLELY RESPONSIBLE FOR THE LEGAL EFFECT OF ANY USE OR MODIFICATION OF THE MATERIAL.

IN NO EVENT SHALL THE STATE BAR BE LIABLE FOR LOSS OF PROFITS OR FOR INDIRECT, SPECIAL, CONSEQUENTIAL, OR PUNITIVE DAMAGES, EVEN IF THE STATE BAR HAS BEEN ADVISED OF THE POSSIBILITY OF THOSE DAMAGES. THE STATE BAR'S AGGREGATE LIABILITY ARISING FROM OR RELATING TO THIS AGREEMENT OR THE MATERIAL IN THE FILES OR IN THE DOCUMENTATION IS

LIMITED TO THE PURCHASE PRICE YOU PAID FOR THE LICENSED COPYRIGHTED PRODUCT. THIS AGREEMENT DEFINES YOUR SOLE REMEDY.

General provisions: This agreement contains the entire agreement between you and the State Bar concerning the license to use the material in the files. The waiver of any breach of any provision of this agreement does not waive any other breach of that or any other provision. If any provision is for any reason found to be unenforceable, all other provisions nonetheless remain enforceable.